Mathematics
an integrated approach

C000152651

Complimentary copy
from
MACMILLAN EDUCATION

(usual price £3.95)

Mathematics
an integrated approach

H. M. KENWOOD B.Sc., AFIMA
(Director of Studies,
King Edward's School, Bath)

G. M. STALEY M.Sc.
(Head of the Mathematics Department,
King Edward's School, Bath)

Consultant Editor: Dr C. Plumpton,
Moderator in Mathematics, University of
London Schools Examination Department;
formerly Reader in Engineering Mathematics,
Queen Mary College, London

Macmillan Education

© H. M. Kenwood and G. M. Staley 1980

All rights reserved. No part of this publication
may be reproduced or transmitted in any
form or by any means, without permission

First published 1980

Published by
MACMILLAN EDUCATION LIMITED
Houndmills Basingstoke Hampshire RG 21 2XS
and London
Associated companies in Delhi Dublin
Hong Kong Johannesburg Lagos Melbourne
New York Singapore and Tokyo

Printed in Hong Kong

British Library Cataloguing in Publication Data

Kenwood, H M
Mathematics.
1. Mathematics – 1961–
I. Title   II. Staley, G M
510   QA39.2
ISBN 0–333–24581–4

Contents

Preface

Since the end of the Second World War the content of mathematics syllabuses at ordinary level has undergone a number of radical changes. Until 1950 mathematics was largely studied as three separate subjects—arithmetic, algebra and geometry, with trigonometry tacked on at the end of one of these. The implementation of the Jeffery Report in the early fifties led to a rapid dispersion of these separate subject boundaries and for the next ten years this process gathered momentum until a majority of pupils were studying mathematics at this level as an integrated subject along the lines suggested in the report.

In the early sixties a further change took place. A few teachers, soon followed by many others, felt that there were fundamental gaps in the subject being taught and they began to introduce topics which have come to be commonly and mistakenly known as 'modern mathematics'. Many of these topics had in fact been taught to undergraduates at university for many years, while others, like computing, had developed at great speed owing to the scientific and industrial needs of war. New syllabuses were developed and their difference from the more traditional ones was perhaps over-emphasised when it should be noted that these had only been operational for around fifteen years. The advent of cheap personal electronic calculators has added a further parameter in the last five years.

Since 1950 there has been a period of great activity and change in school mathematics, not least in the shape and content of what the children between the ages of 14 and 16 are expected to learn, digest and understand. This period has been followed by widespread debate and discussion from which has emerged a recommendation that mathematics syllabuses should be introduced which bring together the modern and traditional approaches and that these revised syllabuses should eventually replace those in existence now. Several examination boards have prepared a syllabus along these lines and this book has been written in support of this unified and co-ordinated approach, although it can also be used for the syllabuses in operation now.

The book has been written for both classroom use and individual study and covers the last two years of courses up to ordinary level. It can be used either as a main course book or for revision. The majority of the content is developed through worked examples followed by exercises. Bookwork, as such, has been kept to a minimum. As far as possible each chapter has been written as a separate entity and there is no set order in which each should be covered. It is hoped that by keeping the work in the main in subject sections, ease of reference to any particular topic will be enhanced.

The majority of topics are developed from first principles and could be read by a student who has missed class teaching through illness, change of school, or by transfer from one set to another within a school. It has been assumed that readers will have access to an electronic calculator and the use of these is well explained in the manuals supplied by the manufacturers. The explicit expression from which a numerical result is calculated should always be written in solutions and this point is emphasised many times in the text. The wide and diverse content of both the present and the proposed syllabuses has meant that more material has been included in the book than that which would be required for any one specific syllabus. Some selection will be necessary from the total content. For example, some syllabuses do not require a knowledge of calculus, while others may not require some of the work covered in geometry. For more able pupils, the inclusion of some extra topics may well prove to be a bonus either after their examinations or during the course itself. The authors hope that pupils studying what may appear to be widely differing syllabuses will find this book both stimulating and unifying in their course of study and that it will provide many with a sound foundation and the stimulus to want to study the subject at advanced level and beyond.

It would be ungracious to conclude this preface without recording our sincere thanks to many friends and colleagues for their help, encouragement and advice; our consultant editor, Dr Plumpton, and Mr Tony Feldman and Mrs Anne Russell, of Macmillan Education Limited; our pupils at King Edward's and Bath High Schools and our families all deserve particular mention. We salute and thank them all. We should also like to record our appreciation to the Public Examination Boards for their help and their permission to print questions from their past papers in the Miscellaneous Exercises.

HMK   GMS

Notation

The following notation is used in the text:

$\{\quad\}$	the set of
$n\{\quad\}$	the number of elements in the set
$\{x:\quad\}$	the set of values of x such that
$\in$	is an element of
$\notin$	is not an element of
$\varnothing$	the empty (null) set
$\mathscr{E}$	the universal set
$\cup$	union
$\cap$	intersection
$\subset$	is a subset of
A'	the complement of the set A
PQ	operation Q followed by operation P
$f: x \rightarrow y$	the function of mapping the set X into the set Y
$f(x)$	the image of x under the function f
f^{-1}	the inverse of the function f
fg	the function f of the function g
—o—o—	open interval on the number line
—●—●—	closed interval on the number line

Acknowledgements

Miscellaneous Exercises

These come after chapters 3, 10, 15, 19, 25 and 27 and are called, A, B, C, D, E, F respectively.
All questions have been selected from past papers of the following examination boards:

University of Cambridge, Local Examinations Syndicate.   (C)
University of London, University Entrance and Schools Examination Council.   (L)
University of Oxford, Oxford Delegacy of Local Examinations.   (O)
The Associated Examining Board   (AEB).
Southern Universities Joint Matriculation Board   (S)
The Joint Matriculation Board   (JMB).
Welsh Joint Education Committee   (W).

The publishers and authors wish to express their gratitude to the Boards for permission to reproduce these questions.

1 Basic arithmetic

The readers of this book will have been using some arithmetical processes for at least ten years. Some will have learnt to use these easily, others will have struggled and gradually won through, while the remainder will still feel unsure in some situations which confront them. As far as mathematics is concerned, competence in and understanding of simple arithmetic is a prerequisite for sound progress because it leads on to the rest of mathematics not only at school but in understanding many situations met in adult life.

In recent years less time has been spent on studying arithmetic than in the past, but its importance remains unique. An ability to understand and accurately use arithmetical processes remains a fundamental social need. As other branches of mathematics are studied, arithmetical competence should provide a foundation for confidence and clarity. Aids like electronic calculators can obtain answers to arithmetical expressions quickly and accurately provided that the user is able to programme a correct sequence of operations; that is, the user has to understand the nature and order of all the steps involved before a calculator is a really effective aid.

The authors assume that readers in their earlier studies have met the sets of numbers defined in (a) to (f) below:

(a) the natural numbers $1, 2, 3 \ldots$,

(b) fractions of the form m/n, where m and n are natural numbers

$$1/1, 2/1, 1/2, 3/1, 3/2, 2/3, 1/3, \ldots$$

(c) the integers $\ldots -3, -2, -1, 0, 1, 2, 3 \ldots$

(d) the rationals which take the form p/q, where p and q are integers and $q \neq 0$.

$$\ldots -1/2, -2/1, -1/1, 0, 1/1, 2/1, 1/2, \ldots$$

(e) the irrationals like $\sqrt{3}$, $\sin 70°$ and π, which cannot be expressed as rational numbers,

(f) the reals, or real numbers, which can be either rational or irrational.

These sets have evolved because of a need to solve practical problems. The problems arose and the formulation of the system followed, often after a considerable period of time. A class discussion could take place about the real number system and how it evolved. Books in the school library can be read to discover about the different number systems which have been used by nations in the past, e.g. the Babylonians, the Greeks, the Romans, the American Indians etc. The choice of 10 as the base of the number system in common use is arbitrary and later in this chapter numbers written in other bases are considered.

Most readers will be very familiar with the worked examples and the exercises which follow on the operations of addition, subtraction, multiplication and division, or combinations of these, on the sets of numbers defined. They are included at the start of this book to encourage the reader to look at them again in the light of his or her growing maturity and to reassess what is now available. The authors have found that this is a fruitful area to discuss with their own pupils as a preliminary to the course and the confidence gained is of real benefit. Unless otherwise stated, the reader should assume that questions refer to the set of real numbers, not only in this chapter but in the book generally.

Operations on fractions

Example 1: *Simplify* $2\frac{1}{3} + 3\frac{1}{4} - 1\frac{5}{6}$.
Written in full this expression means

$$2 + 3 - 1 + \tfrac{1}{3} + \tfrac{1}{4} - \tfrac{5}{6}$$

The lowest common denominator of 3, 4 and 6 is 12.

$$\text{Expression} = 4 + \frac{4 + 3 - 10}{12}$$

$$= 4 - \tfrac{3}{12} = 4 - \tfrac{1}{4} = 3\tfrac{3}{4}.$$

Example 2: *Simplify* $1\frac{5}{9} \times 3\frac{3}{7}$.
Written in full this expression means

$$(1 + \tfrac{5}{9})(3 + \tfrac{3}{7})$$

and by conversion to improper fractions this is reduced to

$$\frac{^{2}\cancel{14}}{\cancel{9}_{3}} \times \frac{\cancel{24}^{8}}{\cancel{7}_{1}} = \frac{2}{3} \times \frac{8}{1} = \frac{16}{3} = 5\tfrac{1}{3}.$$

Note that checking is easier if different types of stroke are used for the different stages of cancelling.

Example 3: *Simplify* $\frac{5}{7} \div \frac{2}{3}$.

$$\frac{5}{7} \div \frac{2}{3} = \frac{\frac{5}{7}}{\frac{2}{3}} = \frac{\frac{5}{7} \times \frac{3}{2}}{\frac{2}{3} \times \frac{3}{2}} = \frac{5}{7} \times \frac{3}{2} = \frac{15}{14} = 1\tfrac{1}{14}.$$

The above example explains why the rule 'dividing by a fraction is the same as turning it upside down and multiplying' works.

Brackets are used to clarify the order in which operations are carried out.

Example 4: *Evaluate (a)* $(2\frac{1}{3} - 1\frac{2}{5}) \div 1\frac{1}{3}$, *(b)* $2\frac{1}{3} - 1\frac{2}{5} \div 1\frac{1}{3}$.

(a) The brackets indicate that $1\frac{2}{5}$ should be subtracted from $2\frac{1}{3}$ and the result divided by $1\frac{1}{3}$.

$$2\frac{1}{3} - 1\frac{2}{5} = 2 - 1 + \frac{1}{3} - \frac{2}{5} = 1 + \frac{5-6}{15} = 1 - \frac{1}{15} = \frac{14}{15}.$$

$$(2\frac{1}{3} - 1\frac{2}{5}) \div 1\frac{1}{3} = \frac{14}{15} \div \frac{4}{3} = \frac{14}{15} \times \frac{3}{4} = \frac{7}{10}.$$

(b) When no brackets are included the convention followed is that multiplication and division precede addition and subtraction.

$$2\frac{1}{3} - 1\frac{2}{5} \div 1\frac{1}{3} = 2\frac{1}{3} - \frac{7}{5} \div \frac{4}{3} = 2\frac{1}{3} - \frac{7}{5} \times \frac{3}{4}$$

$$= 2\frac{1}{3} - 1\frac{1}{20} = 1\frac{20-3}{60} = 1\frac{17}{60}.$$

Exercise 1.1

Evaluate each of the following:

1   $1\frac{2}{3} + 2\frac{5}{6}$

2   $1\frac{3}{4} + \frac{4}{5}$

3   $4\frac{1}{6} - 1\frac{2}{3}$

4   $2\frac{2}{3} - 1\frac{4}{5}$

5   $2\frac{3}{4} + 1\frac{4}{5} + \frac{7}{10}$

6   $1\frac{1}{2} + 2\frac{1}{3} - 1\frac{1}{6}$

7   $3\frac{3}{4} - 4\frac{5}{6} + \frac{5}{12}$

8   $5\frac{2}{5} - 3\frac{9}{10} - \frac{1}{2}$

9   $13\frac{1}{2} - (5\frac{1}{3} + 3\frac{5}{12})$

10   $13\frac{1}{2} - (5\frac{1}{3} - 3\frac{5}{12})$

11   $\frac{2}{5} \times \frac{3}{4}$

12   $2\frac{5}{8} \times 2\frac{2}{7}$

13   $2\frac{7}{9} \times 1\frac{1}{5}$

14   $\frac{1}{6} \div \frac{2}{9}$

15   $7 \div 2\frac{1}{3}$

16   $2\frac{1}{3} \div 7$

17   $2\frac{1}{3} \div 1\frac{3}{4}$

18   $2\frac{1}{4} \div 2\frac{1}{7}$

19   $1\frac{1}{2} \times \frac{4}{9} \times 2\frac{1}{2}$

20   $1\frac{1}{3} \times (4\frac{1}{2} \div 1\frac{1}{4})$

21   $(1\frac{1}{3} \times 4\frac{1}{2}) \div 1\frac{1}{4}$

22   $1\frac{3}{4} \div (1\frac{1}{3} \div 1\frac{5}{9})$

23   $(1\frac{3}{4} \div 1\frac{1}{3}) \div 1\frac{5}{9}$

24   $(3\frac{1}{3} \div 1\frac{1}{2}) \times \frac{3}{5}$

25   $3\frac{1}{3} \div (1\frac{1}{2} \times \frac{3}{5})$.

26   Find the value of $1 + 2x$ when $x = 3$.

27   Find the value of $x/2 + 3$ when $x = 1$.

Note that in 26 and 27 multiplication and division take precedence over addition and subtraction, agreeing with the convention given in example 4(b), above.

28   $(\frac{1}{2} + \frac{1}{6}) \times \frac{1}{3}$

29   $\frac{1}{2} + \frac{1}{6} \times \frac{1}{3}$

30   $\frac{1}{2} - \frac{6}{25} \times 3\frac{1}{3}$

31   $(\frac{1}{2} - \frac{1}{5}) \times (\frac{1}{2} + \frac{1}{5})$

32   $(\frac{1}{7} + \frac{2}{5}) \div (\frac{1}{5} - \frac{1}{8})$

33   $\frac{3}{4}(1\frac{1}{3} - 2) + 2$

34   $\frac{1}{3}(6\frac{1}{2} - 2\frac{1}{4}) - \frac{5}{6}$

35   $\frac{3}{5} \times \frac{1}{2} - 1\frac{1}{2} \times 5$

36   The product of two numbers is 4. If one number is $1\frac{2}{3}$, find the other.

37   Alison, Barbara and Christine share a sum of money so that Alison gets 4/9 and Barbara gets 1/3. Given that Christine gets the rest which is £4, find the amounts the others get.

38   A boy walks 2/5 of the way to school and travels by bus for the remainder, which is $2\frac{1}{4}$ km. Find the distance he walks.

39 By what number must $3\frac{3}{4}$ be multiplied to give $6\frac{2}{3}$?

40 Find which of the fractions 3/14 and 2/9 is the bigger and by how much.

Operations on decimals

A decimal fraction is one whose denominator is a power of 10.

Example 1: $0.37 = 37/100$.

Example 2: $24.967 = 24\frac{967}{1000}$.

Decimals are very widely used because they can be directly applied to slide rules, logarithms and electronic calculators and in many everyday calculations they have superseded common fractions. Hence the reasons for decimalisation of money and the metrication of units of mass, length etc.

In addition and subtraction it is better to write the numbers in columns, the place value of the numbers being preserved by keeping the decimal points vertically aligned.

Example 3: *Find the sum of the numbers 9.8, 1.07 and 69.*

$$
\begin{array}{r}
9.8 \\
1.07 \\
69. \\
\hline
79.87 \quad answer. \\
\hline
\end{array}
$$

Multiplication can be performed in two stages; first, the correct digits are obtained by ordinary multiplication, disregarding the decimal points, and second, the placing of the decimal point is decided by consideration of the place values of the numbers being multiplied.

Example 4: *Evaluate* 3.54×12.7.

$$3.54 \times 12.7 = \tfrac{354}{100} \times \tfrac{127}{10} = 44\,958/1000 = 44.958.$$

The method shown demonstrates the reason in practice for multiplying 354 by 127 to obtain 44 958, followed by the insertion of the decimal point between 4 and 9 because the first number has 2 decimal places and the second 1 decimal place, thus requiring the answer to have $2 + 1 = 3$ decimal places. In practice it is usually prudent to have a rough mental answer available ready to check the final result. This will help to avoid errors, particularly ones which are a long way off, due possibly to pressing the wrong button on a calculator.

Division can be performed by writing the calculation in a fractional form and converting the denominator to a whole number.

Example 5: *Divide 0.009 62 by 0.37*

$$\frac{0.009\,62}{0.37} = \frac{0.009\,62 \times 100}{0.37 \times 100} = \frac{0.962}{37} = 0.026.$$

4

The conversion from decimals to fractions and the reverse

Any decimal can be converted into its fraction equivalent at once (see above).

Any simple fraction can be converted into a decimal or repeated decimal by division.

Example 6: *Convert (a) 2/5, (b) 2/3, (c) 17/99 into decimals.*

(a) 2/5 implies that 2.0 requires division by 5 and is equal to 0.4.

(b) Similarly 2/3 implies division of 2 by 3 but the answer does not terminate and gives 0.6666 . . . . which is called 'point 6 recurring' and is written $0.\dot{6}$.

(c) 17/99 by division converts to 0.171717 . . . , which is called 'point 17 recurring' and is written $0.\dot{1}\dot{7}$.

Example 7: *Convert $12.\dot{2}\dot{3}$ to a rational number.*

Let $n = 12.232323$ . . . and multiply by 100, the order of recurrence,

$100n = 1223.232323$ . . .

Subtraction gives $99n = 1211$ and $n = 1211/99$.

Approximations

The reader will have met in previous work the two ways commonly used for expressing degrees of accuracy, namely decimal places and significant figures. Some cautionary notes however should be stated about approximations. A common fallacy is to believe that increased accuracy may be obtained by continuing a calculation to more figures. When the given numbers in a calculation are only approximate (as they are in practice for all measurement of things like length, time, mass and quantities derived from these like speed, force, area etc), the implied insertion in the answer of a degree of accuracy which is greater than justified by the original figures is both meaningless and wrong. In mathematics, the calculations made are often undertaken without due respect to the practical difficulties involved in measuring data. The important thing to remember is that approximate answers should be correct as far as they go, *especially when the original data is specified to a certain degree of accuracy.* An example is added here to add weight to the caveat given.

Example 1: *The length and the breadth of a rectangle are 8 cm and 6 cm respectively, where each measurement has been given to the nearest cm. Calculate the largest and smallest possible areas of this rectangle.*

The true length of the rectangle lies between 7.5 cm and 8.5 cm.

The true breadth of the rectangle lies between 5.5 cm and 6.5 cm.

Largest possible area $\leqslant 8.5 \times 6.5$ cm$^2 = 55.25$ cm^2.

Smallest possible area $\geqslant 7.5 \times 5.5$ cm$^2 = 41.25$ cm^2.

From the original data all that can be truthfully said is that the area lies somewhere between these extreme values. If the area were given as 48 cm^2, all that can be said is that the 8 is very unreliable and the 4 by no means certain.

Having made this point rather dramatically it should be added that many answers in this book, and others, as well as exam questions in mathematics and science, expect answers to an accuracy which the given data appears to make unattainable. All that can be said in mitigation of this charge is that it is often desirable in studying theoretical mathematics to stand a little aside from the actual practical difficulties. The numbers used in calculations are often made unrealistically simple so that the logical steps are not hidden in a proliferation of arithmetically complicated calculations. This, however, is one of the debating points of the subject and you can have a fruitful discussion about it with your teacher.

Example 2:   The number 372.8259 written correct to
(a) 3 decimal places (3 d.p.) is 372.826,
(b) 3 significant figures (3 s.f.) is 373,
(c) 1 s.f. is 400,
(d) 1 d.p. is 372.8.

Numbers in standard form

The numbers 2.46×10^3, 7.8×10^0 and 9.8×10^{-3} are each expressed in what is called standard form and represent respectively 2460, 7.8 and 0.0098.

In general, any number is in standard form when it is written as

$$a \times 10^n, \text{ where } 1 \leqslant a < 10 \text{ and } n \text{ is an integer.}$$

In practice this is often a convenient way of expressing very large or very small numbers because the relative size of the number is immediately recognisable without counting a lot of zeros in front or behind the decimal point.

Examples: (a) Distance from earth to sun $= 1.5 \times 10^{11}$ m (2 s.f.),
(b) the mass of an electron $= 9.11 \times 10^{-25}$ kg (3 s.f.).

Exercise 1.2

Evaluate each of the following:

1	$2.3 + 5.7 + 6.2$	6	$14.25 - (3.42 + 8.3)$
2	$0.95 + 2.7 + 0.073$	7	$14.25 - 3.42 + 8.3$
3	$28.6 - 9.7$	8	$9 - 3.2 - 2.8$
4	$0.03 - 0.008$	9	$9 - (3.2 - 2.8)$
5	$31 - 13.7$	10	$-8.2 - 2.9 + 13.2$

11   Over a 24 hour period, the lowest temperature is $-2.7°$ C and the highest is $16.4°$ C. Calculate the difference between these extreme temperatures.

12 A naturalist completes a walking tour in four days and covers 18.7 km, 16.6 km, 17.2 km, respectively, on the first three days. Given that the total tour was 73.2 km, calculate the distance covered on the fourth day.

13 A girl records her daily travelling times (in minutes) to school over a week as 17.4, 19.6, 20.7, 15.3 and 16.5. Calculate her total travelling time to school for this week.

14 The rainfall measured at a weather centre over the four weeks of February 1977 was 2.10 cm, 0.34 cm, 3.71 cm and 1.69 cm. Calculate, to 1 d.p., the total rainfall for February.

15 The external diameter of a water pipe is 4.5 cm and the pipe is made of material 0.16 cm thick. Find the internal diameter of the pipe.

Evaluate each of the following: only use your calculator to check an answer once you have worked it out. It is particularly important that the position of the decimal point can be decided with complete confidence and you must be able to do this without relying on your calculator.

16 24×1.3

17 $(0.9)^2$

18 71.3×0.42

19 0.49×0.22

20 $0.1 \times 0.02 \times 0.003$

21 $15 \div 0.2$

22 $9.13 \div 40$

23 $12.351 \div 2.3$

24 $0.0035325 \div 0.015$

25 $316.979 \div 0.037$

26 $(0.9 \div 0.2) \div 0.4$

27 $0.9 \div (0.2 \div 0.4)$

28 Express 7/8 as a decimal.

29 Express 0.65 as a vulgar fraction.

30 Find, to 4 d.p., the difference between $\frac{14}{17}$ and $\frac{9}{11}$.

31 A boy cycles 10.5 km in 35 minutes. Express his average speed in km/h.

32 The line segment AB, of length 14.7 cm, is sub-divided into 9 equal sections each measuring 1.41 cm and a section CB remains. Calculate the length of CB.

33 A boy does an evening paper round from Monday to Saturday inclusive and receives £1.74 per week. He does the round for 48 weeks in the year. Calculate
(a) his daily rate of pay, (b) his annual rate of pay.

34 Find the value of xy^2 when $x = 1.1$ and $y = 0.4$.

35 Find the value of x/y^2 when $x = 2.56$ and $y = 0.08$.

Give each of the following numbers corrected (a) to three s.f., (b) to one d.p.

36 397.694 3   **37** 7.506 1   **38** 400 400.72   **39** 8.009 730

40 0.038 974

Evaluate each of the following, giving your final answer in standard form:

41 $3 \times 10 + 3 \times 10^2$

42 $2.8 \times 10^2 + 6.3 \times 10^2$

43 $5 \times 10^{-1} + 5 \times 10^{-2}$

44 $2.3 \times 10^{-4} + 3.5 \times 10^{-2}$

45 $4.2 \times 10^2 - 6.0 \times 10^1$

46 $3.9 \times 10^9 - 8.9 \times 10^7$

47 $3.5 \times 10^2 \times 2.1 \times 10^2$

48 $7.1 \times 10^{-1} \times 3.0 \times 10^{-2}$

49 $(4.2 \times 10^{-1})^2$

50 $(6.3 \times 10^{-2}) \div (7 \times 10^{-4})$

51 A rectangle measures 5 cm by 9 cm, where each measurement has been made to the nearest cm. Calculate:
(a) the limits within which the perimeter of the rectangle lies,
(b) the limits between which the area of the rectangle lies.

52 The variable numbers x and y are such that $3 \leqslant x \leqslant 4$, $7 \leqslant y \leqslant 9$. Find the least and the greatest possible values of (a) $y - x$, (b) y/x.

53 Written corrected to 1 s.f. the number m is 5 and the number n is 2. Prove that the actual value of $2m + 3n$ must lie between 18.5 and 13.5.

54 The length of a running track is 100 m, correct to the nearest metre. An athlete takes 10.5 s, correct to the nearest 0.1 s, to run along the track. Calculate the limits within which the average speed (in m/s) of the athlete must lie.

55 It is estimated that, to the nearest tonne, there are 100 tonnes of potatoes in a store. The potatoes are put in bags, where each bag contains 2 kg of potatoes, to the nearest 0.1 kg. Calculate the least number of bags that could be filled from the store.

Numbers written to other bases

The idea of using symbols like 1, 2, 3 . . . to represent numbers is thought to have originated from the Hindus and the idea was brought to Europe during the eighth and ninth centuries A.D. when the Moslem empire extended from Spain to India. The new system was slow to develop because few people could write and for mental calculations the abacus was widely used. Over a long period of time two related factors helped to establish the new ideas. The first was a book written by the famous Arab mathematician al-Khowarazmi in the first half of the ninth century and the second was the translation of this book into Latin by Adelard of Bath, a twelfth century English monk. The translation from Arabic into Latin was almost certainly responsible for the name 'arabic numerals' by which the symbols are known today.

An arabic number system has three fundamental features. The first is the use of single code symbols. The second is the principle of place value: the value of a particular symbol within a number depends on its actual position within the number as well as its code meaning. The third is the use of a symbol for zero or 'the empty space' as it was first known. The system actually developed is the one in common use now and is called the denary system because it has a base 10 and requires 10 symbols including one for zero.

Any number could have been taken as the base for a satisfactory number system provided that these three principles are included. It is certainly debatable whether ten is the best, but any change would clearly have world wide repercussions far beyond the scope of mathematics.

Notation

In the following examples and exercises the small number written at the end and just below each number, called a suffix, is used to indicate the base in which the number is expressed.

Example 1: $3456_{10} = 3 \times 10^3 + 4 \times 10^2 + 5 \times 10 + 6.$

Example 2: $403_6 = 4 \times 6^2 + 0 \times 6 + 3 = 144_{10} + 3_{10} = 147_{10}$

The binary system of numbers

This system is based on the two symbols 0 and 1. One, two, three and four in the binary system are represented by 1, 10, 11 and 100 respectively and larger numbers similarly. As only two symbols are required to represent any number, the binary system has far reaching applications. Many mathematical models only require a two state situation – an electric light can be either off or on, or a statement can be either true or false. In particular, the binary system is widely used in digital computers.

Example 1: *Express 29_{10} in binary.*

Successive division gives

		Remainder
2	29	
2	14	1
2	7	0
2	3	1
2	1	1
	0	1

Hence $29_{10} = 1 \times 2^4 + 1 \times 2^3 + 1 \times 2^2 + 0 \times 2 + 1$
$= 11101_2.$

Example 2: *Express 285_{10} in (a) base 9, (b) base 3.*

Successive division by 9 gives

		Remainder
9	285	
9	31	6
9	3	4
	0	3

Hence $285_{10} = 3 \times 9^2 + 4 \times 9 + 6 = 346_9$
$= 1 \times 3^5 + 0 \times 3^4 + 1 \times 3^3 + 1 \times 3^2 + 2 \times 3 + 0 = 101120_3.$
Note the direct conversion from base 9 to base 3, and vice versa, because $3^2 = 9.$

Example 3: *Express 1111011101_2 in (a) octal (base 8), (b) denary.*
Since $2^3 = 8$, any binary number can be converted directly to octal by grouping the symbols of the binary number in 'threes' from the right.

$1|111|011|101 = 1 \times 8^3 + 7 \times 8^2 + 3 \times 8 + 5 = 1735_8.$
$= 512_{10} + 448_{10} + 24_{10} + 5_{10} = 989_{10}.$

Example 4: *Express* 1101.101_2 *in denary.*

$$1101.101_2 = 1 \times 2^3 + 1 \times 2^2 + 1 + 1 \times \tfrac{1}{2} + 1 \times (\tfrac{1}{2})^3 = 13\tfrac{5}{8}.$$

Exercise 1.3

1 Convert the following numbers into base 10:

$$11011_2, \ 1221_3, \ 33_4, \ 324_5, \ 145_6, \ 52_7, \ 76_8, \ 881_9.$$

2 Convert the following denary numbers into (a) octal, (b) binary:

$$42, \ 65, \ 100, \ 1984.$$

3 Write 39_{10} in (a) base 3, (b) base 5, (c) base 7.
4 Write 21201_3 in base 9 and 6572_8 in binary.
5 Express 1000_{10} in (a) base 5, (b) base 8.
6 Express each of the following as mixed numbers in base 10:

$$\text{(a) } 12.12_3, \ \text{(b) } 100.01_2, \ \text{(c) } 16.6_8, \ \text{(d) } 13.35_6.$$

Arithmetical operations applied to numbers in a given base

One example of each is given: the operations follow the same rules as with denary numbers. It must be noted however that different columns no longer stand for powers of ten, but for powers of the base in which the numbers are given.

Example 1: Add 432_6 and 514_6

$$
\begin{array}{r}
432 \\
514 \\
\hline
1350
\end{array}
$$
Ans. 1350_6

Example 2: Subtract 102_3 from 210_3

$$
\begin{array}{r}
210 \\
102 \\
\hline
101
\end{array}
$$
Ans. 101_3

Example 3: Multiply 72_8 by 65_8

$$
\begin{array}{r}
72 \\
65 \\
\hline
5340 \\
442 \\
\hline
6002
\end{array}
$$
Ans. 6002_8

Example 4: Divide 1344_5 by 24_5

$$
\begin{array}{r}
31 \\
24)\overline{1344} \\
132 \\
\hline
24 \\
24 \\
\hline
..
\end{array}
$$
Ans. 31_5

Exercise 1.4

Work out each of the following, giving the answer each time in the base used:

1   $101_2 + 1011_2$

2   $375_8 + 524_8$

3   $201_3 - 122_3$

4   $34_5 \times 21_5$

5   $100_6 \div 13_6$

6   $32_4 - 23_4 + 33_4$

7   $81_9 + 18_9 + 3_9$

8   $330_7 \div 15_7$

9   $1101_2 \times 101_2$

10   $2301_5 - 342_5$

11   $167_8 \times 51_8$

12   $1330_9 \div 41_9$

13   $2254_6 - 324_6 - 1003_6$

14   $101_2 \times 110_2 \times 111_2$

15   $221_3 \times 122_3$

2 Ratio, rate and percentage; some simple commercial examples

Ratio

There are two simple ways of comparing quantities of the same kind: by difference or by ratio. At the end of a Grand Prix race a driver is interested in the difference in distance between his car and that of his rivals. A schoolboy building a model of the racing car would be interested in the scale of his model to that of the original, or in other words, the ratio of the lengths, and the difference in length would be quite meaningless. Every measurement is a ratio because the measurement is set against a standard unit quantity like the metre or the kilogramme or the second. A ratio is used to connect two quantities measured in the same units. Ratios should always be expressed as simply as possible.

Example: In a fifth year class there are 10 boys and 15 girls. The ratio of boys to girls is $10:15 = 2:3$.

Rate

It is often necessary to make a comparison between two quantities not measured in the same units. If a plane travels 5000 km in 4 hours, it moves at an average rate of 1250 km/h. If a length of material is bought in a shop at £2 per metre, this information implies a functional relationship between length and cost; when one is known, the other can be found. A girl with £6 could buy 3 metres of material. A woman needing 7 metres of material will have to spend £14.

Provided that the rate is constant in any particular situation it is possible to illustrate the functional relationship with a straight line graph whose slope is the rate.

Percentages

A percentage is a ratio in which the second number is 100. It is simply a fraction with denominator 100. One advantage of using percentages is that one fraction can easily be compared with another. The choice of 100 is arbitrary, but is now widely accepted. Percentages can be represented by fractions or decimals, and conversely.

Example 1: *Express as percentages (a) 9/25,   (b) 0.57*
(a) 9/25 of 100 $= 36 \Rightarrow 9/25 = 36/100 = 36\%$,
(b) $0.57 = 57/100 = 57\%$.

Example 2: *Express 35% as (a) a vulgar fraction, (b) a decimal.*
(a) $35\% = 35/100 = 7/20$.
(b) $35\% = 35/100 = 0.35$.

Example 3: *Find $7\frac{1}{2}\%$ of £830.*
$7\frac{1}{2}\%$ of £830 $= £(7\frac{1}{2}/100) \times 830 = £(15/200) \times 830 = £62.25$.

Exercise 2.1

1 Express each of the following ratios as simply as possible:
   (a) $5:15$,
   (b) $18:12$,
   (c) $150\,\text{m}:1\,\text{km}$,
   (d) $70\,\text{g}:2\,\text{kg}$,
   (e) $27\,\text{s}:1.5$ minutes.

2 Write each of the following constant rates in simplified form:
   (a) 2000 km in 8 hours,
   (b) 4 kg of sugar for £1.20,
   (c) 72 eggs for £1.80,
   (d) 7 litres of petrol for 38.5 km,
   (e) 8 weeks rent for £100.

3 Express the following as percentages:
   (a) 9/20, (b) 0.59, (c) $1\frac{1}{2}$, (d) the ratio $3:5$.

4 Express the following percentages as fractions and as decimals:
   (a) 75%, (b) 45%, (c) 140%, (d) $2\frac{1}{2}\%$.

5 Express the percentages given in question 4 as ratios.

6 Find the values of the following:
   (a) 5% of £2 (give the answer in pence),
   (b) 17% of 1 kg (give the answer in g),
   (c) 120% of 7 m (give the answer in m),
   (d) 0.5% of 60 cm (give the answer in cm).

7 The length of an oil-tanker is 650 m. A model of the tanker is made of length 13 cm. Find the ratio of the length of the tanker to that of the model.

8 Two cars cost £3000 and £2500 when new. After a year each has lost £600 in value. Find the ratio of their values (a) when new, (b) after a year.

9 In a town a ratepayer pays 82.5 pence for every £1 of the rateable value of his property. Express this as a ratio.
   Find the amount paid in rates by a man whose property has a rateable value of £140.

10 The whole of the rateable value of the property in a town is £2 800 000. Find how much would be obtained if the local authority raised the rates by 3 pence on every pound of rateable value.

11 A salesman's commission is £25 on goods which he sells worth £280. Find the ratio of his commission to his sales.
Find also the commission he would receive for goods that he sold worth £490.

12 A candidate scores 56 marks out of 80 in an examination. Calculate the candidate's percentage score.

13 Find the amount, called the premium, charged to insure a school valued at one million pounds, if the premium is 0.15% of the value.

14 A householder can insure the contents of his home with an annual policy which costs 12 p for every £100 worth of contents.
(a) Express 12 p as a percentage of £100.
(b) Find the annual cost to insure contents worth £6000.
(c) Find the value of the contents of a house for which the annual premium is £10.20.

15 A jeweller charges 2% of a valuation to his customers.
(a) He values some rings for a customer at £1600. Find the cost of the valuation to the customer.
(b) A second customer receives a bill for £42 for the valuation of some silver. Find the amount the silver is valued at.

16 A store makes 12% profit on what is sold. In a particular week the total takings were £1624. Calculate the profit.

17 In a particular year a man paid 25% of his whole salary in tax. Given that he paid £1640 in tax, find how much he had left to spend.

18 The rateable value of a house is £225. In the district where the house is situated rates are charged at 74p in the £. Calculate
(a) the cost of rates to the owner of the house,
(b) the increased cost in rates for this house when the rates are charged at a new rate of 79 p in the £.

19 The scale of a map is 5 cm to 1 km. Express this as a ratio in the form $1:n$.

20 The scale of a plan is 1:32. Find the actual length and breadth of a room which measures 25 cm by 20 cm on the plan.

Proportional parts

Each Christmas the pupils at a school collect money for charity. One year they decided to share out the £75 collected between Oxfam, Help the Aged and the N.S.P.C.A., so that Oxfam gets 1/2, Help the Aged gets 3/10, and the N.S.P.C.A. gets 1/5. This share out can be written in the form of a ratio as

$$1/2 : 3/10 : 1/5 = 5/10 : 3/10 : 2/10 = 5 : 3 : 2.$$

They would send Oxfam £37.50, Help the Aged £22.50, and the N.S.P.C.A. £15, because there are 10 'shares' in all, of which Oxfam get 5, Help the

Aged get 3, and the N.S.P.C.A. get 2. This is an example of what are called proportional parts.

Example: *Two types of tea which cost £2 per kg and £2.50 per kg are mixed so that their weights are respectively in the ratio 5 : 3. Calculate the cost of 20 kg of the mixture.*
8 kg of the mixture will cost $5 \times £2 + 3 \times £2.50 = £17.50$.
20 kg of the mixture will cost $£17.50 \times (20/8) = £43.75$.

Increase and decrease

Increases and decreases can be expressed as a ratio or as a percentage. It is customary to write the ratio as

$$\frac{\text{New quantity}}{\text{Original quantity}},$$

it is greater than 1 for an increase and less than 1 for a decrease. This ratio has important applications in calculations and is called a multiplying factor. When increases or decreases are expressed as percentages the original quantity is always used as the base for comparison.

$$\% \text{ increase (or decrease)} = \frac{\text{Actual increase (or decrease)}}{\text{Original quantity}} \times 100.$$

In the calculation of any percentage change it must be stressed that gain or loss percent is always understood to mean the percentage that the gain or loss is of the original value. In financial transactions the original value is called the *cost price* (C.P.) and the new value is called the *selling price* (S.P.).

Actual gain (or loss) = the difference between S.P. and C.P.

$$\text{Gain (or loss) } \% = \frac{\text{Actual gain (or loss)}}{\text{C.P.}} \times 100.$$

Example 1: *The annual subscription to a sports club is increased from £7.50 to £9. Express this increase as (a) a ratio, (b) a percentage.*
(a) New subscription : old subscription $= £9 : £7.50 = 18 : 15 = 6 : 5$.
(b) Percentage increase $= \dfrac{1.50}{7.50} \times 100 = 20\%$.

Example 2: *A colour television set is bought by a customer from a shop for £350. Some time later the customer sells the set again at a loss of 15%. Calculate the selling price.*
There are two possible methods, of which the second is better, because it implies the method of solution for the harder reverse problem which follows.

Method 1: Actual loss $= \dfrac{15}{100} \times £350 = £52.50$

Selling price = £350 − £52.50 = £297.50.

Method 2: Selling price is 85% of the cost price

$$\text{Selling price} = \frac{85}{100} \times £350 = £297.50.$$

Example 3: *Suppose the last problem had been reversed to read as follows. A customer sells a colour television set for £297.50 and in doing so makes a loss of 15% on the price he originally paid for it. Calculate the original price.* The second solution to the last problem leads directly to the solution required here for the reverse situation, the crucial statement being that 85% of the C.P. is the S.P.

With the S.P. given, the C.P. can be obtained by multiplying the S.P. by 100/85.

$$\text{Cost price} = \frac{100}{85} \times £297.50 = £350.$$

Exercise 2.2

1 (a) Increase 125 by 20%   (b) Decrease 67 by 10%.
   (c) Increase 212 by 35%   (d) Decrease 40 by 80%.
2 (a) Increase 14 in the ratio 4 : 3.   (b) Decrease 100 in the ratio 3 : 5.
   (c) Increase 120 in the ratio 4 : 1.   (d) Decrease 57 in the ratio 2 : 3.
3 Determine the multiplying factor which would
   (a) increase 50 to 75   (b) decrease 39 to 13.
   (c) increase 144 to 240   (d) decrease 69 to 57.5.
4 Given that 6 kg of potatoes cost 39 p, find the cost of 4 kg.
5 Given that a man earns £75 for 30 hours work, find the amount he would earn for 35 hours work, at the same rate per hour.
6 Water flows at the same constant rate through three pipes and fills a swimming bath in 6 hours. Find the time taken to fill the bath when only two of the pipes are used.
7 A mountain outward bound post contains enough supplies to last 6 people for 10 days. Find for how long the supplies would last when there are 15 people present.
8 In a committee of 20 persons the ratio of gentlemen to ladies is 3 : 1. Find the number of ladies required to join this committee so that the ratio is changed to 3 : 2.
9 In 63 g of nitric acid there are 14 g of nitrogen. Calculate the percentage content, by mass, of nitrogen in nitric acid.
10 The proportional parts by mass of potassium, oxygen and hydrogen in caustic potash are 39 : 16 : 1. Find the mass of each in 84 kg of caustic potash.
11 A plank, 1 m long, is cut into three pieces in the ratio 5 : 6 : 9. Find, in cm, the length of each piece.
12 The masses of three boys are in the ratio 5 : 6 : 7. Given that the mass of the lightest boy is 90 kg, find the total mass of the boys.
13 Divide £1000 between three charities in the ratio 3 : 5 : 12.

16

14 Three people A, B and C provide £2500, £3500 and £5000 to buy a business and their share of the profits is proportional to the capital each put up. Find how much each receives when the profits are £2750.

15 After paying income tax at 30 p in the £, a lady has £665 left. Find the amount of tax she has paid.

16 A clock was 2 minutes slow at 0800 and 3 minutes fast at 1800. Given that the clock gained time uniformly, find the time when it showed the correct time during this interval.

17 Divide £112 between A, B, C and D in the ratio $3:5:7:9$.

18 The costs of three motor-cycles P, Q and R are such that the cost of P to the cost of Q is $5:3$, the cost of Q to the cost of R is $5:4$, and R costs £240. Calculate the cost of P.

19 Calculate the S.P. in each of the following:
  (a) C.P. £50, gain 4%
  (b) C.P. £50, loss 4%
  (c) C.P. £32, gain 12%
  (d) C.P. £136, loss 20%.

20 Calculate the gain or loss % in each of the following:
  (a) C.P. £40, S.P. £35
  (b) C.P. £60, S.P. £80
  (c) C.P. £640, S.P. £540
  (d) C.P. £89, S.P. £102.35
  (e) C.P. £50, gain £8
  (f) C.P. 18 p, loss 8 p
  (g) S.P. 18 p, loss 8 p
  (h) S.P. £1000, gain £200.

21 Calculate the C.P. in each of the following:
  (a) S.P. £25, gain 50%
  (b) S.P. £56, loss 20%
  (c) S.P. 36 p, loss 28%
  (d) S.P. £975, gain 25%.

22 A house was bought for £20 000 and sold for £34 000. Find the gain %.

23 A vintage car is bought for £1700 and later sold at a profit of 45%. Calculate the selling price.

24 By selling a vase for £1.50 a dealer makes a profit of 25%. Find the dealer's cost price.

25 The profit on a tape-recorder, sold at a gain of 32.5%, is £6.50. Calculate the cost price.

26 The price of a car tyre is reduced as a special offer from £8.40 to £7. Calculate the percentage reduction.

27 Goods are bought at £25 per tonne and sold at 3.5 p per kg. Calculate the gain %.

28 In a sale a discount of 15% on the marked price of goods is given. Calculate:
  (a) the reduced price of a suite marked at £470
  (b) the marked price of a piano reduced to £765.

29 A supermarket buys sugar at £200 per tonne and sells it at 32 p per kg. The packaging of each tonne costs £20. Calculate the gain %.

30 A man sells his car for £1980 and loses 12% of what he paid for it. Calculate his loss.

Simple interest

If a family live in a house belonging to a local authority (or a private person) they pay money at regular intervals called the rent of the house. If a sum of money, called the **principal**, is invested in a Savings Bank, the principal earns interest which is paid to the investor at regular intervals of time, say monthly or annually. Just as the house in which the family lives remains the property of the local authority, the principal always belongs to the investor. Any money which is loaned or borrowed under conditions which require regular payments of interest, leaving the principal unchanged, is defined to be lent or borrowed at **simple interest**. If the simple interest is added to the principal for a particular period of time, then the sum of the principal and the interest is called the **amount** at simple interest for that period.

Example 1: *A person invests £600 for 4 years with a firm which pays simple interest at a rate of 7% each year. Record the results of this transaction in a table.*

Principal	Annual Rate	Time in years	Interest	Amount
£600	7%	1	£42	£642
£600	7%	2	£84	£684
£600	7%	3	£126	£726
£600	7%	4	£168	£768

The table illustrates that simple interest is directly proportional to the time; the interest accrued in 4 years being 4 times that which accrued in 1 year.

Simple interest can be calculated either by direct proportion or by using a formula.

Suppose that a principle of $£P$ is invested for T years at a rate of $R\%$ simple interest each year.

The interest on $£P$ for 1 year is $\dfrac{R}{100}$ of $£P = £\dfrac{PR}{100}$.

The interest on $£P$ for T years is therefore $£\dfrac{PRT}{100}$.

The simple interest formulae are $A = I + P,$

$$I = \frac{PRT}{100},$$

18

where $£A$ is the amount after time T years, $£I$ is the interest after T years and the rate is $R\%$ per annum (or each year).

Example 2: *The simple interest on $£480$ for 5 years is $£156$. Calculate the rate percent per annum.*

Using the formula, $P = 480$, $T = 5$, $I = 156$ and it is required to find R.

$$\frac{PRT}{100} = I \Rightarrow PRT = 100I \Rightarrow R = \frac{100I}{PT}.$$

$$\text{Hence } R = \frac{100 \times 156}{480 \times 5} = 6.5.$$

The rate is 6.5% per annum.

Example 3: *Find the time in which $£360$ will amount to $£420$ at 4% per annum simple interest.*

$$I = 420 - 360 = 60, \; P = 360, \; R = 4.$$

$$T = \frac{100I}{PR} = \frac{100 \times 60}{360 \times 4} = \frac{25}{6}.$$

Hence time is 4 years 2 months.

Example 4: *Find the principal which will yield $£352$ interest in 4 years at 8% per annum simple interest.*

$$I = 352, \; R = 8, \; T = 4.$$

$$P = \frac{100I}{RT} = \frac{100 \times 352}{4 \times 8} = 1100.$$

The principal is $£1100$.

Example 5: *Find, to the nearest penny, the simple interest on $£2730$ invested at a rate of 7% per annum from 1st August to 9th November in the same year.*

From 1st August to 9th November $= 100$ days; hence $T = \dfrac{100}{365}$, $R = 7$ and $P = 2730$.

$$I = \frac{PRT}{100} = \frac{2730 \times 100 \times 7}{100 \times 365} = 52.356.$$

Interest $= £52.36$ to the nearest penny.

Example 6: *Calculate the principal which amounts to $£546$ in 6 years at 5% per annum simple interest.*

Method 1: Since the interest is directly proportional to the time, 6 years at 5% is the same as 1 year at 30%.

The amount therefore is (130/100) times the principal and it follows that

$$\text{Principal} = £546 \times \frac{100}{130} = £420.$$

Method 2: Using the simple interest formulae with $A = 546$, $T = 6$ and $R = 5$ it follows that

$$P + I = 546 \qquad \dots \quad \text{(i)}$$

$$I = \frac{P \times 6 \times 5}{100}$$

$$I = \frac{3P}{10} \qquad \dots \quad \text{(ii)}$$

Solving (i) and (ii) simultaneously for P gives

$$P + \frac{3P}{10} = 546$$

$$\frac{13}{10}P = 546$$

$$P = \frac{546 \times 10}{13} = 420.$$

Compound interest

In some deals the interest as it falls due is not paid back to the lender but is added on to the principal. The next lot of interest is then calculated on the increased amount and so on. When this happens the money is said to be lent at compound interest.

Depreciation

Many goods like cars, electrical appliances and modern furniture depreciate in value with time. It is common practice to reassess such values annually and then use the reassessed value as the new basis for comparison, leaving the rate of depreciation constant.

In assessing compound interest there is usually a constant growth factor, whereas in depreciation there is a constant decay factor. When the rate of growth or decay is constant over the total time, both of these are examples of what is called the compound interest law. This law can be expressed by the formula

$$A = P \left[1 + \frac{\pm r}{100} \right]^n,$$

where A is the amount which P will grow or decay to after n units of time (usually years), at $r\%$ per unit time, compounded at the end of each unit of time. In cases of growth r is positive and in cases of decay r is negative.

In working examples it is unnecessary to use the formula when the total number of units of time is small; it is quicker to determine the amount accrued at the end of each unit of time by direct calculation.

Example 1: *A man invests £500 at 6% per annum compound interest, compounded yearly. Find, to the nearest penny,*
(a) by direct calculation, the amount at the end of the' third year,
(b) by using the formula, the amount at the end of the tenth year.

(a) Interest for first year $= \dfrac{6}{100} \times £500 \qquad = £30 \qquad$ Amount $= £530$

Interest for second year $= \dfrac{6}{100} \times £530 \qquad = £31.80 \quad$ Amount $= £561.80$

Interest for third year $\quad = \dfrac{6}{100} \times £561.80$

$$= £33.708 \quad \text{Amount} = £595.508$$

The amount at the end of the third year $= £595.51$ (to nearest penny).

(b) Using the formula $\quad A = P\left[1 + \dfrac{r}{100}\right]^{n}$, where $P = 500$, $r = 6$

and $n = 10$, $\qquad A = 500\left(1 + \dfrac{6}{100}\right)^{10} = 500 \times (1.06)^{10}$

$$= 895.423.$$

The amount at the end of the tenth year $= £895.42$ (to nearest penny).

Example 2: *A man buys a colour television set for £400. The value of the set depreciates at 20% per annum, the value for each year being assessed on the value in the immediately preceding year. Calculate the value of the set (a) in the third year, (b) in the seventh year.*
(a) Using the compound interest formula with $P = 400$, $r = -20$ and $n = 2$,

Value in 3rd year $= £400\left(1 - \dfrac{20}{100}\right)^{2} = £400(0.8)^{2} = £256.$

(b) Value in 7th year is given when $n = 6$ and is $£400(0.8)^{6} = £104.857.$
Value in 7th year is $£104.86$ (to nearest penny).

Exercise 2.3

1 Calculate the simple interest and the amount when £500 is invested for 4 years at 6% per annum.
2 Calculate the simple interest and the amount when £324 is invested for 5 years at 7% per annum.
3 Find the time required for £250 to yield £100 simple interest at 8% per annum.

4 Find the time required for £2400 to yield £858 simple interest at 13 % per annum.

5 Find the rate % per annum given that £375 yields £75 simple interest in 4 years.

6 Find the rate % per annum given that £825 yields £77 simple interest in $3\frac{1}{2}$ years.

7 Determine the principal required to give £60 simple interest in 4 years at $2\frac{1}{2}$ % per annum.

8 Determine the principal required to give £191.70 simple interest in 9 years at 6 % per annum.

9 Find the principal which amounts at simple interest to £1308 in 2 years at $4\frac{1}{2}$ % per annum.

10 Find the principal which amounts at simple interest to £752 in 8 years at $7\frac{1}{2}$ % per annum.

11 A finance house charges 1.5 p per month simple interest on every £1 loaned. Calculate the annual interest charge on a loan of £3250.

12 Find the simple interest on £1460 at 7 % per annum from 30th September to 12th December in the same year.

13 A lady invests £16 500 and is paid simple interest at 6.8 % per annum. Show that this investment is worth £93.50 per month to her.

14 A society pays simple interest to its investors at the rate of 7.5 % per annum. Find the time that it will take for an investment of £400 to yield £135 interest.

15 Given that £320 amounts to £344 in 8 months, find the amount it will give in 1 year at the same rate of simple interest.

16 Determine the principal which would amount to £1131 in 4 years at $7\frac{1}{2}$ % per annum simple interest.

17 Find, to the nearest penny, the simple interest on £372 for 73 days at 4 % per annum.

18 Find the principal which will amount to £350 in 3 years at 5 % per annum simple interest; give your answer to the nearest penny.

19 Find the rate % per annum at which £360 will amount to £414 at simple interest in 3 years.

20 Find the time required for £150 to amount to £171 at 4 % per annum simple interest.

21 Calculate the compound interest on £700 for 3 years at 5 % per annum, payable yearly.

22 Calculate the amount at 9 % compound interest, payable yearly, of £640 for (a) 3 years, (b) 10 years.

23 Calculate the simple interest on £1000 for 5 years at 8 % per annum. If this sum had been invested for 5 years at 8 % compound interest, payable yearly, show that the yield would be £69.33 more.

24 A car costing £3000 depreciates at 12 % each year, the depreciation being calculated on the value of the car during the previous year. Show that the value of the car during the 5th year after purchase is £1800 nearly.

25 At the start of a year a man invests £10 000 at 5% per annum. At the end of each year he withdraws £2000, leaving the remainder to gain interest until the next withdrawal. Find the amount of money left in the investment during the third year.

26 A typewriter costing £80 new depreciates at 15% per annum, the value in any year being assessed at 15% less than its value in the immediately preceding year. Calculate the value of the typewriter during its sixth year after purchase.

27 Measured at the end of 5 year periods, the population of a country is known to be growing uniformly at 7% every 5 years with respect to the immediate previous 5 year period. Given that the population was 50 million at the end of 1975, estimate the size of the population at the end of 1985.

28 Show that a rate of approximately 4.5% per annum would allow an investment of £250 to grow to £325.57 over 6 years under compound interest, payable yearly.

29 The value of a car originally costing £3600 was £1600 after 3 years. Assuming its value to depreciate by equal annual percentages, use the compound interest formula to estimate the annual percentage depreciation.

30 Estimate the rate % per annum at which a sum of money should be invested at compound interest, payable annually, in order to double itself in 10 years.

3 Mensuration

Units

The standard unit measure of length is the *metre* (m). Three commonly used derivations of the metre are

the millimetre (mm), where 1 mm $= 1/1000$ m $= 10^{-3}$ m
the centimetre (cm), where 1 cm $\quad = 1/100$ m $\quad = 10^{-2}$ m
the kilometre (km), where 1 km $\quad = 1000$ m $\quad = 10^{3}$ m.

All linear measurements used in a particular calculation should be expressed in the same units.

The area of an enclosed region is measured by finding the number of times a standard unit area will fit into the region.

$$1 \text{ mm}^2 = 10^{-6} \text{ m}^2$$
$$1 \text{ cm}^2 = 10^{-4} \text{ m}^2$$
$$1 \text{ km}^2 = 10^{6} \text{ m}^2.$$

Definition: 1 hectare $= 100^2$ m$^2 = 10^4$ m^2.

The volume of a solid is measured by finding the number of times a standard unit volume will fit into the solid.

$$1 \text{ mm}^3 = 10^{-9} \text{ m}^3$$
$$1 \text{ cm}^3 = 10^{-6} \text{ m}^3$$
$$1 \text{ km}^3 = 10^{9} \text{ m}^3.$$

Definition: 1 litre $\equiv 1000$ cm^3. 1000 litres $\equiv 1$ m^3.

Some standard results (areas)

N.B. Whenever h is used it refers to the *perpendicular height*.
1. **Rectangle** length a, breadth b, **area** $= ab$.
2. All **parallelograms** with a common base and equal height are equal in area.

In Figure 3.1, the line AB is taken as base and the line l is parallel to AB. A general point P is chosen on l and the parallelogram ABPQ completed. Points C and D are taken on l such that ABCD is a rectangle. The triangle

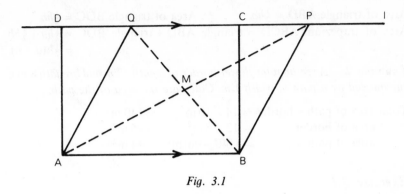

Fig. 3.1

ADQ is mapped onto the triangle BCP by a translation defined by the vector **AB**. These triangles are therefore equal in area.

Rectangle ABCD = triangle ADQ + quadrilateral ABCQ in area.
Parallelogram ABPQ = triangle BCP + quadrilateral ABCQ in area.
Therefore rectangle ABCD = parallelogram ABPQ in area.
Since area of rectangle ABCD = AB × BC,

$$\text{area of a parallelogram} = \text{base} \times \text{height.}$$

3. In Figure 3.1 the diagonals of the parallelogram ABPQ meet at M. Triangle AQB is mapped onto triangle PBQ by a rotation centre M through 180°. These triangles are each equal in area to half the parallelogram ABPQ which is the same as half the area of rectangle ABCD.

$$\text{Area of triangle} = \tfrac{1}{2} \text{ base} \times \text{height.}$$

The areas of plane enclosed regions bounded by straight lines can be calculated by dividing the region into triangles and finding the area of each triangle.

Example 1: *Prove that the area of a trapezium of height h, with parallel sides of lengths a and b, is $\tfrac{1}{2}(a+b)h$.*

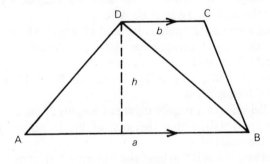

Fig. 3.2

In Figure 3.2, AB is parallel to DC, AB = a, DC = b and the distance between these lines is h.

Area of triangle ABD $= \frac{1}{2}ha,$ Area of triangle BDC $= \frac{1}{2}hb.$

Area of trapezium ABCD $=$ triangle ABD $+$ triangle BDC $= \frac{1}{2}ha + \frac{1}{2}hb$
$$= \frac{1}{2}h(a + b).$$

Example 2: *A rectangular flower border of length 12 m and breadth 8 m is surrounded by a path of width 1 m. Calculate the area of the path.*

Total area of path $+$ border $= 14 \times 10\,\text{m}^2$ $= 140\,\text{m}^2$
area of border $= 12 \times 8\,\text{m}^2$ $= 96\,\text{m}^2$
area of path $= (140 - 96)\,\text{m}^2$ $= 44\,\text{m}^2$

Exercise 3.1

1   Find the area of a rectangle 4.7 m long and 3.8 m wide.

2   Find the area, in m², of one side of a cassette tape which is 1 cm wide and 25 m long.

3   The floor area of a rectangular room 7.5 m in length is 36 m². Calculate the breadth of the room.

4   Calculate, in hectares, the area of a rectangular field of length 175 m and breadth 94 m.

5   The area of a rectangular sports field of length 320 m is 5.92 hectare. Calculate the breadth.

6   A carpet 3.5 m long and 2.6 m wide is laid in a room 4 m square. Find the area of the floor left uncovered.

7   Find the number of square tiles, each tile 15 cm × 15 cm, required to cover the floor of a room 6 m long and 4.5 m wide.

8   A rectangular lounge is 7 m long and 4.5 m wide. Calculate the area of the floor of the lounge.
The floor is partly covered by a rectangular carpet of length 5 m. Given that the floor area not covered is 11.5 m², calculate the width of the carpet.

9   The area of a parallelogram ABCD is 14 cm² and AB = 5 cm. Calculate the perpendicular distance between C and AB.

10   In the triangle ABC, AB = 12 cm and the altitude CH = 8.5 cm. Calculate the area of the triangle ABC.
Given that a second altitude is BP and of length 6.8 cm, find AC.

11   Calculate the area of a trapezium whose parallel sides are of lengths 3.7 cm and 9.7 cm and are 5 cm apart.

12   In the triangle ABC, AB = AC = 10 cm, and BC = 12 cm. Calculate the area of triangle ABC.

13   The parallel sides of a trapezium are of lengths 22 cm and 48 cm and are x cm apart. Given that the area of the trapezium is 252 cm², calculate the value of x.

14   A room of height 4 m is 8 m long and 5 m wide. Calculate the total area of the walls of the room.

15   Each side of a rhombus is 10 cm long and its shorter diagonal is of length 12 cm. Calculate (a) the length of the longer diagonal, (b) the area of the rhombus.

16 Prove that the area of a rhombus whose diagonals are of lengths a and b is $\frac{1}{2}ab$.

17 The area of a rhombus is 240 m². Given that one diagonal is of length 30 m, calculate (a) the length of the other diagonal, (b) the length of a side of the rhombus.

18 A parallelogram ABCD has AB = 12 cm and BC = 8 cm. Given that the area of the parallelogram is 60 cm², calculate the perpendicular distance between (a) AB and DC, (b) BC and DA.

19 Referring to Figure 3.1, prove that triangles ADQ and BCP are congruent. Hence prove that area ABPQ = area ABCD.

20 Referring to Figure 3.1, prove that the area of triangle AQB = area of triangle ADQ + area of triangle BQC.

Some standard results (volumes)

1. **Cuboid**   (rectangular box), length a, breadth b, height h.

$$\text{Volume} = abh.$$

2. **Pyramid**   A solid whose base is a polygon and all the other faces are triangles is called a **pyramid**.

$$\text{Volume} = \tfrac{1}{3} \text{ base area} \times \text{height.}$$

N.B.   A cone can be considered as a pyramid if its volume has to be found.

3. **Solid with uniform cross-section.**

When the uniform cross-section is a triangle, quadrilateral or any polygon, the solid is called a **prism**.

When the uniform cross-section is circular (or elliptical), the solid is called a **cylinder**.

Volume of solid with uniform cross-section = area of cross-section × distance between end faces.

Definition: **Density.** The mass of a unit volume of a particular substance is called its density.

In particular, density = mass/volume: units kg/m³ or g/cm³.

Take 1 m³ of water to be of mass 1000 kg.

Definition: **Specific gravity.** (Relative density)

$$\text{The specific gravity of a substance} = \frac{\text{mass of the substance}}{\text{mass of equal volume of water}}.$$

Example 1:   *A pyramid has a rectangular horizontal base ABCD, where AB = 7 cm and BC = 5 cm. The vertex N of the pyramid is vertically above A and NA = 6 cm. Calculate the volume of the pyramid.*

$$\text{Area of base} = 7 \times 5 \text{ cm}^2 = 35 \text{ cm}^2.$$

$$\text{Volume of pyramid} = \tfrac{1}{3} \times 35 \times 6 \text{ cm}^3 = 70 \text{ cm}^3.$$

Example 2:

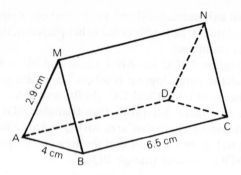

Fig. 3.3

Figure 3.3 shows a solid prism in which the horizontal rectangular base ABCD has AB = 4 cm and BC = 6.5 cm. The edge MN is parallel to BC and MA = MB = NC = ND = 2.9 cm. Calculate (a) the volume, (b) the total surface area of the prism.

Taking the mid-point of AB as X, the height of the prism MX, is given by

$$MX^2 = AM^2 - AX^2 = 2.9^2 - 2^2 = 4.41$$

$$MX = 2.1 \text{ cm}.$$

Area of triangle MAB = area of uniform cross-section of prism.

$$\tfrac{1}{2} \times 4 \times 2.1 \text{ cm}^2 = 4.2 \text{ cm}^2.$$

(a) Volume of prism = 4.2×6.5 cm^3 = 27.3 cm^3.
(b) Total surface area = 2 × triangle MAB + ABCD + 2 × rectangle BCNM

$$= 2 \times \tfrac{1}{2} \times 4 \times 2.1 + 4 \times 6.5 + 2 \times 2.9 \times 6.5 \text{ cm}^2$$

$$= 8.4 + 26.0 + 37.7 \text{ cm}^2$$

$$= 72.1 \text{ cm}^2.$$

Example 3: *Find the mass of a rectangular block of Portland stone, whose specific gravity is 2.1, measuring 30 cm by 20 cm by 12 cm.*

Density of the stone = 2.1×1000 kg/m^3 = 2100 kg/m^3

Volume of stone = $0.3 \times 0.2 \times 0.12$ m^3 = 7.2×10^{-3} m^3.

Mass of stone = volume × density = $7.2 \times 10^{-3} \times 2100$ kg = 15.12 kg.

Exercise 3.2

1 A rectangular oil-tank has internal dimensions 3.4 m by 2.5 m by 1.8 m. Calculate the volume of the tank and its capacity, in litres, when full.

2   A rectangular water tank has a square horizontal base of area 5 m².
    Calculate the length of one of the base edges. Given that the tank, when
    full, holds 8500 litres, find the height of the tank.

3   A swimming bath is 50 m long and 30 m wide. Find the amount of
    water, in litres, required to raise the level by 1 cm.

4   A cattle-trough is 7 m long and its internal uniform cross-section is an
    isosceles triangle of width 0.6 m and depth 0.4 m. Calculate the volume
    of the trough.

5   A metal cuboid is 1.5 m long, 0.4 m wide and 0.24 m high. Given that
    the specific gravity of the cuboid is 7.5, find its mass in kg.

6   A tank holds 800 litres of petrol. Given that the specific gravity of
    petrol is 0.7, calculate the mass of the petrol.

7   A pyramid stands on a rectangular base ABCD, where AB = 18 cm
    and BC = 11 cm. The vertex N of the pyramid is 6 cm vertically above
    the centre of the base. Calculate the volume of the pyramid.

8   A sheet of glass measures 50 cm by 42 cm and is 0.2 cm thick. Given
    that the specific gravity of the glass is 2.6, find the mass, in kg, of the
    sheet of glass.

9   The surface of the water in a swimming bath is a rectangle of length
    60 m and width 35 m. The depth of water decreases uniformly from
    6 m at the deep end to 1.5 m at the shallow end. Calculate the volume of
    water in the pool when it is full.

10 Find, in cm³, the volume of wood required to make a closed
    rectangular cigar box measuring on its outside 12 cm by 8 cm by 3 cm
    from a sheet of wood 0.5 cm thick.

11 The internal dimensions of a closed rectangular tank are 42 cm by
    29 cm by 20 cm. Calculate, in litres, the capacity of the tank. Given that
    the metal in the tank is 0.3 cm thick, find the volume of metal used in
    making the tank.

12 Water is being pumped at the rate of 12 litre/second into a rectangular
    tank whose internal length and breadth are 1.4 m and 0.9 m. Find the
    rate, in cm/s, at which the level of water in the tank is rising.

13 Snow covers a flat horizontal roof measuring 32 m by 22 m to a depth
    of 5 cm. Taking the specific gravity of snow to be 0.4, find the mass, in
    kg, of snow on the roof.

14 A solid metal prism, of length 12 cm, has a uniform cross-section in the
    form of a regular hexagon of side 0.3 cm. Show that the area of the
    hexagonal cross-section is $\dfrac{27\sqrt{3}}{200}$ cm² and hence find, to 2 s.f., the
    volume of the prism.

15 A rectangular lawn measuring 25 m by 18 m is surrounded by a path
    1.5 m wide. Calculate, in m³, the amount of tarmac which would be
    required to cover the path to a uniform depth of 2 cm.

16 The square base of a pyramid has each edge of length 6 cm. Given that
    the volume of the pyramid is 13.2 cm³, find its height.

17 The height of a pyramid with a square base is 8 cm and its volume is
    20 cm³. Calculate the length of a side of the base.

18 A hollow container whose internal uniform cross-sectional area is $0.2\,m^2$ holds 16.5 litres when full. Calculate the internal height of the container.

The circle

The ratio of the circumference of any circle to its diameter is the constant irrational number π. The value of π to 4 figures is 3.142, the rational approximation 22/7 is often used, and a value for π is available on most electronic calculators. In examples the value of π should be taken directly from a calculator or as 3.142, unless instructed otherwise.

The circumference C of a circle radius r is given by

$$C = 2\pi r.$$

The area A of the circle is given by

$$A = \pi r^2.$$

Example 1: *Calculate (a) the circumference, (b) the area of a circle of radius 8.7 cm.*

(a) $C = 2\pi r = 2\pi \times 8.7$ Circumference = 54.7 cm (3 s.f.)
(b) $A = \pi r^2 = \pi \times 8.7 \times 8.7$ Area = 238 cm^2 (3 s.f.)

Example 2: *Calculate the circumference of a circle whose area is 50 m^2.*

$\pi r^2 = 50$, $r^2 = 50/\pi$, $r = \sqrt{(50/\pi)}$ Radius = 3.989 m.

$C = 2\pi r = 2\pi \times 3.989$ Circumference = 25.1 m (3 s.f.).

The right circular cylinder

The radius of the cylinder is r and its height h. The cylinder has two plane circular ends each of area πr^2. If the cylinder is rolled along its curved surface through $360°$ on a flat surface, the area covered is a rectangle of length $2\pi r$ and breadth h. The area of the curved surface of the cylinder is $2\pi rh$.

Total surface area of the cylinder $= 2\pi rh + 2\pi r^2 = \mathbf{2\pi r(h+r)}$.

The cylinder has a uniform circular cross-section of area πr^2 and is of length h.

The volume of the cylinder $= \mathbf{\pi r^2 h}$.   [*N.B.* This is a *closed* cylinder]

Circular pipe

For a circular pipe of inner radius r, outer radius R, height h,

area of uniform
   cross-section $= \pi R^2 - \pi r^2 = \pi(R^2 - r^2) = \mathbf{\pi(R+r)(R-r)}.$

Volume of material in the pipe $= \pi(R^2 - r^2)h = \pi h(R+r)(R-r)$.

Example 1: *A gasometer is in the form of a right circular cylinder of base radius 9 m and height 14 m. Taking π to be 22/7, calculate (a) the volume, (b) the outer curved surface area of the gasometer.*

(a) Volume $= \pi r^2 h = 22/7 \times 9 \times 9 \times 14 \text{ m}^3 = 3564 \text{ m}^3$.
(b) Curved surface area $= 2\pi rh = 2 \times 22/7 \times 9 \times 14 \text{ m}^2 = 792 \text{ m}^2$.

Example 2: *Water flows through a circular pipe of diameter 12 cm at a rate of 44 litre/s, the pipe always being full of water. Calculate, in m/s, the speed of discharge of the water from the pipe.*

Cross-sectional area of water in pipe $= \pi 6^2 \text{ cm}^2 = \dfrac{36\pi}{10\,000} \text{ m}^2$.

Volume of water discharged each second $= \dfrac{44}{1000} \text{ m}^3$.

Speed of discharge of water $= \dfrac{\text{volume of water discharged/s}}{\text{cross-sectional area}}$

$$= \frac{44}{1000} \times \frac{10\,000}{36\pi} \text{ m/s} = 3.89 \text{ m/s}.$$

Right circular cone

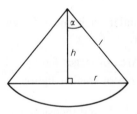

Fig. 3.4

Figure 3.4 shows a right circular cone of base radius r, height h, **slant-height** l and **semi-vertical angle** α.

$$h^2 + r^2 = l^2$$

$$\tan \alpha = r/h.$$

The curved surface area is πrl
The total surface area is $\pi rl + \pi r^2 = \pi r(l+r)$.
The volume is $\frac{1}{3}\pi r^2 h$.
A plane cut taken through the cone, parallel to the base, separates the cone into a smaller cone and a *frustum* of the original cone. The curved surface area and the volume of a frustum are determined by considering the

respective differences between the curved surface areas and the volumes of the original cone and the smaller cone.

Example: *A right circular cone has base radius 5 cm and height 12 cm. Calculate (a) the volume, (b) the total surface area of the cone.*

(a) Volume $= \frac{1}{3}\pi r^2 h = \frac{1}{3}\pi \times 25 \times 12$ cm^3 $= 100\pi$ cm^3 $= 314.2$ cm^3.

(b) $l^2 = h^2 + r^2 = 12^2 + 5^2 = 169.$ $l = 13.$

Total surface area $= \pi r(l+r) = \pi \times 5 \times 18$ cm^2 $= 90\pi$ cm^2 $= 282.8$ cm^2.

The sphere

The surface area S of a sphere, radius r, is given by

$$S = 4\pi r^2.$$

The volume V of the sphere is given by

$$V = \tfrac{4}{3}\pi r^3.$$

Similarity relations: plane figures and solids

Two entities are mathematically similar when one is an enlargement of the other; corresponding angles remain the same and the ratios of corresponding lengths is constant.

Two plane figures are similar, each linear dimension of the larger being n times that of the smaller.

$$\frac{\text{Area of larger figure}}{\text{Area of smaller figure}} = n^2.$$

Two solids are similar, each linear dimension of the larger being n times that of the smaller.

$$\frac{\text{Volume of larger solid}}{\text{Volume of smaller solid}} = n^3.$$

Example 1: *A sphere of radius 3 cm is placed in a fish-tank which is rectangular with square base of side 8 cm. The tank contains sufficient water to completely cover the sphere and none spills over. Calculate, to 0.1 cm, the rise in the height of the water level in the tank.*

Volume of sphere $= \frac{4}{3}\pi \times 3^3$ cm^3

Base area of the tank $= 64$ cm^2

Rise in water level $= \dfrac{\text{volume of sphere}}{\text{base area of tank}} = \dfrac{4 \times \pi \times 27}{3 \times 64}$

$= 1.8$ cm (to 0.1 cm).

Example 2: *A frustum from the cone of base radius 5 cm and height 12 cm is formed by a cut parallel to the base at a distance of 4 cm from the vertex (see Figure 3.5). Calculate (a) the volume, (b) the curved surface area of the frustum.*

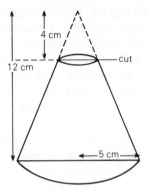

Fig. 3.5

The smaller cone and larger cone are similar, their heights being in the ratio $1:3$. The volumes will be in the ratio $1^3:3^3$ that is $1:27$. The volume of the frustum is $26/27$ of the volume of the larger cone.

Volume of frustum $= \dfrac{26}{27} \times \dfrac{1}{3}\pi \times 25 \times 12 \text{ cm}^3 = 302.6 \text{ cm}^3$.

The curved surface areas of the smaller and larger cones are in the ratio $1^2:3^2 = 1:9$.

The curved surface area of the frustum is $8/9$ of the surface area of the larger cone. The slant height of this cone is 13 cm.

Area of curved surface of frustum $= \dfrac{8}{9} \times \pi \times 5 \times 13 \text{ cm}^2 = 181.5 \text{ cm}^2$.

Example 3: *Two uniform statuettes are similar and made from the same substance, the larger being 5 cm tall and the smaller 2 cm tall. Given that the larger is of mass 1.5 kg, find the mass of the smaller.*

Since the statuettes are made of the same substance, their masses are proportional to their volumes.

Since the statuettes are similar,

$$\frac{\text{volume of larger}}{\text{volume of smaller}} = \frac{5^3}{2^3} = \frac{125}{8}.$$

$$\text{Mass of smaller} = \frac{8}{125} \times 1.5 \text{ kg} = 0.096 \text{ kg}.$$

Exercise 3.3

1   Calculate (i) the circumference, (ii) the area, of a circle whose radius is
(a) 5 cm, (b) 34 m, (c) 0.4 mm.

2   Calculate (i) the radius, (ii) the area, of a circle whose circumference is of length (a) 100 m, (b) 28 cm, (c) 1.7 km.

3   Calculate (i) the radius, (ii) the circumference, of a circle whose area is (a) 5 km², (b) 16π cm², (c) 2 hectare.

4   The two straights AB and DC, each of length 68 m, of a running track are a pair of opposite sides of a rectangle ABCD. The track has semicircular ends with diameters AD and BC. The total perimeter of the track is 400 m. Taking $\pi = 22/7$, calculate (a) the length of AD, (b) the total area, in hectares, enclosed by the track.

5   A rectangular lawn ABCD, where AB = 32 m and BC = 26 m, has a circular flower border of radius 7 m within it. Calculate the area of the lawn.

6   Two circular discs of the same thickness with radii 9 mm and 12 mm are melted down and made into a new circular disc of the same thickness. Calculate the radius of this new disc.

7   Calculate (i) the volume, (ii) the curved surface area, of a right circular cylinder with (a) base radius 10 cm, height 6 cm, (b) base radius 3.4 m, height 6.5 m, (c) base radius 5.6 cm, height 0.1 mm.

8   A cylindrical tub with a horizontal circular base of radius 28 cm contains water to depth of 75 cm. (a) Calculate the amount, in litres, of water in the tub. (b) Find the area on the inside surface of the tub which is in contact with water.

9   A closed cylindrical tin has a circular base, diameter 7 cm. The capacity of the tin is 1.5 litres. Calculate (a) the height, (b) the total surface area, of the outside of the tin.

10   The internal and external radii of a hollow circular cylinder of length 50 cm and open at both ends are 1.2 cm and 1.5 cm respectively. Calculate the volume of material used in making this hollow cylinder.

11   A solid metal cube of side 5 cm is melted down and made into a right circular cylinder whose diameter is equal to its height. Calculate the height of the cylinder and the ratio of its total surface area to that of the original cube.

12   Two similar cylinders are of masses 4 kg and 32 kg. Given that the area of the circular base of the smaller is 24 cm², find the area of the circular base of the larger.

13   Calculate (i) the volume, (ii) the slant height, (iii) the curved surface area, of a right circular cone with
(a) base radius 20 cm, height 21 cm, (b) base radius 3 m, height 4 m, (c) base radius 10 mm, semi-vertical angle 45°.

14   Two right circular cones, each of base radius 8 cm and slant height 10 cm, are joined together by their bases to form a double cone with a common axis. Calculate (a) the total surface area, (b) the volume, of the double cone so formed.

15   Calculate the curved surface area and the volume of a right circular cone with base radius 5 cm and semi-vertical angle 30°.

16   A solid right circular cone of height 35 cm has a volume of 3.3 m³. Taking π to be 22/7, calculate the base radius of the cone.

17 A right circular cone, base radius 7 cm and height 10 cm, and a right circular cylinder, base radius 7 cm and height 5 cm, have their bases stuck together to form a composite solid having a common axis. Calculate (a) the volume, (b) the surface area, of this composite solid.

18 Calculate (i) the volume, (ii) the surface area, of a sphere of radius (a) 2 cm, (b) 1.7 m.

19 A solid sphere of radius 10 cm is bisected into two hemispheres by a plane cut through its centre. Calculate (a) the volume, (b) the total surface area, of a hemisphere so formed.

20 The volume of a sphere is 0.5 m³. Calculate the radius of the sphere.

21 The surface area of a sphere is 100π cm². Calculate its volume.

22 Calculate the volume of a sphere which can just be placed inside a cubical box with internal measurements 5 cm × 5 cm × 5 cm.

23 A cylindrical tank containing water has a circular base of radius 5cm. Four spherical ball bearings, each of radius 1 cm, are placed in the tank and are completely covered by the water, none of which spills. Calculate, to 0.1cm, the rise in water level in the tank.

24 A composite solid consists of a right circular cone, height 8cm and base radius 6cm, and a hemisphere whose plane base coincides with the base of the cone. Calculate (a) the volume, (b) the surface area, of the composite solid.

25 A thin hollow sphere of radius 10cm is half full of water. Find the mass of the water in the sphere and the surface area in contact with water.

26 A pyramid of height 10cm has volume 56cm³.
(a) Find the volume of a similar pyramid of height 15cm.
(b) Find the height of another similar pyramid whose volume is 7cm³.

27 The areas of the bases of two similar cones are in the ratio 25:16. The radius of the base of the larger cone is 15cm. Find the radius of the base of the smaller cone.

28 A sphere of radius 6cm has two separate spherical holes within it of radii 2cm and 3cm, respectively, the remainder of the sphere consisting of uniform material. Calculate the % volume of the whole sphere which is occupied by the uniform material.

29 Given that a wine bottle of height 25cm holds 1 litre, calculate the height of a similar bottle holding 2 litres.

30 Two similar statuettes have masses 6kg and 9kg. Given that the larger has a surface area of 12cm², find the surface area of the smaller.

Miscellaneous Exercise A

1 A party held in a restaurant cost £37.75 plus 12 per cent surcharge. Calculate the total cost. [JMB 1972]

2 Evaluate $(3\frac{3}{4} \div 2\frac{1}{3}) - \frac{1}{4}$. [C 1973]

3 Express as a single fraction in its lowest terms
$$(7\frac{1}{2} - 1\frac{5}{6}) \div 1\frac{7}{8}.$$ [L 1969]

4 A man sells his car for £810 and as a result loses 10 per cent of the price

he paid for it. What was the price he paid for it?   [AEB   1976]

5   A motorway journey takes 3 hours at an average speed of 120 km/h. How long will it take if the average speed is reduced to 80 km/h?
[JMB   1975]

6   £144 is divided into three shares in the ratio 1 : 3 : 5. Find the smallest share.   [C   1975]

7   A table which costs £60 to manufacture is sold at a price which allows 40% profit on the cost price. It is estimated that 10% of the selling price must be set aside to cover overhead expenses. Calculate the net profit.   [L   1975]

8   A diesel train of length 72 m is travelling at 96 km/h on a straight track. Calculate
   (i) the time in seconds taken for the whole train to pass a person standing beside the track,
   (ii) the time in seconds taken for the train to completely pass a platform of length 108 m,
   (iii) the speed in km/h of another train of length 78 m which is travelling in the opposite direction on a parallel track and is passed completely by this train in $3\frac{1}{3}$ seconds.   [AEB   1978]

9   The first £5000 of a sum of money is taxed at 30% and the remainder, if any, is taxed at 40%. Calculate
   (i) the tax on £6805,
   (ii) the sum on which the tax is £1110,
   (iii) the sum on which the tax is £1710.

   On a certain sum, £x, which is greater than £5000, the tax is £$\frac{x}{3}$.

   Express this as an equation in x and hence calculate x.
[JMB   1973]

10   Given that $x = 3.0 \times 10^6$ and $y = 4.0 \times 10^7$, express in the same standard form
   (i) xy;
   (ii) $\dfrac{x}{y}$.   [C   1970]

11   Calculate the Simple Interest on £16.50 invested for 16 months at $7\frac{1}{2}$% per annum.   [C   1971]

12   A man invested £100 in a building society on January 1st each year where the money accumulated at 5% Compound Interest per annum, calculated on 31st December each year. Calculate the amount at the end of each of the 1st, 2nd and 3rd years. He ceased to make any further deposits after 3 years, but the money stayed invested at 5% Compound Interest per annum for a further 9 years. Calculate the amount at the end of the further 9 years, correct to the nearest £1.   [AEB   1975]

13   Two householders from the same town discuss the rates they pay annually. Mr A recalls that he pays £128.25 and his house has a rateable value of £150. Mr B can only remember that each year he pays a total of ten monthly instalments of £15.39. Calculate
   (i) the town rate (as pence in the £1),

(ii) the rateable value of Mr B's house,

(iii) the increase in Mr A's rates bill if house improvements cause his rateable value to be increased to £173 but the town rate falls to 80 p in the £1.

Another town decides to increase its revenue from the rates by 80 %. If in addition the town rateable value is increased by 15 %, by what percentage must the town rate be increased? Give your answer correct to three significant figures. [AEB 1976]

14 When 655 is multiplied by 5 in a certain base, the units digit of the product is 1. Find the three possible values of the base, and give the complete product in each case. [L 1973]

15 (a) Multiply 1111_2 by 101_2 in the binary scale, showing your working in long multiplication form.

(b) p, q and r are positive integers less than 8. Write down their values in each of the following cases.

(i) $143 = 10^2 p + 10q + r$.

(ii) $143 = 8^2 p + 8q + r$.

(c) A rectangular block has a square base whose side is exactly 7 cm. Its height, measured to the nearest millimetre, is 2.1 cm. Find, in cubic centimetres, the greatest possible error in calculating its volume. [C 1976]

16 A plot of land has an area of 8 km². The owner sells $\frac{2}{3}$ of it for farming and $\frac{1}{4}$ of the remainder for building. Calculate the value of the part he keeps if it is worth £51 000 per km². [L 1973]

17 The base of a rectangular tank containing oil is horizontal and measures 1.23 m by 0.78 m. Into this tank are dropped 1200 ball bearings which are completely submerged. Each ball bearing is a solid sphere of diameter 1.75 cm.

Calculate

(a) the volume of one ball bearing,

(b) the area of the base of the tank, in cm²,

(c) the increase, in mm, in the depth of oil when all the ball bearings are submerged,

(d) how many extra ball bearings must be submerged to raise the level of the oil by a further 2 cm.

Volume of a sphere $= \frac{4}{3}\pi r^3$; take π as 3.142 [L 1973]

18 A square brass plate is 2 mm thick and weighs 1.05 kg. Given that 1 cm³ of brass weighs 8.4 g, calculate, in centimetres, the length of the side of the square plate. [W 1977]

19 A uniform cylindrical pipe has an external diameter of 3.2 cm and an internal diameter of 2.6 cm. Show that the volume of material required to construct a metre length of the pipe is approximately 273 cm².

One *cubic metre* of the material used has a mass of 4350 kg. Taking the volume of a metre length to be 273 cm³, calculate the mass of 70 m of such a pipe, giving your answer to the nearest kilogramme. (Take π as 3.142.) [C 1972]

20

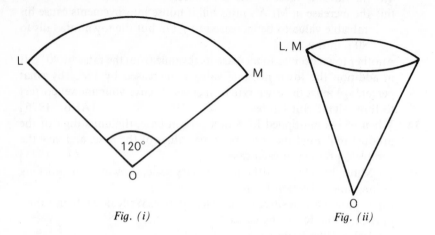

Fig. (i)   *Fig. (ii)*

Fig. (i) shows a sector LOM which has been cut from a circular sheet of thin metal, centre O and radius LO = 30 cm. Calculate the length of the arc LM and the area of the sector LOM.

The edges LO and MO are now joined and the metal is formed into a hollow right circular cone [see Fig. (ii)].
Calculate
(a) the radius of the base of the cone,
(b) the perpendicular height of the cone,
(c) the volume of water which would just fill the cone.   [L   1976]

21 A rectangular swimming pool with vertical sides is 15 m long and 8 m wide. When the pool is full the depth of water increases uniformly from 1 m at one end to 2.5 m at the other. Calculate the volume of water required to fill the pool.
When empty, the pool is filled by means of a pipe at the deep end which allows water to enter at a constant rate. The time taken for the water just to cover the bottom of the pool is 18 minutes. Calculate the further time that will be needed before the pool is completely full.

[S   1977]

22 (a) Calculate the sum of money which, when invested at compound interest, will amount to £1440 at the end of the first year, and to £1620 at the end of the second year.
(b) A tourist changes £120 into francs at a rate of £1 ≡ 8.15 francs and £150 into Deutschmark at a rate of £1 ≡ 3.96 Deutschmark. On his holiday he spends 936 francs and 526 Deutschmark. On his return journey he converts the remainder of his money into £ at the rate of £1 ≡ 8.40 francs and £1 ≡ 4.25 Deutschmark. Calculate the total sum of money (in £) he returned with, and express this as a percentage of the total sum of money he took on holiday.   [W   1978]

23 (a) Convert the binary number 1101110 into a number in base 10.
(b) Evaluate $(75.3 \times 1.7) + (1.7 \times 24.7)$.

(c) Factorise $3a^2 - 10a - 8$.

(d) Express 21609 in prime factors and hence find $\sqrt{(21609)}$.

[W 1977]

24 The cash price of a radiogram is £120 but a customer decides to buy it by Hire Purchase. He pays a deposit of £18 and subsequently makes 24 equal monthly payments. These payments make up the amount owing after the deposit has been paid together with simple interest on this amount for the two year period. The rate of interest is 20% per annum. Calculate what the monthly payment should be and express the total sum paid by the customer as a percentage of the cash price.

Another customer buys a colour television set for which the cash price is £300. He pays a deposit and, over the next three years, 36 monthly payments of £11.20. If the rate of simple interest is 20% per annum for the three year period, what deposit does this customer pay?

[O 1975]

25 A roll of adhesive tape consists of a plastic core in the form of a circular cylinder of radius 2 cm round which 1200 cm of tape is tightly wrapped so that the complete roll is also a cylinder. The thickness of the tape is 0.05 cm. By considering areas on the cross-section calculate the radius of the roll.

Two other such rolls have radii a cm and b cm with cores of radii r cm and $2r$ cm and lengths of tape x cm and $2x$ cm respectively. The thickness of the tape is 0.05 cm as before. Prove that $b^2 = 2(a^2 + r^2)$.

[O 1976]

4 Sets

A set is a collection of objects, so defined that there is no ambiguity as to whether an object is or is not included in that collection. The collection of integers is a set since, given any object, we can determine whether it belongs to the collection or not. The group of people in a school who are alive at this moment form a set, for we should be able to decide whether a person is in the group or not! The collection of fair-haired boys in a school, however, is not a well-defined set since 'fair-haired' is open to different interpretations by different people; some will include a particular boy, others will not.

This simple, basic idea is fundamental to the development of mathematics. The reader could find many branches of mathematics where the language of sets, considered in this chapter, is used.

Sets and elements

If an object x is a member of a set A, x is called an **element** of A, and this is written symbolically as $x \in A$. If the element y is not a member of A, this is written $y \notin A$. Sets themselves are usually denoted by capital letters and the elements of sets by small letters, numbers, or by merely naming each element.

Example 1: If E is the set of positive even integers, $2 \in E$ but $3 \notin E$.

When the number of elements in a set is small they may be listed inside curly brackets (braces).

Example 2: The set B of vowels in the word 'mathematics' may be written, $B = \{a, e, i\}$.
Note that, although 'mathematics' contains two 'a's, only once is 'a' listed in the set **B**. *A set should not record the same element twice.*

This method of describing a set can be used for sets with a large or even infinite number of elements provided that the omitted elements, signified by dots, form a pattern which is clearly recognisable. The set Z_+, of positive integers, and the set $\overline{E}$, of positive even numbers less than 40, may be written as $Z_+ = \{1, 2, 3, 4, \ldots\}$ and $\overline{E} = \{2, 4, 6, \ldots 38\}$ respectively.

Usually the set Z_+ is written as either {positive integers} or {$x: x$ is a positive integer}. In the latter form, used generally when listing is impractical, the ordered contents of the braces are: (a) a typical element of the set, (b) : standing for 'such that', and (c) a complete, unambiguous definition so that every element can be identified.

Example 3: The set of all prime numbers may be denoted by $\{x : x$ is a prime number$\}$.

Example 4: The set of points on the line $x + y = 4$ may be written $\{(x, y) : x + y = 4, x, y \text{ real}\}$.
A typical element in this case is a point and is therefore represented by (x, y).

The order in which elements are listed in a set is immaterial. The set B, defined earlier, may also be represented by $\{i, e, a\}$, for example.

The number of elements in a set A is denoted by $n\{A\}$ or $n(A)$. For the set B, $n(B) = 3$.

Universal set

To list the set of all men older than thirty is not feasible. However, if we are only considering the men in a particular room, or masters of a school, the elements of the set can be listed. In any situation the set to which all the elements under consideration belong is called the **universal set**, denoted by $\mathscr{E}$. It is not a unique set, but is chosen so that it will include every possible element in all other sets under discussion.

If, in a school, lists are made of those children living over five miles from the school, or those who stay for lunch, the children on the two lists form two sets, and a universal set relevant to both would be the set of children in the school.

Exercise

List the elements of the set of people who wear glasses for the following universal sets: (a) members of your class, (b) members of your family, (c) members of your favourite pop group.

Null set

For some readers the set of people who wear glasses in their family will have no members. The set with no elements is called the empty set, or null set, and is denoted by $\{\ \ \}$ or $\varnothing$.

This set, unlike the universal set, is a unique set.

Subset

A set A is a subset of a set B, written $A \subset B$, if every element of A is contained in B, i.e. $x \in A \Rightarrow x \in B$. ('$\Rightarrow$' means implies).

The statement $B \supset A$ (B contains A) also implies that A is a subset of B.

If $A \subset B$ and there is an element of B that is not in A, A is said to be a *proper* subset of B. Any set A is a non-proper subset of itself. (Why is this?). The null set is classed as a non-proper subset of any set.

Example: *List all subsets of the set* $A = \{a, b, c\}$

The subsets are $\{a\}, \{b\}, \{c\}, \{a, b\}, \{b, c\}, \{a, c\}, \{\quad\}, \{a, b, c\}$, the first six being the proper subsets of A.

Equal sets

If $x \in A \Leftrightarrow x \in B$ ('$\Leftrightarrow$' means 'implies and is implied by,' or 'if and only if') the sets A and B are equal.

Note: The implication signs $\Rightarrow$ and $\Leftrightarrow$ should be used carefully. For example, if $A \subset B$ it is not true that $x \in B \Rightarrow x \in A$, unless $A = B$, and, therefore, we cannot use $\Leftrightarrow$ in the definition of a subset.

Exercise 4.1

1 (For discussion). Which of the following are well-defined sets?
   (a) the collection of lively boys in a class,
   (b) the collection of clubs who won the F. A. Cup in the period 1970–75, (If 'clubs' is replaced by 'teams', what difference would there be, if any?)
   (c) the collection of stars in the sky,
   (d) the collection of the top five pop groups in Britain.
   (e) the collection of British kings since 1900?

2 Give a precise description, in words, for each of the following sets, if possible:
   (a) $\{1, 4, 9, 16, 25, \ldots \ldots\}$,   (b) $\{10, 12, 14, 16, 18\}$,
   (c) $\{5, 10, 15, 20, \ldots \ldots 50\}$,   (d) $\{2, 3, 4, 6\}$,
   (e) $\{$Carter, Ford, Nixon, Johnson, Kennedy$\}$,
   (f) $\{\frac{1}{2}p, 1p, 2p, 5p, 10p, 50p\}$.

3 List the elements of the following sets:
   (a) $A = \{x : x$ is a multiple of 5, $6 < x \leqslant 20\}$,
   (b) $B = \{x : x$ is a factor of 30$\}$,
   (c) $C = \{(x, y) : x$ is the square of $y, 1 \leqslant x \leqslant 50, 1 \leqslant y \leqslant 10\}$,
   (d) $D = \{x : x$ is a prime number, $26 < x < 40\}$.

4 Given that $A = \{x : x$ is a Member of Parliament$\}$, describe, in the same notation, three subsets of A.

5 Given that $A = \{x : x$ is a prime number, $a < x < b\}$, choose suitable values of a and b such that $A = \emptyset$

6 Write down the subsets of each of the sets A, B, C where $A = \{u\}$, $B = \{u, v\}$ and $C = \{u, v, w\}$.

    Given that $\overline{A}, \overline{B}, \overline{C}$ are the sets of subsets of A, B and C, respectively, write down: $n(A)$ and $n(\overline{A})$, $n(B)$ and $n(\overline{B})$, $n(C)$ and $n(\overline{C})$, and show that they satisfy the relation, $n(\overline{X}) = 2^{n(X)}$.

If a set has four elements how many subsets would you expect? How many of these are proper subsets?

Intersection and union

Two sets A and B may, or may not, have elements in common. If there are no common elements, the sets are said to be disjoint; if there are, the common set of elements is called the **intersection set** of A and B, denoted by $A \cap B$. Disjoint sets are implied by the statement $A \cap B = \varnothing$.
We may define the intersection set as $A \cap B = \{x : x \in A \text{ and } x \in B\}$, [i.e. $x \in A \cap B \Leftrightarrow x \in A \text{ and } x \in B$].
   The set of elements which are in A or B (including those in A and B) is called the **union set** of A and B, denoted by $A \cup B$.
We may define the union set as $A \cup B = \{x : x \in A \text{ or } x \in B\}$.
[i.e. $x \in A \cup B \Leftrightarrow x \in A \text{ or } x \in B$].

Example 1:   If $A = \{1, 2, 3, 4\}$ and $B = \{2, 4, 6\}$ then $A \cap B = \{2, 4\}$ and $A \cup B = \{1, 2, 3, 4, 6\}$.
The reader should verify that $n(A \cup B) = n(A) + n(B) - n(A \cap B)$.

Example 2:   Let A be the set of prime factors of 42, i.e. $A = \{2, 3, 7\}$, and let B be the set of prime factors of 330, i.e. $B = \{2, 3, 5, 11\}$.
Then $A \cap B = \{2, 3\}$ is the set of prime factors of 6, the H.C.F. of 42 and 330,
and $A \cup B = \{2, 3, 5, 7, 11\}$ is the set of prime factors of 2310, the L.C.M. of 42 and 330.

Note: This method for finding the H.C.F. and L.C.M. of groups of numbers needs modifying if a number has a repeated prime factor. As a set does not include identical elements, a suggested method is to allocate to each repeated prime factor a different suffix.

Example 3:   Denote the set of prime factors of 12 by $A = \{2_1, 2_2, 3\}$ and the set of prime factors of 40 by $B = \{2_1, 2_2, 2_3, 5\}$.
Then $A \cap B = \{2_1, 2_2\}$ is the set of prime factors of 4, the H.C.F. of 12 and 40, and
$A \cup B = \{2_1, 2_2, 2_3, 3, 5\}$ is the set of prime factors of 120, the L.C.M. of 12 and 40.

Complement

The set of elements not in a set A (referred to its universal set) form another set, denoted by A', and called the **complement** of A.

Example: (a) If $\mathscr{E} = \{1, 2, 3, 4, 5, 6\}$ and $A = \{4, 5\}$, then $A' = \{1, 2, 3, 6\}$.
(b) If $\mathscr{E}$ is the set of days in a week and A is the set of days, each of which has more than six letters in its spelling, then $A' = \{\text{Monday, Friday, Sunday}\}$.

Exercise 4.2

1 Given each of the following sets A and B, form the sets $A \cap B$ and $A \cup B$:
   (a) $A = \{1, 2\}$, $B = \{2\}$ (b) $A = \{1, 2\}$, $B = \{1, 2, 3\}$
   (c) $A = \{x:x \text{ prime, } 1 < x < 20\}$ $B = \{x:x \text{ even, } 1 < x < 10\}$
   (d) $A = \{x:x \text{ is a card in a jokerless pack}\}$, $B = \{x:x \text{ is a red ace}\}$
   (e) $A = \{x:x \text{ is a factor of } 120\}$ $B = \{x:x^3 \text{ is even, } 1 < x < 10\}$
   (f) $A = \{x:x \text{ is a score when a die is cast}\}$, $B = \{x:x \text{ is a combined score when two dice are cast}\}$.

2 If $\mathcal{E} = \{\text{natural numbers}\}$, $A = \{2, 4, 6, 8, 10\}$ and $B = \{1, 4, 9, 16\}$ list the elements of the following sets:
   (a) $A \cap B$, (b) $A \cup B$, (c) $A \cap B'$, (d) $A' \cap B$.

3 (a) Given   that $n(A) = 10$, $n(B) = 15$, $n(A \cup B) = 25$,   find $n(A \cap B)$.
   (b) Given that $n(A) = 30$, $n(A \cap B) = 4$, $n(A \cup B) = 40$, find $n(B)$.
   (c) Given that $n(A') = 40$, $n(B') = 30$, $n(A' \cap B') = 6$, find $n(A \cap B)'$.

4 If $\mathcal{E} = \{\text{months in a year}\}$, $A = \{\text{months having 31 days}\}$, $B = \{\text{months beginning with J}\}$, list the elements of: $A, B, A \cap B$, $A' \cap B'$.

5 Find the H.C.F. and the L.C.M. of the following pairs of numbers by letting the set $A = $ prime factors of the first number, and set $B = $ prime factors of the second number, and forming the sets $A \cap B$ and $A \cup B$ respectively (see examples in text): (a) 38 and 72 (b) 66 and 154 (c) 90 and 63.

6 Let A be the set of clubs who won the F.A. Cup in the period 1970–75 inclusive, and B be the set of clubs who were first division league champions in the same period. List the elements of $A, B, A \cap B$ and $A \cup B$, and explain why $n(A) \neq n(B)$.

7 If $A = \{(x, y): x + y = 2\}$, $B = \{(x, y): x = 1\}$, $C = \{(x, y): y = 2x\}$, list the elements of $A \cap B$ and state the values of: $n(A), n(A \cap C)$ and $n(A \cap B \cap C)$.

8 The symmetric difference of two sets A and B, denoted by $A \triangle B$, is defined as the set of elements in $A \cup B$ but not in $A \cap B$. If $A = \{a, b, c, d, e, f\}$ and $B = \{b, c, d, g\}$,   list   the   elements   of $A \triangle B$.

9 If $\mathcal{E} = \{\text{natural numbers less than 30}\}$, $A = \{\text{multiples of 3}\}$, $B = \{\text{prime numbers}\}$ and $C = \{\text{perfect squares}\}$, list the elements of A, B and C and state, with reasons, which of the following statements are true or false:
   (a) $B \subset A'$; (b) $A \cap B = \emptyset$; (c) $n(B) = 10$;
   (d) $n(A) = n(B)$; (e) $n(A \cap C) = 1$; (f) $B' \cap C' = \emptyset$.

10 Let $\mathcal{E}$ be the set of children at a party, B the set of boys, G the set of girls, T the set of children wearing trousers, and F the set of foreign children. Write a sentence equivalent to each of the following statements:
   (a) $B \subset T$; (b) $T' \neq \emptyset$; (c) $F \subset G \cap T'$.

Illustration of sets

The relationship between sets may be illustrated in a diagram, called a **Venn diagram**, after the English mathematician John Venn (1834–1923). The universal set is usually denoted by a rectangle and the subsets of $\mathscr{E}$ by loops such as circles, ovals or rectangles. Some of the sets defined earlier, $A \cap B$, $A \cup B$ and A' are illustrated in the Venn diagrams (Figure 4.1. (a), (b), (c), respectively) by the shaded regions.

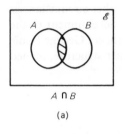
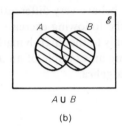
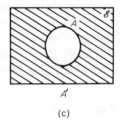

$A \cap B$ $A \cup B$ A'

(a)   (b)   (c)

Fig. 4.1

If $A \cup B = \mathscr{E}$, the rectangle is usually omitted. It should be noted that some relationships can be expressed in several alternative forms.

Example 1: $A \cup B = \mathscr{E} \Leftrightarrow (A \cup B)' = \varnothing \Leftrightarrow A' \cap B' = \varnothing$.
The last two relations in this example suggest the identity

$$(A \cup B)' = A' \cap B'.$$

Venn diagrams may be used to verify, but not prove, the validity of set identities by showing that each side of the relation simplifies to the same set.

Example 2: *For the three sets A, B, C, (as shown in Figure 4.2.) verify that* $A \cap (B \cup C) = (A \cap B) \cup (A \cap C)$.

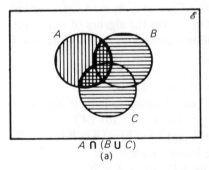
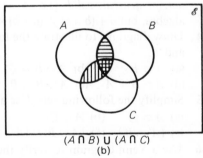

$A \cap (B \cup C)$ $(A \cap B) \cup (A \cap C)$
(a)   (b)

Fig. 4.2

In Figure 4.2(a) the set $B \cup C$ is shown by horizontal shading, the set A by vertical shading and therefore the set $A \cap (B \cup C)$ is represented by the region with both horizontal and vertical shading, bounded by the heavy line.

45

In Figure 4.2(b) the set $A \cap B$ is shown by horizontal shading, the set $A \cap C$ by vertical shading, and therefore the set $(A \cap B) \cup (A \cap C)$ is the same region as $A \cap (B \cup C)$, represented by the region with *either* horizontal or vertical shading, or *both* types of shading.

In this case the operations '$\cap$' and '$\cup$' on the sets A, B, and C act in a similar fashion to the operations of multiplication and addition respectively, on the set of numbers $\{a, b, c\}$. Compare the equivalent identities:

$$A \cap (B \cup C) = (A \cap B) \cup (A \cap C) \text{ in set algebra}$$

and $\qquad a \times (b + c) = (a \times b) + (a \times c)$ in 'ordinary' algebra.

However, these operations behave very differently in other circumstances, as the reader will find in the following exercise. The development of the algebra of sets was due mainly to the English mathematician George Boole (1815–64), this algebra being an example of an abstract structure, named after him, called **Boolean algebra**.

Exercise 4.3

1 If $\mathscr{E} = \{1, 2, 3, 4, 5, 6\}$, $A = \{1, 2, 3, 4\}$, $B = \{2, 3, 4, 5\}$ show the sets in a Venn diagram and list the elements of each of the following sets:
(a) A' (b) B' (c) $A \cap B$ (d) $A \cup B$
(e) $(A \cap B)'$ (f) $(A \cup B)'$ (g) $A' \cap B'$ (h) $A' \cup B'$.

2 If $\mathscr{E} = \{$natural numbers less than $20\}$, $A = \{$prime numbers$\}$, $B = \{$odd numbers$\}$ show the sets in a Venn diagram.
List the elements of (a) $A \cap B$; (b) $(A \cap B)'$; (c) $A \cap B'$.

3 If $A = \{a, b, c, d\}$, $B = \{a, b, d, e\}$ and $C = \{b, c, f\}$, show the sets in a Venn diagram and list the elements of each of the following sets:
(a) $B \cap C$ (b) $A \cup B$ (c) $A \cup C$
(d) $A \cup (B \cap C)$ (e) $(A \cup B) \cap (A \cup C)$ (f) $A \cup (B \cup C)$
(g) $(A \cup B) \cup C$.

   The equality of (d) and (e) demonstrates the fact that in set algebra '$\cup$' **is distributive over '$\cap$'**. The equivalent statement in ordinary algebra, is not, in general, valid. [i.e. $A \cup (B \cap C) = (A \cup B) \cap (A \cup C)$ for set algebra, but $a + (b \times c) \neq (a + b) \times (a + c)$ for the algebra of numbers].

4 Draw diagrams to illustrate the following relations between the sets A and B.
(a) $A \subset B$ (b) $A \cap B = \varnothing$ (c) $A' \cap B = B$
(d) $A \cap B = A$ (e) $A \cup B = B$ (f) $B' \cap A = \varnothing$.

5 Simplify the following sets. Use a Venn diagram to help, if necessary:
(a) $A \cap \varnothing$ (b) $A \cup \varnothing$ (c) $A \cup A$ (d) $(A')'$
(e) $(A' \cap B')$ (f) $(A \cup B) \cap (A \cup B')$ (g) $(A \cap B) \cup (A \cap B')$.

6 Use a Venn diagram to verify the following identities:
(a) $(A \cap B)' = A' \cup B'$ (b) $(A \cup B)' = A' \cap B'$
(c) $(A \cup B) \cup C = A \cup (B \cup C)$ (d) $(A \cap B) \cap C = (A \cap B) \cap C$
(e) $(A \cap B \cap C)' = A' \cup B' \cup C'$ (f) $(A \cup B \cup C)' = A' \cap B' \cap C'$

The identities (a) and (b) are known as **De Morgan's laws**, after the English mathematician Augustus De Morgan (1806–71). They also illustrate the principle of duality in set algebra: if a theorem is true so is the theorem formed by interchanging $\cap$ and $\cup$, and $\mathscr{E}$ and $\varnothing$, if they occur. (c) and (d) are the dual of each other, and so are (e) and (f).

7 Show that $A \cup B = (A \cap B) \cup (A \cap B') \cup (A' \cap B)$ in a Venn diagram. Write down the dual relation and demonstrate its validity in a Venn diagram.

8 If $\mathscr{E} = \{$real numbers$\}$, $A = \{$rational numbers$\}$, $B = \{$irrational numbers$\}$, and $C = \{$natural numbers$\}$, illustrate the relationship of these sets in a Venn diagram.

9 If $\mathscr{E} = \{$all quadrilaterals$\}$, $A = \{$all parallelograms$\}$, $B = \{$all rhombuses$\}$, $C = \{$all squares$\}$, $D = \{$all rectangles$\}$, and $E = \{$all trapezia$\}$, illustrate the relationship between the sets in a Venn diagram.

Problems

Many problems involving sets lend themselves to solution by representing the given data in a Venn diagram.

Example: *In a sixth form of 68 all but 4 of the pupils went on at least one of the university visits arranged to Birmingham (B), Southampton (S) and Reading (R). 11 pupils went to both B and S but not R, 1 went to both B and R but not S, and 5 went on all three visits. Altogether the number of pupils visiting B, S and R were 39, 35 and 14 respectively. Find how many pupils visited (a) only one University, (b) both R and S.*

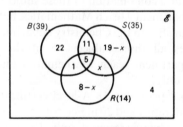

Fig. 4.3

The reader should copy out Figure 4.3, in which $\mathscr{E} = \{$pupils in sixth form$\}$, $B = \{$pupils who visited Birmingham$\}$, $S = \{$pupils who visited Southampton$\}$ and $R = \{$pupils who visited Reading$\}$, and fill in the numbers shown, in the order 4, 11, 1, 5 as they are defined in the problem. As $n(B) = 39$, the number who visited Birmingham only is 22, i.e. $n\{(R \cup S)' \cap B\} = 22$.

Let $n\{(S \cap R) \cap B'\} = x$ then $n\{(B \cup R)' \cap S\} = 19 - x$ as $n(S) = 35$, and $n\{(B \cup S)' \cap R\} = 8 - x$ as $n(R) = 14$.

As $n(B \cup S \cup R) = 64$, we have $19 - x + x + 8 - x = 25 \Rightarrow x = 2$.

The number of pupils who visited only one University $= 22 + 17 + 6 = 45$ and the number of pupils who visited Reading and Southampton $= 5 + 2 = 7$.

47

Problems which can be represented by two intersecting sets are much simpler and the reader is encouraged to try some of these first.

Exercise 4.4

1 Of 50 children questioned 38 owned either a bicycle or a horse or both. 32 children owned a bicycle and 9 owned a horse. Represent the information on a Venn diagram and use it to find:
   (a) the number of children who owned both a bicycle and a horse,
   (b) the number of children that own a bicycle only.

2 A milkman delivers milk and eggs to his customers. On a particular day 240 of his 300 customers required milk, 80 required eggs and 40 required neither. How many required both milk and eggs?
   On a different day 40 did not require milk, 120 did not require eggs and 20 required neither milk nor eggs. How many required both?

3 In a group of 36 people on a coach there are twice as many females as males. Of the females 15 are sitting next to a window and 12 are wearing glasses. Find the minimum number of females that could be both wearing glasses and sitting next to a window.

4 (a) Given that $n(\mathscr{E}) = 50$, $n(A) = 35$, $n(A \cap B) = 5$ and $n(A \cup B) = 45$, find $n(A \cup B)'$ and $n(A' \cap B')$.
   (b) Given that $n(\mathscr{E}) = 60$, $n(A) = 35$, $n(B) = 17$, find the greatest and least values of $n(A \cup B)$ and $n(A \cap B)$.

5 In a school there are 11 members of staff who teach Chemistry, Physics, or Mathematics, or a combination of these subjects. Of the 3 members of the Physics department 2 teach Mathematics, but no one teaches only Physics and Chemistry. In the Chemistry department there are 4 staff, 1 of whom teaches all three subjects. 5 of the 8 members of the Mathematics department teach Mathematics only. How many staff teach Chemistry only?

6 At a recent school prize day 18 A-level certificates were awarded in History, 17 in Geography and 20 in Economics. 3 candidates received all three certificates, while 5 received only History and Geography, 2 received only Geography and Economics, and 9 received only History and Economics. How many candidates were awarded at least one of the certificates?

7 A group of 90 children were asked which books they had read in the following list:
   A David Copperfield, B Animal Farm C Dr No.
   40 had read A, 35 had read B and 16 had read C. 7 had read all three books while of those who had read only two of the books 20 had read A and B, 2 had read B and C and 1 had read A and C. How many children had not read any of the books?

8 In a recent talent contest the 100 people in the audience were asked to vote for as many of the three contestants A, B and C as they wished. 20 people voted for B only and the same number voted for C only. The number of people who voted for all three contestants was the same as

the number who voted for both B and C but not A, and half as many as the number who voted for both A and B but not C. The contest was won by A with 48 votes, B was second with 36 votes, and C was third with 34 votes. Draw a Venn diagram to illustrate the data and find:

(a) the number of people who voted for A only,

(b) the number who refrained from voting.

9 34 children were asked which of the games of chess, Scrabble or draughts they possessed. The replies showed that 16 did not have chess, 17 did not have Scrabble and 22 did not have draughts. 7 children possessed chess only, 6 draughts only, and 7 Scrabble only. Of those who had only two of the games 2 did not have Scrabble. Find: (a) how many children did not have any of the games, and (b) how many had all three.

5 Structure and basic algebra

The Arabs were the first people to use algebraic processes as a form of generalised arithmetic, although some particular problems and their solutions were known to the Chinese and Indians many centuries earlier. The Greeks also solved many algebraic problems by geometrical considerations. The algebra of numbers as we know it today evolved slowly side by side with the base 10 number system. Over many centuries particular algebraic processes, like the solution of certain equations, were discovered in isolation by able scholars who saw patterns and rules which particular sets of numbers followed and obeyed.

During the middle ages the main line of mathematical advance took place in the growing merchant cities of Europe. Reckon masters, as they were called, performed the calculations for the traders and all forms of practical commercial arithmetic flourished and methods of computation improved. With the fall of the Byzantine Empire in 1453 many texts became available to the university teachers and traders, and by the early sixteenth century Italian mathematicians were beginning to develop the notation which is still used now. As subjects like trigonometry and calculus were invented the algebraic notation was extended and refined.

During the last 150 years much attention has been paid to the logical foundations of mathematics and, in particular, the structure of subjects like algebra. It was quickly realised that the classical algebra of numbers was just one structure out of many possible alternatives. Details of some of the laws governing these structures are given in this chapter, but the importance of the basic principles of ordinary classical algebra remains unique and the reader will have been studying it already for several years. At this stage it is important to review the situation and appreciate the existence of other types of algebra which naturally arise when different sets (such as vectors, matrices, sets themselves, and finite number systems) are studied under operations which happen to be either particularly useful, or interesting, or both.

The authors have assumed that readers will have met the number sets listed in Chapter 1 in their earlier work. They have also assumed that readers will have covered the following topics in basic algebra: operations of $+$, $-$, $\times$, $\div$ on directed numbers, the use of brackets and the simplification of simple expressions, and the evaluation of simple expressions for given values of the symbols in them, including an appreciation of the meaning of simple algebraic expressions such as $2x^2$, $(2x)^2$, $2x$, $2+x$, $3xy$ ... etc.

A set of revision exercises is included to give the reader the opportunity of ensuring that these basic topics have been firmly grasped in previous studies. After these exercises, algebraic structures are studied in detail before the return in the subsequent chapters to work which extends the ordinary algebra of numbers from the basis outlined above.

Revision Exercise 5.1

1 Given that $a = 2, b = 1, c = 0, d = -3$, evaluate each of the following:
   (a) $a+b+d$ (b) $a+b-d$ (c) $d-a$ (d) $b-d$
   (e) $3a^2$ (f) d^2 (g) ad (h) $3bc$
   (i) ad^2 (j) $(a-d)^2$ (k) $d(c-a)$ (l) $a(b-d)+d(b-a)$.
2 Simplify each of the following:
   (a) $3(p-2q)-2(q-2p)$ (b) $x(y+z)+y(z+x)-z(x+y)$

   (c) $d(e-2f)+e(2f-3d)$ (d) $\dfrac{a}{2}+\dfrac{a}{3}-\dfrac{a}{4}$

   (e) $\dfrac{x}{3}-\dfrac{2x}{7}$ (f) $\dfrac{x}{3} \div \dfrac{2x}{7}$

   (g) $a(a+b)-b(2a-b)-b^2$ (h) $a(a+7b)+2b(a-3b)-5a(a-b)$.
3 Make a table showing the values of $x-1$, $x-2$ and $(x-1)(x-2)$ when $x = -3, -2, -1, 0, 1, 2, 3$.
4 Given that $A = p(q-r)$, copy and complete the following table:

p	3		$-2\frac{1}{2}$	16
q	4	7		$-4\frac{1}{4}$
r	2	3	12	
A		20	25	4

5 Given that $y = x^3 + 2x^2 - x + 2$, find the values of y when the corresponding values of x are -1, $-\frac{1}{2}$, 0, 1, 2, $2\frac{1}{2}$.

Structure

The elements of a set and a rule for combining these elements are the basic ingredients of an algebraic structure. The choice of ingredients is important, and some structures, like some cakes, are more fruitful than others. In this book some of the algebraic structures considered are those whose sets have elements which are numbers ('ordinary' algebra), sets, vectors, functions and matrices. Some familiar rules of combination, called **operations**, defined on these sets are '$+$' and '$-$' in ordinary algebra, '$\cup$' and '$\cap$' in set algebra, vector 'addition' in vector algebra, 'followed by' in the algebra of functions and matrix 'multiplication' in the algebra of matrices. In order to make mathematical statements in a particular algebra, other symbols like '$=$' and '$>$' are needed to relate the elements of the set. These are called **relations** and are discussed more fully in Chapter 11.

Closure

An operation $*$ is a clearly defined rule which, when applied to any two elements x, y of a set S produces a third element $x * y$, which may, or may not, be a member of S. The set S is **closed** under $*$ if

$$x * y \in S \text{ for all } x, y \in S;$$

in this case $*$ is called a **binary operation** over the set S.

Example 1: The operation $*$ is defined on the set of integers $\mathbb{Z}$ by

$$x * y = x^2 + y^2 + 2xy \text{ for } x, y \in \mathbb{Z}.$$

Find $x * y$ when (a) $x = 2$, $y = 3$, (b) $x = 3$, $y = 2$

(a) $2 * 3 = 2^2 + 3^2 + (2 \times 2 \times 3) = 4 + 9 + 12 = 25$
(b) $3 * 2 = 3^2 + 2^2 + (2 \times 3 \times 2) = 9 + 4 + 12 = 25$.

$\mathbb{Z}$ is *closed* under $*$ since, for all integers, $x^2 + y^2 + 2xy$ is always an integer; $*$ is a *binary operation* over $\mathbb{Z}$.

To show that a set is *not closed* under an operation, one counter-example is sufficient.

Example 2: 1 The set of natural numbers, $\mathbb{N}$, is *not closed* under 'subtract' or 'divide'. The fact that $3 - 5 = -2 \notin \mathbb{N}$ is sufficient to show the first, and $2 \div 4 = \frac{1}{2} \notin \mathbb{N}$ is sufficient to show the second.

Example 3: The set of real numbers $\mathbb{R}$ is *not closed* under the operation $*$ defined by $x * y = \sqrt{xy}$ since,
$$\text{if } x = -1 \text{ and } y = 2, \ -1 * 2 = \sqrt{-2} \notin \mathbb{R}.$$

Exercise 5.2

1 For the following operations $*$ defined over $\mathbb{R}$ find $x * y$ for the given values of x and y. In each case state whether $\mathbb{R}$ is closed under $*$; if it is not, provide a counter-example to illustrate the fact:

(a) $x * y = \dfrac{x + y}{2}$ (the arithmetic mean of x and y) when (i) $x = 2$, $y = 6$,

(ii) $x = 6$, $y = 2$;
(b) $x * y = x^y$ when (i) $x = 2$, $y = 3$, (ii) $x = 3$, $y = 2$;
(c) $x * y$ means 'the L.C.M. of x and y' when (i) $x = 6$, $y = 12$,
(ii) $x = 3$, $y = 5$;
(d) $x * y = \sqrt{xy}$ (the geometric mean of x and y) when (i) $x = 24$, $y = 6$, (ii) $x = 36$, $y = \frac{1}{4}$.
    List four different pairs (x, y) which satisfy $x * y = 2$.
(e) $x * y = 2x^2 y$ when (i) $x = 1$, $y = 1$, (ii) $x = -1$, $y = 1$;
(f) $x * y$ means 'the H.C.F. of x and y' when (i) $x = 8$, $y = 12$, (ii) $x = a$, $y = a + 1$.

2 State which of the following sets are closed under the given operation. If a set is not closed, produce a counter example to substantiate your statement:

(a) $Z = \{\text{integers}\}$ (i) addition, (ii) multiplication, (iii) division, (iv) subtraction;

(b) $Q = \{\text{rationals}\}$ (i) addition, (ii) multiplication, (iii) division, (iv) subtraction;

(c) $E = \{\text{even integers}\}$ (i) addition, (ii) multiplication;

(d) $P = \{\text{primes}\}$ (i) multiplication (ii) subtraction, (iii) addition;

(e) $A = \{x : x > 1, x \in R\}$ (i) multiplication, (ii) division;

(f) $D = \{0, 2, 4, 6, 8\}$ $x * y$ means the unit digit when xy is found,

(g) $D_+ = \{0, 2, 4, 6\}$ $x * y$ means the unit digit when $x + y$ is found,

(h) $J = \{0, \frac{1}{2}, 1, 1\frac{1}{2}\}$ $x * y$ means the greatest integer $\leqslant x + y$.

In the first example of this chapter it was shown that for the defined operation $*$, $2 * 3 = 3 * 2$. The reader would find that for any pair of elements $x, y \in Z$, $x * y = y * x$ is always true. This is a property, a law of algebra, which may, or may not, be possessed by any particular structure.

Commutative law

If an operation $*$, defined over a set S, is such that $x * y = y * x$ for all $x, y \in S$, then $*$ is a **commutative** operation over S.

Example 1: Addition and multiplication are commutative over each of the sets $Z, \mathbb{R}, Q, \mathbb{N}$, since $a + b = b + a$ and $a \times b = b \times a$ for all a, b in any of these sets.

Example 2: The operation $*$ defined by $x * y = x^2 + y^2 + 2xy$ for $x, y \in Z$ is commutative over Z.
$x^2 + y^2 = y^2 + x^2$ since $x^2, y^2 \in Z$ and '$+$' is commutative over Z,
$2xy = 2yx$ since $x, y \in Z$ and '$\times$ is commutative over Z,
$x^2 + y^2 + 2xy = y^2 + x^2 + 2yx \Rightarrow x * y = y * x$ for all $x, y \in Z$.

Example 3: The operations '$\cap$' and '$\cup$' on the set of all sets S are commutative since $A \cap B = B \cap A$ and $A \cup B = B \cup A$ for all $A, B, \in S$.

Another feature of multiplication defined over Z is seen when the result of multiplying three elements of Z is considered. It does not matter whether the result is found by grouping together the first pair and multiplying by the third element, or by taking the first element and multiplying it by the result of the other pair.

Example 4: $2 \times 3 \times 4$ can be found as $(2 \times 3) \times 4$ i.e. $6 \times 4 = 24$,

or as $2 \times (3 \times 4)$ i.e. $2 \times 12 = 24$.

Associative law

The operation $*$ is **associative** over a set S if

$$(x * y) * z = x * (y * z) \text{ for all } x, y, z \in S.$$

The result may be written as $x * y * z$.

Note that this is a law of *grouping*, and not of changing the order of the elements.

This law of structure, like closure and commutativity, may or may not be a feature of the set-operation relationship.

Example: Addition and multiplication are associative over $\mathbb{R}$, since $(x + y) + z = x + (y + z)$ and $(xy)z = x(yz)$ respectively for all $x, y, z \in \mathbb{R}$.

Subtraction is not associative over any of the sets $\mathbb{R}$, $\mathbb{Q}$, $\mathbb{Z}$, or $\mathbb{N}$. As $\mathbb{N} \subset \mathbb{Z} \subset \mathbb{Q} \subset \mathbb{R}$ it is sufficient to give a counter-example for three elements in $\mathbb{N}$.

$(3 - 2) - 1 \neq 3 - (2 - 1) \Rightarrow$ subtraction is not associative over $\mathbb{N}$.

It was seen in Chapter 4 that if A, B and C are three sets, $(A \cap B) \cap C = A \cap (B \cap C)$ and $(A \cup B) \cup C = A \cup (B \cup C)$ and so both '$\cap$' and '$\cup$' are associative over the set of all sets.

Exercise 5.3

1 Find which of the operations $*$, defined in Exercise 5.2. question 1, are (a) commutative, (b) associative, over $\mathbb{R}$. For those which are not, give a counter-example to justify the fact.

2 Give one example for each of the following operations to show that it is not commutative over the defined set:
   (a) (i) subtraction over $\mathbb{R}$ (ii) division over $\mathbb{R}$
   (b) $*$ where $x * y$ means $\dfrac{x + y}{y}$ over $\mathbb{R}$
   (c) $*$ where $x * y$ means $2x - 3y$ over $\mathbb{N}$.

3 The operation $*$ is defined over $\mathbb{R}_+$ such that $x * y = 2x - 5y$.
   Find (a) $10 * 4$ (b) $4 * 10$ (c) $1 * 2$ (d) $2 * 1$.
   Solve the equation $8 * k = 6$.
   Determine whether $\mathbb{R}_+$ is closed under $*$, and whether $*$ is commutative and associative.

4 The operation $*$ is defined over $\mathbb{Z}_+$ in the following cases. Determine whether $\mathbb{Z}_+$ is closed under $*$, and whether $*$ is commutative and associative:

   (a) $x * y = \frac{1}{3}(x + 2y)$ (b) $x * y = x^2 - y$ (c) $x * y = \dfrac{1}{x} + \dfrac{2}{y}$

   (d) $x * y = x^2 + y^2$ (e) $x * y = \dfrac{x + y}{xy}$ (f) $x * y = \dfrac{xy - 1}{x + y}$

5 The operation $*$ is defined as $x * y = x + 5y$.
Find the values of
(a) $1 * (2 * 3)$ (b) $(1 * 2) * 3$ (c) $\frac{1}{2} * (1 * \frac{1}{2})$
(d) $(\frac{1}{2} * 1) * \frac{1}{2}$ (e) $\frac{1}{4} * (\frac{1}{3} * \frac{1}{2})$ (f) $(\frac{1}{4} * \frac{1}{3}) * \frac{1}{2}$.
Is the operation $*$ associative over the set $\mathbb{R}$?

In some sets, under a given operation, there are elements which behave in a special way.

Identity element

An element e is called the identity element of a set S under a given operation $*$ if $x * e = e * x = x$ for all $x \in S$.

Example 1: In the set $\mathbb{R}$ the additive identity is 0 since $x + 0 = 0 + x = x$ for all $x \in \mathbb{R}$.

Example 2: In the set $\mathbb{R}$ the multiplicative identity is 1 since $x . 1 = 1 . x = x$ for all $x \in \mathbb{R}$.

Example 3: In set algebra $\varnothing$ and $\mathscr{E}$ are the identities under '$\cup$' and '$\cap$' respectively, since $X \cup \varnothing = \varnothing \cup X = X$ and $X \cap \mathscr{E} = \mathscr{E} \cap X = X$ for all sets X in the set of all sets.

Inverse element

Suppose a set S has an identity element e under an operation $*$. If elements x and y exist such that $x * y = y * x = e$, then y is called the inverse of x under $*$.
The inverse of x is usually written as x^{-1}. If x and x^{-1} are the same, x is self-inverse.

Example 1: If $x \in R (x \neq 0)$ the inverse of x under multiplication is $\frac{1}{x}$, since $x . \frac{1}{x} = \frac{1}{x} . x = 1$, the multiplicative identity. In this case x^{-1} and $\frac{1}{x}$ are equivalent but, in general, y^{-1} means 'the inverse of y' and its form depends on the operation involved.

Example 2: The inverse of $w \in \mathbb{R}$, under addition, is $-w$, since $w + (-w) = (-w) + w = 0$, the additive identity. In this case $w^{-1} = -w$.

Even when an identity element exists, an element may not have an inverse. For example, in the set of (2×2) matrices the element $\begin{pmatrix} 1 & 0 \\ 0 & 1 \end{pmatrix}$ is the identity under matrix multiplication, but the matrix $\begin{pmatrix} a & b \\ c & d \end{pmatrix}$ only has an inverse if $ad \neq bc$ (See Chapter 21).

Example 3: The operation $*$ defined by $x * y = x + y + 2xy$ on the set $\mathbb{R}$ is a binary operation ($\mathbb{R}$ is closed under $*$); it is also commutative and associative since addition and multiplication are.

Find the identity element and the inverse of (a) 1 and (b) -2 under $*$.

The identity element may be found as follows:

Let e be the identity element

Then $\qquad x * e = x \Rightarrow x + e + 2xe = x$ for all $x \in \mathbb{R}$

$$\Rightarrow e(1 + 2x) = 0.$$

As this must apply for all $x \in \mathbb{R}$ $e = 0$ is the identity element. It is interesting to investigate the significance of the other solution $x = -\frac{1}{2}$.

$$-\tfrac{1}{2} * y = -\tfrac{1}{2} + y - y = -\tfrac{1}{2}.$$

The combination of any element with $-\frac{1}{2}$ gives the result $-\frac{1}{2}$.

The inverse of $-\frac{1}{2}$ under $*$ will be undefined, just as the inverse of 0 is undefined under multiplication.

The inverse of all other elements will be unique.

(a) Let the inverse of 1 be y.

Then $1 * y = 0 \Rightarrow 1 + y + 2y = 0 \Rightarrow y = -\frac{1}{3}$ i.e. $1^{-1} = -\frac{1}{3}$.

The reader should check that the solution of $z * 1 = 0$ is $z = -\frac{1}{3}$.

(b) Let the inverse of -2 be a.

Then $-2 * a = 0 \Rightarrow -2 + a - 4a = 0 \Rightarrow a = -\frac{2}{3}$ i.e. $-2^{-1} = -\frac{2}{3}$.

The reader should check that the solution of $b * -2 = 0$ is $b = -\frac{2}{3}$.

Exercise 5.4

1 (a) Find the multiplicative inverse of the following:

(i) 3   (ii) $\frac{7}{12}$ (iii) $1\frac{1}{2}$ (iv) $-\frac{6}{7}$.

(b) Evaluate $\frac{3}{4} \div \frac{7}{12}$ by multiplying both terms by your answer to part (ii) above.

This shows the reason for the rule 'when dividing two fractions, turn the second one upside down and multiply'.

2 Find the values of a^{-1} and $(a^{-1})^{-1}$ (a) under multiplication and (b) addition, for each of the following values of a.

(i) $a = 5$,   (ii) $a = -2$,   (iii) $a = \frac{3}{5}$.

3 For each of the operations $*$ defined over $\mathbb{R}$, find the identity element, if it exists. Where it does exist, find the inverse elements of (i) 2 and (ii) -1.

(a) $x * y = xy$ (b) $x * y = x + y + 3$ (c) $x * y = -\dfrac{xy}{2} + y + x$

(d) $x * y = x^2 + y^2$ (e) $x * y = x + y - xy$ (f) $x * y = xy + y + x$

Combination tables

A concise way of exhibiting the results, and of investigating the properties of a finite set under a given operation, is by means of a combination table.

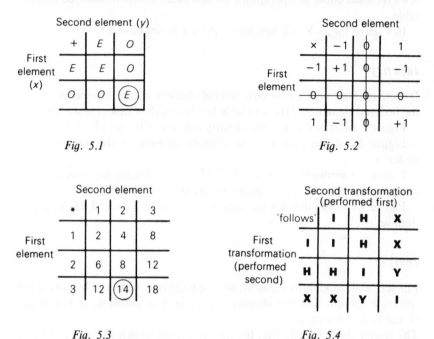

Second element (y)

+	E	O
First element (x) E	E	O
O	O	(E)

Fig. 5.1

Second element

×	−1	0	1
First element −1	+1	0	−1
0	0	0	0
1	−1	0	+1

Fig. 5.2

Second element

*	1	2	3
First element 1	2	4	8
2	6	8	12
3	12	(14)	18

Fig. 5.3

Second transformation (performed first)

'follows'	I	H	X
First transformation (performed second) I	I	H	X
H	H	I	Y
X	X	Y	I

Fig. 5.4

In Figure 5.1 the elements E, O, the classes of even integers and odd integers respectively, are listed as shown and the results of combining them under addition are displayed. The ringed element shows that when any odd integer is added to another odd integer the result is an even integer.

Figure 5.2 displays the results of multiplying elements of the set $\{-1, 0, 1\}$. The element 0 is usually omitted from such a multiplication table since it merely contributes a series of zeros. When 0 is omitted, the table shows a similar pattern to that of Figure 5.1; the two sets behave in the same way under their respective operations and are said to be **isomorphic** (have the same structure).

Figure 5.3 displays the result of combining elements of the set $\{1, 2, 3\}$ under the operation $*$ defined by $x * y = x^2 + y^2 + x - y$. The ringed element shows the result $3 * 2$, which is not equal to the result $2 * 3$. This table clearly shows that $*$ is neither a binary nor commutative operation on the set.

In Figure 5.4 the elements **I, H, X, Y** are the **isometries** (length preserving transformations) of the plane: 'stay put', half turn about the origin, reflect in the x-axis, reflect in the y-axis, respectively. When the operation is defined as 'follows' on the set $S = \{I, H, X\}$, so that **H** $*$ **X** means **H** 'follows' **X**, the results are as shown in the table. The set S is not closed under 'follows'.

Observations

Closure

A set is closed under an operation if no new elements are introduced into the table.

In Figure 5.4 as **Y** is a new entry the set is not closed.

Identity

If there is an element whose row and column entries correspond exactly to the ordered elements of the set (table headings), the element is the identity.

Figure 5.1 shows that E is the identity element of the set $\{E, O\}$ under $+$.

Figure 5.2 shows that 1 is the identity element of the set $\{-1, 0, 1\}$ under $\times$.

Figure 5.3 shows that the set $\{1, 2, 3\}$ has no identity element under $*$ since there is no row whose elements are ordered 1, 2, 3.

Figure 5.4 shows that **I** is the identity element of the set $\{\mathbf{I}, \mathbf{H}, \mathbf{X}\}$ under 'follows'.

Inverse

For sets with an identity element, inverse pairs may be found by noting the row and column that the identity occurs in. For example, in Figure 5.1 O and O are inverse pairs.

The reader should verify that for the structures shown in Figures 5.1, 5.2 and 5.4 the elements are all self-inverse.

Commutativity

The table will exhibit symmetry about the leading diagonal (top left to bottom right) if the operation is commutative.

Exercise 5.5

1 Construct combination tables for the given sets and their respective operations. Investigate each for closure, commutativity, an identity element and inverse elements:

(a) $\{E, O\}$ under multiplication

(b) $\{A, A'\}$ under (i) $\cap$ (ii) $\cup$ [Let A be a non-null set]

(c) $\{-1, 0, 1\}$ under $*$, where (i) $x * y = x^2 + y^2$ (ii) $x * y = x^2 - y^2$

(d) $\{\mathbf{I}, \mathbf{X}\}$ under 'follows'

(e) $\{0, 1, 2, 3\}$ under $*$, where $x * y$ is the remainder when $x + y$ is divided by 4

(f) $\{1, 2, 3\}$ under $*$, where $x * y$ is the remainder when $x . y$ is divided by 4. Are any of these structures isomorphic?

2 In each of the following combination tables the operation is denoted by ∗. In the first four, suggest possible definitions for ∗, and in the others, suggest possible elements and operations which would exhibit the structure.

(a)

∗	1	2
1	1	2
2	2	1

(b)

∗	1	2
1	2	0
2	0	1

(c)

∗	3	10
3	9	1
10	1	8

(d)

∗	1	3	4
1	1	3	4
3	3	9	0
4	4	0	4

(e)

∗	a	b
a	a	b
b	b	a

(f)

∗	a	b	c
a	a	b	c
b	b	c	a
c	c	a	b

Modular arithmetic

The classes E and O of the last section could equally well have been defined as the set of numbers which have no remainder when divided by 2, and the set of numbers which have a remainder of one when divided by 2. If E and O are replaced by 0 and 1, the remainders of all elements in the corresponding classes when divided by 2, the 'addition' and 'multiplication' tables are shown in Figure 5.5 (a) and (b).

+	0	1
0	0	1
1	1	0

(a)

×	0	1
0	0	0
1	0	1

(b)

Fig. 5.5

It may seem strange at first sight; $1 + 1 = 0$, for example, in this system. The numbers 0 and 1, however, are being used to represent all numbers in the classes defined earlier.

It may seem less strange when the reader realises that results like $10 + 3 = 1$ are commonplace in clock arithmetic. If a table were compiled to show the full clock arithmetic it would have the twelve numbers 1, 2, ... 12, or, better, to agree with the previous example, 0, 1, ... 11, and all results are given as elements of this set, the remainder when the combined pairs are divided by 12.

This arithmetic is generally known as **modular arithmetic**. Figures 5.5(a) and 5.5(b) show the combination tables for the set $\{0, 1\}$ under addition modulo 2, and multiplication modulo 2, respectively. The results are the remainders when the relevant pair are divided by 2.

In Exercise 5.5, 1(e) and (f), the reader completed the combination tables for $\{0, 1, 2, 3\}$ under addition (mod 4) and multiplication (mod 4), respectively. In multiplication, 0 is omitted from the table.

Although the operations of 'addition' and 'multiplication' used here are not the usual ones, and nor is the relation '=' taking its usual meaning, we shall continue to use them, but always make their meaning clear, by using (mod n) to indicate the system being used.

Exercise 5.6

1 Construct the combination table for the set $\{0, 1, 2 \ldots (n-1)\}$ under addition (mod n) in each of the cases $n = 2, 3, 4, 5, 6$.
Describe the patterns exhibited in the tables.
Are all sets closed under addition (mod n)?

2 Construct the combination table for the set $\{1, 2, \ldots (n-1)\}$ under multiplication (mod n) in each of the cases $n = 3, 4, 5, 6, 7$ and 8.
Which tables exhibit the more regular patterns? Describe any forms of symmetry shown.
For what values of n are the sets closed under multiplication (mod n)?
State for what values of n there is an identity element and name it in each case.
List the inverse of each element when an identity has been found.
Suggest a condition for n that might produce sets with a unique inverse for each element.

3 Construct the combination tables for the set $\{0, 1, 2, 3, 4\}$ under addition (mod 5) and the set $\{1, 2, 3, 4\}$ under multiplication (mod 5) and use them to solve the following equations in arithmetic modulo 5.
(a) $x + 3 = 2$ (b) $4 + 3 = x$ (c) $2 - 4 = x$
(d) $2x = 1$ (e) $x^2 = 4$ (f) $x^2 = 2$
Does the result for 3(f) surprise you? (Compare with the solutions of $x^2 = -3$, $x \in R$).
(*To evaluate $2 - 4$, look in the addition table for the number that must be combined with 4 to give the result 2. The answer is 3.*)

The reader has seen that multiplication (mod n) does not behave as well as addition (mod n) and consequently there are many simple equations that cannot be solved in the system. For example, if the reader consults his table for multiplication (mod 4) he will see that $2x = 1$ has no solution. In arithmetic modulo 5 there is a solution.

One very great difference between these finite arithmetics and the ordinary algebra of numbers is in the methods employed to solve quadratic equations and equations of higher degree. In a finite arithmetic there are only a finite number of possible solutions and so they can each be tried in turn; a complicated procedure or formula is not needed. There is, however, no set rule for the number of solutions that an equation may have.

Exercise

Use your combination tables to solve $x^2 + x = 2$ (mod n) when $n = 3, 4, 5, 6$.

Some apparently different systems have the same basic structure; some of these occur frequently and are worthy of investigation in their own right. We shall look at the simplest type of algebraic structure for a set with one operation defined over it.

Groups

A set of elements, S, form a group under an operation $*$, if:
  (i) S is closed over $*$ (i.e. $*$ is a binary operation over S),
  (ii) there is an identity element, $e, \in S$,
  (iii) every element has an inverse, and
  (iv) $*$ is associative over S.
  The set $\{a, b, c\}$ under the operation $*$ [Ex. 5.5, Qu. 2(f)] satisfies all these conditions and forms a group under $*$. The set $\{1, 2, 3\}$ under multiplication (mod 4) is also a group. Both of these groups have three elements and are called groups of order 3. These two groups also obey the commutative law. Groups which possess this additional property are called **Abelian groups**, after N. Abel (1802–29), the Norwegian mathematician who studied them.

Example: *Show that the set of functions f_1, f_2, f_3, f_4, defined by $f_1 : x \to x$ $f_2 : x \to \dfrac{1}{x}$, $f_3 : x \to -x$, $f_4 : x \to \dfrac{-1}{x}$ $\{x \in \mathbb{R}, x \neq 0\}$ under the operation $*$, defined by $f_i * f_j$ means f_j 'followed by' f_i, (or f_i follows f_j) form a group.* The combination table for the set under $*$ is shown in Figure 5.6.

$*$	f_1	f_2	f_3	f_4
f_1	f_1	f_2	f_3	f_4
f_2	f_2	f_1	f_4	f_3
f_3	f_3	f_4	f_1	f_2
f_4	f_4	f_3	f_2	f_1

Fig. 5.6

The four conditions are satisfied, since the set is closed under $*$; the identity element is f_1; the inverses of f_1, f_2, f_3, f_4 are themselves, (they are self-inverse); and, since $(f_1 f_2)f_3 = f_1(f_2 f_3)$, etc., the associative law is obeyed. Since $f_1 f_2 = f_2 f_1$ etc, the group is also Abelian.

Exercise 5.7

1 Show that each of the following infinite sets are groups under addition:
   (a) $\mathbb{R}$ (b) $\mathbb{Z}$ (c) $\mathbb{Q}$ (The associative law may be assumed).
   Show that the set of irrational numbers does not form a group under addition.
2 Show that the following sets are groups under multiplication (In (a) and (b) omit zero):
   (a) $\mathbb{R}$ (b) $\mathbb{Q}$ (c) Powers of 2 (The associative law may be assumed).
   Show that the set of integers is not a group under multiplication.
3 Using your combination tables for the sets $\{0, 1, \ldots . (n-1)\}$, under addition (mod n), determine which structures (for $n = 2, 3, 4, 5$) are groups.
4 Using your combination tables for the sets $\{0, 1, 2, \ldots . (n-1)\}$ (for $n = 3, 4, 5, 6, 7$) under multiplication (mod n), determine which structures form groups.
5 Show that the set of (2×2) matrices does not form a group under matrix multiplication. State the group axiom which is not obeyed.
6 The operation $\sim$ means 'the difference between', e.g. $6 \sim 8 = 2$. Show that the set $\mathbb{R}$ is not a group under $\sim$.

Symmetry groups

Transformations which map a shape onto itself are called symmetry transformations. The symmetries of some simple geometrical figures are shown below.

Example 1: An isosceles triangle has two symmetry transformations:

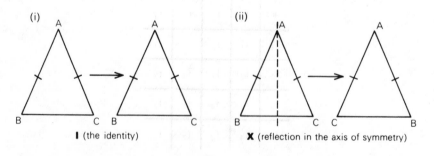

Fig. 5.7

62

Example 2: A rectangle ABCD has four symmetry operations:

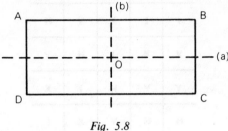

Fig. 5.8

(i) **I**: the 'stay put' identity transformation
(ii) **X**: reflection in the line (a)
(iii) **Y**: reflection in the line (b)
(iv) **H**: rotate through 180° about 0.

Example 3: An equilateral triangle ABC has six symmetries (see Figure 5.9):

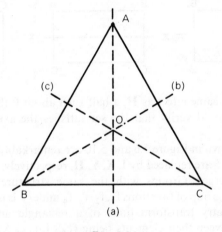

Fig. 5.9

The six symmetries are:
(i) **I**: identity transformation
(ii) **X**: reflection in line (a)
(iii) **Y**: reflection in line (b)
(iv) **Z**: reflection in line (c)
(v) R_1: rotate 120° about 0
(vi) R_2: rotate 240° about 0.

If $A * B$ means 'B followed by A', for any two transformations A and B, these symmetry transformations can be shown to form groups.

Example 4: The symmetries of the rectangle ABCD, defined above, have the following combination table.

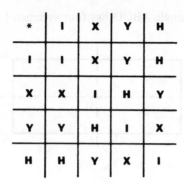

*	I	X	Y	H
I	I	X	Y	H
X	X	I	H	Y
Y	Y	H	I	X
H	H	Y	X	I

Fig. 5.10

The image rectangle (clearly labelled) should be drawn for each of the four transformations so that they can be readily identified. [A cardboard cut-out may be a useful aid].
e.g.

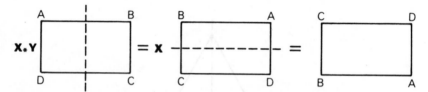

X * Y has the same effect as **H**, a half turn about 0 (See Fig. 5.8).

The reader should verify that the set satisfies the axioms of a group under *.

The tables shown in Figure 5.6 and 5.10 are remarkably similar. If f_1, f_2, f_3, f_4 of Figure 5.6 are replaced by **I, X, Y, H**, respectively, then the table in Figure 5.10 emerges. Groups with the same structure are said to be **isomorphic**. The group of functions f_1, f_2, f_3, f_4 under * is isomorphic to the group of symmetry transformations of a rectangle under *, the correspondence between their elements being $f_1 \leftrightarrow I, f_2 \leftrightarrow X, f_3 \leftrightarrow Y, f_4 \leftrightarrow H$.

Exercise 5.8

1 State the total number of different transformation symmetries for:
(a) a square (b) a rhombus (c) a regular pentagon (d) the letter N.
Define the transformations in each case.

2 Using the operation * where $A * B$ means A 'follows' B, construct the combination tables for the symmetries of:
(a) an isosceles triangle (see Figure 5.7)
(b) an equilateral triangle (see Figure 5.9)
(c) a rhombus
(d) the letter N.
[*The associative law may be assumed to hold for* *].

Show that all of these form groups and state the groups which are isomorphic.

Permutation groups

A permutation is an arrangement of a set of elements. For two coloured balls, red (R) and blue (B) there are just two arrangements (a) RB, (b) BR:

Permutation (a) may be denoted by $P_1 = \begin{pmatrix} R & B \\ R & B \end{pmatrix}$ and

permutation (b) may be denoted by $P_2 = \begin{pmatrix} R & B \\ B & R \end{pmatrix}$.

An operation $*$ is defined on the set of arrangements such that $P_a * P_b$ means P_b 'followed by' P_a.

Example: $P_1 * P_2 = P_1 \begin{pmatrix} R & B \\ B & R \end{pmatrix} = \begin{pmatrix} R & B \\ B & R \end{pmatrix} = P_2$. The set forms a group under $*$ and it is isomorphic to the group of symmetries on the letter N. The reader should compile the combination table for $\{P_1, P_2\}$ under $*$.

Exercise 5.9

1   List the six arrangements for the three coloured balls, red (R) blue (B) and green (G), and define appropriate permutations $P_1, P_2 \ldots P_6$ in a similar manner to the last example. Show that this set forms a group and describe a group isomorphic to it.

2   Write out the combination tables for the following sets S over the defined operation $*$ and show that in each case S is a group of order 2 under $*$:

S	$*$
(a) the permutations on the letters, a, b	defined above
(b) $\{0, 1\}$	addition (mod 2)
(c) $\{E, O\}$	addition
(d) $\{1, 2\}$	multiplication (mod 3)
(e) $\{1, 4\}$	multiplication (mod 5)
(f) $\left\{ I = \begin{pmatrix} 1 & 0 \\ 0 & 1 \end{pmatrix}, A = \begin{pmatrix} 0 & 1 \\ 1 & 0 \end{pmatrix} \right\}$	matrix multiplication

Are all the groups isomorphic to the group of symmetries on an isosceles triangle?

3   Write out the combination tables for the following sets S over the defined operation $*$ and show that they form groups of order 3:

S	$*$
(a) $\{0, 1, 2\}$	addition (mod 3)
(b) $\{I, R_1, R_2\}$ a subset of the set of transformations defined in Figure 5.9	$R_1 * R_2$ means R_1 'follows' R_2
(c) $\{1, w, w^2,$ where $w^3 = 1\}$	multiplication

4 Given that the set $\{a, b, c\}$ forms a group under $*$, where a is the identity element, compile the combination table for the set and show that there is only one possible structure for a group of order 3. Is the group Abelian?

Simplify the combinations $b * b$ (b^2) and $b * b * b (b^3)$

5 Write out the combination tables for the following sets S over the defined operation $*$ and show that they form groups of under 4:

S	$*$
(a) $\{0, 1, 2, 3\}$	addition (mod 4)
(b) $\{1, 2, 3, 4\}$	multiplication (mod 5)
(c) $\left\{ I = \begin{pmatrix} 1 & 0 \\ 0 & 1 \end{pmatrix}, A = \begin{pmatrix} -1 & 0 \\ 0 & 1 \end{pmatrix}, \right.$ $\left. B = \begin{pmatrix} 1 & 0 \\ 0 & -1 \end{pmatrix}, C = \begin{pmatrix} -1 & 0 \\ 0 & -1 \end{pmatrix} \right\}$	matrix multiplication
(d) $\{1, 5, 7, 11\}$	multiplication (mod 12)

Are all of these groups isomorphic to the set of four functions of Figure 5.6?

6 Show that there are two possible structure tables for a group of four elements $\{a, b, c, d\}$ under an operation $*$, by compiling combination tables. (Let a be the identity. Hint: There must be an even number of self-inverse elements.)

If a set of elements form a group under a given operation $*$, then equations of the form $a * x = b$ can be solved for x, given a and b. Consider carefully how you solve $5x = 3$, for example.

The multiplicative inverse of 5 is necessary, the associative law is used, an identity is necessary, and the set of numbers must be closed under multiplication.

In fact the four axioms of a group are necessary and sufficient conditions for equations of the form $a * x = b$ to be solved.

Exercise 5.10

Solve the following equations for x in the groups defined earlier:

1 $4x = 3 \pmod 5$ 2 $3x = 3 \pmod 5$ 3 $f_2 * x = f_4$

4 $f_4 * x = f_1$ 5 $X * x = Y$ 6 $H * x = X$

7　Figure 5.11 shows a combination table for the group $\{a, b, c, d\}$ under the operation $*$. This group is called a **Klein four-group**.

$*$	a	b	c	d
a	a	b	c	d
b	b	a	d	c
c	c	d	a	b
d	d	c	b	a

Fig. 5.11

Solve the following equations for x:
(a) $b * x = c$　　　　　(b) $x * d = a$
(c) $c * (d * x) = d$　　　(d) $(b * x) + c = d$.

If more than one operation is defined on a set S then there may be features of the behaviour of those operations over S that allow a much richer structure.

For the operations of multiplication and addition over the set $\mathbb{R}$ it is true that $a \times (b + c) = (a \times b) + (a \times c)$ for all $a, b, c \in \mathbb{R}$ and this law forms the basis of much of the algebra of numbers.

Distributive law

If two operations, denoted by $*$ and $\circ$, are defined on a set S such that $a * (b \circ c) = (a * b) \circ (a * c)$ for all $a, b, c \in S$ then the operation $*$ is said to be **distributive** over $\circ$ for the set S.

In the algebra of numbers, multiplication is distributive over addition.

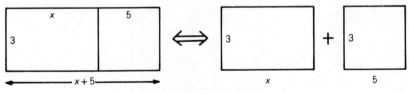

Fig. 5.12

Figure 5.12 demonstrates the fact that

$$3(x + 5) = 3x + (3 \times 5)$$
$$= 3x + 15.$$

67

Note that as $(x + 5)3 = 3(x + 5)$, since multiplication is commutative over $\mathbb{R}$, it follows that $(x + 5)3 = 3(x + 5) = 3x + 15$.

In the algebra of sets it was seen in Chapter 4 that

$$A \cap (B \cup C) = (A \cap B) \cup (A \cap C), \text{ i.e. '} \cap \text{' is distributive over '} \cup \text{',}$$

and $A \cup (B \cap C) = (A \cup B) \cap (A \cup C)$, i.e. '$\cup$' is distributive over '$\cap$'.

Exercise 5.11

1 Draw Venn diagrams to demonstrate the validity of the two set identities stated above.
2 (a) Construct the combination tables for addition (mod 5) and for multiplication (mod 5) on the set $\{0, 1, 2, 3, 4\}$ and evaluate (i) $2 \times (3 + 4)$, and (ii) $(2 \times 3) + (2 \times 4)$ in this system. Is multiplication distributive over addition in arithmetic modulo 5?
  (b) In arithmetic modulo 4 evaluate (i) $2 \times (3 + 1)$, and (ii) $(2 \times 3) + (2 \times 1)$. Is multiplication distributive over addition in this system?
3 The operations $*$ and $\circ$ are defined over $\mathbb{R}$ by $x * y = 2x^2 y$ and $a \circ b = a + 3b$ for all $a, b, x, y \in \mathbb{R}$. Evaluate the following:
  (a) $(1 * 2) \circ 3$ (b) $(1 \circ 3) * (2 \circ 3)$ (c) $(2 \circ 5) * 1$
  (d) $(2 * 1) \circ (5 * 1)$ (e) $(-1 * 2) \circ 0$ (f) $(0 * 2) \circ 4$.

4

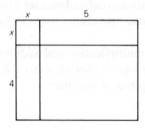

Fig. 5.13

Find the areas of the four sections in Figure 5.13 to demonstrate the statement: $(x + 4)(x + 5) = x^2 + 9x + 20$.

5

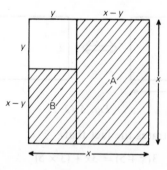

Fig. 5.14

(a) Find the simplest form for the area of the shaded section in Figure 5.14.

(b) The two sections, A and B, can be cut out and rejoined to give one single rectangle. State the lengths of the sides of the rectangle.

Use (a) and (b) to demonstrate that $x^2 - y^2 = (x + y)(x - y)$

Note: This is not a proof. For example, x and y may take negative values. The statement is true, however, for all values $x, y \in \mathbb{R}$.

6

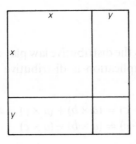

Fig. 5.15

Use Figure 5.15 to demonstrate $(x + y)^2 = x^2 + 2xy + y^2$

7 Draw a diagram to demonstrate $(x - y)^2 = x^2 - 2xy + y^2$.

6 Factorisation and simplification

In the algebra of numbers the distributive law plays a key role. It was shown, in Chapter 5, that multiplication is distributive over addition and subtraction; that is:

$$a \times (b + c) = (a \times b) + (a \times c) = ab + ac$$
and
$$a \times (b - c) = (a \times b) - (a \times c) = ab - ac.$$

As multiplication is also a commutative operation over the set of numbers, it is also true that $(b + c)a = ba + ca = ab + ac$.

Example: $3(x + 5) = (x + 5)3 = 3x + 3 \times 5 = 3x + 15.$

If $(x + 2)$ is substituted for 3 in the above example a further use of the distributive law gives the key to multiplying out a product of two binomial expressions.

$$(x + 2)(x + 5) = (x + 2)x + (x + 2)5$$
$$= x^2 + 2x + 5x + 10$$
$$= x^2 + 7x + 10.$$

The method can be extended to any number of brackets containing any number of terms, but the exercise is rather tedious.

If the reader needs to improve his powers of multiplying out brackets, the following revision exercise should be worked through before proceeding.

Exercise 6.1

Rewrite each of the following expressions without brackets, in descending powers of x, as in the above example:

1	$5(x + 2)$	9	$(x + 5)(x + 8)$
2	$3(x - 7)$	10	$(1 + x)(5 - 2x)$
3	$4(x + 2y)$	11	$(2x + 1)(x + 5)$
4	$x(5 - x)$	12	$(3 + 2x)(x - 8)$
5	$x(1 + 3x)$	13	$(4x + 1)(3x - 1)$
6	$x(x^2 + y)$	14	$(2x + 3)(6x - 1)$
7	$5(x - 2) - 2(x + 3)$	15	$(x + 8)^2$
8	$4(2 - x) - (x - 1)$	16	$(2x + 3)^2$

17	$(5 - x)^2$
18	$(x - 1)(x + 1)$
19	$(2x - 3)(2x + 3)$
20	$(4x - 9)(4x + 9)$
21	$(x^2 - 1)(x^2 + 1)$
22	$(x^2 + 3x + 5)(x + 2)$
23	$x(x + 1)(x + 2)$
24	$x(x + 1)(x - 1)$

The statements $3(x+5)$ and $3x+15$ are equivalent. When an expression like $3x+15$ is rewritten in the bracketed form $3(x+5)$ it is said to be factorised, 3 and $(x+5)$ being the factors of $3x+15$. The distributive law is now being used in the reverse sense to that in the previous section.

As $x^2 + 7x + 10 = (x+2)(x+5)$ the factors of $x^2 + 7x + 10$ are $(x+2)$ and $(x+5)$.

Common factor

The factor 3 of $3x+15$ is called a *common factor* of the expression as it is contained in both $3x$ and 15.

All expressions should first be inspected for a common factor.

Example 1: $3x^2 + 6x^3 + 9x^4 = 3x^2(1 + 2x + 3x^2)$.

Unless the highest common factor is extracted the expression will not be completely factorised.

If an expression contains several variables, the highest common factor will contain the lowest power of each of the common variables.

Example 2: $2x^3y^3 + 8x^4y^2 + 4x^4y = 2x^3y(y^2 + 4xy + 2x)$.
x is common to all terms; its lowest power is three,
y is common to all terms; its lowest power is one.

Exercise 6.2

Factorise the following expressions:

1	$2x+4$	7	$2y + 12y^2$	13	$ab^2c^3 + a^3b^2c$
2	$3x-6$	8	$-3x^2 + 6x^4$	14	$2x^2 + 4y^2$
3	$x^2 - x$	9	$x^2 + x^3 + x^4$	15	$x(x+1) + x$
4	$21 - 7x$	10	$5x^2 - 10x$	16	$x(x-1) - 2(x-1)$.
5	$xy - x^2$	11	$3x + 6x^2$		
6	$p^3 - p^2q$	12	$x + 2x^3 - x^5$		

Difference of two squares

The only two-termed expressions which have real factors are those having a common factor, or those of the form $x^2 - y^2$, *a difference of two squares*. The factors of $x^2 - y^2$ are $(x-y)$ and $(x+y)$.

$$x^2 - y^2 = (x+y)(x-y)$$

Example 1: $16x^2 - 1 = (4x)^2 - (1)^2 = (4x+1)(4x-1)$.
Remember to look for a common factor first.

Example 2: $2 - 32y^2 = 2(1 - 16y^2) = 2(1 + 4y)(1 - 4y)$.

Example 3: $x - x^3 = x(1 - x^2) = x(1 + x)(1 - x)$.

Use of this method can lead to an elegant solution in some arithmetical problems.

Example 4: *Two concentric circles have radii 10.8 cm and 4.2 cm. Calculate, in terms of π, the difference in area between them.*

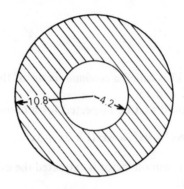

Fig. 6.1

The required area, in cm², (shaded in Figure 6.1,) is,

$$\pi(10.8)^2 - \pi(4.2)^2 = \pi\{(10.8)^2 - (4.2)^2\}$$
$$= \pi\{10.8 + 4.2\}\{10.8 - 4.2\}$$
$$= \pi(15)(6.6)$$
$$= 99\pi.$$

Exercise 6.3

1 Factorise completely:
   (a) $x^2 - 4$ (b) $y^2 - 1$ (c) $p^2 - 49$
   (d) $100 - q^2$ (e) $a^2 - b^2$ (f) $64x^2 - 1$
   (g) $4x^2 - 1$ (h) $4x^2 - 9y^2$ (i) $4 - 25x^2$
   (j) $25y^2 - 9$ (k) $9p^2 - 16q^2$ (l) $16a^2 - 1$
   (m) $27x^2 - 3$ (n) $8x^2 - 50y^2$ (o) $13x^2 - 52$
   (p) $p^2 - p^2q^2$ (q) $x^4 - 1$ (r) $p^2 - p^4$
   (s) $R^2 - r^2$ (t) $ka^2 - kb^2$ (u) $(x + 2)^2 - (x + 1)^2$
   (v) $(x + 1)^2 - (x - 1)^2$ (w) $(x + 1)^2 - 16$ (x) $4 - (2x + 3)^2$.
2 Evaluate, using the difference of two squares:
   (a) $76^2 - 24^2$ (b) $199^2 - 1$ (c) $4.8^2 - 4.2^2$ (d) $6.4^2 - 3.6^2$.
3 Find the area between two concentric circles, whose radii are R cm and r cm, where:
   (a) $R = 3.12, r = 2.12$ (b) $R = 9.08, r = 0.92$, (c) $R = 2.85, r = 2.15$.
   Leave your answers in terms of π.
4 In triangle ABC, $\hat{B} = 90°$, AB $= 24$ cm and AC $= 25$ cm. Using the difference of two squares, calculate the length of BC.

Note that the sums of two squares, like $x^2 + 1$ or $x^2 + y^2$, have no real factors.

Trinomials

Expressions with three terms, like $x^2 + 8x + 15$, $x^2 + 5xy - 16y^2$ and $4x^2 - 16x + 5$, are called **trinomials**. To factorise these it is advisable to separate them into two categories; those where the coefficient of x^2 is unity, and all others.

(A) Coefficient of x^2 is unity

By multiplication $(x + a)(x + b) = x^2 + (a + b)x + ab$.
If an expression like $x^2 + px + q$ can be factorised into $(x + a)(x + b)$, it follows that $a + b = p$ and $ab = q$. The required numbers a and b, have a *sum p* and a *product q*.

Example 1: *Factorise* $x^2 + 8x + 15$.
Two numbers are required whose sum is $+8$ and product is $+15$. The required numbers are $+3$ and $+5$ giving the result $(x + 3)(x + 5)$.
   If the final term is positive, as in this case, both numbers will have the *same* sign as the middle term.

Example 2: $x^2 - 7x + 12 = (x - 4)(x - 3)$.

Example 3: $x^2 + 13x + 36 = (x + 4)(x + 9)$.

Example 4: *Factorise* $x^2 + x - 42$.
   The two numbers must have a product of -42 (they must be opposite in sign) and have a sum of $+1$. The numbers are $+7$ and -6 and the factors are $(x + 7)$ and $(x - 6)$. There are no other possibilities.

$$x^2 + x - 42 = (x + 7)(x - 6).$$

Example 5: $x^2 - 5x - 36 = (x - 9)(x + 4)$.

Example 6: $x^2 + 15x - 34 = (x + 17)(x - 2)$.
   Multiply out the brackets to check the result.
First remember to look for a common factor.

Example 7: $2x^2 - 6x - 80 = 2(x^2 - 3x - 40) = 2(x - 8)(x + 5)$.

Exercise 6.4

Factorise completely:

1 $x^2 - 5x + 4$	9 $y^2 - y - 42$	17 $p^2 - 3p - 108$
2 $x^2 + 5x + 6$	10 $y^2 - 2y - 15$	18 $p^2 + 11pq - 26q^2$
3 $x^2 - 12x + 27$	11 $y^2 + 5y - 14$	19 $5t^2 + 5t - 10$
4 $x^2 + 7x + 12$	12 $y^2 - 7y - 18$	20 $3t^2 - 15t + 18$
5 $x^2 - 6x + 5$	13 $1 + 5x + 6x^2$	21 $2t^2 + 4t - 30$
6 $x^2 + 13x + 40$	14 $1 - 2y - 3y^2$	22 $x^4 - 2x^2 - 3$
7 $y^2 - 4y - 12$	15 $1 + 12x + 27x^2$	23 $x^4 - 6x^3 + 5x^2$
8 $y^2 - y - 12$	16 $p^2 + 5p - 84$	24 $x^2y - 5xy + 4y$.

(B) Coefficient of x^2 is not unity

The expansion of $(2x+3)(5x-2)$ is $10x^2+11x-6$.

In factorising the expression $10x^2+11x-6$, the *four* numbers 2, 3, 5, -2 need to be determined whereas in the last type there were only *two*.

A modification of the method explained in the last section can be used.

Example 1: *Factorise* $10x^2+11x-6$.

Find two numbers which have a product of -60, the outer numbers multiplied together, and a sum of $+11$. These numbers are $+15$ and -4. Using these numbers the given expression is rewritten as

$$10x^2+11x-6 = 10x^2+15x-4x-6.$$

This is then treated in two parts and a common factor is extracted:

$$10x^2+15x = 5x(2x+3)$$

$$-4x-6 \;\;= -2(2x+3).$$

This gives $\qquad 10x^2+11x-6 = 5x(2x+3)-2(2x+3)$

$$= (2x+3)(5x-2).$$

Example 2: *Factorise* $2x^2-9x-5$.

Two numbers are required whose product is -10 and whose sum is -9. These numbers are -10 and $+1$.

Hence $\qquad\qquad 2x^2-9x+5 = 2x^2-10x+x-5$

$$= 2x(x-5)+1(x-5)$$

$$= (x-5)(2x+1).$$

Example 3: *Factorise* $12x^2-31x+9$.

Two numbers are required whose product is 108 and sum is -31. The required numbers are -4 and -27.

Hence $\qquad\qquad 12x^2-31x+9 = 12x^2-4x-27x+9.$

$$= 4x(3x-1)-9(3x-1)$$

$$= (3x-1)(4x-9).$$

Note that $x-y = -(y-x)$.

In the last example if $+9$ had been taken as the common factor of the second pair of terms the expression would appear as $4x(3x-1)+9(1-3x)$, but as $(1-3x) = -(3x-1)$ this is equivalent to the form shown above.

Exercise 6.5

Factorise completely:

1	$2x^2-9x-5$	**5**	$5x^2+26x+5$	**9**	$4x^2-7x+3$
2	$3x^2+8x-3$	**6**	$6x^2-11x-7$	**10**	$2x^2-23x+11$
3	$2x^2-13x-7$	**7**	$7x^2+13x-2$	**11**	$9x^2-3x-2$
4	$6x^2+7x+2$	**8**	$5x^2+12x+4$	**12**	$12x^2-28x-5$

13	$6x^2 - x - 2$	17	$2x^2 + 15x - 27$	21	$6x^2 + 19x + 10$
14	$14x^2 - 19x - 3$	18	$10x^2 + 19x + 6$	22	$4x^2 - 18x - 10$
15	$8 - 14x + 5x^2$	19	$6 + x - 2x^2$	23	$12x^2 + 88x - 180$
16	$15x^2 - x - 2$	20	$2 - 7x^2 + 13x$	24	$2x^3 - 9x^2 - 5x.$

Method of grouping

The method, used in the last section, of arranging the expression into groups so that a common factor may be extracted is called the method of grouping. A four-termed expression is usually grouped into two pairs.

Example 1: $\quad -x^2 + 6x + 6y - xy = x(6 - x) + y(6 - x)$

$$= (6 - x)(x + y).$$

The initial pairings are important; a common factor must emerge for a complete factorisation. Regrouping of the given expression may be necessary.

Example 2: $\quad x^2 - 4x - y^2 + 4y = x^2 - y^2 - 4x + 4y$

$$= (x^2 - y^2) - (4x - 4y)$$

$$= (x - y)(x + y) - 4(x - y)$$

$$= (x - y)(x + y - 4).$$

Sometimes a grouping of three and one is necessary.

Example 3: $\quad x^2 - 4x + 4 - y^2 = (x^2 - 4x + 4) - y^2$

$$= (x - 2)^2 - y^2$$

$$= (x - 2 + y)(x - 2 - y).$$

Five-termed expressions are usually grouped as a trinomial and a binomial.

Example 4: $\quad x^2 + 4x - 5xy - 24y - 6y^2 = (x^2 - 5xy - 6y^2) + (4x - 24y)$

$$= [(x - 6y)(x + y)] + [4(x - 6y)]$$
$$= (x - 6y)(x + y + 4).$$

Exercise 6.6

Factorise the following expressions:

1	$ax + ay + x + y$	9	$x^2 - 4xy - 1 + 4y^2$
2	$3x + 2ay + ax + 6y$	10	$x^2 - 2x + 1 - y^2$
3	$ab + ax + bx + x^2$	11	$9 - 6x + x^2 - 4y^2$
4	$x^2 - y + x - xy$	12	$w^2 - x^2 + 2xy - y^2$
5	$x^2 - 2xy + 3x - 6y$	13	$2x^2 + 12x + 6y + xy$
6	$xy + 2y + 6 + 3x$	14	$x^2 + xy - 5x - 10y - 2y^2$
7	$x^3 - xy^2 + x - y$	15	$x^2 + 11xy - 5x - 5y + 10y^2$
8	$x^2 + x + y - y^2$		

Simplification of algebraic expressions

Factorisation often allows a simplification of algebraic fractions. Given any such fraction the numerator and denominator should always be factorised, if possible. It may then be possible to write the fraction in a simpler form.

Example 1: $\dfrac{a+b}{a^2+ab} = \dfrac{^1\cancel{(a+b)}}{a\cancel{(a+b)}_1} = \dfrac{1}{a}.$

Cancelling is only permissible when the terms have a factor in common. The reader must not be tempted to cancel the a's alone; the terms of the expression are $a+b$ and a^2+ab, not a and a^2.

Example 2: $\dfrac{x^2-4}{x^2+3x-10} = \dfrac{\cancel{(x-2)}(x+2)}{(x+5)\cancel{(x-2)}} = \dfrac{x+2}{x+5}.$

No further simplification is possible. The fraction is in its lowest terms.

Example 3: $\dfrac{x^2-3x}{x^2+2x+1} \Big/ \dfrac{x^2-x-6}{x^2+3x+2}$

$$= \frac{x\cancel{(x-3)}}{\cancel{(x+1)}(x+1)} \cdot \frac{\cancel{(x+2)}\cancel{(x+1)}}{\cancel{(x-3)}\cancel{(x+2)}} = \frac{x}{x+1}$$

The rather complicated expression simplifies to $\dfrac{x}{x+1}.$

Exercise 6.7

Simplify the following expressions, if possible:

1. $\dfrac{x-3}{2x-6}$

2. $\dfrac{x+5}{15+3x}$

3. $\dfrac{2x-8}{x-4}$

4. $\dfrac{3-x}{x-3}$

5. $\dfrac{2x^2-x}{x}$

6. $\dfrac{x+1}{x}$

7. $\dfrac{9x^2-xy}{y-9x}$

8. $\dfrac{x^2-1}{x+1}$

9. $\dfrac{2x+3y}{4x^2-9y^2}$

10. $\dfrac{x^2+y^2}{x+y}$

11. $\dfrac{x^2-3x+4}{x^2-1}$

12. $\dfrac{x^2+9x+20}{x+4}$

13. $\dfrac{x^2-4x-5}{x^2-3x-10}$

14. $\dfrac{x^2-2x+1}{x^2+3x-4}$

15. $\dfrac{2x^2+9x+10}{3x^2-12}$

16. $\dfrac{6x^2+13x-5}{2x^2+3x-5}$

17. $\dfrac{6x^2+x-2}{2x^2+7x-4}$

18. $\dfrac{x^2-1}{(1+x)(1-x)}$

19. $\dfrac{2x+4}{x-5} \Big/ \dfrac{x+2}{x^2-4x-5}$

20. $\dfrac{x^2-1}{x} \Big/ \dfrac{2x+2}{x}$

21. $\dfrac{x^2-3x-4}{x^2-4} \Big/ \dfrac{x^2-1}{2-x-x^2}$

76

Adding or subtracting of algebraic fractions requires care, but it only involves the same processes as adding $\frac{1}{2}$ to $\frac{1}{3}$. The lowest common multiple(L.C.M.) of the denominators is found, each fraction is rewritten with this denominator, and then the numerator is simplified.

Example 1: *Simplify* $\dfrac{x}{2} + \dfrac{x+1}{3}$.

The L.C.M. of 2 and 3 is found and each fraction is written with this as denominator.

As $\qquad \dfrac{x}{2} = \dfrac{3x}{6}$ and $\dfrac{x+1}{3} = \dfrac{2(x+1)}{6}$

$$\frac{x}{2} + \frac{x+1}{3} = \frac{3x + 2(x+1)}{6} = \frac{5x+2}{6}, \text{ after simplifying the numerator.}$$

Example 2: $\dfrac{3}{x} + \dfrac{4}{x+1} = \dfrac{3(x+1)+4x}{x(x+1)} = \dfrac{7x+3}{x(x+1)}$.

The fraction may simplify even further if the numerator factorises.

Example 3: $\dfrac{1}{(x-2)(x+1)} + \dfrac{2}{3(x+3)(x+1)} = \dfrac{3(x+3)+2(x-2)}{3(x-2)(x+1)(x+3)}$

$$= \frac{5x+5}{3(x-2)(x+1)(x+3)}$$

$$= \frac{5(x+1)}{3(x-2)(x+1)(x+3)}$$

$$= \frac{5}{3(x-2)(x+3)}$$

Note the L.C.M. in the above example.

If the reader finds difficulty in forming the L.C.M., the following method, although longer, may prove easier.

Example 4: *Simplify* $\dfrac{1}{x+1} + \dfrac{2}{x^2+x}$.

Denominators should be factorised first, if possible.

$$\frac{1}{x+1} + \frac{2}{x^2+x} = \frac{1}{x+1} + \frac{2}{x(x+1)}$$

If the product $(x+1)x(x+1)$ is used instead of the L.C.M. the expression becomes

$$\frac{x(x+1)+2(x+1)}{(x+1)x(x+1)} = \frac{(x+1)(x+2)}{(x+1)x(x+1)} = \frac{x+2}{x(x+1)}$$

Exercise 6.8

Express the following as single fractions in their lowest terms:

1 $\dfrac{x}{2}+\dfrac{x}{7}$,

2 $\dfrac{x}{5}-\dfrac{x}{4}$,

3 $\dfrac{x+1}{2}-\dfrac{x-2}{3}$,

4 $\dfrac{3}{x}+\dfrac{5}{x^2}$,

5 $\dfrac{2}{x+1}-\dfrac{7}{x}$,

6 $\dfrac{1}{x}+\dfrac{1}{x+1}+\dfrac{1}{x+2}$,

7 $\dfrac{1}{x-3}+\dfrac{1}{x-1}$,

8 $\dfrac{x^2+1}{3x}-\dfrac{x}{3}$,

9 $\dfrac{1}{x^2+x}+\dfrac{1}{x}$,

10 $\dfrac{2}{1-x^2}-\dfrac{3}{1+x}$,

11 $\dfrac{x}{(x+1)(x+2)}-\dfrac{3}{x+2}$,

12 $\dfrac{x}{x^2-2x+1}+\dfrac{1}{x-1}$,

13 $1-\dfrac{12}{x}+\dfrac{15}{x+1}$,

14 $\dfrac{2}{(x-1)(x+4)}+\dfrac{5}{(x+4)(x+1)}$,

15 $\dfrac{1}{x^2-2x-3}-\dfrac{1}{2x^2+3x+1}$,

16 $\dfrac{-3}{(x+1)(x-2)}+\dfrac{7}{(x-2)(x+5)}$,

17 $\dfrac{3}{x^2-3x}-\dfrac{4}{x^2-2x-3}$,

18 $\dfrac{2}{5x^2-5}-\dfrac{1}{2x^2+x-3}$

7 Linear equations and inequations

An equation is a statement of equality between two expressions which contain unknown quantities, and is true only for specific values of the unknowns. The values of the unknowns which satisfy the equation are called solutions, or roots.

Simple equations

Equations in one unknown, where the highest power of the unknown is one, are called simple equations.

If $f(x) = 0$ is a simple equation, it has only one solution.

If the same quantity is added to or subtracted from the expressions on both sides of the equation, the new expressions are equal also.

Example 1: *Solve* $\qquad 4x - 8 = 3x$

Subtract $3x$ and add 8 to both sides
$$4x - 8 - 3x + 8 = 3x - 3x + 8$$
$$x = +8.$$

If the expressions on both sides of the equation are multiplied or divided by the same quantity, the equality is maintained.

Example 2: *Solve* $\qquad 4x = 3.$

Multiply both sides by $\frac{1}{4}$ $\qquad \frac{1}{4} \times 4x = \frac{1}{4} \times 3$
$$x = \tfrac{3}{4}.$$

The equations have been solved by using appropriate additive and multiplicative inverses. In the first example the use of the additive inverses of -8 and $3x$ ($+8$ and $-3x$ respectively), and in the second example the use of the multiplicative inverse of $4(\frac{1}{4})$ have the effect of collecting the x's on one side of the equation and the numbers on the other.

Both of these steps are widely used in the solution of all types of equation and must be mastered.

Exercise 7.1

Solve the equations:

1	$2x = 6$	**7**	$4x = 3$	**13**	$5 - 3x = 1 - 4x$
2	$7x = -7$	**8**	$-6x = 3$	**14**	$9 + 5x = 4 + 4x$
3	$13x = 26$	**9**	$x + 8 = 5$	**15**	$7x - 1 = 8x - 1$
4	$5x = 12$	**10**	$4x - 2 = 3x + 8$	**16**	$2x - 13 = 3x + 2$
5	$12x = 5$	**11**	$5x + 3 = 6x + 4$		
6	$3x = 25$	**12**	$3 - x = 5$		

The more general equations may have brackets or fractions and these must be cleared before the above methods can be used.

Example 1 (Brackets): *Solve*
$$3(1 - x) - 5(2 - 3x) = 2(x - 4).$$

Multiply out brackets $\quad 3 - 3x - 10 + 15x = 2x - 8$

Add $+10 - 3 - 2x$ to both sides, so that like terms are collected together
$$-2x - 3x + 15x = +10 - 3 - 8$$

$$10x = -1$$

Multiply both sides by $\dfrac{1}{10}$ $\qquad x = -\dfrac{1}{10}.$

The reader should cultivate the habit of checking solutions. The proposed solution $x = -\frac{1}{10}$ is substituted in the left-hand side (L.H.S.) of the equation and the result found. The same is then done for the right-hand side (R.H.S.).

Check: $\quad$ L.H.S. $= 3(1 + \frac{1}{10}) - 5(2 + \frac{3}{10}) = -8\frac{1}{5}.$

$\qquad\qquad$ R.H.S. $= 2(-\frac{1}{10} - 4) = 2(-4\frac{1}{10}) = -8\frac{1}{5}.$

As the values agree, the equation has been successfully checked and the proposed solution is confirmed.

Example 2 (Fractional): *Solve* $\dfrac{x}{3} = \dfrac{x - 1}{2}.$

Multiply both sides by 6 (the L.C.M. of 3 and 2)

$$\frac{6x}{3} = \frac{6(x - 1)}{2}$$

$$2x = 3(x - 1)$$

$$2x = 3x - 3.$$

Add $3 - 2x$ to both sides $3 = x \Leftrightarrow x = 3.$

Note: The insertion of the bracket in the first line above is very important. The bracket is not necessary in the given equation, since it is implied by the division line, but as soon as the expression is multiplied by another term, such as 6, it is necessary in order to eliminate any ambiguity.

Exercise 7.2

Solve the equations:

1 $3(x-1) = 9$

11 $\dfrac{x}{2} = \dfrac{4}{3}$

2 $4(2+3x) = 5(1-2x)$

12 $\dfrac{x}{4} = \dfrac{5}{6}$

3 $3(2+x) = 3(2-x)$

13 $\dfrac{3x}{8} = \dfrac{1}{3}$

4 $5-2(x-1) = 5x$

14 $\dfrac{15x}{8} = \dfrac{2}{3}$

5 $6(1+2x) = 5(3+x)$

15 $\dfrac{x}{2} = \dfrac{1-x}{3}$

6 $2(7-x) = 5(1+x)$

16 $\dfrac{1+x}{7} = \dfrac{1-x}{5}$

7 $6(3-x) = 12$

17 $\dfrac{2-x}{3} = \dfrac{x-5}{4}$

8 $4-7x = 2(x-5)$

18 $\dfrac{x}{3} - \dfrac{x}{5} - 2 = 0$

9 $5(x-5) = 2(x-2)$

19 $\dfrac{x}{2} + \dfrac{x}{3} + \dfrac{x}{4} = 4$

10 $1-2(3-x) = 5$

20 $\dfrac{4-3x}{2} = \dfrac{5x}{3}$

It is advisable, in the more complicated equations, to eliminate any fractions first.

Example: Solve $\quad \dfrac{1-5x}{4} - \dfrac{2(1-3x)}{5} = 7.$

Multiply throughout by 20 $\qquad 5(1-5x) - 8(1-3x) = 140$

Then remove brackets $\qquad\qquad 5 - 25x - 8 + 24x = 140$

$$-x = 143$$

Multiply both sides by -1 $\qquad\qquad x = -143.$

Exercise 7.3 (*Miscellaneous*)

1 $\dfrac{x}{2} = 5$

3 $\dfrac{x}{7} = -7$

5 $8x = 7$

2 $3 = \dfrac{x}{3}$

4 $7x = 8$

6 $3(4+x) = 8$

7 $6(1 - 5x) = 2$

8 $7(1 - x) - 4(x - 3) = 2$

9 $x - 6(3 - 5x) = 2(x - 9)$

10 $5 - \dfrac{x}{2} = \dfrac{x}{6}$

11 $1 - \dfrac{4 - 3x}{2} = 5$

12 $\dfrac{x}{3} - \dfrac{2x - 1}{4} = 5$

13 $\dfrac{2}{3}(1 + x) + \dfrac{3}{4}(1 - x) = 1$

14 $\dfrac{1}{4}(1 - x) - \dfrac{1}{7}(x - 3) = 2$

15 $\dfrac{x - 1}{3} + \dfrac{2x - 5}{2} - 1 = 0$

16 $\dfrac{4x - 3}{2x - 5} = \dfrac{3}{4}$

17 $\dfrac{x - 5}{x - 2} + 1 = \dfrac{2x}{x - 1}$

18 $\dfrac{5}{x - 2} = \dfrac{2}{x - 5}$

19 $\dfrac{1 - x}{1 + x} - \dfrac{3}{x} + 1 = 0$

20 $\dfrac{2}{1 - x} + \dfrac{x}{1 + x} = 1$

Simple inequations

The simple equation $x + 1 = 5$ has only the one solution, $x = 4$. This may be represented diagrammatically by a point on the number line. The simple inequation $x + 1 > 5$ is satisfied by all x greater than 4. The solution set, and hence its diagrammatic representation, depends on the domain of x. If the domain of x is the set of integers $\mathbb{Z}$ the solution set may be written as $\{5, 6, 7 \dots\}$ or $\{x : x > 4, x \in \mathbb{Z}\}$; if the domain is the set of real numbers $\mathbb{R}$ the solution set can only be given in the form $\{x : x > 4, x \in \mathbb{R}\}$.

In the first case, the solution set can be clearly represented by the set of discrete points 5, 6, 7, etc., on the number line; in the second case, with domain $\mathbb{R}$, the solution set is represented as in Figure 7.1.

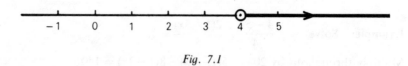

Fig. 7.1

The open ring signifies that the element $x = 4$ is not a member of the solution set.

The set $\{x : x \geqslant 4\}$ would be represented as in Figure 7.1 but with a closed ring. Figure 7.2 shows how to represent the set $\{x : 2 \leqslant x < 4\}$

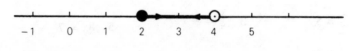

Fig. 7.2

82

The methods used to solve simple equations can be used to find the solution sets of simple inequations, except in the case where it is necessary to multiply or divide both sides of the inequation by a negative number. If the numbers 5 and 6, which are related by the statement $6 > 5$, are multiplied by -1, say, the new numbers -5 and -6 are related by $-6 < -5$.

If an inequation is multiplied, or divided, by a negative number the sign of the inequation must be reversed.

Example 1: *Find the solution set of*
$$2(x-1) > 3x + 8, \ x \ real.$$

Multiply out $\qquad\qquad 2x - 2 > 3x + 8$

$$-x > 10$$

Multiply by -1 $\qquad\qquad x < -10$

$$\text{Solution set is } \{x : x < -10, \ x \in \mathbb{R}\}.$$

Example 2: *Find the greatest integer value of x which satisfies*

$$7(2x + 3) \leqslant 7x - 8.$$

$$14x + 21 \leqslant 7x - 8.$$

$$7x \leqslant -29$$

$$x \leqslant -4\tfrac{1}{7}.$$

Fig. 7.3

The greatest integer value of x is -5 (see Figure 7.3).

Exercise 7.4

1 If x is real, find the solution set of the following:
   (a) $2x > -5$ $\qquad\qquad$ (b) $3x + 1 < 5x - 2$
   (c) $x + 8 < 3x + 9$ $\qquad\quad$ (d) $5x + 2 \leqslant 7x - 8$
   (e) $3(x + 2) < 4(2x - 1)$ $\quad$ (f) $-(x + 1) \geqslant 8$
   (g) $\dfrac{x+1}{5} < \dfrac{2x-1}{4}$ $\qquad$ (h) $\dfrac{x}{7} > \dfrac{x+1}{4}$

2 Give the lowest integer in the solution sets of the following:
   (a) $3x + 8 \geqslant x + 2$ $\qquad$ (b) $5x - 9 \leqslant 6x + 4$ (c) $5(x + 2) > 3x + 9$

   (d) $4x + 13 < 7x + 5$ $\qquad$ (e) $\dfrac{2x + 5}{7} \leqslant \dfrac{8x - 1}{6}$ (f) $\dfrac{x - 9}{3} > 4$

   (g) $2x + 5 \geqslant 7$

3 Illustrate the following solution sets on a number line and, if possible, simplify the set:

(a) $\{x : 3x + 4 > -7\}$ (b) $\{x : 2x - 7 \leqslant 10\}$

(c) $\{x : x + 8 > 3x + 3\}$ (d) $\{x : 5x - 9 < x + 8\}$

(e) $\{x : 2x + 1 \geqslant 4x + 2\} \cap \{x : 3x + 5 > 2x + 3\}$

(f) $\{x : 3x + 4 < 2(x + 2)\} \cap \{x : 5x + 7 > 2x + 19\}$

Formulae

A formula, in mathematics, like $s = vt$, is a symbolic statement of the law governing the quantities involved. In words, $s = vt$ states that (for uniform motion) the distance travelled (s) can be found by multiplying together the speed (v) by the time (t). The units must be compatible. A formula displays the programme to be followed to find one quantity if the others are known.

Example: *Given that apples cost x pence per lb and pears cost y pence per lb, find a formula for the cost C, in pence, of a lb of apples and b lb of pears.*

The cost of a lb of apples at x pence per lb is ax pence. (The reader should consider some numerical examples if necessary).

Similarly the cost of b lb of pears at y pence per lb is by pence.

An expression for the cost of the combination is $(ax + by)$ pence.

When this is related to C, making sure the units are as required, we have the formula $C = ax + by$.

The formula has no units in it and gives a programme for finding the cost of *any* weight of apples and pears at *any* particular costs per lb, provided that a, b and C are in the same units.

In the following exercise the reader is able to practise developing algebraic expressions before attempting to solve problems.

Exercise 7.5

1 Eggs cost p pence each. Find the cost, in pounds, of (a) one dozen eggs, (b) three dozen, (c) g dozen.

2 Two angles of a triangle are $x°$ and $(70 + 3x)°$. Find the other angle in terms of x.

3 The lengths of the sides of a rectangle are x cm and $(x + 2)$ cm. Find expressions for the perimeter P, and area A, in terms of x.

4 On a book shelf there are m books each n cm thick, placed side by side. Find the space, in cm, taken up by the books. How many more similar books can be stacked on the shelf if it is p cm long ($p > mn$)? If the covers of the books are each d cm thick, find the thickness of the paper (a) in each book, (b) in all the books.

5 A toy costs $£x$. Find the cost of y toys (a) in $£$, (b) in pence.

6 An apple costs x pence and an orange costs y pence. Find the cost, in pence, of (a) 2 apples and 5 oranges, (b) d applies and f oranges.

7 The average age of 2 boys is 6 years. If one boy is x years old, find the age of the other boy in terms of x.

8 The total cost of 4 cups of tea and 3 cups of coffee is £1. If the price of a cup of tea is x pence, find the price of a cup of coffee in terms of x.

9 A man can walk at an average speed of 6 km/h. How long will it take him to walk 8 km?
If he can walk at x km/h, find how long, in hours, it will take him to walk y km (a) if he does not stop on the walk, (b) if he stops for 10 minutes on the walk, (c) if he stops for z minutes on the walk.

10 Find the cost of petrol, in pence, used by a car in travelling x km if it can travel y km per litre and the cost of petrol is z pence per litre.

11 A man travels x km in the first two hours of a journey and y km in the next 3 hours. Find his average speed in km/h.

12 For the first 2 km of a journey a car travels at x km/h and for the next 5 km the car travels at y km/h. Find the average speed of the car in km/h.

Problems leading to simple equations

Let the unknown quantity be x and combine the relevant expressions in x to form an equation. This is then solved to find x.

Example 1: *A man is nine times as old as his son. In four years' time he will only be five times as old. How old is the son now?*
Let the son be x years old now.
The father, now, is $9x$ years old.
In four years' time they will be $(x+4)$ yrs old and $(9x+4)$ yrs old, respectively. The expressions $(x+4)$ and $(9x+4)$ are related by

$$9x + 4 = 5(x+4)$$

$$9x + 4 = 5x + 20$$

$$4x = 16$$

$$x = 4.$$

The son is 4 years old.

Example 2: *A boy cycles from his home to the station at 12 km/h and immediately boards a train which then travels at 48 km/h to his destination. The total distance is 64 km and the journey takes the boy 1 h 50 min. How far is it from his home to the station?*

Let the required distance be x km.
The distance from station to destination is then $(64 - x)$ km.

The time taken cycling is $\dfrac{x}{12}$ h (time = distance/speed).

The time taken on train is $\dfrac{(64-x)}{48}$ h

The total time, *in hours*, is $1\frac{5}{6}$

The equation can now be built up.

$$\frac{x}{12}+\frac{64-x}{48}=\frac{11}{6}$$

Multiply by 48: $\qquad\qquad 4x+64-x=88$

$$3x=24$$

$$x=8$$

The distance from home to the station is 8 km.

Exercise 7.6

1   A mother is seven times as old as her daughter. Three years ago she was thirteen times as old. Find the ratio of their ages in four years' time.

2   A man is four years older than his wife and the ratio of their ages is $9:8$. How old are they?

3   After four completed innings a batsman has an average of 48 runs. After a fifth completed innings his average is 60 runs. Find the score in his final innings.

4   The sum of £44.40 is to be divided between two men, A and B. Find how much A receives if the ratio of their shares is $5:7$, respectively.

5   A line AC, of length 5 cm, is divided by a point B in the ratio $3:7$. What is the length of BC?

6   A sum of £65.20 is made up of 50 pence pieces and 10 pence pieces only. If there are 200 coins in all, how many are 10 pence pieces?

7   At the time a buyer was ordering his goods, tea was quoted at £1.20 per lb and coffee at £4 per lb. He decided to buy a certain amount of each. In all 104 lb were bought, at a total cost of £248. How much of each commodity did he buy?

8   A batsman made a very good score of 132. This was made up of twice as many singles as sixes, three times as many fours as sixes, and 12 runs scored in other ways. How many sixes did he score?

9   The angles of a triangle are $x°$, $(3x+5)°$, and $(6x-5)°$. Find x.

10   The sequence of commands in a party game are as follows: Think of a number, double it, add 15, treble the total, take away the number you first thought of, and finally divide your total by 5. If the final result is 14, what was the number first thought of? Make up two sets of instructions for yourself so that (a) you can say what number was chosen, and (b) you can say 'the result is 6' for whatever number was chosen.

11   The distance from London to Bristol is 184 km. A car starts from London and travels at 52 km/h towards Bristol; at the same time a car

starts from Bristol and travels, on the same route, to London at 44 km/h. After how long do they meet and how far from each city are they?

12 Two boys can run at 9 m/s and 8 m/s respectively. How much start, in metres, would the slower boy need so that they dead heat in a race in which the faster boy covers 100 metres?

13 A and B are two points 100 km apart. A cyclist starts from A towards B; at the same time another cyclist, who can move at 3 km/h faster than the first, sets off from B towards A. Given that they meet after 4 hours, find their speeds.

14 The perimeter of a right-angled triangle is 15 cm and the shortest side is 6 cm. Find the lengths of the other two sides.

15 The distance from Whitepool to Blacklake is 154 km. A coach leaves Whitepool at 12.00 h and averages 40 km/h before it stops for 40 minutes for the passengers to lunch. On the second part of the journey the coach is able to average 60 km/h, arriving at Blacklake at 15.46 h. How far from Whitepool was the stop?

Literal equations: change of subject

The equation $ax + b = c$, expressing a relationship between various undefined symbols, is called a literal equation. If a, b and c represent physical quantities it is a formula; if they are replaced by numbers the relation becomes a simple equation. A literal equation, like a formula, cannot be solved numerically, as the simple equations were, but any one of the symbols may be given as a combination of the others. The *isolated symbol* is called the **subject of the equation**.

In the above equation c is the subject, but it is equally true to say that $b = c - ax$ represents the same relationship between the symbols. We say that we have changed the subject of the equation from c to b, or made b the subject of the equation.

To solve a simple equation we have, in effect, made x the subject of the equation. Besides the processes used to solve simple equations we shall use those of squaring and square-rooting. In general, if the same operation is applied to both sides of an equation the equality still holds.

Example 1: *Make x the subject of* $\qquad x^2 = (x - c)(x - d)$

Multiply out the brackets $\qquad\qquad x^2 = x^2 - cx - dx + cd$

Collect x terms on one side $\qquad cx + dx = cd$

Factorise $\qquad\qquad\qquad\qquad x(c + d) = cd$

Divide by $(c + d)$ $\qquad\qquad\qquad\qquad x = \dfrac{cd}{c + d}.$

Note: The subject of the equation must occur only once, isolated, in the equation. A true relationship in the above example is $x = c(d - x)/d$ but x is not the subject of this equation, as x occurs on both sides of the equation.

Example 2: *Make u the subject of* $\dfrac{1}{u} + \dfrac{1}{v} = \dfrac{1}{f}$.

Multiply throughout by uvf $\qquad\qquad vf + uf = uv$

Isolate the terms in u $\qquad\qquad\qquad vf = uv - uf$

Factorise $\qquad\qquad\qquad\qquad\quad vf = u(v - f)$

Divide by $(v - f)$ $\qquad\qquad\qquad \dfrac{vf}{v - f} = u$

Example 3: *Make s the subject of* $\quad x = \sqrt{\dfrac{s - a}{s - b}}$

Square both sides $\qquad\qquad\qquad x^2 = \dfrac{s - a}{s - b}$

Multiply both sides by $(s - b)$ $\quad (s - b)x^2 = s - a$

$\qquad\qquad\qquad\qquad\qquad\quad\ sx^2 - bx^2 = s - a$

Isolate terms in s $\qquad\qquad\quad\ sx^2 - s = bx^2 - a$

Factorise $\qquad\qquad\qquad\ s(x^2 - 1) = bx^2 - a$

Divide by $(x^2 - 1)$ $\qquad\qquad\qquad\ s = \dfrac{bx^2 - a}{x^2 - 1}$.

An alternative method, using flow charts, may be used. The reader should refer to Chapter 11, for a fuller discussion of the notation used.

Example 4: *Make t the subject of* $x = \sqrt{1 + kt}$

The relationship may be considered as a mapping from t to x. The flow chart, Figure 7.4, displays the basic processes in that mapping.

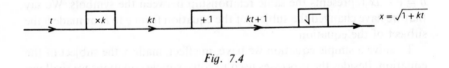

Fig. 7.4

To find t in terms of x is equivalent to feeding in x from the right hand side through a sequence of the inverse processes as shown in Figure 7.5.

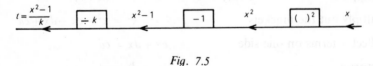

Fig. 7.5

The required relationship is $t = \dfrac{x^2 - 1}{k}$.

The reader should use whichever method is more familiar in the following exercise.

88

Exercise 7.7

For the following equations, make the term in brackets the subject:

1   $V = abc$ (b)

2   $V = \frac{1}{3}\pi r^2 h$ $(h), (r)$

3   $S = ut + \frac{1}{2}at^2$ $(u), (a)$

4   $9C = 5(F - 32)$ (F)

5   $T = 2\pi\sqrt{\dfrac{l}{g}}$ $(l), (g)$

6   $x^2 + y^2 = 9$ (x)

7   $\dfrac{x^2}{4} + \dfrac{y^2}{25} = 1$ (y)

8   $\dfrac{1}{x} + \dfrac{1}{y} = 4$ (x)

9   $\dfrac{1}{c} = \sqrt{b-a}$ (b)

10   $\dfrac{x+a}{x+b} = \dfrac{x+c}{x+d}$ (x)

11   $f = \dfrac{(m-n)g}{m+n}$ (m)

12   $y = \dfrac{1+x}{1-x}$ (x)

13   $P = (M+m)f$ (m)

14   $\dfrac{1}{u} - \dfrac{1}{v} = \dfrac{2}{w}$ $(u), (w)$

15   $y = 1 + \dfrac{1}{x}$ (x)

16   $a = b\sqrt{c+d}$ $(b), (c)$

17   $A = \pi(R-r)(R+r)$ (R)

18   $S = \dfrac{n}{2}\{2a + (n-1)d\}$ $(a), (d)$

8 The straight line

Graphs and linear functions

If a set $\{x\}$ in the domain, and the corresponding set of images $\{y\}$ in the range, of the function $f: x \to mx + c$, are represented by a set of points $\{(x, y)\}$ in the plane, the graph will always be a straight line. The equation of the line is written as $y = mx + c$ and shows the relation satisfied by all points on that line. No other points in the plane have co-ordinates satisfying the relation. A straight line is defined by two points, but at least three should be plotted, so that a check can be made.

Example: *Draw the graph of* $y = 2x + 1$, *representing the mapping of* $f: x \to 2x + 1$.
Choose three points in the domain, say 0, 1, 2, and evaluate their corresponding images.
This is usually shown in a table

x	0	1	2
y	1	3	5

The graph of $y = 2x + 1$ is shown in Figure 8.1

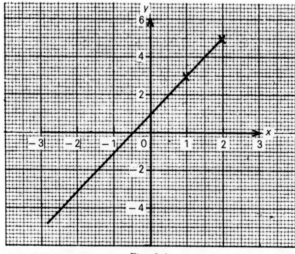

Fig. 8.1

The scales used on the axes need not be the same and should be chosen to give the most accurate graph.

Exercise 8.1

1 Draw the graph of $y = 3x + 5$ for the domain $\{x: -3 \leqslant x \leqslant 3\}$. (Before drawing the graph make a table to find the range of y).
2 Draw the graph of $y = -2x - 3$ for the domain $\{x: -4 \leqslant x \leqslant 2\}$.
3 On the same axes, and using the same scales on each axis (2 cm to represent 1 unit), draw the graphs of the following, for the domain $\{x: -2 \leqslant x \leqslant 3\}$:

$$y = x, \ y = x + 2, \ y = \tfrac{1}{2}x \quad y = 2x + 1, \ y = -x, \ y = -x + 3.$$

In the graph of the function $f: x \to mx + c$ what appears to be the significance of m and c?

Measure the angle that the lines $y = x$ and $y = 2x + 1$ make with the x-axis and use tables to find the values of the tangents of these angles.

Would you expect different results if the scales were not the same?

4 For the domain $\{x: 0 \leqslant x \leqslant 3\}$ draw the graphs of the following, using the same axes and scales in each part. In each case find the co-ordinates of the point of intersection of the lines.
(a) $y = 2x + 5$ and $y = -x + 2$,
(b) $2x + 3y = 6$ and $6x + y = 10$,
(c) $y = 3x + 1$ and $y = 4x - 2$.

Gradient of a line

The gradient of a straight line is the ratio: increase in y/increase in x, measured between two points on the line. This ratio can be either negative or positive. In Figure 8.2(a), the line AB has gradient $\tfrac{3}{2}$ (from A to B the increase in y is 3, increase in x is 2; from B to A the increase in y is -3, the increase in x is -2). In Figure 8.2(b), the line CD has gradient $-\tfrac{5}{3}$. If the

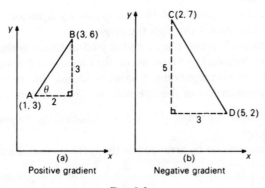

Fig. 8.2

scales are the same on each axis, the angle θ that the line makes with the x axis is related to the gradient m of the line by $m = \tan \theta$.
In Figure 8.2(a), $\tan \theta = 1.5 \Rightarrow \theta = 56° 19'$.
It is useful to be able to sketch the graph of a linear function or form the equation of a line, given sufficient data, without plotting points on graph paper.

General equation of a straight line

Every straight line, unless it is parallel to the y-axis, in which case its equation is $x = k$ (where k is constant), will have an intercept on the y-axis. Let this point be $(0, c)$.
Denote the gradient of the line by m.

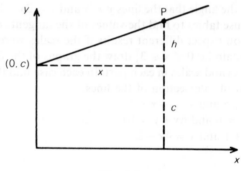

Fig. 8.3

In Figure 8.3, we can see that any point x in the domain has an image $y = h + c$, but $\dfrac{h}{x} = m$, the gradient of the line. All points on the line, therefore, are related by the equation $y = mx + c$.

Conversely, any equation that can be arranged in the form of $y = mx + c$ can be represented by a **straight line whose gradient is m and whose intercept on the y-axis is c.**
If $m = 0$, the line is parallel to the x-axis and its equation is $y = c$.
If $c = 0$, the line passes through the origin.
When the straight line cuts the x-axis the y-co-ordinate of the point is 0. As the equation is satisfied by all points on the line, if $y = 0$ is substituted into the equation the corresponding x value is found. Similarly, substituting $x = 0$ into the equation of the line will give the intercept on the y-axis.

Example: *Sketch the graph of $2x + 3y = 7$, indicating the points in which it crosses the axes.*
As the equation can be arranged in the form $y = mx + c$ it represents a straight line. $\left[2x + 3y = 7 \Rightarrow y = -\dfrac{2}{3}x + \dfrac{7}{3} \Rightarrow m = -\dfrac{2}{3},\ c = +\dfrac{7}{3} \right].$

92

Put $x = 0 \Rightarrow 3y = 7 \Rightarrow y = \frac{7}{3}$. The line crosses the y-axis at $(0, 2\frac{1}{3})$.

Put $y = 0 \Rightarrow 2x = 7 \Rightarrow x = 3\frac{1}{2}$. The line crosses the x-axis at $(3\frac{1}{2}, 0)$.
The sketch is shown in Figure 8.4.

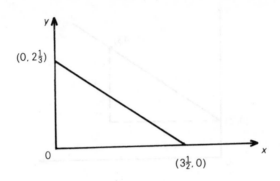

Fig. 8.4

The above method can be used to sketch the graphs of all linear functions.

Exercise 8.2

1 Draw right angled triangles with the line joining A and B as hypotenuse in each of the following cases, and find, (i) the gradient of the line, and (ii) the length of the line segment AB:
(a) A = (2, 5), B = (5, 9) (b) A = (−1, 2), B = (4, −10)
(c) A = (4, −3), B = (−2, 3) (d) A = (0, 0), B = (−4, −3).

2 Calculate the points in which the graphs of the following cut the axes, and in each case state the gradient of the line.
(a) $y = 3x + 5$ (b) $y = 4x − 2$ (c) $y = −x + 1$
(d) $y = −2x + 1$ (e) $x + y = 5$ (f) $2x + 3y = 6$
(g) $7x − y = 5$ (h) $4x + 3y = 1$ (i) $\frac{x}{2} + \frac{y}{3} = 1$.

3 Sketch the graphs of the following, giving the co-ordinates of points where they cross the axes:
(a) $y = 5$ (b) $y = 5x$ (c) $y = 5x − 2$
(d) $x = 3$ (e) $x + y = 3$ (f) $x − y = 3$
(g) $1 + y = 2x$ (h) $y = 4(x − 1)$ (i) $y − 2 = 2(x − 3)$.

To form an equation from given data involves finding m and c.

Example 1: *Find the equation of the line that has a gradient of 7 and passes through the point (5, 43).*
As m is given here we need to find c.

93

In Figure 8.5 we see that $\dfrac{43-c}{5} = 7 \Rightarrow c = 8.$

The equation of the line is $y = 7x + 8$

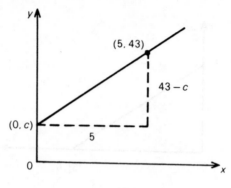

Fig. 8.5

Alternatively, since $m = 7$, the equation is of the form $y = 7x + c$.
As the point $(5, 43)$ satisfies the equation, $43 = 35 + c \Rightarrow c = 8$ and the equation of the line is as above.

Example 2: *Find the equation of the line that cuts the x-axis at $(a, 0)$ and the y-axis at $(0, b)$.*

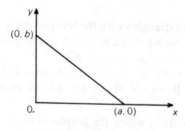

Fig. 8.6

The gradient of the line is $m = -\dfrac{b}{a}$; it meets the y-axis at $(0, b)$

The equation is $y = -\dfrac{b}{a}x + b$

$$\text{or} \quad bx + ay = ab.$$

A neat form of the equation is derived by dividing both sides of the equation by ab:

$$\frac{x}{a} + \frac{y}{b} = 1.$$

If an equation is arranged into this form, a and b are the intercepts on the x and y-axes, respectively.

94

Examples: $\dfrac{x}{3}+\dfrac{y}{4}=1$ cuts the x-axis at $(3, 0)$, the y-axis at $(0, 4)$.

$\dfrac{x}{5}-\dfrac{y}{6}=1 \Rightarrow \dfrac{x}{5}+\dfrac{y}{-6}=1$ cuts the x-axis at $(5, 0)$, the y-axis at $(0, -6)$.

$\dfrac{x}{2}+\dfrac{y}{4}=5 \Rightarrow \dfrac{x}{10}+\dfrac{y}{20}=1$ cuts the x-axis at $(10, 0)$, the y-axis at $(0, 20)$.

Exercise 8.3

1 Find the equations of the straight lines with gradient m passing through the point A in the following cases:
(a) $m = 3$, A $= (0, 4)$ (b) $m = -2$, A $= (0, 1)$ (c) $m = 4$, A $= (-1, 0)$
(d) $m = -1$, A $= (2, 7)$ (e) $m = 6$, A $= (-1, 3)$ (f) $m = \frac{1}{2}$, A $= (2, 3)$.

2 Find the equations of the straight lines joining A and B in the following cases:
(a) A $= (2, 3)$, B $= (6, 11)$ (b) A $= (-1, 8)$, B $= (8, -1)$
(c) A $= (3, 4)$, B $= (8, 4)$ (d) A $= (1, 0)$, B $= (0, 4)$
(e) A $= (3, 0)$, B $= (0, -5)$ (f) A $= (-1, 0)$, B $= (0, -2)$.

3 Find the equation of the straight line parallel to $y = 2x + 5$ and passing through $(2, 3)$.

4 Find the equation of the straight line parallel to $x + y = 8$ and passing through $(6, 0)$.

5 Write down the equations of the four lines forming the sides of the trapezium OABC shown in Figure 8.7.

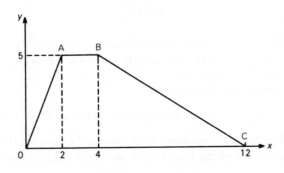

Fig. 8.7

6 Sketch the graphs of the following, giving the co-ordinates of points where they cross the axes:
(a) $y = 2x + 7$ (b) $y = -x + 8$ (c) $2x + 3y = 6$
(d) $\dfrac{x}{2}+\dfrac{y}{8}=1$ (e) $\dfrac{x}{5}-\dfrac{y}{2}=1$ (f) $\dfrac{2x}{3}+\dfrac{3x}{8}=1$.

Simultaneous equations

In the previous section we saw that any equation of the form $ax + by = c$ corresponds to a line in the plane; each number pair (x, y) satisfying the equation corresponds to a point on the line. A linear equation such as $2x + 3y = 6$, therefore, does not have a finite set of solutions like those equations in one unknown; it has an infinite set corresponding to the points on its line graph. If a second linear equation such as $6x + y = 10$ is considered at the same time then we see from their graphs (Figure 8.8) that they have a common solution $x = 1\frac{1}{2}, y = 1$. We say that the equations have been solved simultaneously.

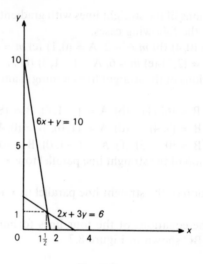

Fig. 8.8

In general, two linear equations will have a unique common solution. There are, however, two special cases to consider, where:

(a) their graphs are parallel.

(b) their graphs are the same line.

The graph of $ax + by = c$ is a line whose gradient is $-\dfrac{b}{a}$. The ratio $\dfrac{b}{a}$, therefore, determines the gradient. If the ratio is the same for two equations then they are either parallel or, in fact, the same straight line.

For example: $2x + 3y = 6$ and $4x + 6y = 7$ are parallel, while
$2x + 3y = 6$ and $4x + 6y = 12$ are the same line.

We conclude that if one equation is a multiple of the other, they have an infinite set of solutions; if this is not the case, but the ratio b/a is the same, they have no common solution. In all other cases there will be a unique solution.

The graphical consideration of simultaneous equations gives an insight into any algebraic analysis. The point of intersection of the two lines is the only point in the plane such that for the same value of x (or y) the equations have the same value of y(or x). This observation leads to the following algebraic method for solving simultaneous equations.

Method of substitution

This is a general method, but in the case of two linear equations it is used when one of the unknowns has a coefficient of unity.

Example 1: *Solve the simultaneous equations* $2x + 3y = 6$ *and* $6x + y = 10$.

The underlined term, having a coefficient of unity, is made the subject of the equation to give $y = 10 - 6x$*.

This is then substituted in the other equation: $2x + 3(10 - 6x) = 6$.
This simple equation is then solved to give $x = 1\frac{1}{2}$.
For this value of x the equations must have the same value of y. The corresponding value of y can be found from*

$$y = 10 - 6(1\tfrac{1}{2}) = 10 - 9 = 1.$$

The solution is $\qquad\qquad x = 1\frac{1}{2}, y = 1.$

Example 2: *Solve the simultaneous equations* $\qquad x + 4y = 13$ $\quad$ (1)

$$2x - 3y = 7 \quad (2)$$

From equation (1) $\qquad\qquad x = 13 - 4y$*.

Substitute for x in equation (2): $2(13 - 4y) - 3y = 7$

$$\Rightarrow 26 - 8y - 3y = 7$$

$$11y = 19$$

$$y = \frac{19}{11} = 1\tfrac{8}{11}.$$

In * $\quad x = 13 - 4(1\tfrac{8}{11}) = 13 - 6\tfrac{10}{11} = 6\tfrac{1}{11}.$

The solution is $x = 6\tfrac{1}{11}, y = 1\tfrac{8}{11}.$

Exercise 8.4

Solve the following pairs of linear equations simultaneously, explaining any special cases:

1	$2x + y = 7$	6	$x + 5y = 14$
	$3x + 5y = 2$		$7x - 3y = 3$
2	$x + 3y = 8$	7	$x + 3y = 6$
	$2x + 4y = 3$		$7x + 21y = 42$
3	$7x + y = 10$	8	$4x + y = 30 = 8x - 13y$
	$14x + 2y = 8$		
4	$5x + y = 10$	9	$5x + 6y = 45$
	$6x - y = 12$		$3y - x = 5$
5	$4x - 3y = 8$	10	$7y + 2x = 36 = 7y - x.$
	$5x + y = 29$		

The method of substitution, although the more logical method of solution, does produce fractional equations when there is not a coefficient of x or y equal to unity. To avoid fractional linear equations the following alternative method may be used:

Method of elimination

Consider the pair of equations, $2x + 3y = 15$ and $3x - 2y = 3$. The equivalent pair of equations, $4x + 6y = 30$ and $9x - 6y = 9$, have the same solution, and by adding these equations we find that $13x = 39$ giving the solution $x = 3$. The value of y can be found, as before. The given equations have a common solution $x = 3$, $y = 3$.

The given equations are each multiplied, if necessary, so that the coefficients of one of the unknowns are equal in size but opposite in sign.

Example: *Solve the equations* $2x + 5y = -3$ (1) *and* $7x + 3y = 4$ (2) simultaneously.

Multiply (1) by 3 $\qquad\qquad\qquad 6x + 15y = -9$

Multiply (2) by -5 $\qquad\qquad -35x - 15y = -20$

Add the equations $\qquad\qquad\qquad -29x = -29$

$$x = 1$$

In (1) when $x = 1$ $\qquad\qquad 2 + 5y = -3 \Rightarrow y = -1$

$$\text{The solution is } x = 1, y = -1$$

Exercise 8.5

1 Use the method of elimination to solve the following pairs of equations simultaneously:

(a) $3x + 2y = 12$
$\quad 4x - 3y = -1$

(b) $3x + 2y = 13$
$\quad 2x + 3y = 12$

(c) $5x + 4y = 22$
$\quad 3x + 5y = 21$

(d) $4y - 7x = 15$
$\quad 2y + 14x = 5$

(e) $4x + 3y = 5 = 12x - \dfrac{y}{3}$

(f) $6x - 5y = 3$
$\quad 2x + 3y = 4$

(g) $5x + 2y = 6$
$\quad 7x - 2y = 6$

(h) $8x + 9y = 12$
$\quad 3x - 2y = 5$

2 Without using a graph, find the intersection of the following straight lines:

(a) $y = 3x + 1$ and $x = 6$
(b) $y = 4x + 2$ and $y = 5$
(c) $y = -2x + 5$ and $y = x + 3$
(d) $2y = 3x + 1$ and $3y = 4x - 5$
(e) $x + y = 7$ and $y = 5x - 1$
(f) $2x + 3y = 4$ and $7x - 2y = 3$

3 Find the co-ordinates of the points A, B, C, D and E shown in Figure 8.9 where CD is parallel to OE

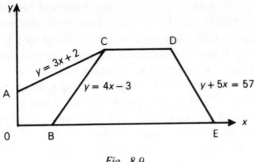

Fig. 8.9

Problems leading to simultaneous equations

The problems in this section involve two unknowns and can be solved by forming two equations in the unknowns x, and y, and solving them simultaneously.

Example: *A man expected to be charged £42.68 for the combination of 7p and 9p stamps he had asked for. In fact, he had mixed up the quantities of each stamp and was only charged £41.16.*
How many of each stamp did he intend to buy?
Let the intended numbers of 7p and 9p stamps to be bought be x and y respectively. The costs, in pence, of the intended and actual purchases would be $(7x + 9y)$ and $(9x + 7y)$ respectively.
  Therefore $7x + 9y = 4268$ and $9x + 7y = 4116$.
  The reader should verify that the common solution of the two equations is
$$x = 224, \quad y = 300.$$
He intended to buy 224 7p stamps and 300 9p stamps.
Note: In this case, addition and subtraction of the two equations lead to $x + y = 524$ and $y - x = 76$; the solution can be more readily found.

Exercise 8.6

1   In a shop apples are marked at x p per kg and oranges at y p each. 5 kg of apples and 30 oranges cost £4.50; 10 kg of apples and 15 oranges cost £6.30. Find (i) the cost of the apples per kg, and (ii) the cost of 15 kg of apples and 45 oranges.

2   For a particular performance at a cinema there were only two prices of seats. Seats in the stalls were 80p, seats in the circle £1.50. When the cinema is full the takings amount to £465.
    On this occasion there were 70 unoccupied seats in the circle and the stalls were two-thirds full. The takings were £280.
    Find the seating capacity of the cinema.

3   The average age of two brothers is three times the age of the younger.

In seven years' time the sum of their ages will be greater than the difference in their ages by 20 years. Find their ages now.

4 The selling price of a television is to be reduced by $x\%$, and that of a radio by $y\%$. If one television and one radio are purchased a saving of £15.10 is made; if two televisions and five radios are purchased the saving is £35. Given that the original selling prices of televisions and radios were £90 and £20 respectively, find x and y.

5 A shop ordered a certain number of large loaves at 18 pence each and some small loaves at 10 pence each. The total cost was £11. After increases of 2 pence on a large loaf and 1 penny on a small loaf, the same order costs £12.20. Find the numbers of each size of loaf ordered.

6 I can walk at 6 km/h and run at 15 km/h.
On a journey I spend as long walking as I do running. If I had walked for twice as long on the journey it would have taken me six minutes longer. Find out how far I ran.

7 A number of two digits is such that four times the ten digit is two less than five times the unit digit. When the digits are reversed the number is decreased by nine in value. Find the number.

8 10 dozen large eggs and 5 dozen standard eggs cost £7.10; 5 dozen large eggs and 6 dozen standard eggs cost £5.02. Find the cost, per dozen, of large and standard eggs.

9 The cost of a large jar of coffee is 10 pence cheaper than the cost of two small jars of the same coffee. The total cost of ten jars of each size is £15.20. What is the cost of a large jar of coffee?

10 Typist A can type at x words per minute while typist B can type at y words per minute. They both work for five minutes and a total of 850 words are typed. At the end of 10 minutes 1560 words have been typed but typist B stopped for 2 minutes during the second session. Find x and y.

11 On a journey of 240 km a car needed 22.5 litres of petrol and $\frac{1}{2}$ litre of oil. The total cost of the fuel was £4.70. Another car made the same journey using 25 litres of petrol and 1 litre of oil. The cost of fuel for this case was £5.40. Find the total cost of 5 litres of petrol and 1 litre of oil. (Do not find them separately).

12 A teacher organised a trip to an international soccer match. The price of tickets for the match was £1.50 for adults and 80p for children. The coach fare was £3.00 for adults and £1 for children. Given that the teacher had to pay £84 for the tickets and £132 for the coaches, find how many people went on the trip. (Exclude the driver!).

Graphs of linear inequations

The solution of a simple equation may be represented by a point on the number line; the solution set of a simple inequation may be represented by a segment, or segments, of the line.
If the co-ordinate plane is used as a means of representing solution sets, then

all linear equations, including the simple equations like $x = 3$, are represented by lines. All points on a line through $(3, 0)$, parallel to the y-axis, for example, satisfy the relation $x = 3$. Any point to the left of the line satisfies the relation $x < 3$, any point to the right of the line satisfies $x > 3$. The line $y = mx + c$ divides the plane into two half planes; one represents the solution set of the inequation $y > mx + c$, the other represents the solution set of $y < mx + c$.

A convenient method of illustrating regions is to shade the outside of the boundary line. We shall adopt the notation of drawing a dotted boundary line if the line is not included in a region; an unbroken line indicates that the points on the line are members of the solution set.

Example 1: *Shade the outer boundary of the half plane $x - y < 1$.*

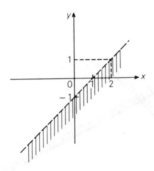

Fig. 8.10

The boundary line $x - y = 1$ is drawn first by finding its intercepts on the axes as shown in Figure 8.10.

The point $(2, \frac{1}{2})$ is clearly below the line and we see that for this point, $x - y = 2 - \frac{1}{2} = 1\frac{1}{2} > 1$. All points below the line are related in this way and so the region we require is *the upper half plane*.

If the relation is rearranged so that y is the subject, e.g. $x - y < 1$ becomes $y > x - 1$, then $>$ will describe 'above' and $<$ will describe 'below'; $\geqslant$ and $\leqslant$ imply that the points on the line are also members of the solution set. The points which satisfy several inequations simultaneously may often be found in a bounded region of the plane.

Example 2: *Sketch the region described by $y \leqslant 2x$, $y \geqslant \frac{1}{2}x$, $y \leqslant 2$, $x \leqslant 3$.* The solution set is represented by region A in Figure 8.11. The vertices of the quadrilateral enclosing A can be found by solving the appropriate simultaneous equations.

Example 3: *Write down the inequations describing the unshaded region B in Fig. 8.12.*
First the equations of the boundary lines are found.

The line passing through $(8, 0)$ and $(0, 4)$ is $\dfrac{x}{8} + \dfrac{y}{4} = 1$ or $x + 2y = 8$.

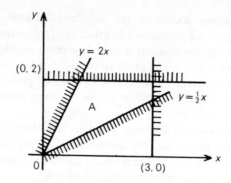

Fig. 8.11

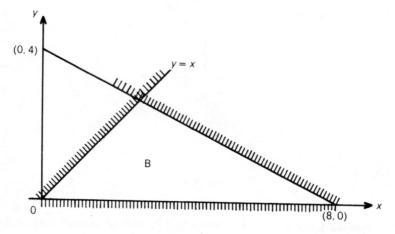

Fig. 8.12

The other two lines have equation $y = 0$ and $y = x$.
Hence the inequations $x + 2y \leqslant 8$, $y \leqslant x$, and $y \geqslant 0$, describe the region.

Exercise 8.7

1 Each of the following inequations describe a half-plane. Draw sketch
   graphs to show this by shading the outside of the boundary line:
   (a) $x < -3$ (b) $y \geqslant -2$ (c) $x \geqslant -1$
   (d) $y < 5$ (e) $y > x$ (f) $y \leqslant x + 3$
   (g) $y \geqslant -x + 1$ (h) $y + x \geqslant 2$ (i) $y - x \geqslant 5$
   (j) $x - y < 4$ (k) $y < 2x + 7$ (l) $y + 3x \geqslant 6$.
2 Draw sketch graphs to show the regions described by the following sets
   of inequations:

   (a) $x \geqslant 0$, $y < 4$, $y > 2x - 1$ (b) $\dfrac{x}{3} + \dfrac{y}{2} > 1$, $y < 2$, $x \leqslant 4$

   (c) $x \geqslant 0$, $y \geqslant 0$, $y \geqslant -x + 1$ (d) $y \geqslant x$, $y \leqslant 2$, $x + y \geqslant 2$

(e) $y > x - 1$, $x + y < 4$, $2x + y > 4$ (f) $x \geqslant 0$, $y \leqslant x$, $5x - y < 10$

(g) $x \geqslant 0$, $y \geqslant 0$, $y \geqslant 3x - 2$, $y - 2x \leqslant 1$.

Find the co-ordinates of the vertices of the regions in each of the above parts.

3   Write down sets of inequations to describe each of the unshaded regions shown in Figure 8.13:

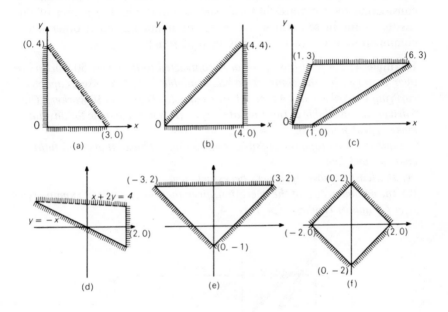

Fig. 8.13

4   (a) List the set S of points in the unshaded region of Figure 8.13 (a) for which both co-ordinates are integers. Find the co-ordinates of the points in S which maximise the value of each of the following: (i) $x + y$, (ii) $2x - y$, (iii) $x + 4$.

(b) List the set of points with integer coefficients in the region in Figure 8.13 (b) for which $x = 2y$.

(c) Find the largest values of (i) $x + y$, (ii) $y - 2x$, for points of the region shown in Figure 8.13 (c).

(d) Find the largest value of $y - x$ for points, whose co-ordinates are integers, in the region shown in Figure 8.13 (d).

(e) Find the range of values of x and of y for the region indicated in Figure 8.13 (d).

Linear programming

The methods of the last section will now be used to solve problems involving an optimum strategy. In industry the question of how best to employ resources subject to certain inevitable constraints is a common one. Their problems, however, usually involve so many variables that a graphical method of solution must be replaced by a computerised one.

We shall concern ourselves only with problems that reduce to linear inequations in two variables; we are more interested here in linear programming than computer programming.

The first step is to translate the constraints into linear inequations and, by considering their graphs, find a feasible solution set. The subset of this feasible solution set, which maximises or minimises some other linear combination of the variables, may then be sought.

Example 1: *A mini-bus operator is contracted to transport 50 workers to their factory. For the contract he has available 3 type A buses, capable of carrying 15 workers, and 4 type B buses, capable of carrying 10 workers. Only 5 drivers are available at this time of the day. (It is not economic for any bus to make repeat journeys).*

Indicate on a graph the possible combinations of buses that could fulfil the contract and find:

(a) the least number of drivers necessary, and

(b) the minimum cost of the operation, given that the expense of running type A is £5 and of running type B is £4.

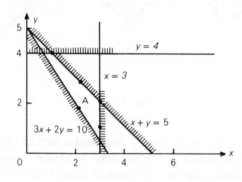

Fig. 8.14

Let the number of type A buses used be x and the number of type B buses used be y.

The total number of passengers capable of being transported is then $(15x + 10y)$.

Therefore $15x + 10y \geqslant 50 \Rightarrow 3x + 2y \geqslant 10$, (why is the relation $\geqslant$ used rather than $= ?$)

The line $3x + 2y = 10$ is drawn and the unwanted half plane is shaded as in Figure 8.14.

The restriction on drivers is written as $x + y \leqslant 5$ and the restriction on buses as $x \leqslant 3$, $y \leqslant 4$.

When these restrictions are added to the graph the feasible solution set is given by the unshaded region, A.

104

The possible combinations (x, y) of type A and type B buses respectively are (1, 4), (2, 2), (2, 3), (3, 1) and (3, 2).

In this case the answers to the problem can be found easily by examining each pair in turn.

The least number of drivers necessary is 4, and the minimum cost of the operation is £18, when two of each type of bus are used.

When the feasible solution set is larger, this method of 'point by point' evaluation is impractical. The method used in such a case is given in the next example.

Example 2:   *A warehouse manager of a departmental store finds that he can store a batch of 3 washing machines in 1 m² and a batch of four freezers in 2 m². He allots 80 m² altogether for this section of his stock and never allows the number of separate items to exceed 200.*

Find the greatest combined number of batches he can store subject to these restrictions.

If a washing machine sells for £140 and a freezer for £210 find what combination of batches he should keep to maintain the greatest possible value of stock.

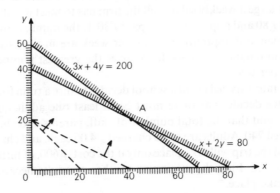

Fig. 8.15

Let the number of batches of washing machines stored be x, and the number of freezers stored be y.

The reader should verify that the restrictions imposed in the problem are represented by the inequations $x + 2y \leqslant 80$ and $3x + 4y \leqslant 200$, together with $x \geqslant 0$, $y \geqslant 0$.

The finite region representing the feasible solution set, is found by drawing lines $x + 2y = 80$, $3x + 4y = 200$, $x = 0$ and $y = 0$.

The greatest value of $x + y$ in the region can be found by finding which line of the family of lines with equation $x + y = c$ has the highest intercept on the y-axis. This is best done by drawing one line of the family ($x + y = 20$ is drawn in Figure 8.15) and finding the line parallel to this which is inside the region and furthest from the origin. The reader should draw a large graph

105

and verify that the line $x + y = 66$ is the required line in the case; the points (64, 2), (65, 1) (66, 0) are the pairs of x and y which give the maximum value of $x + y$.

If there are x batches of washing machines and y batches of freezers in stock the value of the stock is $£(420x + 840y)$. For the greatest possible value of stock we require $420x + 840y$ to be a maximum. This can be determined by finding the line in the family of lines $420x + 840y = c$, which is furthest from the origin but inside the region. In Figure 8.15 the required line {parallel to the dotted line through (40, 0) and (0, 20)} passes through the point $A(40, 20)$.

He should keep 40 *batches of washing machine and* 20 *batches of freezers.*

Exercise 8.8

Appropriate inequations should be formed and solutions found graphically:

1   A small firm can employ up to 20 men, who are either skilled or apprentices. The firm likes to employ at least two apprentices, but there must always be at least twice as many skilled workers as apprentices. Find the largest weekly salary bill the firm has to meet if skilled workers are paid £80 and apprentices are paid £30. If the numbers of hours that skilled men and apprentices work per week are in the ratio 2:3, find which combination of work force gives the greatest number of hours worked per week.

2   To celebrate a special event a school decides to hire a train for a day. The committee decide that there must be at least one adult for every ten children, and that the total number of staff, parents and children must not exceed 240. Adults are to be charged £4.00 each, and children £2.50 each, and the trip will take place only if the cost, £600, of hiring the train is guaranteed. Find the minimum number of adults necessary for the trip to take place.

3   A builder buys some land and divides it into 50 plots. He plans to build two types of house; type A, which requires one plot of land, and type B, a superior house with garage, which requires two plots. He must build at least three times as many type A houses as type B houses, but there is a limit of 35 on the number of the former. There are already 20 type A and 5 type B houses ordered. If the profit on type A and type B houses is £600 and £800, respectively, find his maximum profit. Does he use all the ground in this plan?

4   A shopkeeper decides to stock two kinds of calculator. The 'α' model costs him £8 and the 'β' model costs him £24. As a first venture he is prepared to buy 80 calculators, of which there must be more of model 'α' than model 'β'. He has available up to £960 for the purchase. The 'α' and 'β' models retail at £12 and £32, respectively.
Find how many of each he should buy to maximise his profit.

5   A factory is considering buying two machines which make a special

Machine	Hourly Output	Hourly Profit	Floor space
American	30	£4	15 m^2
English	20	£2.50	12 m^2

component. Information about the machines is given in the table.
The factory is committed to buying at least as many English machines as American machines. At least 240 components must be produced hourly and up to 180 m^2 of floor space is available. Find the combination of machines that should be purchased to maximise the profit. For this combination, how much floor space remains?

6 In an examination consisting of two papers, A and B, both marked out of 100, a candidate is given a mark x for paper A and mark y for paper B. A pass mark is obtained if $x + 2y$ is at least 150, but the candidates must score over 30 marks on paper A and over 40 marks on paper B. Find the lowest value of $x + y$ for any candidate who passed, and give the corresponding values of x and y.

7 In a swimming baths two drinks can be bought from a machine; orange costs 6p per cup and hot chocolate costs 10p per cup. A boy, who never bought more than 2 drinks on any day, worked out that over a 30 day period he had spent at least £2 on drinks. He was sure that he had bought more orange drinks than hot chocolate. Find the least possible number of drinks he could have bought in this period, and the maximum amount he could possibly have spent.

8 A manufacturer plans to build two types of table. For table A the cost of materials is £20, the number of man-hours needed to complete it is 10, and the profit is £15. Table B requires materials costing £12, 15 man-hours of labour and makes the same profit as A.
The total money available for materials is £500 and the labour available is 330 man-hours. Find the maximum profit that can be made and the number of each type of table that should be made to produce it.

9 A factory is to install two types of machine, A and B. Type A requires two operators and occupies 5 m^2 of floor space; type B requires 5 operators and requires 8 m^2 of floor space. The maximum number of operators available is 50 and the floor space available is 110 m^2. Because of the cost of the machines no more than 8 of type B can be bought. Given that the weekly profits on type A and type B machines are £15 and £25, respectively, find the number of each machine that should be bought to maximise the profit, and calculate this profit.

9 Quadratic equations and inequations

Quadratic equations

An important set of equations are those of degree two in one unknown. These are called quadratic equations and can always be rearranged into the form $ax^2 + bx + c = 0$ where a, b, c are constants (b or c may be zero). In general, quadratic equations have two solutions, which may be equal, but if the domain of the unknown, x, is restricted to the set of real numbers, no solution may be forthcoming. For example, the equation $x^2 + 4 = 0$ is a quadratic but there are no real values of x which satisfy it. In the following it is assumed that the domain of x is the set of all real numbers. For each quadratic equation the method of solution is determined by the values that the constants a, b, c may take.

(a) Solution by factorisation

When a quadratic equation has been arranged in the form $ax^2 + bx + c = 0$, it may be possible to factorise the left hand side into the form $pq = 0$, where p and q may be bracketed expressions. The solution of the equation $pq = 0$ is of fundamental importance in the solution of quadratics.

If $pq = 0$, then either $p = 0$ or $q = 0$

Example 1: $(x - 5)(2x + 1) = 0$

Either $x - 5 = 0$ or $2x + 1 = 0$

The solutions are $x = 5$ or $x = -\frac{1}{2}$

Example 2: Solve $x^2 - 7x - 8 = 0$

Factorise $(x - 8)(x + 1) = 0$

Either $(x - 8) = 0$ or $(x + 1) = 0$

                      $x = +8$ or $x = -1$

Exercise 9.1

Solve the following equations for x:

1. $(x - 8)(x + 2) = 0$
2. $(3x - 1)(2x + 5) = 0$
3. $x(x - 5) = 0$
4. $(2x - 13)(x + 5) = 0$

5 $(x+1)(x-2)=0$	13 $5x^2-3x-2=0$
6 $x^2-8x+15=0$	14 $6x^2-23x+7=0$
7 $x^2+3x-10=0$	15 $3x-x^2-2=0$
8 $x^2-x-20=0$	16 $23x+14+3x^2=0$
9 $x^2+15x+56=0$	17 $15x-4x^2=0$
10 $x^2-8x=0$	18 $14x^2-3x-2=0$
11 $2x^2-14x+12=0$	19 $x^2-9x-22=0$
12 $2x^2+13x-7=0$	20 $3x^2-6x-9=0$

It is essential that whatever form the equation is given in it should be rearranged to have a zero on one side.

Example 1:   *Solve $(3x-1)(2x+1) = 6x+5$*

Multiply out
$$6x^2+x-1 = 6x+5$$

Subtract $6x+5$ from both sides $6x^2-5x-6 = 0$

Factorise
$$(3x+2)(2x-3) = 0$$

Either $3x+2 = 0$ or $2x-3 = 0$

Solutions $x = -\tfrac{2}{3}$ or $x = +1\tfrac{1}{2}$.

Example 2:   *Solve $3x^2 = 12x$.*

Subtract $12x$ from both sides $3x^2-12x = 0$

Factorise $3x(x-4) = 0$

Solutions $x = 0$ or $x = 4$.

It is not advisable to cancel in this type of question; the solution $x = 0$ may then be missed.

Exercise 9.2

Solve the following equations for *x*:

1 $x^2+8 = 6x$	5 $x(x-3) = 5(x-3)$	9 $5x(3x-1) = x^2+1$
2 $3x^2+4 = 13x$	6 $(x+1)(x-5) = 16$	10 $(x-1)(x-5) = 21$
3 $3x^2 = 6x$	7 $6x(x-2) = 10-x$	11 $6x^2 = 8x$
4 $x^2+4x = 21$	8 $15x(x+1) = x+8$	12 $2x = 4x^2$.

Quadratic equations may be given in fractional form.

Example: *Solve*
$$\frac{3}{x}+\frac{4}{x+1} = 2$$

Multiply by $x(x+1)$, the L.C.M. of x and $x+1$

$$3(x+1)+4x = 2x(x+1)$$

$$3x+3+4x = 2x^2+2x$$

$$2x^2-5x-3 = 0$$

$$(2x+1)(x-3) = 0$$

Solutions are $x = -\tfrac{1}{2}$ or $x = +3$

Exercise 9.3

Solve the following equations for x:

1 $x = \dfrac{9}{x}$

2 $\dfrac{8}{x} - \dfrac{x}{2} = 0$

3 $x - \dfrac{12}{x+1} = 0$

4 $\dfrac{4-x}{3} + \dfrac{1}{x} = 2$

5 $x + \dfrac{1}{x} = \dfrac{10}{3}$

6 $x = \dfrac{x+4}{x-2}$

7 $\dfrac{2}{x(x-2)} = \dfrac{3}{4(x-2)}$

8 $x = \dfrac{x^2}{4} + 1$

9 $\dfrac{3}{x} + \dfrac{x+7}{x+1} = 7$

10 $\dfrac{5+x}{x} + \dfrac{6}{x+1} = 3$

11 $\dfrac{x+2}{3} = \dfrac{x(x-2)}{4}$

12 $\dfrac{3}{x} + \dfrac{x-3}{x+1} = 2.$

Special case: If the equation is given in the form $(ax+b)^2 = c$ (b may be zero) then, although the usual method may be used, it is quicker to take the square root of both sides of the equation.

Example: *Solve* $(x+3)^2 = 49$.

Square root $x+3 = \pm 7$

Either $x+3 = +7$ or $x+3 = -7$

Solutions are $x = +4$ or $x = -10.$

Exercise 9.4

Solve the following equations for x:

1 $x^2 = 81$

2 $2x^2 = 8$

3 $5x^2 = 125$

4 $2x = \dfrac{1}{2x}$

5 $x = \dfrac{16}{x}$

6 $\dfrac{x}{5} = \dfrac{5}{x}$

7 $(x+1)^2 = 16$

8 $(x-5)^2 = 64$

9 $(x-1)^2 = 9$

10 $(2-x)^2 = 1$

11 $(2x-7)^2 = 25$

12 $(5x+2)^2 = 4$

13 $1-(3x+1)^2 = 0$

14 $2(x+1)^2 = 32$

15 $5(2x+1)^2 = 20.$

Exercise 9.5 (Miscellaneous)

Solve the following equations:

1 $x^2 - 5x - 14 = 0$

2 $(3p-5)(2p+1) = 0$

3 $x = \dfrac{4}{x}$

4 $2x^2 = 6x$

5 $(x+6)^2 = 36$

6 $2x^2 - 7 = 13x$

7 $x^2 + 10 = 7x$

8 $x^3 = x$

9 $p(p-10) = 16(1-p)$

10 $(2x-5)^2 = 1$

11 $x(x+3) = 5(x+3)$

12 $\dfrac{x}{3} - \dfrac{4}{x} = \dfrac{1}{3}$

13 $\dfrac{x(x+1)}{3} = 2$

14 $(2x+1)(x+1) = 6(2x+1)$

15 $y(y-1) = 72$

If the equation cannot be solved by factorisation then one of the following two methods may be used.

(b) Solution by completing the square

The expression $x^2 - 4x + 4$ is a perfect square since it may be written as $(x - 2)^2$. Any expression like $x^2 - 6x$ can be made a perfect square by adding the appropriate constant term. In this case by adding $+9$ the expression becomes $x^2 - 6x + 9$, the perfect square $(x - 3)^2$.

In general, any expression of the form $x^2 + ax$ will become the perfect square $\left(x + \dfrac{a}{2}\right)^2$ by adding the term $\left(\dfrac{a}{2}\right)^2$.

Example 1: *The expression $x^2 + 9x$ becomes the perfect square $(x + \frac{9}{2})^2$ by adding the term $(\frac{9}{2})^2$ or $\frac{81}{4}$.*

This process of completing the square may be used to solve quadratics.

Example 2: *Solve the equation $2x^2 - 10x + 11 = 0$.*
The equation is divided by 2 so that the coefficient of x^2 is unity, to give

$$x^2 - 5x + \frac{11}{2} = 0$$

Subtract $-\dfrac{11}{2}$ from both sides

$$x^2 - 5x = \frac{-11}{2}$$

Add to both sides $\left(\dfrac{-5}{2}\right)^2$, i.e. $\dfrac{25}{4}$, to complete the square on the left hand side

$$x^2 - 5x + \frac{25}{4} = \frac{-11}{2} + \frac{25}{4}$$

or

$$\left(x - \frac{5}{2}\right)^2 = \frac{-22 + 25}{4} = \frac{3}{4}$$

Square root

$$x - \frac{5}{2} = \pm\frac{\sqrt{3}}{2} = \pm\frac{1.732}{2} = \pm 0.866$$

$$x = 2.5 \pm 0.866$$

Solutions are

$$x = 3.366 \quad \text{or} \quad 1.634$$

$$x = 3.37 \quad \text{or} \quad 1.63 \text{ (correct to 2 decimal places)}.$$

Exercise 9.6

Use the method of completing the square to solve the following equations correct to two decimal places.

1	$x^2 - 2x - 4 = 0$	5	$2x^2 - 10x + 6 = 0$	9	$4x^2 + x - 1 = 0$
2	$x^2 + 6x + 4 = 0$	6	$2x^2 - 6x - 1 = 0$	10	$5x^2 + 2x - 4 = 0.$
3	$x^2 - 5x + 5 = 0$	7	$2x^2 - x - 5 = 0$		
4	$x^2 + 3x - 1 = 0$	8	$3x^2 - 6x + 2 = 0$		

If the general quadratic $ax^2 + bx + c = 0$ is taken, and the method of completing the square is used, "the formula" for solving quadratics is derived.

(c) Solution by the formula

Solve $ax^2 + bx + c = 0$ by completing the square.
Subtract c from both sides and divide by a

$$x^2 + \frac{b}{a}x = -\frac{c}{a}$$

Complete the square
$$x^2 + \frac{b}{a}x + \left(\frac{b}{2a}\right)^2 = -\frac{c}{a} + \left(\frac{b}{2a}\right)^2$$

Therefore
$$\left(x + \frac{b}{2a}\right)^2 = \frac{b^2 - 4ac}{4a^2}$$

Square root
$$x + \frac{b}{2a} = \pm\frac{\sqrt{b^2 - 4ac}}{2a}$$

$$x = -\frac{b}{2a} \pm \frac{\sqrt{b^2 - 4ac}}{2a}$$

This should be learnt in the form
$$x = \frac{-b \pm \sqrt{b^2 - 4ac}}{2a}.$$

The value of $b^2 - 4ac$ determines the nature of the roots of the equation.
If $\qquad b^2 > 4ac$ there are two real distinct roots,
$\qquad\qquad b^2 = 4ac$ there is one repeated root,
and if $\qquad b^2 < 4ac$ there are no real solutions.

Example: *Solve the equation* $2x^2 - 10x + 11 = 0$, *using the formula.*
The equation is first arranged in the form $ax^2 + bx + c = 0$.
For $\qquad 2x^2 - 10x + 11 = 0, \qquad a = +2, b = -10, c = +11$
Using the formula

$$x = \frac{-(-10) \pm \sqrt{(-10)^2 - 4(+2)(+11)}}{2(2)}$$

$$x = \frac{+10 \pm \sqrt{100 - 88}}{4}$$

$$x = \frac{+10 \pm \sqrt{12}}{4} = \frac{10 \pm 3.464}{4}$$

$$x = 3.366 \quad \text{or} \quad 1.634$$

$$x = 3.37 \quad \text{or} \quad 1.63 \quad \text{correct to 2 decimal places.}$$

Exercise 9.7

Solve the following equations, using the formula; give answers correct to 2 decimal places:

1 $x^2 - 3x - 3 = 0$ 5 $2x^2 + 7x + 4 = 0$ 9 $2x^2 - 7x - 5 = 0$
2 $x^2 + 2x - 5 = 0$ 6 $5x^2 + 5x - 1 = 0$ 10 $5x^2 - x - 3 = 0$
3 $x^2 - 4x + 1 = 0$ 7 $x^2 - 2x - 2 = 0$ 11 $3x^2 + 5x + 1 = 0$
4 $7x^2 + 2x - 3 = 0$ 8 $x^2 + 7x + 4 = 0$ 12 $4x^2 - x - 1 = 0$

Exercise 9.8 (Miscellaneous)

Solve the following equations, giving answers correct to 2 decimal places, where necessary:

1 $x^2 = 5x$

2 $\dfrac{x}{4} = \dfrac{4}{x}$

3 $x = \dfrac{24}{x}$

4 $x(x - 8) = 0$
5 $x^2 + 6x = 7$
6 $2x^2 + 9x - 5 = 0$

7 $6x^2 + 6 = 13x$

8 $x^2 - x - 1 = 0$

9 $x^2 - 3x + 1 = 0$
10 $2x^2 + 5x + 1 = 0$
11 $3x^2 + x - 5 = 0$
12 $2x^2 - 13x = 7$

13 $3x^2 - 21x + 30 = 0$

14 $(13x - 1)(x + 8) = 0$

15 $(x - 1)(x - 4) = -2$
16 $(x - 1)^2 = 8$
17 $7x^2 - 27x = 4$
18 $2x^2 + 2x - 4 = 0$

Problems leading to quadratic equations

In some problems, although only one symbol needs to be introduced, the resulting equation may be quadratic.

Example: *A teacher orders a set of books at a total cost of £144. When he receives them, the price for each book has risen by 40 p. At this new price, £144 would buy 18 books less than required. How many books were required?*
Let the number of books required be x.

The old price of each book was $£\dfrac{144}{x}$.

Each book has increased in price by 40 p, or $£\frac{2}{5}$

The new price of each book is then $£\left(\dfrac{144}{x} + \dfrac{2}{5}\right)$.

but as the number of books at the new price which can be bought for £144 is $x - 18$, the new price can also be written as $£\dfrac{144}{x - 18}$.

Therefore $\dfrac{144}{x - 18} = \dfrac{144}{x} + \dfrac{2}{5}$

Multiply by $5x(x - 18)$ $720x = 720(x - 18) + 2x(x - 18)$

$$720x = 720x - 12960 + 2x^2 - 36x$$

$$0 = x^2 - 18x - 6480$$

$$0 = (x - 90)(x + 72)$$

$$x = 90 \text{ or } x = -72.$$

The number of books required is 90.

Exercise 9.9

1 The sides of a right angled triangle are of length x cm, $3(x+1)$ cm and $(4x-3)$ cm. Find x.

2 Find the lengths of the sides of a rectangle with perimeter 44 cm and area 117 cm².

3 The length of a rectangle is 2 m longer than the width, and the area is 960 m². Find the length.

4 Find two numbers which differ by 16 and have a sum of squares of 1096.

5 Find two numbers whose sum is 73 and whose product is 1200.

6 An oarsman rows 4 km upstream and back again in a total time of 1 hour. If the current is flowing at 3 km/h, find the speed of the oarsman in still water.

7 There are two routes from A to B. Along the motorway the journey is 35 km; along the alternative route the distance is 25 km. A driver on the former route covered the journey 5 minutes quicker than a driver on the other route, as his average speed was 45 km/h greater. Find their respective times.

8 x articles costing $(2x-3)$ pence each were bought for a total cost of £7.40. Find x.

9 In the triangle ADE, B and C are points on AD and AE respectively such that BC is parallel to DE. If AB $= x$ cm, BD $= 2$ cm, AC $= 18$ cm, and CE $= (x-5)$ cm, find x.

10 A certain number of articles were bought for a total of £120. If the price of each article had been four pence cheaper, 100 more articles could have been bought. How many were bought?

11 If the number of sides of a particular regular polygon is increased by 2, each interior angle is increased by 2°. How many sides does this polygon have?

12 On a journey of 220 km a driver calculated that by increasing his average speed by 4 km/h he would take 30 minutes less. Find his usual average speed.

13 Figure 9.1 shows a rectangle with an isosceles triangle cut off one corner. If the area of the shaded portion is 40 cm², find x.

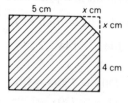

Fig. 9.1

14 A man can row at 5 km/h in still water. He rows 10 km upstream and back again in 6 hours 15 minutes. Find the speed of the current.

Quadratic inequations

The solutions of the equation $(x-2)(x-3) = 0$ are $x = 2$ or $x = 3$. These two values of x divide the number line into three regions, (see Figure 9.2), where the expression $(x-2)(x-3)$ will take values other than zero.

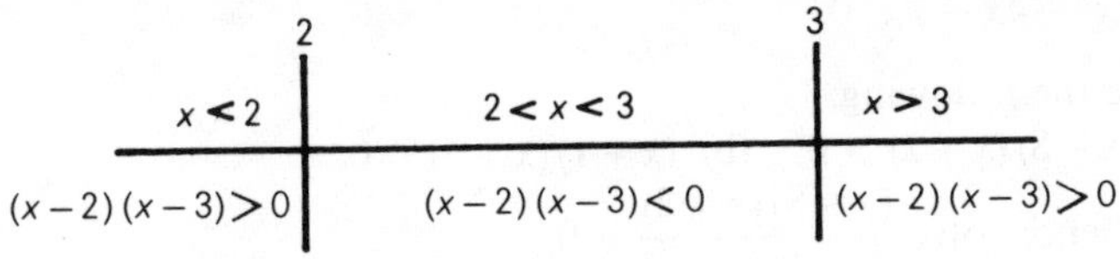

| | $x < 2$ | $2 < x < 3$ | $x > 3$ |

$x < 2$ $2 < x < 3$ $x > 3$

$(x-2)(x-3) > 0$ $(x-2)(x-3) < 0$ $(x-2)(x-3) > 0$

Fig. 9.2

If $x < 2$, each bracket is negative $\Rightarrow (x-2)(x-3) > 0$.
If $2 < x < 3$, $(x-2)$ is positive, $(x-3)$ negative $\Rightarrow (x-2)(x-3) < 0$.
If $x > 3$, each bracket is positive $\Rightarrow (x-2)(x-3) > 0$.

To find the sign of the expression in the defined region, it is sufficient to substitute a particular value of x in that region. For example to find the sign of $(x-2)(x-3)$ when $x < 2$, substitution of $x = 0$, say, will indicate the required sign.

The solution set for the inequation $(x-2)(x-3) < 0$ may be written $\{x : 2 < x < 3\}$, and the complete solution set for $(x-2)(x-3) > 0$ may be written as

$$\{x : x < 2\} \cup \{x : x > 3\}.$$

A convenient method of solving quadratic inequations is shown in the following example.

Example: *Find the solution set of the inequation $x^2 - x - 12 \geqslant 0$.*
Factorise: $(x-4)(x+3) \geqslant 0$

The expression $(x-4)(x+3)$ is equal to zero when $x = +4$ and $x = -3$. These values form part of the solution set in this case. The value of the product $(x-4)(x+3)$ in the three regions $x < -3$, $-3 < x < 4$, $x > 4$ can be found using a table (Figure 9.3.).

	$x < -3$	$-3 < x < 4$	$x > 4$
$x - 4$	$-$ve	$-$ve	$+$ve
$x + 3$	$-$ve	$+$ve	$+$ve
Product	$+$ve	$-$ve	$+$ve
$(x-4)(x+3)$	> 0	< 0	> 0

Fig. 9.3

From the table $(x-4)(x+3) \geqslant 0$ when $x \leqslant -3$ and $x \geqslant 4$.
The solution set is $\{x : x \leqslant -3\} \cup \{x : x \geqslant 4\}$.

Exercise 9.10

1 Give the solution sets of the following inequations:

(a) $x^2 - 2x - 15 > 0$ (b) $x^2 \leqslant 5x$ (c) $x^2 \geqslant 4$

(d) $(x + 5)(3x - 5) < 0$ (e) $(2x - 9)(4x + 3) > 0$ (f) $x(2x + 1) \geqslant 0$

(g) $x^2 - 10x + 16 < 0$ (h) $x^2 - 42 > x$ (i) $2x^2 - 9x - 5 \geqslant 0$

(j) $3x^2 - 4x - 7 \leqslant 0$.

2 Solve the following:

(a) $(x - 8)(x + 2) > 0$,   (b) $(x + 1)(x + 5) < 0$,

and hence solve $\dfrac{(x - 8)(x + 2)}{(x + 1)(x + 5)} < 0$.

The square of an expression must be greater than, or equal to, zero. This fact can be used to find the least, or greatest, values of quadratic expressions.

The expression $x^2 + 10x + 25$, being the perfect square $(x + 5)^2$, is greater than or equal to zero, only being zero when $x = -5$. Its lowest value, then, is zero and it occurs when $x = -5$. Any quadratic expression $x^2 + 10x + c$ can be rewritten in the form $(x + 5)^2 + k$, (where $k = c - 25$), in which case its lowest value is k and occurs when $x = -5$. For example, $x^2 + 10x + 1 = (x + 5)^2 - 24$ and, therefore, has a minimum value of -24 when $x = -5$. All quadratics can be arranged in a similar fashion.

Example 1: *Find the minimum value of $x^2 + 6x - 8$.*

The expression may be written as $(x + 3)^2 - 17$ and, therefore, has a minimum value of -17 when $x = -3$.

Example 2: *Find the greatest value of the expression $6 + 6x - 2x^2$*

$$6 + 6x - 2x^2 = -2[x^2 - 3x - 3] = -2[(x - 1\tfrac{1}{2})^2 - 5\tfrac{1}{4}]$$

$$= -2(x - 1\tfrac{1}{2})^2 + 10\tfrac{1}{2}$$

The greatest value is $10\tfrac{1}{2}$ and occurs when $x = +1\tfrac{1}{2}$.

Exercise 9.11

1 Find the lowest values of the following expressions and give the value of x for which this occurs:

(a) $x^2 + 4x + 4$ (b) $x^2 + 10x - 8$ (c) $x^2 - 2x + 7$

(d) $x^2 - 12x + 7$ (e) $2x^2 + 6x + 4$ (f) $2x^2 - x + 1$

2 Find the minimum value of the expression $x^2 + 4x + 7$.

3 Find the greatest values of the following expressions:

(a) $-x^2 + x + 6$, (b) $3x - 2 - x^2$, (c) $3 + 5x - 2x^2$.

4 Find the minimum value of $(x + 3)^2$ as x varies and the value of x for which it occurs.

5 If $x^2 + 2x + 5$ can be written in the form $(x + a)^2 + b$, find a and b. Hence state the minimum value of $x^2 + 2x + 5$ and the value of x for which it occurs.

Sketch graphs

The graph $y = ax^2 + bx + c$, of the quadratic function $f: x \rightarrow ax^2 + bx + c$, is considered in detail in Chapter 13. However, a good sketch graph can be drawn by finding (a) its intercept on the y-axis, (b) its maximum or minimum point, and (c) its intercepts on the x-axis, if there are any.

Example 1: *Sketch the parabola whose equation is $y = x^2 - 4x + 3$.*
(a) The curve meets the y-axis when $x = 0 \Rightarrow y = +3$.
(b) The equation can be rearranged as $y = (x - 2)^2 - 1$.
The lowest value of y is -1 and occurs when $x = 2$.
The sketch graph is shown in Figure 9.4.

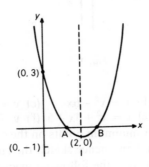

Fig. 9.4

The equation $y = (x - 2)^2 - 1$ also demonstrates the symmetry inherent in parabolas. If two values of x are chosen, equidistant in the domain from $x = 2$, the corresponding values of y are equal. For example, the values of y corresponding to $x = 5$ and $x = -1$ are both equal to 8. The curve is symmetrical about the line $x = 2$.
(c) The intercepts on the x-axis are found by putting $y = 0$ and solving $x^2 - 4x + 3 = 0$. The points A and B in Figure 9.4 are $(1, 0)$ and $(3, 0)$.

The sketching of the graph of the function provides an alternative method of solving quadratic inequations.

Example 2: *Solve $x^2 - x - 12 \geqslant 0$.*
The sketch of the curve whose equation is $y = x^2 - x - 12$ is shown in Figure 9.5.
The values of x for which $x^2 - x - 12 \geqslant 0$ can be seen to be $x \leqslant -3$ and $x \geqslant +4$.

Exercise 9.12

1 In Figure 9.5, calculate the co-ordinates of the point A.
2 For each of the following equations, of the form $y = ax^2 + bx + c$, calculate the value of $b^2 - 4ac$ and hence state the number of intercepts the corresponding curve has on the x-axis:

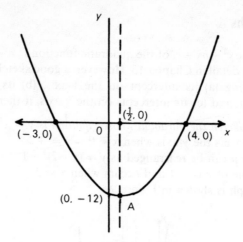

$(\frac{1}{2}, 0)$

$(-3, 0)$

0

$(4, 0)$ x

$(0, -12)$

A

Fig. 9.5

(a) $y = x^2 + 3x + 4$ (b) $y = x^2 - 6x$ (c) $y = x^2 - 4x + 4$
(d) $y = -x^2 + 1$ (e) $y = x^2 + 4x + 5$ (f) $y = 2x^2 - 4x + 3$.

3 Find the maximum or minimum points on the curves whose equations are given in question 2 and hence sketch the curves.

4 Use sketch graphs to solve the following inequations:
(a) $x^2 - 6x - 27 > 0$ (b) $x^2 > 2x - 1$, (c) $x^2 + 7x + 10 \leqslant 0$.

5 Prove that $x^2 + 8x + 17$ is positive for all values of x.

10 Some further topics in algebra

Long multiplication

Example: *Expand* $(3x - 2)(2x^2 - 7x - 4)$ *and arrange in ascending powers of x.*

$$
\begin{array}{ll}
2x^2 - 7x - 4 & \text{(a)} \\
\underline{3x - 2} & \text{(b)} \\
-4x^2 + 14x + 8 & [\text{multiply (a) by } -2] \\
\underline{6x^3 - 21x^2 - 12x} & [\text{multiply (a) by } 3x] \\
6x^3 - 25x^2 + 2x + 8 & [\text{sum of previous two lines}]
\end{array}
$$

The answer, written in **ascending** powers of x, is $8 + 2x - 25x^2 + 6x^3$.

The reader will notice the similarity in the presentation of the above example and that of its counterpart in arithmetic; powers of x should be vertically aligned to ease both working and subsequent checking.

Identities

From the previous example it can be stated that

$$(3x - 2)(2x^2 - 7x - 4) \equiv 6x^3 - 25x^2 + 2x + 8.$$

This statement is true for all values of x and the $\equiv$ sign is used to assert this. Such statements are called **identities**.

Other familiar examples are $(a + b)^2 \equiv a^2 + 2ab + b^2$

and $p^2 - q^2 \equiv (p - q)(p + q),$

which are true for all values of a and b and all values of p and q, respectively.

The reader will appreciate that when an expression is rewritten in its factorised form, an identity is produced; for example, the statement $x^2 - 3x - 4 = (x - 4)(x + 1)$ is true for all values of x.

Identities are widely used in mathematics to replace an expression by a second identical expression, especially when the second is in a more convenient form to complete an argument. In the solution of a quadratic equation, like $x^2 + 5x + 4 = 0$, the left hand side is factorised to give its identical equivalent $(x + 4)(x + 1)$, because the solution, $x = -4$ or -1, can be immediately seen from the factor form of the equation.

Example: *Given that $(2x-1)^2 + (2x+1)^2 \equiv Ax^2 + B$, find the values of A and B.*

Expanding the left hand side gives

$$4x^2 - 4x + 1 + 4x^2 + 4x + 1 = 8x^2 + 2.$$

For the right hand side to be identical, $A = 8$, $B = 2$ (found by comparing coefficients).

Alternative method: As $(2x-1)^2 + (2x+1)^2 = Ax^2 + B$, for all values of x, it must be true for any particular value.

Put $x = 0 \Rightarrow 1 + 1 = B \Rightarrow B = 2$.

Put $x = \frac{1}{2} \Rightarrow \quad 4 = \frac{1}{4}A + 2 \Rightarrow A = 8$.

A combination of both methods may often be the most concise way of tackling such problems.

The use of an identity is seen to great advantage in the following example.

Example: *Given that $a^2 + b^2 = 34$ and that $a + b = 8$ find the value of ab.*

Using the identity $(a+b)^2 = a^2 + 2ab + b^2 = a^2 + b^2 + 2ab$
$$a + b = 8 \text{ and } a^2 + b^2 = 34 \Rightarrow 64 = 34 + 2ab$$
$$\Leftrightarrow 2ab = 30$$
$$\Leftrightarrow ab = 15.$$

A solution by simultaneous equations, involving solving for a and b, is much more cumbersome.

Long division

Example: *Divide $x^2 + x + 5$ by $x - 3$ and find the remainder.*

$$
\begin{array}{r}
x + 4 \\
x - 3 \overline{) x^2 + \ x + 5} \\
\underline{x^2 - 3x} \\
4x + 5 \\
\underline{4x - 12} \\
+ 17
\end{array}
$$

1.
2. (x times $x - 3$)
3. (line 1 − line 2)
4. (4 times $x - 3$)
   (line 3 − line 4)

The presentation is similar to that in arithmetic, the process beginning by dividing the leading term of $x^2 + x + 5$ by the leading term of the divisor $x - 3$ to give the x of the quotient $x + 4$. The process continues, as indicated in parenthesis, until at line 3 a new sequence of events begins, $4x + 5$ replacing $x^2 + x + 5$. Finally, a term emerges of lower degree than the divisor and this is the remainder; in the above example $+ 17$ is the remainder.

We may write $x^2 + x + 5 \equiv (x - 3)(x + 4) + 17$

The above process can be avoided by considering an identity approach. When $x^2 + x + 5$ is divided by $x - 3$, the quotient must be of degree 1, i.e. of the form $Ax + B$, and there will be a remainder, denoted by C.

120

Hence
$$x^2 + x + 5 \equiv (x-3)(Ax+B) + C \qquad \text{(i)}$$
$$\equiv Ax^2 + Bx - 3Ax - 3B + C$$

Equating coefficients of x^2 gives $A = 1$,
equating coefficients of x gives $1 = -3A + B \Rightarrow B = 4$
equating the constant terms gives $5 = C - 3B \Rightarrow C = 17$
hence $x^2 + x + 5 \equiv (x-3)(x+4) + 17$.

The alternative approach may seem rather long at first sight but it produces a general result of great importance. Suppose only the remainder is required when $x^2 + x + 5$ is divided by $x - 3$. The remainder, $+C$ in (i), can be obtained at once by substituting $x = 3$ into $x^2 + x + 5$ since $(x-3)(Ax+B)$ is zero. The general result, illustrated by the example, is called the **Remainder Theorem**.

The remainder theorem

If a polynomial $f(x)$ is divided by $(x-a)$, the remainder is $f(a)$ where $f(a)$ is the value of the polynomial when $x = a$.

Example 1: *Find the remainder when $x^2 + x + 5$ is divided by $x + 2$.*
In the notation above, $f(x) = x^2 + x + 5$ and $a = -2$
 The remainder $= f(-2) = (-2)^2 + (-2) + 5 = 7$.

Example 2: *Find the values of a and b, given that when the expression $ax^3 + bx + 5$ is divided by $x - 1$ the remainder is 9 and when divided by $x + 2$ the remainder is -39.*

$$f(+1) = 9 \Rightarrow a + b + 5 = 9 \Rightarrow a + b = 4$$
$$f(-2) = -39 \Rightarrow -8a - 2b + 5 = -39 \Rightarrow 4a + b = 22.$$

These equations can be solved simultaneously to give $a = 6$, $b = -2$. If the remainder is zero, then a factor of $f(x)$ has been found.

The factor theorem

If $f(a) = 0$, the polynomial $f(x)$ has $(x-a)$ as a factor.

Example 1: *Use the factor theorem to find a factor of $f(x) = x^2 + x - 2$.*
 $f(-2) = (-2)^2 + (-2) - 2 = 0 \Rightarrow (x+2)$ is a factor of $f(x)$, or, alternatively,
 $f(1) = 1 + 1 - 2 = 0 \Rightarrow (x-1)$ is also a factor.
This theorem can be used to find a factor, or factors, of some cubic and higher degree polynomials. Small integer, or simple fractional, values of x are substituted in the polynomial until a zero value of the polynomial is obtained.

Example 2: *Find a factor of $f(x) \equiv x^3 + 2x^2 - x - 2$.*
Substitute $x = 1$: $f(1) = 1 + 2 - 1 - 2 = 0 \Leftrightarrow (x-1)$ is a factor. It can also be shown that $f(-1) = 0$ and $f(-2) = 0$ and so three factors $(x-1)$, $(x+1)$

and $(x+2)$ are found. As the first term of f(x) is x^3, it follows that

$$x^3 + 2x^2 - x - 2 \equiv (x-1)(x+1)(x-2).$$

Example 3: *If $x+1$ is a factor of $ax^3 + 2x + 5$, find the value of a.*
$$x+1 \text{ is a factor} \Leftrightarrow f(-1) = 0,$$

i.e.
$$a(-1)^3 + 2(-1) + 5 = 0$$
$$-a - 2 + 5 = 0$$
$$a = 3.$$

Example 4: *Factorise completely $f(x) \equiv 14x^3 - 11x^2 - 5x + 2$.*
$$f(+1) = 14 - 11 - 5 + 2 = 0 \Leftrightarrow (x-1) \text{ is a factor}$$
$$14x^3 - 11x^2 - 5x + 2 \equiv (x-1)(14x^2 + ax + b)$$
$$\equiv 14x^3 + (a-14)x^2 + (b-a)x - b.$$

Comparing the constant terms $\qquad\qquad 2 = -b \Rightarrow b = -2$
Comparing the coefficients of $x^2 \qquad -11 = a - 14 \Rightarrow a = 3$
$$14x^3 - 11x - 5x + 2 \equiv (x-1)(14x^2 + 3x - 2)$$
$$\equiv (x-1)(7x-2)(2x+1).$$

Exercise 10.1

1 Multiply (a) $x^2 + x + 1$ by $x - 1$, $\quad$ (b) $2x^2 + 5x - 1$ by $2x - 1$,
   (c) $1 - 2x - x^2$ by $1 + 2x - 3x^2$.
2 Find the quotient and remainder when
   (a) $x^3 + 2x^2 - 3x - 2$ is divided by $x + 1$, (b) $2x^2 - 5x - 7$ is divided by $x - 5$.
3 Find the remainder when $x^2 + 7x + 13$ is divided by
   (a) x, (b) $x - 2$, (c) $x + 1$, (d) $x - 3$, (e) $x + 4$.
4 Find the remainder when $x^2 - 3x + 1$ is divided .by
   (a) $x - 10$, (b) $x + 3$, (c) $2x - 1$, (d) $3x$, (e) $3x + 4$.
5 Find one factor of each of the following expressions:
   (a) $x^3 - 2x^2 + x - 2$ $\qquad$ (b) $x^3 + 2x^2 - 2x - 1$
   (c) $x^3 - 1$ $\qquad\qquad\qquad$ (d) $x^3 + 1$.
6 If $x - 5$ is a factor of $x^3 + kx - 135$, find k.
7 Show that $x^3 - a^3 = (x-a)(x^2 + ax + a^2)$ and hence factorise
   (a) $x^3 - 8$, (b) $8x^3 - 27y^3$.
8 Show that $x^3 + a^3 = (x+a)(x^2 - ax + a^2)$ and hence factorise
   (a) $x^3 + 64$ (b) $125x^3 + 8y^3$.
9 Find a and b if $ax^2 + bx + 2$ has remainders of 4 and 8 when divided by $(x-1)$ and $(x+1)$, respectively.
10 Factorise completely the following expressions:
   (a) $2x^3 - 17x^2 + 7x + 8$ $\qquad$ (b) $x^3 + 8x^2 + 5x - 50$
   (c) $x^3 + x^2 - 64x - 64$ $\qquad$ (d) $2x^3 - x^2 - 7x + 6$
   (e) $4x^4 - 8x^3 + 5x^2 - x$ $\qquad$ (f) $6x^3 - x^2 - 46x - 15$.
11 Solve the equations:
   (a) $(x-1)(x+2)(x-5) = 0$ $\qquad$ (b) $x^3 + x^2 - 2x = 0$
   (c) $4x^3 + 4x^2 + x + 1 = 0$ $\qquad$ (d) $5x^3 + 4x^2 - 11x + 2 = 0$

12 Given that $a + b = 6$ and $ab = 2$, show that $a^2 + b^2 = 32$ and $a^2 b^2 = 4$. Find $a^4 + b^4$.

13 If $9x^2 + 30x + k$ is a perfect square of the form $(3x + a)^2$ find the values of k and a.

14 Each of the following statements is either
    (a) true for all values of x,   (b) true for only two values of x,
    (c) true for only one value of x, or (d) never true.

    Distinguish which is which, and, where appropriate, give the solution set in the set of real numbers:
    (i) $(3x - 2)^2 = 9x^2 - 4$ (v) $(x - 3)^2 = 36$
    (ii) $(3x - 2)^2 = 9x^2 - 12x - 4$ (vi) $(x - 3)^2 = 2x^2 + 9$
    (iii) $(3x - 2)^2 = 3x^2 + 12x + 4$ (vii) $(x - 3)^2 = x^2 - 6x + 9$
    (iv) $(3x - 2)^2 = 9x^2 - 12x + 4$ (viii) $(x - 3)^2 = x^2 - 6x + 7$.

15 Find the value of a for which $(x + 2)^2 = x^2 + a^2 x + 2a$ is satisfied,
    (a) by all values of x,   (b) by no value of x.

16 Given that $\quad 1 + nx + \dfrac{n(n-1)x^2}{2} = 1 + ax + a^2 x^2 \quad$ for all x, find a and n.

Indices and logarithms

The reader should be familiar with the following three laws relating to indices:

$$a^p \times a^q = a^{p+q} \qquad \text{(i)} \qquad \text{e.g.} \qquad 3^5 \times 3^2 = 3^7$$

$$a^p \div a^q = a^{p-q} \qquad \text{(ii)} \qquad \text{e.g.} \qquad 2^7 \div 2^3 = 2^4$$

$$(a^p)^q = a^{pq} \qquad \text{(iii)} \qquad \text{e.g.} \qquad (5^2)^3 = 5^6$$

Consequences

(a) $\qquad a^0 = \dfrac{a^p}{a^p} \qquad$ using (ii)

$\qquad \Rightarrow a^0 = 1 \qquad$ e.g. $3^0 = 1$, $7^0 = 1$.

Any number raised to the power zero has the value 1.

(b) As $a^{-p} \times a^p = a^0 = 1$ using (i) and (a),

$$a^{-p} = \frac{1}{a^p} \qquad \text{e.g. } 3^{-4} = \frac{1}{3^4} = \frac{1}{81}.$$

In this way meaning is given to a negative index.

(c) As $(a^{p/q})^q = a^p$ using (iii) (p, q positive integers),

$\qquad a^{p/q} = \sqrt[q]{a^p}$, taking the qth root of both sides.

Note that $a^{p/q} = (a^{1/q})^p = (\sqrt[q]{a})^p$ which is a better form for calculation purposes.

At this level we shall only be concerned with real roots, so that $\sqrt[q]{a}$ will always be real. It is the usual convention, when q is an even, positive integer, for $\sqrt[q]{a}$ to represent the positive qth root of a.

Examples:

1 $\sqrt{9} = +3$ and so the solutions of $x^2 = 9$ are $x = \pm \sqrt{9} = \pm 3$.

2 $(256)^{3/4} = (\sqrt[4]{256})^3 = 4^3 = 64$.

3 $(27)^{-2/3} = \dfrac{1}{27^{2/3}} = \dfrac{1}{(\sqrt[3]{27})^2} = \dfrac{1}{3^2} = \dfrac{1}{9}$.

Exercise 10.2

Simplify

1 $49^{1/2}$		7 5^0		13 $(16^{3/4})^2$		19 $(\frac{121}{169})^{-3/2}$	
2 $(\frac{1}{16})^{1/4}$		8 2^{-3}		14 $(0.01)^{-1/2}$		20 $(3\frac{3}{8})^{-1/3}$	
3 $1024^{2/5}$		9 5^{-2}		15 $(\frac{9}{16})^{1/2}$		21 $3^0 - 4^{-1} + 16^{1/2}$	
4 $125^{1/3}$		10 3^{-4}		16 $(\frac{25}{36})^{-1/2}$		22 $(\frac{1}{2})^{-1} + (32)^{4/5} - (\frac{4}{25})^{-1/2}$	
5 $(-8)^{1/3}$		11 $(16)^{-1/2}$		17 $(\frac{4}{5})^{-2}$			
6 $(-\frac{1}{64})^{2/3}$		12 $(8)^{-2/3}$		18 $(\frac{7}{8})^{-1}$			

Logarithms

Logarithms are closely related to indices.

If $a^x = b$ we say that x is the logarithm of b to the base a; it is the power to which the base a is raised to give the number b.

The logarithm of 100 to the base 10, written $\log_{10} 100$, is 2 since $10^2 = 100$. The reader will be familiar with logarithms to the base 10, but as any statement in indices is equivalent to a corresponding logarithm statement, the base may be any number.

In general, $a^x = b \Leftrightarrow \log_a b = x$

Note: As $a^x > 0$ there is no meaning to $\log_a b$ where $b \leqslant 0$.

Exercise 10.3

Evaluate the following without using tables:

1 $\log_{10} 100$	5 $\log_7 \frac{1}{7}$	9 $\log_2 \frac{1}{8}$	
2 $\log_{10} \frac{1}{10}$	6 $\log_4 64$	10 $\log_9 \frac{1}{81}$	
3 $\log_{10} 0.01$	7 $\log_3 \sqrt{3}$	11 $\log_p p^5$	
4 $\log_5 25$	8 $\log_6 1$	12 $\log_2 2\sqrt{2}$	

Laws relating logarithms

To the three laws of indices given at the beginning of this section there correspond the three following laws of logarithms:

$$\log_a x + \log_a y = \log_a xy \qquad \text{(i)}$$

$$\log_a x - \log_a y = \log_a \left(\frac{x}{y}\right) \qquad \text{(ii)}$$

$$\log_a x^n = n \log_a x \qquad \text{(iii)}$$

The reader will have used the laws of logarithms to the base 10 in some numerical calculations.

For example, to find $\log_{10}(3.24 \times 7.92)$ the values of $\log_{10} 3.24$ and $\log_{10} 7.92$ are found and then added.

The problem is set out in table (a) below left, the final answer being found by the use of antilog. tables, which solve the equation $\log_{10} x = 1.4092$ or, equivalently, $10^{1.4092} = x$.

	No.	Log			No.	Log
3.24×7.92	3.24	0.5105	$(3.28)^7$	3.28	0.5159
$= \mathbf{25.66}$	7.92	0.8987	$= \mathbf{4086}$	$(3.28)^7$	$\times 7$
	25.66	1.4092		4086	3.6113
	(a)			(b)	

The third law, which is useful to solve equations of the form $a^x = b$, such as $3^x = 8$, is illustrated numerically in table (b) above right, where, to find $\log_{10} 3.28^7$, the value of $\log_{10} 3.28$ is found and then multiplied by 7.

The proofs of the above laws use the corresponding index law.

To prove (i)   let $\log_a x = p$ and $\log_a y = q$.

Then $a^p = x$ and $a^q = y \Rightarrow a^{p+q} = xy.$

So $p + q = \log_a xy$

$$\Rightarrow \log_a x + \log_a y = \log_a xy.$$

The other two proofs are left as exercises for the reader.

Examples: *Simplify, without using tables:*
1   $\log_{10} 2 + \log_{10} 50 = \log_{10}(2 \times 50) = \log_{10} 100 = 2.$
2   $\log_8 32 - \log_8 \frac{1}{2} = \log_8 (32/\frac{1}{2}) = \log_8 64 = 2.$
3   $\log_{10} 32 = \log_{10} 2^5 = 5 \log_{10} 2 = 5(0.3010) = 1.505$, *given that* $\log_{10} 2 = 0.3010.$

Exercise 10.4 $(\log a \equiv \log_{10} a)$

Simplify, without using tables, the following:
1   $\log \frac{1}{2} + \log 200$,   5 $2 \log_4 8$,   9 $2 \log 2 + \log 25$,

2   $\log 8 + \log \frac{5}{4}$,   6 $\log_5 80 - \log_5 16$,   10 $\log_6 1 + \frac{1}{3} \log_5 125$,

3   $\log 3.2 - \log 32$,   7 $\dfrac{\log 27}{\log 9}$,   11 $2 \log_5 3 + \log_5 \frac{5}{9}$,

4   $\log_4 8 + \log_4 16$,   8 $\dfrac{\log 25}{\log 5}$,   12 $2 \log (0.1) - \frac{1}{3} \log_3 27.$

Change of base

It may be easier to calculate a logarithm to base a by changing it to a more convenient base c.

Let $\log_a x = b$, then $a^b = x$.

Taking logarithms to base c,

$$\log_c a^b = \log_c x$$
$$\Rightarrow b \log_c a = \log_c x \qquad [\text{using (iii)}]$$
$$\Rightarrow b = \frac{\log_c x}{\log_c a}$$

i.e.
$$\log_a x = \frac{\log_c x}{\log_c a} \qquad \text{(iv)}$$

Example: $\log_3 8 = \dfrac{\log_{10} 8}{\log_{10} 3}$ which can then be evaluated using tables or a calculator to be 1.893

As $\log_c c = 1$ for all c, a special case of (iv) can be seen by letting $c = x$:

$$\log_a c = \frac{\log_c c}{\log_c a} = \frac{1}{\log_c a}.$$

Exercise 10.5 (Tables, or calculator, may be used unless otherwise stated).

1 Evaluate (a) $\log_4 10$, (b) $\log_2 10$, (c) $\dfrac{1}{\log_5 10}$.

2 Evaluate (a) $\log_4 7$, (b) $\log_2 9$, (c) $\log_5 \frac{1}{2}$.

3 Given that $\log 2 = 0.30103$, and $\log 3 = 0.47712$, evaluate the following, correct to four places of decimals: (a) $\log 27 + \log 4$, (b) $2 \log 12 - \log 18$, (c) $\log 3 \sqrt{60}$.

4 Express as single logarithms:
(a) $2 + \log x + \frac{1}{3} \log y$, (b) $4 \log 2 + 2 \log 3 - 2 \log 6$.

5 By taking logarithms to the base 10 of both sides of the equation $3^x = 8$ find x (this is an important use of logarithms).

6 Solve the equations: (a) $7^x = 4$, (b) $(\frac{2}{3})^x = \frac{9}{4}$.

7 Given that $\log_a x + 3 \log_a y = \log_a (x + 1)$, express x in terms of y.

8 Given that $1 + 2 \log x = \log y$, express y in terms of x.

9 The series $y + 2y + 3y + \ldots + ny$ has a sum equal to $\frac{1}{2}n(n + 1)y$. Find the sum of the series $\log 2 + \log 4 + \log 8 \ldots + \log 256$ given that $\log 2 = 0.3010$.

10 The series $1 + y + y^2 + \ldots + y^n$ has a sum equal to $\dfrac{y^{1+n} - 1}{y - 1}$. Find the smallest value of n for $1 + 2 + 4 + \ldots + 2^n$ to have a sum greater than 1500.

Arithmetic and geometric series

A **sequence** is a set of numbers given in a definite order for which there is a rule by which the terms are obtained.

The reader will no doubt be able to suggest the next term in each of the following sequences:

(a) $2, 4, 6, 8, 10 \ldots$ (b) $2, 4, 8, 16, 32, \ldots$

(c) $1, 1, 2, 3, 5, 8, 13, \ldots$ (d) $0, 3, 8, 15, 24, \ldots$

When the sequence is written as a sum, e.g. $1 + 1 + 2 + 3 + 5 + 8 + 13 + \ldots$, it is called a **series**.

By studying the way in which a sequence is constructed, it is possible, in some cases, to derive formulae which will describe any term in the sequence and the sum of a given number of terms for the series. Each of the above sequences have a simple law describing the way in which they are built up, but appearances can be deceptive. Whereas (a), (b) and (d) have simple general terms and the sums of a given number of terms can be found easily, the series corresponding to (c), called a **Fibonacci series**, after the mathematician who studied it, needs more advanced techniques to determine similar expressions.

Derivation of the general term of a series

There is a one–one correspondence between the terms of a sequence and the set of natural numbers. The general term is found by observing the relationship for a few terms and then applying it to the nth term.

Example 1: *Find the nth term of the series* $1, 3, 5, 7, 9, \ldots$
The correspondence

$$
\begin{array}{ccccccc}
1 & 2 & 3 & 4 & 5 & \ldots & n \\
\updownarrow & \updownarrow & \updownarrow & \updownarrow & \updownarrow & & \updownarrow \\
1 & 3 & 5 & 7 & 9 & & \ldots
\end{array}
$$
is set up

The one–one mapping is defined by $n \to 2n - 1$; the value of the nth term is $2n - 1$.

Example 2: *Find the nth term of the series* (d) *above.*
The correspondence

$$
\begin{array}{ccccccc}
1 & 2 & 3 & 4 & 5 & \ldots & n \\
\updownarrow & \updownarrow & \updownarrow & \updownarrow & \updownarrow & & \updownarrow \\
0 & 3 & 8 & 15 & 24 & & \ldots
\end{array}
$$
is set up.

The mapping is defined by $n \to n^2 - 1$; the value of the nth term is $n^2 - 1$.

As the values $1, 2, 3, \ldots$ are substituted for n, the series is constructed.

Exercise 10.6

Write down the nth term of the following series:

1   $2, 4, 6, 8, \ldots$ 5 $1\frac{1}{2}, 2, 2\frac{1}{2}, 3, \ldots$

2   $3, 7, 11, 15, \ldots$ 6 $13, 8, 3, -2, \ldots$

3   $-4, +1, +6, +11, \ldots$ 7 $2, 4, 8, 16, \ldots$

4   $0, 3, 6, 9, \ldots$ 8 $3, 9, 27, 81, \ldots$

9	$4, 8, 16, 32, \ldots$	13	$2, 5, 10, 17, \ldots$
10	$3, 4\frac{1}{2}, 6\frac{3}{4}, 10\frac{1}{8}, \ldots$	14	$-\frac{1}{2}, 3, 12\frac{1}{2}, 31, \ldots$
11	$-2, +4, -8, +16, \ldots$	15	$25, 24, 23, 22, \ldots$
12	$5, 2\frac{1}{2}, 1\frac{1}{4}, \frac{5}{8}, \ldots$	16	$\frac{1}{2}, \frac{1}{2}, \frac{3}{8}, \frac{1}{4}, \ldots$

Two of the more simple types of series are now considered in more detail.

Arithmetic progressions

If the difference between consecutive terms of a sequence remains constant it is called an **arithmetic progression** (A.P. from now on) and the difference is called the **common difference**. In the last exercise, questions 1–6 inclusive and 15 are examples of A.P.s, their corresponding common differences being $+2, +4, +5, +3, +\frac{1}{2}, -5$ and -1, respectively.

Formulae can be found for the nth term and the sum of the first n terms of an A.P. in the following manner:

If the value of the first term of the series is represented by a and the common difference by d, the sequence is

1st term	2nd term	3rd term	4th term	nth term
a	$a+d$	$a+2d$	$a+3d$	$\ldots \; a+(n-1)d$

The value of the nth term is $a+(n-1)d$.

Example 1: *Find the nth term of the A.P.* $5, 9, 13, \ldots$.
$a = 5, d = 4 \Rightarrow n$th term $= 5 + (n-1)4 = 5 + 4n - 4 = 4n + 1$.

Any particular term can then be evaluated. For example, the 20th term $= 81$.

Example 2: *Find the number of terms in the A.P.* $24, 26\frac{1}{2}, \ldots 74$.
Let 74 be the value of the nth term, when $a = 24, d = 2\frac{1}{2}$.
$$74 = 24 + (n-1)2\frac{1}{2} \Leftrightarrow 2\frac{1}{2}n - 2\frac{1}{2} = 50 \Leftrightarrow 2\frac{1}{2}n = 52\frac{1}{2} \Leftrightarrow n = 21.$$

Sum of the first n terms of an A.P.

An A.P. has the property that terms equidistant from each end, when added, give the same result; this is used to find a general formula for a given number of terms of the series. The sum of the first n terms is given by
$$S_n = a + (a+d) + (a+2d) + \ldots + \{a + (n-2)d\} + \{a + (n-1)d\}.$$

If the series is written in reverse the sum remains the same, and therefore
$$S_n = \{a + (n-1)d\} + \{a + (n-2)d\} + \ldots + (a+d) + a.$$

When corresponding pairs are added they each give $\{2a + (n-1)d\}$ and as there are n such pairs we have, on adding both statements:

$$2S_n = n\{2a + (n-1)d\} \Leftrightarrow S_n = \frac{n}{2}\{2a+(n-1)d\}.$$

An alternative form is $S_n = \frac{n}{2}(a + l)$ where l is the last term.

Example 1: *Find the sum of the first 35 terms of the A.P.* 3, 7, 11, . . .

$$a = 3, d = 4, n = 35 \Rightarrow S_{35} = \frac{35}{2}\{6 + (34 \times 4)\} = \frac{35}{2} \times 142 = 2485.$$

Example 2: *Find how many terms of the A.P.* 15, 7, . . . *are needed to give a sum of* -720.

In this case
$$-720 = \frac{n}{2}\{30 - 8(n-1)\}$$

$$\Leftrightarrow -720 = 15n - 4n(n-1)$$

$$\Leftrightarrow 4n^2 - 19n - 720 = 0$$

$$\Leftrightarrow (4n + 45)(n - 16) = 0$$

$$\Leftrightarrow n = -11\tfrac{1}{4} \text{ or } n = 16.$$

16 terms of the series are needed to give a sum of 720.

Arithmetic mean

Consecutive terms of an A.P. are said to be in arithmetic progression. If three numbers a, b, c, are in A.P. b is the **arithmetic mean** of a and c. As they are in A.P.

$$a - b = b - c \Leftrightarrow b = \frac{a + c}{2}.$$

Exercise 10.7

1 Find the 18th term of the A.P.s: (a) -3, $+2$, $+7$, . . ., (b) -12, -2, $+8$, ...
2 Find the 50th term of the A.P.s: (a) 5, $6\tfrac{1}{4}$, $7\tfrac{1}{2}$, . . ., (b) 3, 9, 15 . . ..
3 Find the sum of $1 + 2 + 3 + \ldots + 49$.
4 Find the formula for the sum of the first n natural numbers.
5 Find the sum of the following A.P.s:
   (a) 4, 6, . . . 28   (b) -5, -2, . . . 34
   (c) 12, 5, . . . -72 (d) 1.1, 2.3, . . . 31.1.
6 Find the number of terms of the progressions in the last question.
7 Find the sum of the following A.P.s as far as the term indicated:
   (a) $3 + 9 + \ldots$ 14th term   (b) $12 + 8 + \ldots$ 52nd term.
8 Given that a, b, and 10 are in A.P. and their sum is -56, find a and b.
9 Given that the sum of n terms of a series is $\frac{n}{2}(3n + 2)$, find the first three terms of the series and show that it is an A.P.
10 The third term of an A.P. is 8 and the seventeenth term is 50. Find the first term and the sum of the first 12 terms.

Geometric series

If each term of a sequence is a constant multiple of the preceding term, the terms are said to be in **geometric progression** (G.P.); the corresponding series is called a **geometric series**. The constant multiple involved is called the **common ratio**.

In Exercise 10.6 questions 7 to 12 inclusive are examples of G.P.s, their corresponding common ratios being $2, 3, 2, 1\frac{1}{2}, -2$ and $\frac{1}{2}$, respectively.

Formulae can be found for the nth term and the sum of the first n terms as follows:

Let the first term of the progression be a and the common ratio be r.
The terms of the sequence are then:

1st term	2nd term	3rd term		nth term
a	ar	ar^2	....	ar^{n-1} ...

The nth term is ar^{n-1}

Let the sum of the first n terms of the series be S_n, then

$$S_n = a + ar + ar^2 + \ldots + ar^{n-2} + ar^{n-1}. \tag{1}$$

If both sides are multiplied by r, then

$$rS_n = ar + ar^2 + \ldots + ar^{n-1} + ar^n. \tag{2}$$

Subtracting (2) from (1),

$$(1-r)S_n = a - ar^n = a(1 - r^n)$$

$$\Leftrightarrow S_n = a\frac{(1-r^n)}{1-r} \text{ or equivalently } S_n = a\frac{(r^n - 1)}{r - 1}.$$

If $r < 1$ the former is more appropriate; if $r > 1$ use the latter.

Example: *Find the 13th term of the G.P.* $\frac{1}{8}, \frac{1}{4}, \frac{1}{2}, \ldots$ *and the sum of the first 8 terms.*

If $a = \frac{1}{8}, r = 2$ and $n = 13$ are substituted in the formula for the nth term it is seen to be $\frac{1}{8}(2)^{12} = 512$.

If $a = \frac{1}{8}, r = 2$ and $n = 8$ are substituted in the formula for the sum we have that $S_8 = \frac{1}{8}\frac{(2^8 - 1)}{2 - 1} = 31.875$.

Geometric mean

If a, b, c, are consecutive terms of a G.P. then as the ratio of consecutive terms is constant,

$$\frac{b}{a} = \frac{c}{b} \Leftrightarrow b^2 = ac;$$

this is a condition for three terms a, b, c, to be in G.P.
$\sqrt{ac}$ is the **geometric mean** of the numbers a and c.

Example: The geometric mean of 6 and 216 is $\sqrt{6 \times 216} = 36$

Exercise 10.8

1 Write down the nth term, of each of the following G.P.s for the appropriate value of n:
   (a) $1, 5, 25, \ldots$ $(n = 7)$,   (b) $-8, 24, -72, \ldots$ $(n = 5)$,

   (c) $\dfrac{1}{7}, \dfrac{1}{21}, \dfrac{1}{63}, \ldots$ $(n = 6)$,   (d) $16, -8, 4, \ldots$ $(n = 12)$,

   (e) $13, 2\frac{3}{5}, \dfrac{13}{25}, \ldots$ $(n = 8)$,   (f) $4, 8, 16, \ldots$ $(n = 9)$.

2 Write down S_n for the above G.P.s and for the same values of n. (Leave answers in index form).

3 Find the geometric means of: (a) 2 and 128, (b) 7 and 28.

4 Write down the first three terms of the series for which $S_n = \frac{3}{4}(3^n - 1)$ and deduce that the terms are in G.P.

5 Write down the sum of the series $1 + x + x^2 + x^3 + x^4$. Deduce two factors of $x^5 - 1$.

6 A G.P. whose first term is 3 is such that the 4th term is equal to the sum of the 3rd term and twelve times the 2nd term. Find possible values of the common ratio, and give the first five terms of the sequences in each case. Are there other G.P.s, with different first terms, for which this property holds?

7 The sum of the first five terms of a G.P., whose common ratio is 3, is -242. Find the first term.

8 Given that the third and fifth terms of a G.P. are 4 and 81 respectively, find possible values for the common ratio.

9 Given that the third and sixth terms of a G.P. are 2 and 54 respectively, find the first three terms and write down a formula for S_n.

10 If a man were to agree to pay his son pocket money according to the programme: 1p for the first week, 2p for the second, 4p for the third, etc., how much would his son receive for the twentieth week? (Have a guess first).

11 A ball is dropped from a height of 40 cm. At each bounce it rises to three-quarters of the height from which it fell. How far has it travelled up to the eighth bounce?

Further simultaneous equations

In Chapter 8 methods of solution of two linear equations in two unknowns were discussed. Included in this section is the case where one equation is non-linear, and the case of three linear equations in three unknowns.

The method of substitution can be used when one of the equations is non-linear.

Example 1: *Solve the simultaneous equations $y - 2x = 1$;*
$$5x^2 - y^2 - x - y + 12 = 0.$$
The first equation is rewritten $y = 2x + 1$.

Substitute for y in the second equation:
$$5x^2 - (2x+1)^2 - x - (2x+1) + 12 = 0$$
$$\Rightarrow 5x^2 - 4x^2 - 4x - 1 - x - 2x - 1 + 12 = 0$$
$$\Rightarrow \qquad\qquad\qquad x^2 - 7x + 10 = 0$$
$$\Rightarrow \qquad\qquad\qquad (x-5)(x-2) = 0$$
$$\Rightarrow \qquad\qquad\qquad x = 2 \text{ or } x = 5.$$

When $x = 2$ $y = 4 + 1 = 5$,
when $x = 5$ $y = 10 + 1 = 11$,
The solutions are $x = 2,\ y = 5$ and $x = 5,\ y = 11$

Three linear equations in three unknowns may be solved by eliminating one of the unknowns from two pairs of equations in turn and solving the resulting equations in two unknowns.

Example 2: *Find the values of x, y, z which satisfy the equations*
(a) $2x + 3y - 2z = 3$, (b) $3x - y + z = 9$, and (c) $x - 4y + 2z = -2$, *simultaneously.*
Let us eliminate z from each of two pairs of equations.
Add (a) and (c) $\qquad\qquad\qquad\qquad\qquad\qquad\qquad 3x - y = 1$
Multiply (b) by 2 and add to (a) $\qquad\qquad\qquad\qquad 8x + y = 21$
The two resulting equations can be solved to give $\qquad x = 2,\ y = 5$
These values can then be substituted in one of the given equations to find z.
Using equation (b) $6 - 5 + z = 9 \Rightarrow z = 8$.
The solution is $x = 2$, $y = 5$, $z = 8$.

The geometric interpretation of the above example is that the solution is the unique point in which three planes, defined by the given equations, meet. There will be, therefore, just as in the case of linear equations in two unknowns, special cases to consider. A detailed discussion of these is beyond the scope of the book, but the interested reader may consider the different orientations of three planes in space and list the possible types of solution set.

Exercise 10.9

1 Solve the following pairs of simultaneous equations:
(a) $x^2 - y^2 = 8$ (b) $x^2 + y^2 = 4$
$\quad x + y = 2$ $\qquad\quad y = x + 2$
(c) $2x + 3y = 1$ (d) $x + y = 5$
$\quad 3x^2 + 4xy - y^2 = 6$ $\quad x^2 - 2xy + y^2 = 1$
(e) $3x + 5y = 1$ (f) $2x - y = 7$
$\quad x + 2y = \dfrac{4}{y}$ $\qquad y^2 - x(x+y) = 11.$

2 Find the unique solution (x, y, z) for the following sets of equations:
(a) $2x - 5y + 8z = 5$ (b) $\quad x + y + z = 4$
$\quad x + 2y + 3z = 6$ $\quad 3x - 2y + 2z = 13$
$\quad 4x - 2y + 3z = 5$ $\qquad 2y + z = 2$

(c) $x - 2y + z = 1$
    $2x + 4y - z = 9$
    $-x + 8y + z = 0$

(d) $2x + 3y - 2z = 0$
    $5x + y + 8z = 26$
    $-x - y + z = 1$

3 Given that the expression $ax^2 + bx + c$ has remainders 10, 14, and 37 when divided by $(x - 1)$, $(x + 1)$ and $(x + 2)$ respectively, find a, b and c.

4 Given that the expression $ax^3 + bx + c$ has factors of $x - 1$ and $4x + 1$ and a remainder of -6 when divided by $(x + 1)$, find a, b and c, and the other factor.

Miscellaneous Exercise B

1 The universal set $\mathscr{E} = \{2, 3, 4, 5, 6, 7, 8, 9\}$ has sub-sets $A = \{2, 5, 6, 7\}$, $B = \{3, 4, 7, 9\}$ and $C = \{3, 5, 6, 8\}$.
  (i) List the members of $A' \cap B$.
  (ii) List the members of $A \cup C'$
  (iii) Write down the number of elements in the set $(A' \cap B) \cap (A \cup C')$
                                                                    [JMB 1974]

2 In this question $\mathscr{E} = \{$positive integers less than $100\}$,
                $M_2 = \{$multiples of 2 less than $100\}$,
                $M_3 = \{$multiples of 3 less than $100\}$,
  and M_4, M_5 etc. have similar meanings.
  (i) Name all the members of $M_5 \cap M_6$.
  (ii) Name all the members of $M_9 \cap M'_{18}$.
  (iii) State which of the M sets is the same as
      (a) $M_2 \cap M_3$,   (b) $M_2 \cap M_4$,   (c) $M_4 \cap M_6$.
  (iv) Give the smallest value of n for which $M_9 \cap M_n = \varnothing$.
  (v) Draw a Venn diagram showing the relationship between $\mathscr{E}$, M_6, M_9 and M_{12}.   [L 1979]

3 A and B are two subsets of a universal set $\mathscr{E}$. Which one of the following statements is *not* equivalent to the statement $A \subset B$?
  (a) $B' \subset A'$; (b) $A \cap B' = \varnothing$; (c) $A' \cup B = \mathscr{E}$; (d) $A \cap B = B$;
  (e) $x \in A \Rightarrow x \in B$.   [O 1978]

4 (i) A and B are subsets of a universal set $\mathscr{E}$. If $n(\mathscr{E}) = 60$, $n(A' \cap B)$ $= 10$, $n(A \cap B') = 30$ and $n(A' \cup B') = 48$, calculate, with the help of a Venn diagram or otherwise, $n(A)$ and $n(B)$.
  (ii) The universal set consists of the integers from 36 to 48 inclusive. P, Q and R are subsets, the members of P being multiples of 3, the members of Q being multiples of 4 and the members of R being multiples of 5. By listing the members of the appropriate subsets determine which, if any, of the following statements are true for these subsets:
  (a) $P \cup (Q \cap R) = (P \cup Q) \cap (P \cup R)$;
  (b) $(P \cap Q)' = P' \cup Q'$;
  (c) $(P' \cup Q') \cup (P \cap Q) = \mathscr{E}$.   [O 1976]

5 In a survey the 25 pupils of a class all gave their opinions on music. It was found that 19 liked popular music, 11 liked jazz and 8 liked

classical music. It was also found that 7 pupils like both jazz and popular music, 4 liked both jazz and classical music, and 5 liked both popular and classical music.

Letting x be the number of pupils who liked all three kinds of music, illustrate the results of the survey on a Venn diagram. Hence find the value of x. [C 1972]

6 Given that $a*b$ denotes $a^2 - b^2$,
(i) evaluate $2\frac{1}{2} * 1\frac{1}{2}$,
(ii) find a when $a * 7 = 1 * a$. [C 1972]

7 The operation $*$ is defined on the set of integers by the relation $x * y = xy - (x + y)$.
(i) Evaluate $2 * (3 * 4)$.
(ii) Give an example to illustrate that the operation $*$ is not associative.
(iii) Explain why $*$ is commutative.
(iv) Find the solution set of the equation $x * x = 8$.
(v) Given that $a * y = 0$ and that a is neither 0 nor 1, express y in terms of a. [JMB 1975]

8 A binary operation $\oplus$ is defined on the set of non-zero rational numbers by the rule that

$$x \oplus y = \frac{x}{y} + \frac{y}{x}.$$

(i) Evaluate $2 \oplus 3$, $(2 \oplus 3) \oplus 4$, $\frac{3}{4} \oplus \frac{5}{6}$.
(ii) Solve the equation $1 \oplus x = 2$ and prove that, in general, if $x \oplus y = 2$ then $x = y$.
(iii) Select values of x and y which suggest that this operation is both closed and commutative.
(iv) Solve the equation $(x \oplus x) + (2 \oplus x) - 4 = 0$. [AEB 1975]

9 The operation $*$ is defined such that if $c = a * b$ then c is the remainder when the product ab is divided by 4, e.g. $2 * 3 = 2$.

Copy and complete the table below.

*	1	2	3
1	1	2	3
2	2		2
3	3		

Under the operation $*$,
(i) explain why the set $\{1, 2, 3\}$ is not closed,
(ii) write down the identity element,
(iii) write down the elements of the set $\{1, 2, 3\}$ which have inverses. [W 1978]

10 In this question, $p * q$ denotes 'multiply p by q and delete all digits except the last'. For example, $3 * 4 = 2$ and $3 * 2 = 6$. Construct the operation table for the set $P\{1, 3, 5, 7, 9\}$ under the operation $*$ and explain why $(P, *)$ is not a group.
Find a subset of P which does form a group under the operation $*$, showing clearly that each of the necessary conditions is satisfied. (The property of associativity of $*$ may be assumed.) [L 1972]

11 The operation $*$ is defined on the set of positive integers by $x*y = $ the highest common factor of x and y.

Consider each of the following six statements, state whether each is true or false and illustrate each answer by a carefully worked example.

(i) The operation $*$ is commutative.

(ii) The operation $*$ is associative.

(iii) The operation $*$ is distributive over addition $(+)$.

(iv) The operation multiplication $(\times)$ is distributive over $*$.

(v) $x * 1 = 1$, for all positive integers.

(vi) $x * x = 1$, for all positive integers. [JMB 1974]

12 (i) Factorise
$$2x^2 + x - 6.$$

(ii) Simplify
$$\frac{2x^2 + x - 6}{x^2 - 4}.$$
[C 1970]

13 (a) Factorise completely $px + qx + 2py + 2qy$.

(b) Express
$$\frac{4}{2x-5} - \frac{1}{x+3}$$
as a single fraction. [C 1976]

14 (i) Factorise $6x^2 - x - 15$.

(ii) Solve the equation
$$\frac{3x-1}{4} - \frac{1}{x} = \frac{3(2x+1)}{8}.$$

(iii) Given that $4a - 3x^2 = b^2$, express x in terms of a and b.
[C 1972]

15 (i) A man bought 144 pens at $2x$ pence each and 20 pencils at x pence each. Obtain an expression in terms of x for the amount of change, in pence, he would receive from £10.

(ii) Solve the equations
$$2x - 3y = 12.$$
$$3x - 2y = 13.$$

(iii) Obtain as a single fraction in its simplest form
$$\frac{1}{5}\left\{\frac{2x-y}{3} - \frac{x-3y}{4}\right\}.$$
[L 1977]

16 State whether the following equations are satisfied for (a) one value of x, (b) two values of x, or (c) all values of x.

(i) $(x-3)^2 = x^2 + 6x + 5$.   (iii) $(x-3)^2 = 2x^2 + 9$.

(ii) $(x-3)^2 = x^2 - 6x + 9$.   (iv) $(x-3)^2 = 36$.

Solve those equations which are of type (a) or (b). [C 1968]

17 (a) Solve the equation $x^2 - x - 12 = 0$.

(b) Sketch the curve $y = x^2 - x - 12$.

For what set of values of x is $x^2 - x - 12 \geqslant 0$? [OC 1974]

18 Given that $f(x) = (x+2)(x-3)$, find

(i) $f(5)$,

(ii) the values of x for which $f(x) = 0$,

(iii) the range of values of x for which $f(x) < 0$. [C 1975]

19 Find (a) the range of values of x for which $5x - 3 < x + 1$,
(b) the range of values of x for which $x^2 < 9$.
Indicate both these ranges on a real number line, making it clear which is which, and use your result to express the set
$$\{x: 5x - 3 < x + 1\} \cap \{x: x^2 < 9\}$$
as a single set in the form $\{x: a < x < b\}$. [C 1972]

20 (i) Solve the equation $2x^2 - 8x - 3 = 0$ giving the roots to 2 decimal places. Hence, or otherwise, solve the equation $\dfrac{2}{y^2} - \dfrac{8}{y} - 3 = 0$.

(ii) Simplify $\dfrac{3x}{x^2 - 4} \div \dfrac{6}{2x^2 - 4x}$. [S 1977]

21 Find the values of A and B if the equation
$$2x + 3 = A(x + 1) + B(x - 1)$$
is true for all values of x. [O 1977]

22 (a) If $\dfrac{x + 4y}{x - 2y} = 3$, what is the ratio of x to y?

(b) (i) What number must be added to $x^2 + 17x + 12$ to make the expression exactly divisible by $x + 5$?
(ii) If $4x^2 + px + 49$ is a perfect square, what is a possible value of p? [S 1976]

23 Find the value of x for which $(x + 2)^2 = x^2 + a^2x + 2a$, when $a = 1$.
Find the values of a for which the above equation is satisfied when $x = -1$.
Show that when $a = 2$, the equation is satisfied by all values of x.
Find a value of a for which the equation is satisfied by no value of x. [L 1971]

24 The curve $y = a + bx + cx^2$ passes through the points $(0, 0)$, $(1, 5)$ and $(-1, 3)$.
Calculate the values of a, b and c. [C 1974]

25 The line whose equation is $y + 3x = 5$ meets the y axis at the point $(0, t)$. Find the value of t.
Using your value of t, write down the equation of the line of gradient 3 passing through this point. [C 1970]

26 Find the equation of the straight line joining A$(0, 3)$ and B$(3, 9)$. The line AB meets the straight line whose equation is $x + 2y = 11$ at R. Calculate the coordinates of R.
If T is the point $(13, 0)$, calculate the length of RT. [C 1968]

27 If $x^2 + y^2 = 73$ and $xy = 12$, find the value of $(x + y)^2$. [C 1973]

28 (i) Solve the equations
$$x^2 - 2xy + y^2 = 1.$$
$$2x - y = -1.$$

(ii) Given that $(x + 2)$ and $(x - 1)$ are factors of $2x^3 + ax^2 + bx + 2$, find the values of a and b. [L 1979]

29 (i) Write down an expression for the average cost, in pounds, of a book if the total cost of x books is £50.

(ii) Write down another expression for the average cost, if $(x + 5)$ books cost £60.

(iii) Find x if the average cost in (i) is the same as that in (ii).

(iv) If the average cost in (i) is £1 more than the average cost in (ii), write down an equation for x, and prove that it can be simplified to $x^2 + 15x - 250 = 0$.

(v) Factorize $x^2 + 15x - 250$, and hence find the number of books satisfying the conditions of (iv). [O 1978]

30 A cyclist leaves town A to cycle to town B which is 100 km from A. After cycling for 40 km at an average speed of v, where v is in km/h, he rests for half an hour. He then cycles for the rest of the journey at an average speed of $v + 3$. Write down an expression for the time he takes

(i) to cycle the first part of the journey,

(ii) to cycle the second part of the journey.

Given that he arrives at B $6\frac{1}{2}$ hours after leaving A, form an equation in v and solve it to find v. [JMB 1973]

31 (a) Show, by using the Remainder Theorem, that $2x + 1$ is a factor of $6x^3 + 13x^2 + x - 2$ and find the other two factors.

(b) Factorise completely $2x^2 - 8$.

(c) A man walks at 6 kilometre per hour from his home to town by a path through the fields, a distance of x kilometres. After spending 40 minutes in town, he returns by bus, travelling at an average speed of 30 kilometre per hour. If the journey by road is 1 kilometre longer than the journey by the path, show that the total time taken, T hours, is given by the formula

$$T = \frac{x}{5} + \frac{7}{10}.$$

If the total time taken is 150 minutes, find the value of x.

[W 1978]

32 Of the series, (i) $2 - \frac{1}{2} + \frac{1}{8} - \ldots$

(ii) $2 - \frac{1}{2} + 1 - \ldots$

(iii) $2 - \frac{1}{2} - 3 - \ldots$

one is an arithmetic progression (A.P.), one is a geometric progression (G.P.) and one is neither.

(a) State which is the A.P. and calculate its common difference.

(b) State which is the G.P. and calculate its common ratio.

(c) Calculate the sum of the first 20 terms of the A.P.

(d) The 25th term of the G.P. is equal to 2^n. Find the value of n.

(e) If x is subtracted from each term of the series (ii), a G.P. is formed. Write down, but do not solve, an equation for x. [L 1974]

33 (a) The first term of an arithmetic progression is 3 and its common difference is x. Write down expressions for the second and third terms.

(b) The first term of a geometric progression is 1 and its common ratio is also x. Write down expressions for the second and third terms of this progression.

(c) It is given that the sums of the first three terms of the two progressions are equal. Form an equation in x and solve it to obtain two possible value of x.

(d) For the larger value of x, calculate the sum of the first 40 terms of the arithmetic progression.

(e) For the smaller value of x, calculate the sum of the first 5 terms of the geometric progression.

[L 1975]

34 A family are planning a touring holiday, during which some days (x days) will be spent walking, and the rest of the time (y days) in travelling by bus. Each day they can walk 30 km or travel 80 km by bus, and they wish to travel at least 600 km altogether. Show that this implies that

$$3x + 8y \geqslant 60.$$

Write down inequalities to express the following conditions:

(a) The holiday must not last more than 14 days.

(b) Given that each day walking will cost £10, and each day travelling by bus will cost £70, the holiday must not cost more than £490.

On graph paper, using a scale of 1 cm to 1 unit, draw a graph with straight lines to illustrate these inequalities. [Note that two points on the line $3x + 8y = 60$ are (4, 6) and (12, 3).] Shade your graph so as to leave unshaded the area containing points corresponding to possible values of x and y.

State the values of x and y which give

(i) the cheapest holiday,

(ii) the longest distance travelled. [L 1978]

35 A farmer intends to grow cabbage and lettuce in a field. To plant an acre of cabbage costs £40 and to plant an acre of lettuce costs £30. The farmer has a maximum of £360 to spend on this field. In addition, the farmer can allocate no more than a total of 35 man-days for the planting of the field. An acre of cabbage takes 2 man-days whilst an acre of lettuce takes 7 man-days.

(a) If the farmer plants x acres of cabbage and y acres of lettuce in this field, write down two inequalities connecting x and y.

(b) Using a scale of 2 cm for one acre on both axes, show graphically, by shading, the members of the solution set.

(c) If the profit on each acre of cabbage is £60, and on each acre of lettuce is £90, draw lines on your graph to illustrate the cases of total profit of (i) £180, (ii) £360.

Hence find the amount of land, to the nearest tenth of an acre, that the farmer should plant in this field to produce the largest possible profit. [W 1977]

11 Relations, mappings and functions

Cartesian product

For two sets X and Y the **Cartesian product** $X \times Y$ is the set of ordered pairs (x, y), where $x \in X$ and $y \in Y$.

Example: If $X = \{1, 2\}$ and $Y = \{3, 4, 5\}$ then
$$X \times Y = \{(1, 3), (1, 4), (1, 5), (2, 3), (2, 4), (2, 5)\}$$
and $\quad Y \times X = \{(3, 1), (3, 2), (4, 1), (4, 2), (5, 1), (5, 2)\}$.
Generally $X \times Y \neq Y \times X$ but $n(X \times Y) = n(Y \times X)$.
The Cartesian product of X with itself, $X \times X$, is written as X^2. The Cartesian product $\mathbb{R}^2$ is the set of ordered pairs which represent points in the plane. Any point can be identified by a unique element of this set; the particular ordered pair contains the Cartesian co-ordinates of the point referred to a pair of defined axes.

Plane curves can be considered as subsets of $\mathbb{R}^2$.

Exercise 11.1

1 If $X = \{a, b\}$ and $Y = \{c, d\}$ find $X \times Y$ and $Y \times X$.
2 If $X = \{x : 1 \leqslant x \leqslant 3, x \text{ integer}\}$ and $Y = \{x : 1 < x < 3, x \text{ integer}\}$ find $X \times Y$ and $Y \times X$.
3 If $X = \{x : 0 \leqslant x \leqslant 2, x \in R\}$ and $Y = \{x : 0 \leqslant x \leqslant 1, x \in R\}$, what does $X \times Y$ represent?
4 If $X = \{1, 2, 3\}$, find X^2 and $n(X^2)$.
5 If $X = \{\text{John, Dave, Fred}\}$ and $Y = \{\text{Austin, B.M.W., Citroen}\}$, find $X \times Y$.
6 If $X = \{\text{Aston Villa, Tottenham Hotspur, Arsenal}\}$ and $Y = \{\text{Birmingham, London}\}$, find $X \times Y$.
Write down the largest subset of $X \times Y$ for which there is some relationship between corresponding elements x and y, and state the relationship.

Relations

A **relation** is a statement defined on a set X, or between two sets X and Y, which has meaning; i.e. for an arbitary pair of elements (x, y), $x \in X$, $y \in Y$, associated by the relation ℓ , $x\ell$ y is either true or false.

The relation is a proper subset of the Cartesian product $X \times Y$.

Consider the sets $X = \{1, 2, 3\}$ and $Y = \{1, 2\}$, then
$$X \times Y = \{(1, 1), (1, 2), (2, 1), (2, 2), (3, 1), (3, 2)\}.$$

If $x \in X$, $y \in Y$, then the statement '$x > y$' is meaningful; for any pair (x, y) in $X \times Y$ it is either true or false. '*Is greater than*' is a relation between X and Y defined by the subset $\{(2, 1), (3, 1), (3, 2)\}$.

If $A = \{$all triangles$\}$ and $B = \{$all quadrilaterals$\}$, then the statement '*is greater than*' is not relation between A and B since if $a \in A$ and $b \in B$, $a > b$ has no meaning; whereas '*is equal in area to*' is a relation between A and B since it is possible to determine whether any $a \in A$ is associated with any $b \in B$.

Exercise 11.2 (For discussion)

1 Determine which of the following statements are relations on the set X, or between the sets X and Y:
   (a) 'is the same length as' $X = \{$all lines in space$\}$
   (b) 'was registered in the same town as' $X = \{$all British cars$\}$
   (c) 'has the same make T.V. as' $X = \{$children in a school$\}$
   (d) 'is greater than' $X = \{$all men$\}$, $Y = \{$all women$\}$
   (e) 'is three more than' $X = \{1, 5, 8\}$, $Y = \{2\}$
   (f) 'is the square root of' $X = \mathbb{R}$
   (g) 'is better than' $X = \{$all musical groups$\}$
   (h) 'has had more singles in the top twenty than' $X = \{$all female singers$\}$
   (i) 'is one half of' $X = \mathbb{R}$.
2 Suggest two relations between the sets X and Y of part (d) in the last question.
3 Suggest a relation between the following pairs of sets. For each part give the subset of $X \times Y$ which represents your relation:
   (a) $X = \{$Boycott, Capes, Hunt, Ovett, Piggott$\}$,
      $Y = \{$Motor Car Racing, Soccer, Horse Racing,
         Rugby, Athletics, Cricket.$\}$
   (b) $X = \{$Dickens, Orwell, Austen$\}$
      $Y = \{$David Copperfield, Pride and Prejudice, 1984,
         Animal Farm$\}$
   (c) $X = \{$Cardiff Arms Park, The Oval, Twickenham,
         Wembley, Trent Bridge$\}$
      $Y = \{$Rugby, Soccer, Cricket$\}$
   (d) $X = \{$Paris, Oslo, Helsinki, Rome$\}$
      $Y = \{$Norway, Sweden, Finland, Italy, Germany, France$\}$.

Domain and codomain

A relation, then, associates one element of a set X, called the **domain**, with one or more elements of another set Y, called the **codomain**, which may be the same set as the first.

Consider the relation '*is greater than or equal to*' defined on the set $\{1, 2, 3\}$. The domain and codomain are the same set $\{1, 2, 3\}$.

The relation, defined by the set of ordered pairs $\{(1, 1), (2, 1), (2, 2), (3, 1), (3, 2), (3, 3)\}$, may be illustrated in the following ways:

(a) an arrow graph, as in Figure 11.1,

(b) a **Papygraph** (named after the Belgian mathematician, Georges Papy), as in Figure 11.2,

(c) a Cartesian graph, as in Figure 11.3.

For a relation ℓ, $x \ell y$ is often written as $\ell : x \to y$, which is a symbolic representation of the arrow graph.

In a Cartesian graph the domain $X = \{x\}$ is denoted by points on a horizontal axis and the codomain $Y = \{y\}$ by points on a vertical axis. The set of ordered pairs $X \times Y$ may then be represented by a set of dots in the plane. The relation is illustrated by marking the corresponding subset of points. In Figure 11.3 the relation is denoted by the six closed circles.

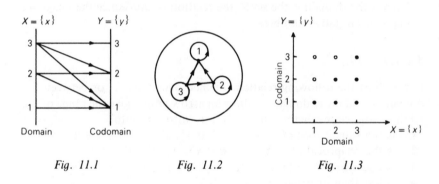

| Fig. 11.1 | Fig. 11.2 | Fig. 11.3 |

The scales on the axes of the graphs need not be the same and in many cases different scales are used to give a more informative picture.

Images and range

An element in the codomain associated with an element in the domain by a relation is called an **image** of that element. An element may have more than one image. In the above example, the image of 1 is 1, the images of 2 are 1 and 2, and the images of 3 are 1, 2 and 3.

The complete set of images is called the **range** of the relation over the given domain. In this example the range is the set $\{1, 2, 3\}$.

If the range and the codomain are the same set, as in this case, the relation is said to be '*onto*', or (surjective), otherwise it is called an '*into*' relation.

Example: *Draw an arrow graph to illustrate the relation 'is the square root of' between the domain $X = \{x : -2 \leqslant x \leqslant 2\}$ and codomain $Y = \mathbb{R}$. Find the range of the relation.*

141

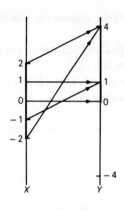

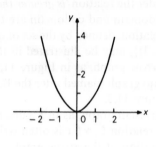

Fig. 11.4   Fig. 11.5

The arrow graph (Figure 11.4) shows that the range of the relation is the set $\{y:0 \leqslant y \leqslant 4\}$ and that the relation is clearly 'into'.

Figure 11.5 shows the corresponding Cartesian graph for the relation.

Even if the domain is the set $\mathbb{R}$, the relation is 'into' since the image set contains no negative numbers.

Exercise 11.3

For each of the following relations defined over a set X, or between the domain X and the codomain Y, draw an arrow graph, give the range of the relation, and state whether the relation is 'into' or 'onto':

1   'is the square root of' $X = \{-1, 0, 1\}$, $Y = \{y:0 \leqslant y \leqslant 1\}$.
2   'is the reciprocal of' $X = \{x:0 < x \leqslant 1\}$, $Y = \mathbb{R}$.
3   'is equal to' $X = \{1, 2, 3\}$, $Y = \{y:1 \leqslant y \leqslant 3\}$.
4   'is less than or equal to' $X = \{1, 2\}$.
5   'is the sum of the digits of' $X = \{2, 3\}$, $Y = \{y:10 \leqslant y \leqslant 30,\ y$ integer$\}$.
6   'is the product of the digits of' $X = \{0, 1, 2\}$, $Y = \{y:10 \leqslant y \leqslant 30, y$ integer$\}$.
7.   'is the number of prime factors of' $X = \{0, 1, 2\}$, $Y = \{3, 4, 5, 6\}$.
8   'is   the   smallest   integer   greater   than' $X = \{1, 2, 3\}$, $Y = \{y:0 \leqslant y \leqslant 3\}$.
9   'is the author of' $X = \{$Charles Dickens, Jane Austin, Dick Francis, Jerome K Jerome$\}$, $Y = \{$Risk, Wuthering Heights, Three Men in a Boat, A Tale of Two Cities, Persuasion$\}$.
10   'was written by' $X = \{$Othello, Jane Eyre, Youth, The Mousetrap, Much Ado About Nothing$\}$, $Y = \{$authors$\}$.
11   ' is higher in the league than' $X = \{$Liverpool, Everton, Manchester United, West Bromwich Albion$\}$,
12   'is manufactured in' $X = \{$Citroen, Datsun, Fiat, Rover$\}$, $Y = \{$countries$\}$
13   'has the same number of lines of symmetry as' $X = \{$square, isosceles

142

triangle, rectangle, circle, parallelogram}, $Y = \{$letters: A, B, C, H, O, X, Y$\}$

14 'was born in an earlier century than' $X = \{$Newton, Napoleon, Charles I, Milton, Shakespeare, Pascal$\}$.

A relation for which each element in the domain has only one image in the range is said to be **one–one**, (or injective); if an element has more than one image the relation is said to be **one–many**.

Example: The relation '*is the author of*,' associating elements of the set of all authors with elements of the set of all books,* is one-many since a given author may have written many books.
[* Books with co-authors are excluded].

If more than one element in the domain has the same image, like the relation '*is the square root of*' defined over ℝ, it is said to be '**many–one**'.

The relation '*is greater than or equal to*' defined on the set $\{1, 2, 3\}$, illustrated in Figure 11.1, is an example of a **many–many** relation.

Exercise 11.4

1 For each of the relations defined in the last exercise, state whether it is 'one–one', 'one–many', 'many–one' or 'many–many'.

2 Classify each of the following relations as in question 1:
  (a) 'is the capital of' relating $X = \{$capital cities$\}$ and $Y = \{$countries$\}$
  (b) 'attends the same school as' defined over $X = \{$children in Bristol$\}$
  (c) 'is a football team in' relating $X = \{$football teams$\}$ and $Y = \{$English cities$\}$
  (d) 'is married to' defined over $X = \{$all people$\}$
  (e) 'teaches' relating $X = \{$teachers in your school$\}$ and $Y = \{$subjects they teach$\}$.

3 Each of the following relations is defined on the set ℝ. Find the range and classify the relation as in question 1:
  (a) 'is the cube root of'
  (b) 'is the square root of'
  (c) $x \rightarrow 3x + 1$
  (d) $x \rightarrow x^2 + 1$.

4 Illustrate the relation 'is a brother of' on the set consisting of Mr. and Mrs. Dickson and their children David, Michael and Clare. What type of relation is it?

5 In a mathematics exam the top four pupils were David, who gained 98 %, Elizabeth 92 %, Mark 87 %, and Jane 84 %. Illustrate the relation 'scored more than' on the set David, Elizabeth, Mark, Jane. What type of relation is it?

Equivalence relations

Relations possessing particular properties are given special names:

Reflexive

A relation $\mathcal{R}$ is **reflexive** if $x \mathcal{R} x$ for all x in the domain. The relation, '*is greater than or equal to*' is reflexive over $\mathbb{R}$, for example, since every number is greater than or equal to itself. The relation '*is greater than*' over $\mathbb{R}$ is not reflexive. The property is shown up in the Papygraph by loops at each of the elements, as in Figure 11.2.

Symmetric

A relation $\mathcal{R}$ is **symmetric** if when $x \mathcal{R} y$ then $y \mathcal{R} x$ and vice versa, i.e. $x \mathcal{R} y \Leftrightarrow y \mathcal{R} x$. If a family consists of three sons and their parents, for example, the relation '*is a brother of*' is symmetric, but for the Dickson family (Ex. 11.4, No. 4) the relation '*is a brother of*' is not symmetric since, although Michael is a brother of Clare, Clare is not a brother of Michael!

Transitive

A relation $\mathcal{R}$ is **transitive** if when $x \mathcal{R} y$ and $y \mathcal{R} z$ then $x \mathcal{R} z$ is implied. The relation '*is a brother of*' on the set of all people is transitive, for if x is a brother of y, and y is a brother of z then x must be a brother of z.

A relation which is reflexive, symmetric and transitive is called an **equivalence relation**.

Example 1: The relation '*has the same nationality as*' is an equivalence relation for the set of all men, because:
(a) it is reflexive: A 'has the same nationality as' A is true for all A.
(b) it is symmetric: If A ' has the same nationality as' B then B 'has the same nationality as' A and vice versa.
(c) it is transitive: If A 'has the same nationality as' B, and B 'has the same nationality as' C, then A 'has the same nationality as' C.

Example 2: The relation '*weighs within* 1 *kg of*' for members of a rugby team is *not* an equivalence relation, since it is not transitive.

If A 'weighs within 1 kg of' B, and B 'weighs within 1 kg of' C, then A does not necessarily 'weigh within 1 kg of' C.
e.g. Their weights may be A, 95.8 kg; B, 95 kg and C, 94.6 kg.

Exercise 11.5

For the following relations defined over the domain X, find which are
(a) reflexive, (b) symmetric and (c) transitive, and hence deduce which are equivalence relations:
1 'is greater than' $X = \mathbb{Z}_+$
2 'is a subset of' $X = \{\text{all sets}\}$
3 'is similar to' $X = \{\text{all triangles}\}$
4 'is congruent to' $X = \{\text{all triangles}\}$
5 'has the same area as' $X = \{\text{all quadrilaterals}\}$
6 'is a factor of' $X = \mathbb{Z}_+$

7 'is parallel to' $X = \{$all lines in space$\}$
8 'is the reciprocal of' $X = \mathbb{R}$, excluding 0
9 'is a team mate of' $X = \{$all first division footballers$\}$
10 'is the same height as' $X = \{$all children in a school$\}$
11 'is married to' $X = \{$all people$\}$
12 'is the same colour as' $X = \{$all cars in a garage$\}$
13 'has the same oddness or eveness as' $X = \mathbb{Z}_+$
14 'has the same remainder as when divided by 4' $X = \mathbb{Z}_+$.

Functions

If a relation associates with each element of the domain X one and only one element of the codomain Y, i.e. *it is either a many–one or a one–one relation*, it is called a **function** from X to Y, or a **mapping** from X into Y.

In terms of the corresponding arrow graph for a function, there must be only one arrow leaving each element of the domain; in terms of the Cartesian graph, there must be only one point of the relation on any vertical line drawn through the elements of the domain; and in terms of the ordered pairs (x, y) of $X \times Y$ no pair may have the same x.

In some texts the term 'mapping' may be defined in a different manner, but here it is used as a synonym for 'function'. The term 'function' is used more widely when numbers are being considered; the term 'mapping' emphasises the selection of ordered pairs and helps to convey a pictorial image – it is readily associated with the arrow graph where one element is 'mapped' onto another element.

Notation

Given that the function f (small letters are used to represent functions) maps the set $\{x\}$ of the domain X into the set $\{y\}$ of the codomain Y (x is called the **independent variable,** y the **dependent variable**), we write:

$f: X \rightarrow Y$ or, more simply, $f: x \rightarrow y$, where the relation between object and image is clear.

The image of x is written as $f(x)$, so that for the function $f: x \rightarrow y$ the relation is conveyed by the *equation* $y = f(x)$, and we say that y is a function of x.

The reader will realise that many of the relations already encountered in this Chapter are functions. Many of these functions can be expressed symbolically in terms of familiar mathematical functions.

Example 1: The relation *'is one half of'* defined over $\mathbb{R}$ is a one–one function f, mapping an element of $\mathbb{R}$ onto double its value and may be defined by $f: x \rightarrow 2x$.

The functional relation between object, x, and image, y, is expressed in the form $y = 2x$. The graph of the function is a straight line through the origin.

Example 2: *For the function f defined over* ℝ *by* $f: x \to x^2 + 5$ *find* $f(-1)$, $f(1)$ *and* $f(0)$.

$f(-1)$, the image of -1 under f, is given by $f(-1) = (-1)^2 + 5 = 6$,

$$\text{similarly} \qquad f(1) = (1)^2 + 5 = 6,$$
$$\text{and} \qquad f(0) = (0)^2 + 5 = 5.$$

The function f is many–one. The reader should verify that the range of f is $f(x) \geqslant 5$, which may be written as the set $\{y: y \leqslant 5\}$. (See Chapter 9. Ex. 9.11).

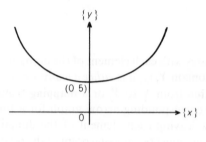

Fig. 11.6

The Cartesian graph of the function $f: x \to x^2 + 5$ is shown in Figure 11.6. The equation of the curve is $y = x^2 + 5$.

For many functional relationships, however, there may not be a simple expression for the relationship.

Example 3: The transformation $P \to P'$ mapping points P of the plane onto their images P' by a rotation of 30°, say, about a fixed point in the plane is an example of a one–one function. (The reader may be able to suggest a matrix equation to represent the function but at this level this is not easy.)

Example 4: If the body temperature T of a patient is recorded at time t hours during the day the relation mapping $t \to T$ is a function, which may be many–one. We say that T is a function of t, although there may be no simple expression to convey the relationship.

Example 5: The relation m defined as m: { Members of Parliament } → { Political Parties } is a many–one function, since a given M.P. is only a member of one political party.

Note that if domain and, codomain are interchanged, the resulting relation may not be a function, *as in the above example.*

When a relation is defined over the set ℝ it may be that particular numbers have to be excluded from the domain for the relation to be a function.

Example 6: The relation $f: x \to \dfrac{1}{x}$ is a one–one function defined over the subset of ℝ, $\{x: 1 \leqslant x \leqslant 2\}$, but if the subset $\{x: -1 \leqslant x \leqslant 1\}$ is being considered, the element $x = 0$ must be excluded. (What is the image of 0 under this relation ?).

The relation f is a function over the domain $\{x: -1 \leqslant x \leqslant 1, x \neq 0\}$.

In the following exercises the reader should assume that if the domain is not stated it is suitably defined.

Exercise 11.6

1 (For discussion)

(a) Determine which of the following relations are functions:

$r_1 : \{\text{books}\} \rightarrow \{\text{authors}\}$

$r_2 : \{\text{different words on this page}\} \rightarrow \{\text{numbers of letters in their spelling}\}$

$r_3 : \{\text{shirt collar sizes}\} \rightarrow \{\text{boys in a school with that collar size}\}$

$r_4 : \{\text{boys in a school}\} \rightarrow \{\text{shirt collar sizes}\}$

$r_5 : \{\text{football clubs}\} \rightarrow \{\text{home grounds}\}$

$r_6 : \{\text{types of aircraft leaving Heathrow on a particular day}\} \rightarrow \{\text{countries of destination}\}$

$r_7 : \{\text{children in a school}\} \rightarrow \{\text{distances travelled to reach school}\}$

$r_8 : \{\text{T.V. news readers}\} \rightarrow \{\text{T.V. channel they work for}\}$

$r_9 : \{\text{capital cities}\} \rightarrow \{\text{countries}\}$.

(b) Copy and complete the following:

r_1 (Under Milk Wood) $= \ldots$; r_2 (this) $= \ldots$;

r_5 (Birmingham City) $= \ldots$; r_9 (Paris) $= \ldots$.

(c) In each of the following, give one value of x and state whether it is unique:

$r_1(x) =$ Hammond Innes; $r_2(x) = 3$; $r_6(x) =$ U.S.A.; $r_8(x) =$ BBC 1; $r_9(x) =$ Norway.

2 For each of the following relations, define the largest subset of $\mathbb{R}$ so that the relation is a function:

(a) $f_1 : x \rightarrow 3x^2$ (b) $f_2 : x \rightarrow \sin x°$

(c) $f_3 : x \rightarrow x + 5$ (d) $f_4 : x \rightarrow \sqrt{x}$ ($\sqrt{x}$ means the positive square root of x)

(e) $f_5 : x \rightarrow \dfrac{1}{x - 1}$ (f) $f_6 : x \rightarrow \log_{10} x$.

3 (a) For the following functions defined over the domain X, find the range:

$f_1 : x \rightarrow 2x + 5$ $X = \{-1, 0, 1, 2\}$,

$f_2 : x \rightarrow 7x - 2$ $X = \{x: -1 \leqslant x \leqslant 1\}$,

$f_3 : x \rightarrow 2x^2$ $X = \{x: -3 \leqslant x \leqslant 3\}$,

$f_4 : x \rightarrow \sin x°$ $X = \{x: -90 \leqslant x \leqslant 90\}$,

$f_5 : x \rightarrow \dfrac{x - 1}{x}$ $X = \{x: 1 \leqslant x \leqslant 2\}$,

$f_6 : x \rightarrow |x|$ $X = \mathbb{R}$ $\left[\begin{array}{l} |x| \text{ is the positive value of } x, \\ \text{e.g. } |-3| = 3 \end{array}\right]$

$f_7 : x \to [x]$ $X = \mathbb{R}$ $\begin{bmatrix} [x] \text{ is the largest integer less} \\ \text{than or equal to } x, \\ \text{e.g. } [2.7] = 2, [3] = 3 \end{bmatrix}$

$f_8 : x \to \{x\}$ $X = \mathbb{R}$ $\begin{bmatrix} \{x\} \text{ is the decimal part of } x \\ \text{e.g. } [3.14] = 0.14, \{2\} = 0 \end{bmatrix}$

$f_9 : x \to \log_{10} x$ $X = \{x : \dfrac{1}{10} \leqslant x \leqslant 100\}$.

(b) Find the following:
    (i) $f_2(\frac{1}{7})$, $f_4(45)$, $f_5(1.5)$, $f_8(2\frac{1}{4})$,
    (ii) the values of x for which $f_3(x) = 8$, $f_5(x) = 0$, $f_7(x) = 5$.

(c) Draw the graphs of $y = f_1(x)$, $y = f_4(x)$, $y = f_6(x)$, $y = f_7(x)$ and $y = f_8(x)$ for the appropriate domains, and hence check your answers for the range.

4   For the following functions find a domain for the given range:
    (a) $f_1 : x \to 4x + 3$, range $= \{y : 0 < y < 6\}$,
    (b) $f_2 : x \to x^2$, range $= \{y : 1 \leqslant y \leqslant 4\}$,
    (c) $f_3 : x \to x^2$, range $= \{y : 0 \leqslant y \leqslant 4\}$,
    (d) $f_4 : x \to \log_{10} x$, range $= \{y : 0 \leqslant y \leqslant 2\}$.

Composite functions

Many functions are compounds of more than one basic function. The one – one function $f_1 : x \to 3x - 2$ is a combination of the 'trebling' function, $g : x \to 3x$ and the 'subtract two' function, $h : x \to x - 2$.

The order in which these two basic functions g and h must be carried out, if they are to produce the same mapping as the function f_1 is unambiguous.

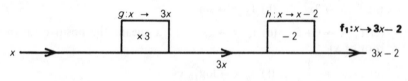

Fig. 11.7

The flow diagram (Figure 11.7) makes this quite clear; *the function g must be applied first and then function h.*

If the order is reversed then a new function $f_2 : x \to 3x - 6$ is formed (Figure 11.8).

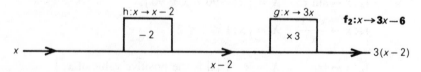

Fig. 11.8

148

In Figure 11.9 a few selected elements from the domain ℝ are shown as they are mapped by the composite function 'g *followed by h*'. In such a mapping the range of g becomes the domain for the mapping h.

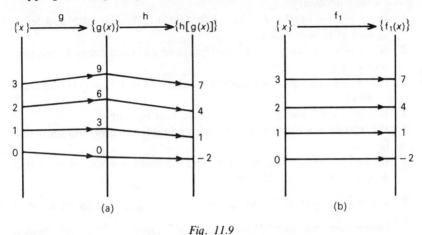

Fig. 11.9

The image of 3 under the function g, g(3), is 9; the image of 9 under the function h, h(9) is 7. The image of 3 under the composite function 'g followed by f' is 7.

The sequence is

$$3 \xrightarrow{\;g(x)\;} g(3) \xrightarrow{\;h(x)\;} h[g(3)] = 7.$$

Similarly, the images of 0, 1, 2, under this composite function are $h[g(0)]$, $h[g(1)]$ and $h[g(2)]$, respectively.

In general, a point x in the domain has image $h[g(x)]$, written in future more simply as $hg(x)$, in the range of the composite function.

The composite function 'g followed by h', is then written as hg.

In the above example hg is equivalent to f_1 and we write $hg: x \rightarrow 3x - 2$ (See Figures 11.9(a) and (b)).

Example: *If* $f: x \rightarrow x^2 + 1$ *and* $g: x \rightarrow x - 5$, *find* $fg(2)$ *and* $gf(2)$ *and give the definitions of these composite functions in terms of* x.

$$fg(2) = f[g(2)] = f(-3) = (-3)^2 + 1 = 10$$
$$gf(2) = g[f(2)] = g(5) = 0$$

For any point x is the domain.

$$fg(x) = f[g(x)] = f(x-5) = (x-5)^2 + 1 = x^2 - 10 + 26.$$
$$fg: x \rightarrow x^2 - 10x + 26,$$

whereas $gf(x) = g[f(x)] = g(x^2 + 1) = (x^2 + 1) - 5 = x^2 - 4$

$$gf: x \rightarrow x^2 - 4.$$

The ranges of these quadratic functions can be found using the methods of Chapter 9. If x is mapped onto y in the range of fg then $y = x^2 - 10x + 26$ $= (x-5)^2 + 1$. The range of fg is, therefore, $y \geqslant 1$.

The reader should verify that the range of the function gf is $\{y : y \geqslant -4\}$.

Exercise 11.7

In this exercise, assume that the domain is the set $\mathbb{R}$. Any restrictions are given where necessary.

1. If $f: x \rightarrow 2x+1$ and $g: x \rightarrow 5x-4$, find $fg(5)$, $fg(\frac{4}{5})$, $gf(0)$, $gf(5)$ and define fg and gf in terms of x.

2. If $f: x \rightarrow x-5$ and $g: x \rightarrow x^2$, find $fg(1)$ and $gf(1)$ and define fg and gf in terms of x.

3. If $f: x \rightarrow 4x$ and $g: x \rightarrow x^2$, find the solutions of $f(x) = g(x)$ and $fg(x) = gf(x)$.

4. If $f: x \rightarrow x+7$ and $g: x \rightarrow x-4$, show that $fg = gf$

5. If $f: x \rightarrow 4x-3$ and $g: x \rightarrow -5x+6$, find $fg(4)$ and $gf(4)$ and show that $fg = gf$

6. If f and g are linear functions $f: x \rightarrow ax+b$ and $g: x \rightarrow cx+d$, show that if $fg = gf$ then $d(a-1) = b(c-1)$.

7. If $f:x \rightarrow \dfrac{1}{x-1}$ $(x \neq 1)$ and $g:x \rightarrow x^2$, define fg and gf in terms of x.

   Determine whether there are any values of x for which $fg(x) = gf(x)$.

8. If $f: x \rightarrow \sin x$ and $g: x \rightarrow \dfrac{1}{x}$, find $fg(\frac{1}{90})$, $gf(90)$, $gf(-90)$, $gf(270)$. Choose a suitable domain so that gf can be defined in terms of x for all values of the domain.

9. If $f: x \rightarrow ax$ and $g: x \rightarrow x^2+2$ show that $fg \neq gf$ unless $a = 1$. If $a = 2$ find a value of x for which $fg(x) = gf(x)$, and show that if $a = -2$ there is no such value of x.

10. The four functions f_1, f_2, f_3, f_4 are defined by:

    $f_1:x \rightarrow x$, $f_2:x \rightarrow \dfrac{1}{x}$, $f_3:x \rightarrow \dfrac{-1}{x}$, $f_4:x \rightarrow -x$ $(x \neq 0$ for f_2 and $f_3)$

    Show that $f_2{}^2 = f_3{}^2 = f_4{}^2 = f_1$ ($f^2(x)$ means $f[f(x)]$) and define $f_2f_3f_4$, $f_3f_2f_4$, and $f_4f_2f_3$ in terms of x.

    Compile the combination table for this set of functions and show that they form a group under the defined rule of combination. State the inverse of each function.

11. The six functions f_1, f_2, f_3, f_4, f_5, f_6 are defined by:

    $f_1:x \rightarrow x$, $f_2:x \rightarrow \dfrac{1}{1-x}$, $f_3:x \rightarrow \dfrac{x-1}{x}$,

    $f_4:x \rightarrow 1-x$, $f_5:x \rightarrow \dfrac{1}{x}$, $f_6:x \rightarrow \dfrac{x}{x-1}$, $(x \neq 0, 1)$.

    Show that $f_2f_5 = f_6$, $f_5f_2 = f_4$, $f_4f_3 = f_5$ and $f_6{}^2 = f_1$.

    Compile the combination table for this set of functions and show that they form a group under the defined rule of combination. State the inverse of each function.

12. In each of the following, find the range of the composite function fg for the given domain X:

    (a) If $f:x \rightarrow 3x+5$ and $g:x \rightarrow 7x-2$ $X = \{2, 3, 4\}$

(b) If $f:x \to x^2 + 1$ and $g:x \to 2x + 3$ (i) $X = \{0, 1, 2\}$

                                           (ii) $X = \{x: -2 \leqslant x \leqslant 2\}$

(c) If $f:x \to \dfrac{1}{x}$ and $g:x \to 3x$ (i) $X = \{-1, 2, 3\}$

                                           (ii) $X = \{x:1 \leqslant x \leqslant 3\}$

(d) If $f:x \to 2x + 3$ and $g:x \to x^2 + 1$ (i) $X = \{0, 1, 2\}$

                                           (ii) $X = \mathbb{R}$.

13 For the following functions f and g, defined over suitable domains, define the composite functions fg and gf in the same manner:

(a) $f:x \to 3x - 2$, $g:x \to \dfrac{x+2}{3}$ (b) $f:x \to 5x - 2$, $g:x \to \dfrac{x+2}{5}$.

(c) $f:x \to x^2 + 2$, $g:x \to \sqrt{x - 2}$ (d) $f:x \to 10^x$, $g:x \to \log_{10} x$.

14 In each of the following, define g in terms of x if:

(a) $f:x \to 2x$ and $fg:x \to x$

(b) $f:x \to \dfrac{x}{7}$ and $fg:x \to x$

(c) $f:x \to x + 5$ and $fg:x \to x$.

Inverse of a function

In the last exercise several pairs of one–one functions f and g were such that the composite function gf mapped all points in the domain onto themselves, i.e. gf was the identity mapping $gf:x \to x$. Figure 11.10 illustrates the mapping gf for a few elements of the domain when f and g are defined as

$f:x \to 3x - 2$ and $g:x \to \dfrac{x+2}{3}$ (See Ex. 11.7, 13(a)).

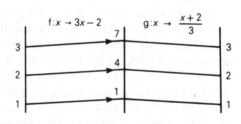

Fig. 11.10

The reader should verify that $gf(1) = 1$, $gf(2) = 2$, $gf(3) = 3$ and that gf is the identity mapping $gf:x \to x$.

When a function like g maps the range of f back onto the domain of f it is called the **inverse function** of f, written f^{-1}.

If $f:x \to 3x - 2$ then $f^{-1}:x \to \dfrac{x+2}{3}$.

It is left as an exercise for the reader to show that $fg:x \to x$ and that $g^{-1}:x \to 3x - 2$.

A function has an inverse function *only if it is one–one*.

If a function is many–one its inverse relation is not a function.

In Figure 11.11 we see that for the function $f:x \to x^2$ the relation g, required to 'map' the points in the range of f onto their corresponding points in the domain, is a one–many relation and is, therefore, not a function.

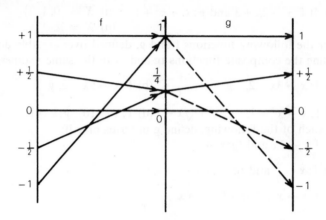

Fig. 11.11

The inverse relation of f over this domain is $g:x \to \pm \sqrt{x}$.

If the domain is restricted to make the function one–one over this domain then an inverse function can be defined. In the above example, the widest possible domains for f to have an inverse function are $\{x:x \geqslant 0, x \in \mathbb{R}\}$ in which case the inverse function is $f^{-1}:x \to + \sqrt{x}$, and $\{x:x \leqslant 0, x \in \mathbb{R}\}$ for which the inverse function is $f^{-1}:x \to - \sqrt{x}$.

As many trigonometric functions are many–one, the process of restricting the domain so that the function can have an inverse function is common, but very important in higher Mathematics. The function $f:x \to \sin x°$ is many–one [find the values of $f(60)$, $f(120)$, $f(420)$], but if the domain is restricted to the set $\{x: -90 \leqslant x \leqslant 90\}$, then f has an inverse function, written $f^{-1}:x \to \sin^{-1}x$. This set of values forming the domain is called the **set of principal values**. Similarly, the set of principal values for $\cos x$ and $\tan x$ are $\{x:0 \leqslant x \leqslant 180\}$ and $\{x: -90 \leqslant x \leqslant 90\}$, respectively, and we then write $\cos^{-1}x$ and $\tan^{-1}x$ for their inverse functions.

Definition of inverse functions

In the above example we saw that the inverse of the function $f:x \to 3x - 2$ was the function $f^{-1}:x \to \dfrac{x+2}{3}$. We shall now consider how to determine the form of the inverse for a given function.

The inverse of simple functions can be written down immediately. The inverse of the function $f:x \to x + 5$ is $f^{-1}:x \to x - 5$, since adding and subtracting are inverse processes. Similarly, if $f:x \to 4x$, then $f^{-1}:x \to x/4$, since multiplication and division are inverse processes.

In Figure 11.7 a flow diagram was used to illustrate how the function $f: x \rightarrow 3x - 2$ is related to the basic functions $g: x \rightarrow 3x$ and $h: x \rightarrow x - 2$. To find the inverse function we may work back, from right to left, inverting each basic process as we meet it.

Example: The flow diagram for $f: x \rightarrow 3x - 2$ is illustrated in Figure 11.12

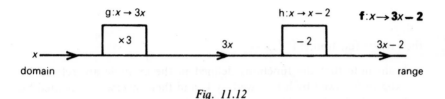

Fig. 11.12

The inverse function is illustrated in Figure 11.13

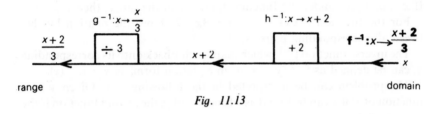

Fig. 11.13

and defined as $f^{-1}: x \rightarrow \dfrac{x+2}{3}$.

Figure 11.13 demonstrates also that the inverse functions f^{-1}, g^{-1}, h^{-1} are related by $f^{-1} = g^{-1} h^{-1}$, whereas the function f, g and h are related by $f = hg$.

The result that $(hg)^{-1} = g^{-1} h^{-1}$ is a general result for functions h and g that have inverse functions.

Example: *Find the inverse of the function* $f: x \rightarrow 2 + \dfrac{3}{x}$ *defined over a suitable domain.*
The flow diagram for f is

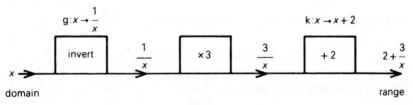

Fig. 11.14

The flow diagram for the inverse is:

153

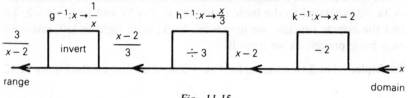

Fig. 11.15

the inverse function is $f^{-1}: x \rightarrow \dfrac{3}{x-2}$.

Again note that the functions defined in the example are related by $f = khg$ (g followed by h followed by k, and their inverses are related by $f^{-1} = g^{-1}h^{-1}k^{-1}$; i.e. $(khg)^{-1} = g^{-1}h^{-1}k^{-1}$.

Alternative method

If x is mapped, under the function f, onto y in the range, then $y = f(x)$.

For the function $f: x \rightarrow 3x - 2$, $y = 3x - 2$ shows the relationship between all corresponding pairs (x, y).

The inverse function f^{-1}, which maps each y back onto its corresponding x, can be defined as $f^{-1}: y \rightarrow x$ or, in equation form, as $x = f^{-1}(y)$.

The problem can be interpreted in the following way. Given y as a function of x, if x can be found as a function of y, the second function is the inverse of the first.

In this case $y = 3x - 2 \Leftrightarrow x = \dfrac{y+2}{3}$.

The first equation represents the mapping $f: x \rightarrow 3x - 2$, and the second represents the mapping $g: y \rightarrow \dfrac{y+2}{3}$

The set $\{y\}$ forms the range of f, but as it is the domain for f^{-1} the inverse function is defined as

$$f^{-1}: x \rightarrow \frac{x+2}{3},$$

where the domain of f^{-1} is the range of f.

This 'change of subject of an equation' approach may be more familiar to some readers.

Example 1: *Find the inverse of the function* $f: x \rightarrow \dfrac{x+1}{x-2}$ $(x \neq 2)$

Write $y = \dfrac{x+1}{x-2}$ and make x the subject of the equation.

The reader should verify that $x = \dfrac{2y+1}{y-1}$.

The inverse function is defined as $f^{-1}: x \rightarrow \dfrac{2x+1}{x-1}$ $(x \neq 1)$

If the function f is defined over the domain $\{x:3 \leqslant x \leqslant 5\}$ the range of f is $\{y:2 \leqslant y \leqslant 4\}$. The domain of f^{-1} is then $\{x:2 \leqslant x \leqslant 4\}$ and its corresponding range $\{y:3 \leqslant y \leqslant 5\}$.

Example 2: *Find the inverse of the function* $f:x \to x^2 + 8$ *over* $\mathbb{R}$.

Write $y = x^2 + 8 \Rightarrow x = \pm \sqrt{y-8}$.

Hence $f^{-1}:x \to \pm \sqrt{x-8}$. f^{-1} is not a function, as it is a one–many correspondence; for example, $f^{-1}(12) = \pm 2$.

If the domain of f is defined as $\{x:x \geqslant 0\}$, then an inverse function f^{-1} exists and is defined as $f^{-1}:x \to \sqrt{x-8}$. Similarly, if the domain is restricted to $\{x:x \leqslant 0\}$, the inverse function $f^{-1}:x \to -\sqrt{x-8}$ could be defined.

Exercise 11.8 (The reader should use either method for finding the inverse function.)

1   Find the inverse of each of the following functions. Assuming that a suitable subset of $\mathbb{R}$ has been defined for the domain,

(a) $f:x \to 2x - 5$ (b) $f:x \to \frac{1}{3}(x+2)$
(c) $f:x \to 3x - 4$ (d) $f:x \to -\frac{1}{5}x + 4$

(e) $f:x \to 1 - 3x$ (f) $f:x \to \dfrac{2}{x}$

(g) $f:x \to \dfrac{1}{x+1}$ (h) $f:x \to \dfrac{1}{x} + 1$

(i) $f:x \to 4 + \dfrac{1}{1-x}$ (j) $f:x \to \sqrt{x+1}$

(k) $f:x \to 2x^3$ (l) $f:x \to \dfrac{x-2}{x+3}$

(m) $f:x \to \dfrac{2x-1}{x-2}$ (n) $f:x \to x^2 + 2$.

2   Choose a subset of $\mathbb{R}$ such that each of the following functions f has an inverse function, and define the inverse in the same manner as f.
(a) $f:x \to 2x^2$ (b) $f:x \to x^2 + 2$
(c) $f:x \to (x-1)^2$ (d) $f:x \to \sin x°$

3   Find the inverse functions of f, g and fg and verify that $(fg)^{-1} = g^{-1}f^{-1}$ in each case:
(a) $f:x \to \frac{1}{2}x + 1$, $g:x \to 1 - 2x$, $X = \mathbb{R}$

(b) $f:x \to 7x + 2$, $g:x \to \dfrac{x-2}{7}$, $X = \mathbb{R}$

(c) $f:x \to x^3$, $g:x \to x + 1$, $X = \mathbb{R}$

(d) $f:x \to x^2$, $g:x \to 5x + 2$, $X = \{x:x \geqslant 0\}$.

Graphs of inverse functions

If the graphs of a function and its inverse are drawn on the same axes, having the same scales, it will be noticed that the line $y = x$ is a line of symmetry. The graph of a function can be mapped onto the graph of its inverse by a reflection in the line $y = x$. Consequently, if a graph is symmetrical about this line, the function is its own inverse.

Exercise 11.9

Draw, on the same set of axes in each case, the graphs of the following functions, and their inverses. In each case define the inverse function with its appropriate domain:

1   $f: x \rightarrow \frac{1}{2}x + 1,$ $X = \{x: -3 \leqslant x \leqslant 3\}$
2   $f: x \rightarrow 3 - x,$ $X = \{x: -3 \leqslant x \leqslant 3\}$
3   $f: x \rightarrow x^2 + 6x + 9$ $X = \{x: -3 \leqslant x \leqslant 0\}$
4   $f: x \rightarrow 3\sqrt{x}$ $X = \{x: 0 \leqslant x \leqslant 4\}.$

12 Variation

Variation is concerned with the ways in which one variable depends on one or more other variables. Although, for example, $y = 3x$ and $y = 3x + 1$ are the equations of linear functions, the dependence of y (the dependent variable) on x (the independent variable) is quite different. In the first case the ratio $y : x$ is always constant ($= 3$) and so if x is doubled y is doubled, if x is halved y is halved, etc; in the second case this property is lacking, e.g. $x = 1 \Rightarrow y = 4$ but $x = 2 \Rightarrow y = 7$. The variation of y with x is clearly related to ratio and proportion, considered in Chapter 2.

Direct proportion

If two variables x and y are related in such a way that the ratio $y : x$ is a constant value for all pairs (x, y), we say that y is *directly proportional to x*, or that y *varies as* x, and write $y \propto x$.

As $y/x = $ a constant (k), the equation $y = kx$ represents such a relationship. The graph of y against x is a straight line through the origin. (See Chapter 8).

Example 1: The circumference C of a circle is related to the radius r by the equation $C = 2\pi r$; C is directly proportional to r or C varies as r.

Note also that $r \propto C$ since $r = \dfrac{1}{2\pi}C$.

Example 2: If a man walks at a constant speed of 4 km/h then the distance travelled, s km, is directly proportional to the time taken, t hours, since $s = 4t$.

If the ratio $y : x^2$ is constant, i.e. $\dfrac{y}{x^2} = k$ or $y = kx^2$, we say that y is *directly proportional to x^2* or that y *varies as* x^2.
In this case if x is doubled, y is four times greater than its previous value; if x is halved, y is four times smaller than its previous value.

The graph of y against x in this case is a parabola. (See Chapter 9).

Example 3: The area A of a circle is related to the radius r by the equation $A = \pi r^2$; A varies as the square of r.

Example 4: The distance s travelled by a particle dropped from rest under gravity is related to the time t by the equation $s = \frac{1}{2}gt^2$ $(g \simeq 10\,\text{m/s}^2)$; s varies as t^2.

In the same way if y varies as x^3 we may write $y = kx^3$; if y is proportional to the square root of x then $y = k\sqrt{x}$. Note that the variation of x with y can be found by changing the subject of the equation so that, for example,

$$y = kx^3 \Rightarrow x = \frac{1}{k}\sqrt[3]{y}, \quad \text{i.e. } x \propto \sqrt[3]{y}.$$

Example 5: *Given that y varies as the cube of x, and that $y = 189$ when $x = 3$, find the value of y when $x = \frac{1}{2}$.*

$$y \propto x^3 \Leftrightarrow y = kx^3$$

When $x = 3$, $y = 189$ $\quad \therefore 189 = 27k \Leftrightarrow k = 7$

$$y = 7x^3$$

When $x = \frac{1}{2}$ $\quad\quad\quad\quad y = 7\left(\frac{1}{8}\right) = \frac{7}{8}.$

Alternative method

As $y \propto x^3$, if x is doubled, (its scale factor is 2), y is eight times its previous value (its scale factor is 2^3). In this case the scale factor for x is $\frac{1}{6}$ and therefore the scale factor for y is $(\frac{1}{6})^3 = \frac{1}{216}$. Therefore $y = \frac{189}{216} = \frac{7}{8}$.

In general, if $y \propto x^n$ we may write $y = kx^n$.

Exercise 12.1

1 The following familiar formulae relate two variables. State their relationship in the form '. . . varies as . . .':

(a) $V = \frac{4}{3}\pi r^3$, (b) $T = 2\pi\sqrt{\dfrac{l}{10}}$, (c) $A = 6x^2$.

2 Write down formulae relating the variables in the following:
(a) The cost, C, of painting circular posters varies as the square of the radius, r, of the circle
(b) The weight, W, of a ball-bearing of a particular metal varies as the cube of its radius, r
(c) The distance, d, of the horizon varies as the square root of the height, h, of the observer above sea level
(d) The rate, r, at which a colony of bacteria increase varies as the number, n, of cells present at that time.

3 In each of the following cases it is given that y varies as x^n. For each particular value of n find the value of y when $x = 1$, given that $y = 6$ when $x = 4$; (a) $n = 3$, (b) $n = \frac{1}{2}$, (c) $n = -2$.

4 (a) If the area of a circle is halved, what happens to its radius?
(b) If the height of a cylinder is fixed and its radius trebled, what happens to its volume?
(c) If the radius of a sphere is trebled, what happens to its volume?

5 Copy and complete the following table, given that in each case y varies as x^n (n is different in each part):

	x	1	2	3	4
(a)	y		14	21	
(b)	y	4			8
(c)	y	$\frac{1}{2}$	8		

6 Assume that the distance of the horizon at sea varies as the square root of the height of the eye above sea level. The distance is 16 km when the height is 20 m. Find the distance when the height is (a) 80 m, (b) 125 m, and find the height for which the horizon is 8 km.

7 The time which a simple pendulum takes to swing from one side to the other is proportional to the square root of the length of the string. The time of swing is 2 s when the length of string is 4 m. Find the time of swing when the length is 3 m, and find what length has a time of swing of 4 s.

8 The braking distance on a dry road for a car in good condition varies as the square of the speed of the car. Given that a car travelling at 40 km/h has a braking distance of 9.6 m, find the braking distance when the speed is 80 km/h.

Find the speed corresponding to a braking distance of 4.8 m.

9 Given that y^2 varies as x^3 and that $y = 3$ when $x = 2$, find a value of y when $x = 8$.

10 The volume, V cm^3, and the surface area, S cm^2, of a sphere are related by the formula $V^2 = kS^3$. For a particular sphere the ratio $V:S = 2$, and $S = 144\pi$. Find V when $S = 16\pi$.

Inverse proportion

If y varies as x^{-n}, where n is positive, we say that y is *inversely proportional* to x^n.

For example, if $y \propto \dfrac{1}{x}$ ($y \propto x^{-1}$) then y is inversely proportional to x; if

$y \propto \dfrac{1}{x^2}$ ($y \propto x^{-2}$) then y is inversely proportional to x^2.

If variables are inversely proportional then increasing one decreases the other and vice versa.

Example 1: *Given that y is inversely proportional to x^2, and that $y = 8$ when $x = \frac{1}{2}$, find the value of y when $x = 3$.*

$$y \propto \frac{1}{x^2} \Leftrightarrow y = \frac{k}{x^2}.$$

$$x = \tfrac{1}{2}, \, y = 8 \Rightarrow 8 = 4k \Leftrightarrow k = 2$$

The relationship between x and y is $y = \dfrac{2}{x^2}$.

When $x = 3$, $\hspace{4cm} y = \dfrac{2}{9}$.

We see that the scale factor for x is 6 whereas the scale factor for y is $\frac{2}{9} : 8 = \frac{1}{36}$; when x is increased by a factor 6, y is decreased by a factor $(\frac{1}{6})^2$.

Example 2: *The speed at which an artificial satellite needs to travel to perform circular orbits around the earth is inversely proportional to the square root of the distance of the satellite from the centre of the earth. Given that it needs a speed of 7 km/s to travel in circular orbit 1630 kilometres above the earth's surface (radius of the earth = 6370 km), find the speed needed for an orbit 5150 km above the earth's surface.*

In the first case the speed, $v_1 = 7$ km/s when the radius of the orbit, R_1, = 8000 km.

In the second case the radius, R_2, is 11520 km.

The ratio $R_2 : R_1 = 11520/8000 = 36/25$.

As v is inversely proportional to $\sqrt{R}$, if R is *increased* in the ratio $36/25$, v will be *decreased* in the ratio $\sqrt{36/25} = 6/5$.

The required velocity is $\frac{5}{6} \times 7 = \frac{35}{6} = 5\frac{5}{6}$ km/s.

Exercise 12.2

1 Given that y is inversely proportional to x^2, and that $y = \frac{1}{2}$ when $x = 2$, find the value of: (a) y when $x = 4$, (b) y when $x = 2\frac{1}{2}$, (c) x when $y = 2$.

2 Given that y is inversely proportional to x and that $y = 5$ when $x = 5$, find the value of: (a) y when $x = 6$, (b) y when $x = 1$, (c) x when $y = 2$.

3 Copy and complete the table, given that in each case y is inversely proportional to x^n (n is different in each part).

	x	1	2	$2\frac{1}{2}$	4
(a)	y		12		3
(b)	y	1		0·4	
(c)	y	64			1

4 The radius of a cone, of given volume, is inversely proportional to the square root of its height. If the height is doubled what happens to the radius?

If a cone of radius 16 cm, height 20 cm has the same volume as a cone with radius 40 cm, height h cm, find the value of h.

5 The pressure, p, of a given mass of gas at constant temperature is inversely proportional to its volume, v. (Boyle's law). Write down an equation relating p and v. Given that when the pressure is increased from 600 mm to p mm the volume changes from 120 cm^3 to 100 cm^3, find the value of p.

6 The number of spherical balls which can be made from a given volume of metal varies inversely as the cube of the radius of the required ball. When the radius is 1.5 cm the number of balls is 128. How many balls of radius 2 cm can be made from the same volume?

7 Newton's law of gravitation implies that the weight of a body is inversely proportional to the square of its distance from the centre of the earth.

Given that a satellite has a weight of 32 kg.f. at a distance of 8000 km, find the weight when the distance from the centre of the earth is 10 000 km. Deduce also the weight of the satellite at take off. (Radius of earth is 6400 km).

8 If y^2 is inversely proportional to x and $y = 1.5$ when $x = \frac{2}{3}$, find the value of y when $x = 6$.

9 Given that y varies inversely as $(x + 3)^2$ and that $y = 5$ when $x = 0$ find y when $x = 2$.

10 Given that $y - 2$ is inversely proportional to the square root of x and that $y = 18$ when $x = 4$, find y when $x = 16$.

For a given value of n, the graph of $y = kx^n$ is a family of curves as k varies. When a corresponding pair of values (x, y) is given, a particular curve of the family is selected, and hence if a further value of x (or y) is given, the corresponding value of y (or x) can be read off.

A typical curve in the family is given for some of the more familiar relationships (Figure 12.1).

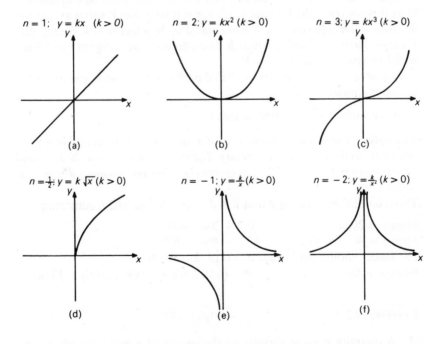

$n = 1; y = kx \ (k > 0)$ (a)

$n = 2; y = kx^2 \ (k > 0)$ (b)

$n = 3; y = kx^3 \ (k > 0)$ (c)

$n = \frac{1}{2}; y = k \sqrt{x} \ (k > 0)$ (d)

$n = -1; y = \frac{k}{x} (k > 0)$ (e)

$n = -2; y = \frac{k}{x^2} \ (k > 0)$ (f)

Fig. 12.1

It should be noted that if y is plotted against x^n, rather than against x, the graph of $y = kx^n$ is a straight line through the origin, with gradient k. This fact is often used to verify the validity of relationships between two variables.

Joint variation

The formula for the volume of a cylinder, $V = \pi r^2 h$, shows that the volume V varies as r^2 and also as h. V is said to vary *jointly* as r^2 *and* h. The effects of variations in r and h are *multiplied* to give the variation in V.

Example: *If r is doubled and h is trebled find the scale factor for V.*
Since $V \propto r^2$, if r is scaled up by a factor of 2, then V is scaled up by a factor of 4.
Since $V \propto h$, if r is scaled up by a factor of 3, then V is scaled up by a factor of 3.
The scale factor for V is $+12$ (i.e. 4×3).

In general, if y varies jointly as x^m and z^n, we write $y = kx^m z^n$ (k constant).

Compound variation

If the three quantities V, r and h are connected by the formula $V = \pi r^2 + 5\pi h$, the difference between this and the last case must be emphasised. Here it is *not true* that V varies as r^2, nor is it true that V varies as h; if r is doubled and h kept constant V is *not* scaled up by a factor of 4. We say that V varies *partly* as r^2 and *partly* as h. The effects of variations in r and h are *added* to give the variation in V.

In general, if y varies partly as x^m and partly as z^n, we write $y = ax^m + bz^n$ (a and b constant).

Many variables are related in this way.

Example: *The stopping distance, d, of a car varies partly as the velocity, v, and partly as the square of the velocity. The stopping distances at 20 km/h and 40 km/h are 6.2 m and 17.2 m, respectively. Find the stopping distance at 60 km/h.*
The relationship between d and v is $d = av + bv^2$ (a and b constant);
when $v = 20$, $d = 6.2$ $6.2 = 20a + 400\,b$,
when $v = 40$, $d = 17.2$ $17.2 = 40a + 1600\,b$.
The reader should verify that $a = 0.19$, $b = 0.006$
When $v = 60$ $d = (0.19 \times 60) + (0.006 \times 3600) = 33$ m.

Exercise 12.3

1   A quantity y varies directly as the square of x and inversely as the square root of w.

(a) If $y = 32$ when $x = 4$ and $w = 25$, find the value of y when $x = 25$ and $w = 4$, and the value of w if $x = 4$ and $y = 20$.

(b) If y is unchanged, how must x be changed if w is scaled up by a factor of 4?

2   Given that y varies jointly as x and w^2, and that $y = 4$ when $x = 1/10$ and $w = 5$, find the value of y when $x = 1$ and $w = 2\frac{1}{2}$.

3   The kinetic energy of a body varies as the mass and the square of the speed. If one body has a mass double that of another and a speed half that of the other, how are their kinetic energies related?

A car of mass 800 kg travelling at 108 km/h has a kinetic energy of 360 kJ (J stands for joules). Find the kinetic energy of a car of mass 1600 kg travelling at 54 km/h.

4   When a thin hollow inverted cone is used to store a liquid, the amount stored varies jointly as the height of the cone and the square of the radius of the base. Given that a cone of the radius 21 cm and height 30 cm holds 13.8 litres find the capacity of a cone of radius 10.5 cm and height 25 cm.

5   The light received at a point varies jointly as the power of the source and inversely as the square of its distance from the source. Assuming that bulbs have similar characteristics, find which of the following bulbs gives the better result:

(a) a 60 W bulb at 2 m, or (b) a 100 W bulb at $2\frac{1}{2}$ m.

6   The cost per head of catering for a party is partly constant and partly inversely proportional to the number of people expected. The cost per head for a party of 100 people is £1.20; the cost per head for 60 people is £1.80. Find the cost per head for a party of 50.

7   The annual cost of running a certain car is partly constant and partly varies as the distance covered by the car in the year. The owner worked out that if he covered 14 400 km in the year the running cost would be £610, and if he covered 16 800 km the running cost would be £600. Find the estimated running cost if the car travels 20 000 km in the year.

8   The sum, S, of the first n positive integers varies partly as n and partly as n^2. Write down the relationship between S and n and, by considering the cases $n = 1$ and $n = 2$, deduce the formula for the sum of the first n integers. Find the sum of the first 50 integers.

9   If a book sells more than a specified number, n, the author receives a sum of money which is partly constant and partly varies as the number of books sold in excess of n. When the excess is 2000 the author receives £1000, and when it is 3000 he receives £1100. If the author receives £1400, find how many books are sold in excess of n.

10   In uniformly accelerated motion the distance travelled, s, varies partly as the time and partly as the square of the time. When the time is 1.5 s the distance travelled is 54 m, and when the time is 2.5 s the distance travelled is 102.5 m. Find the distance travelled in 3 s, and the time taken to travel a distance of 1062 m.

13 Graphs

Graphs of linear functions have been considered in Chapter 8. Although sketch graphs of other functions have been included elsewhere, where useful (e.g. quadratic functions in Chapter 9), it is important to be able to plot the graphs of the more common functions.

If the plotted points do not lie on a straight line, a straight edge must not be used to join them up.

Quadratic functions

Consider the quadratic function $f: x \rightarrow ax^2 + bx + c$. For a value of x in the domain, the corresponding image y in the range is determined and the resulting number pair (x, y) can be represented by a point in the plane. The set of all such points form the graph of $y = ax^2 + bx + c$ for that domain. The graph of a quadratic function is called a **parabola**.

Care must be exercised in determining the number pairs. Readers may find it useful to set out their working in the form of a table.

Example: *Draw the graph of $y = x^2 - x - 2$ taking values of x from -3 to $+3$.*
[The domain of x is $\{x : -3 \leqslant x \leqslant 3\}$].

x	-3	-2	-1	0	1	2	3
x^2	$+9$	$+4$	$+1$	0	1	4	9
$-x$	$+3$	$+2$	$+1$	0	-1	-2	-3
-2	-2	-2	-2	-2	-2	-2	-2
y	10	4	0	-2	-2	0	4

The symmetry of the graph can clearly be seen and it is an aid to drawing to find the value of y on the line of symmetry. When $x = \frac{1}{2}$, $y = \frac{1}{4} - \frac{1}{2} - 2 = -2\frac{1}{4}$.

If the scales are changed a different picture is seen, but the details relative to the axes remain the same.

The graph of $y = ax^2$, for $a > 0$, is a parabola with vertex downwards, and with the y-axis as its axis of symmetry. The reader will see in Exercise 13.1

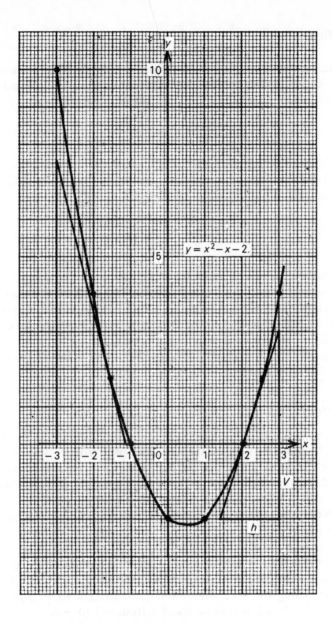

Fig. 13.1

that the graph of $y = ax^2 + bx + c$ is very much related to that of the basic parabola $y = ax^2$. If a tracing of the graph of $y = ax^2$ is made and redrawn elsewhere on your graph paper, such that its axis of symmetry remains parallel to the y-axis, its equation will be $y = ax^2 + bx + c$, the values of b and c being dependent on the co-ordinates of the vertex.

In particular, the graph of $y = ax^2 + bx + c$ is a parabola with vertex downwards if $a > 0$, and with vertex upwards if $a < 0$.

165

Gradient

The gradient of a straight line was defined in Chapter 8 and has a constant value. As the graphs of non-linear functions are curves, the gradient is constantly changing and we can only talk of *the gradient at a particular point.*

This is defined as the gradient of the tangent to the curve drawn at that point.

In Figure 13.1 the gradient at the point where $x = 2$ is found by drawing a tangent at the point and finding the gradient of this line as in Chapter 8. The gradient

$$\frac{V}{h} = \frac{5}{1.6} \simeq 3.1.$$

Note that the values of V and h are found with respect to the axes, and not by measuring lengths or counting squares. The gradient of a curve at the point is then not dependent on the scale used; all readers should find a value close to 3 whatever scales they use, although clearly the steeper the curve at a point the more difficult it is to draw the tangent.

The gradient at any point whose x value is less than $\frac{1}{2}$ in the graph of Figure 13.1 is *negative*.

Exercise 13.1

1 Draw the graphs of (a) $y = x^2$, (b) $y = x^2 - 2x$ and (c) $y = x^2 + 3x - 4$ on the same set of axes, taking values of x from -3 to $+3$. Use a scale of 2 cm to represent 1 unit for x and 1 cm to represent 2 units for y.

Make a tracing of curve (a) and place, in turn, over each of the other two curves. What observations can be made?

Write down the co-ordinates of the lowest point on each of graphs (b) and (c).

Re-arrange the equations of (b) and (c) in the form $y = (x + p)^2 + q$. What significance have p and q to the lowest point on the graph?

Give a rough sketch of (i) $y = x^2 + x$ and (ii) $y = x^2 - 2x + 1$.

2 Draw, using the same scales and axes, the graphs of $y = 2x^2$ and $y = 2x^2 - 5x + 2$, taking values of x from -1 to $+4$.

Do the curves have the same shape? (check with a tracing).

Give the equation of the line of symmetry and the co-ordinates of the lowest point of each graph. What is the minimum value of $2x^2 - 5x + 2$ for the given domain of x?

3 Draw, using the same scales and axes, the graphs of $y = -x^2$ and $y = -x^2 - x + 2$ for values of x from -3 to $+3$.

What is the maximum value of $-x^2 - x + 2$ for the given domain of x?

Describe a transformation of the plane which will map $y = -x^2$ onto $y = -x^2 - x + 2$.

For what values of x is the gradient of $y = -x^2 - x + 2$ negative as x increases?

4 Draw the graph of $y = x^2 - 4x$ for the domain $\{x: -1 \leqslant x \leqslant 4\}$. (Let 2 cm represent 1 unit on both axes).

Use your graph to find the gradient of $y = x^2 - 4x$ at the points where (a) $x = 3$,   (b) $x = 1$.

At what point on the graph is the gradient zero?

Give the subset of the domain for which $y < 1$.

5 Draw the graph of $y = x^2 - 2x + 3$ taking values of x from -3 to $+3$. How many values of x have a corresponding y value of (a) 1, (b) 2, (c) 3?

6 Draw the graph of $y = x(x - 1)(x - 3)$ (cubic) for values of x from -1 to $+4$.

How many values of x are there for which the value of y is (a) 2, (b) 0, (c) -4?

Find the gradient of the curve at the point where $x = 3$.

7 Draw the graph of $y = \dfrac{1}{x}$ (rectangular hyperbola) for the domain $\{x: -1 \leqslant x \leqslant 1, x \neq 0\}$. (Suggested scale: 2 cm represent $\frac{1}{4}$ unit for x, 1 cm represent 1 unit for y).

Find the gradient at the point whose x co-ordinate is $\frac{1}{4}$. Give sketch graphs of the following: (a) $y = 1 + \dfrac{1}{x}$, (b) $y = \dfrac{1}{x-1}$, (c) $y = x + \dfrac{1}{x}$.

Intersecting graphs

In Figure 13.1 the curve crosses the x-axis at the points $(-1, 0)$ and $(2, 0)$. These points lie on the x-axis and the curve and so their co-ordinates satisfy both equations $y = 0$ and $y = x^2 - x - 2$, simultaneously. The x-co-ordinates of these points, therefore, are the solutions of the equation $x^2 - x - 2 = 0$.

If the line $y = 1$ is drawn in Figure 13.1, the points of intersection with the curve have co-ordinates which satisfy $y = 1$ and $y = x^2 - x - 2$; i.e. their x-co-ordinates satisfy the equation $1 = x^2 - x - 2$, or $x^2 - x - 3 = 0$.

As any two points on the curve also lie on a line, the process can be extended. The points of intersection of the line $y = x + 1$ and $y = x^2 - x - 2$ provide the solutions of the equation $x + 1 = x^2 - x - 2$, or $x^2 - 2x - 3 = 0$.

The graph has been used to solve equations. Generally the solutions are not as accurate as those obtained by algebraic methods, but once one curve has been drawn it can be used to solve many equations quickly.

Example: *Draw the graph of $y = x^2 - 2x - 3$, taking values of x from -2 to 4, and use it to solve the equations. (a) $x^2 - 2x - 3 = 0$,   (b) $x^2 - 2x - 5 = 0$ and   (c) $y = x^2 - 3x - 3 = 0$.*

x	-2	-1	0	1	2	3	4
x^2	4	1	0	1	4	9	16
$-2x$	4	2	0	-2	-4	-6	-8
-3	-3	-3	-3	-3	-3	-3	-3
y	5	0	-3	-4	-3	0	5

(a) To solve $x^2 - 2x - 3 = 0$ is equivalent to asking which points on the curve have a y-co-ordinate of 0. The solutions are -1 and $+3$, the x-co-ordinates of the points where the curve crosses the x-axis.

(b) The equation $x^2 - 2x - 5 = 0 \Rightarrow x^2 - 2x - 3 = 2$, by adding 2 to both sides. The solutions of this equation are the x-co-ordinates of the points of intersection of the curve $y = x^2 - 2x - 3$ and the line $y = 2$.
Using Figure 13.2 the solutions are -1.45 and 3.45.

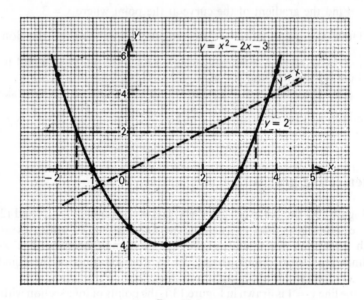

Fig. 13.2

(c) The equation $x^2 - 3x - 3 = 0 \Rightarrow x^2 - 2x - 3 = x$, by adding x to both sides. The solutions are -0.8 and 3.8, the x-co-ordinates of the points of intersection of the line $y = x$ and the curve.

Exercise 13.2

1   Given that the graph of $y = x^2 - 5x + 2$ has been drawn, determine the equations of the lines that should be drawn so that the graph may be used to solve each of the following equations:
   (a) $x^2 - 5x + 2 = 0$ (b) $x^2 - 5x + 3 = 0$ (c) $x^2 - 5x = 0$
   (d) $x^2 - 5x + 8 = 0$ (e) $x^2 - 6x + 4 = 0$ (f) $x^2 - 3x = 0$.

As part (d) has no solutions, what can be said about the corresponding line and curve?

Explain, in terms of the graph $y = ax^2 + bx + c$, how we can tell whether the equation $ax^2 + bx + c = 0$ has *real* solutions.

2 Given that the graph of $y = 2x^2 - 5x + 2$ has been drawn, determine the equations of the lines that should be drawn to solve the following equations:

(a) $2x^2 - 5x + 2 = 0$ (b) $(2x - 3)(x - 1) = 0$ (c) $2x(x - 2) = x - 1$
(d) $2x^2 - 6x + 3 = 0$ (e) $4x^2 - 11x + 4 = 0$ (f) $x^2 - 3x = 0$.

3 Draw, using the same scales and axes, the graphs of $y = -x^2 + 2x$ and $y = \frac{1}{2}x$, taking values of x from 0 to 3. Write down the x-co-ordinates of the points of intersection of the graphs, and form the equation having these values as solutions.

For what values of x is the gradient of $y = -x^2 + 2x$ negative?

4 Draw, using the same scales and axes, the graphs of $y = x(x - 2)^2$ and $y = -\frac{1}{3}x + 1$, taking values of x from 0 to 3. (For the curve plot points at x intervals of $\frac{1}{4}$).

(a) Write down the co-ordinates of the highest point of the curve in the interval $0 \leqslant x \leqslant 2$.

(b) Use your graphs to solve the equation $x(x - 2)^2 = -\frac{1}{3}x + 1$.

(c) Write down the values of x for which $x(x - 2)^2 \geqslant -\frac{1}{3}x + 1$.

5 Draw, using the same scales and axes, the graphs of $y = x^2$ and of $y = x + 6$, taking values of x from -3 to $+3$.

Give the values of x for which (a) $x^2 = x + 6$,   (b) $x^2 < x + 6$.

6 Draw the graph of $y = x^2 - 3x - 4$, taking values of x from $-1\frac{1}{2}$ to $+4\frac{1}{2}$. Use your graph to solve the equations: (a) $x^2 - 3x - 4 = 0$, (b) $x^2 - 3x - 6 = 0$,   (c) $x^2 - 4x + 1 = 0$,   (d) $x(x - 2) = 4$.

In each case give the equation of the line used, together with the solutions.

7 Draw the graph of $y = 2x^2 + x - 5$ taking values of x from -3 to $+3$. By drawing suitable lines, which should be stated, solve the following equations:

(a) $2x^2 + x - 9 = 0$,   (b) $2x(x + 1) = 5$ (c) $4x^2 + 3x - 20 = 0$.

Find points on the curve for which the value of the y-co-ordinate is twice the value of the x-co-ordinate.

8 Draw the graph of $y = \dfrac{1}{x^2}$ for the domain $\{x. -6 \leqslant x \leqslant 6, x \neq 0\}$.

(a) On the same axes, draw the graph of $20y = -x + 6$ and find its points of intersection with the given curve. Hence form the equation whose solutions are the values of the x-co-ordinates of these points.

(b) By drawing a suitable straight line, solve the equation
$$5x^3 + 33x^2 - 110 = 0.$$

9 Given that $y = x + \dfrac{2}{x} - 4$, copy and complete the following table:

x	0.5	1	1.5	2	3	4	5	6
y			-1.17			0.5		2.33

Taking 2 cm to represent 1 unit on the x-axis, and 4 cm to represent 1 unit on the y-axis, draw the graph of $y = x + \dfrac{2}{x} - 4$ for values of x from $+0.5$ to $+6$.

(a) Use the graph to solve the equation $x + \dfrac{2}{x} - \dfrac{7}{2} = 0$.

(b) Find the gradient of the graph at the point where $x = 5$.

10.

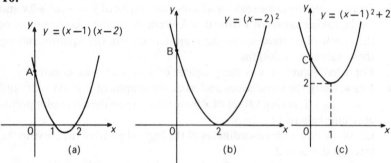

(a) $y = (x-1)(x-2)$
(b) $y = (x-2)^2$
(c) $y = (x-1)^2 + 2$

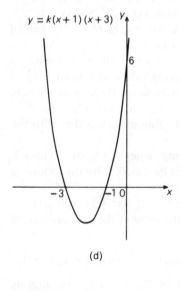

(d) $y = k(x+1)(x+3)$

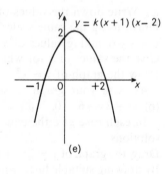

(e) $y = k(x+1)(x-2)$

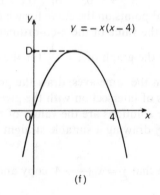

(f) $y = -x(x-4)$

Fig. 13.3

The graphs shown in Figure 13.3 are all of quadratic functions. In (a), (b), (c), (f) find the co-ordinates of A, B, C, D, respectively. For the graphs (d) and (e), write down the appropriate value of k. Using the corresponding graph, state how many real solutions the following equations possess:

(a) $x^2 - 3x - 4 = 0$ (b) $x^2 - 4x + 5 = 0$ (c) $(x-1)^2 + 1 = 0$
(d) $2(x+1)(x+3) = -x$ (e) $(x+1)(x-2) = 5$ (f) $x(4-x) = x$.

Travel graphs

If the x-axis represents time and the y-axis the distance from a particular point, the graph of y against x is called a travel graph. The gradient of the graph at a point represents the speed at a particular time; if the speed varies, the graph is a curve, if the speed is constant, the graph will be a straight line. In this section we shall concern ourselves with straight line travel graphs.

Example: *The distance from Bristol to Birmingham, on a route through Stratford-upon-Avon, is 160 km. Two families, one in Bristol and one in Birmingham, decide to travel by car and meet in Stratford. The former family leave at 10.00 h and, apart from a 9 minute stop after 60 km, maintain a steady speed of 80 km/h. The other family leave Birmingham at 10.30 h and maintain a steady speed of 50 km/h. Given that Stratford is 120 km from Bristol, find: (a) which family arrives in Stratford first, and by how long; (b) the distance the cars were apart at 11.00 h; (c) the time and place of meeting if the one family had not waited at Stratford.*

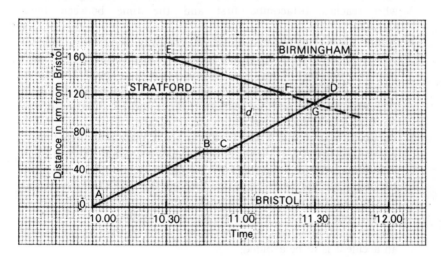

Fig. 13.4

The travel graphs of the two cars are shown in Figure 13.4. The line BC represents the 9 minute stop for the car from Bristol; AB and CD represent the sections of the journey when the car was travelling at 80 km/h. The other car's journey is represented by the line EF, whose gradient is -50.

171

(a) The cars reach Stratford at 11.36 h and 11.18 h respectively; the Birmingham family arrive first and have to wait 18 minutes.

(b) At 11.00 h the distance apart is approximately 66 km (represented by d in Figure 13.4).

(c) The point of intersection G, of the travel graphs represents their meeting. They would have met at approximately 11.30 h, about 10 km from Stratford on the Bristol side.

Exercise 13.3

1   The distance from Bristol to Edinburgh is 580 km. The 11.35 h train from Bristol arrives in Edinburgh at 18.42 h; the 07.30 train from Edinburgh arrives in Bristol at 13.44 h. Assuming that both trains maintain steady speeds, find the time at which the trains pass each other and their distance from Bristol at this time.

2   A man drives from Oxford to Cambridge at a steady speed of 60 km/h, arriving in Cambridge at 14.00 h. A student leaves Cambridge at 11.40 h for Oxford in a coach which maintains a speed of 40 km/h. Find, graphically, the distance from Cambridge when the car and coach pass.

3   A man sets out at 10.00 h to walk from Barnstaple to Ilfracombe, a distance of 22 km, and maintains a steady speed of 6 km/h. A cyclist from Ilfracombe to Barnstaple passes the man at 11.30 h, and continues to Barnstaple, where he rests for 15 minutes before returning to Ilfracombe at the same steady speed of 15 km/h. Find, graphically, who reaches Ilfracombe first and the time between their arrivals.

4   A family is moving to a new house 100 km away. The removal men set off at noon and maintain a steady speed of 40 km/h until 13.15 h, when they stop for lunch. They then continue at the same speed. The family set off at 13.30 h in their car and maintain a speed of 60 km/h. Given that they pass the removal men at 15.00 h, find the duration of the removal men's lunch break.

5   Between two stations A and B, 40 km apart, there is a single line. A goods train leaves A at 10.00 h and maintains a speed of 30 km/h when in motion. After 15 km it waits in a siding for 10 minutes, to allow the passing of an express which passed through B at 10.15 h and travels at 80 km/h on this section of the track. Find, graphically:

(a) the time at which the express passed the siding,

(b) the maximum and minimum steady speeds the express can have if an accident is to be avoided,

(c) the time of the collision if the express is 5 minutes late passing through B and travels at only 70 km/h.

6   A boy takes a river trip from A to B and then walks back, along the riverbank, to meet his family who had started walking from A to B at the same time as their son began his trip. Given that the boat travelled at 10 km/h, the boy walked at 6 km/h, the family maintained a speed of

4 km/h, and that they met up again after 45 minutes, find graphically the distance from A to B.

7   A coach leaves Weymouth at 10.00 h and arrives in Lyme Regis, 50 km away, at 11.30 h. At 11.50 h it continues the journey to Torquay, a further 100 km away, at a steady speed of 50 km/h. At 08.00 h a cyclist sets out from Torquay and travels towards Weymouth along the same route. Given that the cyclist maintains a speed of 16 km/h for the first two hours and then reduces his speed to a steady 12 km/h for the remainder of the journey, find how far from Lyme Regis the cyclist meets the coach. Find the distance between coach and cyclist at 12.30 h.

8   A salesman leaves Bristol at 12.00 h and travels along the M32 and M4 motorways to meet an appointment in Cardiff, 70 km away. If he maintains a steady speed of 100 km/h he will arrive in Cardiff with 18 minutes to spare. Until he reaches the Severn Bridge, a distance of 24 km, he is able to maintain this speed, but there he meets a traffic-jam. Find, graphically, the longest delay he can suffer if he is to meet the appointment without breaking the speed limit of 112 km/h.

9   A man sets out from Birmingham at 11.30 h to walk to Sutton Coldfield at 6 km/h. After twenty minutes a bus travelling from Sutton Coldfield to Birmingham passes him. The bus waits in the Birmingham bus station for ten minutes and then returns, along the same route, to Sutton Coldfield. Given that the bus travels at 30 km/h, find the time and place that the bus overtakes the man.

10   A motorcyclist leaves Kendal for Carlisle, 75 km away, at the same time as a car leaves Carlisle for Kendal. Given that the motorcyclist reaches Carlisle twenty-five minutes before the car reaches Kendal, and that they pass each other 30 km from Carlisle, find their steady speeds.

Exercise 13.4   (Miscellaneous)

1   Temperatures are measured on both Centigrade and Fahrenheit thermometers. For a value of C (the temperature in $^\circ$ Centigrade) there is a corresponding value of F (the temperature in $^\circ$ Fahrenheit), given by the formula $F = \frac{1}{5}(9C + 160)$. Plot F against C for values of C from -40 to $+100$ and find:
(a) the value of C when $F = 98$,   (b) the value of F when $C = 65$,
(c) the change in C when F increases from 80 to 120,
(d) when F and C are equal.

2   At noon a coach leaves Bristol and travels 180 km to London at a steady speed of 56 km/h. A man who sets out by car on the same journey, 30 minutes after the coach left, overtakes the coach after driving at a steady speed for half an hour. After a further 15 minutes he stops for half an hour and then continues at a steady speed of 80 km/h to London. Draw a travel graph and use it to find:
(a) when the car overtakes the coach for a second time, and
(b) the car's time of arrival in London.

3 The time-table for part of a coach journey is:

Distance (km)	Stop	Arrive	Depart
0	York		10.00
30	Malton	10.37	10.40
43	Pickering	10.54	11.00
70	Scarborough	11.42	

Draw a travel graph to show the data and state which was the fastest part of the journey.

An express coach passes through York at 10.30 h and maintains a speed of 80 km/h on the same route to Scarborough. Find where this coach overtakes the other.

4 The speed of a car (v m/s) is recorded after a time (t s) in the table below.

t(s)	0	1	2	3	4	5	6	7
v(m/s)	0	5	7.6	8.0	6.2	4.9	4.6	3.8

Draw a graph of v against t and find:
(a) the maximum speed attained in the period,
(b) the rate at which the car is slowing after 4 seconds,
(c) for how long the car is travelling faster than 4 m/s.

5 The table shows how far you can see over a calm sea for various heights above sea-level:

Distance seen d(km)	11.3	16	19.5	22.6	25.2	27.6
Height above sea-level, h(m)	10	20	30	40	50	60

Draw a graph of d against h and use it to find:
(a) the distance of the horizon when h is 35 m,
(b) the value of h necessary to see a distance of 25 km.

6 A stone is thrown vertically upwards with a speed of 10 m/s from the edge of a cliff. After t seconds the stone is s metres above the edge of the cliff, where $s = 10t - 5t^2$.

Draw a graph of s against t for values of t from 0 to 4 and find:
(a) for how long the stone is more than 3 m above the edge,
(b) the maximum height reached,
(c) the time at which the stone is 10 m below the edge.

7 A rectangular piece of cardboard, 6 cm by 5 cm, has squares of side x cm cut from its corners, as shown in Figure 13.5. The four 'flaps' are then folded up so that the cardboard forms an open drawer of volume V cm^3. Show that $V = x(5 - 2x)(6 - 2x)$, and draw a graph of V against x for values of x from 0 to 3.

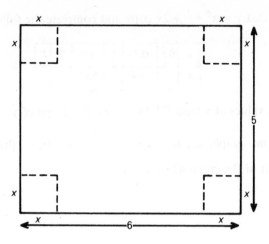

Fig. 13.5

Use your graph to find:
(a) the value of x that gives a maximum volume for the box,
(b) the range of values of x if the volume must lie between 4 cm³ and 5 cm³.

8 Draw the graph of $y + 4 = x^2$ and $y = \dfrac{3}{x}$ on the same axes and using the same scales, for various values of x from -4 to $+4$.
Use your graphs to find:
(a) the solutions of $x^3 - 4x - 3 = 0$,
(b) the square root of 5,
(c) the range of values of x for which $\dfrac{3}{x} > x^2 - 4$.

9 The cost C of running a ship is related to its speed s by the 'equation'
$$C = \frac{8000}{s} + s^2.$$
Draw a graph of C against s for values of s from 10 to 30 and estimate the most economic speed for the ship.

10 Two straight lines intersect at right angles at O. A particle A, on one line, starts moving towards O, 10 km away, at 1 m/s; a particle B, 5 m from O on the other line, starts to move towards O at 2 m/s at the same time as A. State their distances from O after t seconds and prove that they are then d metres apart, where $d^2 = 5(t^2 - 8t + 25)$.
Draw a graph of d^2 against t for values of t from 0 to 6 and hence find their minimum distance apart and the corresponding value of t.

11 A hemispherical bowl of radius 4 cm is used to collect water. When the depth of water is x cm the volume, V cm³, is given by $V = \pi x^2(4 - \frac{1}{3}x)$.
Plot V/π against x for values of x from 0 to 4. Use your graph to find:
(a) the volume of water collected, in terms of π, when $x = 2$,
(b) the value of x that gives a volume of $12\,\pi$ cm³.

12 Given that $y = x^2 + \dfrac{1}{x} + 2x$ copy and complete the following table

x	0.5	0.75	1	1.5	2	3
y		3.4		5.91		

Taking values of x from 0.5 to 3, draw the graph of $y = x^2 + \dfrac{1}{x} + 2x$.

Use your graph: (a) to solve $x^2 + \dfrac{1}{x} = 4 - 2x$, (b) to find the gradient of the curve when $x = 15$.

14 Simple differentiation and some of its applications.

The fundamental problem for which the process called **differentiation** provides a solution can initially be framed in terms of simple examples which describe the motion of a particle moving in a straight line.

Example 1: *A particle is moving in a straight line at 5 m/s. Sketch graphs to show the relation between: (a) time and speed (the time–speed graph), (b) time and distance (the time–distance graph).*

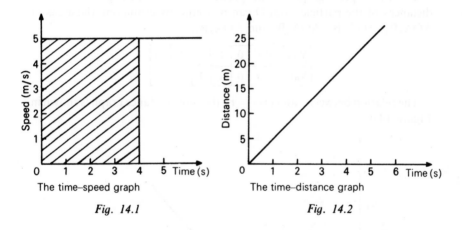

Fig. 14.1   Fig. 14.2

In Figure 14.1, the distance covered in 4 s by the particle is 20 m and is represented by the shaded area.

In Figure 14.2, the speed of the particle is represented by the gradient of the straight line showing the relation between time and distance.

In general, this simple illustration can be summarised by the relation $s = 5t$, where s metres is the distance covered in t seconds. Conversely, if $s = 5t$ were given, the speed v m/s is given by $v = 5$, which is the gradient of the line $s = 5t$.

Example 2: *A particle starts at a point O and moves in a straight line. At time t seconds after leaving O the speed of the particle is v m/s where v = 2t. Sketch the time–speed graph, and hence tabulate the distance s metres covered by the particle from O when t = 0, 1, 2, 3 and 4. Deduce the relation between t and s and sketch the time–distance graph.*

177

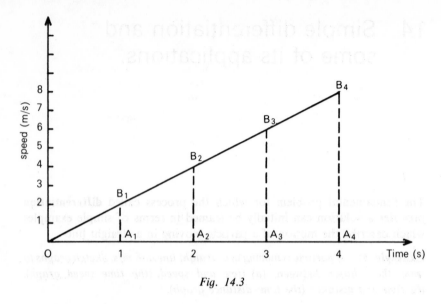

Fig. 14.3

The time–speed graph of the particle is shown in Figure 14.3. The distances of the particle from O can be found by evaluating the areas of ΔOA_1B_1, ΔOA_2B_2, ΔOA_3B_3 and ΔOA_4B_4.

Value of t	0	1	2	3	4
Value of s	0	1	4	9	16

The relation between s and t is $s = t^2$; the time–distance graph is shown in Figure 14.4.

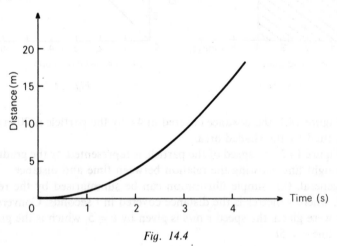

Fig. 14.4

If the relation $s = t^2$ had been given as the initial data, the speed of the particle for any particular value of t could be determined by drawing a tangent to the curve at the required point and evaluating the gradient of this tangent (see Chapter 13).

The gradient of a curve at a particular point is defined to be the same as the gradient of the tangent to the curve at the point. The previous example shows a more general result. The gradient *at any point* on the curve $s = t^2$ is given by $v = 2t$, where v is the gradient of the curve at the point (t, t^2). It can be added that v is the speed of the particle at time t and an equivalent statement could be that for the function $s = t^2$, the rate of change of distance with respect to time, that is v, is $2t$.

From the first example, the rate of change of $5t$ with respect to time is 5.

Differential calculus is the branch of mathematics where rates of change of one or more variables with respect to another related variable are studied. This branch of mathematics, and also **integral calculus**, were developed during the latter part of the seventeenth century by Newton (1642–1727) and Leibnitz (1646–1716). The work in this book is restricted to the differentiation of simple polynomials which are expressed explicitly as the sum or difference of integer powers of one independent variable. No attempt is made to give a formal introduction to the subject through a detailed study of limiting processes, because this is outside the scope of work at this level. Some further examples are added at this stage to illustrate as simply as possible the methods used in more advanced work and to introduce the notation generally used.

When an algebraic function is given in the form of a mapping as
$$f: x \to x^2 \qquad \text{where } x \in \mathbb{R},$$
a convenient way of expressing the function for this work is to write $y = x^2$ or, in general, $y = f(x)$, where $f(x)$ is the image of x under the function f.

The gradient function of $y = x^2$ is then written as
$$D_x(y) \quad \text{or} \quad D_x(x^2) \quad \text{or} \quad \frac{dy}{dx}.$$

The third of these does *not* mean '*d times y divided by d times x*'; it is read as '*dy by dx*' and represents the result of differentiating y with respect to x.

Writing the results of the two previous examples in this notation gives

$$D_x(x^2) = 2x \qquad \text{or} \qquad y = x^2, \qquad \frac{dy}{dx} = 2x$$

$$D_x(c) = 0 \qquad \text{or} \qquad y = c, \qquad \frac{dy}{dx} = 0,$$

where c is a fixed number, called a **constant**.

Example 3: *Given that $y = x^3$, find $D_x(y)$.*
Choose two points P and Q on the curve $y = x^3$ with coordinates (x, x^3) and $[(x + h), (x + h)^3]$ respectively, see Figure 14.5.

179

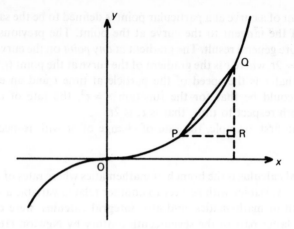

Fig. 14.5

The gradient of the chord $PQ = \dfrac{QR}{PR} = \dfrac{(x+h)^3 - x^3}{(x+h) - x}$

$$= \frac{x^3 + 3x^2h + 3xh^2 + h^3 - x^3}{h}$$

$$= 3x^2 + 3xh + h^2.$$

Let the point Q approach the point P along the curve. This will have the effect of making h get smaller and smaller. In fact h can be chosen to be as small as required. As this limiting process continues the gradient of successive chords approaches nearer and nearer to the value $3x^2$ and the successive chords themselves are an increasingly better approximation to the tangent to the curve at P. In the limit when $h = 0$,

$$D_x(x^3) = 3x^2$$

and the gradient of the tangent at any particular point on the curve can be accurately evaluated.

Example 4: *Given that* $y = \dfrac{1}{x}$, *find* $D_x\left(\dfrac{1}{x}\right)$

Choose two points P and Q on the same branch of the curve, with coordinates $\left(x, \dfrac{1}{x}\right)$ and $\left[(x+h), \dfrac{1}{x+h}\right]$, respectively (see Figure 14.6).

The gradient of the chord PQ is $-\dfrac{PR}{RQ} = -\dfrac{1/x - 1/(x+h)}{x+h-x}$

$$= -\frac{x+h-x}{hx(x+h)}$$

$$= -\frac{1}{x(x+h)}.$$

180

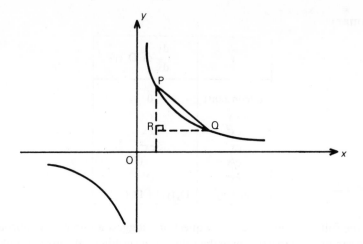

Fig. 14.6

As Q approaches P along the curve, h approaches zero and in the limit

$$D_x\left(\frac{1}{x}\right) = -\frac{1}{x^2}.$$

In more advanced courses the general result

$$D_x(x^n) = nx^{n-1}$$

is proved.

The reader should check the five special cases: c, x, x^2, x^3 and x^{-1} which have been established by intuitive methods.

Example 5: *Find the value of $D_x\left(x^2 - \dfrac{1}{x}\right)$ when $x = 2$.*

This question is equivalent to asking for the gradient of the curve $y = x^2 - \dfrac{1}{x}$ at the point on it where $x = 2$.

$D_x(x^2) = 2x$,

$$D_x\left(\frac{1}{x}\right) = D_x(x^{-1}) = (-1)x^{-2} = -\frac{1}{x^2},$$

$$D_x\left(x^2 - \frac{1}{x}\right) = 2x - \left(-\frac{1}{x^2}\right) = 2x + \frac{1}{x^2}.$$

The value of $D_x\left(x^2 - \dfrac{1}{x}\right)$ when $x = 2$ is $4 + \frac{1}{4} = 4\frac{1}{4}$.

Summary

y	$\dfrac{dy}{dx}$ or $D_x(y)$
c (constant)	0
cx	c
cx^2	$2cx$
cx^3	$3cx^2$
c/x	$-c/x^2$
cx^n	ncx^{n-1}
$y_1 \pm y_2$	$D_x(y_1) \pm D_x(y_2)$

In the following exercise, a few questions suggest a numerical approach which can be used to determine the value of the gradient at a given point on a curve. The reader should work these, preferably with the help of an electronic calculator, to reinforce the methods already used in the text.

Exercise 14.1

1 Calculate the gradient of the chord AB of the curve $y = x^2$, given that A is the point $(1, 1)$ and the x-co-ordinate of B is:
   (a) 2, (b) 1.5, (c) 1.1, (d) 1.01, (e) 1.001, (f) $1 + h$.
2 Repeat the work in question 1 when the x-co-ordinate of B is:
   (a) 0, (b) 0.5, (c) 0.9, (d) 0.99, (e) 0.999, (f) $1 - h$.
3 Give a brief explanation why it is necessary to carry out both the investigations in question 1 and question 2 before stating that the gradient of $y = x^2$ at $(1, 1)$ is 2.
4 Use a similar investigation to that in the first three questions to find the gradient of the curve whose equation is $y = 2/x$ at the point $(2, 1)$.
5 Find the gradient function $D_x(y)$ for each of the following curves whose equations are:
   (a) $y = 7$ (b) $y = -4$ (c) $y = -2x$ (d) $y = 3x^2$ (e) $y = x^4$
   (f) $y = 1/x^2$ (g) $y = 5x^3$ (h) $y = x^{-3}$ (i) $y = 5x^{-1}$ (j) $y = -2x^{-4}$
6 A particle moving in a straight line starts from a point O. At time t seconds after leaving O the particle is s metres from O, where $s = 2t^3$. Find the speed of the particle when:
   (a) $t = 4$, (b) $s = 250$.
   (c) Find the value of t when the particle has speed 37.5 m/s.
   (d) Find the value of s when the particle has speed 54 m/s.
7 The time–speed graph of a particle moving in a straight line is a straight line passing through the origin 0. Given that this particle covers 48 m in the first 4 s of its motion, find:
   (a) the distance covered by the particle in the first 6 s,
   (b) the speed of the particle after it has been moving for 6 s.
   Sketch the time–distance graph.
8 Sketch a time–distance graph for a particle moving in a straight line

which covers s metres in t seconds, where $s = 10t^3$. Take values of t from 0 to 4. Calculate:

(a) the distance covered by the particle during this interval,

(b) the speed of the particle when $t = 3$,

(c) the distance covered by the particle in the fourth second of motion.

9 Find, in each case, the numerical value of $\dfrac{dy}{dx}$ for the curve at the point whose x-co-ordinate is given:

(a) $y = x^3 + x^2$ at $x = 3$

(b) $y = 3x + 1/x$ at $x = 1$

(c) $y = \dfrac{1}{x^2} - 2x^2$ at $x = 2$

(d) $y = 3x^2 - \dfrac{2}{x}$ at $x = -1$

(e) $y = 2x^2 - 7x + 5$ at $x = -1$ (f) $y = ax^2 + bx + c$ at $x = -b/2a$

10 (a) Find the value of $D_x(x^3 - x^2 + x)$ when $x = 2$.

(b) Find the value of $D_x\left(\dfrac{x^2 - x}{x^3}\right)$ when $x = 3$.

(c) Find the value of $D_x\left(\dfrac{1 - x^2}{x}\right)$ when $x = -\frac{1}{2}$.

The equations of tangents and normals

The equation of the straight line of slope m passing through the point (h, k) is $y - k = m(x - h)$ (See Chapter 7). This form of the equation of the line has wide uses in calculus and should be memorised.

Definition: The straight line drawn perpendicular to the tangent to a curve at the point of contact is called the **normal** to the curve at the point. In particular, for a tangent of slope m, the associated normal will have slope $-1/m$.

Example: *Find the equations of the tangent and normal to the curve $y = x^3$ at the point where $x = 2$.*

At $x = 2$, $y = 2^3 = 8$. The co-ordinates of the point of contact are $(2, 8)$.

$\dfrac{dy}{dx} = 3x^2$ and the slope of the tangent at $(2, 8)$ is $3 \times 2^2 = 12$.

Equation of tangent at $(2, 8)$ is $y - 8 = 12(x - 2)$ or $12x - y - 16 = 0$.

At $(2, 8)$ the slope of the normal is $-1/12$.

Equation of normal at $(2, 8)$ is $y - 8 = -\frac{1}{12}(x - 2)$ or $x + 12y - 98 = 0$.

The location of maximum and minimum values

Figure 14.7 shows the graph of a curve $y = f(x)$ whose gradient function $\dfrac{dy}{dx}$ takes a zero value at both the points A and B. That is, the tangents to the curve at A and B are parallel to Ox. Given that the x-co-ordinates of A and B are a and b, respectively, then $f(a)$ is called a **minimum** value of $f(x)$ and $f(b)$ is called a **maximum** value of $f(x)$. It is also worth noting that *greater* values

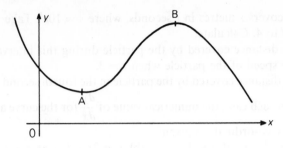

Fig. 14.7

than f(b) and *smaller* values than f(a) of f(x) may occur when the graph is considered as a whole.

For a minimum value f(a) to occur at $x = a$ on the curve $y = f(x)$, the following conditions are *all* needed:

(i) $\dfrac{dy}{dx} = 0$ at $x = a$,

(ii) $\dfrac{dy}{dx} < 0$ for values of x just less than a,

(iii) $\dfrac{dy}{dx} > 0$ for values of x just greater than a.

For a maximum value f(b) to occur at $x = b$ on the curve $y = f(x)$, the following conditions are *all* needed:

(i) $\dfrac{dy}{dx} = 0$ at $x = b$,

(ii) $\dfrac{dy}{dx} > 0$ for values of x just less than b,

(iii) $\dfrac{dy}{dx} < 0$ for values of x just greater than b.

In actual examples, conditions (ii) and (iii) can often be seen to be satisfied from a sketch graph of $y = f(x)$ and this would be sufficient for confirmation of a maximum or minimum value.

Example 1: *Find the stationary values of y, where $y = 2x^3 - 3x^2 - 12x$ and determine the nature of each.*

$$\frac{dy}{dx} = 6x^2 - 6x - 12$$

For stationary values of y, $\dfrac{dy}{dx} = 0$.

These occur when $6x^2 - 6x - 12 = 0$

$$\Rightarrow 6(x - 2)(x + 1) = 0$$

$$\Rightarrow x = 2, x = -1.$$

When $x = 2$, $y = 16 - 12 - 24 = -20$.

When $x = -1$, $y = -2 - 3 + 12 = 7$.

184

x	$x < -1$	$x = -1$	$-1 < x < 2$	$x = 2$	$x > 2$
$\dfrac{dy}{dx}$	> 0	$= 0$	< 0	$= 0$	> 0
General direction of tangent	↗	$\overrightarrow{\text{MAX}}$	↘	$\overrightarrow{\text{MIN}}$	↗

The ranges in the table imply that near the stationary point $(-1, 7)$ the gradients of tangents change from $+$ to $-$ as x increases through the value -1, confirming that $y = 7$ is a *maximum* value of y.

The ranges also imply that near the stationary point $(2, -20)$ the gradients of tangents change from $-$ to $+$ as x increases through the value 2, confirming that $y = -20$ is a *minimum* value of y.

Figure 14.8 shows the general shape of the graph of $y = 2x^3 - 3x^2 - 12x$.

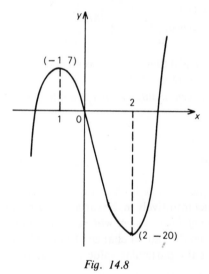

Fig. 14.8

Example 2: *A farmer wishes to construct a rectangular sheep-pen using an existing wall as one of the sides with 60 m of fencing. Calculate the dimensions of the pen which would allow the maximum grazing area.*

In Figure 14.9 the equal fenced sides are each of length x m and the remaining side opposite the wall is of length $(60 - 2x)$ m. The area of the pen, A m^2, is given by $A = x(60 - 2x) = 60x - 2x^2$.

$$\frac{dA}{dx} = 60 - 4x$$

$$\frac{dA}{dx} = 0 \text{ when } x = 15.$$

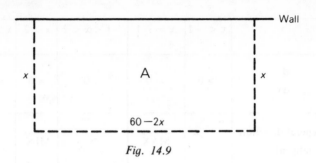

Fig. 14.9

x	$x < 15$	$x = 15$	$x > 15$
$\dfrac{dA}{dx}$	> 0	$= 0$	< 0
gradient of tangent	/	$\overrightarrow{\text{MAX}}$	\

It could also be confirmed that $x = 15$ gives a maximum value of A by using a sketch graph of $A = 60x - 2x^2$.

The dimensions of the pen required to give a maximum enclosed area are 30 m by 15 m.

Rates of change

The rate at which one variable is changing with respect to another related variable has been met intuitively in the earlier work of this chapter. *Velocity is the rate of change of displacement with respect to time.* In general, if f is a function of time, then the rate of change of f at time t can be measured by evaluating df/dt for the particular value of t required.

Example: *A circular oil-slick has radius r metres at time t seconds, where* $r = 10 + \dfrac{t}{100}$. *Find, in terms of π, the rate of increase of the area of the slick when $t = 3600$.*

$A = \pi\left(10 + \dfrac{t}{100}\right)^2$, where A m^2 is the area of the slick at time t second.

$A = 100\pi + \dfrac{20\pi t}{100} + \dfrac{\pi t^2}{10\,000}$

$\dfrac{dA}{dt} = \dfrac{\pi}{5} + \dfrac{\pi t}{5000}.$

186

When $t = 3600$, $\dfrac{dA}{dt} = \dfrac{\pi}{5} + \dfrac{\pi \times 3600}{5000} = \dfrac{46\pi}{50} = 0.92\pi$.

The rate of increase of the area of the slick at $t = 3600$ is $0.92\pi \ m^2/s$.

Exercise 14.2

1 Find the equations of the tangent and the normal to the following curves at the given points: (a) $y = x^2$ at $(2, 4)$, (b) $y = \dfrac{x^3}{12}$ at $(6, 18)$, (c) $y = \dfrac{2}{x^2}$ at $(-1, 2)$, (d) $y = 3x - x^2$ at $(3, 0)$, (e) $y = \dfrac{1}{x} - x^2$ at $(-1, -2)$.

2 Find the co-ordinates of the point P on the curve $y = 3x^2 - 6x$ where $dy/dx = 12$. Find the equation of the normal to the curve at P.

3 Prove that any line with slope $-1/m$ is perpendicular to the line $y = mx$.

4 Find the equation of the tangent to the curve $y = 18/x^3$ at the point P on the curve whose x-co-ordinate is 2.

5 Find the equations of the tangent and normal to the curve $8y = x^4$ at the point $P(2, 2)$. The tangent cuts the x-axis at A and the normal cuts the x-axis at B. Calculate the distance AB.

6 For each of the following curves, find the co-ordinates of any points where stationary values of y occur. Determine the nature of each stationary point found and sketch the curve: (a) $y = x^2 - 4x + 3$, (b) $y = 2 - x - x^2$, (c) $y = x^2 + 2x + 2$, (d) $y = x^3 - 3x$, (e) $y = x + \dfrac{4}{x}$.

7 Find the equations of the tangent and normal at the point $(\frac{1}{2}, 3)$ to the curve $y = 12x^2$. Given that the tangent cuts the co-ordinate axes at A and B, and the normal cuts the co-ordinate axes at C and D, find the areas of the triangles OAB and OCD, where O is the origin.

8 Find the minimum value of $(x + 5)(2x - 3)$ as x varies.

9 Show that for all real x, $(x + 4)(6 - x)$ never exceeds 25.

10 Prove that the tangent at $(2, -2)$ to the curve $y = x^3 - 4x^2 + 3x$ passes through the origin.

11 The sum of two positive variable numbers is 10. Prove that their greatest possible product is 25.

12 An enclosed rectangular oil-tank has a square base of side x m and its volume is 27 m^3. Show that the height of the tank is $27/x^2$ m and that the total surface is $(2x^2 + 108/x)$ m^2. Find the value of x for which the surface area of the tank is a minimum.

13 Show that a rectangle with given perimeter encloses the greatest area when the rectangle is a square.

14 A cylindrical tin holds 1 litre. Calculate, in cm, the height and base radius of the tin, given that its total closed surface area is a minimum.

15 An open cylinder of base radius x cm and height h cm has a capacity of 10 litres. Show that the surface area, A cm^2, is given by

$$A = \pi x^2 + \frac{20\,000}{x}.$$

As x varies, find the greatest value of A and the corresponding value of h.

16 A rectangle of length x cm has an area of 12 cm^2. Find an expression, in terms of x, for the perimeter p cm, of this rectangle. Find the minimum value of p.

17 A rectangular sheet of cardboard measures 8 cm by 6 cm. At each corner squares of side x cm are removed and the remainder is folded to make a rectangular box with no lid. Show that the volume V cm^3 of this box is $V = 4x(4-x)(3-x)$. Find the maximum value of V.

18 The velocity v m/s of a car moving in a straight line at time t seconds is given by $v = 4t^2 + 3t$. Find the acceleration of the car when $t = 2$.

19 At time t seconds the radius r cm of an expanding sphere is given by $r = 2 + 0.1t$. Find the rate at which the surface area of the sphere is expanding when $t = 4$.

20 The radius r cm of an expanding circular ink-blot at time t seconds is given by $r = 3 + 0.3t$. Calculate the rate of increase of the area of the blot when $t = 5$.

21 At time t seconds the radius r cm of an expanding sphere is given by $r = \dfrac{t}{3}$. Find the rate at which (a) the volume, (b) the surface area, of the sphere is increasing when $t = 6$.

22 At time t seconds, a side, length x cm, of a contracting square metal plate is given by $x = 80 - 0.2t$. Find the rate at which the area of the plate is contracting when $t = 5$.

15   Simple integration and some of its applications

Integration as the reverse process of differentiation

At the beginning of chapter 14, some simple illustrations were discussed about a particle moving in a straight line. When the distance s and the time t, each measured from a fixed point in the line, are given in the form $s = f(t)$, the velocity v of the particle at time t is ds/dt. The problem of finding s in terms of t when v is given as a function of t requires the steps used in the differentiation of s to find v to be reversed, if this is possible. This reverse process is called **integration**.

Example 1:   *A particle P, moving in a straight line, passes through a point O. The velocity v m/s of P at time t seconds after passing through O is given by $v = t^3 + 3t$. Find the distance of P from O at time t.*
If the distance $OP = s$ metres at time t seconds,

$$\frac{ds}{dt} = t^3 + 3t.$$

Since $D_t(t^4/4) = t^3$ and $D_t(3t^2/2) = 3t$,
it follows that $D_t(t^4/4 + 3t^2/2) = t^3 + 3t.$
Hence $s = \dfrac{t^4}{4} + \dfrac{3t^2}{2}.$

Although the above answer is correct, there has been an element of good fortune in arriving at the correct solution. The choice of O as the point from which s is measured is crucial, because this makes $s = 0$ when $t = 0$. The following section illustrates the reason why a further term should have been included in the expression for s obtained above.
Each of the expressions $3x^2, 3x^2 - 4, 3x^2 + 7$, and $3x^2 \pm$ any constant, when differentiated with respect to x, give the answer $6x$. This is because the differential coefficient of any constant is 0. This fact must be taken into account when integration is undertaken.
The information contained in the differential equation $dy/dx = 6x$ is the same as the information given by $y = 3x^2 + c$, where c is called an **arbitrary constant**. Figure 15.1 shows sketches of the curves with equations $y = 3x^2$, $y = 3x^2 - 4$ and $y = 3x^2 + 7$ which can be described as 'parallel' to each other.

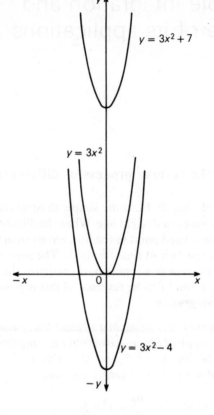

Fig. 15.1

For different values of c, the equation $y = 3x^2 + c$ represents a family of curves all of which are 'parallel' to each other, no two ever passing through the same point. The equation of any particular member of the family can be easily identified when a point on it is given.

Example 2: *Given that* $\dfrac{dy}{dx} = 6x$ *and that* $y = 3$ *when* $x = -2$, *find* y *in terms of* x.

The general solution of $dy/dx = 6x$ is $y = 3x^2 + c$, where c is a constant. Using the data that $y = 3$ when $x = -2$ in this general solution gives

$$3 = 12 + c \text{ and therefore } c = -9.$$

Hence $y = 3x^2 - 9$ is the required expression of y in terms of x.
This equation would represent the member of the family of curves, described above, which passes through the point $(-2, 3)$.

In the first example, the general solution of the differential equation $ds/dt = t^3 + 3t$ is $s = t^4/4 + 3t^2/2 + c$, where c is a constant. This constant is 0 because the position from which s is measured makes $s = 0$ when $t = 0$.

190

Example 3: *A particle P moving in a straight line passes through a point O with speed 5 m/s. The acceleration at time t seconds of P after passing through O is (6t + 4) m/s². Calculate: (a) the velocity of P when t = 3, (b) the distance covered by P between the instants when t = 2 and t = 4.*

(a) Let v m/s be the velocity of P at time t, hence

$$\frac{dv}{dt} = 6t + 4.$$

Integrating with respect to t gives $v = 3t^2 + 4t + A$, where A is a constant. At O, $v = 5$ when $t = 0$, therefore $5 = 0 + 0 + A$ and $A = 5$.

$$\text{Hence } v = 3t^2 + 4t + 5.$$

When $t = 3$, $v = 27 + 12 + 5 = 44$.
The velocity of P when t = 3 is 44 m/s.

(b) Let s metres be the distance of P from O at time t, hence

$$\frac{ds}{dt} = 3t^2 + 4t + 5.$$

Integrating with respect to t gives $s = t^3 + 2t^2 + 5t + B$, where B is a constant.

When P is at O, $s = 0$ and $t = 0$ and therefore $B = 0$.

$$\text{Hence } s = t^3 + 2t^2 + 5t.$$

When $t = 2$, $s = 8 + 8 + 10 = 26$ i.e. the distance between O and P is 26 m.

When $t = 4$, $s = 64 + 32 + 20 = 116$ i.e. the distance between O and P is 116 m.

$\therefore$ *the distance covered by P between t = 2 and t = 4 is $(116 - 26)$ m = 90 m.*

Integral notation and indefinite integrals

A summary of the work covered in integration to this point could be expressed as follows:

The solution of the differential equation $dy/dx = f(x)$, where f is a function of x, can be expressed in the form $y = g(x) + c$, where g is another function of x such that $g(x)$, when differentiated with respect to x, becomes a function of x, called g', and $g'(x)$ only differs from $f(x)$ by a constant. A proviso is necessary because certain functions can be chosen for f, e.g. $f(x) = 1/x$, which give rise to a function g outside the scope of this book, and others can be chosen for which there is no corresponding function g. The process of integration is of such importance in mathematics that a special symbol is used. In the notation of this paragraph it is written as

$$\int f(x)\, dx = g(x) + c.$$

The left hand side should be read as '**the integral of f(x) with respect to x**'.

$\int$ is called the **integral sign**, $f(x)$ is called the **integrand** and, at this stage, the dx should be taken as indication of the variable with respect to which the integration process is being carried out. The process of finding g(x) is called 'integrating f(x) with respect to x' and is called **indefinite integration** because of the inclusion of an arbitrary constant. When boundary conditions are given, as in the previous examples, which allow the value of an arbitrary constant of integration to be evaluated, the integration is called **definite** and limits are written in the integral as will be shown in the next part of this chapter.

Examples: *Evaluate the following indefinite integrals:*

(a) $\displaystyle\int 7x^4\, dx$ (b) $\displaystyle\int \frac{dx}{x^4}$ (c) $\displaystyle\int \left(x - \frac{1}{x}\right)^2 dx.$

(a) $\dfrac{d}{dx}(x^5) = 5x^4 \Rightarrow \displaystyle\int 7x^4\, dx = \frac{7}{5}x^5 + c.$

(b) $\dfrac{d}{dx}(x^{-3}) = -3x^{-4} \Rightarrow \displaystyle\int \frac{dx}{x^4} = \int x^{-4}\, dx = -\frac{1}{3}x^{-3} + c$

(c) $\left(x - \dfrac{1}{x}\right)^2 = x^2 - 2 + \dfrac{1}{x^2} = x^2 - 2 + x^{-2}$

$\dfrac{d}{dx}(x^3) = 3x^2, \quad \dfrac{d}{dx}(x) = 1, \quad \dfrac{d}{dx}(x^{-1}) = -x^{-2}$

$\Rightarrow \displaystyle\int \left(x - \frac{1}{x}\right)^2 dx = \int (x^2 - 2x^0 + x^{-2})\, dx = \frac{1}{3}x^3 - 2x^1 - x^{-1} + c$

$$= \frac{1}{3}x^3 - 2x - \frac{1}{x} + c.$$

Exercise 15.1

1 A particle P, moving in a straight line, passes through a point O. The velocity v m/s of P at time t seconds after passing through O is given by $v = 4t + 5$. (a) Show that the acceleration of P is constant. (b) Calculate the distance covered by P in the first 4 s after passing through O.

2 A particle, falling vertically, has velocity $10t$ m/s at time t seconds after being released from rest. Find the distance covered by the particle in the 4th second of its motion.

3 The acceleration of a particle moving in a straight line is $12t$ m/s² at time t seconds after it starts from rest at the point O. The particle is at the point P when $t = 4$. Calculate OP and find the average speed of the particle over this distance.

4 A particle moving in a straight line has velocity $(6t^2 + 4)$ m/s, at time t seconds after passing through a point O. Calculate the acceleration when $t = 1.5$ and the distance covered between the instants when $t = 1$ and $t = 4$.

5 A particle moving in a straight line, with constant acceleration a m/s²,

covers a distance s metres in time t seconds, and its velocities at the start and end of this interval are u m/s and v m/s, respectively. Prove that: (a) $v = u + at$, (b) $s = ut + \frac{1}{2}at^2$, (c) $v^2 = u^2 + 2as$.

6 Draw a sketch to show the graph of $y = 2x + c$ for: (a) $c = 0$, (b) $c = 2$, (c) $c = -2$. Write down a differential equation to describe all members of the family of lines represented by $y = 2x + c$. Find the equation of the member of this family which passes through $(5, -4)$.

7 Find the general solution of the differential equation $dy/dx = -2x$ and illustrate with a sketch graph. Find the particular solution for which $y = 4$ when $x = 4$.

8 Write down the value of $D_x(x^6)$ and hence write down the general solution of $dy/dx = 8x^5$.

9 Write down the value of $D_x(1/x^6)$ and hence write down the general solution of $dy/dx = 8/x^7$.

10 For all values of s and t it is given that $ds/dt = 7 - 10t$. Also $s = 4$ when $t = 0$. Find s in terms of t.

11 If $dy/dx = -4/x^2$ and $x = 1$ when $y = -1$ find y in terms of x.

12 Find the particular solution of the differential equation $\dfrac{dy}{dx} = x - \dfrac{1}{x^3}$

for which $y = 4$ when $x = -1$.

13 The gradient of the curve $y = f(x)$ is $4x^3 - 2x$ for all values of x and the curve passes through the point $(-2, 3)$. Find $f(x)$.

Evaluate each of the following indefinite integrals:

14 $\displaystyle\int 6x^3 \, dx$

15 $\displaystyle\int x^{-2} \, dx$

16 $\displaystyle\int (2x - 5) \, dx$

17 $\displaystyle\int x^2(x - 3) \, dx$

18 $\displaystyle\int (x - 1)^2 \, dx$

19 $\displaystyle\int \left(3 + \frac{2}{x^3}\right) dx$

20 $\displaystyle\int \left(\frac{3 - x^3}{x^2}\right) dx$.

Areas of regions bounded by lines and curves

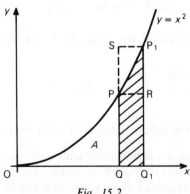

Fig. 15.2

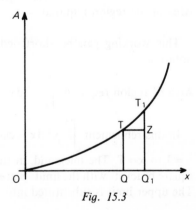

Fig. 15.3

In Figure 15.2, the graph of the curve $y = x^2$ is shown for $x \geqslant 0$. Points P, P_1 on the curve have co-ordinates (x, x^2) and $[x+h, (x+h)^2]$, respectively. The area bounded by the arc OP, PQ and Ox is A. It is required to express A in terms of x.

Let the shaded region bounded by PQ, QQ_1, Q_1P_1 and arc PP_1 be of area u.

$$\text{Rectangle } QQ_1RP < u < \text{rectangle } QQ_1P_1S$$
$$hx^2 < u < h(x+h)^2$$
$$x^2 < u/h < (x+h)^2.$$

As P_1 approaches P along the curve, h approaches zero and the value of u/h approaches x^2.

In Figure 15.3, the graph of A against x is shown; Q is the point $(x, 0)$ and Q_1 is the point $(x+h, 0)$; $QT = A$ and $Q_1T_1 = A+u$. Hence $T_1Z = u$. As P_1 approaches P along the curve $y = x^2$, T_1 will approach T along the graph of A. The gradient of the chord TT_1 is u/h and this ratio will approach the value of the gradient of the tangent at T on the graph of A as h approaches zero. The gradient of the tangent is $\dfrac{dA}{dx}$, and hence

$$\frac{dA}{dx} = x^2.$$

Integrating this differential equation gives

$$A = \tfrac{1}{3}x^3 + c.$$

In this case it can be seen that $A = 0$ when $x = 0$, hence $A = \tfrac{1}{3}x^3$.

Once the function A has been found, the area of any region bounded by the curve, the x-axis and any specific ordinates can be determined.

Example 1: *Find the area of the region bounded by the curve $y = x^2$, the x-axis and the ordinates $x = 3$ and $x = 5$.*

In Figure 15.2, first suppose that PQ is the line $x = 3$, then
$$A_3 = \tfrac{1}{3}(3)^3 = 9.$$
Now suppose that PQ is the line $x = 5$, then
$$A_5 = \tfrac{1}{3}(5)^3 = 125/3.$$
Area of the region required $= A_5 - A_3 = 125/3 - 9 = 98/3 = 32\tfrac{2}{3}$.

This working can be shortened and refined by using the following notation:

Area of region required $\displaystyle\int_3^5 x^2 \, dx = \left[\frac{x^3}{3}\right]_3^5 = \frac{5^3}{3} - \frac{3^3}{3} = 32\tfrac{2}{3}$.

In this refinement $\displaystyle\int_3^5 x^2 \, dx$ is called 'the definite integral of $x^2 \, dx$ from $x = 3$ to $x = 5$'. The integrand, in this case x^2, is integrated and written in square brackets with the limits placed outside the right hand end as shown. The upper limit is substituted into the integrated expression and a minus sign then precedes the substitution of the lower limit. This numerical expression is then simplified to give the answer.

Subject to any modifications imposed by a particular function, the method of determining areas illustrated here for the curve $y = x^2$ can be generalised. For the curve $y = f(x)$, the area of a region enclosed by the curve, the x-axis and the ordinates $x = a$ and $x = b$, where $a < b$, is given by the definite integral

$$\int_a^b f(x)\,dx \qquad \text{(see Figure 15.4).}$$

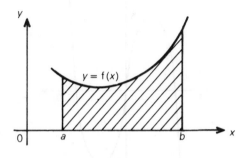

Fig. 15.4

The following examples have been chosen to illustrate the technique of evaluating areas under curves. A sketch graph should always be drawn when working examples of this sort.

Example 2: *Calculate the area of the finite region bounded by the curve* $y = 1/x^2$, *the x-axis and the ordinates* $x = 1$ *and* $x = 5$.
In Figure 15.5, the region is shown shaded.

$$\text{Area of region} = \int_1^5 \frac{dx}{x^2} = \left[-\frac{1}{x} \right]_1^5 = -\tfrac{1}{5} - (-1) = \tfrac{4}{5}.$$

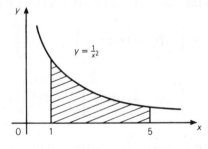

Fig. 15.5

Example 3: *Evaluate* $\displaystyle\int_{-2}^2 x(x^2 - 4)\,dx$. *Sketch the graph of* $y = x(x^2 - 4)$ *for* $-2 \leqslant x \leqslant 2$. *Find the sum of the areas of the finite regions enclosed*

195

between the curve and the x-axis.

$$\int_{-2}^{2} x(x^2-4)\,dx = \int_{-2}^{2}(x^3-4x)\,dx = \left[\frac{x^4}{4}-2x^2\right]_{-2}^{2} = (4-8)-(4-8)$$
$$= 0.$$

The graph of the curve is shown in Figure 15.6.

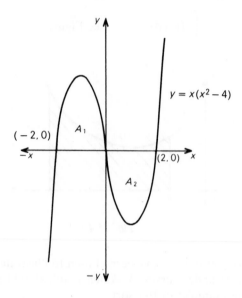

$y = x(x^2-4)$

$(-2, 0)$ A_1

$-x$ $(2, 0)$ x

A_2

Fig. 15.6

The curve crosses Ox when $x(x^2-4) = 0$, that is $x(x-2)(x+2) = 0$, giving the points $(0, 0)$, $(2, 0)$ and $(-2, 0)$. For large x, y is $+$, and for large negative x, y is $-$. There should be no need to find the stationary points in sketch curves like this, but they can be found to act as a check if the reader wishes.

$$\text{Area of region } A_1 = \int_{-2}^{0}(x^3-4x)\,dx = \left[\frac{x^4}{4}-2x^2\right]_{-2}^{0} = 0-0-(4-8)$$
$$= 4.$$

$$\text{Area of region } A_2 = \int_{0}^{2}(x^3-4x)\,dx = \left[\frac{x^4}{4}-2x^2\right]_{0}^{2} = 4-8-(0-0)$$
$$= -4.$$

Note that the negative sign of A_2 indicates that this region is *below* the x-axis.

Sum of the areas required $= 4+4 = 8$.

Care must be exercised in evaluating the area of a finite region which does not lie completely on one side of the x-axis. It is usually necessary to find each part separately.

Example 4: *Calculate the area of the finite region bounded by the line* $y = 2x$ *and the curve* $y = 4x - x^2$.

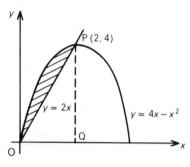

Fig. 15.7

In Figure 15.7, the co-ordinates of P are given by $2x = 4x - x^2$, that is $x^2 - 2x = 0$, $x(x - 2) = 0$, $x = 0$ (at O), $x = 2$ (at P), and $y = 4$.

Area of region bounded by arc OP, PQ and Ox
$$= \int_0^2 (4x - x^2)\,dx = \left[2x^2 - \frac{x^3}{3} \right]_0^2.$$
$$= 8 - \tfrac{8}{3} = 16/3.$$

Area of triangle $OPQ = \int_0^2 (2x)\,dx = \left[x^2 \right]_0^2 = 4$

(or using $\frac{1}{2}$ base $\times$ height, $= \frac{1}{2} \times 2 \times 4 = 4$).

Area of finite region = area under curve − area of triangle
$$= 16/3 - 4 = 4/3 = 1\tfrac{1}{3}.$$

Volumes of revolution

In Figure 15.8, the graph of the curve $y = x^2$ is shown for $x \geqslant 0$. Points P and P_1 on the curve have co-ordinates (x, x^2) and $[x + h, (x + h)^2]$, respectively. The area of the region bounded by arc OP, PQ and Ox is rotated completely about Ox to form a **solid of revolution** of volume V. It is required to express V in terms of x.

Suppose the shaded area bounded by PQ, QQ_1, Q_1P_1 and arc PP_1 is rotated about Ox to form a solid of volume w. The volume of the cylinder of radius PQ and thickness h is *less* than w and the volume of the cylinder of radius P_1Q_1 and thickness h is *greater* than w. Algebraically this can be expressed as

$$\pi x^4 h < \quad w \quad < \pi(x + h)^4 h$$

that is
$$\pi x^4 < w/h < \pi(x + h)^4.$$

As P_1 approaches P along the curve, h approaches zero and the value of w/h approaches πx^4.

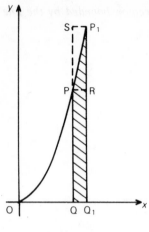

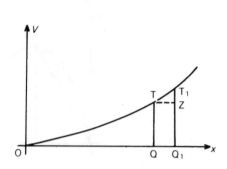

Fig. 15.8   Fig. 15.9

In Figure 15.9, the graph of V is shown, Q is the point $(x, 0)$ and Q_1 is the point $(x + h, 0)$; $QT = V$, $Q_1T_1 = V + w$, $T_1Z = w$.

As P_1 approaches P along the curve, $y = x^2$, T_1 will approach T along the graph of V. The gradient of TT_1 is w/h and this ratio will approach the gradient of the tangent at T on the graph of V as h approaches zero.

The gradient of the tangent is $\dfrac{dV}{dx}$ and hence $\dfrac{dV}{dx} = \pi x^4$.

Integrating this differential equation gives $V = \dfrac{\pi x^5}{5} + c$.

In this case it can be seen that $V = 0$ when $x = 0$, hence $V = \pi x^5/5$.

Once the function V has been found, the volume of any solid generated by the complete revolution about Ox of a region bounded by the curve, the x-axis and any specified ordinates can be determined.

Example 1: *Find the volume generated when the region bounded by the curve $y = x^2$, the x-axis and the ordinates $x = 3$ and $x = 5$ is completely rotated about Ox.*

Using definite integral notation, the required volume is given by

$$\int \pi y^2 \, dx = \int_3^5 \pi x^4 \, dx = \left[\frac{\pi x^5}{5} \right]_3^5 = \frac{\pi}{5}(5^5 - 3^5)$$

$$= \frac{\pi}{5}(3125 - 243) = \frac{2882\pi}{5}.$$

Answers for volumes are usually left in terms of π. Generally, for the curve $y = f(x)$, the volume of the solid, V, generated by the complete rotation of the finite area bounded by $y = f(x)$, the x-axis and the ordinates $x = a$ and $x = b$, where $a < b$, is given by:

$$V = \int \pi y^2 \, dx = \int_a^b \pi [f(x)]^2 \, dx.$$

198

Example 2: *A finite region is bounded by the curve* $y = x^3 + 2$, *the x-axis and the ordinates* $x = -1$ *and* $x = 2$. (a) *Calculate the area of the region.*

The region is rotated through 4 right-angles about the x-axis. (b) *Calculate the volume of the solid formed.*

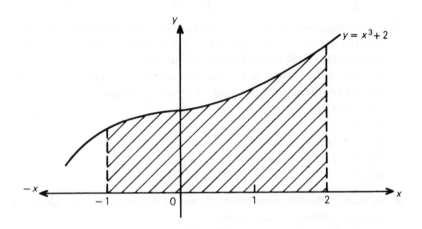

Fig. 15.10

Area of the shaded region $= \int y \, dx = \int_{-1}^{2} (x^3 + 2) \, dx = \left[\dfrac{x^4}{4} + 2x \right]_{-1}^{2}$

$$= 4 + 4 - \left(\dfrac{1}{4} - 2 \right) = 4 + 4 - \dfrac{1}{4} + 2 = 9.75$$

Volume of the solid formed $= \int \pi y^2 \, dx = \int_{-1}^{2} \pi (x^3 + 2)^2 \, dx$

$$= \int_{-1}^{2} \pi (x^6 + 4x^3 + 4) \, dx$$

$$= \pi \left[\dfrac{x^7}{7} + x^4 + 4x \right]_{-1}^{2}$$

$$= \pi \left[\dfrac{128}{7} + 16 + 8 - \left(-\dfrac{1}{7} + 1 - 4 \right) \right]$$

$$= \pi \left(\dfrac{128}{7} + 16 + 8 + \dfrac{1}{7} - 1 + 4 \right) = \dfrac{318\pi}{7}.$$

Exercise 15.2

1 Evaluate each of the following definite integrals:

(a) $\displaystyle\int_{0}^{3} 4x \, dx$ 　　　　(b) $\displaystyle\int_{1}^{3} 6x^2 \, dx$ 　　　　(c) $\displaystyle\int_{1}^{2} \dfrac{dx}{x^2}$

(d) $\displaystyle\int_{-2}^{-1} \frac{dx}{x^3}$ (e) $\displaystyle\int_{-1}^{1} (2x^3 - 4x)\,dx$ (f) $\displaystyle\int_{0}^{2} (x^2 + 1)^2\,dx$

(g) $\displaystyle\int_{-2}^{2} (x-1)(x+1)\,dx$ (h) $\displaystyle\int_{2}^{5} \frac{x^2 - 2}{x^2}\,dx.$

2   Use integration to find the area of the trapezium enclosed by the x-axis, and the lines $y = x$, $x = 2$ and $x = 5$. Confirm the answer you obtain by calculating the area of the trapezium directly.

3   In each of the following, find the area of the finite region bounded by the x-axis, the given curve and the given ordinates:
   (a) $y = x^2$ $x = 1$ $x = 3$
   (b) $y = x^3$ $x = 2$ $x = 4$
   (c) $y = 2x - x^2$ $x = 2$ $x = 5$
   (d) $y = 1/x^2$ $x = -4$ $x = -1$
   (e) $y = (x^2 - 2)^2$ $x = -\sqrt{2}$ $x = +\sqrt{2}.$

4   In each of the following, find the area of the finite region enclosed by the given curve and the x-axis:
   (a) $y = 5x - x^2$ (b) $y = 3x^2 - 9x$ (c) $y = -6 + 5x - x^2$
   (d) $y = x^2 - x - 6.$

5   Given that $y = x + 1$, evaluate: (a) $\displaystyle\int_{0}^{1} y\,dx$, (b) $\displaystyle\int_{1}^{2} y\,dx$, (c) $\displaystyle\int_{0}^{2} y\,dx$
   and check each answer by evaluating the areas represented from a diagram.

6   Given that $y = 2x - x^2$, find the non-zero value of k for which $\displaystyle\int_{0}^{k} y\,dx$
   $= 0$. By drawing a sketch graph, illustrate this result.

7   Find the area of the finite region enclosed by the x-axis and the curve
   (a) $y = 6x - x^2$, (b) $y = x^2 - 6x$. Display the regions on sketch graphs.

8   Find the finite area enclosed by the curve $y = 4 - x^2$ and the line $y = 3$.

9   Find the area in the first quadrant of the region bounded by the curve $y = x^2$, the line $y = 2 - x$ and the x-axis.

10   Find the area of the finite region in the first quadrant bounded by the curve $y = 12 - x^2$, the line $y = x$ and the y-axis.

11   The finite region bounded by the curve $y = x^2$, the x-axis and the ordinates $x = 1$ and $x = 4$ is completely rotated about Ox. Find the volume of the solid so formed.

12   The finite region bounded by the lines $y = 3x$, $x = 2$ and $y = 0$ is completely rotated about the x-axis. Find, by integration, the volume of the cone so formed. Check your answer by direct calculation.

13   In each of the following, a finite region is bounded by the lines and curves whose equations are given. Each region is rotated about Ox to form a solid of revolution. Find the volume of each solid so formed:
   (a) $y = 1/x$, $x = 1$, $x = 4$, $y = 0$
   (b) $y = 1 - x^2$, $x = 0$, $y = 0$

(c) $y = 3/x^2$, $x = -3$, $x = -1$, $y = 0$

(d) $y = \sqrt{(x+3)}$, $x = 1$, $x = 6$, $y = 0$.

14 The circle, centre the origin and radius r, has the equation $x^2 + y^2 = r^2$. By completely revolving the upper half of this circle about Ox, show that the volume of a sphere of radius r is $\frac{4}{3}\pi r^3$.

15 A hollow sphere of internal radius 10 cm contains water to a depth of 5 cm. By considering a complete revolution of part of the circle with equation $y^2 = 100 - x^2$, and evaluating the definite integral representing the volume so formed, find the volume of water in the sphere.

Approximate integration: the trapezium rule

Example: *The following data was collected about the speed of an electric train over a continuous interval of 1 minute.*

Time (s)	0	10	20	30	40	50	60
Speed (m/s)	0	9	17	24	30	32	33

Illustrate this information graphically and estimate the distance covered by the train during this interval.

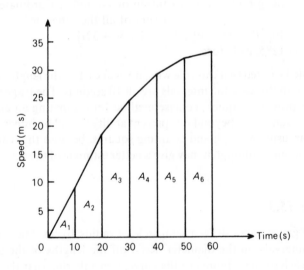

Fig. 15.11

The graph illustrating these data is shown in Figure 15.11. As only seven readings are given, one must assume that the motion between each plot point is reasonably steady and the overall pattern seems to support this. In many high speed trains a device is now installed which draws a continuous time–speed graph as the train moves along. This type of graph derived from a practical situation can sometimes be represented by a complicated mathematical equation, but more often it is not possible to express the relation between speed and time in this form at all. Readings, however, can be taken from the graph and these are then used to produce estimated results.

In order to estimate the distance covered, an approximate evaluation of the area under the speed–time 'curve' is required. One such estimate can be found by using what is called the **Trapezium Rule**. The successive plotted points are joined by straight line segments as shown in Figure 15.11 and the areas A_1, A_2, A_3, A_4, A_5 and A_6 are calculated. It will be noticed that each of these, except the first, are trapezia.

Estimate of total area

$$= A_1 + A_2 + A_3 + A_4 + A_5 + A_6$$
$$= \tfrac{1}{2} \times 10 \times 9 + \tfrac{1}{2} \times 10 \times (9 + 17) + \tfrac{1}{2} \times 10 \times (17 + 24)$$
$$+ \tfrac{1}{2} \times 10 \times (24 + 30) + \tfrac{1}{2} \times 10 \times (30 + 32) + \tfrac{1}{2} \times 10 \times (32 + 33)$$
$$= 10 \left[(\tfrac{1}{2} \times 33) + 9 + 17 + 24 + 30 + 32 \right]$$
$$= 1285.$$

Hence, during this period, the train has travelled about 1300 metre.

A scrutiny of the above calculation will reveal that there is a very simple rule to obtain an estimate of the area by this method.

Estimate of area

$= $ (length of interval) $\times$ (mean of 1st and last ordinates

$+$ sum of all the other ordinates)

$$= 10 \left[\tfrac{1}{2}(0 + 33) + (9 + 17 + 24 + 30 + 32) \right]$$
$$= 1285, \text{ as before.}$$

It should be noted that this rule will only work when the length of interval is *constant*, in this case the intervals are all 10 seconds. The trapezium rule, therefore, provides a quick, concise method for estimating an area which cannot be found, or is beyond our present ability to find by integration; it is better than using a graph and counting squares, because that can be very time consuming, although it may give a better estimate of the actual answer.

Exercise 15.3

1 Using graph paper draw a semicircle of radius 10 cm. Mark points at 2 cm intervals on the diameter. Read off the lengths of the ordinates from each of these points to the curve, remembering that the first and last are both zero. Use the trapezium rule to estimate the area enclosed by the semi-circle. Find the % error in your estimate by using the formula $A = \tfrac{1}{2}\pi r^2$.

2 The speed of a train was recorded at 10 s intervals as shown in the table:

Time (s)	0	10	20	30	40	50	60
Speed (m/s)	0	6	9	11	13	15	16

Estimate the distance travelled by the train in this 1 minute interval.

3 Sketch a graph for the data given in the table:

x	1	2	3	4	5	6	7	8	9	10	11	12
y	0	7	8	11	15	17	20	18	13	9	4	0

Using the trapezium rule, estimate the area between (a) the graph and the x-axis, (b) the graph, the ordinates $x = 3$, $x = 10$ and the x-axis.

4 Taking unit intervals on the x-axis, estimate the area of the finite region bounded by the curve $y = \sqrt{(x^2 + 1)}$, the ordinates $x = 0$, $x = 5$ and the x-axis.

5 Sketch the graph of the curve $y = 1/x$ from $x = 1$ to $x = 5$. Estimate the area of the finite region bounded by the curve, the ordinates $x = 1$, $x = 5$ and the x-axis.

Miscellaneous Exercise C

1 If $f : x \rightarrow x^2 - 4x$, find
   (i) the range set, whose domain set is $\{-1, 0, 1\}$,
   (ii) the domain set, whose range set is $\{-3, 0\}$.   [L   1973]

2 The functions f and g are defined as follows:
   $f : x \rightarrow x^2$,
   $g : x \rightarrow ax - b$, where a and b are constants.
   Given that $f(1) = g(1)$ and that $f(4) = g(4)$, show that $a = 5$, and find the value of b.
   With these values of a and b
   (i) find the range of values of x for which $f(x) - g(x) < -2$,
   (ii) find the value of x for which $fg(x) = gf(x)$,
   (iii) show that for all other values of x, $fg(x) - gf(x) > 0$.
                                                              [L   1979]

3 The functions f and g map x onto $3x - 2$ and $2x^2 + 1$ respectively. Show that fg maps x onto $6x^2 + 1$, and find the mapping of the function gf.
   A third function, h, maps x onto $ax + b$, where a and b are positive constants, and is such that fgh maps x onto $6x^2 + 12x + 7$.
   Find the values of a and b and also that of fgh (-2).
   Find the two values of x for which $fgh(x) = 25$.   [L   1973]

4 (a) Functions f and g are defined by
$$f = \{(1, 3), (2, 2), (3, 1)\},$$
$$g = \{(1, 2), (2, 1), (3, 3)\}.$$

Define, as sets of ordered pairs, the inverse functions f^{-1} and g^{-1}, and the composition functions $f \circ g$ and $g \circ f$. Hence show that

   (i) $f^{-1} \circ g^{-1} = (g \circ f)^{-1}$,
   (ii) $f \circ (g \circ f) = (f \circ g) \circ f$.

(b) If $R = \{2, 5\}$ and $T = \{60, 90\}$, define the Cartesian product $R \times T$. The polar coordinates of a point are (r, θ), where $r \in R$, $\theta \in T$; r is measured in cm and θ is measured in degrees. Illustrate $R \times T$ by a set of such points in a diagram.

Which pair of points in this set are closest together?

Calculate the distance between the two points which are closest together, giving your answer correct to two decimal places.

[AEB 1976]

5 (a) Functions f and g are defined for all values of x by

$$f: x \to \frac{x}{2} + 1 \text{ and } g: x \to x^2.$$

(i) Write down the definitions, in terms of x, of the composition functions $f(g(x))$ and $g(f(x))$. Find the range of values of x for which $f(g(x)) \leqslant g(f(x))$.

(ii) Define the inverse function f^{-1} in terms of x and find the ranges of f, g and f^{-1}, if the domains of f and g are restricted to $-2 \leqslant x \leqslant 2$.

(b) A, B, C, D, E are members of a family. A relation is defined on $S \times S$, where $S = \{A, B, C, D, E\}$, by the statement "x is related to y, if x is older than y". A subset of this relation is defined by the set of ordered pairs $T = \{(C, A), (B, E), (D, B), (E, C)\}$.

Find the correct order of age in this family and state your answer, starting with the youngest member. Give a clear explanation for your conclusions.

[AEB 1976]

6 Let $X = \{1, 2, 3, \ldots, 21\}$. A function f is defined for the members of X as follows: take any element $x \in X$ and write it in the form

$$x = 3a + b$$

where a is an integer or zero and b is 0, 1, or 2, then

$$f(x) = a + 7.$$

(i) Copy and complete the following table of values for $f(x)$.

x	1	2	3	4	5	.	.	.	20	21
$f(x)$			8							

(ii) Solve the equations

(a) $f(x) = 10$;   (b) $f(x) = 15$

where x is a member of X.

(iii) What are the possible values of $f(f(x))$ when $x \in X$?

(iv) Write down the solutions of the equation $f(f(x)) = 11$ where $x \in X$.

(v) What is the value of $f(f(f(x)))$ when $x \in X$?

[O 1977]

7 Three quantities x, y and z are such that x varies inversely as y and y varies as the square of z. Given that when $x = 1$, $y = 4$, and $z = 2$, calculate the value of x when $z = 1$.

[JMB 1975]

8 (a) When a car travelling at a speed of V kilometres per hour is brought to a stop by a resistance of R newtons, the distance, D metres, in which the car stops is proportional to the square of the speed and inversely proportional to the resistance. Express D in terms of V, R and a constant of variation k and hence calculate

(i) the value of k if $D = 20$ when $V = 50$ and $R = 11\,000$,

(ii) the value of R if $D = 33$ when $V = 60$,

(iii) the value of V if $D = 23$ when $R = 8096$ [AEB 1978]

9 Given that $y = 3x - 2x^2$, copy and complete the following table:

x	-2	$-1\frac{1}{2}$	-1	0	1	2	$2\frac{1}{2}$	3
y		-9		0		-2		

Taking 10 small squares to represent 1 unit on the x-axis, and 5 small squares to represent 1 unit on the y-axis, draw the graph of $y = 3x - 2x^2$ from $x = -2$ to $x = 3$.

Using the same axes draw the graph of $y = \frac{3}{2}(x - 5)$, and write down the values of x at the points where your graphs meet. Write down also the equation of which these values are the solutions and rearrange this equation into the form $ax^2 + bx + c = 0$, where a, b and c are whole numbers.   [C 1971]

10 Write down the two values missing from the following table which gives values of $3x^2 - 8x - 7$ for values of x from -2 to 5.

x	-2	-1	0	1	2	3	4	5
$3x^2 - 8x - 7$	21		-7	-12	-11		9	28

Draw the graph of $y = 3x^2 - 8x - 7$ for values of x from -2 to 5, taking 2 cm as one unit on the x-axis and 2 cm as 4 units on the y-axis.

(i) Use your graph to estimate the members of the sets

$$P = \{x : 3x^2 - 8x - 7 = 0\},$$
$$Q = \{x : 3x^2 - 8x = 19\}.$$

(ii) By drawing, find the rate of change of y with respect to x, when $x = 3$.   [W 1977]

11 A rectangular box without a lid has a square base of side x cm. Given that its total internal surface area is 40 cm^2, show that its volume, y cm^3, is given by the formula

$$y = \tfrac{1}{4}x(40 - x^2).$$

Draw the graph of $y = \frac{1}{4}x(40 - x^2)$ for values of x from 0 to 6, taking 2 cm as one unit on the x-axis, and 2 cm as 5 units on the y-axis. Use your graph to find

(a) the volume of the box when $x = 4.75$,

(b) the range of values of x for which the volume is greater than 15 cm^3,

(c) the maximum volume of the box,

(d) the value of x which gives this maximum volume.   [L 1974]

12 Draw the graph of $y = \dfrac{16}{x}$ for values of x from 1 to 6. As scales use 2 cm to represent 1 unit on the x-axis and 2 units on the y-axis.

On the same sheet of graph paper and with the same axes draw the graphs of $y = 5x$ and $y = 18 - 4x$.

Show how the intersection of $y = 5x$ with $y = \dfrac{16}{x}$ can be used to estimate $\sqrt{3.2}$ and obtain such an estimate from your graphs.

Show how the intersections of $y = 18 - 4x$ and $y = \dfrac{16}{x}$ can be used to solve a particular quadratic equation. State this equation in its simplest form and the solutions obtained from your graphs.

[O   1978]

13 Copy and complete the table of values of the function $y = x - 4 + \dfrac{11}{x}$ giving values of x correct to two decimal places.

x	1	2	3	4	5	6	7
-4	-4	-4	-4	-4	-4	-4	-4
$\dfrac{11}{x}$	11			2.75			1.57
y	8			2.75			4.57

Using a scale of 2 cm to represent 1 unit on each axis, draw the graph of the function for these values.

From your graph find

(a) the minimum value of $x - 4 + \dfrac{11}{x}$ and the value of x at which it occurs,

(b) the roots of the equation $x + \dfrac{11}{x} = 8$.

From the point $(1, 1)$ draw a tangent to the curve and find its gradient.

[L   1976]

14 Draw the graph of $y = x^2 - 5x + 13$ for values of x from -1 to 7.
[Scales: take 2 cm to represent 1 unit on the x-axis and 1 cm to represent 1 unit on the y-axis.]

(i) Use the Trapezoidal Rule (with 14 intervals) to estimate the area bounded by the curve, the positive x-axis, the positive y-axis and the ordinate $x = 7$.

(ii) Use a calculus method to calculate the area bounded by the curve, the positive x-axis, the positive y-axis, and the ordinate $x = 7$.

[AEB   1976]

15 (i) Calculate the maximum value of the function

$$5 - 2x - 3x^2.$$

(ii) The area bounded by the x-axis, the lines $x = 2$ and $x = 3$, and the curve $y = x - \dfrac{1}{x}$ is rotated completely about the x-axis.

Calculate the volume of the solid formed. [L 1972]

16 A rectangular block has square ends of edge x cm and its length is y cm. Given that the total surface area is 96 cm², prove that

(i) $y = \dfrac{24}{x} - \dfrac{x}{2}$,

(ii) the volume V cm³ is given by $V = 24x - \dfrac{x^3}{2}$

Given that x varies while the surface area remains constant, find the maximum volume of the block. [JMB 1976]

17 The diagram shows part of the graph of $y = \frac{1}{2}x^2 - 2x + 5$.

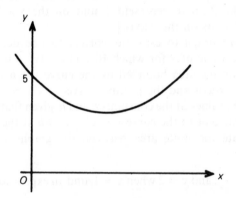

(a) Find the value of the gradient $\dfrac{dy}{dx}$ of this graph when $x = 4$.

(b) Show that there is a minimum point when $x = 2$, and find the corresponding minimum value of y.

(c) Calculate the area of the region between the curve, the line $y = 0$ and the lines $x = 0$ and $x = 4$.

(d) Show that the area of the region enclosed by the curve and the line $y = 5$ is $5\frac{1}{3}$ square units. [L 1978]

18 The points P and Q on the curve $y = x^2 - \dfrac{1}{x} + 2$ have coordinates $(\frac{1}{2}, a)$ and $(-1, b)$ respectively, referred to the usual axes of coordinates Ox, Oy. The tangents to the curve at P and Q meet at R.

(i) Find the values of a and b and also the co-ordinates of R.

(ii) The tangent to the curve at Q meets the y-axis at C and the x-axis at D. Calculate the ratio QC:QD. [AEB 1976]

19 Calculate the co-ordinates of the points where the curve $y = 4 - x^2$ cuts the x and y axes and *sketch* the curve. Calculate

(a) the area enclosed by the curve and the x-axis,

(b) the volume of the solid of revolution formed by rotating this area about the y-axis. [L 1972]

20 It is given that $y = 8x - \dfrac{27}{x^2}$.

Calculate the value of

(i) y when $x = 1.2$,

(ii) x when $y = 0$,

(iii) $\dfrac{dy}{dx}$ when $x = 2$,

(iv) $\displaystyle\int_1^3 y\,dx$. [JMB 1974]

21 Show the curve $y = 6 + 11x - 2x^2$ meets the x-axis at the points where $x = -\frac{1}{2}$ and $x = 6$.

Draw the graph of $y = 6 + 11x - 2x^2$ for values of x from -1 to 7. [Scales: take 2 cm to represent 1 unit on the x-axis and 2 cm to represent 4 units on the y-axis.]

(i) *Use your graph* to estimate, correct to one decimal place, the positive value of x for which $10 + 11x - 2x^2 = 0$.

(ii) Calculate the area bounded by the curve $y = 6 + 11x - 2x^2$, the positive x-axis and the positive y-axis. [AEB 1978]

22 (i) Find the values of the constants a and b, given that the line $y = 2x$ is the tangent to the curve $y = x^2 + ax + b$ at the point $(2, 4)$.

(ii) Calculate the finite area between the graphs $y = x^2 + 3x$ and $y = 4x$. [O 1977]

23 If $\dfrac{dy}{dx} = 2 + \dfrac{1}{x^2}$, and $y = 2$ when $x = 1$, find an expression for y in terms of x. [L 1976]

24 A particle moves from rest in a straight line. Its velocity, v cm per second, after t seconds, is given by $v = 5t - 2t^2$. Calculate

(a) the velocity after 2 seconds,

(b) the time taken for the particle to come to rest again,

(c) the acceleration after 3 seconds,

(d) the velocity when the acceleration is zero,

(e) the distance travelled in the first 2 seconds. [L 1975]

25 A particle moves in a straight line such that its velocity v metres per second is given after time t seconds by the equation

$$v = 7 + 5t - t^2.$$

Calculate

(i) the acceleration after 1 second,

(ii) the maximum velocity,

(iii) the distance travelled in the third second. [W 1977]

16 Basic geometrical concepts

Literally the word 'geometry' means 'the measurement of the earth.' Its practical origins are as old as when man first began to build shelters and shape primitive tools, and the subject has gradually evolved over at least the last thirty centuries. The number π and many other details about the dimensions of buildings are mentioned in the Bible in Kings II. Books on the history of mathematics can provide a rich source of information for project work on the development of geometry from its origins as a practical necessity to an academic discipline founded on logical structure. A knowledge of surveying was necessary to the ancient Egyptians every time the Nile flooded its banks in order that the boundaries of land ownership could be fairly re-established. Their civil engineering expertise culminated in the building of the pyramids, which are recognised as one of the greatest engineering feats of all time. As trade developed and expanded, the techniques of navigation at sea were established and by the fifth century B.C. man had accumulated a vast amount of practical knowledge and experience about building, navigation and surveying.

The Greeks made an immeasureable contribution to geometry by formalising this practical knowledge and recording their work in the famous books of Euclid. There were many renowned contributors and, by the third century B.C., the subject was held in such high esteem that Plato, in his book *The Republic*, insisted that a knowledge of geometry was a necessity in the education of future statesmen.

After this period, often called 'the golden age of Greece,' the development of geometry remained more or less static until the middle ages, when a new approach using co-ordinate systems led to a rebirth of interest. In spite of this, the Greek influence remained very strong right up to the present century. During the last 200 years many new branches of the subject have been invented and developed and a university mathematician of the present day recognises, and studies, many different geometries, depending on the rules, called axioms, with which he starts each time.

In the next four chapters some of the theoretical and practical aspects of elementary geometry are developed. Most of the work will be confined to a study of figures in two dimensions, but the extension to three dimensions is undertaken where appropriate. The sequence of results is built up in a logical order. It is assumed that readers will be familiar with the basic notions of measuring lines and angles, but for easy reference a number of definitions and the meanings of some frequently used words and phrases are stated.

No attempt is made to define a point, a straight line or a plane. These three elements are intuitive, but some relations exist between them which experience and commonsense should allow the reader to accept.

(a) *Two co-planar lines meet in a point, except when these lines are parallel.*
(b) *A straight line can be drawn joining two points.*
(c) *Two intersecting lines lie in one and only one plane.*
(d) *Three points lie in one and only one plane, provided that the three points are not collinear.*
(e) *Two intersecting planes meet in one and only one line.*
(f) *A straight line and a point, not in the line, lie in one and only one plane.*
(g) *Three intersecting planes meet either in a point, or a line or in three parallel lines.*

Angles and definitions

Complementary angles have a sum of 90°; **supplementary angles** have a sum of 180°.

Angle $\theta°$, such that $0 < \theta < 90$, is called **acute**.

Angle $\theta°$, such that $90 < \theta < 180$, is called **obtuse**.

Angle $\theta°$, such that $180 < \theta < 360$, is called **reflex**.

$90° = 1$ **right angle**; $180° = 2$ right angles, sometimes called a **straight angle**. If three points A, B and C are such that angle ABC $= 180°$, then A, B and C lie in a straight line and are called **collinear** points. If three or more lines all pass through a point, the lines are called **concurrent**.

Example:

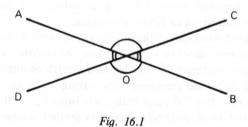

Fig. 16.1

Figure 16.1 shows two lines AB and CD which intersect at O.

Angle AOC + angle COB $= 180°$ (straight line).
Angle BOD + angle COB $= 180°$ (straight line).

Since both of the angles AOC and BOD are equal to $180° -$ angle COB, it follows that angle AOC = angle BOD.

210

The angles AOC and BOD are called **vertically opposite** and are always equal. Another pair of equal and vertically opposite angles are AOD and BOC.

Note on proofs: The method of proof used in the example will appear many times and should be noted carefully.

If $x = y$ and $x = z$, it follows that $y = z$. In the language of algebra, this is known as **the transitive rule**.

Parallel lines

A pair of straight lines which lie in the same plane but never meet are called **parallel**. There are three types of angles which occur when two parallel lines are cut by a third line, called a **transversal**:

(a) **Alternate Angles**   (b) **Corresponding Angles**   (c) **Interior Angles**

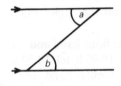   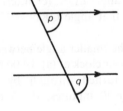   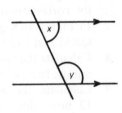

| Fig. 16.2 | Fig. 16.3 | Fig. 16.4 |

The *alternate angles* a and b are equal

$$a = b$$

The *corresponding angles* p and q are equal

$$p = q$$

The *interior* (or *allied*) *angles* x and y are supplementary.

$$x + y = 180°$$

Exercise 16.1

1   State the angle which is complementary to (a) 32°, (b) 43°, (c) $67\frac{1}{2}°$.
2   State the angle which is supplementary to (a) 47°, (b) 113°, (c) $67\frac{1}{2}°$.

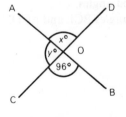   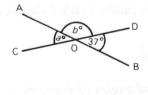   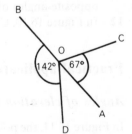

| Fig. 16.5 | Fig. 16.6 | Fig. 16.7 |

211

3 Given that AOB and COD are straight lines, find x and y in Figure 16.5.

4 Given that AOB and COD are straight lines, find a and b in Figure 16.6.

5 In Figure 16.7, AOB is a straight line, find angles BOC and AOD.

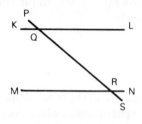

Fig. 16.8

6 In Figure 16.8, name the angle which is (a) alternate to angle KQR, (b) corresponding to angle LQR, (c) interior to angle MRQ.

7 In Figure 16.8, given that angle QRN $= 139°$, find the angles PQL, QRM and LQR.

8 Calculate the size of the smaller angle between the hour hand and the minute hand of a 12 hour clock at (a) 14.00 h, (b) 16.40 h, (c) 18.30 h.

9 Calculate the angle turned through by the minute hand of a 12 hour clock in (a) 30 minutes, (b) 5 minutes, (c) 57 minutes, (d) 100 minutes.

10 The hour hand and the minute hand of a 12 hour clock exactly overlap at noon. Find, in minutes, the time before they next exactly overlap.

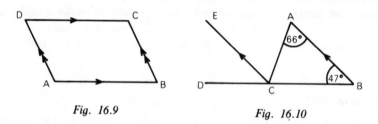

Fig. 16.9   *Fig. 16.10*

11 In Figure 16.9, the opposite sides of ABCD are parallel. Prove that the opposite angles of ABCD are equal, using allied angles.

12 In Figure 16.10, CE is parallel to BA. Calculate angles BCE and ACD.

Practical applications

Angles of elevation and angles of depression

In Figure 16.11, the point B is higher than the point A, AH is horizontal and B, A and H are in the same vertical plane. The angle marked e is called the **angle of elevation** of B from A.

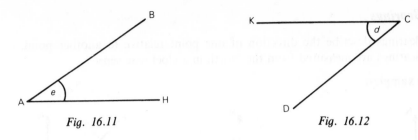

Fig. 16.11

Fig. 16.12

In Figure 16.12, the point D is lower than the point C, CK is horizontal and D, C and K are in the same vertical plane. The angle marked d is called the **angle of depression** of D from C.

In practice, the instrument used for measuring such angles is called a theodolite and one could be made at school. A surveyor's office usually has one which has been manufactured and will possibly offer to loan it.

The compass

The discovery that a stone containing magnetised iron oxide points to the magnetic north or south poles was known to the Chinese in the 3rd millennium B.C. and was probably known in Europe by 1000 B.C. In spite of this, man has only used this property for navigation and surveying in the last 1000 years. In 1840 the Royal Navy introduced a new **magnetic compass** in their ships and this compass, which used 4 parallel magnetised needles, proved so successful that most seafaring nations quickly adopted the instrument. There was still, however, one snag about this compass; the user had to standardise the reading of magnetic north with true north by a calculation or by using tables. In 1911 the **gyroscopic compass**, which always indicates true north, superseded the magnetic compass and it is still in use today.

In Figure 16.13, the sixteen major points of the compass are shown and the angle between adjacent directions is 360/16 degrees = $22\frac{1}{2}°$.

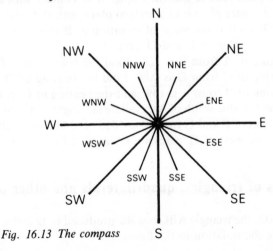

Fig. 16.13 The compass

Bearings

Bearings describe the direction of one point relative to another point. Bearings are measured from the North in a clockwise sense.

Examples:

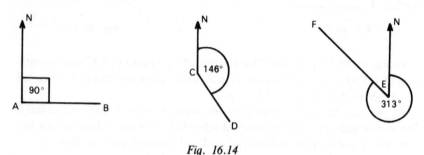

Fig. 16.14

In Figure 16.14, the bearing of B from A is 090°, the bearing of D from C is 146° and the bearing of F from E is 313°.

Back-bearings

If the bearing of B from A is given, the bearing of A from B is known as the back-bearing.

In Figure 16.14, the bearing of A from B is 270°, the bearing of C from D is 326° and the bearing of E from F is 133°.

Exercise 16.2

1 The angle of elevation of B from A is 30°. State the angle of depression of A from B.
2 A square plate ABCD has the corner A in contact with a horizontal table. The square plate is in a vertical plane with B, C and D all higher than A. Given that the angle of elevation of B from A is 37°, find the angles of elevation of C and D from A.
3 The bearing of A from B is 228°. Find the bearing of B from A.
4 The bearing of C from D is 009°. Find the bearing of D from C.
5 The bearing of B from A is 149° and the bearing of C from B is 217°. Given that C is due south of A, calculate (a) angle ABC, (b) angle ACB.
6 The bearings of F and G from E are 328° and 067° respectively. Given that F is due west of G, calculate (a) angle EFG, (b) angle EGF.

The angles of triangles, quadrilaterals and other polygons.

In Figure 16.15, the triangle ABC has BC produced to D and CE is parallel to BA. Using the notation in the figure,

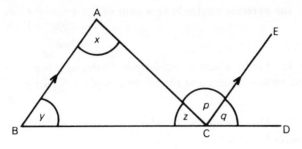

Fig. 16.15

$x = p$ (alternate angles)   and $y = q$ (corresponding angles).

It follows that $x + y = p + q$. That is, angle ACD = angle A + angle B.

An exterior angle of a triangle is equal to the sum of the interior opposite angles.

At the point C, $p + q + z = 180°$ (straight line).

Therefore $x + y + z = 180°$.

The sum of the angles of a triangle is 180°, or the angles of a triangle are supplementary.

The interior and exterior angle sums of polygons

Any closed plane figure which is bounded by straight lines is called a **polygon** and the corners of the figure are called **vertices**. The number of vertices of any polygon is the same as the number of its sides. The simplest polygon is the triangle whose interior angle sum is 180°. Polygons having 4, 5, 6, 7, 8, 9 and 10 sides are called quadrilaterals, pentagons, hexagons, heptagons, octagons, nonagons and decagons respectively. A polygon which has all its sides of the same length and all its interior angles equal is called **regular**. The **equilateral triangle** and the **square** are the regular polygons with three and four sides, respectively. A **convex** polygon has all interior angles less than 180°. A quadrilateral can be divided into two triangles by a line, called a **diagonal**, joining two opposite vertices. Since the interior angles of a triangle add up to 180°, the interior angles of a quadrilateral add up to $2 \times 180° = 360°$.

A pentagon (5 sides) can be divided into three triangles by drawing two diagonals from a vertex. The sum of the interior angles of a pentagon is therefore $3 \times 180° = 540°$. By extending this process we can see that a convex polygon, having n sides, can be divided into $(n-2)$ triangles by drawing $(n-3)$ diagonals from a vertex of the polygon. **The sum of the interior angles of a convex polygon with n sides is, therefore, $180° \times (n-2)$ $= 180n° - 360°$.**

At each vertex of the polygon the interior angle and the exterior angle add up to 180°.

For n vertices, the sum of all the exterior and interior angles $= 180n°$. The interior angles have a sum of $180(n-2)°$.

Therefore **the exterior angles have a sum of** $180n° − 180(n − 2)°$
$$= 180n° − 180n° + 360°$$
$$= \textbf{360}°.$$

Example 1: *Find the sum of the interior angles of a heptagon.*
A heptagon has 7 sides and the interior angles add up to $180(7 − 2)°$
$$= 900°.$$

Example 2: *Find the number of sides of a regular polygon, each of whose interior angles is 156°.*
If each interior angle $= 156°$, each exterior angle $= 180° − 156° = 24°$.
Sum of the exterior angles $= 360°$.
Number of sides of the polygon $= \dfrac{360}{24} = 15$.

Example 3: *The sum of the interior angles of a regular polygon is 3420°. Calculate: (a) the number of sides, (b) the size of an exterior angle.*

(a) If the polygon has x sides, then $180x − 360 = 3420$
$$x − 2 = 19 \text{ and } x = 21.$$
The polygon has 21 sides.

(b) Size of an exterior angle $= \dfrac{360}{21}$ degrees $= 17\tfrac{1}{7}$ degrees.

Exercises 16.3

1   A line XAY is drawn parallel to BC, where ABC is a triangle. If angle $XAB = 32°$ and $YAC = 77°$, calculate the angles of the triangle ABC.
2   The angles of a triangle are in the ratio $1 : 2 : 3$; calculate the size of each angle in this triangle.
3   The angles A, B and C of the triangle ABC are $(3x + 7)$, $(2x + 3)$, and $(4x − 1)$ degrees, respectively. Find the value of x and the size of each angle in the triangle.
4   The interior angles of a quadrilateral are $(3y + 5)$, $(5y + 1)$, $(3y − 21)$ and $4y$ degrees. Find the value of y and hence show that one pair of opposite sides of this quadrilateral are parallel.
5   Three angles in a pentagon are equal and the remaining two angles are supplementary. Calculate the size of one of the three equal angles.
6   Find the sum of the interior angles of a 15 sided polygon.
7   Find the size of an exterior angle of a regular 20 sided polygon. Hence, deduce the size of one of its interior angles.
8   Find the number of sides in a regular polygon, each of whose interior angles is 165°.
9   Find the number of sides in a regular polygon, each of whose exterior angles is one third that of each of its interior angles.
10   Six of the angles of an octagon are each equal to 140° and the remaining two angles are each $x°$. Find the value of x.
11   Prove that a regular hexagon consists of six equal equilateral triangles.

12 The interior angles of a polygon have a sum of $1260°$. Calculate the number of sides of this polygon. Three of the interior angles of the polygon are each $x°$ and the remainder are each $y°$. If $2y = 3x$, calculate the values of x and y.

13 The interior angles of a regular polygon with x sides have a sum which is the same as the total sum of the interior angles of a quadrilateral and a pentagon. Find the value of x.

14 Five of the exterior angles of a polygon are each equal to $30°$. The remaining exterior angles are each equal to x. Given that the sum of the interior angles of this polygon is 4 times the sum of the exterior angles, find: (a) the number of sides of this polygon, (b) the value of x.

15 Two regular polygons have a total of 44 sides and each of their respective exterior angles has a difference of $3°$. Find the number of sides of each of these polygons.

17 The logical development of proofs: congruence and similarity

There are often several methods of proof available for the solution of a geometrical problem at the level of this book. In the books of Euclid, each step forward is justified by deductions from a store of knowledge already established in earlier work. In this way a logical structure is built up, whose foundations depend on the rules (*axioms*) which were laid down at the start. The tools available for solving geometrical problems are much more varied now and, as experience of using these grows, a choice of method is often possible. Elegance, beauty and brevity are factors which help to determine the choice made. The **symmetry** contained in a situation should be utilised. The **plane transformations** described in Chapter 22 are often employed in establishing cases of congruency and similarity. **Vectors** (see Chapter 20) are used for proving properties of incidence, concurrence and collinearity. In more advanced three-dimensional work, vector methods have taken over the longer traditional methods with clarity and much grace. Some of the geometrical work connected with areas of plane figures has been covered in Chapter 3.

It is impossible in a few short chapters to illustrate all the possible geometrical work which could be covered. There should be no dichotomy, however, about the different approaches to geometrical proof. The only ultimate test which should be applied is the logical one, and that in turn implies a clear statement about what is being assumed at the start of a particular problem. For any student, the choice of method with respect to elegance, beauty and brevity, can usually be made only retrospectively, after all the various approaches have been considered in the course of study.

In the development of geometry, practical work usually precedes generalisation, and it is assumed that readers are familiar from their earlier studies with the practical construction exercises which follow. Reference should also be made to Chapter 19.

Congruent triangles

The lengths of the three sides and the sizes of the three angles of any triangle are six items, often called **elements.** These six elements are not independent. The angles of a triangle are supplementary; when two angles are known, the third can be calculated. The sum of the lengths of two sides of a triangle must always exceed the length of the third side. The largest side of a triangle is opposite the largest angle; the smallest side is opposite the smallest angle. The following practical construction exercises are intended to build on these intuitive ideas and to provide experience in deciding the least number of facts which need to be given about a triangle in order to make it unique.

Exercise 17.1

In each of the following, some elements of a triangle are given. If possible, construct the triangle, measure the remaining elements and state whether there are more solution sets than one. If the triangle is impossible to construct, say why.

1 $AB = 5$ cm, $BC = 6$ cm, $CA = 8$ cm.
2 $AB = 5$ cm, $BC = 6$ cm, $CA = 11$ cm.
3 $AB = 5$ cm, $B = 60°$, $C = 70°$.
4 $AB = 5$ cm, $CA = 8$ cm, $A = 48°$.
5 $B = 60°$, $C = 70°$.
6 $AB = 4$ cm, $BC = 6$ cm, $A = 90°$.
7 $AB = 6$ cm, $BC = 4$ cm, $A = 90°$.
8 $AB = 4$ cm, $AC = 5$ cm, $A = 90°$.
9 $AC = 7$ cm, $BC = 5$ cm, $A = 30°$.
10 $AC = 7$ cm, $BC = 3$ cm, $A = 30°$.
11 $AC = 7$ cm, $BC = 3.5$ cm, $A = 30°$.
12 $AB = AC = BC = 7$ cm, $A = 80°$.

In working these exercises, the reader should have found that unique triangles, in the sense that all their elements remained unchanged no matter how many times they were constructed and differently orientated, were obtained in questions 1, 3, 4, 6, 8 and 11; in questions 2, 7, 10 and 12, it is impossible to construct a triangle from the data; in question 5, it is possible to construct an infinite number of triangles, all of which have the same shape but not the same size; in question 9, it is possible to construct two triangles which fit the data.

Further practice and analysis would show that there are four sets of data which *always* lead to a unique triangle, provided, of course, that the inequality rule about the lengths of sides is observed in the case where all three lengths are given. These four sets are:
(a) lengths of all sides given, (see question 1),
(b) lengths of two sides and the size of the angle between them, (see questions 4 and 8),
(c) the sizes of two angles and the length of one side, (see question 3),
(d) a right angle, the length of the hypotenuse and the length of another side, (see questions 6 and 11; in 11 the result is concealed, but still true). These four sets of data give sufficient conditions for two separate triangles to be equal in all respects; such pairs of triangles are called congruent. Two triangles are said to be congruent if, by reasoned argument, it can be shown that one of the following is true:

(a) *Three sides of one triangle are equal to the three sides in the second triangle. (SSS)*

(b) *Two sides and the included angle of one triangle are equal to two sides and the included angle in the second triangle. (SAS)*

(c) *Two angles and a side in one triangle are equal to two angles and the corresponding side in the second triangle. (AAS).*

(d) *Two right-angled triangles have equal hypotenuses and another side of the first is equal to a second side of the other. (RHS).*

If two triangles ABC and PQR are congruent, with A, B and C corresponding to P, Q and R, respectively, then a convenient notation is to write 'The triangles $\frac{ABC}{PQR}$ are congruent'. Equal elements can be identified easily; in this case they are:

$AB = PQ$, $BC = QR$, $CA = RP$, $\hat{A} = \hat{P}$, $\hat{B} = \hat{Q}$ and $\hat{C} = \hat{R}$.

Many of the early results in Euclidean geometry are dependent on proving pairs of triangles congruent. This can be done by finding, with valid reasons, sufficient pairs of equal elements and stating the appropriate case of congruency. Two triangles can also be proved congruent by finding one or a series of isometric transformations (such as translations, reflections, or rotations) which map one triangle onto the other. The following examples illustrate the methods which can be used.

Example 1:   Figure 17.1 shows the triangle ABC in which AB = AC and AD is perpendicular to BC.

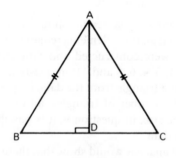

Fig. 17.1

Since BDC is a straight line, angle ADB = angle $ADC = 90°$.
$$AB = AC \text{ (given)},$$
$$AD = AD \text{ (same line)}$$

Therefore triangles $\frac{ABD}{ACD}$ are congruent (RHS)

Since the triangles are congruent, angle BAD = angle CAD, BD = CD and angle ABC = angle ACB, these being the remaining three pairs of elements which were not proved equal in the case of congruency used. The reader should note that for an isosceles triangle ABC, in which AB = AC, the line of symmetry AD can be described in three different ways. The line AD bisects angle BAC, it joins A to the mid-point of BC and AD is

220

perpendicular to BC. It is left as an exercise for the reader to check that each of these descriptions would give rise to a different case of congruency, but still clinch the same final result.

Note: In a triangle which is *not* isosceles, the three descriptions of the line AD given in the last paragraph would produce three different lines called the **internal angle bisector,** the **median** and the **altitude** from A to BC, respectively.

Example 2: *A triangle ABC has equilateral triangles X AB and Y AC drawn as shown in Figure* 17.2. *Prove that XC = YB.*

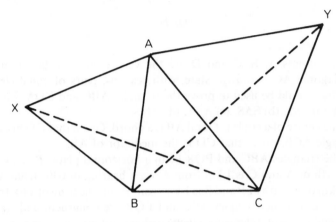

Fig. 17.2

Since triangles XAB and YAC are equilateral, angle XAB = angle YAC = 60°.
It follows that angle XAC = angle YAB (both are 60° + angle BAC)
$$\text{Also} \quad AX = AB \quad \text{(sides of an equilateral triangle)}$$
$$\text{and} \quad AC = AY \quad \text{(sides of an equilateral triangle)}$$
$$\text{Therefore triangles} \quad \begin{matrix} AXC \\ ABY \end{matrix} \quad \text{are congruent (SAS).}$$
The third sides of the congruent triangles are equal; therefore XC = YB.

In a more complicated case of proving congruency, such as this, where the triangles overlap, the reader will probably find it helpful to sketch the triangles separately, marking in equal elements, as shown in Figure 17.3.

An alternative proof: A counter-clockwise rotation, centre A, through 60° on triangle AXC maps A onto A, X onto B and C onto Y. This implies that under this rotation (an isometry), triangle AXC maps onto triangle ABY, thus making the triangles congruent.

Exercise 17.2

1   In the triangle XYZ, XY = XZ and XM is a median. Prove that the triangles XYM and XZM are congruent.

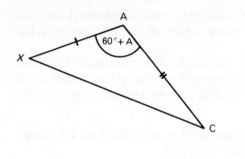
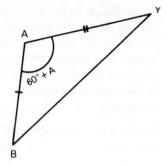

Fig. 17.3

2 The points A, B, C and D are the vertices of a rectangle and the diagonal AC is drawn. State, with reasons, pairs of equal elements which could be used to prove the triangles ABC and CDA congruent by (a) SSS, (b) SAS, (c) ASA, (d) RHS.

3 The centre of a circle is C and AB is a chord. Given that CD bisects the angle ACB, prove that CD is the mediator of AB.

4 The triangles ABC and PQR lie in a horizontal plane; B is 2 km due north of A and C is 1 km from A, on a bearing of 040° from A; Q is 2 km due south of P and R is 1 km from P, on a bearing of 140° from P. Prove that the triangles ABC and PQR are congruent and state the remaining equal elements which you have not used in your proof. Find the acute angle between AC and PR.

5 In the triangle LMN, LM = LN and points X and Y are taken on LM and LN, respectively, such that LX = LY. Prove that MY = NX.

6 The points X and Y are taken on the sides AB and BC of a square ABCD, such that XB = YC. Prove that CX = DY and that DX = AY.

7 The circles, centres A and B, intersect at C and D. Prove that the triangles ACB and ADB are congruent.

8 A quadrilateral whose opposite sides are parallel is called a parallelogram. Using this definition to prove a pair of triangles congruent, deduce that:
(a) the opposite sides of a parallelogram are equal,
(b) the opposite angles of a parallelogram are equal,
(c) the diagonals of a parallelogram bisect each other.

9 The lines AB and CD are at right angles and intersect at P. Given that CP = PD, use congruent triangles to prove that:
(a) the triangles ACD and BCD are isosceles,
(b) the triangles ACB and ADB are congruent.

10 The lines AB and DC are both equal and parallel. Prove that ABCD is a parallelogram.

11 A rhombus is a parallelogram with all sides equal in length. Prove that:
(a) a diagonal divides a rhombus into two congruent isosceles triangles.
(b) the diagonals of a rhombus bisect each other at right angles.

12 The triangle ABC has AB = AC. A line XAY is parallel to BC and AX = AY. Prove that BY = CX.

13 See Figure 17.4.

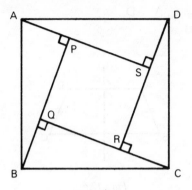

Fig. 17.4

(a) Starting with the right angled triangle ABP, in which AB = x, BP = y and AP = z, describe how this figure could be drawn.

(b) Describe a pair of transformations which, when taken in order, would map triangle ABP onto triangle ADS.

Hence, prove that triangles APD, ASD, DRC and CQB are congruent.

(c) Show that PQ = $y - z$.

(d) By considering areas, show that $(y - z)^2 + 2yz = x^2$.

(e) Deduce that $x^2 = y^2 + z^2$, a proof of the Theorem of Pythagoras.

Special quadrilaterals – a summary of results

Trapezium

Definition: One pair of opposite sides parallel.

No axes of symmetry.

A trapezium is the difference of two similar triangles OR the sum of a parallelogram and a triangle.

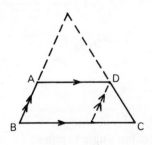

Fig. 17.5

223

Isosceles Trapezium

Definition: A trapezium whose non-parallel sides are equal in length, AB = DC.
Angle properties B = C, A = D.
One axis of symmetry.

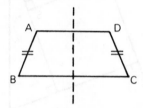

Fig. 17.6

Kite

Definition: One diagonal, AC, is *an axis of symmetry.*
Properties: AB = AD, CB = CD.
angle B = angle D.
AC is perpendicular to BD.
One axis of symmetry.

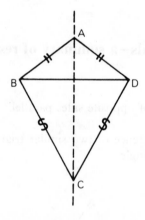

Fig. 17.7

Arrowhead
(Reflex kite)

Definition: As for a kite, but angle C reflex.
Properties: As for kite, but note: AC *produced* is perpendicular to BD.

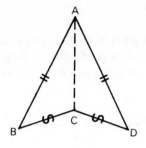

Fig. 17.8

Parallelogram

Definition: Opposite sides parallel.
Properties: AB = DC, AD = BC.
Opposite angles equal.
Diagonals bisect each other.
Rotational symmetry of order 2; *no axes of symmetry.*

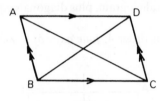

Fig. 17.9

Rhombus

Definition: A parallelogram with all sides equal.
Properties: As for a parallelogram plus diagonals are perpendicular to each other.
Diagonals bisect opposite angles.
Rotational symmetry of order 2; *two axes of symmetry.*

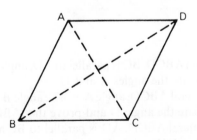

Fig. 17.10

Rectangle

Definition: A parallelogram with all angles equal.
Properties: As for a parallelogram, plus the diagonals are equal in length.
Rotational symmetry of order 2; *two axes of symmetry.*

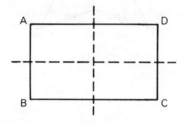

Fig. 17.11

Square

Definition: A parallelogram with all sides equal and all angles equal.
Properties: As for parallelogram, plus diagonals equal and perpendicular to each other.
Rotational symmetry of order 4; *four axes of symmetry.*

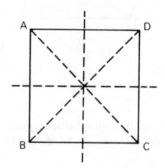

Fig. 17.12

Exercise 17.3

1   In the trapezium ABCD, BC is parallel to AD, angle B = 72° and angle C = 42°. Calculate the angles A and D.
2   In the quadrilateral ABCD, angle A = 47°, angle B = 59° and angle C = 121°. Calculate the angle D and prove that ABCD is a trapezium.
3   In the quadrilateral ABCD, AD is parallel to BC and $\hat{A} = \hat{D} = 116°$. Prove that AB = DC and find angle B.
4   In the arrowhead ABCD, AC is the axis of symmetry and the interior

angles BAD and BCD are 48° and 228°, respectively. Calculate angle ABC and prove that BC produced is perpendicular to AD.

5 In the quadrilateral ABCD, AB = AC = AD and the angles B and D are 70° and 65°, respectively. Prove that angle A is 90°.

6 In the parallelogram ABCD, angles BDC and DCA are equal. Prove that ABCD is a rectangle.

7 In the parallelogram ABCD, angles BDC and DBC are equal. Prove that ABCD is a rhombus.

8 An equilateral triangle ABX is drawn with one side coinciding with a side of the square ABCD, such that X lies inside the square. Calculate the size of the angle CXD.

9 The kite ABCD has AB = AD = 6 cm, and BC = CD = 8 cm. Calculate the area of the kite and the distance BD, given that $\hat{B} = \hat{D} = 90°$.

10 Given that $P = \{$parallelograms$\}$, $R = \{$rhombuses$\}$, $T = \{$rectangles$\}$ and $S = \{$squares$\}$, display this information in a labelled Venn diagram.

11 The universal set is all quadrilaterals having one, and only one, axis of symmetry. Use a labelled Venn diagram to classify the different sets of quadrilaterals with this property.

12 In the isosceles trapezium ABCD, AB = 2a and AD = DC = CA = a. Prove that angle ADC = 120°.

13 Through each corner of the rectangle ABCD a line is drawn parallel to a diagonal of the rectangle. Prove that these lines are the sides of a rhombus.

14 Through each corner of a parallelogram ABCD a line is drawn which bisects the respective interior angle of the parallelogram. Prove that the four lines so drawn form the sides of a rectangle.

15 A line AB is divided internally in golden section at C if the area of the rectangle with sides AB and BC is equal to the area of the square with sides of length AC. If AB = 10 cm, find the length of AC. (*Hint:* Take AC = x cm, CB = $(10-x)$ cm, form a quadratic equation and solve it.)

Similar triangles

Definition: Two polygons are **similar** if, and only if, corresponding angles are equal and the ratios of the lengths of corresponding sides are all the same.

Three sets of conditions ensure that a pair of triangles are similar:

(a) *If two triangles are equiangular, they are similar.*

(b) *If the ratios of the lengths of two sides of one triangle are the same as the ratios of the lengths of two sides of a second triangle, and the angles between these sides are equal, the triangles are similar.*

(c) *If the ratios of the lengths of all sides in one triangle are equal to the ratios of the lengths of all sides in the second triangle, the triangles are similar.*

These three conditions can be verified in the same way as the cases of congruency were checked, by drawing. They can also be proved generally but the proofs are no longer expected to be written formally by students. The recognition of the existence of similar triangles, or other similar figures, in a given situation is extremely important and can save much time and space in writing solutions. The whole system of calculations used in trigonometry, involving ratios like sine, cosine and tangent, has been built up from a use of similar right-angled triangles. Every time a set of trigonometry tables is used in a calculation a similarity relation is being applied.

Note: A word of caution is needed in conclusion about the conditions required to make two figures similar. *For triangles, they are similar if they are equiangular and they are equiangular if they are similar. This is not generally true for other polygons.* A rectangle and a square are equiangular, but they are clearly not similar.

Example 1:

In Figure 17.13, $\dfrac{OA}{OC} = \dfrac{OB}{OD}$, *$OA = 4$ cm, $OC = 5$ cm and $AB = 6$ cm. Prove that AB is parallel to DC and find the length of CD.*

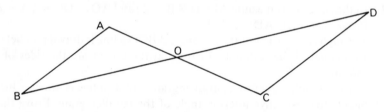

Fig. 17.13

The angles AOB and COD are equal (vertically opposite). Since the sides of the triangles AOB and COD enclosing these equal angles are in the same ratio (given), the triangles are similar. Since the triangles AOB and COD are similar, they are also equiangular. In particular, angle OAB = angle OCD and these are alternate angles for the lines AB and DC. *Therefore AB is parallel to DC.*

Since the sides of similar triangles are in the same ratio,

$$\frac{OA}{OC} = \frac{AB}{DC} \Rightarrow \frac{4}{5} = \frac{6}{DC} \Rightarrow DC = 7.5 \text{ cm}$$

Example 2: *In Figure 17.14, the triangle ABC is right angled at B and BP is perpendicular to AC. Prove that (a) triangles ABC, APB and BPC are similar, (b) $AB^2 = AP.AC$, (c) $AB^2 + BC^2 = AC^2$.*

(a) If angle ACB = x, angle PBC = $90° - x$ (angle sum of triangle)
Therefore angle ABP = x.
The triangles ABC, APB and BPC are equiangular and are therefore similar.

(b) From the similar triangles ABC and APB, $\dfrac{AB}{AC} = \dfrac{AP}{AB} \Rightarrow AB^2 = AP.AC$

228

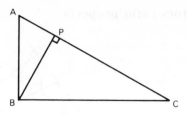

Fig. 17.14

(c) From the similar triangles ABC and BPC, $\dfrac{BC}{AC} = \dfrac{PC}{BC} \Rightarrow BC^2 = PC \cdot AC$

Adding these results gives $AB^2 + BC^2 = AC(AP + PC) = AC^2$, which proves the Theorem of Pythagoras.

Exercise 17.4

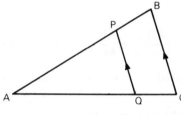

Fig. 17.15

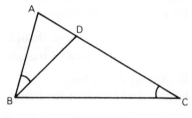

Fig. 17.16

Questions 1–5 refer to Figure 17.15 and questions 6–8 refer to Figure 17.16.

1 Given that AP = QC = 3 cm and AQ = 4.5 cm, find PB.
2 Given that AB = 6 cm and AQ = 2 QC, find PB.
3 Given that AQ:AC = 3:5, AB = 7.5 and PQ = 4 cm, find AP and BC.
4 Given that PQ = QC = 4 cm, BC = 5 cm and AB = 18 cm, find AQ and PB.
5 Given that angle ABC = 90°, AB = 24 cm, BC = 10 cm and AP = 18 cm, find AC and AQ.
6 Prove that triangles ABC and ADB are similar (Figure 17.16).
7 Given that AB = 7 cm and AC = 10.5 cm, find AD.
8 Given that AD = 4 cm and DC = 5 cm, find AB.
9 Any point P is taken on the line joining the fixed points A and B. Prove that for any line through P the ratio of the perpendicular distances from A and B to this line are constant.
10 Two fixed lines AB and CD intersect at O. Given that AC is parallel to DB, prove that triangles OAC and OBD are similar. If AO = 3 cm, BO = 5 cm and CD = 10 cm, find OD.

The angle bisectors ratio property

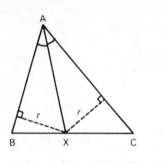

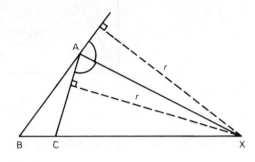

Fig. 17.17

Fig. 17.18

In Figure 17.17, AX is the internal bisector of angle A in triangle ABC. In Figure 17.18, AX is the external bisector of angle A in triangle ABC. In both figures the point X is equidistant from AB and AC (The locus property of an angle bisector, or congruent triangles, could be used to prove this). Using the notation in the figures:

$$\frac{\text{area of triangle ABX}}{\text{area of triangle ACX}} = \frac{\frac{1}{2}AB.r}{\frac{1}{2}AC.r} = \frac{AB}{AC} \qquad \text{(i)}$$

Regarding BC as base line the triangles ABX and ACX have a common height, the altitude of the triangle ABC.

Therefore $\qquad \dfrac{\text{area of triangle ABX}}{\text{area of triangle ACX}} = \dfrac{\frac{1}{2}BX.\text{altitude}}{\frac{1}{2}XC.\text{altitude}} = \dfrac{BX}{XC} \qquad$ (ii)

From (i) and (ii) $\qquad \dfrac{BX}{XC} = \dfrac{AB}{AC} \qquad$ (iii)

The internal and external bisectors of the vertical angle of a triangle divide the base, internally and externally respectively, in the ratio of the other two sides.

Example: *Using the notation above, consider the triangle ABC in which AB = 7 cm, AC = 5 cm and BC = 9 cm.*
Taking BX = x cm and CX = $(9-x)$ cm and applying (iii) in Figure 17.17
$x/(9-x) = 7/5$, that is $5x = 63 - 7x$ ∴ $12x = 63$ ∴ $x = 5.25$.
Taking BX = y cm and CX = $(y-9)$ cm and applying (iii) in Figure 17.18
$y/(y-9) = 7/5$, that is $5y = 7y - 63$ ∴ $2y = 63$ ∴ $y = 31.5$.
In this triangle the internal and external bisectors of angle A cut BC at points whose distances from B are 5.25 cm and 31.5 cm respectively.

Exercise 17.5

Questions 1 to 4 refer to a triangle ABC, in which the internal and external angle bisectors of the angle A cut BC and BC produced at X and Y, respectively.

1 Given that AB = 4 cm, BC = 5 cm and CA = 2 cm, find BX and BY.
2 Given that AB = 10 cm, BC = 12 cm and CA = 5 cm, find CX and CY.
3 Given that AB = 6 cm, BC = 8 cm and BX = 5 cm, find AC and BY.
4 Given that AC = 4 cm, BC = 6 cm and CY = 12 cm, find AB and CX.
5 In the triangle ABC, the mid-point of BC is D. The internal bisectors of angles ADB and ADC meet AB and AC at X and Y, respectively. Prove that $\dfrac{AX}{XB} = \dfrac{AY}{YC}$.

18 Circle properties

All points on a curve called a **circle** are at the same distance (the **radius**) from a fixed point (the **centre**). In everyday language there are two meanings of the word circle; it can mean the curve itself, or it can mean the region bounded by the curve. When there is a possibility of ambiguity, the curve itself can be distinguished by calling it the **circumference** of the circle.

Any line which passes through the centre of a circle and reaches the circumference at each end is called a **diameter**. All diameters are axes of symmetry. A diameter divides a circle into two **semi-circles**. Any line, not passing through the centre of a circle, which intersects the circumference and splits the circle into two regions is called a **secant**; the part of a secant which lies within a circle and includes the two intersection points with the circumference is called a **chord**. When a chord is drawn, the smaller region into which the circle is partitioned is called the **minor segment** and the larger is called the **major segment**; the boundaries of segments which are parts of the circumference of the circle are called **arcs**. Any line which touches a circle is called a **tangent**; a tangent meets the circumference of a circle at one and only one point, called the **point of contact**.

Two circles having different centres but equal radii are congruent; in particular they have the same area and can be completely superimposed one on the other. Two circles with the same centre but different radii are called **concentric**; a diameter of the larger contains the corresponding diameter of the smaller. The line joining the centres of two circles of different radii is clearly an axis of symmetry for both.

If the reader has not met any of the terms given in this introduction in previous work, it is suggested that a large diagram is drawn and labelled to show the meanings of each term.

The symmetrical properties of chords of a circle

Example 1: *To show that the perpendicular bisector of a chord of a circle passes through the centre of the circle.*
In Figure 18.1, AB is a chord of the circle, centre C. The perpendicular bisector of AB is, by definition, the line for which any member point P has the property that AP = BP.
Since C is the centre of the circle, CA = CB = the radius of the circle and it follows that C is a member of the set of points defined by P.

232

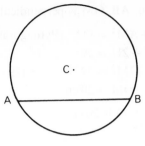

Fig. 18.1

The following properties can be deduced from the last result, or proved by congruent triangles. The notation in Figure 18.1 is used.

(a) The straight line which joins C to the mid-point of AB is perpendicular to AB.

(b) The line drawn from C perpendicular to AB cuts AB in half.

In Figure 18.2, the chords AB and CD are of the same length, O is the centre of the circle.

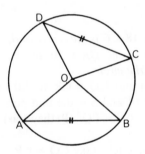

Fig. 18.2

OA = OC = OB = OD (radii)
and AB = CD (given)

Therefore triangles $\dfrac{\text{OAB}}{\text{OCD}}$ are congruent, SSS. Chords of equal length are the same distance from the centre of the circle, since the corresponding altitudes of the congruent triangles are equal in length.

The converse of this result is also true. If two chords are equidistant from the centre of a circle, they are equal in length. The proof is left as an exercise for the reader.

Since the triangles OAB and OCD are congruent it also follows that the angles AOB and COD are equal. The angle AOB is often called the angle at the centre for chord AB, or the angle at the centre subtended by the chord (or minor arc) AB.

Example 2: *In Figure 18.3, the chord AB is of length 42 cm and the radius of the circle is 29 cm. Find the distance of AB from the centre O.*

If M is the mid-point of AB, OM is perpendicular to AB. AM = 21 cm.

$$OM^2 + AM^2 = OA^2 \text{ (Pythagoras)}$$
$$OM^2 + 21^2 = 29^2$$
$$OM^2 = 29^2 - 21^2 = (29 - 21)(29 + 21) = 400$$
$$OM = 20 \text{ cm.}$$

The distance of AB from O is 20 cm.

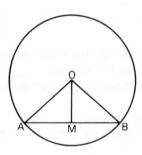

Fig. 18.3

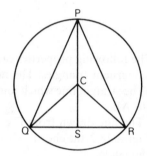

Fig. 18.4

Example 3: *In Figure* 18.4, *C is the centre of the circle passing through P,
Q and R; PQ = PR = 13 cm, QR = 10 cm and PCS is a straight line.
Calculate the radius of the circle.*

Since PQ = PR (given) and CQ = CR (radii) the line PCS is the perpendicular bisector of QR and S is the mid-point of QR. QS = 5 cm.
In triangle PQS, $PS^2 + QS^2 = PQ^2$ (Pythagoras). $PS^2 = 13^2 - 5^2 = 144$
$$PS = 12 \text{ cm.}$$

As C is the centre of the circle, take CQ = CP = r cm. CS = $(12 - r)$ cm.
In triangle CQS, $CQ^2 = CS^2 + QS^2$ (Pythagoras), giving the equation
$$r^2 = (12 - r)^2 + 5^2$$
$$r^2 = 144 - 24r + r^2 + 25$$
$$24r = 169 \text{ and } r = 169/24 = 7\tfrac{1}{24}.$$

Therefore radius = $7\tfrac{1}{24}$ cm.

Exercise 18.1

1   In figure 18.3, AM = MB = 9 cm and OM = 12 cm. Find the radius of
    the circle.

2   In Figure 18.3, AM = MB = 8 cm and the radius of the circle is 15 cm.
    Calculate OM.

3   A chord HK of length 16 cm is placed in a circle, centre C, of radius
    10 cm. Calculate the distance from C to HK.

4   An equilateral triangle, each side of length 10 cm, is inscribed in a
    circle. Calculate the radius of this circle.

5   The point X is on the diameter AB of a circle; AX = 4 cm and XB
    = 16 cm. Find the length of the chord through X perpendicular to AB.

6 Two parallel chords of a circle, of radius 6.5 cm, are of lengths 5 cm and 12 cm. Given that the chords are on opposite sides of the centre, find the distance between them.

7 In a circle of radius 7.5 cm, several chords of length 12 cm are drawn. Show that the centres of all these chords lie on a circle. Find the radius of the circle.

8 Two circles, centres P and Q, intersect at R and S. The mid-point of RS is M. Prove that P, M and Q are collinear.

9 The lines AB and AC are equal in length and chords of a circle, centre O. Prove that the bisector of angle BAC passes through O.

10 Two concentric circles have radii 6 cm and 10 cm. The line ABCD cuts the first circle at B and C and the second circle at A and D. Given that BC = 8 cm, prove that AB = 4($\sqrt{5}$ − 1) cm.

11 In Figure 18.4, C is the centre of the circle passing through P, Q and R; PQ = PR = 20 cm, QR = 24 cm, and P, C and S are collinear. Calculate the radius of the circle.

12 Two circles of different radii intersect at P and Q. Parallel lines APB and CQD are drawn, A and C being on the circumference of the first circle and B and D being on the circumference of the second circle. Prove that AB = CD.

13 Two circles, centres A and B, of radii 10 cm and 17 cm, respectively, intersect at P and Q. Given that PQ = 16 cm, calculate the distance AB.

14 Take perpendicular co-ordinate axes Ox and Oy on graph paper. Draw any two circles which have their centres on Ox and pass through the point (4, 3). Find the co-ordinates of their second point of intersection.

15 The co-ordinates of the centre of a circle of radius r are (a, b). Show that for any point (x, y) on the circumference of the circle
$$(x - a)^2 + (y - b)^2 = r^2.$$

Angle properties

The angle which an arc of a circle subtends at the centre is double any angle which the same arc, or an equal arc, subtends at any point on the remaining part of the circumference.

The fixed points A and B are on the circumference of a circle, centre O. A point P is taken on the major arc AB, as shown in Figure 18.5. The line PO is produced to K.

Since OA = OP (radii), denoting angle APO by x, angle PAO = x.

Since the exterior angle of a triangle is equal to the sum of the interior opposite angles, angle AOK = $x + x = 2x$.

Denoting angle BPO by y, it follows by the same argument that
$$\text{angle BOK} = 2y.$$

The angle subtended by AB at the centre is AOB = $2x + 2y = 2(x + y)$.
The angle subtended by AB at the circumference = APB = $x + y$.
Therefore angle AOB is twice angle APB.

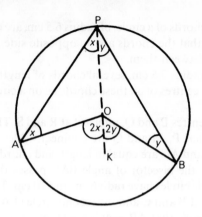

Fig. 18.5

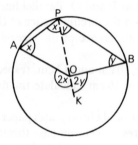

Fig. 18.6

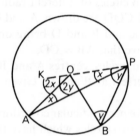

Fig. 18.7

Figure 18.6 shows the situation when A and B take positions such that angle AOB is reflex. The argument used for Figure 18.5 applies, the result being that *the reflex angle AOB is twice angle APB*.

Figure 18.7 shows the situation when P takes a position for which the line AP crosses the line OB and in this case a modification to the final stages of the proof is required.

Angle subtended by AB at the centre = angle AOB
$$= 2y - 2x = 2(y - x).$$
Angle subtended by AB at P = angle APB = $y - x$.

The angle AOB is twice the angle APB for all positions of A, B and P.

Three very important angle properties of a circle can be deduced from this fundamental result.

(a) The angle subtended in a semicircle is a right angle.

In Figure 18.8, AOB is a diameter of the circle, centre O and P is any point on the circumference.

Angle AOB = 180° (straight line) and this is the angle subtended by AB at the centre.

The angle APB is therefore 90°, half the angle subtended at the centre.

236

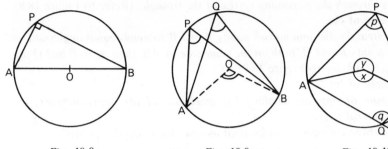

| Fig. 18.8 | Fig. 18.9 | Fig. 18.10 |

(b) Angles in the same segment are equal.

In Figure 18.9, O is the centre of the circle, the points A, B, P and Q being on the circumference.

Angle AOB = twice angle APB   (The angle subtended at the centre is
Angle AOB = twice angle AQB   twice the angle subtended at the
                                                            circumference by the same arc.)

Therefore angle APB = angle AQB = any other angle subtended by AB in this segment.

(c) Angles subtended in opposite segments are supplementary.

In Figure 18.10 the points A, B, P and Q are on the circumference and the angles subtended at the centre and circumference by the major and minor arcs AB are shown. Using the notation in the figure.

$x = 2p$ (The angle subtended at the centre is twice the angle
$y = 2q$ subtended at the circumference)

But $x + y = 360°$ since their sum is the complete revolution at the centre. *It follows that $p + q = 180°$, and since p and q can represent any angle in their respective segments, angles subtended in opposite segments are supplementary.*

It is always possible to construct a circle to pass through three non-collinear points (see chapter 19, Figure 19.2).

If four, or more, points, lie on the circumference of a circle they are called **concyclic** points. In particular, when four points lie on a circle, the quadrilateral formed by the straight lines joining them is called a **cyclic quadrilateral**. In Figure 18.10, the quadrilateral APBQ is cyclic. Since $p + q = 180°$ and the angle sum of any quadrilateral is 360°, **the opposite angles of a cyclic quadrilateral are supplementary**. In Figure 18.10 produce AQ to X as shown.

Since AQX is a straight line, angle BQX + q = 180°
Since APBQ is cyclic, $p + q = 180°$
Therefore   angle BQX = p.

The interior angle of a cyclic quadrilateral is equal to the exterior opposite angle.

The converses of the results given and proved in (a), (b) and (c) are true and are now stated:

Converse of (a)

The circle drawn on the hypotenuse of a right angled triangle as diameter

237

passes through the remaining vertex of the triangle. (Refer to Figure 18.8).

Converse of (b)

If the straight line joining two points A and B subtends equal angles at two other points P and Q, both on the same side of AB, then A, B, P and Q are concyclic. (Refer to Figure 18.9).

Converse of (c)

If a pair of opposite angles of a quadrilateral are supplementary, the quadrilateral is cyclic.

The three converses can be used as tests for concyclic points.

Example 1: *In Figure 18.11, ABC and AOQ are straight lines and O is the centre of the circle. Given that angle PBC = 56° and angle PAB = 30°, calculate the angles AQP, QAP and BOQ.*

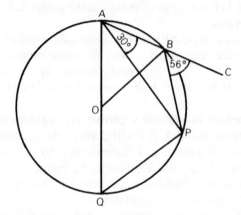

Fig. 18.11

The quadrilateral ABPQ is cyclic, angle AQP = angle PBC = 56° (interior angle equals exterior opposite angle)

The angle APQ is 90° (angle in a semicircle, since AOB is a diameter)

Therefore angle QAP is 34° (third angle of triangle AQP)

Angle QOB is twice angle QAB (angle at centre twice that at circumference)

But angle QAB = 34° + 30° = 64°

Therefore angle QOB is 128°.

Example 2: *In Figure 18.12, ABCD is a cyclic quadrilateral whose sides when produced meet at P and Q as shown. Using the notation in the figure, find v in terms of x and y.*

Since the exterior angle of a triangle is equal to the sum of the interior opposite angles,

angle BAD = $v + y$ and angle BCD = $v + x$.

Since ABCD is cyclic, angle BAD + angle BCD = 180° (opposite angles supplementary)

Therefore $v + y + v + x = 180°$

That is $v = \frac{1}{2}(180° - x - y)$.

Example 3: *In Figure 18.13, BM and CN are altitudes of triangle ABC. Prove that (a) B, C, M and N are concyclic, (b) angle NBM = angle NCM.*

238

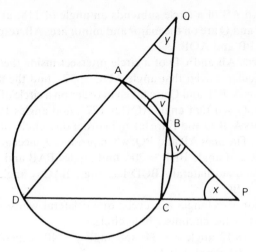

Fig. 18.12

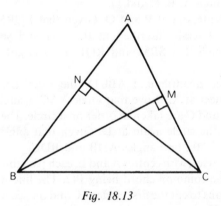

Fig. 18.13

Since the angles BNC and BMC are equal (both right angles) by the converse of angles in the same segment are equal, it follows that B, C, M and N are concyclic. (It is worth noting that in this case the circle passing through these points has BC as a diameter.)

Since the points are concyclic, quadrilateral BCMN is cyclic and for the chord MN the angles NBM and NCM are in the same segment and are therefore equal.

Exercise 18.2

1   A circle, centre O, passes through the points A, B and C. Given that angle AOB = 120° and angle BOC = 140°, find the angles of triangle ABC.

239

2 The chord AB of a circle subtends an angle of 118° at the centre O. Points P and Q are on the major and minor arcs AB, respectively. Find angles APB and AQB.

3 The chords AB and CD of a circle intersect inside the circle and are perpendicular. Given that angle ADC = 32°, find the angle DCB.

4 The points A, B, P and Q are taken in order on a circle of which AB is a diameter. Given that angle AQP is 127°, find angles PBA and PAB.

5 The points A, B, Q and P are taken in order on a circle, of which AB is a diameter. The lines AB and PQ, when produced, meet at R. Given that BP = BR and angle BRP = 20°, find angles PAB and QBR.

6 The cyclic quadrilateral ABCD has angle BAC = angle ADB. Prove that BA = BC.

7 Prove that a rectangle is a cyclic quadrilateral whose diagonals are diameters of the circumscribing circle.

8 In Figure 18.12, angle $x = 34°$ and angle $y = 40°$. Calculate the angles of the quadrilateral ABCD.

9 In Figure 18.12, angle D = 56° and angle A = 100°. Find x and y.

10 The diagonals of the cyclic quadrilateral ABCD meet at O; angle BOC = 98° and angle BDC = 49°. Prove that O is the centre of the circle passing through A, B, C and D.

11 Two circles intersect at P and Q. Given that PQRS and PQLM are cyclic quadrilaterals inscribed in the first and second circles, respectively, such that SPM and RQL are straight lines, prove that RS ∥ LM.

12 In the cyclic quadrilateral ABCD, the sides BA and CD, when produced, meet at X. Prove that angle XAC = angle XDB.

13 Points A, B and C are taken in order on a circle. The bisector of angle ABC meets the circle again at D. Given that angle ABC = 58° and angle BAD = 70°, find angles ADB and BDC.

14 Two equal circles, with centres A and B, each pass through the centre of the other, the common chord being PQ. The line AB is produced in both directions to cut the first circle at C and the second at D. Calculate the angle CPD.

15 A square ABCD is inscribed in a circle and any point P is taken on the minor arc AB. Calculate the values of angles DPC and APB. Prove that angle PDA + angle PCB = 45°.

16 A regular pentagon ABCDE is inscribed in a circle, centre O. Calculate the angles AOB, ACB and OAC.

17 Three points A, B and C are chosen on the circumference of a circle, such that triangle ABC is acute-angled. The diameters BX and CY of the circle are drawn. Prove that angle XAC = angle YAB.

18 Two chords of a circle, PQ and PR, are equal in length. The bisector of angle PQR meets the circle at X. The lines PX and QR are produced to meet at Y. Prove that PR = RY.

19 Take a diameter AB of a circle centre O and any point P on the circumference. By considering the isosceles triangles OPA and OPB, prove that the angle APB = 90°.

20 Draw any cyclic quadrilateral ABCD and its circumscribing circle, centre O. Join AO, BO, CO and DO. By considering the isosceles triangles so formed (e.g. triangle OAB) prove from first principles that the opposite angles of a cyclic quadrilateral are supplementary.

21 Name the quadrilateral which has (a) the properties of both a parallelogram and a cyclic quadrilateral, (b) the properties of both a rhombus and a cyclic quadrilateral.

22 (a) Prove that any isosceles trapezium is a cyclic quadrilateral. (b) A cyclic quadrilateral has one pair of opposite sides equal; prove that the other pair of opposite sides are parallel.

23 An equilateral triangle ABC has BD as the bisector of angle ABC, and DC is perpendicular to BC. Prove that A, B, C and D are concyclic.

24 In the triangle ABC, AP is an altitude and N is the mid-point of AB. By considering the circle drawn on AB as diameter, prove that triangle PNB is isosceles.

The mid-points of BC and AC are L and M, respectively. Prove that the points P, L, M and N, when joined, form an isosceles trapezium. Hence, deduce that these points are also concyclic.

25 Through the vertex A of a rectangle ABCD a line is drawn perpendicular to AC, to meet CD produced at P and CB produced at Q. Prove that the points B, D, P and Q are concyclic.

Tangent properties

A line which meets a circle in one and only one point, no matter how far it is produced in either direction, is called a **tangent**, it being assumed that the line and the circle are in the same plane.

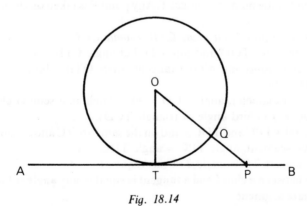

Fig. 18.14

Figure 18.14 shows a circle, centre O and radius r, and a tangent AB which meets (touches) the circle at T.

Take any point P on the tangent and join OP to cut the circle at Q.
$$OP = OQ + QP = r + QP.$$

Since OT = r, OP ⩾ OT for all positions of P on AB, and equality occurs only when P and T are coincident.

OT is therefore the shortest distance from O to AB.

It follows that angle OTP = 90°.

The radius of a circle drawn to the point of contact of a tangent is perpendicular to the tangent.

Conversely, a line drawn perpendicular to the tangent of a circle at the point of contact passes through the centre of the circle.

The alternate segment property

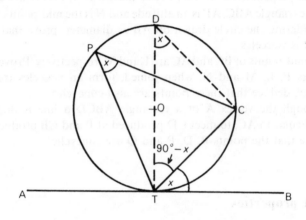

Fig. 18.15

In Figure 18.15, ATB is a tangent to the circle centre O and CT is a chord with one end at the point of contact T. Any point P is taken on the major arc TC.

It is required to prove that angle CTB = angle CPT.

Draw the diameter TOD and join CD. Let angle CTB = x.

Since OT is a radius and ATB a tangent, angle OTB = 90°.

Angle OTC = 90° − x.

Since TD is a diameter, angle TCD = 90°. (Angle in a semi-circle)

Angle TDC = x (Third angle of triangle TCD).

Since the angles TPC and TDC stand on the same arc TC and are subtended in the same segment, angle TPC = angle TDC = x.

Therefore angle CTB = angle TPC, as required.

The angle between a chord and a tangent is equal to any angle subtended in the alternate segment.

Tangents from an external point to a circle

In Figure 18.16, O is the centre of a given circle and P any external point.

242

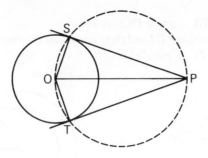

Fig. 18.16

The circle drawn on OP as diameter cuts the given circle at S and T as shown. Join PS, PT, OS and OT.

Since OP is a diameter of the dotted constructed circle, angles OSP and OTP are each 90° (angles in semicircles).

Since OS and OT are radii and angles OSP and OTP are 90°, the lines PS and PT are the tangents from P to the given circle.

The line OP is an axis of symmetry and S maps onto T under reflection in the line OP. *The triangles OSP and OTP are congruent and the tangents PS and PT are equal in length.*

Two tangents can be drawn from an external point to a circle. The tangents are equal in length.

Example 1: *In Figure* 18.17, *ATB is a tangent and PT, CT and QT are chords. Given that angle CTA = 136° and TC = TP, find angles CQT and PTA. Deduce that PC is parallel to AB.*

The angle CTA is between chord CT and tangent AT and angle CQT is subtended by CT in the alternate segment.

Therefore angle CTA = angle CQT = 136°.

Angle CPT + angle CQT = 180° (CQTP is a cyclic quadrilateral)

Therefore angle TPC = 44°.

Since PT = TC, angle PCT = 44°.

The angle PTA is between chord PT and tangent TA and angle PCT is subtended by PT in the alternate segment.

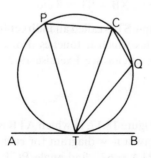

Fig. 18.17

Therefore angle PTA = angle PCT = 44°
Since angle CPT = angle PTA and these angles are alternate between PC and AB, it follows that PC is parallel to AB.

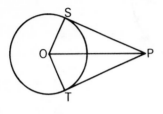

Fig. 18.18

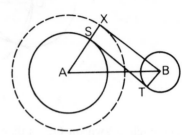

Fig. 18.19

Example 2: *In Figure* 18.18, *PS and PT are tangents to the circle centre O. Given that OS = 7 cm and OP = 25 cm, find the length of PS.*
The angle OSP is 90° (radius perpendicular to tangent).
$OS^2 + SP^2 = OP^2$ (Pythagoras). Therefore $SP^2 = 25^2 - 7^2 = 625 - 49$
$$= 476$$

The length of SP = 24 cm.

Example 3: *In Figure* 18.19, *ASX is a straight line, BX is a tangent to the dotted circle whose centre is A, and ST is a common tangent to both the other circles. Given that AS = 4 cm, BT = 2 cm and AB = 10 cm, find: (a) the radius of the dotted circle, (b) the length of ST.*
Since X, S and T are contact points of tangents and AX, AS and BT are the respective radii, the angles AXB, AST and BTS are all 90°.
Therefore XSTB is a rectangle.
SX = TB = 2 cm and AX = (4 + 2) cm = 6 cm.
The radius of the dotted circle is 6 cm, the *sum* of the radii of the other two circles.
In the right angled triangle AXB, $AX^2 + XB^2 = AB^2$ (Pythagoras).
$$6^2 + XB^2 = 10^2$$
Therefore $XB^2 = 10^2 - 6^2 = 64$
$$XB = 8 \text{ cm.}$$
Since XSTB is a rectangle, XB = ST = 8 cm.

Note: In this last example ST is called an **indirect (or transverse) common tangent** to the two circles which it touches. For an example of a **direct common tangent** to two circles, see Exercise 19.2, questions 9 and 10.

Exercise 18.3

Questions 1–6 refer to Figure 18.17, in which ATB is a tangent and PT, CT and QT are chords. Draw a new diagram for each question.
1   Given that angle PTA = 62°, find angle PCT.
2   Given that angle CTB = 55°, find angles TPC and TQC.

3 Given that angle TCQ = 32° find angle QTA.

4 Given that angle TPC = 40°, find angles CQT and CTA.

5 Given that angle CTB = angle CTP = 57°, find angles CPT, PCT and CQT.

6 Given that angle PCT = 67° and angle TCQ = 42°, find angles ATQ and PTQ.

Questions 7–12 refer to Figure 18.18, in which PS and PT are tangents to the circle, centre O. Draw a new diagram for each question.

7 Given that angle TOP = 53°, find angle SPO.

8 Prove that quadrilateral SOTP is cyclic. Deduce that angle SPO = angle STO.

9 Given that PS = 16 cm and OP = 20 cm, find OS.

10 Given that OS = 5 cm and OP = 13 cm, find the perimeter of the quadrilateral SOTP.

11 If OS = SP, prove that angle STO is 45°.

12 If OP = 10 cm and angle SPT = 60°, find OS.

13 Two circles centres A and B, of different radii, touch each other externally at T. Prove that ATB is a straight line. (See Figure 18.20).

14 Two circles centres A and B, touch each other internally at T. Prove that ABT is a straight line. (See Figure 18.21).

15 In Figure 18.22, O is the centre of both circles and the chord AB of the larger is a tangent of the smaller. If the radii of the circles are 8 cm and 17 cm, find the length of AB.

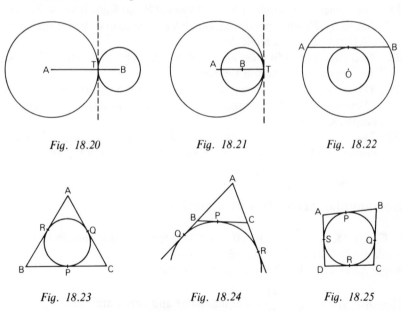

Fig. 18.20   Fig. 18.21   Fig. 18.22

Fig. 18.23   Fig. 18.24   Fig. 18.25

Questions 16–18 refer to Figure 18.23, in which AB, BC and CA are tangents to the circle and P, Q and R are points of contact.

16 Prove that AR + BP + CQ = QA + RB + PC.

If AB = 5 cm, BC = 6 cm and CA = 7 cm, find the length of BP.

17 Given that A = 50° and B = 64°, calculate the angles of triangle PQR.

18 Given that angle PQR = 60° and angle PRQ = 70°, calculate the angles of triangle ABC.

Questions 19–21 refer to Figure 18.24, in which the lines BPC, ABQ and ACR touch the circle at P, Q and R, respectively.

19 Prove that AB + BP = AC + CP.

 If AB = 5 cm, BC = 6 cm and CA = 7 cm, find the length of BP.

20 Given that B = 60° and C = 74°, find the angles of triangle PQR.

21 Given that angle PQR = 34° and angle PRQ = 40°, find the angles of triangle ABC.

22 In Figure 18.25, A = 122°, B = 75° and C = 90°. Find the angles of the quadrilateral PQRS.

23 In Figure 18.25, prove that AB + CD = BC + DA.

24 A circle has a diameter AB and T is a point on the circumference of the circle. The tangent at T meets AB produced at C. Given that angle BTC = 35°, find angles TAB and TCA.

25 Points A, B, C are taken on the circumference of a circle. The tangent at C meets AB produced at T. Given that BC = BT prove that CT = CA.

26 Two circles of different radii intersect at B and D. From a point A on the circumference of the smaller circle, lines AB and AD are drawn and produced to meet the circumference of the larger circle at C and E respectively. Prove that CE is parallel to the tangent at A to the smaller circle.

27 The tangents to a circle at A and B meet at P and angle BAP = 50°. The diameter BD, when produced, cuts PA produced at C. Prove that angle CAD is four times angle ACD.

28 Two circles of radii 4 cm and 9 cm touch each other externally. Find the length of a common tangent.

29 The centres of two circles, of radii 11 cm and 5 cm, are at a distance 20 cm apart. Find the lengths of their direct and transverse common tangents.

30 Two circles touch internally at P. A chord AB of the larger circle is a tangent at Q to the smaller circle. Prove that angle APQ = angle BPQ.

Rectangular properties of a circle

In Figure 18.26, the chords AB and CD intersect inside the circle at X.

Angle BAD = angle BCD (same segment)

Angle AXD = angle CXB (vertically opposite)

Therefore triangles $\dfrac{\text{AXD}}{\text{CXB}}$ are equiangular and hence are similar.

Since the corresponding sides of similar triangles are proportional,

$$\frac{\text{XA}}{\text{XC}} = \frac{\text{XD}}{\text{XB}}, \text{ that is } \mathbf{XA.XB = XC.XD} \qquad \text{(i)}$$

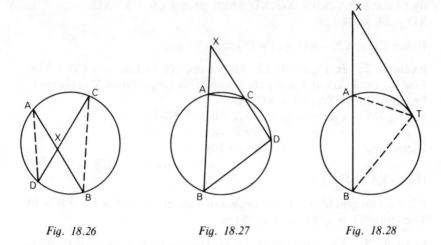

| Fig. 18.26 | Fig. 18.27 | Fig. 18.28 |

In Figure 18.27, the chords BA and DC meet, when produced, outside the circle at X. Since the quadrilateral ABDC is cyclic,
Angle XAC = angle XDB (exterior angle = interior opposite angle)
Angle AXC is common.

Therefore triangles $\dfrac{XAC}{XDB}$ are equiangular and hence are similar.

Since the corresponding sides of similar triangles are proportional,

$$\frac{XA}{XD} = \frac{XC}{XB}, \text{ that is } \mathbf{XA.XB = XC.XD} \tag{ii}$$

In Figure 18.28, AB is a chord and XT a tangent to the circle, where BA produced meets the tangent at X.
Angle XTA = angle TBA (alternate segment)
Angle AXT is common.

Therefore triangles $\dfrac{XAT}{XTB}$ are equiangular and hence are similar.

Since the corresponding sides of similar triangles are proportional,

$$\frac{XA}{XT} = \frac{XT}{XB}, \text{ that is } \mathbf{XA.XB = XT^2} \tag{iii}$$

The results proved above and numbered (i), (ii) and (iii) are known as **the rectangular properties of the circle.**
The converses of the above results are true and may be used as tests for possible concyclic points. For example, the converse of (i) is **if two line segments AB and CD intersect each other internally in the point X and XA.XB = XC.XD, the points A, B, C and D are concyclic.**

Example 1: *In Figure 18.26, AX = 4 cm, XB = 6 cm and CX = 5 cm; find CD.*

247

By (i) above XA.XB = XC.XD which gives $4 \times 6 = 5 \times XD$.
XD = 24/5 = 4.8 cm .

Hence CD = CX + XD = (5 + 4.8) cm = 9.8 cm.

Example 2: *In Figure* 18.27, *AB* = 6 *cm*, *XC* = 5 *cm and CD* = 3 *cm. Find* (*a*) *the length of X A*, (*b*) *the length of the tangent from X to the circle.*
From (ii) above XA.XB = XC.XD
Taking XA = x cm, this gives $x(x + 6) = 5(5 + 3)$
$$x^2 + 6x - 40 = 0$$
Factorising $(x - 4)(x + 10) = 0$
$$x = 4 \quad (\text{or } x = -10)$$
Hence XA = 4 cm.

If XT is a tangent from X to the circle, using (iii) above $XT^2 = XA.XB = 40$.
Therefore XT = $\sqrt{40}$ cm = 6.325 cm.

Example 3: *The diagonals of the quadrilateral ABCD cross at O. Given that the distances of O from A, B, C and D are 4 cm, 8 cm, 6 cm and 3 cm respectively, prove that ABCD is a cyclic quadrilateral.*
OA.OC = $4 \times 6 = 24$ and OB.OD = $8 \times 3 = 24$.
Therefore OA.OC = OB.OD
By the converse of (*i*), *A, B, C and D are concyclic points and ABCD is a cyclic quadrilateral.*

Exercise 18.4

1   In Figure 18.26, XB = 10 cm, XC = XD = 9 cm. Find XA.
2   In Figure 18.26, XA = 4 cm, AB = 10 cm and XC = 8 cm. Find CD.
3   In Figure 18.27, XA = 6 cm, XB = 10 cm and XC = 5 cm. Find CD.
4   In Figure 18.27, XC.XD = 75 cm^2, and XB = 20 cm. Find XA.
5   In Figure 18.28, XA = 7 cm and AB = 1.75 cm. Find XT.
6   In Figure 18.28, XA = 4 cm and XT = 6 cm. Find AB.
7   In Figure 18.26, XA = 4 cm, XB = 3 cm and CD = 8 cm. If XC = y cm, find the possible values of y.
8   In Figure 18.27, XC = 5 cm, CD = 9 cm and AB = 3 cm. Find XA.
9   In Figure 18.28, XT = 6 cm and XA = AB. Find AB.
10   Water stands to a depth of 6 cm in a spherical fish bowl of radius 15 cm. Calculate the diameter of the surface of the water.
11   The straight edge of a semicircle is AB. From a point P on the semicircle a line is drawn perpendicular to AB, meeting AB in X. If AX is of length 9 cm, and PX = 4 cm, find the radius of the semicircle.
12   The vertical cross-section of a tunnel is a major segment of a circle with a horizontal line as base. The radius of the circle is 6.25 m and the height of the tunnel is 4.5 m. Calculate the width of the base of the tunnel.
13   The triangle ABC has B = 90°, and P is on AC such that angle BPC = 90°. Prove that $AB^2 = AP.AC$.
Deduce that the circle through B, P and C has AB as a tangent at B.

14 Two circles intersect at X and Y, their radii being different. The line XY is drawn and produced to O, from which tangents OA and OB are drawn, one to each circle. Prove that $OX.OY = OA^2 = OB^2$.

15 A tangent is drawn at B to a circle with diameter AB. A line is drawn from A to meet the circle at P and the tangent at Q.
   Prove that $AB^2 = AP.AQ$.

19 Loci and constructions

The path which a variable point takes as it moves under given conditions is called the **locus** of the point.

Example: A point P moves so that its distance from a fixed point C is always *r*.

If P is restricted to a plane, its locus is a circle of radius *r* and centre C. If P is not restricted to a plane, its locus is a sphere of radius *r* and centre C.

Many geometrical constructions can be performed which involve the use of a straight edge and a pair of compasses only. Some of these basic, simple constructions are shown in the following illustrations. Locus properties associated with these constructions are listed for ease of reference. Detailed instructions of how to undertake the constructions are not given verbally. The reader should undertake each construction using drawing instruments. The proofs are left as an exercise.

The perpendicular bisector (mediator) of a line AB

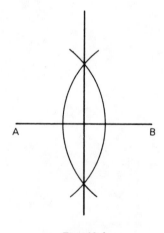

Fig. 19.1

Any point P on mediator has PA = PB

The circumcircle of a triangle

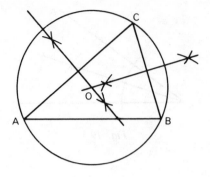

Fig. 19.2

Centre O is such that OA = OB = OC

The perpendicular at a point P in a line AB

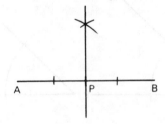

Fig. 19.3

The perpendicular from a point P to a line AB

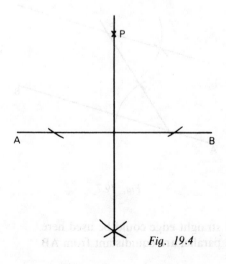

Fig. 19.4

251

The bisector of an angle ABC

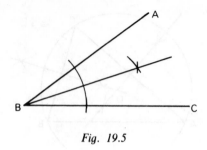

Fig. 19.5

Any point P on bisector is the same distance from AB as from BC.

The copying of a given angle ABC

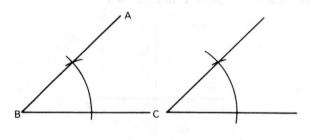

Fig. 19.6

Line parallel to AB through P

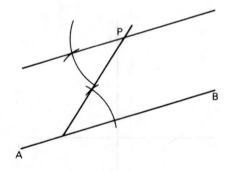

Fig. 19.7

A set-square and straight edge could be used here.
All points on the parallel are equidistant from AB.

The division of AB into 5 equal parts

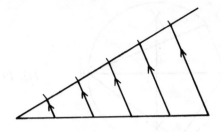

Fig. 19.8

Use a set square and straight edge for drawing the parallels.

To construct an angle of 60°

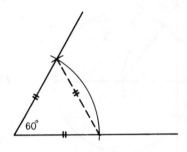

Fig. 19.9

The construction of 30°, 120° etc are simple extensions of this.

To construct an angle of 45°

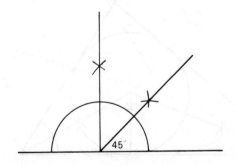

Fig. 19.10

The construction of 135°, 22.5° etc are simple extensions of this.

A and B are fixed. **The locus of P such that angle APB = 90°**

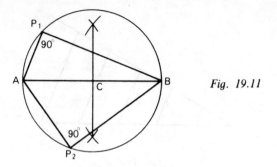

Fig. 19.11

P lies on a circle, diameter AB.

The tangent from T to a circle, centre C

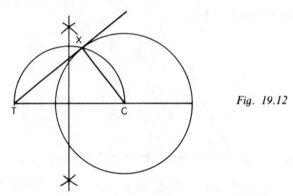

Fig. 19.12

Angle TXC = 90°

The incircle of a triangle ABC

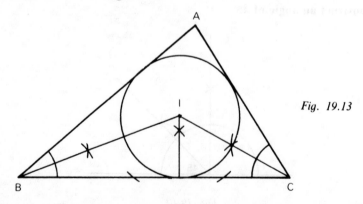

Fig. 19.13

The incentre **I** is such that its distance from AB, BC and CA is *r*, the radius of the incircle.

254

The constant angle locus

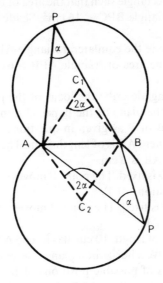

Fig. 19.14

For all positions of P on the arcs shown, the angle APB is α. One arc is the reflection of the other in AB.

Exercise 19.1: Loci

In each of the following, describe the locus of the point P, whose position is restricted to the plane of the paper (2 dimensions), and construct the locus.

1 The points A and B are fixed and AB = 5 cm. For all positions of P, AP = PB.

2 The points A and B are fixed and AB = 4 cm. For all positions of P, the area of triangle APB is 6 cm².

3 Two fixed parallel lines are distance 5 cm apart. The point P moves so that it is equidistant from each parallel line.

4 Two fixed lines intersect at a point O. The point P moves so that in any position its perpendicular distance to each fixed line is the same.

5 The points A and B are fixed and AB = 6 cm. The point P moves so that the angle APB is always 30°.

6 A fixed circle has centre C and radius 4 cm. The point P is the centre of circles of radius 1 cm, all of which touch the given circle, centre C.

7 The line AB is of length 7 cm. The point P moves in such a way that P can always be the centre of a circle, whose radius can vary, which passes through A and B.

8 The square ABCD is fixed with AB = 4 cm. The point P moves inside the square so that PA < PB and PA < PD. Shade the region in which P must lie.

9 The rectangle ABCD has AB = 6 cm and BC = 8 cm. The point P moves inside the rectangle such that the area of triangle APB < 12 cm² and the area of triangle BPC < 16 cm². Shade the region in which P must lie.

10 A point P lies inside the equilateral triangle ABC, where AB = 8 cm, and is such that the area of triangle APB ≥ 6 cm². Shade the area in which P must lie.

In each of the following, describe the locus of the point P, when P is *not* restricted to move in the plane of the paper (3 dimensions).

11 Describe the locus of P as given in questions 1 and 4.

12 The fixed line segment AB is of length 5 cm. The point P moves so that its distance from AB is 3 cm.

13 The square ABCD is fixed. The point P moves so that AP = BP = CP = DP for all positions of P.

14 The triangle ABC is fixed. The point P moves so that AP = BP = CP for all positions of P.

15 A straight rod AB, of length 10 cm, has its end A hinged to a fixed point 8 cm vertically above a horizontal plane. The end B rests on this plane. Describe the locus of possible positions of B.

A ring R is threaded on the rod AB and can take all positions between A and B. Describe, precisely, the surface on which R must lie.

Examples on constructions

Example 1: *Construct the triangle ABC in which AB = 4.3 cm, BC = 6.5 cm and angle CAB is 120°. Construct the circle which passes through C and has AB as a tangent at A. Measure the radius of this circle.*

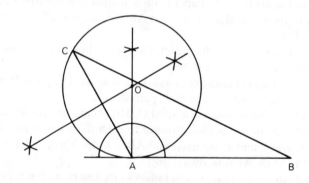

Fig. 19.15

Explanation: Draw AB = 4.3 cm and construct an angle of 120° at A with AB as one arm. Centre B, radius 6.5 cm, draw an arc to cut the second arm of the 120° angle at C. The required triangle is ABC, as shown in Fig. 19.15. The centre of the required circle is found as the intersection of two loci, the mediator of AC and a line through A perpendicular to AB. The first of these loci ensures that the circle will pass through A and C, the second ensures that the line AB will be a tangent to the circle. The required circle has centre O, radius OA, and AB is a tangent since angle OAB = 90°. Radius of circle by measurement is 1.8 cm.

Example 2: *Construct a triangle ABC of area 10 cm² in which AC = 8 cm and B = 90°.*

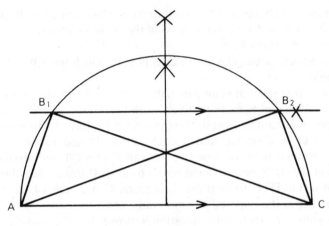

Fig. 19.16

Explanation: Draw AC = 8 cm and construct the semicircle on AC as diameter, as shown in Figure 19.16. Since ∠ABC = 90°, B lies on this arc. Taking AC as base, the height of the triangle is 2.5 cm to give an area of 10 cm². The positions of B can therefore be found by drawing a line parallel to AC and at a distance 2.5 cm from it. Either of the triangles AB₁C or AB₂C fit the required data.

Exercise 19.2

Note: For constructions of triangles from given data, refer to Exercise 17.1.

1 Show by construction how to divide the line AB, of length 9 cm, internally at the point X, such that AX : XB = 3 : 2.
   (Hint: divide AB by construction into 5 equal parts.)

2 Show by construction how to divide the line PQ, of length 5 cm, externally at the point Y, such that PY : YQ = 3 : 1.

3 Construct the circumcircle of a triangle ABC in which:
   (a) AB = 6 cm, BC = 7 cm, CA = 8 cm,
   (b) AB = 6 cm, BC = 8 cm, CA = 10 cm,
   (c) AB = 6 cm, BC = 7 cm, CA = 10 cm.
   Measure the radius in each case.

4 Reconstruct the triangles given in question 3 and then construct the incircle for each triangle. Measure the radius in each case.

5   Draw a circle, centre C, of radius 5 cm. Take any point P, such that PC is of length 8 cm. Construct the tangents from P to the circle and measure their lengths. Check your measurements by direct calculation.

6   Construct a cyclic quadrilateral in which two sides, of lengths 4.3 cm and 5.6 cm, are adjacent and at right angles and the other two sides are of equal lengths.

7   Draw a circle, centre O and radius 5 cm. Choose a point P such that OP = 3.5 cm. Construct a chord of the circle which passes through P and is of length 8 cm.

8   Construct a triangle ABC, of area 14 cm^2, which has AB = 8 cm and angle C = 45°.

9   On a large sheet of plain paper, draw two circles, centres C and D, of radii 4 cm and 6 cm, respectively, such that CD = 12 cm. Construct a direct common tangent to these two circles. (Hints: Draw a semicircle on CD as diameter, and a circle centre D and radius 2 cm; the intersection point of these two loci call T; join DT and produce it to meet the circle, centre D and radius 6 cm, at P; draw a line through C parallel to DTP, to meet the circle centre C and radius 4 cm at Q; the line PQ is the required common tangent.)

10   In your construction for question 9, prove that the triangle TCD is right-angled and prove that PQCT is a rectangle.

11   The square ABCD has AB = 3 cm and M is the mid-point of CD. Find the centre of the circle which passes through M and has AD as a tangent with contact point A. Measure the radius of this circle.

12   Draw a triangle ABC with unequal sides. Verify by construction that the altitudes of the triangle are concurrent.

13   Construct an equilateral triangle OAB, of side 3 cm. With centre O and radius OA draw a circle. By rotating this triangle about O through successive angles of 60°, construct a regular hexagon ABCDEF, all of whose vertices lie on the circle.

14   Construct the triangle ABC, in which AB = 5.6 cm, BC = 6.3 cm and CA = 4.3 cm. Locate by further construction the point X, such that XA = XB, XC = 3 cm and X is inside the triangle ABC. Measure XA.

15   In the quadrilateral ABCD, AB is parallel to DC; BC = CD = 4 cm, DA = 3 cm and AB = 10 cm. Construct this quadrilateral. Measure BD. (Hint see Figure 17.4)

16   Construct the quadrilateral ABCD in which AB = 3 cm, BC = 4 cm, CD = 7 cm, DA = 6 cm and BD = 5 cm.
Construct a line through C parallel to BD, to meet AD produced at E. The triangles BCD and BED are equal in area because they have the same base BD and equal heights (BD parallel to CE). The area of the quadrilateral ABCD is equal to the area of the triangle ABE.

17   For the quadrilateral ABCD described in question 15, construct a triangle equal in area to this quadrilateral.

18   Construct a rectangle ABCD, in which AB = 8 cm and BC = 6 cm. Produce AB to E such that BE = 6 cm. Draw a semicircle on AE as

diameter on the opposite side to the rectangle ABCD. Produce CB to meet this semicircle at F.

The rectangle area AB . BC = AB . BE = $(r + OB)(r - OB)$, where O is the centre of the semicircle and r is the radius.

But $(r + OB)(r - OB) = r^2 - OB^2 = FB^2$, by Pythagoras, in triangle FOB.

∴ *A square with one side FB is equal in area to rectangle ABCD.*

Miscellaneous Exercise D

1 ABCDE is a regular pentagon and ABF is an equilateral triangle inside the pentagon. Calculate the size of ∠ EFA. [L 1973]

2 In the triangle ABC, the side BC is produced to X and the bisectors of AB̂C and AĈX meet at D. Given that BÂC = 60° and AĈB = 48°, calculate BD̂C. [C 1977]

3 The diagram shows a circle with centre C and two parallel chords which are equal in length. Draw the lines of symmetry of the figure.

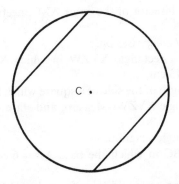

[JMB 1975]

4 PQRS is a rhombus in which ∠SPQ = 64°. Equilateral triangles PXQ and QYR are drawn outside the rhombus on the sides PQ and QR. Calculate the angles of △QXY. [L 1975]

5 In a quadrilateral, the largest angle is twice the size of each of the other angles. Calculate the size of each of the four angles. [JMB 1974]

6 Each exterior angle of an n-sided polygon is 24°. Calculate n. [C 1973]

7 O is the centre of the circle XYZ and XY is a diameter. If ∠OYZ = 40°, calculate angles YOZ and OZX. [L 1977]

8 A triangular plot of land PQR is bounded by straight fences with PQ = 80 m, PR = 100 m and the angle RPQ = 60°. *Using ruler and compasses only*, construct a scaled diagram of the triangular plot and mark on it the position of a telegraph post T that is equidistant from RP and RQ, and is on the perpendicular from Q to PR. Measure and state the length QT. [AEB 1976]

9 AB and CD are two parallel chords of a circle. The lines AD and BC intersect at E. Prove that AE = BE. [JMB 1976]

10 In the isosceles triangle ABC, the sides AB and AC are equal. A straight line XAY is parallel to BC and XA = AY. Prove that the triangles XAB and YAC are congruent. [C 1975]

11 △PXY has a fixed base XY of length 6 cm. State clearly the locus of P in two dimensions in each of the following cases:
(a) When PX = PY.
(b) When the area of △PXY = 9 cm². [L 1976]

12 Two circles touch externally at A. The tangent at a point B on one circle cuts the second circle at C and D (so that the order of points on the tangent is BCD). The line DA is produced to cut the first circle at E. The common tangent at A meets BD at T. Prove that
(i) ∠TAB = ∠BED,
(ii) ∠EAB = ∠BAC,
(iii) ∠BAC + ∠BAD = 180°. [O 1977]

13 (a) In a circle two chords AXB and CXD meet at a point X. Given that AX = 5 cm, CX = 9 cm, AC = 7 cm and BX = 7.2 cm, calculate
(i) the length of DX,
(ii) the ratio of the area of the triangle AXC to the area of the triangle BXD.

Given that the bisector of the angle AXC meets AC at E, calculate the length of AE.

(b) *Use ruler and compasses only*
(i) to construct a rectangle XYZW in which XW = 6 cm and the diagonal YW = 13 cm,
(ii) to find the length of the side of a square which has an area equal to that of the rectangle XYZW. Measure and state this length.

[AEB 1976]

14 Construct in a single diagram
(i) a triangle ABC in which the base AB = 6 cm, CÂB = 90° and BC = 9 cm,
(ii) the locus of points equidistant from A and B,
(iii) the locus of the centres of the circles which touch CB at B,
(iv) the circle which touches CB at B and passes through A.
Measure and write down the radius of this circle. [C 1977]

15 ABCD is a rectangle in which AB = 2BC. The diagonal AC is drawn, and a point X is taken on AB such that BĈX = DĈA.
Prove that
(i) △BXC is similar to △DAC,
(ii) BX = ¼BA,
(iii) BC is a tangent to the circle which passes through A, X and C,
(iv) the bisector of DÂB bisects DC. [C 1977]

16 An acute-angled triangle ABC is inscribed in a circle. The point D is the foot of the perpendicular from A to BC; the line AD produced cuts the circle at E. The point F on AD is such that FD = DE; the line BF produced cuts AC at G and the circle at H.

Prove that
(i) triangles BFD, BED are congruent,
(ii) ABDG is cyclic,
(iii) triangles AFG, AHG are congruent,
(iv) DG = ½EH.   [JMB 1977]

17 Construct the rectangle ABCD given that AB = DC = 9 cm, AD
= BC = 5 cm. On AB as base construct an isosceles triangle ABE
equal in area to ABCD and having AE = EB.
On the same diagram, and without calculation, construct a square
equal in area to ABCD.   [JMB 1973]

18 In △ABC, the internal bisector of ∠BAC meets BC at P. Prove that
BP:PC = AB:AC.
In the same triangle, a line is drawn through P parallel to BA meeting
AC at Q. Prove that
(a) PC:BC = PQ:BA,
(b) PQ:BP = AC:BC.
It is given that AB = 5 cm, BP = 2 cm, and PC = 3 cm. Calculate PQ
and QC.   [L 1979]

19

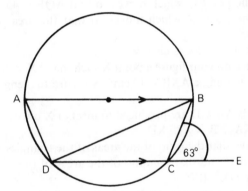

ABCD is a cyclic quadrilateral in which AB is a diameter and DC is
parallel to AB. The side DC is produced to E and ∠BCE = 63°.
Calculate ∠DBC.   [L 1977]

20

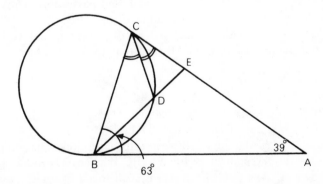

In the diagram, AB is the tangent to the circle at B and DC bisects BĈA.

The line BD produced meets AC at E. Given that $B\hat{A}C = 39°$ and $A\hat{B}C = 63°$, calculate $B\hat{C}D$ and $C\hat{B}D$. [C 1976]

21 ABCD is a cyclic quadrilateral, AC is a diameter, $\angle ABD = 20°$ and $\angle BDC = 36°$. Calculate (i) $\angle BAD$, (ii) $\angle BCD$, (iii) the acute angle between CD and the tangent at C. [O 1975]

22 A circle has a diameter AB and A, D, C and B are four points in order on its circumference. DC is parallel to AB and $A\hat{C}D = 31°$. Calculate $A\hat{D}C$. [W 1978]

23 (a) The internal bisectors of the three angles of the triangle PQR meet at I. PI produced meets QR at the point K and PI : IK = 2 : 1. Prove that PQ + PR = 2QR.

(b) AN and BM are perpendicular to the line AB, and on the same side of AB, AM and BN intersect at the point X. Prove that XA.XB = XM.XN. [W 1976]

24 Draw a line AB 6 cm long and approximately 10 cm from the top of the page.

In a single diagram draw accurately the locus of
 (i) the point P which moves so that AP = PB,
 (ii) the point Q which moves so that $A\hat{Q}B = 45°$,
(iii) the point R which moves so that the area of triangle ARB is 12 cm².

Label each locus clearly.

Mark on your figure a point X such that AX < XB, $A\hat{X}B = 45°$ and area of triangle AXB = 12 cm². Measure the lengths AX and BX.

[C 1974]

25 Chords AB, CD are produced to meet at X outside their circle. Prove that XA . XB = XC . XD.

Prove that the ratio of the areas of the triangles AXC, DXB equals $CX^2 : BX^2$ and that the ratio of the areas of the triangles AXD, CXB equals $DX^2 : BX^2$.

In each case, name a ratio of squares of sides or diagonals of ABCD which equals the ratio of the areas. [S 1976]

20 Vectors

The expression $ax + by$, where a and b are real variables, is commonplace in algebra. For each pair (a, b) a particular combination of x and y is formed. For example $(3, 4)$ generates $3x + 4y$, one element in the infinite set of all such combinations. There is a one–one correspondence between a pair (a, b) and the expression $ax + by$. In ordinary algebra x and y are usually considered to be real variables such that, for given values of x and y, the expression can be evaluated. That is a, b, x and y are all considered as the same type of quantity, namely **numbers**.

Consider the expression $3\mathbf{b} + 4\mathbf{g}$, used to represent a group of 3 boys and 4 girls. This is a completely different type of expression. The letters $\mathbf{b}$ and $\mathbf{g}$ certainly cannot be replaced by numbers; they represent 'units of identification', while the numbers 3 and 4 specify how many of each unit is present. This type of expression is called a vector and should be written $3\mathbf{b} + 4\mathbf{g}$, or as $3\underset{\sim}{b} + 4\underset{\sim}{g}$. When you are writing vectors, the second way is probably easier to use, where a vector is shown by the wavy line, called a tilde. The separate parts $3\mathbf{b}$ and $4\mathbf{g}$ are called the **components** of the vector.

A vector may have any number of components, providing that they are independent. If a stock vector is formed to describe all the records and cassettes owned by a member of your class, it might be shown as $10\mathbf{s} + 5\mathbf{l} + 3\mathbf{c}$ (10 singles, 5 long-players, 3 cassettes); this vector has three components. A stock vector giving the number of cars in a garage at a particular time may contain 10, or more, components.

In all the above illustrations of vectors the associated numbers have been taken as natural numbers, but this is not general. The displacement of one town from another may be written as $8\mathbf{n} - 7.5\mathbf{e}$. In this case what might $\mathbf{n}$ and $\mathbf{e}$ represent? Would merely north and east be acceptable?

The dimensions of a rectangle could be written as $2.5\mathbf{l} + 1.5\mathbf{b}$, but some indication of the unit of distance being used would also have to be given. In any given family (or set) of vectors, the non-scalar quantities, e.g. $(\mathbf{s}, \mathbf{l}, \mathbf{c})$ in the record stock illustration, form the basis of every vector in the family, and the scalar quantities, (numbers, lengths, etc.) as they vary, generate the complete set of vectors for that family; every vector in the set is of the form $\alpha\mathbf{s} + \beta\mathbf{l} + \gamma\mathbf{c}$. The vectors $\mathbf{s}$, $\mathbf{l}$ and $\mathbf{c}$ are special members of the set, since they may be written as $\mathbf{s} = 1\mathbf{s} + 0\mathbf{l} + 0\mathbf{c}$, $\mathbf{l} = 0\mathbf{s} + 1\mathbf{l} + 0\mathbf{c}$ and $\mathbf{c} = 0\mathbf{s} + 0\mathbf{l} + 1\mathbf{c}$ respectively; $\mathbf{s}$, $\mathbf{l}$ and $\mathbf{c}$ are called base vectors of the set.

Exercise 20.1

1 The following vectors are used to describe the composition of the Maths sets in the third year of a school.
$s_1 = 15b + 16g$, $s_2 = 20b + 12g$, $s_3 = 15b + 17g$, $s_4 = 14b + 14g$ and $s_5 = 5b + 0g$.
(a) What do the vectors **b** and **g** represent?
(b) Could the vectors s_1, s_2 etc., have more components?
(c) Find the total number of girls who study maths in this year.
(d) Find the total number of boys who study maths in this year.
(e) Name two sets which contain the same number of boys in each.
(f) Given that 3 boys are moved from s_2 to s_1 and that 1 boy and 1 girl are moved from s_1 to s_2, write down new vectors for s_1 and s_2.

2 Undertake a survey to find the record stock vector for each member of your class, using the base vectors **s**, **l** and **c**. Are there any members having the same total number of records? Are there any with the same record vector?

3 A garage owner deals in Audi, BMW, Citroen and Datsun cars only. His stock vector on a particular day is $5a + 3b + 6c + 2d$.
(a) Find the total number of cars in the garage.
(b) Find the new stock vector, given that he sells 1 Audi and 1 Datsun and he has delivered 3 Audi and 5 Citroen cars.

In question 2 of the last exercise, it is possible that someone in the class recorded the vector $0s + 0l + 0c$ because they did not own any records or cassettes. This vector is called **the null vector** and is written simply as **0**. The null vector plays a similar role in the manipulation of vectors to that of zero in ordinary algebra. The record vector $10s + 5l + 3c$ can be written as the **row vector**,

$$(10 \quad 5 \quad 3)$$

or as the **column vector**,

$$\begin{pmatrix} 10 \\ 5 \\ 3 \end{pmatrix}$$

always provided that it is known what each component and its position within the bracket stands for.

The Algebra of vectors

Two people with record stock vectors $10s + 5l + 3c$ and $25s + 14l + 2c$ decide to combine their collections for a party. The sum of their collections, obtained by adding like components, is $35s + 19l + 5c$.
The sum of two vectors is found by adding respective components.
The difference between two vectors is defined in a similar way.

264

Example: $(25s + 14l + 2c) - (10s + 10l + c) = 15s + 4l + c$.

The difference between two vectors is found by subtracting the respective components in the second from those in the first.

An operation for two vectors analogous to multiplication in ordinary algebra is not obvious. In fact, in more advanced work, two product operations are defined, but they are outside the scope of work at this level.

A product that *does* have immediate meaning and *can* be demonstrated is that of a vector by a scalar.

If three people have the same record vector $10s + 5l + 3c$, the sum is $30s + 15l + 9c$ and it would be logical to write

$$3(10s + 5l + 3c) = 30s + 15l + 9c.$$

If a vector is multiplied by a scalar, each component of the vector is multiplied by the scalar.

The three operations defined above characterise vectors; if a quantity behaves like the stock vector it may be considered to be a mathematical vector.

Example: *Given that* $x = 5a + 10b$ *and* $y = 2a - b$, *write* $2x + 3y$ *in terms of* a *and* b.

$2x = 2(5a + 10b) = 10a + 20b$ and $3y = 3(2a - b) = 6a - 3b$,

Therefore $2x + 3y = 10a + 20b + 6a - 3b = 16a + 17b$.

Exercise 20.2

1 Simplify each of the following:

(a) $(2a + 3b) + (a + 5b)$ (b) $(a + 5b) + (2a + 3b)$

(c) $(5a + 2b) + (2a - 4b)$ (d) $(2a - 4b) + (5a + 2b)$

(e) $\begin{pmatrix} 9 \\ 12 \end{pmatrix} + \begin{pmatrix} 3 \\ -2 \end{pmatrix}$ (f) $\begin{pmatrix} 1 \\ 2 \end{pmatrix} + \begin{pmatrix} 6 \\ 0 \end{pmatrix}$

(g) $[(a - b) + (-2a + b)] + (6a - 2b)$

(h) $(a - b) + [(-2a + b) + (6a - 2b)]$.

2 Simplify each of the following:

(a) $(2a + 9b) - (3a + 2b)$ (b) $(3a + 2b) - (2a + 9b)$

(c) $(a + b) - (a - b)$ (d) $(a - b) - (a + b)$

(e) $\begin{pmatrix} 5 \\ 6 \end{pmatrix} - \begin{pmatrix} 2 \\ 3 \end{pmatrix}$ (f) $\begin{pmatrix} 2 \\ 1 \end{pmatrix} - \begin{pmatrix} -3 \\ 4 \end{pmatrix}$.

3 Simplify each of the following:

(a) $5(6a + 2b)$ (b) $3(a - b)$ (c) $3(a + b) + 2(a - b)$

(d) $4\begin{pmatrix} 1 \\ -2 \end{pmatrix}$ (e) $2\begin{pmatrix} 6 \\ 1 \end{pmatrix} + 3\begin{pmatrix} -1 \\ 2 \end{pmatrix}$ (f) $5\begin{pmatrix} 0 \\ 1 \end{pmatrix} - 2\begin{pmatrix} 5 \\ -4 \end{pmatrix}$.

The graphical representation of a vector

Consider a record stock vector with two components, singles and long-players. Take co-ordinate axes Ox and Oy to represent singles and long-players respectively, choosing scales as shown in Figure 20.1.

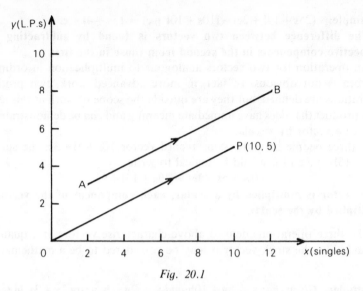

Fig. 20.1

If a third component were needed for cassettes, a three co-ordinate axes system would be required to illustrate this, and this would use three dimensions; vectors with more components than this do not lend themselves easily to geometrical illustration but can be dealt with by algebraic methods, as has been suggested earlier in the chapter.

In Figure 20.1, the stock vector $10s + 5l$ can be represented by the point P(10, 5). There is a one–one correspondence between points in the plane of the co-ordinate axes and all such record stock vectors. To every point like P there exists a **unique** directed line segment like OP, shown in Figure 20.1, written as **OP** (or $\overrightarrow{OP}$) and called **the position vector of P**. Any vector having two components can be represented in this unique way by using a co-ordinate system, whose axes need not necessarily be rectangular, but are commonly taken so. In addition, a two component vector has associated with it.

(a) length OP, called the **modulus** or the **magnitude** of the vector, written as $|\mathbf{OP}|$ or $|\overrightarrow{OP}|$ or just OP,

(b) **direction**, given by angle xOP, measured as positive in the anticlockwise direction. The direction is shown by an arrow, as in Figure 20.1.

In Figure 20.1, the line segment **AB** joining A(2, 3) and B(12, 8) has the same magnitude and direction as **OP** and could equally well represent the vector $10s + 5l$. The vector, therefore, can be represented by an infinite number of directed line segments, similar to **AB**, called **shift vectors**, but only *one point* P, with position vector **OP**, actually represents the vector $10s + 5l$.

The shift vector $\begin{pmatrix} 10 \\ 5 \end{pmatrix}$ is then a directed line segment joining points (p, q) and $(p + 10, q + 5)$, for any (p, q) in the co-ordinate system. The shift vector $\begin{pmatrix} 10 \\ 5 \end{pmatrix}$ can also be used to represent a translation of the plane, the point P

266

with position vector $\begin{pmatrix} 10 \\ 5 \end{pmatrix}$ being the image of the origin under this translation.

At this level of work, a vector may be defined as any quantity that can be represented by a directed line segment. Many physical quantities such as force, displacement, velocity, acceleration and momentum are **vectors**, whereas quantities such as time, mass, speed, temperature and energy only have magnitude and are **scalars**.

Unit vectors

As $\begin{pmatrix} 10 \\ 5 \end{pmatrix} = 10\begin{pmatrix} 1 \\ 0 \end{pmatrix} + 5\begin{pmatrix} 0 \\ 1 \end{pmatrix}$, and any other shift vector can be written as a combination of the base vectors $\begin{pmatrix} 1 \\ 0 \end{pmatrix}$ and $\begin{pmatrix} 0 \\ 1 \end{pmatrix}$, which are of magnitude 1 unit and parallel to the x-axis and y-axis respectively, these base vectors are given a special notation, and called **i** and **j** respectively.

Hence $\begin{pmatrix} 10 \\ 5 \end{pmatrix}$ can be written just simply as $10\mathbf{i} + 5\mathbf{j}$.

In general, any vector, like the special ones **i** and **j** just defined, which has a modulus 1 is called a **unit vector**.

Example: *The position vectors of the points A and .B, relative to origin O, are* **a** *and* **b** *respectively. Given that* $\mathbf{a} = 4\mathbf{i} + 3\mathbf{j}$ *and* $\mathbf{b} = \mathbf{i} + 2\mathbf{j}$, *show these points on a diagram and calculate the moduli of* **a**, **b** *and* $\mathbf{a} + \mathbf{b}$.

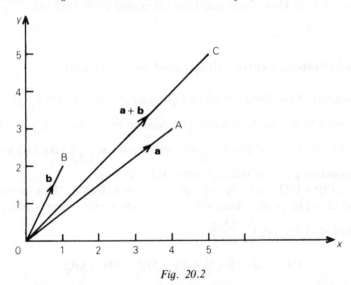

Fig. 20.2

In Figure 20.2, A is (4, 3) and B is (1, 2).
$|\mathbf{a}|$ = length of OA = 5, by the theorem of Pythagoras.
$|\mathbf{b}|$ = length of OB = $\sqrt{5}$, similarly.

$$\mathbf{a} + \mathbf{b} = 4\mathbf{i} + 3\mathbf{j} + \mathbf{i} + 2\mathbf{j} = 5\mathbf{i} + 5\mathbf{j}.$$
$|\mathbf{a} + \mathbf{b}| = $ length of OC, where C is (5, 5)
$$= \sqrt{25 + 25} = \sqrt{50} = 5\sqrt{2}.$$
Note that $|\mathbf{a} + \mathbf{b}| \neq |\mathbf{a}| + |\mathbf{b}|$.

Exercise 20.3

1 Given that $\mathbf{a} = \begin{pmatrix} 7 \\ 8 \end{pmatrix}$ and $\mathbf{b} = \begin{pmatrix} 2 \\ -1 \end{pmatrix}$, represent $\mathbf{a}$ and $\mathbf{b}$ in a diagram and calculate: (a) $|\mathbf{a}|$, (b) $|\mathbf{b}|$, (c) $|\mathbf{a} - \mathbf{b}|$, (d) $|3\mathbf{a} + 4\mathbf{b}|$.
2 The points A and B have position vectors $\mathbf{i} + 2\mathbf{j}$ and $5\mathbf{i} + 6\mathbf{j}$, respectively, relative to an origin O. Show these vectors in a sketch and express $\mathbf{AB}$ in terms of $\mathbf{i}$ and $\mathbf{j}$. Find the position vector of the point P, such that $\mathbf{OP} = \mathbf{AB}$.
   Find $|\mathbf{OA}|$, $|\mathbf{OB}|$ and $|\mathbf{AB}|$ and hence calculate angle AOB.
3 Draw sketches to show each of the following shift vectors and for each, calculate (i) the modulus, (ii) the angle made by the vector with Ox.
   (a) $\mathbf{OA} = \begin{pmatrix} 1 \\ 1 \end{pmatrix}$, (b) $\mathbf{OB} = \begin{pmatrix} -3 \\ 4 \end{pmatrix}$, (c) $\mathbf{OC} = \begin{pmatrix} -1 \\ -2 \end{pmatrix}$ (d) $\mathbf{OD} = \begin{pmatrix} 12 \\ -5 \end{pmatrix}$.
4 Draw a co-ordinate system where the axes, Ox and Oy, are inclined at $60°$. The lines of the grid are drawn parallel to these axes. Mark scales on the axes. Draw directed line segments $\mathbf{OA}$, $\mathbf{OB}$ and $\mathbf{OC}$ representing $\begin{pmatrix} 4 \\ 3 \end{pmatrix}$, $\begin{pmatrix} 1 \\ 2 \end{pmatrix}$ and $\begin{pmatrix} 2 \\ 2 \end{pmatrix}$, respectively. Measure these lengths in the scales you have chosen. How could you have calculated these lengths?

The addition of vectors illustrated geometrically

Any member of the family of vectors given by the shift vector $\begin{pmatrix} a \\ b \end{pmatrix}$ can be represented by the position vector $\mathbf{OP}$, relative to an origin O, where $\mathbf{OP}$ $= a\mathbf{i} + b\mathbf{j}$. For a second family, whose shift vector is $\begin{pmatrix} c \\ d \end{pmatrix}$, take $\mathbf{OQ}$ as the corresponding position vector, where $\mathbf{OQ} = c\mathbf{i} + d\mathbf{j}$.
   Now $\mathbf{OP} + \mathbf{OQ} = a\mathbf{i} + b\mathbf{j} + c\mathbf{i} + d\mathbf{j} = (a + c)\mathbf{i} + (b + d)\mathbf{j}$. This result is illustrated in Figure 20.3. Take $\mathbf{OR}$ as the position vector representing the family of shift vectors $\begin{pmatrix} a + c \\ b + d \end{pmatrix}$.

$$\mathbf{OR} = (a + c)\mathbf{i} + (b + d)\mathbf{j} \Rightarrow \mathbf{OR} = \mathbf{OP} + \mathbf{OQ}.$$

   Some deductions can be made at once from this geometrical illustration:
(1) The vector $\mathbf{PR}$, joining (a, b) and $(a + c, b + d)$, has the same magnitude and direction as the vector $\mathbf{OQ}$, joining $(0, 0)$ and (c, d). Hence $\mathbf{OQ} = \mathbf{PR}$.
Therefore $\mathbf{OP} + \mathbf{OQ} = \mathbf{OR} \Rightarrow \mathbf{OP} + \mathbf{PR} = \mathbf{OR}$.

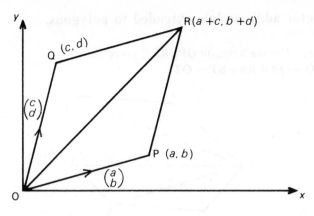

Fig. 20.3

In terms of displacements, this implies that a journey from O to P **followed by** a journey from P to R is equivalent to a direct journey from O to R. This property is called the **Triangular Law** of addition of vectors.

By a similar argument it can be established that

$\quad\quad$ **OP = QR** and **OQ + QR = OR**.

(2) Given that the position vectors of P and Q are **p** and **q** respectively then the position vector of R is **p + q**.

As $OP = |\mathbf{p}|$, $OQ = PR = |\mathbf{q}|$, $OR = |\mathbf{p+q}|$
and as $\quad\quad OR \leqslant OP + PR$, since OPR form a triangle,

$\quad\quad |\mathbf{p+q}| \leqslant |\mathbf{p}| + |\mathbf{q}|,$

the equality being true only when O, P, Q lie on the same straight line, i.e. when O, P, Q are collinear.

(3) Since **OQ** and **PR** have the same magnitude and the same direction, it follows at once that the quadrilateral OPRQ is a **parallelogram**. Both this property and the triangular law of addition have many uses, particularly in mechanics. The vectors **OP** and **OQ** could represent two forces acting at a point O. The resultant of these forces is represented by the vector **OR**, where R is the fourth vertex of the parallelogram OPRQ.

Example: *Use the notation in Figure 20.3 to show that vectors are (a) commutative under addition, (b) associative under addition.*

(a) In triangle OQR, **OQ + QR = OR** and **OP = QR** ⇒ **OQ + OP = OR**. In triangle OPR, **OP + PR = OR** and **OR = PR** ⇒ **OP + OQ = OR**. Hence **OQ + OP = OP + OQ**, showing *vectors are commutative under addition*.

(b) Consider **(OQ + QR) + RP = OR + RP = OP**,
$\quad$ and $\quad$ **OQ + (QR + RP) = OQ + QP = OP**.

Both of the above require the triangular law to be applied twice and are most easily seen by using the notion of journeys already described. Hence **(OQ + QR) + RP = OQ + (QR + RP)** and both of these expressions can now be written as **OQ + QR + RP**; the additions may be taken in any order. *Vectors are associative under addition.*

The vector addition law extended to polygons.

Example: *For the hexagon OPQRST, prove that*
$\mathbf{OP} + \mathbf{PQ} + \mathbf{QR} + \mathbf{RS} + \mathbf{ST} = \mathbf{OT}$.

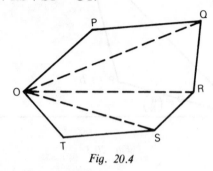

Fig. 20.4

In Figure 20.4, using the triangle law of addition in each case,
$$\mathbf{OP} + \mathbf{PQ} = \mathbf{OQ},$$
$$\mathbf{OQ} + \mathbf{QR} = \mathbf{OR},$$
$$\mathbf{OR} + \mathbf{RS} = \mathbf{OS},$$
$$\mathbf{OS} + \mathbf{ST} = \mathbf{OT}.$$
Adding all these results gives
$\mathbf{OP} + \mathbf{PQ} + \mathbf{OQ} + \mathbf{QR} + \mathbf{OR} + \mathbf{RS} + \mathbf{OS} + \mathbf{ST} = \mathbf{OQ} + \mathbf{OR} + \mathbf{OS} + \mathbf{OT}$.
Hence $\mathbf{OP} + \mathbf{PQ} + \mathbf{QR} + \mathbf{RS} + \mathbf{ST} = \mathbf{OT}$, as required.

Note: By writing $\mathbf{OT} = -\mathbf{TO}$, in the above result and bringing this term to the left-hand side, another important property for vectors in a closed polygon is illustrated:
$$\mathbf{OP} + \mathbf{PQ} + \mathbf{QR} + \mathbf{RS} + \mathbf{ST} + \mathbf{TO} = \mathbf{0}.$$
The sum of the vectors taken in order around a closed polygon of any number of sides is the zero vector.

The subtraction of vectors illustrated geometrically

Using the same notation as in the previous paragraphs and referring to Figure 20.5, $\mathbf{OP} - \mathbf{OQ} = a\mathbf{i} + b\mathbf{j} - (c\mathbf{i} + d\mathbf{j}) = (a - c)\mathbf{i} + (b - d)\mathbf{j}$.

Take S to be the point with position vector $(a - c)\mathbf{i} + (b - d)\mathbf{j}$, representing the family of shift vectors $\begin{pmatrix} a - c \\ b - d \end{pmatrix}$

$\mathbf{OS} = (a - c)\mathbf{i} + (b - d)\mathbf{j} \Rightarrow \mathbf{OS} = \mathbf{OP} - \mathbf{OQ}$.
In Figure 20.5, $-\mathbf{OQ} = \mathbf{QO} = \mathbf{OZ}$.
The parallelogram OPSZ is completed, which makes
$$\mathbf{OS} = \mathbf{OP} + \mathbf{OZ} = \mathbf{OP} - \mathbf{OQ}.$$
Note: $\mathbf{OS} = \mathbf{OP} + \mathbf{PS} = \mathbf{OP} + \mathbf{QO} = \mathbf{QO} + \mathbf{OP} = \mathbf{QP}$, the second diagonal of parallelogram OPRQ, and in examples, the vector $\mathbf{QP}$ is often used to represent the difference between the vectors $\mathbf{OP}$ and $\mathbf{OQ}$. In fact, a simple single application of the triangle addition rule gives
$$\mathbf{QP} = \mathbf{QO} + \mathbf{OP} = -\mathbf{OQ} + \mathbf{OP} \text{ at once.}$$

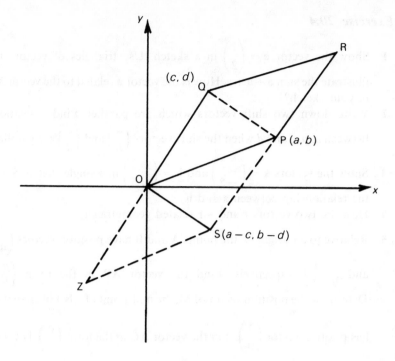

Fig. 20.5

Example: *In the triangle ABC, AB = **p**, AC = **q** and D is the mid-point of BC. Express, in terms of **p** and **q**, the vectors (a) **BC**, (b) **BD**, (c) **AD**. (See Figure 20.6.)*

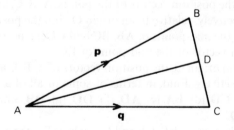

Fig. 20.6

(a) $\mathbf{BC} = \mathbf{BA} + \mathbf{AC} = -\mathbf{AB} + \mathbf{AC} = -\mathbf{p} + \mathbf{q} = \mathbf{q} - \mathbf{p}$.
(b) $\mathbf{BD} = \frac{1}{2}\mathbf{BC} = \frac{1}{2}(\mathbf{q} - \mathbf{p})$.
(c) $\mathbf{AD} = \mathbf{AB} + \mathbf{BD} = \mathbf{p} + \frac{1}{2}(\mathbf{q} - \mathbf{p}) = \mathbf{p} + \frac{1}{2}\mathbf{q} - \frac{1}{2}\mathbf{p} = \frac{1}{2}\mathbf{p} + \frac{1}{2}\mathbf{q} = \frac{1}{2}(\mathbf{p} + \mathbf{q})$.
The last result could also be obtained by realising that D is the mid-point of the diagonals of the parallelogram, having AB and AC as two of its sides.

Exercise 20.4

1 Show the vector $\mathbf{a} = \begin{pmatrix} 1 \\ 2 \end{pmatrix}$ in a sketch. Use triangles of vectors to illustrate the sum $\mathbf{a} + \mathbf{a} + \mathbf{a}$. How is the vector $\mathbf{a}$ related to the vector $3\mathbf{a}$ in your sketch?

2 Write down two shift vectors which are parallel. Find a relation between a, b, c and d when the shift vectors $\begin{pmatrix} a \\ b \end{pmatrix}$ and $\begin{pmatrix} c \\ d \end{pmatrix}$ are parallel.

3 Show the vectors $\mathbf{a} = \begin{pmatrix} 2 \\ -5 \end{pmatrix}$ and $\mathbf{b} = \begin{pmatrix} -2 \\ 5 \end{pmatrix}$ in a single sketch. State the relationship between $\mathbf{a}$ and $\mathbf{b}$.

4 How are two vectors $\mathbf{r}$ and $-\mathbf{r}$ related geometrically?

5 Relative to an origin O, the points A and B have position vectors $\begin{pmatrix} 2 \\ 4 \end{pmatrix}$ and $\begin{pmatrix} 1 \\ -2 \end{pmatrix}$ respectively. Find the vector $\mathbf{AB}$ in the form $\begin{pmatrix} a \\ b \end{pmatrix}$. Determine the position vector of M, the mid-point of AB. Given that C has position vector $\begin{pmatrix} \frac{4}{3} \\ 0 \end{pmatrix}$, find the vector $\mathbf{AC}$ in the form $\begin{pmatrix} c \\ d \end{pmatrix}$. Is C on the line AB? If so, in what ratio does it divide AB?

6 Taking O as origin, use graph paper to plot the points A and B, whose position vectors are $(3\mathbf{i} + 4\mathbf{j})$ and $(\mathbf{i} + 2\mathbf{j})$, respectively. Locate points C, D, E, F and G such that $\mathbf{OC} = 3\mathbf{OA}$, $\mathbf{OD} = 4\mathbf{OB}$, $\mathbf{OE} = 3\mathbf{OA} + 4\mathbf{OB}$, $\mathbf{OF} = 2\mathbf{OA} + \mathbf{OB}$ and $\mathbf{OG} = \frac{1}{3}\mathbf{OA} + \frac{1}{2}\mathbf{OB}$. Is there any point in the plane of the co-ordinate axes which cannot be represented by a combination of the vectors $\mathbf{OA}$ and $\mathbf{OB}$? Can $\mathbf{OG}$ be represented by any combination of $\mathbf{OA}$ and $\mathbf{OB}$ other than the one given?

7 Given that the position vectors of the points, A, B, C, and D are $\mathbf{a}$, $\mathbf{b}$, $\mathbf{c}$ and $\mathbf{d}$, respectively, relative to an origin O, find the position vectors of E, F and G, the mid-points of AB, BC and CD, respectively. Find also the position vector of the mid-point of EG.

8 Relative to an origin O, the position vectors of A, B, C and D are $\mathbf{a}$, $\mathbf{b}$, $\mathbf{c}$ and $\mathbf{d}$, respectively. Find, in terms of some or all of $\mathbf{a}$, $\mathbf{b}$, $\mathbf{c}$, $\mathbf{d}$: (a) $\mathbf{AB}$, (b) $\mathbf{BC}$, (c) $\mathbf{CD}$, (d) $\mathbf{BA}$, (e) $\mathbf{AD}$, (f) $\mathbf{DO}$, (g) $\mathbf{DB}$. Simplify $\mathbf{OA} + \mathbf{AB} + \mathbf{BC} + \mathbf{CD}$.

Express the vectors $\mathbf{BE}$, $\mathbf{CE}$ and $\mathbf{OE}$, where E is the mid-point of BC, in terms of some or all of $\mathbf{a}$, $\mathbf{b}$, $\mathbf{c}$, $\mathbf{d}$.

If F is on OC such that $\mathbf{OF}:\mathbf{FC} = 3:1$, find $\mathbf{FD}$ in terms of $\mathbf{c}$ and $\mathbf{d}$.

9 Given that $\mathbf{AB} = \mathbf{a}$ and $\mathbf{AC} = \mathbf{b}$, find $\mathbf{BC}$ in terms of $\mathbf{a}$ and $\mathbf{b}$. If $\mathbf{CD} = 2\mathbf{BC}$, find $\mathbf{AD}$ in terms of $\mathbf{a}$ and $\mathbf{b}$.

10 Given that $\mathbf{OA} = 3\mathbf{i} + 4\mathbf{j}$ and $\mathbf{OB} = 2\mathbf{i} - \mathbf{j}$, where O is the origin, find: (a) $\mathbf{OC}$ such that $\mathbf{OC} = 2\mathbf{OA} - \mathbf{OB}$, (b) $\mathbf{OD}$ such that $\mathbf{OD} = -3\mathbf{OA} + 4\mathbf{OB}$.

Equality of vectors

Two vectors represented by the directed line segments AB and CD are equal if, and only if, the translation defined by the mapping of A on to B also maps C on to D. This statement implies the following: the line segments AB and CD must be *equal* in length AND either *parallel* or such that *A, B, C and D all lie in the same line.*

In component form this can be expressed as:

$$\begin{pmatrix} a \\ b \end{pmatrix} = \begin{pmatrix} c \\ d \end{pmatrix} \Leftrightarrow a = c \text{ and } b = d.$$

Parallel vectors

If two non-zero vectors, **a** and **b**, are parallel, it is always possible to find two scalars, h and k, such that $h\mathbf{a} = k\mathbf{b}$.

Conversely, if $h\mathbf{a} = k\mathbf{b}$, then either **a** and **b** are parallel or *both* h and k are zero.

Example 1: *The vectors **a** and **b** are not parallel. Given that $3\mathbf{a} + h\mathbf{b} = k\mathbf{a} + 2\mathbf{b}$, find the values of the scalars h and k.*

The vector equation can be rewritten as $3\mathbf{a} - k\mathbf{a} = 2\mathbf{b} - h\mathbf{b}$,

$$\text{that is} \qquad (3 - k)\mathbf{a} = (2 - h)\mathbf{b}.$$

As **a** and **b** are not parallel, *both* $3 - k$ and $2 - h$ must be zero.

$$\text{Therefore } k = 3 \text{ and } h = 2.$$

Example 2: *The position vectors of three points A, B and C, relative to an origin O are **a**, **b** and $\frac{9}{8}\mathbf{a} + \frac{11}{8}\mathbf{b}$ respectively. The point D on AB is such that $AD = \frac{1}{3} DB$. Write down, in terms of **a** and **b**, the vectors **AB** and **AD** and hence find the vectors **OD** and **BC**. What deduction can be made about the quadrilateral OBCD?*

In Figure 20.7, $\mathbf{AB} = \mathbf{AO} + \mathbf{OB} = -\mathbf{OA} + \mathbf{OB} = -\mathbf{a} + \mathbf{b}$,

$$\mathbf{AD} = \tfrac{1}{3}\mathbf{DB} = \tfrac{1}{4}\mathbf{AB} = \tfrac{1}{4}(-\mathbf{a} + \mathbf{b})$$
$$\mathbf{OD} = \mathbf{OA} + \mathbf{AD} = \mathbf{a} + \tfrac{1}{4}(-\mathbf{a} + \mathbf{b}) = \tfrac{3}{4}\mathbf{a} + \tfrac{1}{4}\mathbf{b} = \tfrac{1}{4}(3\mathbf{a} + \mathbf{b})$$
$$\mathbf{BC} = \mathbf{BO} + \mathbf{OC} = -\mathbf{b} + (\tfrac{9}{8}\mathbf{a} + \tfrac{11}{8}\mathbf{b}) = \tfrac{9}{8}\mathbf{a} + \tfrac{3}{8}\mathbf{b} = \tfrac{3}{8}(3\mathbf{a} + \mathbf{b}).$$

As $2\,\mathbf{BC} = 3\,\mathbf{OD}$, **BC** is parallel to **OD** and $|\mathbf{BC}| = \frac{3}{2}|\mathbf{OD}|$.

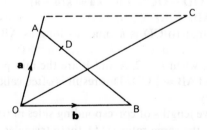

Fig. 20.7

Therefore OBCD is a trapezium, as it has one pair of parallel, but not equal sides OD and BC.

Example 3: *Given that* $\mathbf{OA} = -2\mathbf{i} + 3\mathbf{j}$, $\mathbf{OB} = \mathbf{i} + 2\mathbf{j}$ *and* $\mathbf{OC} = 7\mathbf{i}$, *referred to O as origin, prove that A, B and C are collinear.*
$\mathbf{AB} = \mathbf{AO} + \mathbf{OB} = \mathbf{OB} - \mathbf{OA} = (\mathbf{i} + 2\mathbf{j}) - (-2\mathbf{i} + 3\mathbf{j}) = 3\mathbf{i} - \mathbf{j}$.
$\mathbf{BC} = \mathbf{BO} + \mathbf{OC} = \mathbf{OC} - \mathbf{OB} = 7\mathbf{i} - (\mathbf{i} + 2\mathbf{j}) = 6\mathbf{i} - 2\mathbf{j}$.
Hence $\mathbf{BC} = 6\mathbf{i} - 2\mathbf{j} = 2(3\mathbf{i} - \mathbf{j}) = 2\,\mathbf{AB}$.
The vectors $\mathbf{BC}$ and $\mathbf{AB}$ have the same direction, defined by the shift vector $3\mathbf{i} - \mathbf{j}$, and they also have a common point B.
Therefore the points A, B and C are collinear.

A further geometrical illustration

The use of vectors can produce many elegant proofs of geometrical properties and this application should be utilised whenever appropriate. Vectors can be particularly useful in extracting ratios of lengths and areas from similar figures.

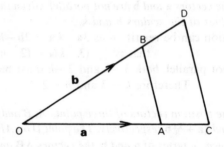

Fig. 20.8

In Figure 20.8, $\mathbf{OA} = \mathbf{a}$ and $\mathbf{OB} = \mathbf{b}$, referred to O as origin. The points C and D are taken on OA produced and OB produced such that $\mathbf{OC} = k\,\mathbf{OA}$ and $\mathbf{OD} = k\,\mathbf{OB}$, where k is some fixed number.
Hence $\mathbf{OC} = k\mathbf{a}$ and $\mathbf{OD} = k\mathbf{b}$.
$\mathbf{AB} = \mathbf{AO} + \mathbf{OB} = \mathbf{OB} - \mathbf{OA} = \mathbf{b} - \mathbf{a}$
$\mathbf{CD} = \mathbf{CO} + \mathbf{OD} = \mathbf{OD} - \mathbf{OC} = k\mathbf{b} - k\mathbf{a} = k(\mathbf{b} - \mathbf{a})$.
Therefore $\mathbf{CD} = k\,\mathbf{AB}$.
This result implies that (i) CD is k times as long as AB, and (ii) CD is parallel to AB.

In the special case when $k = 2$, A and B are the mid-points of OC and OD, respectively, and $\mathbf{AB} = \frac{1}{2}\,\mathbf{CD}$. This result is often called the **mid-point theorem** in geometry.

Since the respective lengths of corresponding sides in triangle OAB and triangle ACD are in the same ratio $(1:k)$, these triangles are similar. The ratios of their respective areas will be $1:k^2$. Referring again to the special case when $k = 2$, it can be shown that the area of triangle OAB is $\frac{1}{4}$ of the area of triangle OCD and the area of trapezium ACDB is $\frac{3}{4}$ of the area of triangle OCD.

Exercise 20.5

1   Given that $\mathbf{a} = \begin{pmatrix} 2 \\ 4 \end{pmatrix}$, $\mathbf{b} = \begin{pmatrix} 3 \\ 6 \end{pmatrix}$, $\mathbf{c} = \begin{pmatrix} 6 \\ 12 \end{pmatrix}$ and $\mathbf{d} = \begin{pmatrix} 1 \\ 3 \end{pmatrix}$ find, where possible, scalars, k, m and n in the following vector equations:
(a) $\mathbf{c} = k\mathbf{a}$, (b) $\mathbf{c} = m\mathbf{b}$, (c) $\mathbf{a} = n\mathbf{d}$.

2   Using graph paper and choosing suitable scales, illustrate the vectors $\mathbf{a}$, $\mathbf{b}$, $\mathbf{c}$, $\mathbf{d}$ of question 1 on the same axes. Write down any observations about these shift vectors from your diagram.

3   In the regular hexagon OABCDE, $\mathbf{OA} = \mathbf{a}$ and $\mathbf{ED} = \mathbf{b}$. Find, in terms of $\mathbf{a}$ and $\mathbf{b}$, (a) $\mathbf{AB}$, (b) $\mathbf{CD}$, (c) $\mathbf{OC}$, (d) $\mathbf{OB}$, (e) $\mathbf{BC}$.

4   Given that $h\mathbf{b} + 3\mathbf{a} = k(\mathbf{b} - \mathbf{a})$, find the scalars h and k.

5   Given that $h\begin{pmatrix} 3 \\ 5 \end{pmatrix} + k\begin{pmatrix} 2 \\ -1 \end{pmatrix} = \begin{pmatrix} 3 \\ 6 \end{pmatrix}$, find the scalars h and k.

6   Given that $\mathbf{a} = 3\mathbf{b}$ and that $\mathbf{b} = 4\mathbf{c}$, write $\mathbf{c}$ in terms of $\mathbf{a}$ and find the ratio $|\mathbf{a}| : |\mathbf{c}|$.

7   In the quadrilateral ABCD, $\mathbf{AB} = \mathbf{a}$, $\mathbf{BC} = \mathbf{b}$, $\mathbf{CD} = \mathbf{c}$ and $\mathbf{DA} = \mathbf{d}$. Prove that the quadrilateral formed by joining the mid-points of the sides of the quadrilateral ABCD is a parallelogram. (Hint: express $\mathbf{AC}$ in vectors in two different ways).

8   In the parallelogram OABC, $\mathbf{OA} = \mathbf{a}$ and $\mathbf{OC} = \mathbf{c}$. Name the special type of parallelogram when: (a) $|\mathbf{a} + \mathbf{c}| = |\mathbf{a} - \mathbf{c}|$, (b) $|\mathbf{a}| = |\mathbf{c}|$.

9   In the triangle OAB, the mid-points of AB and OA are C and D respectively. Given that $\mathbf{OA} = 2\mathbf{a}$ and $\mathbf{OB} = 2\mathbf{b}$, express, in terms of $\mathbf{a}$ and $\mathbf{b}$, the vectors: (a) $\mathbf{OD}$ (b) $\mathbf{AB}$, (c) $\mathbf{CD}$, (d) $\mathbf{BD}$. Deduce that: (e) the triangles OBD and ABD are equal in area, (f) the area of triangle ADC is $\frac{1}{4}$ area of triangle OAB. Find the area of the quadrilateral OBCD in terms of the area of triangle OAB.

10   Prove that the points with position vectors $\mathbf{a} + \mathbf{b}$, $2\mathbf{a} - \mathbf{b}$ and $-5\mathbf{a} + 13\mathbf{b}$ relative to an origin O all lie on the same line.

11   Give a sketch to illustrate the relationship between the origin O and the points A, B, C, D if $\mathbf{OA} = \mathbf{a}$, $\mathbf{OC} = 5\mathbf{a}$, $\mathbf{OB} = \mathbf{b}$ and $\mathbf{OD} = 5\mathbf{b}$. Find $\mathbf{DC}$ in terms of $\mathbf{BA}$ and deduce the ratio: area of trapezium BDCA/area of triangle OBA.

12   A and B have position vectors $\mathbf{a}$ and $\mathbf{b}$ relative to an origin O. C is the point on AB such that AC:CB = 5:3. Express $\mathbf{AB}$, $\mathbf{AC}$ and $\mathbf{OC}$ in terms of $\mathbf{a}$ and $\mathbf{b}$. D is a point on OB such that $\mathbf{OD} = \lambda\mathbf{b}$. Express $\mathbf{DC}$ in terms of $\mathbf{a}$, $\mathbf{b}$ and λ.
Find the value of λ when
(a) OA is parallel to DC, and
(b) DC is parallel to the diagonal OE of parallelogram OAEB.

13   The rectangle OACB has one vertex at the origin O and A and B have position vectors $\mathbf{a}$ and $\mathbf{b}$ relative to O. D is a point on AB such that

AD : DB = 2 : 1 and E is a point on BC such that BE = EC. Express **DB**, **BE**, **DE** in terms of **a** and **b**. Using a vector method find the position vector of the point F, on OC produced, such that AF is parallel to DE, and in this case find the ratio AF : DE.

14 Given that $|\mathbf{a}| = 3, |\mathbf{b}| = 3$, and the angle θ between **a** and **b** is 60°, find:
(a) $|\mathbf{a} - \mathbf{b}|$, and (b) $|\mathbf{a} + \mathbf{b}|$.
Repeat the exercise when $|\mathbf{a}| = 4$, $|\mathbf{b}| = 3$ and $\theta = 40°$.

15 The points A, B, C, D, E, F, G have position vectors given by $\binom{3}{4}, \binom{4}{3},$
$\binom{5}{0}, \binom{0}{5}, \binom{-3}{4}, \binom{\sqrt{2}}{\sqrt{23}}$ and $\binom{1}{\sqrt{24}}$, respectively.
Find the distance of each point from the origin. On what curve do the points lie?
If a point P has variable position vector **p** relative to O, what is the locus traced out by P if $|\mathbf{p}| = 5$?

16 The fixed point A has position vector **a** relative to an origin O. If the moving point P has variable position vector **p**, such that $|\mathbf{p} - \mathbf{a}| = 2$, find the locus of P.
[Hint: draw a diagram and identify $\mathbf{p} - \mathbf{a}$].
If the fixed point B has position vector **b**, find the locus of P if $|\mathbf{p} - \mathbf{a}| = |\mathbf{p} - \mathbf{b}|$.

Navigation problems

We shall now use the addition law for vectors, applied specifically to velocities, to solve problems in air and sea navigation. A simple model is taken where (for example, in the case of air navigation), the wind has constant velocity.

An aircraft is capable of producing a certain speed in still air, called its **airspeed**. If a journey from A to B were undertaken in still air the aircraft would head in the direction **AB**, and the time taken for the journey would be calculated as distance AB/airspeed.

If the same journey were undertaken in a wind of constant velocity **w** the pilot must make allowance for this and would head in a direction (shown as AC in Figure 20.9(a)) so that its actual flight path is **AB**. The time taken for the journey in this case is distance AB/resultant speed.

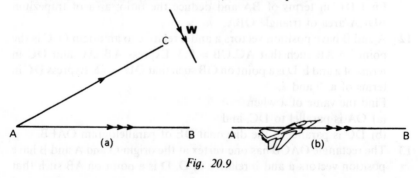

Fig. 20.9

Definitions:

Course (heading)   The direction in which the aircraft is headed, the directions in which it would fly in still air, is called the course.

Track   The direction in which the aircraft actually flies is called the track. It is the path of the aircraft relative to an observer on the ground. (Figure 20.9 (b) shows the observer's view of the aircraft).

Note: The course and track of an aircraft can only be identical when the wind is blowing directly at, or directly behind, the aircraft, i.e. when there is a head wind or tail wind, respectively.

Drift   The angle between the course and the track is called the drift.

Wind direction   The wind direction is the direction *from* which the wind is blowing.

Knot   A speed of 1 nautical mile per hour is called a knot. We shall use n.m. for nautical mile in the following work.

The resultant speed of the aircraft, in the direction of the track, is called its **ground speed. The time of flight** is then **distance travelled/ground speed**.

In the problems to be considered there are three velocities: **a**, *the velocity of the aircraft in still air*, **w**, *the wind velocity*, and **r**, *the resultant velocity of the aircraft*. The magnitudes of these vectors are the *airspeed*, *wind speed* and *ground speed*, respectively; their corresponding directions are the *course, wind direction* and *track*. We shall set up the triangle of vectors **r** = **a** + **w** and either solve by calculation, using trigonometry, or by scale drawing. The arrow convention shown in Figure 20.10 (one for **a**, two for **w**, and three for **r**) serves as a useful check; whichever route is chosen from A to B, there should be a total of three arrows in that direction.

Example 1:   *An aircraft can fly at 250 km/h in still air. The wind is blowing from the North at 30 km/h. Find the ground speed and the track when the aircraft is headed due east.*

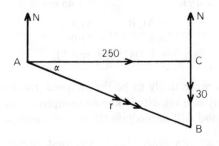

a	w	r
090°	000°	090°+α°
250 k	30 k	r

Fig. 20.10

The triangle of vectors is shown in Figure 20.10.

Using Pythagoras' Theorem: $r^2 = 30^2 + 250^2 = 63400$

$$r = 252 \text{ (3 s.f.)}.$$

There is less likelihood of error if the scaled down numbers 3 and 25 are used, but remember to scale up again, by the same factor, when finding *r*.

277

α can be found since $\tan \alpha = \dfrac{3}{25} = 0.12 \Rightarrow \alpha = 6.84°$

$$= 7° \text{ (nearest°)}.$$

The track is 097°; the ground speed is 252 km/h.

The reader should also solve the problem using a scale drawing.

Example 2: *An aircraft whose airspeed is 250 knots sets a course of 320°. If it is observed to have a track of 310° and a ground speed of 260 knots, find the wind velocity.*

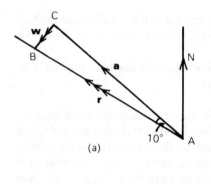
(a)

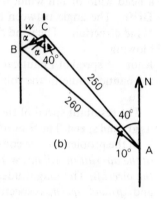
(b)

Fig. 20.11

From the triangle of vectors (Figure 20.11(a)) it is clear that **CB** represents the wind velocity. With the notation of Figure 20.11(b), w and α can be found as follows.

Using the Cosine Rule:
$$w^2 = 250^2 + 260^2 - 2 \times 250 \times 260 \cos 10°$$
$$w = 45.6 \text{ (3 s.f.)}.$$

Using the Sine Rule: $\dfrac{\sin ACB}{260} = \dfrac{\sin 10°}{45.6} \Rightarrow \sin ACB = \dfrac{260 \sin 10°}{45.6} = 0.9901$

$$\Rightarrow ACB = 81.9°$$
$$\Rightarrow \alpha = 41.9°.$$

Wind speed is 45.6 km/h and its direction is 042° (nearest °).

In practice the known data is more likely to be the airspeed, the wind velocity and the track. When only one velocity is known completely, as in this case, the scale drawing method will necessitate the use of a compass.

Example 3 (drawing): *An aircraft with airspeed 220 knots wants to make a track of 090° in a wind blowing at 40 knots from 020°. Find the course to be set and the ground speed.*

A rough triangle of velocities is formed (Figure 20.12(a)) so that the positioning of the scale drawing can be considered.

CB, representing the wind velocity, is drawn first, using a suitable scale (Figure 20.12(b)). An arc, centre C, radius $5\frac{1}{2}$ cm is drawn to cut the track at A.

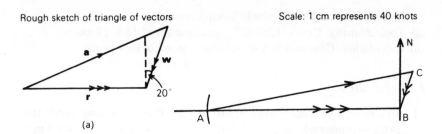

Rough sketch of triangle of vectors

Scale: 1 cm represents 40 knots

(a)

(b)

Fig. 20.12

AC represents **a**; the direction of **AC** is the course.

AB represents **r**; *AB* (5.1 cm) represents the ground speed.

By measurement the ground speed is 204 knots and the course is 080°.

The reader should check these by calculation.

Problems in sea navigation are solved in the same manner. A craft has a speed in still water, provided by the oars or a motor, but if a current is flowing the craft will have an effective speed, or resultant speed, different to its speed in still water. If **a** is *the velocity of the craft in still water,* **c** *the velocity of the current,* and **r** *the resultant velocity of the craft,* the triangle of vectors is

$$\mathbf{r} = \mathbf{a} + \mathbf{c}$$

Example 4: *A launch whose speed relative to the water is 16 knots makes good a track of 040° in a current flowing at 4 knots in a direction of 110°. Find the course set and the resultant speed of the launch.*

Figure 20.13(a) gives the solution by scale drawing while Figure 20.13(b) shows the data for calculation purposes.

Scale: 1 cm represents 4 knots

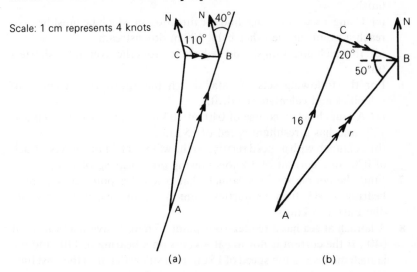

(a)

(b)

Fig. 20.13

The reader should verify the following results:

(a) *Scale drawing: Course 026–027°, resultant speed 16.8–17 knots.*

(b) *Calculation: Course is 026.4°, resultant speed is 16.9 knots.*

Exercise 20.6

1 In a pool, a swimmer takes 50 s to travel 100 m. How long would the same swimmer take to cover 100 m in a stream whose current is 1.5 m/s if he swims: (a) with the current, (b) against the current?

2 A man can row a boat at 4 m/s in still water. How long does it take him to row 210 m upstream and back again in a stream whose current is 3 m/s? What is his average speed for the complete journey?

3 An aircraft has an airspeed of 200 knots. Find the time taken to travel 1000 n.m. if there is a tail wind of 5 knots.

4 For each of the following problems find the missing entries:

	Airspeed	Course	Wind velocity		Ground speed	Track
(a)	220 knots	000°	40 knots,	090°	——	——
(b)	200 knots	310°	30 knots,	060°	——	——
(c)	300 knots	095° ·	——,	——	320 knots	090°
(d)	150 knots	260°	——,	——	125 knots	250°
(e)	220 knots	——	45 knots,	120°	——	020°
(f)	240 knots	——	40 knots,	090°	——	250°

5 An oarsman who can row at 5 m/s in still water rows across a river 200 m wide flowing due West at 2 m/s.

(a) In what direction must he head if he is to reach a point on the other bank directly opposite to his starting point? (His resultant velocity is straight across). Find his resultant speed and the time taken to cross.

(b) If he heads straight across the river, how far downstream does he finish?

(c) Using a scale drawing, find the direction in which he must head to reach a point on the other bank 100 m downstream.

(d) In which direction should he head to cross the river in the shortest time?

6 For the following sets of data, sketch the appropriate triangle of velocities and calculate the drift:

(a) A launch sets a course of 040° at 10 knots in a current flowing at 120° and has a resultant speed of 15 knots.

(b) A launch with a speed relative to the water of 8 knots makes a track of 070° in a current of 3 knots flowing on a bearing of 150°.

7 Find the course set by a launch that reached a point 20 n.m. on a bearing of 045° from its starting point in 2 hours in a current flowing due East at 3 knots.

8 A launch at sea has a rendez-vous point 15 n.m. away on a bearing of 040°. If the current is flowing at 4 knots on a bearing of 110° and the launch moves at a top speed of 15 knots in still water, find the least time taken to reach the rendez-vous point and the course that is set.

9 A pilot calculates that with an airspeed of 200 knots and a course due

north, in a westerly wind of 30 knots, he will reach his destination in 3 hours. What is the bearing of the destination and how far is it from the take-off point?

10 In a wind blowing at 50 knots from 250°, an aircraft whose airspeed is 250 knots needs to set a course due north to make the journey from A to B. On the return journey the wind velocity and the airspeed remain the same. What course should be set to reach A?

11 A helicopter, on a training flight, has to cover a square course ABCDA of side 25 n.m., with B due north of A, and C due east of B. The helicopter's airspeed is 80 knots and the wind is blowing from the west at 20 knots. Find the course set for each section of the journey and the time taken (to the nearest minute) for the 'round' trip.

12 An aircraft is flying with an airspeed of 250 knots on a course of 070°. The navigator fixes his position at half-hourly intervals. The distance and direction of the second fix from the first is 100 n.m. and 080° respectively. Find the wind velocity.

13 An aircraft has a rendez-vous point 100 n.m. from its base on a bearing of 036°. The pilot misreads the bearing as 063° and sets his course accordingly. The plane has an airspeed of 220 knots and the wind is blowing at 20 knots from 120°. Find, to the nearest n.m., the distance of the plane from the rendez-vous after 30 minutes.

21 Matrices

A **matrix** is a list of numbers, letters or symbols, called **elements**, written as a rectangular array with each element occupying a definite position, with the whole array enclosed by a bracket.

In many practical situations matrices provide a neat and concise way of storing information. What is more, if the information in one matrix is related to that in another, it is often possible to process the data and extract further information by the application of a few simple operations. The **stock vectors**, described at the start of Chapter 20, are particular examples of matrices which have either only one row or only one column.

Example 1: Each week a family sends sheets, pillow-cases and towels to a laundry. The table shows the numbers sent each week over three successive weeks.

	Sheets	Pillow-cases	Towels
Week 1	10	8	12
Week 2	5	8	7
Week 3	8	7	10

$$\begin{pmatrix} 10 & 8 & 12 \\ 5 & 8 & 7 \\ 8 & 7 & 10 \end{pmatrix}$$

Table   *Information in matrix form*

This tabulated information can be written in matrix form as shown. Each slot in the matrix has a fixed position and a definite meaning relative to all the other slots.

Example 2: The matrix

$$\begin{pmatrix} 8 & 8 & 10 \\ 9 & 7 & 6 \\ 5 & 7 & 8 \end{pmatrix}$$

shows the same information over the same three week period for a neighbouring family using the same laundry.

$$\begin{pmatrix} 10 & 8 & 12 \\ 5 & 8 & 7 \\ 8 & 7 & 10 \end{pmatrix} + \begin{pmatrix} 8 & 8 & 10 \\ 9 & 7 & 6 \\ 5 & 7 & 8 \end{pmatrix} = \begin{pmatrix} 18 & 16 & 22 \\ 14 & 15 & 13 \\ 13 & 14 & 18 \end{pmatrix}.$$

The addition of these matrices, as shown in the example, has some practical meaning; the **sum matrix** gives the total numbers of sheets, pillow cases and towels sent by the families each week. This would be the matrix describing the position if the two families had parcelled their laundry together each week and sent it as one bundle.

The reader will have appreciated already that the simple laws developed for stock vectors can equally well be applied to matrices. In particular, both examples (a) and (b) which follow can be given a practical meaning at once.

$$\text{(a)} \quad \begin{pmatrix} 10 & 8 & 12 \\ 5 & 8 & 7 \\ 8 & 7 & 10 \end{pmatrix} + \begin{pmatrix} 10 & 8 & 12 \\ 5 & 8 & 7 \\ 8 & 7 & 10 \end{pmatrix} = \begin{pmatrix} 20 & 16 & 24 \\ 10 & 16 & 14 \\ 16 & 14 & 20 \end{pmatrix}$$

$$= 2 \begin{pmatrix} 10 & 8 & 12 \\ 5 & 8 & 7 \\ 8 & 7 & 10 \end{pmatrix}.$$

$$\text{(b)} \quad \begin{pmatrix} 18 & 16 & 22 \\ 14 & 15 & 13 \\ 13 & 14 & 18 \end{pmatrix} - \begin{pmatrix} 8 & 8 & 10 \\ 9 & 7 & 6 \\ 5 & 7 & 8 \end{pmatrix} = \begin{pmatrix} 10 & 8 & 12 \\ 5 & 8 & 7 \\ 8 & 7 & 10 \end{pmatrix}.$$

The first, (a), shows that if all the items in a matrix **A** are doubled, this can be written simply as $2\mathbf{A}$.

The second, (b), shows how matrices could be subtracted in a meaningful and practical way.

The next step in this illustration shows how it is possible to attach both a practical meaning and a reason for the combination of two matrices under an operation which is called **matrix multiplication**.

At the laundry, the respective costs for laundering a sheet, pillow-case and towel are 12 p, 6 p and 5 p.

The total cost therefore for the first family in week 1 for its laundry is given by $(10 \times 12 + 8 \times 6 + 12 \times 5)$ pence $= (120 + 48 + 60)$ pence $= 228$ p, and similar calculations would yield the total cost for week 2 and week 3. This overall calculation can be expressed concisely in terms of matrices as follows:

$$\begin{pmatrix} 10 & 8 & 12 \\ 5 & 8 & 7 \\ 8 & 7 & 10 \end{pmatrix} \begin{pmatrix} 12 \\ 6 \\ 5 \end{pmatrix} = \begin{pmatrix} 10 \times 12 + 8 \times 6 + 12 \times 5 \\ 5 \times 12 + 8 \times 6 + 7 \times 5 \\ 8 \times 12 + 7 \times 6 + 10 \times 5 \end{pmatrix} = \begin{pmatrix} 228 \\ 143 \\ 188 \end{pmatrix}.$$

Suppose the laundry had introduced a special offer for the period and priced the laundering for a sheet, pillow-case and towel at 10 p, 5 p and 4 p, respectively. This special offer and the standard price could be illustrated in one matrix product as

$$\begin{pmatrix} 10 & 8 & 12 \\ 5 & 8 & 7 \\ 8 & 7 & 10 \end{pmatrix} \begin{pmatrix} 12 & 10 \\ 6 & 5 \\ 5 & 4 \end{pmatrix} = \begin{pmatrix} 228 & 188 \\ 143 & 118 \\ 188 & 155 \end{pmatrix}.$$

The following sections develop the algebra of matrices.

Order

A matrix with m rows and n columns is said to be of order $(m \times n)$.

Equality

Two matrices are equal if, and only if, they are of the same order and the elements of one are equal to the corresponding elements of the other.

Example: $\begin{pmatrix} 3 & 4 \\ 1 & 2 \end{pmatrix} = \begin{pmatrix} 3 & x \\ 1 & y \end{pmatrix}$ if, and only if, $x = 4$ and $y = 2$.

Addition of matrices

Matrices can be added (subtracted), if and only if, they are of the *same order*, the resulting matrix being formed by the addition (subtraction) of the corresponding elements.

Multiplication of a matrix by a scalar (number)

A matrix multiplied by a scalar, k, forms a matrix of the same order with each corresponding element k times those in the original matrix.

Exercise 21.1

1 Given that $\mathbf{A} = \begin{pmatrix} 3 & 4 \\ 1 & 2 \end{pmatrix}$, $\mathbf{B} = \begin{pmatrix} 5 & 2 \\ 3 & 1 \end{pmatrix}$, and $\mathbf{C} = \begin{pmatrix} 2 & 5 \\ 4 & -3 \end{pmatrix}$, simplify:

(a) $\mathbf{A} + 2\mathbf{B} + 3\mathbf{C}$, (b) $2\mathbf{A} + 3\mathbf{B}$, (c) $\mathbf{B} - \mathbf{C}$, (d) $3\mathbf{A} - 2\mathbf{B}$,
(e) $(\mathbf{A} + \mathbf{B}) + \mathbf{C}$,
(f) $2\mathbf{A} + (2\mathbf{B} + \mathbf{C})$, (g) $\mathbf{C} - \mathbf{B}$, (h) $(\mathbf{A} + \mathbf{C}) + (\mathbf{B} - \mathbf{C})$.

2 Show that matrices, of the same order, are both commutative and associative under matrix addition.

Multiplication of two matrices

Two matrices, $\mathbf{A}$ and $\mathbf{B}$, form a product $\mathbf{AB}$, if, and only if, the number of columns in $\mathbf{A}$ is equal to the number of rows in $\mathbf{B}$. Similarly, the product $\mathbf{BA}$ can be formed if, and only if, the number of columns of $\mathbf{B}$ is equal to the number of rows in $\mathbf{A}$.

The following examples illustrate how matrix products are built up.

Example 1: *Product* $\quad$ (1 $\quad$ 2) $\begin{pmatrix} 3 \\ 4 \end{pmatrix}$

$\qquad\qquad$ *Order* $\qquad$ $(1 \times \underline{2})$ $\quad$ $(\underline{2} \times 1)$

The product exists because the first matrix has 2 *columns* and the second matrix has 2 *rows*.
The product matrix $= (1 \times 3 + 2 \times 4) = (11)$.
The order of the product matrix is (1×1).

Example 2: *Product* $\qquad$ $\begin{pmatrix} 3 \\ 4 \end{pmatrix}$ (1 $\quad$ 2)

$\qquad\qquad$ *Order* $\qquad$ $(2 \times \underline{1})$ $\quad$ $(\underline{1} \times 2)$

The product exists because the first matrix has 1 column and the second matrix has 1 row.

The product matrix $= \begin{pmatrix} 3 \times 1 & 3 \times 2 \\ 4 \times 1 & 4 \times 2 \end{pmatrix} = \begin{pmatrix} 3 & 6 \\ 4 & 8 \end{pmatrix}$.

The order of the product matrix is (2×2).

$\quad$ These examples show that, in general, matrices are *not* commutative under matrix multiplication.

Example 3: *Given that* $\mathbf{A} = \begin{pmatrix} 1 & 2 & 3 \\ 4 & 5 & 6 \end{pmatrix}$ *and* $\mathbf{B} = \begin{pmatrix} 7 & 8 \\ 9 & 10 \end{pmatrix}$, *show that it is*

not possible to form the product **AB** *and find the product* **BA**.

Order

$$
\begin{array}{cccc}
\mathbf{A} & \mathbf{B} & \mathbf{B} & \mathbf{A} \\
(2 \times \underline{3}) & (\underline{2} \times 2) & (2 \times \underline{2}) & (\underline{2} \times 3)
\end{array}
$$

It is *not* possible to form the product **AB** because **A** has 3 columns and B has 2 rows. The product **BA** will have order $\underline{(2 \times 3)}$.

$\mathbf{BA} = \begin{pmatrix} 7 & 8 \\ 9 & 10 \end{pmatrix} \begin{pmatrix} 1 & 2 & 3 \\ 4 & 5 & 6 \end{pmatrix}$

$= \begin{pmatrix} 7 \times 1 + 8 \times 4 & 7 \times 2 + 8 \times 5 & 7 \times 3 + 8 \times 6 \\ 9 \times 1 + 10 \times 4 & 9 \times 2 + 10 \times 5 & 9 \times 3 + 10 \times 6 \end{pmatrix} = \begin{pmatrix} 39 & 54 & 69 \\ 49 & 68 & 87 \end{pmatrix}$.

Conclusions

The matrix **A**, order $(m \times \underline{n})$, and the matrix **B**, order $(\underline{p} \times q)$, can be combined to form a product **AB** if, and only if, $n = p$. The matrix **AB** will have order $(m \times q)$. In general, matrices are *not commutative* under matrix multiplication. It can be shown that, when the products exist, matrices are *associative* under matrix multiplication.

Exercise 21.2

1 Perform the following matrix products:

(a) $\begin{pmatrix} 3 & 4 \\ 5 & 6 \end{pmatrix} \begin{pmatrix} 2 \\ 1 \end{pmatrix}$
(b) $\begin{pmatrix} 2 & -1 \\ 6 & 0 \end{pmatrix} \begin{pmatrix} 4 \\ -2 \end{pmatrix}$
(c) $(6 \quad 4 \quad 1) \begin{pmatrix} 2 \\ 0 \\ 3 \end{pmatrix}$

(d) $\begin{pmatrix} 6 & 4 & 1 \\ 3 & 0 & 2 \end{pmatrix} \begin{pmatrix} 2 & 3 & 7 \\ 0 & 1 & 2 \\ 3 & 5 & 4 \end{pmatrix}$
(e) $(4 \quad 5) \begin{pmatrix} 3 & 5 \\ 1 & 6 \end{pmatrix}$
(f) $\begin{pmatrix} 1 & 0 \\ 0 & 1 \end{pmatrix} \begin{pmatrix} 3 & 4 \\ 5 & 6 \end{pmatrix}$

(g) $\begin{pmatrix} 5 \\ 2 \end{pmatrix} (3 \quad 7)$
(h) $\begin{pmatrix} 5 & 1 \\ 2 & 4 \end{pmatrix} \begin{pmatrix} 3 & 7 \\ 2 & -1 \end{pmatrix}$
(i) $\begin{pmatrix} 3 & 7 \\ 2 & -1 \end{pmatrix} \begin{pmatrix} 5 & 1 \\ 2 & 4 \end{pmatrix}$.

2 Given that $A = \begin{pmatrix} 3 & 4 \\ 1 & 2 \end{pmatrix}$ and $B = \begin{pmatrix} 5 & 2 \\ 3 & 1 \end{pmatrix}$, find:

(a) A^2, (b) B^2, (c) $(A + B)^2$, (d) AB, (e) BA, (f) $A^2 + AB + BA + B^2$,
(g) $A^2 + 2AB + B^2$, (h) $A^2 - B^2$.

3 (a) If $A = \begin{pmatrix} 1 & 2 \\ 3 & 6 \end{pmatrix}$, show that $A^2 = 7A$.

(b) If $B = \begin{pmatrix} 4 & -6 \\ 2 & -3 \end{pmatrix}$, show that $B^2 - B = 0$.

(c) If $C = \begin{pmatrix} k & 1 \\ k^2 & k \end{pmatrix}$, show that $C^2 = 2kC$.

4 Given that $A = \begin{pmatrix} 2 \\ 5 \end{pmatrix}$, $B = \begin{pmatrix} 2 & 1 \\ 6 & 4 \end{pmatrix}$, $C = \begin{pmatrix} 2 & 1 \\ 3 & 4 \\ 9 & -2 \end{pmatrix}$,

$D = \begin{pmatrix} 1 & 2 & 1 \\ 7 & 8 & 9 \end{pmatrix}$, $E = \begin{pmatrix} 1 & 0 \\ 0 & 1 \end{pmatrix}$, $F = (3 - 12)$, $G = \begin{pmatrix} 4 & -1 \\ -6 & 2 \end{pmatrix}$,

$H = (2 \quad 4 \quad 11)$,

state which of the following products can be performed and find the
resulting matrix in these cases:
(a) BC, (b) CB, (c)AF, (d) FA, (e) G^2, (f) GE, (g) EG, (h) BG,
(i) GB, (j) FB, (k) BD, (l) F(BD), (m) (FB)D.

Note: Parts (l) and (m) illustrate a verification of the associative rule
for matrices under matrix multiplication.

5 (a) Find the matrix $A = \begin{pmatrix} a & b \\ c & d \end{pmatrix}$ such that

$$\begin{pmatrix} 6 & 11 \\ 1 & 2 \end{pmatrix} \begin{pmatrix} a & b \\ c & d \end{pmatrix} = \begin{pmatrix} 1 & 0 \\ 0 & 1 \end{pmatrix}.$$

(b) Find the matrix $B = \begin{pmatrix} d & e \\ f & g \end{pmatrix}$ such that

$$\begin{pmatrix} d & e \\ f & g \end{pmatrix} \begin{pmatrix} 6 & 11 \\ 1 & 2 \end{pmatrix} = \begin{pmatrix} 1 & 0 \\ 0 & 1 \end{pmatrix}.$$

6 Evaluate: (a) $\begin{pmatrix} 3 & 2 \\ 6 & 4 \end{pmatrix}\begin{pmatrix} -2 & 4 \\ 3 & -6 \end{pmatrix}$ (b) $\begin{pmatrix} 2 & 1 \\ 4 & 2 \end{pmatrix}\begin{pmatrix} 1 & 5 \\ -2 & -10 \end{pmatrix}$.

Is it necessarily true that $\mathbf{AB} = 0 \Rightarrow \mathbf{A} = 0$ or $\mathbf{B} = 0$?

7 Show that the matrix equation $\begin{pmatrix} 4 & 5 \\ 2 & 3 \end{pmatrix}\begin{pmatrix} x \\ y \end{pmatrix} = \begin{pmatrix} 8 \\ 9 \end{pmatrix}$, is equivalent to

writing $4x + 5y = 8$ *and* $2x + 3y = 9$ in algebra.

Definition 1: The **unit** or **identity** matrix of order 2 is $\begin{pmatrix} 1 & 0 \\ 0 & 1 \end{pmatrix}$.

This matrix plays a similar role in the algebra of (2×2) matrices to that of the number 1 in ordinary multiplication.

Example: $\begin{pmatrix} a & b \\ c & d \end{pmatrix}\begin{pmatrix} 1 & 0 \\ 0 \cdot & 1 \end{pmatrix} = \begin{pmatrix} 1 & 0 \\ 0 & 1 \end{pmatrix}\begin{pmatrix} a & b \\ c & d \end{pmatrix} = \begin{pmatrix} a & b \\ c & d \end{pmatrix}$.

Definition 2: The **null** or **empty** matrix of order 2 is $\begin{pmatrix} 0 & 0 \\ 0 & 0 \end{pmatrix}$.

This matrix plays a similar role in the algebra of (2×2) matrices to that of the number 0 in ordinary arithmetic.

Example: $\begin{pmatrix} 0 & 0 \\ 0 & 0 \end{pmatrix}\begin{pmatrix} a & b \\ c & d \end{pmatrix} = \begin{pmatrix} 0 & 0 \\ 0 & 0 \end{pmatrix}$.

$$\begin{pmatrix} 0 & 0 \\ 0 & 0 \end{pmatrix} + \begin{pmatrix} a & b \\ c & d \end{pmatrix} = \begin{pmatrix} a & b \\ c & d \end{pmatrix}.$$

The inverse of a 2×2 matrix

The **inverse** of a square matrix $\mathbf{A}$, written $\mathbf{A}^{-1}$, is that matrix, if it exists, which satisfies the equation $\mathbf{AA}^{-1} = \mathbf{I}$, where $\mathbf{I}$ is the unit (identity) matrix of order two.

The procedure for finding this matrix may have been deduced from working question 5 of the last exercise, but the algebraic treatment of the problem formalises the approach and indicates a possible point of breakdown.

Given that $\mathbf{A} = \begin{pmatrix} a & b \\ c & d \end{pmatrix}$, the matrix $\mathbf{A}^{-1} = \begin{pmatrix} u & v \\ w & x \end{pmatrix}$ is required such that

$$\begin{pmatrix} a & b \\ c & d \end{pmatrix}\begin{pmatrix} u & v \\ w & x \end{pmatrix} = \begin{pmatrix} 1 & 0 \\ 0 & 1 \end{pmatrix}.$$

Reducing the L.H.S. gives $\begin{pmatrix} au + bw & av + bx \\ cu + dw & cv + dx \end{pmatrix} = \begin{pmatrix} 1 & 0 \\ 0 & 1 \end{pmatrix}$.

As the matrices are equal, the following equations are obtained by equating corresponding elements

$$au + bw = 1 \qquad av + bx = 0$$
$$cu + dw = 0 \qquad cv + dx = 1.$$

The first pair of equations are simultaneous in u and w (a, b, c, d, are known, since they are the elements of the given matrix), and the second pair are simultaneous in v and x.

Solving the first pair gives $u = \dfrac{d}{(ad - bc)}$ and $w = \dfrac{-c}{(ad - bc)}$.

Solving the second pair gives $v = \dfrac{-b}{(ad - bc)}$ and $x = \dfrac{a}{(ad - bc)}$.

The inverse matrix then is

$$\begin{pmatrix} \dfrac{d}{ad - bc} & \dfrac{-b}{ad - bc} \\[2mm] \dfrac{-c}{ad - bc} & \dfrac{a}{ad - bc} \end{pmatrix} \quad \text{or} \quad \dfrac{1}{ad - bc} \begin{pmatrix} d & -b \\ -c & a \end{pmatrix}.$$

The expression $(ad - bc)$ is called the **determinant** of the matrix $\begin{pmatrix} a & b \\ c & d \end{pmatrix}$ and is often written as $\begin{vmatrix} a & b \\ c & d \end{vmatrix}$.

The process of finding an inverse can be broken down into three stages:

(a) Change over the elements in the leading diagonal so that $\begin{pmatrix} a & \\ & d \end{pmatrix}$ becomes $\begin{pmatrix} d & \\ & a \end{pmatrix}$.

(b) Change the sign of the other elements so that $\begin{pmatrix} a & b \\ c & d \end{pmatrix}$ becomes $\begin{pmatrix} d & -b \\ -c & a \end{pmatrix}$.

(c) Divide each element by the determinant of the given matrix to give $\dfrac{1}{ad - bc} \begin{pmatrix} d & -b \\ -c & a \end{pmatrix}$.

Example: *Find the inverse of* $\begin{pmatrix} 5 & 2 \\ 4 & 3 \end{pmatrix}$.

The determinant $\begin{vmatrix} 5 & 2 \\ 4 & 3 \end{vmatrix} = (5 \times 3) - (2 \times 4) = 15 - 8 = 7.$

The inverse is $\dfrac{1}{7} \begin{pmatrix} 3 & -2 \\ -4 & 5 \end{pmatrix}$ or $\begin{pmatrix} 3/7 & -2/7 \\ -4/7 & 5/7 \end{pmatrix}$.

Note: Any square matrix commutes with its inverse, if it exists, and the common product is the identity matrix of the same order.

Singular matrices

The process of finding an inverse will break down when the determinant $(ad - bc)$ is equal to zero. A matrix, whose determinant is zero, is said to be **singular**, and has no inverse.

Examples of singular matrices are $\begin{pmatrix} 4 & 5 \\ 16 & 20 \end{pmatrix}$ and $\begin{pmatrix} -1 & 5 \\ 2 & -10 \end{pmatrix}$.

Exercise 21.3

1 Evaluate the determinants of the following matrices:

(a) $\begin{pmatrix} 1 & 3 \\ 1 & 4 \end{pmatrix}$ (b) $\begin{pmatrix} 5 & 6 \\ 4 & 5 \end{pmatrix}$ (c) $\begin{pmatrix} -1 & 0 \\ 0 & 1 \end{pmatrix}$ (d) $\begin{pmatrix} 1 & 0 \\ 0 & 1 \end{pmatrix}$

(e) $\begin{pmatrix} 0 & 1 \\ 1 & 0 \end{pmatrix}$ (f) $\begin{pmatrix} 1 & 0 \\ 0 & -1 \end{pmatrix}$ (g) $\begin{pmatrix} 6 & -3 \\ 1 & 2 \end{pmatrix}$ (h) $\begin{pmatrix} 6 & 3 \\ 2 & 0 \end{pmatrix}$

Find the inverse of the matrices given.
[The matrices given in parts (c), (d), (e) and (f) are their own inverses (self-inverse)].

2 Find the inverse matrix of each of the following matrices:

(a) $\begin{pmatrix} 5 & 3 \\ 13 & 8 \end{pmatrix}$, (b) $\begin{pmatrix} 2 & 0 \\ 0 & 2 \end{pmatrix}$, (c) $\begin{pmatrix} 7 & 3 \\ 2 & 1 \end{pmatrix}$, (d) $\begin{pmatrix} -2 & 4 \\ -3 & 5 \end{pmatrix}$,

(e) $\begin{pmatrix} -1 & -2 \\ -3 & -4 \end{pmatrix}$.

3 (a) Evaluate (i) $\begin{pmatrix} 2 & 1 \\ 4 & 2 \end{pmatrix}\begin{pmatrix} 3 \\ 5 \end{pmatrix}$, (ii) $\begin{pmatrix} 2 & 1 \\ 4 & 2 \end{pmatrix}\begin{pmatrix} 5 \\ 1 \end{pmatrix}$, (iii) $\begin{pmatrix} 6 & 9 \\ 2 & 3 \end{pmatrix}\begin{pmatrix} 10 \\ -9 \end{pmatrix}$,

(iv) $\begin{pmatrix} 6 & 9 \\ 2 & 3 \end{pmatrix}\begin{pmatrix} 1 \\ -3 \end{pmatrix}$.

(b) Evaluate (i) $\begin{pmatrix} 2 & 1 \\ 4 & 2 \end{pmatrix}\begin{pmatrix} 3 & 4 \\ 5 & 2 \end{pmatrix}$, (ii) $\begin{pmatrix} 2 & 1 \\ 4 & 2 \end{pmatrix}\begin{pmatrix} 5 & 5 \\ 1 & 0 \end{pmatrix}$,

(iii) $\begin{pmatrix} 6 & 9 \\ 2 & 3 \end{pmatrix}\begin{pmatrix} 10 & 1 \\ -9 & 1 \end{pmatrix}$, (iv) $\begin{pmatrix} 6 & 9 \\ 2 & 3 \end{pmatrix}\begin{pmatrix} 1 & -2 \\ -3 & 3 \end{pmatrix}$.

If **A, B, C** are matrices such that $\mathbf{AB} = \mathbf{AC}$, what deductions can be made?

4 State which of the following matrices are singular, and find the inverse matrix for those which are not:

(a) $\begin{pmatrix} 1 & 2 \\ -1 & 2 \end{pmatrix}$,   (b) $\begin{pmatrix} 6 & 12 \\ 2 & 4 \end{pmatrix}$,   (c) $\begin{pmatrix} -1 & 5 \\ 1 & -5 \end{pmatrix}$,   (d) $\begin{pmatrix} 1 & 0 \\ 0 & 1 \end{pmatrix}$,

(e) $\begin{pmatrix} 3 & 0 \\ 8 & 0 \end{pmatrix}$,   (f) $\begin{pmatrix} 3 & 6 \\ 0 & 2 \end{pmatrix}$.

The use of an inverse matrix

The solution of the algebraic equation $2x = 5$ can be found by dividing both sides by 2, or alternatively multiplying both sides by $\frac{1}{2}$, multiplication and division being inverse processes. In matrix algebra there is no meaning to the division of two matrices, but the equivalent step of multiplying both sides of the equation by the inverse matrix may be applied.

If the matrix equation $AB = C$ is premultiplied by A^{-1}
then it becomes $\qquad\qquad A^{-1}AB = A^{-1}C$
which reduces to $\qquad\qquad IB = A^{-1}C$
or $\qquad\qquad B = A^{-1}C$

providing that A is non-singular and that $A^{-1}C$ exists.

Simultaneous equations

Example: *Solve the equations* $2x + 3y = 3$, $x + 7y = -4$

(a) Using the inverse of the coefficient matrix

The equations are written in matrix form as

$$\begin{pmatrix} 2 & 3 \\ 1 & 7 \end{pmatrix}\begin{pmatrix} x \\ y \end{pmatrix} = \begin{pmatrix} 3 \\ -4 \end{pmatrix} \qquad\qquad (1)$$

Pre-multiplying both sides of (1) by the inverse of $\begin{pmatrix} 2 & 3 \\ 1 & 7 \end{pmatrix}$,

i.e. $\begin{pmatrix} 7/11 & -3/11 \\ -1/11 & 2/11 \end{pmatrix}$

gives $\quad \begin{pmatrix} 1 & 0 \\ 0 & 1 \end{pmatrix}\begin{pmatrix} x \\ y \end{pmatrix} = \begin{pmatrix} 7/11 & -3/11 \\ -1/11 & 2/11 \end{pmatrix}\begin{pmatrix} 3 \\ -4 \end{pmatrix}$.

which reduces to $\begin{pmatrix} x \\ y \end{pmatrix} = \begin{pmatrix} 33/11 \\ -11/11 \end{pmatrix} = \begin{pmatrix} 3 \\ -1 \end{pmatrix}$.

giving the solution $x = 3$, $y = -1$.

(b) Using the adjoint matrix

It may be easier, if the inverse is not specifically required, to use the 'incomplete inverse' where the elements have *not* been divided by the determinant. This 'incomplete inverse' is called the **adjoint**.

Using the same example, pre-multiplying both sides of (1) by $\begin{pmatrix} 7 & -3 \\ -1 & 2 \end{pmatrix}$

gives $\begin{pmatrix} 11 & 0 \\ 0 & 11 \end{pmatrix}\begin{pmatrix} x \\ y \end{pmatrix} = \begin{pmatrix} 7 & -3 \\ -1 & 2 \end{pmatrix}\begin{pmatrix} 3 \\ -4 \end{pmatrix}.$

which reduces to $\begin{pmatrix} 11x \\ 11y \end{pmatrix} = \begin{pmatrix} 33 \\ -11 \end{pmatrix}$

giving the solution $x = 3$, $y = -1$, as before.

The above methods for solving simultaneous equations are less elegant and longer than the methods explained in Chapter 8. Their importance becomes much greater, however, for systems of n simultaneous equations in n unknowns, where $n \geq 3$. If the inverse matrix of the coefficient matrix can be found, the rest of the work is routine and all of it, including the determination of the inverse, can be undertaken by using a computer.

Example 1: *Solve the equations* $3x - 4y = 5$, $6x - 8y = 10$.

The matrix of coefficients $\begin{pmatrix} 3 & -4 \\ 6 & -8 \end{pmatrix}$ is singular and has no inverse. The first method of solution, therefore, breaks down immediately. The second method requires the matrix equation to be pre-multiplied by $\begin{pmatrix} -8 & 4 \\ -6 & 3 \end{pmatrix}$ to

give $\begin{pmatrix} -8 & 4 \\ -6 & 3 \end{pmatrix}\begin{pmatrix} 3 & -4 \\ 6 & -8 \end{pmatrix}\begin{pmatrix} x \\ y \end{pmatrix} = \begin{pmatrix} -8 & 4 \\ -6 & 3 \end{pmatrix}\begin{pmatrix} 5 \\ 10 \end{pmatrix}.$

$$\begin{pmatrix} 0 & 0 \\ 0 & 0 \end{pmatrix}\begin{pmatrix} x \\ y \end{pmatrix} = \begin{pmatrix} 0 \\ 0 \end{pmatrix}.$$

Clearly x and y are not unique. It is helpful to consider the graphical representation of the given equations. The two equations represent the same straight line and so further search for a unique solution is futile. There are an infinite number of solutions, the set of points on the line.

Example 2: *Solve the equations* $x + 2y = 4$, $3x + 6y = 7$.

Again the matrix of coefficients is singular; the second method leads to the equation $\begin{pmatrix} 6 & -2 \\ -3 & 1 \end{pmatrix}\begin{pmatrix} 1 & 2 \\ 3 & 6 \end{pmatrix}\begin{pmatrix} x \\ y \end{pmatrix} = \begin{pmatrix} 6 & -2 \\ -3 & 1 \end{pmatrix}\begin{pmatrix} 4 \\ 7 \end{pmatrix},$

which simplifies to give $\begin{pmatrix} 0 & 0 \\ 0 & 0 \end{pmatrix}\begin{pmatrix} x \\ y \end{pmatrix} = \begin{pmatrix} 10 \\ -5 \end{pmatrix}.$

Clearly there are no values of x and y which satisfy the equation.

Considered graphically this result is not surprising, because the given equations represent parallel lines.

Exercise 21.4

In equations 1–6, solve the following pairs of equations simultaneously, using a matrix method. Check your solutions by also solving the equations by a method described in Chapter 8:

1 $2x + y = 8,$
   $x + y = 5.$

2 $3x - 2y = 13,$
   $2x - y = 8.$

3 $3x + 2y = 5,$
   $x - y = -5.$

4 $5x - 3y = 20,$
   $3x - 2y = 11.$

5 $4x - 9y = 24,$
   $5x + 2y = 3.5.$

6 $4x = 5y + 13,$
   $2x = 3y + 7.$

7 Find a and b if $\begin{pmatrix} 5 & a \\ b & -2 \end{pmatrix}\begin{pmatrix} 1 \\ 4 \end{pmatrix} = \begin{pmatrix} 2 \\ 5 \end{pmatrix}.$

8 Find possible values of x and k if $\begin{pmatrix} x & k \\ 3 & 4 \end{pmatrix}\begin{pmatrix} x \\ 2 \end{pmatrix} = \begin{pmatrix} 1 \\ 7 \end{pmatrix}.$

9 Find possible values of x and k if $\begin{pmatrix} x^2 & x \\ 3 & k \end{pmatrix}\begin{pmatrix} 1 \\ 2 \end{pmatrix} = \begin{pmatrix} 8 \\ x \end{pmatrix}.$

10 Find x and y if $\begin{pmatrix} 3 & 1 \\ 1 & -2 \end{pmatrix}\begin{pmatrix} x \\ y \end{pmatrix} = \begin{pmatrix} 2 \\ 3 \end{pmatrix}.$

11 Find x and k if $\begin{pmatrix} x^2 & x \\ 2 & 3 \end{pmatrix}\begin{pmatrix} 2 \\ -9 \end{pmatrix} = \begin{pmatrix} 5 \\ k \end{pmatrix}.$

12 Find x and y if $\begin{pmatrix} 3x & x \\ 3 & 2 \end{pmatrix}\begin{pmatrix} x \\ 5 \end{pmatrix} = \begin{pmatrix} 2 \\ y \end{pmatrix}.$

13 If the determinant of $\begin{pmatrix} x & 7 \\ 4 & 2 \end{pmatrix}$ is 6, find x.

14 If the matrix $\begin{pmatrix} x & 4 \\ 1 & x \end{pmatrix}$ is singular find possible values of x.

15 Solve the following pairs of simultaneous equations, if possible:

(a) $2x - 5y = 2,$
    $3x + 2y = 4.$

(b) $2x - y = 5,$
    $4x - 2y = 6.$

(c) $6x - 6y = 3,$
    $x + 6y = 5.$

(d) $3x - 2y = 5,$
    $6x - 4y = 10.$

Matrices related to networks

Figure 21.1 shows a network consisting of three **nodes** A, B, C, four **regions** a, b, c, d, and five **arcs** linking various nodes.

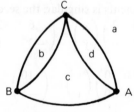

Fig. 21.1

A network may be used as a convenient representation of a problem. The relationship between the nodes, arcs and regions is the important factor; the form of the network is immaterial, provided that this particular relationship is preserved.

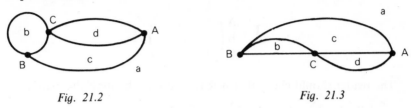

Fig. 21.2   Fig. 21.3

Figures 21.2 and 21.3 show networks equivalent to that shown in Figure 21.1.

Route matrices

A one-stage route between two nodes of a network is defined as a route which does not pass through any other node.

Copy and complete the 3×3 matrix **R** which shows the number of different one-stage routes between each of the nodes of the network shown in Figure 21.1.

R is called the one-stage route matrix for the network.

$$\mathbf{R} = \text{from} \quad \begin{array}{c} \\ A \\ B \\ C \end{array} \begin{array}{c} \overset{\text{to}}{} \\ \overset{A \quad B \quad C}{\left(\begin{array}{ccc} 0 & 1 & \\ & 0 & \\ 2 & & 0 \end{array} \right)} \end{array}$$

A two stage route is defined as a route which passes through one other node on the way, and two examples are given to explain this.

Example 1: The number of different two-stage routes between A and C (or C and A) is two and these are:

Example 2: The number of different two-stage routes from A to A is five and these are:

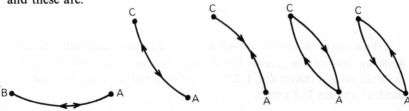

293

By finding the total number of each of the remaining two-stage routes between the nodes, copy and complete the 3×3 matrix **T** which is used to display this information.

$$
\mathbf{T} = \begin{array}{c} \\ A \\ B \\ C \end{array} \begin{array}{ccc} A & B & C \\ \left(\begin{array}{ccc} 5 & & 2 \\ & & \\ 2 & & \end{array} \right) \end{array}
$$

The reader should check that if **R** is multiplied by itself the matrix

$$
\mathbf{R}^2 = \left(\begin{array}{ccc} 0 & 1 & 2 \\ 1 & 0 & 2 \\ 2 & 2 & 0 \end{array} \right) \left(\begin{array}{ccc} 0 & 1 & 2 \\ 1 & 0 & 2 \\ 2 & 2 & 0 \end{array} \right) = \left(\begin{array}{ccc} 5 & 4 & 2 \\ 4 & 5 & 2 \\ 2 & 2 & 8 \end{array} \right) = \mathbf{T}.
$$

A one-stage route matrix combined with itself under matrix multiplication gives the two-stage route matrix for the network. The process can be extended; the reader should form the matrix $\mathbf{R}^3$ and verify that this is the three-stage route matrix for the network.

Note: The method applied in the above example is true generally, and is an important application of matrices.

In the network above there was no restriction on the route that may be taken from one node to another. In such a case the one-stage route matrix will be symmetrical about its leading diagonal, the elements of which will be even numbers, or zero. (Why do these results follow?)

If one-way routes are imposed on the network, as they may well be in a street plan, for example, this symmetry may disappear.

Incident matrices

A network may be described by matrices in other ways.

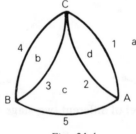

Fig. 21.4

If the arcs are labelled as shown in Figure 21.4 the relationship between nodes and arcs can be recorded by noting which arcs each node lies on. For example, node A lies on arcs 1, 2, 5 but not on 3 and 4; we say that node A is **incident** on arcs 1, 2 and 5.

The results are recorded in $\mathbf{X}$, the 3×5 matrix showing the incidence of nodes on arcs.

$$
\mathbf{X} = \begin{array}{c} \\ A \\ B \\ C \end{array}\begin{array}{c} 1 \ 2 \ 3 \ 4 \ 5 \\ \left(\begin{array}{ccccc} 1 & 1 & 0 & 0 & 1 \\ 0 & 0 & 1 & 1 & 1 \\ 1 & 1 & 1 & 1 & 0 \end{array}\right) \end{array}
\qquad
\mathbf{X}' = \begin{array}{c} \\ 1 \\ 2 \\ 3 \\ 4 \\ 5 \end{array}\begin{array}{c} A \ \ B \ \ C \\ \left(\begin{array}{ccc} 1 & 0 & 1 \\ 1 & 0 & 1 \\ 0 & 1 & 1 \\ 0 & 1 & 1 \\ 1 & 1 & 0 \end{array}\right) \end{array}
$$

If the rows and columns of $\mathbf{X}$ are interchanged, the matrix $\mathbf{X}'$, called the **transpose** of $\mathbf{X}$, is formed. The reader should verify that this matrix shows the incidence of arcs on nodes.

The product $\mathbf{X}\mathbf{X}'$ differs from the one-stage route matrix $\mathbf{R}$ only in the elements of the leading diagonal. The reader should verify that

$$
\mathbf{X}\mathbf{X}' = \begin{pmatrix} 3 & 1 & 2 \\ 1 & 3 & 2 \\ 2 & 2 & 4 \end{pmatrix}
$$

and explain why it is so related to $\mathbf{R}$.

For the network of Figure 21.4 the matrices $\mathbf{Y}$ and $\mathbf{Z}$ showing the incidence of arcs on regions and nodes on regions, respectively, are:

$$
\mathbf{Y} = \begin{array}{c} \\ 1 \\ 2 \\ 3 \\ 4 \\ 5 \end{array}\begin{array}{c} a \ \ b \ \ c \ \ d \\ \left(\begin{array}{cccc} 1 & 0 & 0 & 1 \\ 0 & 0 & 1 & 1 \\ 0 & 1 & 1 & 0 \\ 1 & 1 & 0 & 0 \\ 1 & 0 & 1 & 0 \end{array}\right) \end{array}
\qquad
\mathbf{Z} = \begin{array}{c} \\ A \\ B \\ C \end{array}\begin{array}{c} a \ \ b \ \ c \ \ d \\ \left(\begin{array}{cccc} 1 & 0 & 1 & 1 \\ 1 & 1 & 1 & 0 \\ 1 & 1 & 1 & 1 \end{array}\right) \end{array}
$$

The matrices $\mathbf{X}$, $\mathbf{Y}$ and $\mathbf{Z}$ can be multiplied only in certain instances, depending on their respective orders.

Example:

$$
\mathbf{X}\mathbf{Y} = \begin{pmatrix} 1 & 1 & 0 & 0 & 1 \\ 0 & 0 & 1 & 1 & 1 \\ 1 & 1 & 1 & 1 & 0 \end{pmatrix}\begin{pmatrix} 1 & 0 & 0 & 1 \\ 0 & 0 & 1 & 1 \\ 0 & 1 & 1 & 0 \\ 1 & 1 & 0 & 0 \\ 1 & 0 & 1 & 0 \end{pmatrix} = \begin{pmatrix} 2 & 0 & 2 & 2 \\ 2 & 2 & 2 & 0 \\ 2 & 2 & 2 & 2 \end{pmatrix} = 2\mathbf{Z}
$$

but $\mathbf{Y}\mathbf{X}$ cannot be evaluted. Why is $\mathbf{X}\mathbf{Y} = 2\mathbf{Z}$?

Incident matrices will not always have only 1 and 0 as their elements.

In the network of Figure 21.5, node A is incident on arc 1 twice, node A is incident on region 'a' twice, and region 'a' is incident on node B three times, for example.

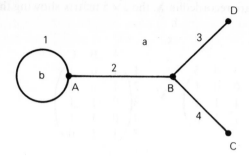

Fig. 21.5

Example: *Find the matrices X and X' for the above network, and hence find the product X X'.*

$$
X = \begin{array}{c} \\ A \\ B \\ C \\ D \end{array}
\begin{array}{cccc} 1 & 2 & 3 & 4 \\ \end{array}
\left(\begin{array}{cccc}
2 & 1 & 0 & 0 \\
0 & 1 & 1 & 1 \\
0 & 0 & 0 & 1 \\
0 & 0 & 1 & 0
\end{array} \right)
\text{ and } X' = \begin{array}{c} \\ 1 \\ 2 \\ 3 \\ 4 \end{array}
\begin{array}{cccc} A & B & C & D \\ \end{array}
\left(\begin{array}{cccc}
2 & 0 & 0 & 0 \\
1 & 1 & 0 & 0 \\
0 & 1 & 0 & 1 \\
0 & 1 & 1 & 0
\end{array} \right)
$$

$$
XX' = \left(\begin{array}{cccc}
5 & 1 & 0 & 0 \\
1 & 3 & 1 & 1 \\
0 & 1 & 1 & 0 \\
0 & 1 & 0 & 1
\end{array} \right)
$$

The reader should form the one-stage route matrix **R** for the network (assume no one-way arcs) and compare with **XX'**.

The matrices **Y** and **Z** should be found for the network and the relationship between **X**, **Y** and **Z** stated.

Only a few illustrations of the use of matrices have been given in this Chapter, due to lack of space, but another important application can be seen in Chapter 22.

Exercise 21.5

1 A garden shop sells three packs of bulbs A, B and C.
   Pack A contains 20 daffodils, 10 tulips, 35 crocus;
   Pack B contains 10 daffodils, 20 tulips, 30 crocus, 6 lilies;
   Pack C contains 30 daffodils, 20 tulips, 50 crocus, 10 lilies.
   Arrange this information as a matrix with the types of bulbs in columns and the different packs in rows.
   The prices of single bulbs are, daffodil 3 p, tulip 5 p, crocus 2 p, and lily 20 p.
   Write down a cost matrix and multiply the two matrices to find the costs of packs A, B and C.

2 A Supermarket stocks four different soups: tomato, chicken, vegetable and consomme; and each of these are sold in three sizes of cans: small, medium and large. On a particular day the following numbers of cans of soup were sold:

	Tomato	Chicken	Vegetable	Consomme
Small	77	65	57	84
Medium	59	54	117	96
Large	102	25	69	34

The respective prices for small, medium and large cans are 10 p, 20 p and 40 p.

(i) Use a matrix multiplication method to find the money taken for selling each brand of soup.

(ii) Explain the meaning of the matrix addition.

$$\begin{pmatrix} 77 \\ 59 \\ 102 \end{pmatrix} + \begin{pmatrix} 65 \\ 54 \\ 25 \end{pmatrix} + \begin{pmatrix} 57 \\ 117 \\ 69 \end{pmatrix} + \begin{pmatrix} 84 \\ 96 \\ 34 \end{pmatrix}.$$

Use the result of this addition to determine the total cash taken by the Supermarket from selling cans of soup on this particular day.

3 Draw the networks described by each of the following matrices:

(a) $\begin{matrix} & \text{arcs} \\ & \begin{matrix} 1 & 2 \end{matrix} \\ \text{nodes} \begin{matrix} A \\ B \end{matrix} & \begin{pmatrix} 1 & 0 \\ 1 & 2 \end{pmatrix} \end{matrix}$ (b) $\begin{matrix} & \text{arcs} \\ & \begin{matrix} 1 & 2 & 3 & 4 \end{matrix} \\ \text{nodes} \begin{matrix} A \\ B \end{matrix} & \begin{pmatrix} 1 & 1 & 2 & 0 \\ 1 & 1 & 0 & 2 \end{pmatrix} \end{matrix}$

(c) $\begin{matrix} & \text{regions} \\ & \begin{matrix} a & b & c \end{matrix} \\ \text{nodes} \begin{matrix} A \\ B \\ C \\ D \end{matrix} & \begin{pmatrix} 2 & 1 & 0 \\ 2 & 0 & 1 \\ 2 & 0 & 1 \\ 1 & 0 & 0 \end{pmatrix} \end{matrix}$ (d) $\begin{matrix} & \text{regions} \\ & \begin{matrix} a & b & c \end{matrix} \\ \text{arcs} \begin{matrix} 1 \\ 2 \\ 3 \end{matrix} & \begin{pmatrix} 0 & 1 & 1 \\ 1 & 1 & 0 \\ 1 & 0 & 1 \end{pmatrix} \end{matrix}.$

4 Write down the one-stage route matrix **R** for each of the networks in Figure 21.6(a), (b), (c).

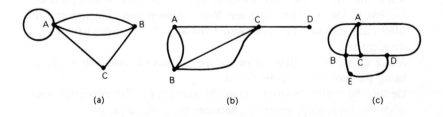

(a)　　　　　(b)　　　　　(c)

Fig. 21.6

In each case find R^2 and compare with the two-stage route matrix for the network.

Find the three-stage route matrices in each case.

5 Repeat the exercise for the directed networks (showing one way systems) in Figures 21.7(a), (b), (c).

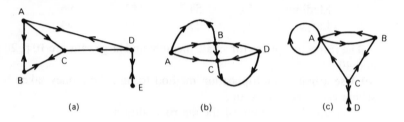

(a) (b) (c)

Fig. 21.7

6 (a) For each of the networks of Figure 21.8, find the matrices **X**, **Y** and **Z**, defined in the text.

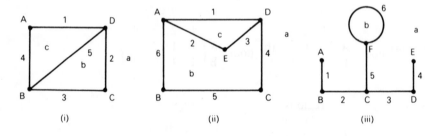

(i) (ii) (iii)

Fig. 21.8

(b) Write down the matrices **X′**, **Y′** and **Z′** and define them.

(c) Find **XY** in each case and relate to **Z**.

(d) Find **Y′X′** in each case and relate to **Z′**.

(e) Find **XX′** and **R** for each network and compare the results.

7 There are two motorways, M6 and M45, between Northampton and Coventry. The M1 runs between Northampton and Leicester and the M69 runs between Leicester and Coventry. Show these routes on a diagram.

Make up a 3×3 matrix for one-stage journeys between these places, using the motorway routes listed.

Deduce by matrix multiplication the numbers of (a) two-stage journeys, (b) three-stage journeys, between these three places.

8 Take a section of a map of the London Underground system linking Victoria, Oxford Circus and Charing Cross and make up a one-stage

route matrix between these stations. From your matrix, deduce the number of two-stage and three-stage routes between them.

9 Choose three or four towns in your home area and draw a network showing the main roads joining them. Analyse this network by finding one-stage and two-stage route matrices.

22 Geometrical transformations in two dimensions

When a set of points is mapped onto a second set of points the operation is called a **transformation**. If the first set of points define a geometrical figure, then the second set will also produce a geometrical figure, called the **image** of the first figure. In more advanced mathematics, transformations are studied in which the sets of points belong to three dimensional space or even a space of n dimensions, but at the level of this book all the transformations will be studied as mappings in two dimensions: the notation (x, y) is often used to indicate that the set of points under discussion are members of the plane containing the x-axis and the y-axis. Any point P in this plane can be identified uniquely by the number pair (x, y) called the co-ordinates of P, where x and y are the distances, in suitable units, from the y-axis and the x-axis, respectively. The position vector of P can be written as the column vector $\begin{pmatrix} x \\ y \end{pmatrix}$. If P is mapped onto P' under a transformation **T** we write $\mathbf{T}(P) = P'$.

Isometries

An isometry is a transformation under which the original figure and the image figure have the same shape and the same size. The original figure and the image figure are **congruent**. Under any transformation a point which maps onto itself is called an **invariant** point.

Translation

A transformation which maps every point $P(x, y)$ onto a new point $P'(x', y')$ under the vector relation
$\begin{pmatrix} x' \\ y' \end{pmatrix} = \begin{pmatrix} x \\ y \end{pmatrix} + \begin{pmatrix} a \\ b \end{pmatrix}$, where a and b are fixed numbers, is called a **translation**. The vector $\begin{pmatrix} a \\ b \end{pmatrix}$ is called the **shift vector** of the translation. (See chapter 20.)

In general, a translation has no invariant points.

300

Example 1: *The points $A(3, 1)$, $B(-2, 5)$ and $C(-4, -3)$ are mapped onto A', B' and C', respectively, by the translation $\mathbf{T}$, whose shift vector is $\begin{pmatrix} 3 \\ -2 \end{pmatrix}$.*

Calculate the coordinates of A', B' and C'.

The equation of the transformation is $\begin{pmatrix} x' \\ y' \end{pmatrix} = \mathbf{T} \begin{pmatrix} x \\ y \end{pmatrix} = \begin{pmatrix} x \\ y \end{pmatrix} + \begin{pmatrix} 3 \\ -2 \end{pmatrix}$.

The position vector of A' is given by $\begin{pmatrix} 3 \\ 1 \end{pmatrix} + \begin{pmatrix} 3 \\ -2 \end{pmatrix} = \begin{pmatrix} 6 \\ -1 \end{pmatrix}$.

The position vector of B' is given by $\begin{pmatrix} -2 \\ 5 \end{pmatrix} + \begin{pmatrix} 3 \\ -2 \end{pmatrix} = \begin{pmatrix} 1 \\ 3 \end{pmatrix}$.

The position vector of C' is given by $\begin{pmatrix} -4 \\ -3 \end{pmatrix} + \begin{pmatrix} 3 \\ -2 \end{pmatrix} = \begin{pmatrix} -1 \\ -5 \end{pmatrix}$.

The coordinates of A', B' and C' are $(6, -1)$, $(1, 3)$ and $(-1, -5)$ respectively.

Example 2: *All points in the plane of the co-ordinate axes are successively subjected to the translations which have shift vectors*

$$\begin{pmatrix} -3 \\ 2 \end{pmatrix}, \begin{pmatrix} -1 \\ -3 \end{pmatrix} \text{ and } \begin{pmatrix} 5 \\ -2 \end{pmatrix}.$$

Find the translation $\mathbf{T}$ which will restore all points to their original positions. Let the associated shift vector be $\begin{pmatrix} a \\ b \end{pmatrix}$.

$$\text{Then } \begin{pmatrix} -3 \\ 2 \end{pmatrix} + \begin{pmatrix} -1 \\ -3 \end{pmatrix} + \begin{pmatrix} 5 \\ -2 \end{pmatrix} + \begin{pmatrix} a \\ b \end{pmatrix} = \begin{pmatrix} 0 \\ 0 \end{pmatrix} \Rightarrow \begin{pmatrix} a \\ b \end{pmatrix} = \begin{pmatrix} -1 \\ 3 \end{pmatrix}.$$

$$\mathbf{T} \begin{pmatrix} x \\ y \end{pmatrix} = \begin{pmatrix} x \\ y \end{pmatrix} + \begin{pmatrix} -1 \\ 3 \end{pmatrix}.$$

Exercise 22.1

1 Plot the triangles ABC and A'B'C' from the first example on graph paper and show that the lines AA', BB' and CC' are parallel.

2 In each of the following apply the translation T to the point P and find the co-ordinates of the point P', the image of P:

P	Shift vector for T	P	Shift vector for T
(a) (3, 2)	$\begin{pmatrix} 4 \\ -2 \end{pmatrix}$	(b) (5, −4)	$\begin{pmatrix} -4 \\ 9 \end{pmatrix}$
(c) (−1, −2)	$\begin{pmatrix} -6 \\ -6 \end{pmatrix}$	(d) (12, 16)	$\begin{pmatrix} 0 \\ 5 \end{pmatrix}$

Calculate the length of the line PP' in each case.

3 The position vector of A is $\begin{pmatrix} 4 \\ 5 \end{pmatrix}$. Under a translation, A is mapped onto

the point A' whose position vector is $\begin{pmatrix} 5 \\ -4 \end{pmatrix}$. Under the same translation the point B is mapped onto the point B', (2, 4). Find the co-ordinates of B.

4 The translation **T** has shift vector $\begin{pmatrix} -3 \\ 4 \end{pmatrix}$. Find the co-ordinates of the images of the vertices of the triangle ABC, given that the co-ordinates of A, B and C are (1, 0), (4, −3) and (2, −1), respectively.

5 Given that three of the vertices A, B, C of a parallelogram ABCD are (0, 0), (2, 3), (3, 8), respectively, find the fourth vertex D.

Reflection

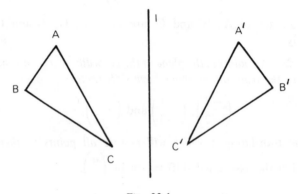

Fig. 22.1

In Figure 22.1, the points A, B and C are mapped onto A', B' and C', respectively, under the operation of reflection in the line (axis) l. Under this transformation, the lines AA', BB' and CC' are each perpendicular to l, the triangles ABC and A'B'C' are congruent, and the respective distances of A and A', B and B' and C and C' from l are equal.

The axis of reflection is an **axis of symmetry** for triangle ABC and triangle A'B'C'.

The image (triangle A'B'C') can be obtained by folding the plane of the paper containing triangle ABC along l.

All points on the line l are invariant under the operation of reflection in l.

Example: *Find the co-ordinates of A', B', C', the images of A(3, 0) B(1, 4) and C(−2, −3) respectively under the transformation* **X** *which reflects all points of the plane in the x-axis.*
A' = **X**(A) = (3, 0), B' = **X**(B) = (1, −4) and C' = **X**(C) = (−2, 3). The point (3, 0) is invariant under **X**.

Exercise

1 Write down the equation of any line for which every point on it is invariant under **X**. (Such a line is said to be '**point invariant**').
2 Write down the equation of any lines which are invariant, but not point invariant.

If $P(x, y)$ is mapped onto $P'(x', y')$ under **X**, the transformation is characterised by the pair of equations
$$x' = x \qquad y' = -y.$$
This statement is equivalent to the matrix equation

$$\begin{pmatrix} x' \\ y' \end{pmatrix} = \begin{pmatrix} 1 & 0 \\ 0 & -1 \end{pmatrix} \begin{pmatrix} x \\ y \end{pmatrix}$$

where $\begin{pmatrix} x \\ y \end{pmatrix}$ is the position vector of P, and $\begin{pmatrix} x' \\ y' \end{pmatrix}$ is the position vector of P', the image of P under **X**. The matrix $\begin{pmatrix} 1 & 0 \\ 0 & -1 \end{pmatrix}$ is the matrix associated with the transformation **X**.

As this application of matrices is a useful one, and used widely in this chapter, the reader is advised to read the next section carefully.

Representation of transformations by 2×2 matrices

As $\begin{pmatrix} a & b \\ c & d \end{pmatrix} \begin{pmatrix} 0 \\ 0 \end{pmatrix} = \begin{pmatrix} 0 \\ 0 \end{pmatrix}$ only transformations for which the origin is invariant can be represented by 2×2 matrices.

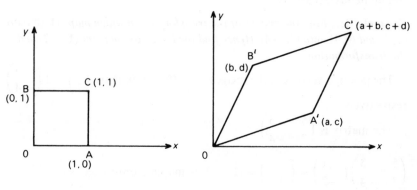

Fig. 22.2   *Fig. 22.3*

The *unit square* $OACB$ (Figure 22.2) will be mapped, in general, onto the parallelogram OA'C'B' (Figure 22.3) by a transformation represented by a 2×2 matrix.

303

If this matrix is $\begin{pmatrix} a & b \\ c & d \end{pmatrix}$, the position vectors of the image points can be found as follows:

$$\mathbf{OA'} = \begin{pmatrix} a & b \\ c & d \end{pmatrix}\begin{pmatrix} 1 \\ 0 \end{pmatrix} = \begin{pmatrix} a \\ c \end{pmatrix}; \qquad \mathbf{OB'} = \begin{pmatrix} a & b \\ c & d \end{pmatrix}\begin{pmatrix} 0 \\ 1 \end{pmatrix} = \begin{pmatrix} b \\ d \end{pmatrix};$$

$$\mathbf{OC'} = \begin{pmatrix} a & b \\ c & d \end{pmatrix}\begin{pmatrix} 1 \\ 1 \end{pmatrix} = \begin{pmatrix} a+b \\ c+d \end{pmatrix}.$$

The point $(1, 0)$ is mapped onto the point (a, c); $\begin{pmatrix} a \\ c \end{pmatrix}$ is the first column of the matrix.

The point $(0, 1)$ is mapped onto the point (b, d); $\begin{pmatrix} b \\ d \end{pmatrix}$ is the second column of the matrix.

The point $(1, 1)$ is mapped onto the point $(a + b, c + d)$; $\begin{pmatrix} a+b \\ c+d \end{pmatrix}$ is the sum of $\begin{pmatrix} a \\ c \end{pmatrix}$ and $\begin{pmatrix} b \\ d \end{pmatrix}$.

Exercise

Prove that the figure OA′C′B′ is a parallelogram.

If the images of the points $(1, 0)$ and $(0, 1)$ are known under a transformation, the corresponding matrix is formed immediately. If the images of any two points are given the matrix can be found by using simultaneous equations.

Example 1: *Find the matrix of the transformation which maps $(1, 0)$ onto $(5, 7)$ and $(0, 1)$ onto $(3, -4)$. Hence find the image of the point $(1, -2)$ under the transformation.*

The position vectors of the images of $(1, 0)$ and $(0, 1)$ are $\begin{pmatrix} 5 \\ 7 \end{pmatrix}$ and $\begin{pmatrix} 3 \\ -4 \end{pmatrix}$ respectively.

The matrix is $\begin{pmatrix} 5 & 3 \\ 7 & -4 \end{pmatrix}$.

$\begin{pmatrix} 5 & 3 \\ 7 & -4 \end{pmatrix}\begin{pmatrix} 1 \\ -2 \end{pmatrix} = \begin{pmatrix} -1 \\ 15 \end{pmatrix} \Rightarrow (1, -2)$ is mapped onto $(-1, 15)$.

Example 2: *Find the matrix of the transformation which maps $(1, 0)$ onto $(3, 1)$ and $(1, 1)$ onto $(8, 3)$. Deduce the matrix which maps $(3, 1)$ onto $(1, 0)$ and $(8, 3)$ onto $(1, 1)$.*

Since $(1, 0) \rightarrow (3, 1)$, the matrix is of the form $\begin{pmatrix} 3 & b \\ 1 & d \end{pmatrix}$

The image of (1, 1) has position vector $\begin{pmatrix} 3 & b \\ 1 & d \end{pmatrix}\begin{pmatrix} 1 \\ 1 \end{pmatrix} = \begin{pmatrix} 3+b \\ 1+d \end{pmatrix}$.

As $\begin{pmatrix} 3+b \\ 1+d \end{pmatrix} = \begin{pmatrix} 8 \\ 3 \end{pmatrix}$, $b = 5$, $d = 2$.

The matrix is $\begin{pmatrix} 3 & 5 \\ 1 & 2 \end{pmatrix}$.

The inverse mapping will be represented by the inverse matrix $\begin{pmatrix} 2 & -5 \\ -1 & 3 \end{pmatrix}$.

The reader should check that when $\begin{pmatrix} 3 \\ 1 \end{pmatrix}$ and $\begin{pmatrix} 8 \\ 3 \end{pmatrix}$ are pre-multiplied by this matrix the results are $\begin{pmatrix} 1 \\ 0 \end{pmatrix}$ and $\begin{pmatrix} 1 \\ 1 \end{pmatrix}$, respectively.

Example 3: *Find the matrix which maps (2, 3) onto (5, -1) and (3, -1) onto (2, 4).*

Let the matrix be $\begin{pmatrix} a & b \\ c & d \end{pmatrix}$.

Then $\begin{pmatrix} a & b \\ c & d \end{pmatrix}\begin{pmatrix} 2 & 3 \\ 3 & -1 \end{pmatrix} = \begin{pmatrix} 5 & 2 \\ -1 & 4 \end{pmatrix}$ represents the mapping.

Solving the pairs of simultaneous equations

$$2a + 3b = 5, \quad \text{and} \quad 2c + 3d = -1$$
$$3a - b = 2 \qquad\qquad 3c - d = 4$$

gives $a = 1$, $b = 1$, $c = 1$ and $d = -1$.

The matrix is $\begin{pmatrix} 1 & 1 \\ 1 & -1 \end{pmatrix}$.

Note: The identity matrix, $\begin{pmatrix} 1 & 0 \\ 0 & 1 \end{pmatrix}$, maps every point in the plane onto itself, and the null matrix, $\begin{pmatrix} 0 & 0 \\ 0 & 0 \end{pmatrix}$, maps every point onto the origin O.

Exercise 22.2

1 Determine the 2 × 2 matrices which map:
   (a) (1, 0) onto (9, -13) and (0, 1) onto (3, 0)
   (b) (1, 0) onto (3, 4) and (1, 1) onto (5, 12)
   (c) (0, 1) onto (2, 6) and (1, 1) onto (3, -5)
   (d) (1, 0) onto (-3, -4) and (6, 2) onto (1, 9)
   (e) (2, 5) onto (1, 0) and (3, 4) onto (0, 1)
   (f) (2, 0) onto (3, 1) and (1, 2) onto (4, 0)
   (g) (1, 0) onto (2, 1) and (3, -1) onto (4, 2).
   In case (g), find the images of four other points under this transformation. What do you notice about these image points?
2 Find the matrix which maps (1, 0) onto (7, 6) and (0, 1) onto (2, 5).
   Deduce the matrix which maps (7, 6) onto (1, 0) and (2, 5) onto (0, 1).

3 Sketch the image of the unit square OACB under the transformation represented by the matrix $\begin{pmatrix} 5 & 2 \\ 0 & 6 \end{pmatrix}$. Find the area of the transformed figure. Calculate the determinant of the matrix.

4 Plot on graph paper the points $(2, -1), (2, 1), (-2, 1)$ and $(-2, -1)$ and join up, in order, to form a rectangle. Plot their images under the transformation represented by the matrix $\begin{pmatrix} 2 & 3 \\ 0 & 1 \end{pmatrix}$. Find the ratio of the area of the image figure to the area of the given rectangle. Calculate the determinant of the matrix.

5 Sketch the image of the unit square OACB under the transformation represented by the matrix $\begin{pmatrix} 3 & 6 \\ 1 & 2 \end{pmatrix}$. Find the area of the image figure, and calculate the determinant of the matrix.

6 The unit square OACB is mapped onto OA′C′B′ by transformations represented by the following matrices. Draw OACB and OA′C′B′ on the same axes in each case and describe, in words, the effect of the transformation on the plane.

(a) $\begin{pmatrix} -1 & 0 \\ 0 & -1 \end{pmatrix}$ (b) $\begin{pmatrix} 4 & 8 \\ 1 & 2 \end{pmatrix}$ (c) $\begin{pmatrix} 3 & 0 \\ 0 & 3 \end{pmatrix}$ (d) $\begin{pmatrix} 0 & 1 \\ 1 & 0 \end{pmatrix}$.

7

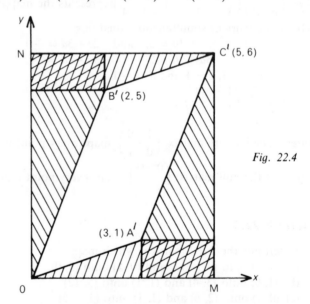

Fig. 22.4

For the parallelogram OA′C′B′, shown in Figure 22.4, calculate its area by finding the area of rectangle OMC′N and subtracting from it the shaded areas which are either rectangles or right-angled triangles. Hence, calculate the area of the image figure of the unit square OACB under the transformation represented by the matrix $\begin{pmatrix} 3 & 2 \\ 1 & 5 \end{pmatrix}$. How is this related to the determinant of the matrix?

Exercise

Copy out Figure 22.3 and, using the method of question 7, show that the area of parallelogram OA'C'B' is $ad - bc$, the determinant of the matrix $\begin{pmatrix} a & b \\ c & d \end{pmatrix}$.

The positive value of a determinant, $|ad - bc|$, is the ratio:

$$\frac{\text{Area of image figure}}{\text{Area of original figure}}.$$

If the non-null matrix is singular, all points of the plane map onto a line whose equation can be found.

Example: *Find the image of the point (a, b) under the transformation represented by* $\begin{pmatrix} 4 & 8 \\ 1 & 2 \end{pmatrix}$.

$$\begin{pmatrix} a' \\ b' \end{pmatrix} = \begin{pmatrix} 4 & 8 \\ 1 & 2 \end{pmatrix}\begin{pmatrix} a \\ b \end{pmatrix} = \begin{pmatrix} 4a + 8b \\ a + 2b \end{pmatrix} \Rightarrow b' = \tfrac{1}{4}a'.$$

All points lie on the line $y = \tfrac{1}{4}x$.

The following example shows how to find the matrix of a transformation described in words:

Example: *Find the matrix which represents the transformation* **Y**, *reflection of the plane in the y-axis.*

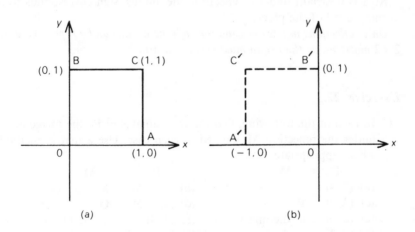

Fig. 22.5

Figure 22.5(a) shows the unit square OACB and Figure 22.5(b) its image square OA'C'B' under **Y**

$$(1, 0) \rightarrow (-1, 0); \quad (0, 1) \rightarrow (0, 1) \Rightarrow \text{matrix is } \begin{pmatrix} -1 & 0 \\ 0 & 1 \end{pmatrix}.$$

307

$\begin{pmatrix} -1 & 0 \\ 0 & 1 \end{pmatrix}$ maps all points in the plane onto their images under **Y**.

It is expected that the reader will work through the following as exercises, using the method of this example, to check that the matrix corresponds to the given transformation.

Reflection in the y-axis, $\qquad\qquad \begin{pmatrix} -1 & 0 \\ 0 & 1 \end{pmatrix}$

Reflection in the x-axis, $\qquad\qquad \begin{pmatrix} 1 & 0 \\ 0 & -1 \end{pmatrix}$

Reflection in the line $y = x$ $\qquad \begin{pmatrix} 0 & 1 \\ 1 & 0 \end{pmatrix}$

Reflection in the line $y = -x$ $\qquad \begin{pmatrix} 0 & -1 \\ -1 & 0 \end{pmatrix}$

These reflections will be referred to as **Y**, **X**, **P** and **Q** respectively for the remainder of the chapter.

Exercise

Verify that the matrices corresponding to **Y**, **X**, **P** and **Q** are self-inverse.

Note that the determinant of each of the above matrices is -1.

Area is invariant under a reflection; the 'minus' sign corresponds to a 'turning over' of the plane.

Only reflections in lines passing through the origin can be represented by 2×2 matrices, as the origin must remain invariant.

Exercise 22.3

1 In each of the following, find the co-ordinates of P′, the image of P, under the reflection **M**, defined in each case. Use a matrix method where appropriate:

	P	M		P	M
(a)	(3, 4)	**Y**	(b)	(−2, 5)	**X**
(c)	(3, 3)	**P**	(d)	(4, −5)	**Q**
(e)	(2, 0)	in the line $x = 3$	(f)	(3, 4)	in the line $x = -4$
(g)	(−2, 3)	in the line $y = -1$	(h)	(0, 1)	in the line $y = x + 1$

2 The vertices of the rectangle OABC are O(0, 0), A(2, 0), B(2, 1) and C(0, 1). The rectangle is reflected in the line $x = -1$. Find the co-ordinates of the vertices of the image rectangle.

3 The triangle ABC, with vertices A(3, 0), B(3, 4) and C(5, 1), is reflected in a line parallel to the y-axis so that the image of the point C has co-ordinates $(-3, 1)$. Calculate the equation of the axis of reflection and the co-ordinates of the images of A and B.

4 The point P′ is the image of P under a reflection. Find the equation of the axis of reflection in each of the following cases:

	P	P′		P	P′
(a)	(3, 4)	(−3, 4)	(b)	(7, −8)	(7, 8)
(c)	(1, −2)	(2, −1)	(d)	(−3, 5)	(−3, 4).
(e)	(8, −6)	(−6, 8)	(f)	(−1, −1)	(1, 1)
(g)	(8, 0)	(4, 0)	(h)	(3, 6)	(3, −8)

5 Use the appropriate (2 × 2) matrix to find the image of the point P under the given reflection. State the matrix in each case:

	P	reflection		P	reflection
(a)	(4, −7)	**Y**	(b)	(2, 5)	**X**
(c)	(−5, 5)	**P**	(d)	(−5, 5)	**Q**

6 A rectangle ABCD is mapped onto A′B′C′D′ by a reflection in a line L. Which of the following statements are necessarily true:
(a) The two figures are equal in area
(b) If the lettering ABCD is anticlockwise then so is A′B′C′D′
(c) If BD is on the line L, the rectangle maps onto itself
(d) A′B′C′D′ is a rectangle?

7

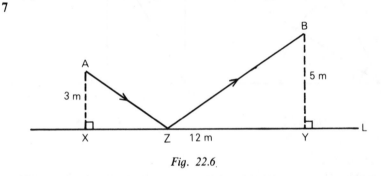

Fig. 22.6.

A small ball rolls along the ground from a point A, strikes a smooth vertical wall and rebounds to pass through a point B. Figure 22.6 shows a plan of this arrangement where L represents the wall. Given that AX and BY are perpendicular to the wall and the lengths of AX, XY and BY are 3 m, 12 m and 5 m, respectively, calculate the length XZ, where Z is the point at which the ball meets the wall. How would you construct the point Z? (Assume angle AZX = angle BZY.)

8 Find the images of (0, 1), (1, 3), (3, 7) under a reflection in the line $y = x$. Under the same reflection the line $y = 2x + 1$ is mapped onto $y = mx + c$. Find m and c.

9 Draw a sketch graph of $y = x^2$ and on the same axes sketch the image of the curve under a reflection in the line $y = x$. What is the equation of the image curve?

10 (Harder). Show that the matrix representing a reflection in the line $y = x \tan \alpha$ is $\begin{pmatrix} \cos 2\alpha & \sin 2\alpha \\ \sin 2\alpha & -\cos 2\alpha \end{pmatrix}$.

309

Rotation

In Figure 22.7, the point A is mapped onto the point A' under the operation of rotation, about O as centre, in an anticlockwise sense, through an angle θ.

The lines OA and OA' are equal.

The sign convention adopted for the operation of rotation is + for anticlockwise rotation and − for clockwise rotation. An important property of all rotations, shown in Figure 22.7, is that the mediator (perpendicular bisector) of AA' passes through O and bisects angle AOA'. It follows, that, given two points and their image points, the centre of rotation can be constructed by finding the point of intersection of the mediators of the first point and its image, and the second point and its image.

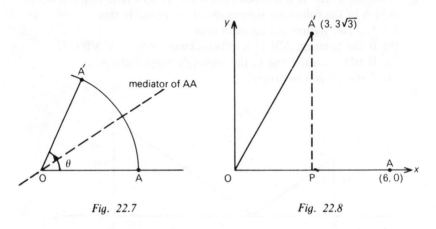

Fig. 22.7   Fig. 22.8

Example: *The point A(6, 0) is mapped onto the point A'(3, 3 $\sqrt{3}$) under a rotation whose centre is the origin O. Find the size of the angle of rotation.*

In Figure 22.8, A'P is perpendicular to the x-axis, OP = 3 and A'P $= 3 \sqrt{3}$. Hence, $\tan \angle AOA' = A'P/OP = \sqrt{3}$, giving the angle of rotation as 60°, (or $-300°$).

The reader should check, by finding the image of the unit square OACB, that the matrices corresponding to the following *rotations about the origin* are:

90° anticlockwise (+90°) $\begin{pmatrix} 0 & -1 \\ 1 & 0 \end{pmatrix}$

90° clockwise (−90°) $\begin{pmatrix} 0 & 1 \\ -1 & 0 \end{pmatrix}$

180° (half-turn) $\begin{pmatrix} -1 & 0 \\ 0 & -1 \end{pmatrix}$

360° (identity) $\begin{pmatrix} 1 & 0 \\ 0 & 1 \end{pmatrix}$.

We shall denote these rotations by $\mathbf{R}_+$, $\mathbf{R}_-$, **H** and **I**, respectively.

310

Note: Only rotations about the origin can be represented by 2×2 matrices.

The determinants of the above matrices are $+1$; rotations preserve area. The image figure is directly congruent to the original figure under a rotation.

Exercise 22.4

1 Use graph paper to find the image of the point P under the following rotations. The co-ordinates of P, the angle of rotation, θ, and the centre of rotation, C, are given in each case:

P	θ	C		P	θ	C
(a) (4, 0)	$+90°$	(1, 0)	(b)	(0, -4)	$180°$	(0, 2)
(c) (2, -3)	$180°$	(2, 0)	(d)	(-1, -3)	$-90°$	(0, -1)
(e) (1, 2)	$+90°$	(3, 4)	(f)	(-1, -2)	$180°$	(1, 1).

2 Under a rotation, the point A(6, 1) maps onto the point A'(5, 4) and the point B(1, 6) maps onto the point B'(-2, 5). Calculate: (a) the co-ordinates of the centre of rotation, (b) the positive angle of the rotation.

Verify your result for (a) by constructing, on graph paper, the centre of rotation.

3 The triangle whose vertices have co-ordinates $(-2, 2), (-4, 2), (-6, 4)$ is mapped, under a rotation, onto the triangle whose co-ordinates are $(2, -1), (4, -1), (6, -3)$, respectively. Find the centre of rotation.

4 The diagonals of the square ABCD intersect at the origin O and A is the point with position vector $\begin{pmatrix} 4 \\ 3 \end{pmatrix}$. Calculate the position vectors of B, C and D.

5 For the following rotations **R** about the origin use the matrix method to find the co-ordinates of P', the image of P:

	P	R			P	R
(a)	(5, 0)	$\mathbf{R}_+$	(b)		(0, -3)	$\mathbf{R}_-$
(c)	(3, 4)	$\mathbf{H}$	(d)		(-1, 7)	$\mathbf{R}_+$

6 A flag is formed by joining the points with co-ordinates (6, 4), (6, 6), $(5, 5\frac{1}{2})$ and (6, 5) in that order. Find the co-ordinates of the images of these points under $\mathbf{R}_+$, using a matrix method. Check your results by constructing the image flag on graph paper.

7 By considering the image of the unit square under a rotation of $\theta°$ anticlockwise about the origin, show that the matrix representing this transformation is $\mathbf{R}_\theta = \begin{pmatrix} \cos\theta & -\sin\theta \\ \sin\theta & \cos\theta \end{pmatrix}$.

The equilateral triangle ABC, lettered anticlockwise, has its centre at the origin and the position vector of A is $\begin{pmatrix} 2 \\ 0 \end{pmatrix}$. By letting $\theta = 120°$ in $\mathbf{R}_\theta$, deduce the position vector of B. State the position vector of C.

8 The centre of a regular hexagon ABCDEF is O and A is (4, 0). Calculate the co-ordinates of B, C, D, E and F.

Bilateral and rotational symmetry

If a plane figure is mapped onto itself under a reflection, it is said to have **bilateral** or **line symmetry** and the axis of reflection is called an **axis of symmetry**.

If a plane figure is mapped onto itself under a rotation of angle θ, where θ is less than $360°$, it is said to have **rotational symmetry**, the centre of rotation being the centre of symmetry. A figure with rotational symmetry of an even order is said to possess **point symmetry**.

Example: When an equilateral triangle maps onto itself under rotation, where the centre of the triangle is the centre of rotation, the angles of rotation are $120°$, $240°$ and $360°$ (or $0°$) and it is said to possess rotational symmetry of order 3.

The order of symmetry of a figure is the largest value of n for which a rotation of $360°/n$ maps the figure onto itself.

Exercise 22.5

1   For each of the following figures, state the number of axes of symmetry they possess, if any, and also the order of any rotational symmetry they may possess. Draw a diagram to illustrate your answers:
    (a) an equilateral triangle (b) an isosceles triangle (c) a parallelogram (d) a rhombus (e) an isosceles trapezium (f) a kite (g) a square (h) a rectangle (i) a circle (j) a regular pentagon (k) an ellipse (l) a semi-circle.
    Which of the above have point symmetry?
2   Name two geometrical figures in each part, possessing: (a) only one line of symmetry, (b) two lines of symmetry, (c) a diagonal as its only line of symmetry, (d) no lines of symmetry

Summary:

The identity transformation and each of the transformations translation, reflection and rotation are isometries, the image figure being congruent to the original figure.

Further transformations:

Enlargements

In Figure 22.9, the points A, B and C are mapped onto A', B' and C', respectively, under an enlargement centre A and scale factor k. The points A and A' are the same, the centre of enlargement being invariant under the transformation. The triangles ABC and A'B'C' are similar, with BC parallel to B'C'.

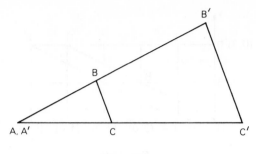

Fig. 22.9

In particular, A'B'/AB = B'C'/BC = C'A'/CA = k,
and Area of triangle A'B'C'/Area of triangle ABC = k^2.
Note: In an enlargement, the scale factor k can be positive or negative, and greater than or less than 1.

Under an enlargement, centre the origin and scale factor k,
$$(1, 0) \rightarrow (k, 0) \text{ and } (0, 1) \rightarrow (0, k).$$
The matrix representing this transformation is, therefore, $\begin{pmatrix} k & 0 \\ 0 & k \end{pmatrix}$.

Example: *The co-ordinates of A, B and C are* (2, 0), (3, 2) *and* (1, 3), *respectively. The triangle ABC is mapped onto the triangle A'B'C' by an enlargement E, centre 0 and scale factor* -2. *Find the co-ordinates of A', B' and C'.*

The matrix representing **E** is $\begin{pmatrix} -2 & 0 \\ 0 & -2 \end{pmatrix}$.

$\mathbf{E}(A) = \begin{pmatrix} -2 & 0 \\ 0 & -2 \end{pmatrix} \begin{pmatrix} 2 \\ 0 \end{pmatrix} = \begin{pmatrix} -4 \\ 0 \end{pmatrix}$, the position vector of A',

$\mathbf{E}(B) = \begin{pmatrix} -2 & 0 \\ 0 & -2 \end{pmatrix} \begin{pmatrix} 3 \\ 2 \end{pmatrix} = \begin{pmatrix} -6 \\ -4 \end{pmatrix}$, the position vector of B',

$\mathbf{E}(C) = \begin{pmatrix} -2 & 0 \\ 0 & -2 \end{pmatrix} \begin{pmatrix} 1 \\ 3 \end{pmatrix} = \begin{pmatrix} -2 \\ -6 \end{pmatrix}$, the position vector of C'.

Exercise

Draw the triangles ABC and A'B'C' of the last example on graph paper and verify that: (a) the corresponding sides of the triangles, e.g. AC and A'C', are parallel, and their lengths are in the ratio 2:1; (b) the lines AA', BB', CC' all pass through O, the centre of enlargement..

Shear

In Figure 22.10, the rectangle OAED is mapped onto the parallelogram OAE'D' by a transformation called a **shear**. All points on the line OA are

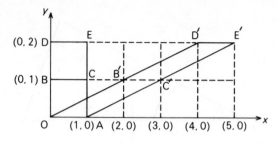

Fig. 22.10

invariant and any two points on a line parallel to OA are mapped onto points in the same line, such that the distance between them is invariant, e.g. DE and D′E′ are the same length. The distance of a point from the invariant line, therefore, remains fixed.

Area is invariant under a shear.

Shears having either of the axes as the invariant line may be represented by 2×2 matrices, since the origin is invariant. In Figure 22.10, the image of $(1, 0)$ is $(1, 0)$ and the image of $(0, 1)$ is $(2, 1)$. The matrix for this shear is $\begin{pmatrix} 1 & 2 \\ 0 & 1 \end{pmatrix}$.

In general, if a shear with the x-axis invariant maps $(0, 1)$ onto $(k, 1)$, its matrix is $\begin{pmatrix} 1 & k \\ 0 & 1 \end{pmatrix}$.

The reader should show that the shear with y-axis invariant that maps $(1, 0)$ onto $(1, k)$ is $\begin{pmatrix} 1 & 0 \\ k & 1 \end{pmatrix}$.

Example: *The rectangle ABCD is mapped onto A′B′C′D′ under a shear with y-axis invariant which maps $(1, 0)$ onto $(1, 6)$. If the co-ordinates of A, B, C and D are $(-1, 0), (1, 0), (-1, 4)$ and $(1, 4)$, respectively, find the co-ordinates of A′, B′, C′ and D′.*

The matrix representing the shear is $\begin{pmatrix} 1 & 0 \\ 6 & 1 \end{pmatrix}$.

The position vectors of A′, B′, C′ and D′ can be found, as follows:

$$\begin{pmatrix} 1 & 0 \\ 6 & 1 \end{pmatrix} \begin{pmatrix} -1 & 1 & -1 & 1 \\ 0 & 0 & 4 & 4 \end{pmatrix} = \begin{pmatrix} -1 & 1 & -1 & 1 \\ -6 & 6 & -2 & 10 \end{pmatrix}.$$

The co-ordinates of A′, B′, C′ and D′ are $(-1, -6), (1, 6), (-1, -2)$, and $(1, 10)$, respectively.

The reader should draw ABCD and A′B′C′D′ on graph paper to see the effect, geometrically, of the given shear.

Stretch

The transformation that maps the square OACB onto OA′C′B (Figure 22.11) is called a **one-way stretch**. In a stretch of the plane, one line remains

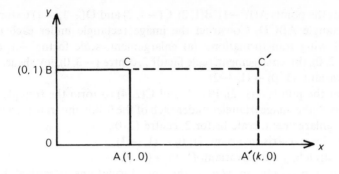

Fig. 22.11

(point) invariant; the rest of the plane is pulled, as if elastic, at right angles away from the line.

By considering the effect on the unit square OACB, the matrix representing the stretch with the y-axis invariant, mapping $(1, 0)$ onto $(k, 0)$ (shown in Figure 22.11), is seen to be $\begin{pmatrix} k & 0 \\ 0 & 1 \end{pmatrix}$.

The matrix representing the stretch with the x-axis invariant, mapping $(0, 1)$ onto $(0, k)$ is $\begin{pmatrix} 1 & 0 \\ 0 & k \end{pmatrix}$.

In terms of vectors, the operation called a two-way stretch can be defined as $\begin{pmatrix} x \\ y \end{pmatrix} \rightarrow \begin{pmatrix} ax \\ by \end{pmatrix}$. The equivalent matrix equation is

$$\begin{pmatrix} x' \\ y' \end{pmatrix} = \begin{pmatrix} a & 0 \\ 0 & b \end{pmatrix}\begin{pmatrix} x \\ y \end{pmatrix};$$ if $a = b$, this is an enlargement.

Exercise 22.6

1 In each of the following, find the co-ordinates of P′, the image of P, under the transformation named in each part:

P	Transformation
(a) (3, 2)	enlargement, scale factor $+3$, centre O
(b) $(-6, 7)$	enlargement, scale factor $\frac{1}{2}$, centre (2, 0)
(c) $(4, -8)$	enlargement, scale factor -2, centre (1, 2)
(d) (2, 4)	shear, x-axis invariant, mapping (0, 1) onto (3, 1)
(e) $(4, -5)$	shear, y-axis invariant, mapping (1, 0) onto $(1, -2)$
(f) (1, 3)	stretch, y-axis invariant, mapping (1, 0) onto (4, 0)
(g) $(3, -4)$	stretch, x-axis invariant, mapping (0, 1) onto (0, 2.5)

2 On graph paper, draw the image of the unit square under each of the following transformations and hence find their corresponding matrices:
(a) enlargement, scale factor 5, centre O, (b) shear, x-axis invariant $(0, 1) \rightarrow (5, 1)$, (c) stretch, y-axis invariant, $(1, 0) \rightarrow (2, 0)$, (d) enlargement, scale factor -1, centre O. Give a transformation equivalent to (d).

315

3 Plot the points A(1, −1), B(1, 2), C(−1, 2) and D(−1, −1) to form the rectangle ABCD. Construct the image rectangle under each of the following transformations: (a) enlargement, scale factor −1, centre (−2, 0), (b) enlargement, scale factor 2, centre (−3, 0), (c) shear, y-axis invariant, (1, 0) → (1, −2).

4 Plot the points A(1, 2), B(1, 4) and C(2, 4) to form the triangle ABC. Sketch the image triangles under each of the following transformations:
(a) enlargement, scale factor 2, centre (2, 0),
(b) shear, y-axis invariant, (1, 0) → (1, −1),
(c) stretch, y-axis invariant, (1, 0) → (3, 0).

5 Define precisely, in words, the transformations described by the following matrices:

(a) $\begin{pmatrix} \frac{1}{2} & 0 \\ 0 & \frac{1}{2} \end{pmatrix}$ (b) $\begin{pmatrix} 5 & 0 \\ 0 & 1 \end{pmatrix}$ (c) $\begin{pmatrix} 1 & 4 \\ 0 & 1 \end{pmatrix}$ (d) $\begin{pmatrix} -1 & 0 \\ 0 & -1 \end{pmatrix}$

(e) $\begin{pmatrix} 0 & -1 \\ -1 & 0 \end{pmatrix}$ (f) $\begin{pmatrix} 0 & 1 \\ 1 & 0 \end{pmatrix}$ (g) $\begin{pmatrix} 1 & 0 \\ -2 & 1 \end{pmatrix}$ (h) $\begin{pmatrix} 3 & 6 \\ 2 & 4 \end{pmatrix}$.

6 Find the image of the unit square under each of the following transformations and find the matrix, if possible, to describe the inverse mapping.

(a) $\begin{pmatrix} x \\ y \end{pmatrix} \rightarrow \begin{pmatrix} -2 & 0 \\ 0 & -2 \end{pmatrix}\begin{pmatrix} x \\ y \end{pmatrix}$

(b) $\begin{pmatrix} x \\ y \end{pmatrix} \rightarrow \begin{pmatrix} 1 & 2 \\ 0 & 1 \end{pmatrix}\begin{pmatrix} x \\ y \end{pmatrix}$

(c) $\begin{pmatrix} x \\ y \end{pmatrix} \rightarrow \begin{pmatrix} 4 & -1 \\ 3 & 2 \end{pmatrix}\begin{pmatrix} x \\ y \end{pmatrix}$

(d) $\begin{pmatrix} x \\ y \end{pmatrix} \rightarrow \begin{pmatrix} 6 & 4 \\ 3 & 2 \end{pmatrix}\begin{pmatrix} x \\ y \end{pmatrix}$.

Successive transformations

The point P(3, 4) is mapped, under **X**, onto the point P_1. The point P_1 is mapped, under $\mathbf{R}_+$, onto the point P_2. Find the co-ordinates of P_1 and P_2 and state, in words, the transformation which maps P directly onto P_2.

Figure 22.12 shows the successive transformations **X** 'followed by' $\mathbf{R}_+$. $\mathbf{X}(P) = (3, -4)$; $\mathbf{R}_+(3, -4) = (4, 3) \Rightarrow \mathbf{R}_+[\mathbf{X}(P)] = (4, 3)$ or more simply $\mathbf{R}_+\mathbf{X}(P) = (4, 3)$.
In general, if **A** and **B** are two transformations, we denote **A** 'followed by' **B** (or **B** 'follows' **A**) by the 'product' **BA**.

In the example, the point P can be mapped directly onto P_2 under reflection in the line $y = x$. This is conveyed by the statement $\mathbf{R}_+\mathbf{X} = \mathbf{P}$, where **P** is the transformation, 'reflect in $y = x$'.

Figure 22.13 shows the successive transformations $\mathbf{R}_+$ 'followed by' **X**, i.e. $\mathbf{X}\mathbf{R}_+$, where P maps onto $P_3(-4, 3)$ under $\mathbf{R}_+$, and P_3 maps onto P_4 (−4, −3) under **X**.

The point P can be mapped directly onto P_4 under reflection in the line $y = -x$.

This example illustrates that, in general, successive transformations are *not commutative* under the defined law of composition.

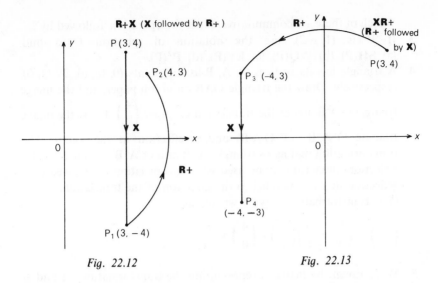

Fig. 22.12   Fig. 22.13

It is instructive to consider the above solution in terms of matrices.

X can be represented by $\begin{pmatrix} 1 & 0 \\ 0 & -1 \end{pmatrix}$ and **R**$_+$ by $\begin{pmatrix} 0 & -1 \\ 1 & 0 \end{pmatrix}$.

$$\mathbf{R}_+ \mathbf{X} \begin{pmatrix} 3 \\ 4 \end{pmatrix} = \begin{pmatrix} 0 & -1 \\ 1 & 0 \end{pmatrix} \begin{pmatrix} 1 & 0 \\ 0 & -1 \end{pmatrix} \begin{pmatrix} 3 \\ 4 \end{pmatrix} = \begin{pmatrix} 0 & 1 \\ 1 & 0 \end{pmatrix} \begin{pmatrix} 3 \\ 4 \end{pmatrix} = \begin{pmatrix} 4 \\ 3 \end{pmatrix}.$$

The triple product can be evaluated in several ways, since matrices are associative, but in the above it is clear that $\begin{pmatrix} 0 & 1 \\ 1 & 0 \end{pmatrix}$ is the matrix of the single transformation equivalent to **X** 'followed by' **R**$_+$. This matrix represents reflection in the line $y = x$ (see page 308).

The reader should confirm the result shown in Figure 22.13 by a matrix method.

Exercise 22.7

1 **T** is the translation $\begin{pmatrix} -3 \\ 4 \end{pmatrix}$, **X, Y, P, Q** the reflections defined earlier, **R**$_+$, **R**$_-$, **H, I** the rotations defined earlier, **S** the shear with x-axis invariant, mapping $(0, 1)$ onto $(3, 1)$, **V** the shear with y-axis invariant, mapping $(1, 0)$ onto $(1, 2)$, **E** the enlargement scale factor 2, centre O, and **W** is reflection in the line $y = 2$. Draw the image of the unit square under each of the following successive transformations and deduce the matrix, where possible, representing the single transformation having the same effect.
   (a) **XY**   (b) **XR**$_-$ (c) **SH**   (d) **EV**   (e) **R**$_+$**S**
   (f) **P**^{2} (g) **PQ**   (h) **R**$_+$^{2} (i) **TP**   (j) **WQ**.
   Replace these 'products' by a single transformation defined in the question, if possible. (**P**^{2} means **P** 'followed by' **P**.)

2 Repeat question 1 with the transformations in the reverse order.

Which of these are commutative under the operation 'followed by'?

3 If P is $(1, -2)$, use the notation of question 1 to find: (a) $\mathbf{SH}(P)$, (b) $\mathbf{WQ}(P)$, (c) $\mathbf{EV}(P)$, (d) $\mathbf{P}^2(P)$.

4 A triangle has its vertices O, A, B at the points $(0, 0)$, $(0, 2)$, $(3, 0)$, respectively. Draw the triangle OAB on graph paper, and the image triangle O′A′B′ under the translation given by $\begin{pmatrix} 4 \\ 0 \end{pmatrix}$. Draw the image triangle O″A″B″ of O′A′B′ under reflection in the x-axis. The transformation that maps triangle OAB into O″A″B″ is called a glide-reflection; the term may be used when a translation is followed by a reflection in a line parallel to the direction of the translation. (The transformation may be written as

$$\begin{pmatrix} x' \\ y' \end{pmatrix} = \begin{pmatrix} 1 & 0 \\ 0 & -1 \end{pmatrix} \begin{pmatrix} x \\ y \end{pmatrix} + \begin{pmatrix} 4 \\ 0 \end{pmatrix}.)$$

5 Write down the matrices representing the transformations **A** and **B** and find the single matrix representing **A** 'followed by' **B** in each of the following cases:

A	B
(a) Shear with x-axis invariant, $(0, 1) \to (3, 1)$	reflection in the line $y = x$
(b) reflection in the x-axis	enlargement, scale factor 5, centre O
(c) enlargement, scale factor -2, centre O	reflection in the line $y = -x$
(d) reflection in the y-axis	half turn about the origin.

Find the inverses of the matrices representing **A**, **B** and **BA** and verify that $(\mathbf{BA})^{-1} = \mathbf{A}^{-1}\mathbf{B}^{-1}$, in each case.

6 Write down the matrix which represents a shear, S, with x-axis invariant, mapping $(0, 1)$ onto $(-3, 1)$. Deduce the matrix of S^5, and

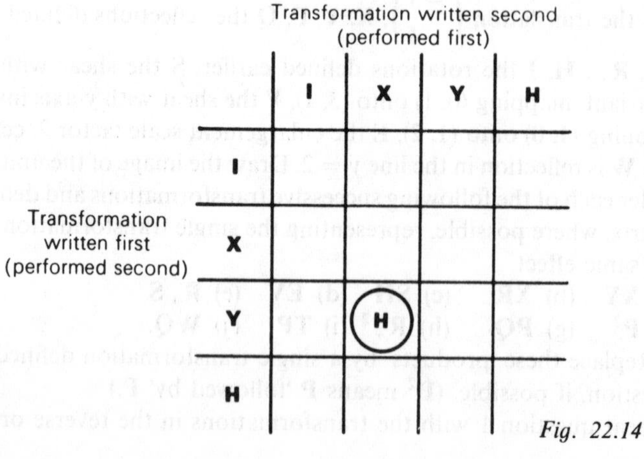

Transformation written second
(performed first)

	I	X	Y	H
I				
X				
Y			H	
H				

Transformation written first (performed second)

Fig. 22.14

the area of the image of a quadrilateral of area 10 cm^2 under $\mathbf{S}^5$. If P is (3, 4), find $\mathbf{S}(P)$ and $\mathbf{S}^5(P)$.

7 Write down the matrix for $\mathbf{R}_-$. Deduce $\mathbf{R}_-^5$ and $\mathbf{R}_-^{12}$. (Think geometrically).

8 Repeat question 7 for $\mathbf{P}$.

9 Fig. 22.14 shows the combination table for the four transformations $\mathbf{I}$, $\mathbf{X}$, $\mathbf{Y}$ and $\mathbf{H}$. The ringed entry is found, since $\mathbf{YX}$ means 'X first then Y', which is equivalent to $\mathbf{H}$. Copy and complete the table and discuss any properties exhibited.

These transformations form a **group** (Chapter 5), which is necessarily commutative since all groups of order 4 or less are Abelian.

10 Repeat question 9 for (a) the four rotations $\mathbf{I}$, $\mathbf{R}_+$, $\mathbf{R}_-$ and $\mathbf{H}$,
(b) the five transformations $\mathbf{I}$, $\mathbf{X}$, $\mathbf{Y}$, $\mathbf{P}$, $\mathbf{Q}$,
(c) the six transformations $\mathbf{I}$, $\mathbf{P}$, $\mathbf{Q}$, $\mathbf{X}$, $\mathbf{Y}$, $\mathbf{H}$

Do the tables exhibit closure and commutativity?

23 Right-angled triangles and graphs

The study of trigonometry grew from the need to calculate particular distances and angles in plane figures when the sizes of other sides and angles were already known. This need can be fulfilled to some extent by scale drawing, but the calculation methods used in trigonometry are more accurate and take less time. The word trigonometry itself means 'measurement of a triangle' and the early basic work is developed from a study of right-angled triangles.

The three basic ratios in a right-angled triangle

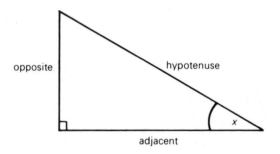

Fig. 23.1

In Figure 23.1, the sides of the triangle marked opposite, adjacent and hypotenuse, refer to the angle marked x. The ratios $\sin x$, $\cos x$ and $\tan x$ are defined as:

$$\sin x = \frac{\text{opposite}}{\text{hypotenuse}}, \quad \cos x = \frac{\text{adjacent}}{\text{hypotenuse}}, \quad \tan x = \frac{\text{opposite}}{\text{adjacent}}.$$

The values of $\sin x$, $\cos x$ and $\tan x$ are tabulated for 1 minute intervals from 0–90° as natural sine, natural cosine and natural tangent tables. These values are also easily available from a scientific calculator which contains keys for the trignometrical ratios. The natural sine, cosine and tangent ratios for angles from 0–90° are also tabulated separately in their respective equivalent logarithm form, as $\log_{10} \sin x$, $\log_{10} \cos x$ and $\log_{10} \tan x$; this has been done in order to facilitate access to these values when logarithms are used in calculations.

In the difference columns of the tables for sines and tangents the differences are ADDED.

Examples: $\sin 34° \, 11' = 0.5606 + 0.0012 = 0.5618$
$\tan 71° \, 38' = 3.006 + 0.006 \quad = 3.012.$

In the difference columns for cosines the differences are SUBTRACTED.

Examples: $\cos 50° \, 39' = 0.6347 - 0.0007 = 0.6340$
$\cos x \qquad = 0.8612 = 0.8616 - 0.0004 \Rightarrow x = 30° \, 33'.$

The theorem of Pythagoras

This important result, relating the lengths of the sides of a right-angled triangle, is frequently used with the trigonometric ratios.
In the notation of Figure 23.1 the result is
$$(\text{hypotenuse})^2 = (\text{adjacent})^2 + (\text{opposite})^2.$$
When the lengths of two sides of a right-angled triangle are known, the length of the third side can be determined using this result.

Example 1: *In the triangle ABC, $B = 90°$, $C = 27° \, 11'$ and $AC = 20$ cm. Calculate the lengths of AB and BC.*

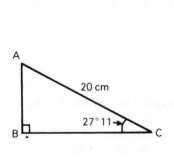

Fig. 23.2

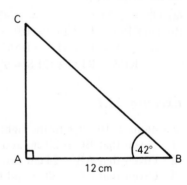

Fig. 23.3

See Figure 23.2
$AB/20 = \sin 27° \, 11' \Rightarrow AB = 20 \sin 27° \, 11' = 20 \times 0.4568 = 9.136$ cm
$BC/20 = \cos 27° \, 11' \Rightarrow BC = 20 \cos 27° \, 11' = 20 \times 0.8895 = 17.79$ cm.

Example 2: *In the triangle ABC, $A = 90°$, $AB = 12$ cm and $B = 42°$. Calculate AC and BC.*
See Figure 23.3
$AC/12 = \tan 42° \Rightarrow AC = 12 \tan 42° = 12 \times 0.9004 \approx 10.80$ cm.
$12/BC = \cos 42° \Rightarrow BC = 12/\cos 42°$ (a calculator or logs should be used)
$\qquad\qquad BC = 16.14$ cm.

To find BC, Pythagoras could be used $BC = \sqrt{12^2 + 10.8^2} = 16.14$ cm.
The first method for finding BC is superior because it uses only given

data; if an error had been made in calculating AC, the second method carries the error forward into the second answer, too.

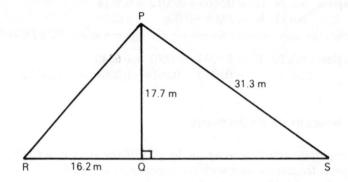

Fig. 23.4

Example 3: *In Figure* 23.4, *PQ* = 17.7 *m, RQ* = 16.2 *m, PS* = 31.3 *m and the line PQ is perpendicular to the line RQS. Calculate:* (a) *the length of QS,* (b) *the angle RPS.*

(a) $QS = \sqrt{31.3^2 - 17.7^2} = \sqrt{979.7 - 313.3} = \sqrt{666.4} = 25.81$ m.

(b) $\tan R\hat{P}Q = 16.2/17.7 = 0.9153$ ∴ $R\hat{P}Q = 42° 28'$.

$\cos Q\hat{P}S = 17.7/31.3 = 0.5655$ ∴ $Q\hat{P}S = 55° 34'$.

∴ $R\hat{P}S = R\hat{P}Q + Q\hat{P}S = 98° 02'$.

Exercise 23.1

Questions 1–10 refer to the right-angled triangle ABC, where B = 90°.

1 Given that BC = 20 cm and C = 20°, calculate AB.
2 Given that AB = 24 cm and C = 41°, calculate BC.
3 Given that AC = 30 m and C = 27°, calculate AB and BC
4 Given that AC = 24.6 m and A = 31°, calculate AB and BC.
5 Given that AB = 5 cm and BC = 12 cm, calculate AC and angle C.
6 Given that AC = 50 m and AB = 14 m, calculate BC and angle A.
7 Given that C = 24° 36′ and AC = 14.5 cm, calculate AB and BC.
8 Given that A = 49° 14′ and BC = 22.4 m, calculate AB and AC.
9 Given that A = 76° 49′ and BC = 16.7 m, calculate AB and AC.
10 Given that AC = 68.3 cm, BC = 35.6 m, calculate AB and angle C.
11 In the triangle LMN, LM = MN = 17 cm and LN = 16 cm. The mid-point of LN is X. Calculate the length of MX and the angle MLN.
12 In the rhombus ABCD, where AB = 10 cm, the shorter diagonal BD is of length 12 cm. Calculate the length of the longer diagonal AC and the angles of the rhombus.
13 The equal sides of an isosceles triangle are each of length 23.5 m and the equal angles are each 56° 24′. Calculate the length of the remaining side of the triangle.

322

14 The length of a rectangle is 23 cm and the breadth 14 cm. Calculate the length of a diagonal and the acute angle between the diagonals.

15 The area of a square is 24 m². Calculate the length of a diagonal of the square.

Example 1: *In a mountain district the observation points B, A and C are situated in the same vertical plane such that the angle of elevation of B from A is 32° and the angle of depression of A from C is 46°. Given that the horizontal distances between A and B and between A and C are each 5 km, calculate:* (a) *the height of C above B,* (b) *the angle of depression of B from C.*

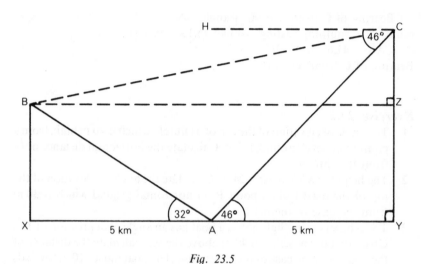

Fig. 23.5

In Figure 23.5, XAY, BZ and HC are horizontal lines.
From the given data, $\hat{BAX} = 32°$, $\hat{HCA} = 46°$, $XA = AY = 5000$ m.
$\hat{CAY} = \hat{HCA} = 46°$ (alternate angles).
In the triangle BXA, $BX/5000 = \tan 32° \Rightarrow BX = 5000 \tan 32° = 3124$ m.
In the triangle CAY, $CY/5000 = \tan 46° \Rightarrow CY = 5000 \tan 46° = 5178$ m.
Height of C above B $= 5178 - 3124 = 2054$ m.
In the triangle BCZ, $\tan \hat{CBZ} = 2054/10\,000 = 0.2054 \Rightarrow \hat{CBZ} = 11.6°$.
Angle of depression of B from C $= \hat{HCB} = \hat{CBZ} = 11.6°$, or $11° \, 36'$.

Example 2: *Three villages, A, B and C are all situated at the same horizontal level such that $AB = 10$ km, $BC = 17$ km. The bearing of B from A is 075° and the bearing of C from B is 161°. Calculate* (a) *the easting of C from A,* (b) *the southing of C from A,* (c) *the bearing of C from A.*
In Figure 23.6, $\hat{BAX} = 15°$ and $\hat{BCY} = 71°$.
(a) Easting of C from A $= AX + CY = 10 \cos 15° + 17 \cos 71°$
$$= 9.659 \qquad + 5.535 = 15.19 \text{ km.}$$
(b) Southing of C from A $= BY - BX = 17 \sin 71° - 10 \sin 15°$
$$= 16.07 \qquad - 2.58 = 13.49 \text{ km.}$$

323

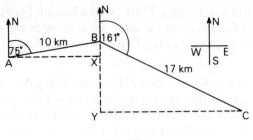

Fig. 23.6

(c) Bearing of C from A $= 90° +$ angle CAX

$\tan \text{C}\hat{\text{A}}\text{X} = \text{southing/easting} = 13.49/15.19 = 0.8881$

$\quad \text{C}\hat{\text{A}}\text{X} = 41.6°$ or $41° 36'$

Bearing of C from A $= 131.6°$.

Exercise 23.2

1   The angle of elevation of the top of a church, which is 40 m high, from a point O on level ground, is 25°. Calculate the horizontal distance of O from the church.

2   The height of a TV mast is 24 m. Calculate the angle of elevation of the top of the mast from a point P on horizontal ground which is 30 m from the base of the mast.

3   To an observer in a lighthouse a boat has an angle of depression of 39°. Given that the observer is 40 m above the sea, calculate the distance of the boat from the base of the lighthouse. The boat moves 10 m towards the lighthouse; calculate the new angle of depression of the boat from the observer.

4   A helicopter, flying horizontally, at 180 km/h at a height of 4 km, passes directly over an observer on the ground. Calculate the angle of elevation of the helicopter: (a) 5 minutes later, (b) 10 minutes later, from the observer.

5   A man walks from A for 5 km due west and then for 4 km due south to B. Calculate (a) AB, (b) the bearing of B from A.

6   The point A is 22 km from the point B, and the bearing of A from B is 252°. Calculate: (a) the westing, (b) the southing, of A from B.

7   A helicopter travels from P for 45 km on a bearing 332° and follows this by travelling for 35 km on a bearing 300° to Q. Calculate: (a) the westing, (b) the northing, (c) the bearing of Q from P.

8   The bearing of B from A is 047°. The bearing of C from A is 317°. Given that BC = 127 m and AB = 60 m, calculate, to the nearest metre, the distance AC.

9   One stage of a funicular railway AB rises 52 m vertically and the straight cable joining A and B is of length 96 m. Calculate: (a) the angle of depression of A from the higher point B, (b) the horizontal distance between A and B.

324

10 From a harbour H, a boat sails on a bearing 007° for 16 km to a point Q. From Q the boat sails on a bearing 123° for 7 km to a point R. Calculate: (a) the northing, (b) the easting, (c) the bearings, of H and Q from R.

11 A tree is 40 m high and stands on horizontal ground. Two points A and B are on the ground 50 m south and 65 m east of the tree, respectively. Calculate: (a) the angles of elevation of the top of the tree from A and B, (b) the distance AB, (c) the bearing of A from B.

12 The points A, B, C and D are the vertices of a square marked out on horizontal ground, with AB = 12 m. A vertical pole AP is 10 m high. Calculate: (a) the angles of elevation of P from B and C, (b) the distances BP and PC.

Some special right-angled triangles

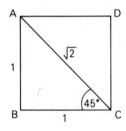

Fig. 23.7

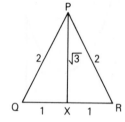

Fig. 23.8

Example 1: *In Figure 23.7, ABCD is a square of side 1 unit. By drawing the diagonal AC, calculate the trigonometric ratios for 45°.*
By Pythagoras, $AC^2 = AB^2 + BC^2 = 1^2 + 1^2 = 2$.
The length of AC is $\sqrt{2}$ units.
$\sin 45° = \cos 45° = 1/\sqrt{2}$ and $\tan 45° = 1$.

Example 2: *In Figure 23.8, PQR is an equilateral triangle of side 2 units. By drawing the perpendicular PX, calculate the trigonometric ratios of 30° and 60°.*
By Pythagoras, $PX^2 + QX^2 = PQ^2 \Rightarrow PX^2 = PQ^2 - QX^2 = 2^2 - 1^2 = 3$.
The length of PX is $\sqrt{3}$ units.
$\sin 30° = \cos 60° = 1/2$.
$\cos 30° = \sin 60° = \sqrt{3}/2$.
$\tan 30° = 1/\sqrt{3}$, $\tan 60° = \sqrt{3}$.

Example 3: *Show that the triangle with sides of lengths $m^2 + n^2$, $m^2 - n^2$ and 2 mn is right-angled.*
$(m^2 + n^2)^2 = m^4 + 2m^2n^2 + n^4$
$(m^2 - n^2)^2 = m^4 - 2m^2n^2 + n^4$
$(2mn)^2 = 4m^2n^2$.

Adding the last two lines gives $(m^2 + n^2)^2 = (m^2 - n^2)^2 + (2mn)^2$. By applying the converse of the theorem of Pythagoras, the result is established.
By taking values for m and n, it is possible to find sets of three numbers p, q and r for which $p^2 = q^2 + r^2$, where $p = m^2 + n^2$, $q = m^2 - n^2$ and $r = 2mn$. In particular, $m = 2$ and $n = 1$ gives $p = 5$, $q = 3$ and $r = 4$;
$m = 3$ and $n = 2$ gives $p = 13$, $q = 5$ and $r = 12$,
both of which are well known right-angled triangles whose sides are of integral length.

The graphs of sin x, cos x and tan x

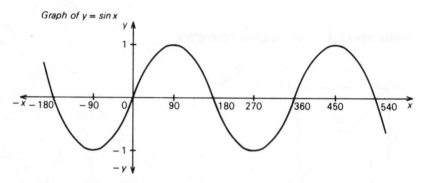

Fig. 23.9

In physics, engineering and more advanced mathematics, it is necessary to extend the basic definitions of sine, cosine and tangent in order that the ratios of angles of any size, both positive and negative, may be used and evaluated. The graphs of these functions are shown in Figures 23.9, 23.10 and 23.11. By using these graphs, and the tables of sine, cosine and tangent for values between 0° and 90°, it is possible to find the value of a ratio for any angle.

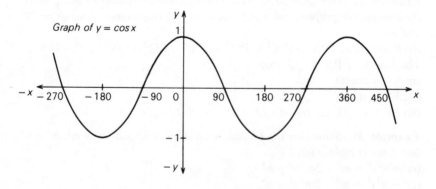

Fig. 23.10

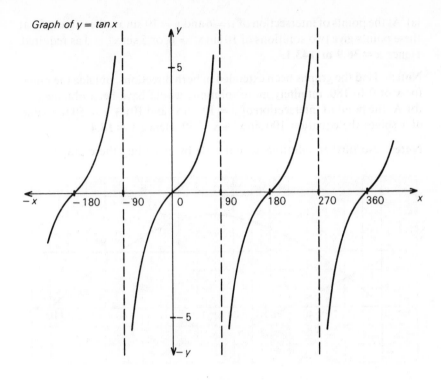

Graph of $y = \tan x$

Fig. 23.11

In order to grasp the following sections of work to be covered, a complete understanding of the graphs of the three functions $y = \sin x°$, $y = \cos x°$ and $y = \tan x°$ is essential. Before proceeding with further reading, the student should plot each of these on a large sheet of graph paper. In the cases of $y = \sin x°$ and $y = \cos x°$, intervals of $10°$ should be taken along the x-axis from 0 to 360. In the case of $y = \tan x°$, $10°$ intervals from 0 to 180 will suffice.

Example 1: *Taking values of x at $10°$ intervals, draw the graph of* **$y = 10 \sin x°$** *for values of x from 0 to 180.*

By adding the graphs of the lines $y = 6$ and $10y + x = 50$, solve the equations: (a) $5 \sin x° = 3$, (b) $100 \sin x° = x + 50$.

Make up a table of values for $y = 10 \sin x°$:

	0	10	20	30	40	50	60	70	80	90
x	180	170	160	150	140	130	120	110	100	
$\sin x$	0	0.17	0.34	0.5	0.64	0.77	0.87	0.94	0.98	1
$10 \sin x$	0	1.7	3.4	5	6.4	7.7	8.7	9.4	9.8	10

Plot the graph as shown in Figure 23.12
Add the lines $y = 6$ and $10y + x = 50$, as shown.

327

(a) At the points of intersection of $y = 6$ and $y = 10 \sin x°$, the values of x at these points give two solutions of $10 \sin x° = 6$, or $5 \sin x° = 3$ as required. Hence $x = 36.9$ or 143.1.

Note: Had the graphs been extended in both directions, outside the range for x of 0 to 180, infinitely more solutions would have been obtained.
(b) At the point of intersection of $y = 10 \sin x°$ and $10y + x = 50$ the value of x solves the equation $100 \sin x° + x = 50$. Hence $x = 18.4$

Note: No further solutions would arise by extending these graphs.

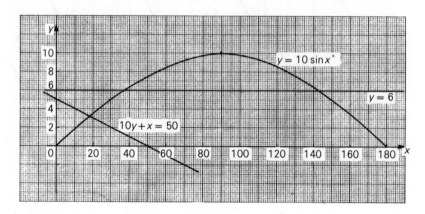

Fig. 23.12

Example 2: *Taking values of x at $20°$ intervals, draw the graph of $y = 3 \sin x° - 5 \cos x°$ for values of x from -100 to $+200$.*
Use your graph to estimate the maximum and the minimum values of y and the values of x at which these occur.
Make up a table of values:

x	-100	-80	-60	-40	-20	0	20	40	60	80	100
y	-2.09	-3.82	-5.10	-5.76	-5.72	-5	-3.67	-1.90	.01	2.09	3.82
x	120	140	160	180	200						
y	5.10	5.76	5.72	5	3.67						

Plot the graph, as shown in Figure 23.13. From the graph, the maximum value of y is 5.83, when $x = 149$; the minimum value for y is -5.83, when $x = -31$.

Example 3: *Using the graph in the last example, draw by eye using a ruler a tangent to the curve $y = 3 \sin x° - 5 \cos x°$ which passes through the origin. For this tangent, estimate: (a) the slope, (b) the co-ordinates of the point of contact with the curve.*
(a) Slope $= 2.5/60 = 0.04$ (approx.)
(b) Co-ordinates of point of contact (124, 5.3).

328

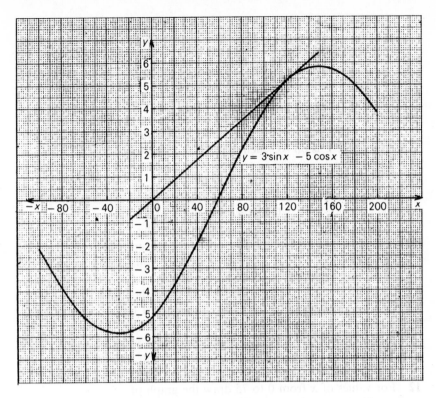

$y = 3\cdot\sin x - 5\cos x$

Fig. 23.13

Exercise 23.3

1 In the triangle ABC, B = 90°, AB = 4 cm, AC = 5 cm. Calculate:
   (a) BC, (b) sin C, (c) cos A, (d) cos C, (e) tan C.

2 In the triangle PQR, P = 90°, PQ = 7 m, PR = 24 m. Calculate:
   (a) QR, (b) tan R, (c) sin R, (d) cos Q, (e) sin Q.

3 In the triangle XYZ, XY = 8 cm, YZ = 15 cm, ZX = 17 cm.
   (a) Prove that XY is perpendicular to YZ. Calculate:
   (b) tan X, (c) cos X, (d) sin X, (e) the area of triangle XYZ,
   (f) the perpendicular distance from Y to ZX.

4 In the triangle ABC, the point D lies on BC such that AD is
   perpendicular to BC; AD = 5 cm, DC = 12 cm and BD = 3.75 cm.
   Calculate: (a) AC, (b) AB, (c) sin B, (d) cos C, (e) the area of the
   triangle ABC.

5 In the triangle DEF, G is on EF and DE = 25 cm, DF = 17 cm, DG
   = 15 cm and FG = 8 cm. Prove that angle DGF = 90°. Calculate:
   (a) GE, (b) the area of the triangle DEF, (c) sin F, (d) cos E.

6 The length of the diagonal AC of the square ABCD is 6 cm. Points X
   and Y are taken on AC such that AX = XY = YC = 2 cm. Show that
   (a) AB = 3 $\sqrt{2}$ cm, (b) BX = $\sqrt{10}$ cm. Use these values to find
   (c) sin BX̂C, (d) cos BX̂C.

7 The triangle ABC is equilateral and BC = 4 cm. The mid-point of BC is L and the mid-point of AL is M. Calculate (a) AL, (b) MC, and show that $\cos L\hat{C}M = 2/\sqrt{7}$.

8 In the triangle ABC, AB = AC and D is the mid-point of BC, BC = 16 cm and O is on AD such that OA = OB = OC, and OD = 6 cm. Calculate: (a) OB, (b) AB, and show that $\tan A\hat{B}D = 2$.

9 A trigonometry proof of the theorem of Pythagoras. The triangle ABC has B = 90°, AB = c, BC = a and AC = b. Draw BP perpendicular to AC, where P is on AC such that AP = x and CP = $b - x$. In triangle APB: $\cos A = x/c$ and in triangle ABC $\cos A = c/b$.

$$\text{Therefore } bx = c \tag{1}$$

In triangle BPC: $\cos C = (b - x)/a$ and in triangle ABC: $\cos C = a/b$

$$\text{Therefore } b(b - x) = a^2 \tag{2}$$

Add (1) and (2), $b^2 = a^2 + c^2$, which proves the theorem.

10 Taking values of x at 10° intervals, draw the graph of $y = 10 \cos x°$, for values of x from -90 to $+90$. Use your graph to solve the equations: (a) $\cos x° = 0.75$, (b) $x = 10 \cos x°$, for $-90 < x < 90$.

11 Taking values of x from -75 to $+75$ draw the graph of $y = \tan x°$.
(a) Use your graph to solve the equations (a) $\tan x° = 2$ and $\tan x° = -2$ for $-75 < x < 75$.
(b) Using a ruler, draw by eye a tangent to $y = \tan x°$, which passes through the point (10, 0). For this tangent estimate: (i) the co-ordinates of the point of contact with the curve, (ii) the slope.

12 For values of x from 0 to 75 draw the graph of
$y = 20 \sin x° - 10 \tan x°$, plotting at least 10 co-ordinates. Use your graph to estimate:
(a) the maximum value of $20 \sin x° - 10 \tan x°$ for $0 < x < 75$,
(b) the values of x for which $2 \sin x° = \tan x°$,
(c) by drawing a tangent, the slope of the curve at the point on the curve where $x = 30$.

24   The general triangle and three-dimensional work

Standard notation

In the following sections, the work refers to a triangle ABC, BC = a, CA = b, AB = c, and the capital letters A, B and C are used to represent the angles BAC, ABC and ACB, respectively.

The sine rule

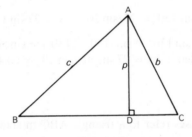

Fig. 24.1

Draw AD perpendicular to BC. Let AD = p.
In the triangle ABD: $\sin B = p/c \Rightarrow p = c \sin B$,
In the triangle ACD: $\sin C = p/b \Rightarrow p = b \sin C$.
Hence $b \sin C = c \sin B \Rightarrow b/\sin B = c/\sin C$.
Similarly by drawing the altitude from B to AC it can be shown that
$a/\sin A = c/\sin C$, giving the general result
$$a/\sin A = b/\sin B = c/\sin C.$$
This result is known as the **Sine Rule**.

Example 1:   *From the data given in Figure 24.2 calculate the values of x and y.*

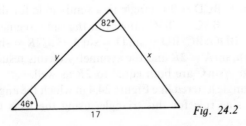

Fig. 24.2

331

$x/\sin 46° = 17/\sin 82° \Rightarrow x = 17 \sin 46°/\sin 82° = 12.34$.

Since the three angles of a triangle add up to 180°, the angle opposite the unknown side y is 52°.

$y/\sin 52° = 17/\sin 82° \Rightarrow y = 17 \sin 52°/\sin 82° = 13.53$.

From the graph of $y = \sin x°$ (see Figure 23.9) it can be seen that the sine of an obtuse angle = the sine of the supplement. For example $\sin 124°$ = $\sin (180° - 124°) = \sin 56°$.

Example 2: *From the data given in Figure 24.3, calculate x.*

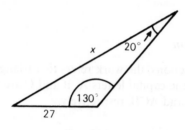

Fig. 24.3

By the sine rule, $x/\sin 130° = 27/\sin 20° \Rightarrow x = 27 \sin 130°/\sin 20°$

$$\text{But } \sin 130° = \sin (180° - 130°) = \sin 50°,$$
$$\text{Hence} \quad x = 27 \sin 50°/\sin 20° = 60.47$$

Exercise 24.1

The following exercises refer to a triangle ABC in standard notation.

1 Given that $a = 8$ cm, A = 30°, C = 70°, calculate b and c.
2 Given that $b = 7$ cm, A = 82° and B = 58°, calculate a and c.
3 Given that $a = 16$ cm, A = 110°, C = 27°, calculate b and c.
4 Given that $c = 10$ cm, A = 64° 48′, C = 45° 12′, calculate a and b.
5 Given that $c = 12$ cm, A = 150°, C = 13°, calculate a and b.
6 Given that $a = 12$ cm, B = 47°, C = 72°, calculate b and c.
7 Given that $a = 15.3$ cm, B = 39°, C = 27°, calculate b and c.
8 Given that $c = 14.7$ cm, B = 117°, A = 32°, calculate a and b.
9 **An alternative proof of the sine rule.**
   See Figure 24.4. Take a triangle ABC and the circle passing through A, B and C, whose radius is R and centre is O. This is the circumcircle of triangle ABC. Join BO and produce to meet the circle again at D. In this figure, $B\hat{C}D = 90°$ (angle in a semi-circle for diameter BD)
   $$B\hat{A}C = B\hat{D}C \text{ (angles in the same segment)}$$
   In triangle BDC: $BC/BD = \sin D = \sin A \Rightarrow a/2R = \sin A$
   This gives $a/\sin A = 2R$ and the symmetry of this result implies that $b/\sin B$ and $c/\sin C$ are both equal to $2R$ as well.
10 Draw a triangle lettered like Figure 24.4 in which the angle A is obtuse. Prove the sine rule for this triangle, using the facts that angles in

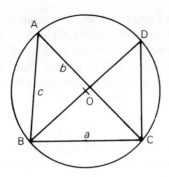

Fig. 24.4

opposite segments of a circle are supplementary and that the sine of an obtuse angle is equal to the sine of its supplement.

11 Calculate the radius of the circumcircle for the triangles given in questions 1, 2 and 3 of this exercise.

12 In triangle ABC, A = 60°, B = 40° and R = 10 cm. Calculate a, b and c.

The use of the sine rule when two sides and a non-included angle of a triangle are known

Example: *Construct the three triangles for the given sets of data:*
(a) AC = 4 cm, BC = 2 cm and A = 30°,
(b) AC = 4 cm, BC = 3 cm and A = 30°,
(c) AC = 4 cm, BC = 5 cm and A = 30°.
Figures 24.5, 24.6 and 24.7 show the triangles (half size).
Apply the sine rule in each case as sin A/a = sin B/b and explain how the construction and calculation give the same result in each case.

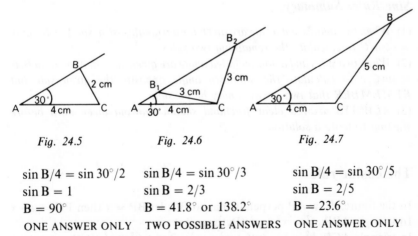

| *Fig. 24.5* | *Fig. 24.6* | *Fig. 24.7* |

$\sin B/4 = \sin 30°/2$	$\sin B/4 = \sin 30°/3$	$\sin B/4 = \sin 30°/5$
$\sin B = 1$	$\sin B = 2/3$	$\sin B = 2/5$
$B = 90°$	$B = 41.8°$ or $138.2°$	$B = 23.6°$
ONE ANSWER ONLY	TWO POSSIBLE ANSWERS	ONE ANSWER ONLY

Notes: When two sides and a non-included angle are known for a triangle, the student should note that the side opposite the given angle is the critical

333

value to investigate. In Figure 24.5 BC is as small as it can possibly be and the circle centre C, radius 2 cm touches AB at B. In Figure 24.6, known as **the ambiguous case,** two solutions are possible. In Figure 24.7 only one solution is possible because BC is greater than AC. In the following exercises a realistic freehand sketch is essential for each question.

Exercise 24.2

The following exercises refer to a triangle ABC in standard notation. In some questions two possible sets of answers are required. (See Figure 24.6 in the previous example.)

1 Show by construction and by using the sine rule that a triangle cannot be constructed from the following data: AB = 6 cm, BC = 4 cm and A = 60°.
2 Given that AB = 6 cm, BC = 8 cm and A = 60°, calculate C.
3 Given that AB = 6 cm, BC = 5.5 cm and A = 60°, calculate the possible values of C.
4 Given that BC = 10 cm, AC = 11 cm and B = 42°, calculate A and c.
5 Given that BC = 10 cm, AC = 8 cm and B = 42°, calculate the two possible values of A. For each of these find the corresponding length of AB.
6 Given that A = 117°, c = 6 cm, a = 9 cm, calculate C.
7 Given that b = 13 cm, c = 10 cm and C = 45°, calculate the possible values of B and the corresponding lengths of BC in each case.
8 In the triangle ABC, B = 50° and BC = 9 cm.
   (a) Calculate the least possible length of AC when this triangle exists.
   (b) Calculate the two possible values of A when AC = 8 cm.
   (c) Calculate the value of A when AC = 12 cm.

Sine Rule: Summary

(1) *When two angles and a side are given for a triangle, use $a/\sin A = b/\sin B = c/\sin C$ to calculate the remaining two sides.*

(2) *When two sides and a non-included angle are given, use $\sin A/a = \sin B/b = \sin C/c$ to calculate the unknown angle opposite the given side but REMEMBER that two answers may be possible.*

(3) *ALWAYS draw a clear freehand sketch showing given data before starting to write a solution.*

The cosine rule

In the figure, draw AP perpendicular to BC; let BP = x then PC = $a - x$
In triangle ABP: $c^2 = x^2 + p^2$ (Pythagoras)
In triangle ACP: $b^2 = (a-x)^2 + p^2 = a^2 - 2ax + x^2 + p^2$ (Pythagoras)
Writing c^2 for $x^2 + p^2$ gives $b^2 = a^2 + c^2 - 2ax$.
But in triangle ABP, $x = c \cos B$.

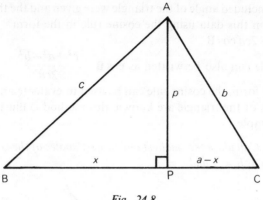

Fig. 24.8

Hence $$b^2 = a^2 + c^2 - 2ac \cos B.$$

This result is known as the **Cosine Rule**.

Note: The student should take a second triangle in which the angle B is obtuse: in this case, with the same notation, $b^2 = a^2 + c^2 + 2ax$ and $x = c \cos (180° - B)$. As the angle B is now obtuse, $x = -c \cos B$ because $\cos (180° - B) = -\cos B$, as can be seen at once from the graph of $y = \cos x°$ (See Figure 23.10). Also when $B = 90°$, $\cos B = 0$, giving $b^2 = a^2 + c^2$ (Pythagoras).

In *all* triangles, acute-angled, right-angled and obtuse-angled, the result $b^2 = a^2 + c^2 - 2ac \cos B$ is true.

Example 1: *In Figure 24.9 and 24.10, find the value of b in each case.*

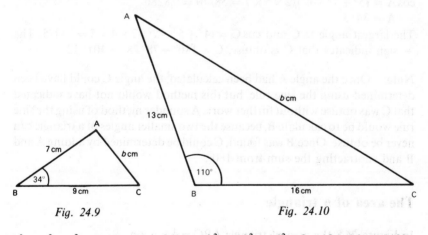

Fig. 24.9   Fig. 24.10

$$b^2 = 7^2 + 9^2 - 2 \times 7 \times 9 \cos 34° \qquad b^2 = 13^2 + 16^2 - 2 \times 13 \times 16 \cos 110°$$
$$= 49 + 81 - 104.5 \qquad\qquad = 169 + 256 + 2 \times 13 \times 16 \cos 70°$$
$$= 25.5 \qquad\qquad\qquad\qquad = 169 + 256 + 142.3$$
$$b = 5.05 \qquad\qquad\qquad\qquad = 567.3$$
$$\qquad\qquad\qquad\qquad\qquad b = 23.8$$

In both parts of the example just worked, it should be noted that two

sides and the included angle of the triangle were given and the third side was calculated from this data using the cosine rule in the form
$b^2 = c^2 + a^2 - 2ca \cos B$.

The above rule can also be written as $\cos B = \dfrac{c^2 + a^2 - b^2}{2ca}$

In this second form, the cosine rule can be used to evaluate an angle when the three sides of the triangle are known; this method is illustrated in the following example.

Example 2: *Calculate the smallest and largest angles of the triangle ABC, given that $a = 4$, $b = 5$ and $c = 7$.*

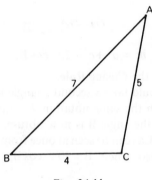

Fig. 24.11

The smallest side of a triangle is opposite the smallest angle, hence the angle required is A.
$\cos A = (5^2 + 7^2 - 4^2)/2 \times 5 \times 7 = 58/70 = 0.8286$
$A = 34° 3'$.
The largest angle is C and $\cos C = (4^2 + 5^2 - 7^2)/2 \times 4 \times 5 = -1/5$. The $-$ sign indicates that C is obtuse, $C = 180° - 78° 28' = 101° 32'$.

Note: Once the angle A had been calculated, the angle C could have been determined using the sine rule, but this method would not have indicated that C was obtuse without further work. A sounder method of using the sine rule would be to calculate B, because the two smaller angles of a triangle can never be obtuse. Once B was found, C could be determined by adding A and B and subtracting the sum from 180°.

The area of a triangle

In Figure 24.8 the area of triangle $ABC = \frac{1}{2} \times a \times p$
But $p = c \sin B$.
Hence, the **area of triangle ABC** $= \frac{1}{2}ac \sin B$ or, in words, *'one half of the product of two sides times the sine of the angle between these sides'*.
When three sides of a triangle are known, the formula:
Area of triangle ABC $= \sqrt{(s)(s-a)(s-b)(s-c)}$, where $s = \frac{1}{2}(a+b+c)$, can be used.

Cosine Rule: Summary

(1) *When two sides and the included angle are given, use the cosine rule in the form $b^2 = c^2 + a^2 - 2ac \cos B$ to calculate the unknown side b.*

(2) *When the three sides of a triangle are given, use the cosine rule in the form $\cos B = (a^2 + c^2 - b^2)/2ac$ to work out the angle B.*

(3) *Always draw a clear freehand sketch giving data before starting to write a solution.*

Exercise 24.3

The following exercises refer to a triangle ABC in standard notation:

1 Given that $a = 3$ cm, $b = 5$ cm and $C = 60°$, calculate c.

2 Given that $b = 13$ cm, $c = 15$ cm and $A = 60°$, calculate a.

3 Given that $a = 20$ cm, $c = 17$ cm and $B = 44°$, calculate b.

4 Given that $a = 3$ cm, $b = 5$ cm and $C = 120°$, calculate c.

5 Given that $b = 15$ cm, $c = 12$ cm and $A = 112°$, calculate a.

6 Given that $a = 4$ cm, $b = 5$ cm and $c = 6$ cm, calculate B.

7 Given that $a = 6$ cm, $b = 7$ cm and $c = 9$ cm, calculate the smallest angle of this triangle.

8 Calculate the largest angle of triangle ABC where $a = 12$ cm, $b = 14$ cm and $c = 11$ cm.

9 Given that $a = 5$ cm, $b = 6$ cm and $c = 7$ cm, calculate the angles of the triangle ABC.

10 Given that $a = 37$ cm, $b = 42$ cm and $c = 30$ cm, calculate the angles of the triangle ABC.

11 Given that $a = 6$ cm, $b = 9$ cm and $C = 30°$, calculate the area of the triangle ABC.

12 Given that $b = 14$ cm, $c = 19$ cm and $A = 30°$, calculate the area of the triangle ABC.

13 Given that $c = 56$ m, $a = 60$ m and $B = 76°$, calculate the area of the triangle ABC.

14 Given that $a = 4$ cm, $b = 6$ cm and $c = 7$ cm, calculate the area of the triangle ABC.

15 Given that $a = 8$ cm, $b = 9$ cm and $C = 150°$, calculate the area of the triangle ABC.

16 Given that $a = 6$ cm, $b = 9$ cm and $c = 10$ cm, calculate the area of the triangle ABC.

17 Given that $a = 14$ cm, $b = 23$ cm and $C = 156°$, calculate the area of the triangle ABC.

18 In the triangle XYZ, $XY = 12$ cm, $YZ = 7$ cm and angle $XYZ = 56°$. Calculate: (a) the area of triangle XYZ, (b) ZX, (c) angle XZY.

19 In the triangle PQR, $PQ = 10$ cm, $QR = 13$ cm and $RP = 15$ cm. Calculate: (a) angle PQR, (b) the area of the triangle PQR.

20 In the triangle LMN, $MN = 45$ m, $NL = 58$ m and angle $LNM = 135°$. Calculate: (a) the area of triangle LMN, (b) LM.

Situations often arise where both the sine and cosine rules are required.

These rules should not be used in right-angled triangles because, even though they are valid, direct use of the three basic ratios will lead to a shorter solution, with less chance for error.

Example: *A power-boat race is organised on a large inland lake. The point A is 15 km due west of B; C is south of AB and D is north of AB such that BC = 11 km, BD = 19 km and angle CBD = 131°. The bearing of D from A is 019°. Given that the boats move around the perimeter of the quadrilateral ABCD once, calculate: (a) the bearing of D from B, (b) the total length of the race course.*

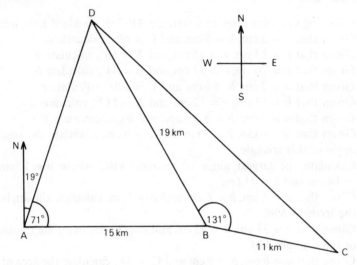

Fig. 24.12

(a) Sine rule in triangle ABD: $\sin D/15 = \sin 71°/19$
   $\sin D = 15 \sin 71°/19 \Rightarrow D = 48.3°$
   Angle ABD $= 180° - (71° + 48.3°) = 60.7°$
   Bearing of D from B $= 270° + 60.7° = 330.7°$.

(b) Sine rule in triangle ABD: $AD/\sin 60.7° = 19/\sin 71°$
   $AD = 19 \sin 60.7°/\sin 71° = 17.52$ km.
   Cosine rule in triangle BCD: $\quad CD^2 = 11^2 + 19^2 - 2 \times 11 \times 19 \cos 131°$
   $$CD^2 = 121 + 361 + 2 \times 11 \times 19 \cos 49°$$
   $$CD^2 = 121 + 361 + 274.2 = 756.2$$
   $$CD = 27.50 \text{ km}.$$
   Length of race course $= 15 + 11 + 17.52 + 27.50 = 71.02$ km.

Exercise 24.4

1 From P a boat sails 8 km due north to Q. From Q the boat sails 8 km on a bearing 120° to R. Calculate: (a) PR, (b) the bearing of R from P.

2 The town X is 12 km due west of the town Y. The bearings of a town Z are 040° and 330° from X and Y, respectively. A helicopter flies from X

to Y to Z to X. Calculate the distance covered by the helicopter.

3 The hour hand and the minute hand of a church clock are of lengths 0.3 and 0.4 metres, respectively. Calculate the distance between the tips of these hands at: (a) 0300 h, (b) 0200 h, (c) 0400 h.

4 Two radar stations P and Q are 10 km apart and P is due north of Q. A third station R is to be situated 8 km from Q and the bearing of R from P is 150°. Show that there are two possible sitings for R and calculate the distance of each of these from P.

5 Two camps, P and Q, are situated in a flat desert region where P is 8 km due west of Q. A third camp R bears 030° and 290° from P and Q, respectively. Calculate the distance between: (a) P and R, (b) Q and R.

6 A hiker walks 10 km due N from A to B and then 7 km on a bearing 327° from B to C. Calculate: (a) the distance AC, (b) the bearing of C from A.

7 The area of a triangular plot of ground is 1 400 m². Two of the sides of the plot enclose an obtuse angle θ and are of length 80 m and 70 m, respectively. (a) Show that $\theta = 150°$. (b) Calculate the perimeter of the plot.

8 A helicopter flies on a bearing 225° from A to B, where AB = 58 km. It then flies on a bearing 149° from B to C, where C is due south of A. Calculate the distance AC.

9 The angle of elevation of the top of a tree is 29° from a point A and 52° from another point B, 50 m nearer the base of the tree, which lies on the horizontal line AB produced. Calculate the height of the tree.

10 Three straight rods are of lengths 3 m, 5 m, 7 m. They are joined to form a triangle. Calculate the largest angle of this triangle.

11 Two ships, P and Q, leave a small port and move at constant speeds in the directions 060° and 110°, respectively. Given that P is moving at 20 km/h and Q is moving at 24 km/h, find the distance between P and Q $\frac{1}{2}$ hour after they leave the port.

12 In the quadrilateral ABCD, AD is parallel to BC; AD = DC = 6 cm, AB = 5 cm and BC = 10 cm. Sketch this quadrilateral. By adding a line through D, parallel to AB show that the quadrilateral consists of a parallelogram and a triangle. Calculate: (a) the angle DCB, (b) the angle ABC, (c) the area of the quadrilateral ABCD.

Three-dimensional work

The plumb-line and level have been used as practical building aids for many centuries and have enabled man to check vertical and horizontal alignment in building.

Two directions are defined by any straight line, and vertical and horizontal lines are no exception; for example, a vertical line could define either 'upwards' or 'downwards'. Care must always be taken in defining an angle. Any line which is not horizontal makes two angles with the vertical, one with the upward vertical and its supplement with the downward vertical. One way used to define such an angle uniquely is to say the acute angle made by the line with the vertical.

In three dimensions it is possible to draw infinitely many horizontal straight lines through a single point P. All of these lines, however, lie in one horizontal plane. Any straight line l through P which is not horizontal has a member l' of the set of horizontal lines through P, uniquely related to it by an operation called projection. The line l' is the intersection of the vertical plane containing l and the horizontal plane through P, or, in other words, it is the shadow of l on the horizontal plane. The acute angle between l and the horizontal is defined to be the acute angle between l and l'.

Definition: The acute angle between a line l and a plane p is the acute angle between l and the projection of l on p.

Two non-parallel planes, p and q, intersect in a common straight line, c. Choose any point T on c and draw the two lines, m and n, where m lies in p and is perpendicular to c and n lies in q and is perpendicular to c.

Definition: The acute angle between the lines m and n is the acute angle between the planes p and q.

When particular situations are presented in three dimensions, it is always necessary in finding a solution to undertake a series of steps which in themselves require calculations to be confined to two dimensions in each step. The following examples illustrate the methods used in calculations of this kind.

Example 1: *A rectangular block ABCDEFGH stands on a horizontal table, as shown in Figure* 24.13. *Given that AB* = 12 *cm, BC* = 5 *cm and AE* = 9 *cm, calculate:*
(a) *the angle made by EC and the horizontal,*
(b) *the angle made by the plane EFCD and the horizontal,*
(c) *the longest straight pin-hole which could be bored through this block.*

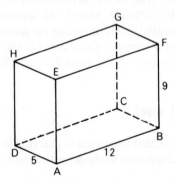

Fig. 24.13

(a) Working in the plane ABCD, $AC^2 = 5^2 + 12^2 = 169 \Rightarrow AC = 13$. Working in plane EACG the angle made by EC with the horizontal is angle ECA, $\tan E\hat{C}A = EA/AC = 9/13 \Rightarrow E\hat{C}A = 34.7°$.

(b) The acute angle between the planes EFCD and ABCD is required and this angle is the same as $E\hat{D}A$ or $F\hat{C}B$

$\tan E\hat{D}A = EA/AD = 9/5 \Rightarrow E\hat{D}A = 60.9°$.

(c) The longest straight pin-hole which could be bored would be from a top corner to the opposite bottom corner, say from E to C. Working in the plane EACG and using Pythagoras:

$EC^2 = EA^2 + AC^2 \Rightarrow EC^2 = 81 + 169 = 250 \Rightarrow EC = 15.8$ cm

Example 2: *A vertical flag-pole AP, 10 m high, stands at the corner A of a rectangular horizontal parade ground ABCD. The angles of elevation of P from B and C are 21.8° and 11.3° respectively. Calculate, to the nearest m, the lengths of: (a) AB, (b) AC, (c) AD. (d) Calculate, to the nearest degree, the angle made by the plane PBD with the horizontal.*

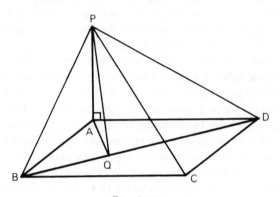

Fig. 24.14

(a) In the plane PAB: $AB = 10/\tan 21.8 = 25.00 \rightarrow 25$ (nearest m).

(b) In the plane PAC: $AC = 10/\tan 11.3 = 50.05 \rightarrow 50$ (nearest m).

(c) In the plane ABCD: $AD = \sqrt{(AC^2 - DC^2)} = 43.35 \rightarrow 43$ (nearest m).

(d) In the plane ABCD, the altitude from A to BD meets BD at Q.

Area of triangle $ABD = \frac{1}{2}AB.AD = \frac{1}{2}BD.AQ$.

Hence $AQ = AB.AD/BD = 21.66$ (using answers above)

In the plane PAQ, the acute angle made by plane PBD and the horizontal is PQA

$\tan P\hat{Q}A = PA/AQ = 10/21.66$

$P\hat{Q}A = 24.8° \rightarrow 25°$ (nearest degree).

In both of the previous examples the reader should work through the example, sketching the plane figure to which each stage refers. As experience is gained, these intermediate sketches can be mentally visualised but many will prefer to actually draw them every time they tackle problems in 3 dimensions.

Plans and elevations

An architect prepares scaled diagrams from which a builder constructs a new house, a new school, a hospital, an office block, an extension or a reconstruction of an existing or damaged building. These detailed drawings are called **plans and elevations** and they are an essential part of engineering and the construction industry. Such drawings are studied when planning consent from a local authority is required and everyone should understand the basic principles used in their construction, as they form an essential part of everyday life. When a very complicated building is being planned, these drawings form a very early stage only and it is often necessary to produce a three dimensional model of the building as well before any actual building is started. When a construction is relatively simple, a builder will work directly from a set of drawings.

Many of the readers of this book will be familiar with the simple illustrations which follow, because they are studying practical subjects like woodwork, metalwork, engineering science or technical drawing. The work is outlined here for those who have not had the opportunity to study these subjects; any reader who wishes to delve more deeply and learn the technical language should consult a textbook on technical drawing.

Plans and elevations are basically two-dimensional drawings of what can be seen when a solid is viewed from different directions; the plan is a horizontal projection viewed either from above or below the solid, and elevations are projections onto certain vertical planes taken through the solid. Hidden lines from the direction of viewing are represented by dotted lines, and lines that can be seen are represented by continuous lines. Plans and elevations are constructed in relation to one another in order that the parts can be seen in relation to the whole. The following simple examples are included to illustrate the way in which this is done. Lines which relate a plan to an elevation are drawn in feint continuous lines.

Example 1: *A solid right circular cylinder of radius 1.5 cm and height 2 cm standing with a circular face on a horizontal plane.*

Full scale

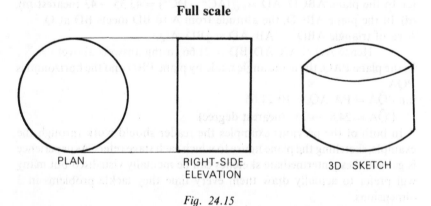

PLAN   RIGHT-SIDE   3D SKETCH
           ELEVATION

Fig. 24.15

Example 2: *A hollow right circular cylinder of radius 2 cm and heigh 3 cm stands on a horizontal plane and is surmounted by a sphere of radius 2.5 cm.*
Draw full scale (a) the plan, (b) the front elevation. Measure the total height of the model.

342

Full Scale

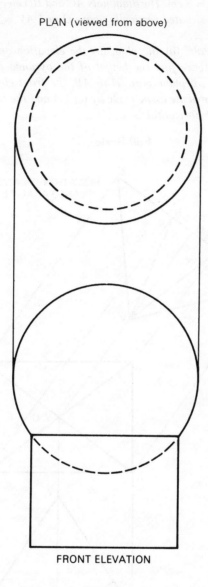

FRONT ELEVATION

Fig. 24 16

The plan consists of two concentric circles of radii 2.5 cm and 2 cm, the inner one being drawn in a broken line because it cannot be seen from above.

The front elevation consists of a rectangle 4 cm by 3 cm and a circle of radius 2.5 cm, the part below the level of the top of the rectangle being shown by a broken line as it cannot be seen.

Height of model = height of front elevation = 7 cm.

Example 3: *A pyramid has a rectangular horizontal base ABCD, where AB = 4 cm and BC = 3 cm. The diagonals AC and BD meet at O. The vertex V of the pyramid is situated vertically above O and AV = BV = CV = DV = 4 cm.*

Construct, full scale, (a) the plan, (b) the elevation on a vertical plane parallel to VAC. Hence find the height of the pyramid and construct the elevation on a vertical plane parallel to AB, the front elevation. Use your elevations to find the acute angle made by (c) VA and the horizontal, (d) the plane VDA and the horizontal.

Full Scale

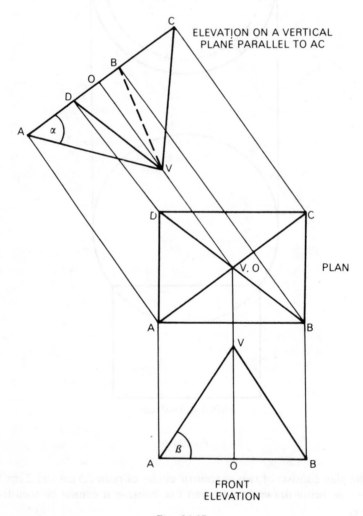

Fig. 24.17

Description of the construction and answers
(a) Construct the plan, as shown in Figure 24.17.

344

(b) Draw in the relation lines from A and C, perpendicular to AC in the plane and add the relation line through V parallel to these. At a convenient distance along these lines draw AC for the elevation on a vertical plane parallel to AC and using compasses locate V such that VA = VC = 4 cm. As a check, note that the arcs should meet on the third relation line which joins V in the plan to V in the elevation. Measure the height of the pyramid 3.1 cm from this elevation. Draw the relation lines perpendicular to AB and at a convenient distance draw AB for the elevation on a vertical plane parallel to AB and use the height obtained above to add the position of V.

(c) The angle marked α is the acute angle between VA and the horizontal; by measurement $\alpha = 51°$.

(d) the angle marked β is the acute angle made by the plane VDA and the horizontal; by measurement $\beta = 57°$.

Exercise 24.5

1 One face of a cube stands on a horizontal table. Calculate the acute angle made by a diagonal of the cube and the horizontal.

2 A sloping rectangular desk-lid ABCD, where AB = 90 cm and BC = 60 cm, has AB and DC horizontal and DC 10 cm higher than AB. Calculate: (a) the acute angle made by the plane ABCD and the horizontal, (b) the acute angle made by AC and the horizontal.

3 A line AE is drawn on the surface of the desk-lid (see Q.2) such that angle DAE = 40°. Calculate the acute angle made by AE with the vertical.

4 Two points P and Q are at the same level as the base B of a vertical tower AB; P is 30 m due east of B and Q is 60 m due south of B. The angle of elevation of A from P is 37°. Calculate: (a) AB, (b) the angle of elevation of A from Q.

5 The edges of a rectangular match-box are of lengths 8 cm, 4.5 cm and 1.5 cm. Calculate the acute angle made by a diagonal with: (a) one of the largest plane faces, (b) one of the smallest plane faces.

6 Two vertical television masts AP and BQ are of heights 10 m and 8 m, respectively. Their bases P and Q are on the same level as a third point R; Q is 20 m due east of P, and R is 15 m due south of P. Calculate the angle of elevation of: (a) A from R, (b) B from P, (c) B from R. Calculate the distance between A and B.

7 A pyramid has a square horizontal base ABCD where AB = 6 cm and the vertex N of the pyramid is 4 cm vertically above A. Calculate the acute angle made by: (a) NB and the horizontal, (b) NC and the horizontal, (c) the plane NBD and the horizontal.

8 In the equilateral tetrahedron ABCD, the six edges are all of length 10 cm and M is the centre of the face BCD. Calculate: (a) BM, (b) AM, (c) the acute angle between AB and plane BCD, (d) the acute angle between planes ABC and BCD.

9 The horizontal base of a pyramid is a regular hexagon ABCDEF and the centre of the base is O. The vertex P of the pyramid is vertically

above O; $AB = 4$ cm and $PO = 3$ cm. Show that triangle AOB is equilateral. Calculate: (a) the acute angle between PA and the horizontal, (b) the acute angle between plane PAB and the horizontal, (c) the acute angle between plane PAC and the horizontal.

10 The triangle ABC has $AB = 6$ cm, $BC = 4$ cm and angle $B = 30°$. Show that the area of the triangle ABC is 6 cm^2 and calculate the length of the perpendicular from A to BC.

The triangle is hinged along BC, which is horizontal, and rotated about this hinge until A is 2 cm higher than the level of BC. Calculate: (a) the acute angle made by plane ABC and the horizontal, (b) the acute angle made by AB and the horizontal.

11 By taking some measurements from actual models and choosing a suitable scale, draw plans and elevations to illustrate: (a) a cylindrical tin, (b) a pencil, (c) a garden frame, (d) a lamp-shade, (e) an ice-cream cone, (f) a milk bottle, (g) a roll of sellotape, (h) an electric light bulb, (i) a garden shed, (j) a bucket.

12 A right circular cone of base radius 3 cm and height 4 cm is standing with its base on a horizontal table. Draw full scale: (a) the plan, (b) the elevation on a vertical plane containing the axis of the cone. A horizontal cut is made to the cone at a distance 2 cm from its base to form a smaller cone and a frustum. Draw full scale the plan and the elevation of the frustum when it is standing with its smaller plane face in contact with the table.

13 Draw full scale the plan and elevations on vertical planes parallel to the vertical faces of the match-box in Q5.

14 An equilateral tetrahedron ABCD has each of its edges of length 5 cm and the face ABC rests on a horizontal table. Draw full scale: (a) the plan, (b) the elevation on a vertical plane parallel to AD. Using your drawings, estimate the height and total surface area of the tetrahedron.

15 A pyramid ABCDE has a horizontal rectangular base ABCD in which $AB = 7$ cm and $BC = 4$ cm. The vertex E is at a height 5 cm vertically above A. Construct, full scale: (a) the plan, (b) the elevation on a vertical plane parallel to (i) AB, (ii) AD, (iii) AC. Use your diagrams to find the acute angle between the horizontal and EB, ED, EC, and the plane EBD.

16 A pyramid ABCDP has a square horizontal base, $AB = 5.4$ cm. The vertex P is vertically above the centre of the base and $PA = 4$ cm. Draw full scale: (a) the plan, (b) the elevation on a vertical plane parallel to AC. Find the acute angle made by the line AP and the horizontal, and by further drawing find the acute angle made by the plane PAB and the horizontal.

17 Three equal spheres, each of diameter 4 cm, are placed in contact on a horizontal table with their centres forming the vertices of an equilateral triangle. A fourth equal sphere is placed symmetrically on top of the three. By drawing the plan and a relevant elevation, find the total height of this model.

18 Three equal cubical boxes are so placed on a horizontal table that a lower edge and upper edge of each form a side of two horizontal equilateral triangles. Each edge of the boxes is of length 4 cm. A sphere of radius 3 cm is placed symmetrically on the top of the boxes, in contact with the edges forming the upper equilateral triangle. Draw the plan. By further drawing, determine the height of the model.

25 The general angle, circular measure, longitude and latitude

Example 1:   *Refer to Figure* 23.9 (page 326)
Find the exact values of (a) sin 150°, (b) sin 240°, (c) sin 315°.
From the graph of $y = \sin x°$, (a) $\sin 150° = \sin 30° = 1/2$
$$\text{(b) } \sin 240° = -\sin 60° = -\sqrt{3}/2.$$
$$\text{(c) } \sin 315° = -\sin 45° = -1/\sqrt{2}.$$

Example 2:   *Refer to Figures* 23.9, 23.10 *and* 23.11 *(pages 326–7)*
Using tables, find the values as decimals of:
(a) cos 137°, (b) tan 238°, (c) sin (−128°), (d) cos 465°.
(a) From the graph of $y = \cos x°$, $\cos 137° = -\cos 43° = -0.7314$.
(b) From the graph of $y = \tan x°$, $\tan 238° = +\tan 58° = 1.600$.
(c) From the graph of $y = \sin x°$, $\sin (-128°) = -\sin 52° = -0.7880$.
(d) From the graph of $y = \cos x°$, $\cos 465° = -\cos 75° = -0.2588$.

An alternative method of solution to Examples 1 and 2

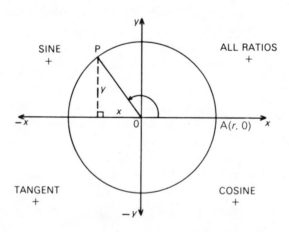

Fig. 25.1

Figure 25.1 shows a circle, of radius r and centre O, and OP is any radius of this circle. The point A has co-ordinates $(r, 0)$ referred to the axes Ox and Oy. Starting from the line OA and measuring in an anticlockwise sense, the trigonometric ratios of the angle AOP are given by:

$$\sin A\hat{O}P = \frac{y \text{ co-ordinate of P}}{r}, \quad \cos A\hat{O}P = \frac{x \text{ co-ordinate of P}}{r},$$

$$\tan A\hat{O}P = \frac{y \text{ co-ordinate of P}}{x \text{ co-ordinate of P}} \text{ for all positions of P on the circumference}$$

of the circle.

The ratio of any angle AOP is numerically the same as the ratio of the acute angle made between OP and the axis $-xOx$; the sign of the ratio depends on which quadrant P lies in.

$$\text{First Quadrant: all ratios} +$$
$$\text{Second Quadrant: only SINE} +$$
$$\text{Third Quadrant: only TANGENT} +$$
$$\text{Fourth Quadrant: only COSINE} +$$

Example 1: *Using Figure* 25.1
(a) 150° is in second quadrant, sine $+$: $\sin 150° = \sin 30° = 1/2$,
(b) 240° is in third quadrant, sine $-$: $\sin 240° = -\sin 60° = -\sqrt{3}/2$,
(c) 315° is in fourth quadrant, sine $-$: $\sin 315° = -\sin 45° = -1/\sqrt{2}$.

Example 2: *Using Figure* 25.1
(a) 137° is in second quadrant, cos $-$: $\cos 137° = \cos 43° = -0.7314$,
(b) 238° is in third quadrant, tan $+$: $\tan 238° = \tan 58° = 1.600$,
(c) $-128°$ is in third quadrant, sin $-$: $\sin(-128°) = -\sin 52°$
$$= -0.7880.$$

(d) 465° is in second quadrant, cos $-$: $\cos 465° = -\cos 75° = -0.2588$.

In each of the above examples the reader should draw a sketch and check the solution given.

In Figure 25.1, for all positions of $P(x, y): x^2 + y^2 = r^2$ by using the theorem of Pythagoras.

Divide by r^2 to give $(x/r)^2 + (y/r)^2 = 1$

That is $\quad \mathbf{cos^2\theta + sin^2\theta = 1}$, where $\theta = A\hat{O}P$.

Also $\tan \theta = y/x = y/r \div x/r = \sin \theta/\cos \theta$.

That is $\mathbf{tan\,\theta = sin\,\theta/cos\,\theta}$.

These two results are known as **identities**, because they hold for all values of θ. Many more of these will be met in more advanced work.

Circular measure : radians

In Figure 25.1, the length of the circular arc $AP = \dfrac{\theta}{360} \times 2\pi r$ and the area of

the sector $AOP = \dfrac{\theta}{360} \times \pi r^2$. In both cases it has been assumed that θ is

measured in degrees. In more advanced work, a new angle measure is used to avoid having repeatedly to use the conversion factor $\pi/180$., which appears in both of the above formulae.

The angle measure 1 radian is defined as $180/\pi$ degrees $\approx 57° \ 17.7'$, and the relation π radians $= 180$ degrees can be used to express any angle in either degrees or radians. Conversion tables are available for this and a key is usually built in on a scientific calculator.

When θ is measured in radians, the formulae for the arc length AP and the sector area AOP are given by

$$\text{Arc AP} = r\theta$$
$$\text{Area of sector AOP} = \tfrac{1}{2}r^2\theta.$$

Example 1: *Express the following angles in radians: (a)* $90°$, $225°$, $80°$, *and express the following angles, given in radians, in degrees: (b)* $\pi/3$, $5\pi/8$, 3.4.

(a) $90° = \pi/2$, $225° = 225 \times \pi/180 = 5\pi/4$, $80° = 80 \times \pi/180 = 1.40$ rad.
(b) $\pi/3 = 60°$, $5\pi/8 = 5\pi/8 \times (180/\pi) = 112.5°$, 3.4 rad $= 3.4 \times 180/\pi = 194.8°$

Example 2: *In Figure 25.2, C is the centre of the sector CAB, angle ACB $= 100°$ and $CA = CB = 5$ cm. Calculate:(a) the length of the arc AB, (b) the area of the sector CAB, (c) the area of the shaded segment.*

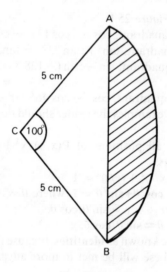

Fig. 25.2

Method 1: (a) length of arc $AB = \dfrac{100}{360} \times 2 \times \pi \times 5 = 8.727$.

(b) Area of sector $CAB = \dfrac{100}{360} \times \pi \times 5^2 = 21.82$.

(c) Shaded segment $=$ sector $CAB - \triangle ACB$
$$= 21.82 - \tfrac{1}{2} \times 5 \times 5 \times \sin 100°$$
$$= 21.82 - 12.31 = 9.51.$$

Method 2: for (a) and (b) (using radians). $100° = 1.7453$ radian.
(a) Length of arc $AB = \theta r = 1.7453 \times 5 = 8.727$.
(b) Area of sector $CAB = \tfrac{1}{2}\theta r^2 = \tfrac{1}{2} \times 1.7453 \times 25 = 21.82$.

350

Exercise 25.1

1   Find the values of: (a) $\cos 30°$, (b) $\cos 150°$, (c) $\cos 210°$, (d) $\cos 330°$.

2   Find the values of: (a) $\tan 45°$, (b) $\tan 135°$, (c) $\tan 225°$, (d) $\tan 315°$.

3   Find the values of: (a) $\sin 150°$, (b) $\sin 300°$, (c) $\sin 600°$, (d) $\sin 720°$.

4   Given that $\sin 52° \approx 0.788$, use this approximation to find:
(a) $\sin 128°$, (b) $\sin 308°$, (c) $\cos 38°$, (d) $\cos 322°$.

5   Given that $\tan 31° \approx 0.6$, use this approximation to find:
(a) $\tan 149°$, (b) $\tan 211°$, (c) $\tan 391°$, (d) $\tan 59°$.

6   Convert the following angles, given in degrees, into radians, in terms of
π: (a) $60°$, (b) $45°$, (c) $75°$, (d) $150°$, (e) $270°$, (f) $300°$.

7   Convert the following angles, given in degrees, into radians, to 3 s.f.:
(a) $56°$, (b) $20°$, (c) $87°$, (d) $137°$, (e) $34.6°$, (f) $78°32'$.

8   Convert the following angles, given in radians in terms of π, into
degrees: (a) $\pi/5$, (b) $2\pi/3$, (c) $5\pi/6$, (d) $8\pi/3$, (e) $13\pi/5$.

9   Convert the following angles, given in radians, into degrees to 3 s.f.:
(a) 1.2, (b) 0.55, (c) 0.08, (d) 2.3, (e) 5.

10   The centre of a circle of radius 5 cm is O. The points A and B are on
the circumference of this circle, such that $A\hat{O}B = 2$ rad. Calculate the
length of the minor arc AB and the area of the sector AOB.

11   The centre of a circle is C, the radius is 8 cm and A and B are points on
the circumference such that $A\hat{C}B = 30°$. (a) Express $A\hat{C}B$ in radians in
terms of π. (b) Calculate the area of the sector ACB.

12   The length of the arc of a circular sector is 12 cm and the angle between
the bounding radii of the sector is 1.2 radians. Calculate: (a) the radius
of the circle of which the sector is a part, (b) the area of the sector.

13   Given that θ is obtuse and $\sin \theta = 3/5$, calculate the values of:
(a) $\cos \theta$, (b) $\tan \theta$.

14   Given that ϕ is reflex and $\cos \phi = 5/13$, find (a) $\tan \phi$, (b) $\sin \phi$.

15   Write down the values of (a) $\sin \pi/6$, (b) $\tan 3\pi/4$, (c) $\cos 5\pi/3$.

16   A wheel of radius 0.6 m is rotating at 3 rad/s. Find the speed, in m/s, of
a point on the rim of the wheel.

17   Each point on the rim of a rotating circular disc has a speed of 20 m/s.
Given that the radius is 12 m, calculate, in rad/s, the angular
speed.

18   A straight rod AB of length 5 m is pivoted at one end A so that the rod
can rotate horizontally about A. Given that the speed of B is 19 m/s,
calculate (a) the angular speed, in rad/s, of AB, (b) the time taken for the
rod to complete one revolution, (c) the speed of the point C on AB
where $AC = 2$ m.

19   A circular sector of radius 10 cm and central angle 60° is cut out of thin
cardboard and used for the curved surface of a right circular cone.
Calculate the height of this cone.

20   A hollow right circular cone is of height 3 cm and base radius 4 cm.
Find the central angle of the sector from which the curved surface of
this cone was made.

Longitude and latitude

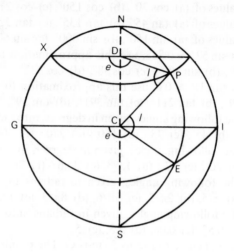

Fig. 25.3

The earth is taken to be a sphere. In Figure 25.3, N and S are the north and south poles and C is the centre of the earth. All circles which have centre C and the same radius as the earth are called **great circles.** An infinite number of great circles, called **meridians,** pass through N and S with centre C. The meridian which passes through Greenwich has been selected to act as a reference for all the others. In Figure 25.3, the Greenwich meridian is shown as NGS and the other half of this great circle NIS is called the **International date line.** The great circle perpendicular to the line NCS is called the **equator.** Take a general point P on the surface of the earth and draw the great circle through P, N and S which cuts the equator at E. The circle drawn on the surface of the earth passing through P and parallel to the equator is called a **small circle** of the earth and its centre is D on the line NS as shown.

Angle XDP = angle GCE $\equiv e^\circ$ say, since XD is parallel to GC and DP is parallel to CE.

Also angle PCE = angle DPC (alternate angles CE parallel to DP)
$$= l^\circ, \text{ say.}$$
The point P has longitude e° East and latitude l° North. By this means any point on the earth's surface can be uniquely identified.

Taking the radius of the earth to be R and DP = r, since angle CDP = 90°, it follows that $r = R \cos l$. **The radius of a small circle is equal to the radius of the earth multiplied by the cosine of the latitude of the small circle.**

Since $2\pi r = 2\pi R \cos l$, it follows that the ratio of the circumferences of a small circle to a great circle is equal to the cosine of the latitude of the small circle. This fact is more often used in calculations than the radii themselves.

Units

(a) When distances are measured in km, the earth can be taken as a **sphere of circumference 40 000 km. (21 600 n.m.).**

(b) **The nautical mile** was specifically invented for navigation purposes on the earth's surface and was originally defined as the arc length subtended on a great circle by a central angle of 1 minute. To fit in with the system of internationally adopted units now in current use, for conversion purposes the nautical mile is taken as **1852 metres exactly.**

1 knot is a speed of **1 nautical mile per hour.**

For places around the earth with different longitudes the clock times are usually zoned, e.g. Greenwich Mean Time and Eastern Standard Time are the names of two of these zones. Mathematically, since the earth rotates in 24 hours through $360°$ of longitude, it can be said that the difference in time for one degree of longitude is $(24 \times 60)/360 = 4$ minutes.

Example 1: *Find (a) in nautical miles, (b) in km, the distance measured on a great circle route between Thule (Greenland) $76°$ N, $69°$ W and Rio Gallegos (Argentina) $52°$ S, $69°$ W.*

The latitude change is $76 + 52$ degrees $= 128°$, the second being due south of the first.

(a) Distance $= 128 \times 60$ n.m. $= 7680$ n.m.

(b) Distance $= \dfrac{128}{360} \times 40000$ km $= 14\,220$ km.

Example 2: *Find the distance, in n.m., measured along the circle of latitude joining Long Beach (California) $34°$ N, $118°$ W and Hiroshima (Japan) $34°$ N $133°$ E.*

The longitude change $= 360 - (133 + 118)$ degrees $= 109°$.

Distance $= 109 \times 60 \times \cos 34°$ n.m. $= 5422$ n.m.

Note: This is not the shortest route, by any means, but it is possible to find a great circle passing through both places which would be the shortest route by way of the earth's surface. The routes discussed in this book are confined to journeys on meridians or circles of latitude only.

Example 3: *A plane leaves an airport in central England $52°$ N, $2°$ W and flies due west for 2400 km to a point B; it then flies for 1500 km due south to a point C. Find the positions of B and C.*

For the first stage to B, the latitude remains unchanged. Lat. B is $52°$ N.

Angle change during first stage $= \dfrac{2400 \times 360}{40\,000 \cos 52°} = 35.1°$, a small circle route.

Long. of B is $35.1 + 2$ degrees West $= 37.1°$ W.

During the second stage of the journey from B to C, the longitude remains unchanged. Long. of C is $37.1°$ W.

Angle change during second stage $= \dfrac{1500 \times 360}{40\,000} = 13.5°$, a great circle route.

353

Latitude of C is $52 - 13.5$ degrees North $= 38.5°$ N.
Answers B is 52° N, 37.1° W, and C is 38.5° N, 37.1° W.

Exercise 25.2

1   Find the distances (in n.m. or km, as preferred) between the following
    pairs of places, measured on the great circle joining them:
    (a) Greenwich (London 51.5° N, 0°, and the North Pole.
    (b) Rio de Janiero (Brazil) 22° S, 43° W and Cowell (Australia) 34° S,
    137° E,
    (c) Berlin (Germany) 53°N, 13°E and Tripoli (Lybia) 33°N, 13°E,
    (d) Byrd (Antarctica) 80° S, 120° W and Carson City (Nevada) 39° N,
    120° W,
    (e) Quito (Equador) 0°, 79° W and Pontianak (Indonesia) 0°, 109° E.
2   Find the distances (in n.m. or km, as preferred) between the following
    pairs of places, measured on the circle of latitude joining them:
    (a) Aabenraa (Denmark) 55° N, 9° E, and Gretna (Scotland) 55° N,
    3° E,
    (b) St. Helier (Jersey) 49° N, 2° W and Volgograd (USSR) 49° N, 44° E,
    (c) Bath (England) 51° N, 2° W and Quatsino (Canada) 51° N, 128° W,
    (d) Tokyo (Japan) 36° N, 140° E to Nashville (USA) 36° N, 87° W,
    (e) Vostok (Antarctica) 78° S, 107° E and Ellsworth (Antarctica) 78° S,
    41° W.
3   At noon a ship is at position A 55° N, 18° W and is sailing due south at
    25 knots. Calculate the position of the ship at noon the next day.
4   An aircraft leaves a point A 43° S, 70° E and flies due north for 1800 km
    to a point B. Find the latitude of B. It then flies for 1600 km due west to
    a point C. Calculate the longitude of C.
5   Calculate the total perimeter of the circle of latitude 48° S, giving your
    answer in km.
6   Tapelbala is 1 020 n.m. due south of Taunton (51° N, 3° W) Calculate
    the position of Tapelbala.
7   An aircraft leaves Rockhampton 22.5° S, 150° W and flies due East for
    2 500 n.m. to a point A. From A it flies due north to a point B on the
    equator. Calculate: (a) the longitude of A, (b) the distance AB.
8   An aircraft is flying due east on a circle of latitude, 840 n.m. due north
    of the equator. Find the latitude in which the aircraft is flying. From a
    point due south of Greenwich on this circle the aircraft flies 1 200 n.m.
    due east to a point P. Calculate the longitude of P.
9   Two places on the equator differ in local time by 9 hours. Find the
    distance, in km, between them measured along the equator.
10 A ship sailing due west at 24 knots is changing longitude at the rate of
    0.2 degrees per hour. Find the latitude in which the ship is sailing.
11 A ship is moving at 20 knots along the international date line. At 0100
    hours the latitude is 6° N. Given that the ship is moving south, find: (a)
    when she crosses the equator, (b) her latitude at 2300 hours the same
    day.

12 Two places A and B have co-ordinates (36° N, 55° E) and (36° N, 125° W), respectively. (a) State their difference in local time, and find, in km, (b) the distance between A and B, measured on a great circle route over the North Pole, (c) the distance between A and B, measured along the parallel of latitude 36° N.

Miscellaneous Exercise E

1 In the figure, which is not drawn to scale, OABC is a quadrilateral and M is the mid-point of CB. P is on AM such that AP = 3 PM.

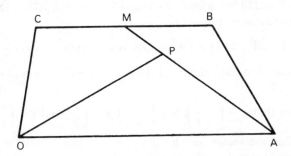

If **OA** = 3**a**, **CB** = 2**a** and **OC** = **b** write down the following in terms of **a** and **b**:
(i) **AM**; (ii) **AP**; (iii) **OP**; (iv) **OB**.
Write down a relationship between **OP** and **OB**, and interpret this geometrically.   [W 1978]

2 (i) Draw accurate diagrams showing vectors **a**, **b** and **x**, where **x** = 2**a** + 3**b**, in each of the following cases:
(a) **a** and **b** are perpendicular vectors each of magnitude one unit;
(b) **a** and **b** are inclined at an angle of 150°, **a** has magnitude 2 units and **b** has magnitude 1 unit.
   Calculate the magnitude of **x** in case (*a*), and measure the magnitude of **x** in case (*b*).
(ii) OABC is a rectangle, and the vectors **OA** and **OC** are given by **OA** = 4**i**, **OC** = 3**j** where **i**, **j** are perpendicular vectors each of magnitude one unit. M and N are the mid-points of AB and BC respectively, and AN meets OM at X. Prove that **OX** may be expressed as $p(4\mathbf{i} + 1.5\mathbf{j})$ and also as $4\mathbf{i} + q(3\mathbf{j} - 2\mathbf{i})$, where p and q are scalars. By equating these two expressions prove that **OX** = 3.2**i** + 1.2**j**.   [O 1978]

3 (i) Name the type of quadrilateral PQRS which is such that **PQ** = **p**, **QR** = **q**, **RS** = **r** and **PS** = 2**q**.
Express **r** in terms of **p** and **q**.

(ii) O is the origin, **OA** = **a** and **OB** = **b**. The point X is on AB such that AX = 2XB and Y is the mid-point of OX.

Find $\overrightarrow{OX}$ and hence show that $\overrightarrow{BY} = \frac{1}{6}\mathbf{a} - \frac{2}{3}\mathbf{b}$.

BY produced meets OA at Z. Using the facts that

$$\overrightarrow{OZ} = \mathbf{b} + k\overrightarrow{BY} \text{ for some value of } k$$

$$\text{and } \overrightarrow{OZ} = h\mathbf{a} \text{ for some value of } h,$$

find the position vector of Z. [C 1972]

4 (i) If $\overrightarrow{AB} = \begin{pmatrix} 5 \\ 1 \end{pmatrix}$, $\overrightarrow{AC} = \begin{pmatrix} 7 \\ -2 \end{pmatrix}$ and A is a point with co-ordinates $(-3, 2)$ referred to rectangular Cartesian axes with origin O, write down the co-ordinates of the points B and C.

(ii) Find the co-ordinates of a point D such that ABCD(in order) is a parallelogram.

(iii) P and Q are points such that $\overrightarrow{AB} = \overrightarrow{BP}$ and $\overrightarrow{AD} = \overrightarrow{DQ}$. Find the co-ordinates of P and Q.

(iv) If $\overrightarrow{OP} + k\overrightarrow{PD} = \overrightarrow{OQ} + l\overrightarrow{QB}$, show that $k = l = \dfrac{2}{3}$ and hence calculate the co-ordinates of the point of intersection of the lines PD and QB. [AEB 1978]

5 Given that $\mathbf{a} = \begin{pmatrix} 2 \\ -1 \end{pmatrix}$, $\mathbf{b} = \begin{pmatrix} -5 \\ 3 \end{pmatrix}$, $\mathbf{s} = \begin{pmatrix} 1 \\ 0 \end{pmatrix}$ and $\mathbf{t} = \begin{pmatrix} 0 \\ 1 \end{pmatrix}$,

(i) find the vector $3\mathbf{a} + \mathbf{b}$,

(ii) find the real numbers p and q such that $p\mathbf{a} + q\mathbf{b} = \mathbf{t}$. A 2×2 matrix M is such that $M\mathbf{a} = \begin{pmatrix} 1 \\ 0 \end{pmatrix}$ and $M\mathbf{b} = \begin{pmatrix} 1 \\ 1 \end{pmatrix}$. Use your previous results to work out $M\mathbf{s}$ and $M\mathbf{t}$. Hence, or otherwise, obtain the matrix M. [JMB 1974]

6 $A = \begin{pmatrix} 1 & 2 \\ 0 & 3 \end{pmatrix}$ and $B = \begin{pmatrix} 1 \\ 4 \end{pmatrix}$.

Calculate where possible

(i) $A + B$, (ii) AB, (iii) A^{-1}. [AEB 1975]

7 The matrices $A = \begin{pmatrix} 3 & 0 \\ 0 & 4 \end{pmatrix}$ and $B = \begin{pmatrix} a & b \\ 0 & c \end{pmatrix}$ are such that

$AB = A + B$, Find a, b and c. [C 1973]

8 Matrices A and B are defined,

$$A = \begin{pmatrix} 3 & 1 \\ 5 & 2 \end{pmatrix}, B = \begin{pmatrix} 2 & 0 \\ -1 & 1 \end{pmatrix}.$$

Write down the inverse matrices A^{-1} and B^{-1}. Use these to determine 2×2 matrices P and Q such that

$$AP = B \text{ and } BQ = A.$$

Evaluate (i) $(AB)^{-1}$, (ii) $A^{-1}B^{-1}$, (iii) $(BA)^{-1}$. Which of these expressions are equal? [O 1978]

9 $M = \begin{pmatrix} a-1 & a \\ a & a+1 \end{pmatrix}$, $N = \begin{pmatrix} a-1 & a^2-1 \\ 1 & a+1 \end{pmatrix}$.

Find which of M and N is singular for all values of a, and find the inverse of the other.

Also find and simplify the matrix $M - N$. [L 1971]

10 $M = \begin{pmatrix} 1 & 1 \\ 1 & 2 \end{pmatrix}$, $N = \begin{pmatrix} 0 & 1 \\ 1 & 1 \end{pmatrix}$, $I = \begin{pmatrix} 1 & 0 \\ 0 & 1 \end{pmatrix}$.

(i) Show that $MN = NM$ and that $M = N^2$.

(ii) Show that $(M+N)(M+2N)$ can be expressed in the form $N^4 + 3N^3 + 2N^2$.

(iii) Verify, numerically, that $N^2 = N + I$.

(iv) Using your results from (ii) and (iii), or otherwise, show that $(M+N)(M+2N)$ can be expressed in the form $pN + qI$, where p and q are integers. State the values of p and q. [AEB 1976]

11 Calculate $\begin{pmatrix} 1 & 2 \\ 0 & 1 \end{pmatrix} \begin{pmatrix} 1 & 0 \\ 1 & 1 \end{pmatrix}$.

Name the type of transformation determined by the matrix $\begin{pmatrix} 1 & 2 \\ 0 & 1 \end{pmatrix}$.

Solve the simultaneous equations
$$3x + 2y = 9$$
$$x + y = 4.$$

The transformation K determined by the matrix $\begin{pmatrix} 3 & 2 \\ 1 & 1 \end{pmatrix}$ maps B onto B′, and D onto D′.

If B is $(3, 2)$ and D′ is $(9, 4)$ calculate the co-ordinates of B′, and state the co-ordinates of D.

OABC is a rectangle where O is the origin, A is $(3, 0)$, B is $(3, 2)$ and C is $(0, 2)$. OABC is mapped onto OA′B′C′ by K. Find the area of OA′B′C′. [W 1977]

12 (i) Determine the matrix $\begin{pmatrix} a & b \\ c & d \end{pmatrix}$

which transforms $\begin{pmatrix} 1 \\ 1 \end{pmatrix}$ into $\begin{pmatrix} 4 \\ 1 \end{pmatrix}$ and $\begin{pmatrix} 1 \\ 2 \end{pmatrix}$ into $\begin{pmatrix} 7 \\ 0 \end{pmatrix}$.

(ii) R is the set of all points on the line $y = 2x$. Under the matrix $\begin{pmatrix} 5 & 4 \\ -4 & 2 \end{pmatrix}$, the set R is mapped onto the set S.

Describe geometrically the set S and state the invariant point of the transformation. [C 1972]

13 O, A, B, C are the vertices of a square such that $\overrightarrow{OA} = \begin{pmatrix} 1 \\ 0 \end{pmatrix}$.

$\overrightarrow{OB} = \begin{pmatrix} 1 \\ 1 \end{pmatrix}$, $\overrightarrow{OC} = \begin{pmatrix} 0 \\ 1 \end{pmatrix}$.

The transformation T with matrix $\begin{pmatrix} 1 & \frac{1}{2} \\ \frac{1}{2} & 1 \end{pmatrix}$ maps OABC

Calculate the vectors $\overrightarrow{OA'}$, $\overrightarrow{OB'}$ and $\overrightarrow{OC'}$ and show the square and its image in a diagram.

(i) Find the area of OA′B′C′ in square units.

(ii) Show that OB′ and A′C′ are perpendicular.

(iii) Calculate the size of angle C′OB′. [JMB 1974]

14 O is the origin and A, B and C have position vectors $\begin{pmatrix} 1 \\ 1 \end{pmatrix}$, $\begin{pmatrix} 0 \\ 2 \end{pmatrix}$ and $\begin{pmatrix} -1 \\ 1 \end{pmatrix}$ respectively. A′, B′ and C′ are the points whose position vectors are obtained by pre-multiplying the position vectors of A, B and C by the matrix

$$\mathbf{M} = \begin{pmatrix} 2 & 1 \\ -1 & 0 \end{pmatrix}.$$

Draw a diagram showing the figures OABC and OA′B′C′. State what type of transformation **M** represents, and calculate the area of OA′B′C′.

OPAR is the square with co-ordinates (0, 0), (1, 0), (1, 1) and (0, 1) respectively. Find the matrix which maps OPAR to OABC.

Calculate the single matrix which maps OA′B′C′ to the square OPAR.   [O   1977]

15 In an Athletics match, Mr. Allen wanted to award 5 points for a first, 3 for a second, 2 for a third and 1 for a fourth place, but Mr. David wanted to award 4 points for a first, 2 for a second, 2 for a third and 1 for a fourth place. Represent this information in a 2×4 matrix **P**.

In the match, North obtained 4 firsts, 8 seconds, 4 thirds and 4 fourths, whilst South obtained 6 firsts, 2 seconds, 6 thirds and 6 fourths. Represent this in a 4×2 matrix **Q**. Calculate the product **PQ** and state what information this shows about the results of the match under the two systems of scoring.   [O   1978]

16

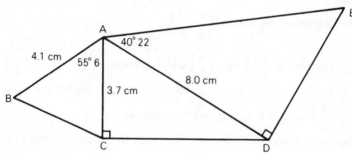

In the diagram
A$\hat{\text{C}}$D = A$\hat{\text{D}}$E = 90°, B$\hat{\text{A}}$C = 55° 6′, D$\hat{\text{A}}$E = 40° 22′,
AB = 4.1 cm., AC = 3.7 cm. and AD = 8.0 cm.
Calculate (i) A$\hat{\text{D}}$C; (ii) AE; (iii) the area of triangle ABC.
                                                              [C   1971]

17

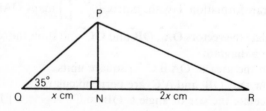

N is the foot of the perpendicular from P to the side QR of △ PQR. If QN = x cm, NR = 2x cm and PQ̂R = 35°, write down an expression for PN in terms of x, and hence calculate PR̂Q.　　　[C 1975]

18 In the trapezium ABCD, AB is parallel to DC, DA = AB = BC = 4.2 cm and ∠ADC = ∠BCD = 67°. Calculate (i) the perpendicular distance between AB and DC, (ii) the length of CD, (iii) the area of the trapezium.　　　[O 1975]

19 In the diagram, BNCD is a straight line, angle B = 65°, angle ACN = 40°, AN is perpendicular to BD, AC = CD and AB = 10 cm.

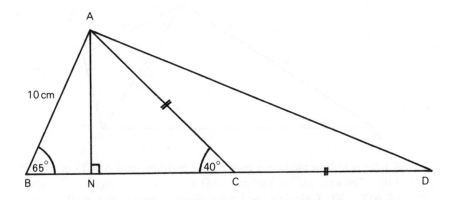

Calculate the lengths of (i) AN; (ii) AC; (iii) AD; (iv) BD.　　　[O 1978]

20 A vertical tower AT, of height 50 m, stands at a point A on a horizontal plane. The points A, B and C lie in the same horizontal plane, B is due west of A and C is due south of A. The angles of elevation of the top, T, of the tower from B and C are 25° and 30° respectively. Calculate
(a) the distances AB, AC and BC, giving your answers to the nearest metre,
(b) the angle of elevation of T from the mid-point M of AB.
　　　[L 1976]

21

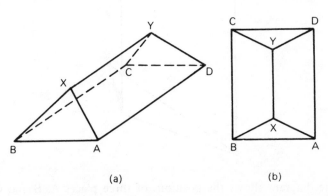

(a)　　　　　　　　　　　　(b)

Fig (a) represents the roof of a house, the plan of which is shown in Fig (b). The horizontal ridge XY is 6 m long and it is placed symmetrically

3 m above the horizontal rectangle ABCD formed by the walls. Given that AD = BC = 10 m and that AB = DC = 7.5 m, calculate

  (i) the angle of inclination of the triangular "end" XBA to the horizontal,
  (ii) the angle of inclination of the trapezium XADY to the horizontal,
  (iii) the angle AX makes with the horizontal.   [JMB 1975]

22 ABCD is a square of side 4 cm. H is the mid-point of AB and K is on AD, between A and D, so that DK = 1 cm. CK cuts DH at O.

  Calculate (i) ∠DCK, (ii) ∠DOK, (iii) DO.   [O 1976]

23

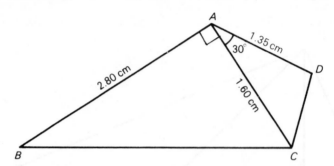

A field is represented on a map by the quadrilateral ABCD in which AB = 2.80 cm, AC = 1.60 cm, AD = 1.35 cm, ∠BAC = 90° and ∠CAD = 30°. Calculate the length of the diagonal BD on the map.

  The scale of the map is such that the length of the side of the field represented by AB is 420 metres.

Calculate

(a) the length in metres, of the diagonal of the field represented by BD.
(b) the area, in square metres, of the field,
(c) the length, in metres, of the side of a square field of equal area.
                    [L 1974]

24

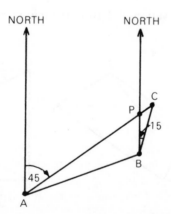

The diagram shows the positions of three places A, B and C. The bearings of C from A and B are 045° and 015° respectively. The point P is on AC and is due north of B.

Given that AB = BC = 20 km and that the bearing of B from A is 075°, calculate

(i) the distance of B from the line AC,

(ii) the length of AC,

(iii) the length of BP. [C 1975]

25 Prove the cosine rule for an acute-angled triangle.

In quadrilateral ABCD, the line AB = 2.1 cm, BC = 5.6 cm, CD = 4.7 cm, the diagonal BD = 3.9 cm and $A\hat{B}D = 113° 15'$. Calculate (i) AD, (ii) $C\hat{B}D$. [C 1972]

26 A triangle ABC is such that AB = 40 cm, BC = 78.1 cm and CA = 111.8 cm; D is the foot of the perpendicular from C onto AB produced. Calculate (i) the size of $C\hat{A}B$, (ii) the length of CD, (iii) the length of BD. [W 1977]

27

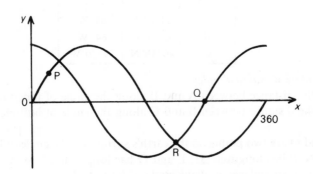

The diagram shows the graphs of $y = \sin x°$ and $y = \cos x°$ for values of x from 0 to 360.

Complete the co-ordinates of the given points P, Q and R.

P is (30, ...)

Q is (. . . . ., . 0.)

R is (. . . . ., ...) [C 1975]

28 θ is an angle between 0° and 360°, and $\cos \theta = -0.5$.

(a) Either $\theta = 120°$ or $\theta = 240°$;

(b) either $\theta = 120°$ or $\theta = 300°$;

(c) either $\theta = 240°$ or $\theta = 300°$;

(d) either $\theta = 120°$ or $\theta = 240°$ or $\theta = 300°$;

(e) none of (a), (b), (c), (d) is true. [O 1978]

29 A boat, which travels at 5 knots in still water is set on a course of $x°$, where $0 < x < 90$, in a current flowing at 6 knots from due north.

Illustrate this information on a sketch, labelling the sides representing the 5 knots and 6 knots, and also labelling the angle $x°$.

Given that $\cos x° = \frac{3}{5}$, **calculate** the resultant speed of the boat and the direction in which it travels.

If, however, the boatman wishes to sail on a track of 135°, find, by drawing or by calculation, the two possible courses he can set. [C 1974]

30 The pilot of a light aircraft wishes to fly from X to Y, where Y is due east of X. The air-speed of the aircraft is 120 knots and the wind is blowing from south to north at 15 knots. Sketch the velocity triangle, indicating the data clearly, and **calculate** the course the pilot should set, giving your answer to the nearest degree.

If the pilot sets his course due east and the distance XY is 140 nautical miles, **calculate** his distance from Y after he has flown for exactly one hour. [C 1975]

31 A nautical mile is defined as the length of an arc of a great circle which subtends an angle of 1 minute at the centre of the earth. From this definition calculate the circumference of the earth in nautical miles and hence the radius of the earth.

Position	Latitude	Longitude
A	24° 27′ S	64° W
B	40° 18′ N	64° W
C	40° 18′ N	59° 30′ W

Calculate in *nautical miles*
 (i) the distance between A and B along the circle of longitude,
 (ii) the distance between B and C along the circle of latitude.

[O 1978]

32 P and Q are two points on the earth's surface on the circle of latitude 35° N. P has longitude 31° E and Q has longitude 17° W. Calculate
 (i) the circumference of the circle of latitude 35° N,
 (ii) the shorter distance PQ measured along the circle of latitude 35° N,
 (iii) the ratio of the circumference of the circle of latitude 35° N to the length of the equator,
 (iv) the angle of latitude at which the circumference of the circle of latitude is equal to half the length of the equator.
(Take π as 3.142 and the radius of the earth as 6380 km.)

[JMB 1976]

33 P and Q are two points on the same parallel of latitude 66° 25′ S, whose longitudes differ by 120°.

Assuming the Earth to be a sphere with centre O and radius 6370 km, calculate in kilometres
(a) the radius of the parallel of latitude,
(b) the distance of P from Q measured along the parallel of latitude.

By calculating the length of the straight line PQ, show that $\angle$ POQ is about $40\frac{1}{2}°$. Using this value of $\angle$ POQ calculate the shortest distance in nautical miles between P and Q measured on the surface of the Earth.

[L 1974]

34 A right circular cone, of height 7 cm, stands on a horizontal circular base of radius 4 cm. The cone is cut by a plane VAB, where V is the vertex of the cone and AB, of length 5 cm, is a chord of the base circle.

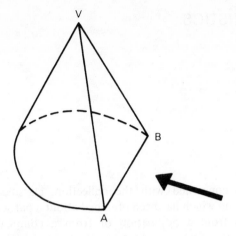

The smaller portion is removed to leave the solid illustrated in the diagram.

Draw full size and correctly positioned

(i) the plan of this solid,

(ii) its elevation on a vertical plane perpendicular to AB,

(iii) its elevation, on a vertical plane parallel to AB, as viewed from X.

[C 1975]

35

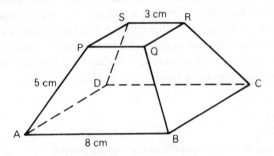

The diagram shows a frustum of a solid pyramid with a square base ABCD of side 8 cm standing on a horizontal table. The sloping edges AP, BQ, CR and DS, each of length 5 cm, are equally inclined to the horizontal. PQRS is a square of side 3 cm.

Draw, full size, the plan of the solid and hence, without calculation, draw an elevation on a vertical plane parallel to AC. Measure the height of PQRS above the base of the frustum. [C 1972]

26 Statistics

This chapter is concerned with the collection, classification and interpretation of data which has been obtained about a particular feature of either a sample from a population or from a complete population. Originally, **statistics** developed because of a need to keep government records about the number of people living in a country at a particular time, the amount of tax they should pay and the relative value of the property they owned. Statistics has now developed into a wide ranging subject and is used extensively in commerce, industry and government, not only as a means of keeping records, but as an aid to communications, future policy making and the quality control of goods produced by industry. Indeed it would be unusual now to find any daily paper or news broadcast which did not contain some mention of statistical data. The analysis and interpretation of data often requires a considerable knowledge of advanced mathematical techniques. In this chapter, the basic ideas about graphical representation and the estimation of a few common measures for a set of data are described and a reader who wishes to pursue the subject further should consult a specialist book on statistics.

Variables

Variables can be either **qualitative** or **quantitative**.
Colour of hair: blond, brunette, red-head, etc . . .
Nationality: English, American, Welsh, Russian, etc . . .
Sex: male, female
are all examples of qualitative variables.
Quantitative variables involve numbers and are either **continuous** or **discrete**. A continuous variable can take all values in a certain range. A discrete variable takes only whole number (integral) values in a certain range.
The number of apples on each tree in an orchard is a discrete variable.
Height (in cm) of the children in a class is a continuous variable.

Graphical representation of data

Example 1: *A class of 30 children recorded and classified the numbers of* *brothers and sisters each of them had and the results are shown in the table.*

Numbers of brothers and sisters	Number of children	Frequency
0	⦃⦄ //	7
1	⦃⦄ ⦃⦄ /	11
2	⦃⦄ /	6
3	///	3
4	/	1
5	//	2
		30

In this simple survey the tally system is not really needed because the children could just raise their hands to be counted; it is included to show how to keep control of the figures in a survey where the numbers involved are much greater.

The data could be illustrated by a **bar chart**, as shown in Figure 26.1, where each frequency is proportional to the **height** of the bar which represents it. The thickness of the bar is irrevelant and is merely a matter of choice.

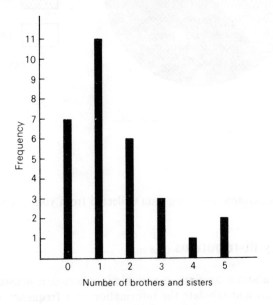

Fig. 26.1

Exercise

Repeat this illustration for your own class.

Example 2: *In the summer term, this class of 30 children can opt to take* *part in one of the following sports: athletics, swimming, tennis or cricket, and the table shows how they made their choice.*

Sport	Athletics	Swimming	Tennis	Cricket
Number of children	8	11	5	6

Show this information on a pie chart.
Angle of sector representing athletics $8/30 \times 360° = 96°$
Angle of sector representing swimming $11/30 \times 360° = 132°$
Angle of sector representing tennis $5/30 \times 360° = 60°$
Angle of sector representing cricket $6/30 \times 360° = 72°$.
Figure 26.2 shows the information on a pie chart.

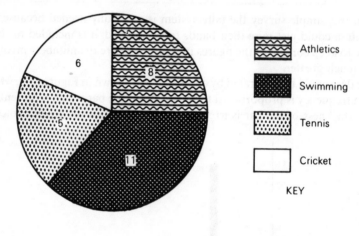

Fig. 26.2

Exercise

Repeat this example for some data collected from your class.

Frequency distributions

When data about a continuous variable is collected, it is usual to choose class intervals and tabulate the information in a **frequency distribution**. There is no definite rule about the number of class intervals for a distribution but it is usually convenient to have not less than 5 and not more than about 15. It is also preferable to define the limits of each class interval, so that every value of the variable can be placed without ambiguity into one, and only one, class interval. If this is not achieved, then a rule must be made about values of the variable which could be placed in more than one interval. For example, suppose the class intervals 20–30, 30–40, ... were being used. Any value given as 30 could be placed in either of the intervals and it is usual in this case to give each interval 1/2 of the total frequency for the value 30.

Histograms

A histogram is often used to display the information contained in a frequency distribution. The essential differences between a histogram and a bar chart are:

(a) in a histogram, frequency is proportional to the area of the corresponding rectangle, whereas in a bar chart frequency is proportional to the height of the corresponding bar,

(b) in a histogram, the horizontal axis is marked as a continuous variable, whereas in a bar chart only the actual readings at which bars are drawn are marked.

Example 1: *The height (in cm) of each member in a class of 30 children is measured and tabulated as shown.*

Height (cm)	145–	150–	155–	160–	165–	170–	175–	180–	185– up to but not including 190
Frequency	1	1	3	4	7	9	0	3	2

(145– means greater than or equal to 145 and less than 150)

Display this information as a histogram and complete the associated frequency polygon.

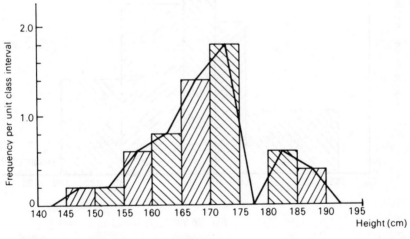

Fig. 26.3

The histogram is shown in Figure 26.3 and the frequency polygon is obtained by joining the successive mid-points of the tops of each rectangle.

367

Example 2:   A Histogram with Unequal Class Intervals

Re-classify the information in the previous example as a frequency distri-bution having class intervals 145 −, 160 −, 165 −, 170 −, 180 −. *Display the re-classification as a histogram.*

The new table is:

Height (cm)	145 −	160 −	165 −	170 −	180 −
Frequency	5	4	7	9	5

Since the class intervals are unequal, the following steps are re-quired

Length of class interval	15	5	5	10	10
Height of class interval	5/15	4/5	7/5	9/10	5/10

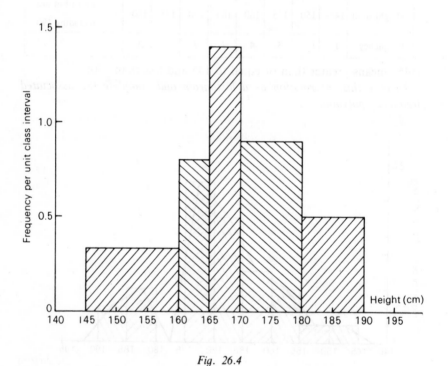

Fig. 26.4

Figure 26.4 shows the required histogram. The reader should check that this representation makes the area of a rectangle proportional to the frequency it represents.

The pictograph

Another form of graphical representation which is popular is the pictograph, often called a **pictogram** or **ideograph**.

Example 1: *The data given earlier about the way in which the members of a class of 30 pupils chose their summer sport options could be shown as in the Figure 26.5.*

Sport	Number of children	
Athletics	웃 웃 웃 웃 웃 웃 웃 웃	
Swimming	웃 웃 웃 웃 웃 웃 웃 웃 웃 웃 웃	
Tennis	웃 웃 웃 웃 웃	
Cricket	웃 웃 웃 웃 웃 웃	

KEY

웃 = 1 child

Fig. 26.5

This form of graphical representation, although simple and attractive, needs care.

Example 2: *An advertiser wishes to show by means of pictographs that the sales of loaves of bread have doubled during a five year interval. Figure 26.6 shows two sets of diagrams (a) and (b). Explain which set gives a true display of the fact requiring representation.*

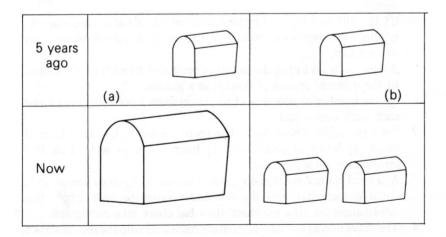

Fig. 26.6

In (a) each linear dimension has been doubled and this gives a false representation, because the second volume will be 8 times the first.

In (b) this is a true representation, because for every loaf produced five years ago, two are produced now.

Summary

Any attempt at graphical representation should make the data easier to understand and contain sufficient information, by labelling or in a key, for a reader to fully appreciate what is represented without ambiguity. A title should usually be included.

A bar chart and histogram must have both axes marked to be meaningful, otherwise scales can be distorted to mean more or less anything.

A pie chart should have frequencies included and must be accompanied by a key, or the items and their respective frequency must both be written on the diagram.

In any pictograph, care must be taken not to mix up lengths, areas and volumes; otherwise scales are totally distorted.

Exercise 26.1

1 State which of the following variables are (i) qualitative, (ii) quantitative. For the variables which are quantitative, state whether they are continuous or discrete:
(a) The different makes of car in a school car park,
(b) the number of tomatoes produced by each plant in a greenhouse,
(c) the height (in cm) of each tomato plant in a greenhouse,
(d) the number of bottles of milk delivered on a particular morning to each house in a street,
(e) the distance (in km) travelled by a lorry on each working day for a month,
(f) the different types of breakfast cereal on sale at a supermarket,
(g) the total number of words written by each entrant to an essay competition,
(h) the mass (in kg) of the potatoes produced by each of 100 plants,
(i) the different species of flowers in a garden,
(j) the number of people sent to prison from a certain county court each week over a year.

2 On a particular school day a class spent 3 hours in lessons, 1 hour at lunch, $1\frac{1}{2}$ hours at games and $1\frac{1}{2}$ hours on a project. Show this information on a pie chart.

3 At a local council election 40% voted labour, 15% voted liberal, 35% voted conservative and the remainder failed to vote. Show this information on: (a) a pie chart, (b) a bar chart, (c) a pictograph.

4 The masses (in kg) of 100 children are measured with the results shown in the following table:

Mass (kg)	40–	45–	50–	55–	60–	65–	70–	75–	80–but less than 85
Frequency	3	7	8	17	28	19	12	5	1

(a) Display these results in a histogram and add the corresponding frequency polygon.

(b) Re-classify the data into the five intervals
Mass (kg) 40– 50– 60– 65– 70– but less than 85.
Display the re-classified distribution on another histogram.

5 The rainfall (to the nearest cm) was measured for monthly periods over a year by a school class and the results are shown in the table.

Month	J	F	M	A	M	J	J	A	S	O	N	D
Rainfall (cm)	6	9	7	13	2	4	5	1	3	6	15	11

Display this information as a bar chart.

6 Out of every £1 spent by a local authority, 55p is spent on education, 22.5p on hospitals, 10p on recreation, 7.5p on sewerage and 5p on miscellaneous requirements.
Show this information on a pie chart.

7 The areas of the four sectors of a pie chart are in the ratios $1:2:3:4$. Find the angle of the largest sector.

8

Variable	0–1	1–3	3–6	6–10
Frequency	3	2	6	4

A histogram is required to show these results. Given that the height of the rectangle representing the frequency in the interval 3–6 is chosen to be 6 cm, find the heights of the rectangles representing the remaining frequencies. Hence, draw this histogram.

9 For a school day, write down the amount of time you spend
(a) studying, (b) eating, (c) relaxing, (d) travelling, (e) sleeping.
Display this information on a bar chart.

10 Take a local or national newspaper on a day when last week-end's football results are printed.
(a) Draw a bar graph to show the attendances at 10 games selected from the first division.
(b) Make a table to show the number of first division games played in (a) London, (b) the Midlands, (c) the North-east, (d) the remainder of the country, on this particular Saturday. Illustrate your table using a pie chart.
(c) Find the total numbers of goals scored in each game for the four English divisions and make a table. Illustrate your findings using a pictograph.
(d) Find the number of home wins, away wins, score draws and goal-less draws for this Saturday for all the games in the four divisions. Illustrate with two suitable diagrams and discuss briefly the relative merits of the diagrams you have drawn.

11 Use a copy of the Radio Times or TV Times where programmes for a whole week are given.

(a) Find the total amount of time for each day that a particular channel is on the air. Illustrate this for the seven days by means of a bar chart.

(b) For a particular day of your choice tabulate the amount of time devoted to (i) Music, (ii) Comedy, (iii) Sport, (iv) Drama, (v) News and Current Affairs, (vi) other programmes.
Illustrate your findings by means of a bar chart and a pie chart.

(c) Watch some adverts of ITV and, using a watch, record (in seconds) the time allocated to each advert. Repeat for 3 sessions of adverts. Display your findings in a pictograph.

(d) Write a short description about how you think the ten most popular programmes in order of choice for a week could be determined by questioning the public.

The calculation of measures of central position

Three important measures of central position, or central tendency as they are sometimes called, are the **mean**, the **mode** and the **median** of a list of numbers, or of a frequency distribution. The methods used in the calculations of these measures are now illustrated.

The mean

The mean is the **common average** obtained by dividing the total sum of all the members in the list, or distribution, by the frequency.

Example 1: *Find the mean of the numbers* 4, 5, 8, 9, 11, 16, 17.
Mean = $\frac{1}{7}$ (4 + 5 + 8 + 9 + 11 + 16 + 17) = 70/7 = 10.

Example 2: *Find the mean of the numbers* 404, 405, 408, 409, 411, 416, 417.
Each member of this list of numbers has been obtained by adding 400 to each member of the list of numbers in the previous example.
Mean = $400 + \frac{1}{7}$ (4 + 5 + 8 + 9 + 11 + 16 + 17) = 410.

If every member of a list of numbers is increased (or decreased) by the addition (or subtraction) of a constant, the mean of the new list is obtained by this constant being added to (or subtracted from) the original mean.

Example 3: *Find the mean of the numbers* 24, 30, 48, 54, 66, 96, 102, *where each member of the list of numbers given in the first example has been multiplied by 6 to give this list of numbers.*
Mean = $6 \times \frac{1}{7}$ (4 + 5 + 8 + 9 + 11 + 16 + 17) = 60.

If each member of a list of numbers is multiplied by a constant, the mean of the new list so formed can be obtained by multiplying the mean of the original numbers by the constant.

When the number of members in the list is small, the methods illustrated in the two previous examples do not save much time or labour, but when the number of members in the list is large, the saving in time is substantial and the arithmetic is simplified. This is particularly true when estimating the mean of a frequency distribution. The reader should note that there is a fundamental difference between finding the mean of a list of numbers and finding the mean of a frequency distribution. For a frequency distribution, the original figures are not usually available and only an estimate for the mean of the original figures can therefore be found. It is assumed that the members of a distribution with readings falling into a particular class interval are evenly distributed throughout the interval and the mid-point of the interval is taken as representative for all members in this interval when calculating an estimate of the mean of the whole distribution.

Example 4: *The mean age of a class of 30 children*

A long and unnecessarily arduous way of finding the mean would be to write down every child's actual age to the nearest month, add all these ages together and divide by 30. A neater and quicker method results from the following steps:

Ask four or five children at random around the class for their age in years and months. Suppose the following answers were given 16 years 3 months, 16 years 5 months, 15 years 6 months and 15 years 11 months. Take an age roughly in the middle of these say 16 years 0 months and ask each child to write down by how much his or her age differs from this in months, placing a minus sign in front for a lower age and a plus sign for a higher age.

For the answers above the response would be $+3$, $+5$, -6, -1. Now obtain this information for every child in the class in turn. A running total can be kept as each response is given and the answers given below need not be actually recorded.

Children's responses $+3$, $+5$, -6, -1, 0, -4, $+6$, $+7$, $+2$, $+3$, $+8$, -4, -2, 0, $+5$, -5, $+2$, $+7$, $+6$, $+4$, -3, $+5$, -5, $+2$, $+7$, $+6$, $+4$, -3, $+5$, $+1$

Running total $+3$, $+8$, $+2$, $+1$, $+1$, -3, $+3$, $+10$, $+12$, $+15$, $+23$, $+19$, $+17$, $+17$, $+22$, $+17$, $+19$, $+26$, $+32$, $+36$, $+33$, $+38$, $+33$, $+35$, $+42$, $+48$, $+52$, $+49$, $+54$, $+55$.

The estimate taken for the mean, often called the working origin, was 16 years 0 months. When all the ages of the children are considered there are 55 months too many on the $+$ side of the working origin.

$$\text{Actual mean age} = 16 \text{ years} + 55/30 \text{ months}$$
$$= 16 \text{ years } 2 \text{ months (to the nearest month).}$$

Exercise

Repeat the above example with your own class. Show by repeating the exercise with a different choice of working origin that the same answer is obtained irrespective of the choice of working origin.

Example 5: *Refer to the information shown in Figure 26.3 about the heights of 30 children. Estimate the mean height.*

Class interval	Mid-interval	Frequency		Working origin	
	m	*f*	*fm*	*x*	*fx*
145–	147.5	1	147.5	−4	−4
150–	152.5	1	152.5	−3	−3
155–	157.5	3	472.5	−2	−6
160–	162.5	4	650.0	−1	−4
165–	167.5	7	1172.5	0	0
170–	172.5	9	1552.5	+1	9
175–	177.5	0	0	+2	0
180–	182.5	3	547.5	+3	9
185–190	187.5	2	375.5	+4	8
			5070.0		−17 + 26

In the table the calculation of the estimate of the mean height has been performed in two ways which are explained below.

Method 1:
Each mid-interval height has been multiplied by its corresponding frequency to obtain the figures written in column 4 under *fm*. These are then added up and divided by 30 to give
Estimate of mean height = 5070/30 = 169 cm.

Method 2:
Here a working origin has been employed which even in an example like this, with only 30 total frequency, considerably reduces the complexity of the arithmetic.

In column 5, 167.5 has been chosen as the origin and each successive mid-interval value, both above and below, has been rescaled with + or − steps, appropriately, as shown in the table. The final column, *fx*, is completed by multiplying each *f* by its corresponding value of *x*, the sign being retained.

The column *fx* is totalled, with due regard to the signs of its members, giving a sum of 26 − 17 = +9 steps in the scale of *x*.
Estimate of mean height = $167 \cdot 5 + 5 \times 9/30$
$$= 167 \cdot 5 + 1 \cdot 5$$
$$= 169 \text{ cm.}$$

By taking the working origin at 167·5, it was found that this was 9 '*x* steps' away from what is actually required. Each '*x* step', however, represents 5 cm in the original scale, because this is the distance between each successive mid-interval value.

Exercise

Repeat the above example using 162·5 as the position of the working origin. The same result should be obtained.

Exercise 26.2

1 Find the mean of each of the following lists of numbers:
   (a) 1, 1, 2, 4, 8, 8, 9, 11, 12, 14
   (b) 10, 10, 11, 13, 17, 17, 18, 20, 21, 23
   (c) 7, 7, 14, 28, 56, 56, 63, 77, 84, 98.
2 The mean of four numbers is 6. A fifth number is added to the list and the mean of the five numbers is 5. Find this fifth number.
3 The masses of 5 boys are 26 kg, 27 kg, 30 kg, 32 kg and 40 kg. Find their mean mass.
   A sixth boy joins the group and increases the mean mass by 1 kg. Calculate the mass of this sixth boy.
4 A small firm employs 4 mechanics who each earn £82 per week, 2 secretaries who earn £63 per week, and a salesman who earns £85 a week. Calculate the mean weekly wage for these people.
5 By using 350 as a working mean, calculate the mean of the numbers: 346, 348, 351, 355, 357, 361.
   Use your answer to state the mean of 3.46, 3.48, 3.51, 3.55, 3.57, 3.61
6 The mean of one list of 6 numbers is 12·5 and the mean of a second list of 10 numbers is 6·9. Find the mean of the 16 numbers when considered as one list.
7 The mean of the numbers a, b and c is 4 and the mean of the numbers a, b, c, d, e, f, g, is 8. Calculate the mean of the numbers d, e, f and g.
8 The sum of 4 numbers is 76 and the sum of a further 7 numbers is 89. Calculate the mean of all 11 numbers.
9 The top 70% of the entry in an exam had a mean of 67 marks and the remaining 30% had a mean of 37 marks. Calculate the mean of the whole entry for this exam.
10 A school play ran for five performances and the attendance figures were 243, 272, 290, 312, 323. Calculate the mean number of people who attended a performance. By how much would this mean be increased if the total attendance had been 1500 people?
11 During a week the following data was collected at a garage about the time (in minutes) taken to undertake a short service to 80 cars.

Time (minutes)	35–	40–	45–	50–	55–	60–	65–	70–	75–	80–but less than 85
Frequency	2	5	12	18	15	10	6	4	4	4

   Using a working origin centred at 57.5, estimate, to the nearest minute, the mean time taken to service a car.
12 A survey was conducted to find out the amounts of pocket money (in pence) received weekly by 100 children. The results are given in the table.

Pocket money (pence)	–20	–40	–60	–80	–110	–120	–140	–160	–180
Frequency	4	5	5	9	18	30	19	7	3

Find, using a working origin, an estimate of the mean amount of pocket money received by a child from this group.

13 A hundred apple trees produced the masses (in kg) of apples shown in the table during one season.

Mass (kg)	0 –5	–10	–15	–20	–25	–30	–35	–40	–45	–50
No. of trees	3	7	11	13	19	12	18	8	8	1

Estimate the mean mass produced by a tree.

14 The frequency distribution of the marks obtained by 500 candidates in a Mathematics examination is shown in the table:

Marks	1–20	21–30	31–40	41–50	51–60	61–70	71–80	81–100
No. of candidates	19	39	100	134	98	75	28	7

Use a working origin to estimate the mean mark.

15 **Experiment:** A flat table, a metre rule and a penny are needed for this "shove-penny" experiment. Place the metre rule along an edge of the table and draw a chalk line at right angles to the metre rule at the 50 cm mark, measured from the "shoving" edge. One pupil attempts to shove the penny as near as possible to this line. Allow about 20 practice turns and then record the distance (in cm) of the centre of the penny from the chalk line for 100 turns.

Use a calculator and work out the mean of these distances.

Classify the results in a frequency distribution at 5 cm intervals and estimate the mean from the distribution.

Compare the two results you have obtained.

The mode

For a list of numbers, the **mode** is defined as *'the number which most frequently occurs.'* This measure can be particularly useful to manufacturers of shoes, clothes and food, etc.

Example 1: *State the mode of the list of numbers* 1, 2, 2, 2, 3, 3, 4, 5, 5, 5, 5.
The mode is 5, because 5 occurs more often than any other number.
An estimate of the mode for a frequency distribution can be determined by using the histogram. The modal class of a frequency distribution, which has equal class intervals, is the class having the greatest frequency.

Example 2: *The number of minutes each child in a class of 30 took to solve a particular problem is shown in the table:*

Number of minutes	–1	–2	–3	–4	–5	–6	–7	–8
Frequency	1	3	4	8	6	4	3	1

Draw a histogram for this distribution and estimate the modal time.
Figure 26.7 shows the histogram.

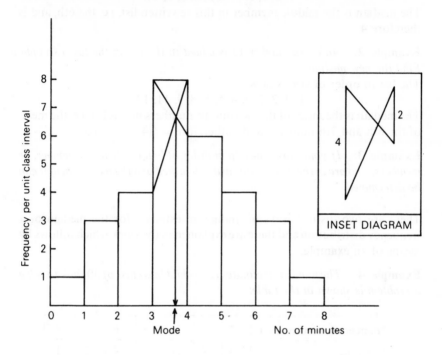

Fig. 26.7

The modal class is 3–4. It is assumed that the mode lies in this class and divides the class in proportion to the differences between the frequencies in the modal group and in those groups immediately above and below. The simplest way to obtain this estimate is to join the lines shown and read off the estimate of the mode on the horizontal axis at their point of intersection.

Estimate of mode = 3.7 minutes.

Since the triangles shown in the inset diagram are similar, an estimate for the mode can be made by calculation. In this case, the ratio of lengths of corresponding sides in the similar triangles is 2:1 and the estimate of the mode is therefore $3\frac{2}{3}$ minutes.

The median

The **median** of a list of numbers is obtained by rewriting, if necessary, the list in order of size and selecting the central number when the total number in the list is odd, or the *two* central members when the total number in the list is even. In the first case, the median is the central member, and in the second, the median is the mean of the two central members.

Example 1: *Find the median of the numbers* 2, 1, 9, 8, 3, 4, 11, 2, 5, 3, 5.
Rearrange in order of size
$$1, 2, 2, 3, 3, 4, 5, 5, 8, 9, 11.$$
The median is the middle member in this rewritten list, i.e. the 6th, and is therefore 4.

Example 2: *An extra number* 13 *is added to the list in the last example. Find the new median.*
The list in order of size is now
$$1, 2, 2, 3, 3, 4, 5, 5, 8, 9, 11, 13.$$
The median is the mean of the two middle numbers in this list, i.e. the mean of the 6th and 7th numbers and is therefore $= \frac{1}{2}(4 + 5) = 4.5$

Example 3: *If your class lines up in order of height, then the member, or members, who are in the middle are easily identified and the median height can be determined.*

There are two distinct ways of finding an estimate for the median of a frequency distribution and these are explained in the work which follows by means of an example.

Example 4: *The number of minutes each child in a class of 30 took to solve a problem is shown in the table:*

Number of minutes	-1	-2	-3	-4	-5	-6	-7	-8
Frequency	1	3	4	8	6	4	3	1

(a) *Draw a histogram for this distribution and estimate the median time.*
(b) *Draw a cumulative frequency diagram for this distribution and estimate the median time.*
(a) Figure 26.8 shows the histogram, which is the same as that for the example about the mode dealt with earlier.

By considering the distribution, it is obvious that the median lies in the class interval 3–4.

In a histogram, the frequencies in each of the class intervals are proportional to the respective areas and because of this the median must take the position where it will cut the total area into two equal parts. Suppose that this occurs at a distance x to the right of the start of the class interval 3–4 (see Figure 26.8). For the areas on each side of the dotted line to be equal, it follows that:
$$1 + 3 + 4 + 8x = 8(1 - x) + 6 + 4 + 3 + 1$$
$$\text{Hence} \qquad x = \tfrac{7}{8}.$$
$$\text{Estimate of median} \quad = 3\tfrac{7}{8} \text{ minutes.}$$
(b) From the frequency distribution table it follows that

Minutes	< 0	< 1	< 2	< 3	< 4	< 5	< 6	< 7	< 8
Cumulative frequency	0	1	4	8	16	22	26	29	30

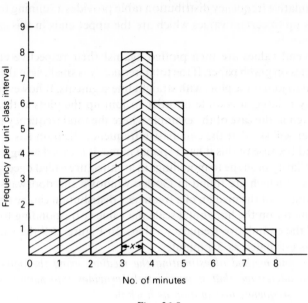

Fig. 26.8

This set of values is called a **cumulative frequency distribution table** and it is always wise to record this before drawing a cumulative frequency diagram, which is shown in Figure 26.9.

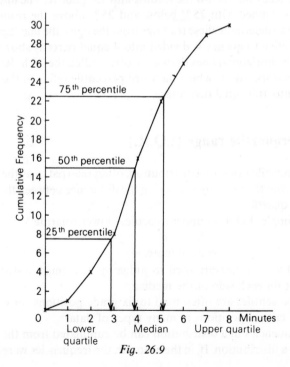

Fig. 26.9

A cumulative frequency distribution table provides a running total of the numbers up to certain values which are the upper ends in this case of the class intervals.

These end values are then plotted against their respective cumulative frequencies on graph paper. If the total frequency is small, as in the example, it is usual to join these plots with straight line segments. If however the total frequency is large, it is quite in order to join up the plots with a smooth curve. Even in the case of the example where the total frequency is only 30, the reader will see that the cumulative frequency diagram has a definitive shape and because of this it has a special name. It is called an **ogive** because of its similarity in shape to mouldings in architecture called ogee, particular examples of which are found in Gothic windows and doorways.

An estimate of the median of a frequency distribution can be determined by reading off on the horizontal scale the value corresponding to the mid-point of the cumulative frequency values. In Figure 26.9 the value of the median is estimated as 3.9 minutes.

This second method of estimating the median, using the ogive, has the additional advantage that it immediately provides information about the cumulative frequency distribution as a whole.

The quartiles

The **lower quartile** of a frequency distribution is the reading at which 25 % of the frequency falls below the reading and 75 % above. The **upper quartile** is similarly defined with 75 % below and 25 % above the reading.

In order to determine these readings from the ogive the line segment giving the cumulative frequency is divided into 4 equal parts as shown in Figure 26.9 and the horizontal lines drawn are often called the 25th, 50th and 75th percentiles respectively, where the word percentile refers to the division of this line into 100 equal divisions.

The interquartile range (I.Q.R.)

The interquartile range of a distribution, often referred to as the I.Q.R., can be found from the ogive by measuring the difference between the upper and the lower quartiles.

In the example, I.Q.R. = upper quartile − lower quartile
$$= 5.1 - 2.8$$
$$= 2.3 \text{ minute.}$$

The I.Q.R. is a measure used to judge by how much a distribution is spread out on each side of the median.

Other percentiles are often used to fix grade positions for exam marks and select critical positions in many types of data.

The frequencies in a distribution can be cumulated from the top or the bottom of a distribution. If, in the example, the frequencies were cumulated from the top, a second ogive would be obtained which would be the mirror image of the ogive shown, obtained by reflection in the line parallel to the cumulative frequency axis through the median.

Exercise 26.3

1 Find the mode and the median of the following lists of numbers:
  (a) 1, 1, 2, 2, 2, 3, 4, 4, 5, 6, 6, 7, 8.   (c) 4, 1, 7, 3, 4, 9, 8, 9, 11, 2, 9.
  (b) 7, 8, 9, 9, 10, 10, 10, 12.   (d) 27, 23, 25, 23, 24, 26.
2 A class of 30 girls had the shoe sizes shown in the table:

Size	$3\frac{1}{2}$	4	$4\frac{1}{2}$	5	$5\frac{1}{2}$	6	$6\frac{1}{2}$	7
No. of girls	1	3	2	4	7	9	3	1

State the modal size and find the median size. Explain briefly why the mode provides a better measure of central position here than the median.
3 The number of bottles of milk delivered at each of 60 houses in a road on a particular morning is shown in the table.

Number of bottles of milk	0	1	2	3	4	5	6
Number of houses	3	11	17	20	6	2	1

Calculate (a) the mean, (b) the mode, (c) the median number of bottles of milk delivered.
4 A number of children were asked to estimate the height, in metres, of a tree. They obtained the following results:

9, 11, 12, 13, 8, 9, 7, 11, 12, 7, 12, 10, 10, 12, 11, 14, 6, 10, 11, 13, 8, 9, 12, 10, 9.

Find (a) the mode, (b) the median of the estimated heights.
Find also the I.Q.R. of the estimated heights.
5 The following table gives the results of a Physics test taken by 2 classes.

Mark	0	1	2	3	4	5	6	7	8	9	10
Freq. Class A	2	5	17	4	2	2	0	0	0	0	0
Freq. Class B	3	5	4	4	3	2	1	4	4	2	0

Find the mean, mode and median mark for each class.
6 A Freezer Repair Service received the following number of calls from customers on 28 consecutive working days:

18, 17, 13, 9, 12, 10, 15, 15, 17, 16, 14, 14, 13, 12, 11, 18, 17, 16, 14, 15, 16, 14, 17, 14, 14, 17, 15, 16.

Calculate the mean, the mode and the median number of calls per day.

7 At a factory bottles are filled with paint stripper which are then sold to the public. Two hundred bottles are selected at random from the production line and their volume of paint stripper was measured in millilitres. The results are shown in the table.

Volume (ml)	496–	498–	500–	502–	504–	506–508
Frequency	8	25	45	53	47	22

Using graphical methods, estimate: (a) the mode, (b) the median volume of this sample.

8 Calculate the mean, median and mode of the list of numbers:
3, 3, 3, 7, 7, 7, 7, 7, 8, 8, 8, 8, 8, 8, 10, 10, 10, 12, 12, 24.
When 5 more numbers, all of which are equal, are added to this list, the mean is increased by 0.5. Find these additional numbers.

9 A motorist averages 60 km/h for 2 hours and x km/h for 3 hours. Given that his overall average speed for the 5 hours is 50 km/h, find the value of x and the total distance covered for the whole journey.

10 The information in the following table relates to the parental income of 200 university students selected at random:

Income ($\pounds$)	–2500	–3000	–3500	–4000	–4500	–5000	–5500	–6000	–8000	–10000	–12000
Frequency	2	15	24	39	36	30	14	10	14	8	8

Draw the ogive for this information and deduce an estimate for: (a) the median, (b) the I.Q.R.

11 The heights (in cm) and the masses (in kg) of 100 girls in the same year at a school are found and the results are shown in the following table.

Heights (cm)	Frequency	Masses (kg)	Frequency
140–	2	40–	1
145–	6	45–	0
150–	8	50–	10
155–	9	55–	11
160–	10	60–	22
165–	15	65–	26
170–	17	70–	12
175–	24	75–	8
180–	5	80–	7
185–	2	85–	3
190–195	2	90–95	0

(a) By drawing histograms, estimate the mode height and the mode mass.

(b) By drawing ogives, estimate the median height and the median mass. In addition for each distribution, estimate the I.Q.R.

Speed (km/h)	under 10	10–19	20–29	30–39	40–49	50–59	60–69	70–79
No. of cars	1	4	11	27	38	12	4	3

12

The above table shows the speeds of 100 cars, moving in the same direction along a road, as recorded by a radar speed detector. The speeds were recorded to the nearest km/h before entry in the table. Explain why the greatest speed possible for the one car classified in the interval 'under 10' is 9.5 km/h.

Make up a table showing cumulative frequency for the speeds of the 100 cars and draw an ogive to display this information. Use your graph to estimate (a) the median speed, (b) the number of cars, out of this sample of 100, which were travelling at a speed greater than 55 km/h past the check point.

27 Probability

The first recorded study of the subject now called **probability** was in the seventeenth century, when a gambler called Chevalier de Méré asked Pascal, a famous mathematician, to explain a result he had noticed when betting on the outcomes of throwing a number of dice. The result which Pascal was asked to explain was, "*why does it pay in the long run to back the appearance of at least one six when a single die is thrown four times, whereas it does **not** pay to back the appearance of at least one double six when two dice are thrown 24 times?*" The solution of the problem will be given later in the chapter. Probability theory now assists in the interpretation of data collected from wide-ranging subject areas which include statistics, the social and physical sciences, economics, biology, geography, insurance and education, as well as testing, quality control and future planning in industry.

Each time that a question is raised about the probability of a particular event taking place, a satisfactory model of the situation is required so that possible deductions can be made. Games of chance are often used to provide the data for discussion, because in most cases it is fairly easy to attach definite numerical values to the set of possible outcomes for these games. When a particular action takes place, there is usually a number of different possible outcomes. In the language of probability theory it is said that a **trial** (experiment) takes place, and, as a result, certain **outcomes** (often called events) are possible and some of these outcomes may be more likely to occur than others. When all the outcomes can be either described completely in words or all written down separately, then this is called the **sample space** (or possibility space) for the trial. The sample space may contain just a few outcomes or infinitely many. In each case the aim is to attach a **probability measure** to a particular event, or events, taken from a sample space and the following examples illustrate the methods used.

Example 1: *A single unbiased die is thrown. State the sample space and find the probability of each score.*

The sample space has six equally likely outcomes with scores
$$1, 2, 3, 4, 5, 6.$$
The probability of a particular score, say 2, from this sample space is $1/6$.

Example 2: *A bag contains 4 red marbles, 7 blue marbles and 2 green marbles, all of which are identical except for colour. A marble is selected at* *random from the bag. State the sample space and find the probability that the marble selected will be blue.*

The sample space has 13 equally likely outcomes, in that each marble has the same chance of selection. Of these selections, 7 are blue marbles, and hence the probability that a blue marble will be selected is 7/13.

Example 3: *The point P lies in the line segment AB such that $AP = 3PB$. A point X in AB is selected at random. State the probability that $AX > AP$.*

The sample space has an infinite number of equally likely outcomes because X can be any point between A and B. If a large number of trials took place, X would tend to be placed between A and P 3 times as often as it would between P and B because AP is 3 times as long as BP. The probability that $AX > AP$ is therefore taken to be 1/4.

Notation

Events are denoted by capital letters *A, B, C* etc.
The probability that the event *A* will occur is written as $p(A)$, and the value of $p(A)$ will lie between 0 and 1 inclusive.
If $p(A) = 0$, the event *A* never happens.
If $p(A) = 1$, the event *A* always happens.
There are often many different ways in which the complete sample space of an experiment can be satisfactorily described. This is exactly analogous to the fact that elements which are members of a particular set can be described in different ways, the only conditions being that each element can be identified uniquely and that each element can be recognised as belonging to the set under discussion.

Example 4: *A single unbiased die is thrown. Find the probability that the score will be (a) even, (b) a multiple of 3, (c) greater than 2.*

The scores 1, 2, 3, 4, 5, 6 are the outcomes in the sample space. Of these, the scores 2, 4, 6 are even; the scores 3, 6 are multiples of 3; the scores 3, 4, 5, 6 are greater than 2. Hence, the required probabilities will be:

$$\text{(a) } 1/2, \text{ (b) } 1/3, \text{ (c) } 2/3.$$

In this example, the six outcomes with scores 1, 2, 3, 4, 5, 6 are called **simple events** and together they make up the complete sample space. Events like "the score is even" are called **compound events** because they are the union of two or more simple events.

Example 5: *Two unbiased dice are thrown simultaneously and the numbers showing on the uppermost faces are added to obtain the score. Draw a diagram to show the total possibility space and hence find the associated probabilities for these scores.*

Each die produces 6 possible outcomes and when these are combined under addition, there will be a possibility space with 36 outcomes. Figure 27.1 (over leaf) shows these, and the associated probabilities are displayed in the table below it.

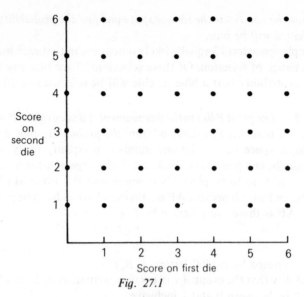

Fig. 27.1

Score	The ways in which this can be obtained	p(score)
2	(1, 1)	1/36
3	(1, 2), (2, 1)	2/36
4	(2, 2), (3, 1), (1, 3)	3/36
5	(3, 2), (2, 3), (4, 1), (1, 4)	4/36
6	(3, 3), (4, 2), (2, 4), (5, 1), (1, 5)	5/36
7	(4, 3), (3, 4), (5, 2), (2, 5), (6, 1), (1, 6)	6/36
8	(4, 4), (5, 3), (3, 5), (6, 2), (2, 6)	5/36
9	(5, 4), (4, 5), (6, 3), (3, 6)	4/36
10	(5, 5), (6, 4), (4, 6)	3/36
11	(6, 5), (5, 6)	2/36
12	(6, 6)	1/36

Example 6: *Using the previous example, find the probability that the score will be: (a) even, (b) a multiple of 3, (c) greater than 2.*

Each of these events for which the probability is required are compound events which are the union of some of the 36 simple events completely described above. The reader should check the following results by making copies of Figure 27.1 and using coloured pens to identify the events required.

(a) p(score is even) = 1/2

(b) p(score is a multiple of 3) = 1/3

(c) p(score is greater than 2) = 35/36.

Exercise 27.1

1 A random number selector is made so that on a single spin it is equally likely to produce one of the numbers 1, 2, 3, 4, 5 and no others. Find, for a single spin, the probability that it will produce: (a) an odd number, (b) a number > 2, (c) a number which lies between 2 and 5 exclusive.

2 Two identical random number selectors, as described in question 1, are spun simultaneously and the numbers on each are added to get the

386

score. Draw a diagram to show all the possible scores and hence evaluate the associated probability for each score.

3   A bag contains 15 red balls, 3 white balls and 7 black balls; all the balls are of identical size. A ball is selected at random from the bag. Calculate the probability that the selected ball will be: (a) red, (b) not black.

4   A class of 30 children contains 17 boys. If a child is selected at random, find the probability that a boy will be selected. A number of boys join the class and the probability is 2/3 that a child selected at random from the enlarged class is a boy. Find the total number of children in the enlarged class.

5   A bag contains n balls of identical size, some coloured red and the rest green. The probability is 2/5 that a ball selected at random from the bag is red and there are 21 green balls in the bag. Find n.

6   The sets of numbers A and B are defined as:
$$A = \{x : x \text{ is an even integer and } 1 < x < 20\},$$
$$B = \{y : y \text{ is a multiple of 3 and } 3 < y < 22\}.$$
A number is selected at random from the set C where
$$C = \{z : z \text{ is an integer and } 1 < z < 22\}.$$
Calculate the probability that the number selected is a member of the set (a) A, (b) B, (c) $A \cup B$, (d) $A \cap B$.

7   A card is selected at random from a normal pack of 52 playing cards. Find the probability that the card selected will be: (a) an ace, (b) a heart, (c) a red card, (d) a card whose value lies between 2 and 8 inclusive.

8   The 12 letters of the word *MATHEMATICAL* are written one each on 12 identically-sized cards which are then well shuffled. A card is selected at random. Calculate the probability that the card will have: (a) an A on it, (b) a consonant on it, (c) one of the first five letters of the alphabet on it.

9   Two unbiased coins are tossed. List the four possible outcomes. Hence, find the probability that one, and only one, head turns up.

10 A girl has 2 ten-pence coins and 2 two-pence coins in her purse and she selects 2 coins simultaneously at random. Write down the total possibility space. Hence, calculate the probability that she will have selected sufficient money to pay for a chocolate bar costing 12 pence.

11 Two unbiased dice are thrown simultaneously and the numbers which turn up are multiplied together to give the score. Show the total sample space of possible scores on a diagram and tabulate the associated probability for each score. Hence, find the probability that the score is: (a) odd, (b) a multiple of 6, (c) 14.

12 A set of dominoes consists of all the 28 possible different pieces, on each of which are represented two numbers, possibly equal, from the set $\{0, 1, 2, 3, 4, 5, 6\}$. Draw a diagram to show the 28 dominoes. A domino is selected at random from the full set. Calculate the probability that it will be: (a) a double, (b) one where the total number of dots adds up to an odd number.

13 The line segment PQ has length 7.5 cm and the point R divides PQ such that $PR:RQ = 3:2$. A point X is selected at random in PQ. Find the probability that $PX < RQ$.

14 A rectangular piece of cardboard is 8 cm long and 7 cm wide. Three non-intersecting circles, each of radius 1 cm, are drawn on the cardboard. If a point is selected at random on one face of the cardboard, find the probability that the point selected will lie within: (a) any one of the circles, (b) a particular circle. (Give your answers to 2 decimal places.)

15 Buffon's experiment. Take a large sheet of drawing paper and construct a series of parallel lines, distance 3 cm apart. A thin rod of length 2 cm (a needle or piece of wire will do) is thrown at random on to the paper 100 times and the number of times that the rod crosses any of the parallel lines is recorded. This result provides an experimental result for the probability of the rod crossing a line. By advanced mathematics it is possible to show that the theoretical value of this probability is $4/3\,\pi$. Use your result to find an approximate value for π.

Note: The general result of this example is true and can be expressed in this way. Suppose the distance between an adjacent pair of parallels is a and the length of the rod b, where $b < a$. The probability that the rod will cross a line when thrown at random is $2b/a\pi$. Take some different values for a and b and repeat the experiment.

Mutually exclusive events

Suppose a sample space S is defined and the compound event E is a subset of S. That is, the event E occurs if, and only if, the outcome of a trial corresponds to a simple event which is contained in E. A second compound event F is a subset of S and contains no simple events which are members of E. The events E and F are said to be **mutually exclusive**. In a single trial, if E occurs, then F cannot occur.

In set language this implies that $E \cap F = \emptyset$ and the situation is shown in Figure 27.2.

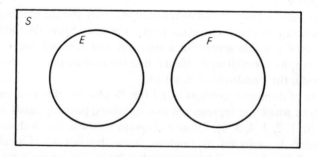

Fig. 27.2

For the events E and F it follows that $p(E) + p(F) = p(E \cup F)$; in words, this is the probability of E or F is the same as the sum of the probabilities of each event considered separately.

Complementary events

An event A of a sample space S is defined. The event A', called the complement of A or 'not A', is defined as *'the union of all the remaining simple events of S which are not included in A'*. The events A and A' are mutually exclusive and, in particular, $p(A) + p(A') = 1$ or, in words, in every trial one of the events A or 'not A' must occur.

Example 1: *A card is selected at random from a pack of 52 playing cards. Find the probability that the card selected will be: (a) a spade, (b) not a spade.*

The sample space has 52 simple events of which 13 are spades and 39 are not spades.
(a) p(a spade is selected) $= 13/52 = 1/4$.
(b) p(a spade is not selected) $= 39/52 = 3/4$.
OR since the events 'a spade is selected' and 'a spade is not selected' are mutually exclusive once the first probability has been found, the second follows at once by subtraction from 1.

Example 2: *Two unbiased dice are thrown and the numbers obtained are added to give the score. Find the probability that the score will be: (a) < 5, (b) > 8, (c) < 5 or > 8.*
As described before, the sample space of possible scores contains 36 simple events (see Figure 27.1).
(a) p(score < 5) $= p$(score is 2 or 3 or 4) $= 1/36 + 2/36 + 3/36 = 1/6$.
(b) p(score > 8) $= p$(score is 9 or 10 or 11 or 12)
$$= 4/36 + 3/36 + 2/36 + 1/36 = 10/36 = 5/18.$$
(c) Since the two events above whose probabilities have been found are mutually exclusive,
p(score < 5 or > 8) $= 1/6 + 5/18 = 8/18 = 4/9$.

Events which are not mutually exclusive

Suppose a sample space T is defined and the compound events G and H are defined as subsets of T where $G \cap H \neq \emptyset$. This would mean that some of the simple events of the sample space T are contained in both G and H. In this case

$$p(G) + p(H) = p(G \cup H) - p(G \cap H).$$

The situation is shown diagrammatically in Figure 27.3.

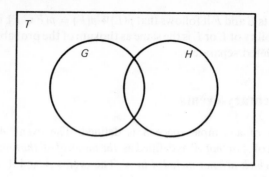

Fig. 27.3

Example 1: *A card is selected at random from a pack of 52 playing cards. Find the probability that the card selected will be: (a) a spade, (b) an ace, (c) an ace or a spade.*

(a) $p(\text{spade}) = 13/52 = 1/4.$

(b) $p(\text{ace}) \quad = \quad 4/52 = 1/13.$

(c) $p(\text{ace and a spade}) = p(\text{ace of spades}) = 1/52.$

$p(\text{ace or spade}) = p(\text{ace}) + p(\text{spade}) - p(\text{ace and a spade})$
$$= 1/13 + 1/4 - 1/52$$
$$= 16/52$$
$$= 4/13.$$

Example 2: *Two unbiased dice are thrown and the numbers obtained are added to give the score. Find the probability that the score will be (a) even, (b) a multiple of 3, (c) an even multiple of 3.*

(a) $p(\text{score is even}) = p(\text{score is 2 or 4 or 6 or 8 or 10 or 12})$
$$= 18/36 = 1/2$$

(b) $p(\text{score is a multiple of 3}) = p(\text{score is 3 or 6 or 9 or 12})$
$$= 12/36$$
$$= 1/3.$$

(c) $p(\text{score is an even multiple of 3}) = p(\text{score is 6 or 12})$
$$= 5/36 + 1/36$$
$$= 1/6.$$

Exercise 27.2

1 A random number selector chooses one member from the set A, where $A = \{1, 2, 3, 4, 5, 6, 7\}$ in such a way that each member of the set has an equal chance of selection for each trial. Calculate the probability that the number chosen in a single trial will be: (a) odd, (b) even, (c) odd or even, (d) an even multiple of 3.

2 A random number selector chooses one member from the set B, where $B = \{3, 4, 5, 7, 9, 11, 13, 15\}$ in such a way that each member of the set has an equal chance of selection for each trial. Calculate the probability

that the number chosen in a single trial will be: (a) exactly divisible by 3, (b) an even number, (c) a prime number, (d) an even number or a prime number.

Name two events for which you have found the probability which are mutually exclusive.

3 Two unbiased dice are thrown and the numbers obtained are added to give the score. Find the probability that the score will be (a) 7, (b) a multiple of 4. Explain why the events for which you have found the probability are mutually exclusive. (c) Find the probability that the score will be even.

Name two events from the three which have been described which are not mutually exclusive and explain why.

4 A card is selected at random from a pack of 52 playing cards. Find the probability that the card selected will be: (a) a heart or a club, (b) a red card, (c) a card whose face value lies between 3 and 9 inclusive.

Deduce the probability that the card selected will be red and lie in face value between 3 and 9, inclusive.

5 From a set of dominoes, as described in Exercise 27.1, question 12, a domino is selected at random. Find the probability that the selected domino will be: (a) a double, (b) a domino where the sum of the total spots is odd, (c) either a double or a domino where the sum of the total spots is odd.

6 From the same set of dominoes, find the probability that a domino selected at random will have the sum of its spots even. Hence, find the probability that a domino selected at random will have the sum of its spots even and not be a double.

7 The events A and B are mutually exclusive. Given that $p(A) = 3/5$ and $p(A \cup B) = 11/15$, find $p(B)$.

Find also $p(A')$, $p(B')$ and $p(A' \cup B')$. What deduction can you make about the events A' and B'?

8 The events A and B are mutually exclusive. Given that $p(A) = 1/4$ and $p(A \cup B) = 2/3$, find $p(B)$.

9 The events A and B are mutually exclusive. Given that $p(A') = 5/6$ and $p(B') = 3/4$, find $p(A \cup B)$.

10 Given that $p(A) = 1/3$, $p(B) = 2/5$ and $p(A \cap B) = 1/4$, find $p(A \cup B)$.

11 Given that $p(A) = 2/5$, $p(A \cup B) = 9/10$, $p(A \cap B) = 1/10$, find $p(B)$.

12 Given that $p(A) = 9/14$, $p(B) = 1/2$ and $p(A \cap B) = 2/7$, find $p(A' \cap B')$.

13 The sets S, A, B, and C are defined as:

$S = \{x : x \text{ is an integer such that } 3 < x < 20\}$
$A = \{y : y \text{ is an even integer such that } 3 < y < 20\}$
$B = \{5, 11, 13, 17, 19\}$
$C = \{z : z \text{ is an odd integer such that } 3 < z < 20\}$.

An element of S is selected at random. Given that $p(A)$ is the probability that the selected integer is an element of A, etc, find the values of $p(A)$, $p(B)$, $p(C)$, $p(A \cup B)$, $p(B \cup C)$, $p(C \cup A)$, $p(A \cap B)$, $p(B \cap C)$, $p(C \cap A)$.

14 Two unbiased dice are thrown simultaneously and the numbers appearing on their uppermost faces are multiplied together to give the score. Calculate the probability that the score will be: (a) odd, (b) a multiple of 3, (c) odd and a multiple of 3, (d) either odd or a multiple of 3.

15 A number is selected at random from the set A where
$$A = \{x : x \text{ is an integer such that } 2 \leqslant x \leqslant 100\}.$$
Calculate the probability that the number selected will be:
(a) even, (b) a multiple of 5, (c) an even multiple of 5,
(d) either even or a multiple of 5, but not both.

Independent events

The events A and B of a sample space S are independent if the probability of each event is unaffected by the occurrence of the other and, in particular, $p(A \cap B) = p(A).p(B)$, provided that $p(A) \neq 0$ and $p(B) \neq 0$.

Example 1: *An unbiased die is thrown and an unbiased coin is spun. The event A is the score on the die is a multiple of 3 and the event B is a head turns up. Prove that A and B are independent events.*

The possible scores from the die are 1, 2, 3, 4, 5, 6. Hence $p(A) = 2/6$. The coin can give either a head or a tail. Hence $p(B) = 1/2$. The sample space of the trial has 12 equally likely simple outcomes. These are 1H, 2H, 3H, 4H, 5H, 6H, 1T, 2T, 3T, 4T, 5T, 6T of which 3H and 6H are members of the set $A \cap B$. Hence $p(A \cap B) = 2/12$.

$p(A)p(B) = 2/6 \times 1/2 = 2/12 = p(A \cap B)$ and because this rule holds, A and B are independent events.

Example 2: *A card is selected at random from a pack of 52 cards. The event A is the card selected is red and the event B is the card selected is a king. Show that the events A and B are independent.*

$p(A) = 26/52 = 1/2$ and $p(B) = 4/52 = 1/13$.
$p(A \cap B) = p(\text{the card selected is a red king}) = 2/52 = 1/26$.
Hence $p(A \cap B) = p(A).p(B)$ and the events are therefore independent.

Repeated trials

When a trial or experiment is repeated, provided that the conditions are unaltered, each trial can be considered as independent. If the conditions are changed, the above rule can often be adapted, as shown in the second of the following examples.

Example 3: *A bag contains 4 red, 5 blue and 7 green marbles which are all identical except for colour. A marble is selected at random from the bag, its colour is noted and it is returned to the bag. A second marble is selected. Find the probability that the marbles selected are: (a) both red, (b) of the same colour.*

Since replacement of the marble selected after the first trial takes place, the probability of a red marble being selected is the same for each trial and is $4/16 = 1/4$.

(a) Hence p(the two marbles are red) $= 1/4 \times 1/4 = 1/16$.

(b) Probability that both marbles are same colour = probability that both are either red or blue or green $= (1/4)^2 + (5/16)^2 + (7/16)^2$

$$= 90/256$$
$$= 45/128.$$

Example 4:   *A bag contains 4 red, 5 blue and 7 green marbles which are all identical except for colour. A marble is selected at random, the colour is noted and it is not replaced in the bag. A second marble is selected at random from those remaining in the bag. Find the probability that the marbles selected are: (a) both red, (b) of the same colour.*

Since replacement does not take place after the first trial, the probability is not the same for the first trial and the second trial. The probability in the second trial depends on what happened in the first trial.

(a) The probability that the first marble selected is red $= 4/16 = 1/4$.

If the first marble selected is red, the probability that the second marble selected will also be red $= 3/15 = 1/5$.

p(both marbles red) $= 1/4 \times 1/5 = 1/20$.

(b) The probability that both marbles will be of the same colour

$= p$(both red) or p(both blue) or p(both green)

$= 4/16 \times 3/15 + 5/16 \times 4/15 + 7/16 \times 6/15 = 74/240 = 37/120.$

Probability tree diagrams

Another way of illustrating the repeated trials in the last two examples is by means of a probability tree diagram.

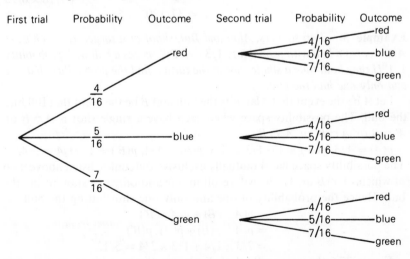

Fig. 27.4 Tree diagram for first marble replaced

Figures 27.4 and 27.5 show the examples where the first marble is replaced in the bag and not replaced in the bag, respectively.
Follow the tree through the two trials selecting events required.
(a) p(the two marbles are red) $= 4/16 \times 4/16 = 1/16$.
(b) p(the two marbles are the same colour $= (4/16)^2 + (5/16)^2 + (7/16)^2$
$$= 45/128.$$

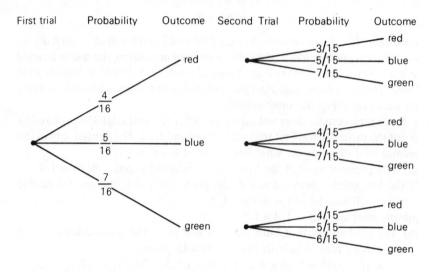

Fig. 27.5 Tree diagram for first marble not replaced

(a) p(both marbles are red) $4/16 \times 3/15 = 1/20$
(b) p(both marbles are same colour) $= 4/16 \times 3/15 + 5/16 \times 4/15 +$
$$+ 7/16 \times 6/15$$
$$= 37/120.$$

Example 5: *Two soldiers, Alan and Bill, shoot at a target. On each shot, Alan scores a bull with probability 1/3 and Bill scores a bull with probability 1/4. If they both take a single shot at the target, find the probability that one and only one hits the bull.*

Let A be the event that Alan hits the bull and B be the event that Bill hits the bull. The possibility space when each have a single shot is $A \cap B$ or $A' \cap B$ or $A \cap B'$ or $A' \cap B'$.

$p(A) = 1/3$, $p(A') = 1 - 1/3 = 2/3$; $p(B) = 1/4$, $p(B') = 1 - 1/4 = 3/4$.
The possibility space has 4 mutually exclusive outcomes, listed above, two of which, $A' \cap B$ or $A \cap B'$, will result in one and only one shot hitting the bull. Hence the probability of one and only one shot hitting the bull
$$= p(A' \cap B) + p(A \cap B')$$
$$= p(A') \cdot p(B) + p(A) \cdot p(B')$$
$$= 2/3 \times 1/4 + 1/3 \times 3/4 = 5/12.$$

Figure 27.6 shows a method of displaying the possible outcomes after each soldier has taken one shot.

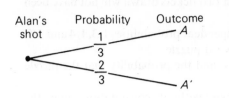

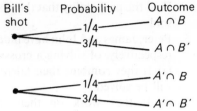

Fig. 27.6

The events required are $A \cap B'$ or $A' \cap B$ and these are mutually exclusive.
$p(\text{required}) = 2/3 \times 1/4 + 1/3 \times 3/4 = 5/12$.

Example 6: *There are three sets of traffic lights which a man has to drive past each day on his way to work. The probability that the man will have to stop at any one of these lights is 1/3. Calculate, for a particular morning, the probability that the man will have to stop at: (a) none of the three sets of lights, (b) at least one of the three sets of lights.*

(a) p(man will have to stop at none of the three sets of lights)
$= 2/3 \times 2/3 \times 2/3 = 8/27$.

(b) Since the events 'the man will have to stop at none of the three sets of lights' and 'the man will have to stop at at least one of the sets of lights' are mutually exclusive, their union makes up the total possibility space.
p(that the man will have to stop at at least one set of lights) $= 1 - 8/27$
$$= 19/27.$$

Example 7: *The question asked by Chevalier de Méré to Pascal can now be solved (refer to the first paragraph of this chapter).* The probability of the appearance of at least one six when a single die is thrown four times $= 1 - (5/6)^4 = 0.518$.

The probability of the appearance of at least one double six when two dice are thrown 24 times $= 1 - (35/36)^{24} = 0.491$.

One can only say that this gambler must have had plenty of practice to notice this result merely from observation.

Exercise 27.3

1 An unbiased die is thrown and an unbiased coin is spun. Calculate the probability that the score will be odd and a head will be obtained.

2 The probability that Mary beats Jane in a game of table tennis is 3/5. Two games are played. Calculate the probability that Jane will win both games.

3 A committee consists of 10 members from whom 2 are chosen at random to represent the committee at a dinner. Calculate the probability that two particular members will be chosen.

4 In a raffle at a disco, 900 of the 1 000 tickets are sold. Unfortunately the 1 000 counterfoil tickets have all been placed in a bag from which two are to be drawn at random, without replacement, for the two prizes.

395

Find the probability that the first two tickets drawn will not have been sold.

5 Peter, James and John have independent probabilities 1/3, 1/4 and 3/5, respectively, of solving a crossword puzzle.

(a) If they combine their talents, find the probability that the puzzle will be solved.

(b) If they work on their own, without consultation, find the probability that one, and only one of them, solves the puzzle.

6 A man has 5 yale keys on his key ring, one of which fits his front door. On a dark night he chooses from the 5 keys at random, without replacement, until his front door key is located. Find the probability that he will be able to unlock his front door after trying: (a) 2 keys, (b) 3 keys.

7 Two football teams, R and S, play each other home and away. The table shows the probabilities of some of the possible results for each game.

Team	p(win)	p(draw)	p(lose)
R (home)	4/7		1/7
R (away)	2/5	1/10	

Copy and complete the table and hence find the probability that: (a) R and S will both win their home games, (b) at least one draw will result, (c) S will win one, and only one, game.

8 A bag contains 5 yellow, 7 blue and 8 black marbles, all of the same size. Three marbles are selected at random from the bag. Find the probability that the three selected are all of different colour when the selection is made: (a) with replacement, (b) without replacement.

9 Three unbiased coins are spun simultaneously. Draw a tree diagram to show the possibility space and the associated probabilities. Hence find the probability that: (a) three heads appear, (b) at least one head appears.

10 At an observation post on a particular main road it is estimated that 45% of the cars which pass are moving at a speed greater than 75 km/h. For two cars, selected at random, estimate the probability that the first is moving at a speed exceeding 75 km/h but the second is not.

11 From a class of 30 children, 9 come from district A, 13 come from district B, and the rest from district C. Two children are selected at random from the class. Find the probability that the two selected children will come from: (a) district C, (b) either district A or district B, (c) one from district A and the other from district B.

12 A card is selected at random from a pack of 52 playing cards. The event A is the card selected is either a king or a queen. The event B is the card selected is a spade. Given that $p(A)$ and $p(B)$ are the respective probabilities of events A and B occurring, find: (a) $p(A)$, (b) $p(B)$, (c) $p(A \cap B)$, (d) $p(A \cup B)$.

Explain why the events A and B are not mutually exclusive.

Explain why the events A and B are independent.

13 Two cards are selected at random from a pack of 52 playing cards. If the first card is replaced before the second is selected, calculate the probability that both cards are: (a) diamonds, (b) aces, (c) cards with face values lying between 3 and 8, inclusive.

14 On any schoolday morning there is a probability 1/3 that the school bus will be late. Find the probability that the bus will be late on Monday and not late on Tuesday and late on Wednesday next week.

Find also the probability that the bus will be late at least once out of 5 days chosen at random.

15 Out of a class of 30 children, 18 have been inoculated against catching measles. A measles epidemic occurs and 9 of the children who have not been inoculated get the illness and 4 of those who have been inoculated get the illness. If a child is selected at random from the class, calculate the probability that the child will have (a) been inoculated and caught measles, (b) not been inoculated and not caught measles.

Miscellaneous Exercise F

1 The mean of five numbers is 15 and the mean of a further eight numbers is 2. Calculate the mean of all thirteen numbers.
[AEB 1976]

2 (i) The mean of the five numbers x, 2, 3, 5 and 9 is 3. Find x.
(ii) A pie-chart is drawn to represent three commodities. The angles of two of the sectors are 107° and 208°. Express the third sector as a percentage of the whole pie-chart. [C 1972]

3 The mean of five integers is 5 and their median is 4. The integers are all different and none is less than 1. Find the range of possible values of the largest of them. [L 1971]

4 In an election for a sixth form representative, 72 voted for Brown, 16 for Jones and 8 for Smith. Represent this information on a circular diagram. [JMB 1975]

5 The circular diagram illustrates how a young lady spends her wages each week.

If she pays £4.50 rent each week, find how much she spends on
(i) heating, (ii) food. What is her weekly wage? [JMB 1974]

6 A local authority has 200 houses of a certain type (Type *A*). The following table gives an analysis of the numbers of houses in which 1, 2, 3, 4, 5 or 6 people live. (This type of house will not hold more than six people.)

Number of people	1	2	3	4	5	6
Number of houses	5	25	40	75	33	22

Calculate the mean number of people per house.

Calculate what percentage of this population is living fewer than four to a house.

The authority also has 100 houses of another type (Type *B*); the mean number of people living in each of these is 2.12. Find the mean number of people per house in all 300 houses.

It is suggested that all those who live fewer than four in a Type *A* house should be moved to other houses, and their houses filled by larger families. Find the largest possible increase in the number of people living in Type *A* houses, if this were done.   [L 1979]

7 One hundred pods of a new variety of garden pea were opened to find the number of peas in each pod. The frequency distribution is given below:

Number of peas per pod	1	2	3	4	5	6
Number of pods	2	15	30	25	20	8

Find the values of the mode and the median of this distribution, labelling each answer, and calculate the mean number of peas per pod.

If two pods are selected at random, find the probability that they both contain 4 peas.   [C 1974]

8 The tables below show the numbers of pupils in three different groups who scored 0, 1, 2, 3, or 4 marks in a test question:

(i)

Marks	0	1	2	3	4
Number of pupils	1	1	3	1	x

Give the value of x if the median is 3 marks.

(ii)

Marks	0	1	2	3	4
Number of pupils	11	12	y	7	5

Give a possible value of y if the modal class is 2 marks.

(iii)

Marks	0	1	2	3	4
Number of pupils	z	4	3	2	1

Calculate z if the mean is 1 mark.   [C 1975]

9 The table below gives information concerning the masses at birth of the first 100 babies born in a maternity home in 1975.

Mass in kg		No. of babies
Exceeding	Not exceeding	
1.5	2.5	2
2.5	3.0	4
3.0	3.5	18
3.5	4.0	38
4.0	4.5	28
4.5	5.0	8
5.0	6.0	2

Represent this information by
 (i) a histogram,
 (ii) a cumulative frequency polygon.
   Find
 (iii) the median of the masses at birth of these 100 babies,
 (iv) the number of babies whose masses at birth were within 1 kg of this median. [JMB 1975]

10 In order to find out how many miles per gallon of petrol a new model of car would cover, 100 drivers were asked to keep records of the amount of petrol they used. The table below summarizes the results.

No. of miles per gallon	24–25	25–26	26–27	27–28	28–29	29–30	30–31	31–32
No. of drivers	6	2	23	39	17	10	2	1

 (i) Illustrate these figures by means of a cumulative frequency graph, and find the median of the distribution.
 (ii) Calculate an estimate of the mean number of miles per gallon obtained.
   Later, a second sample of 200 drivers produced a mean value of 27.84 miles per gallon. Calculate the combined mean value for all 300 drivers. [O 1977]

11 The following table shows a grouped frequency distribution of percentage marks obtained by 500 candidates in an examination.

Mark	Frequency	Mark	Frequency
1–10	10	51–60	88
11–20	28	61–70	50
21–30	42	71–80	30
31–40	90	81–90	15
41–50	142	91–100	5

Draw a histogram to illustrate this data. Draw another histogram, using the same scales, to illustrate the given information rearranged in mark groups 1–30, 31–50, 51–70, 71–100. Use the table to estimate the pass mark if 45 per cent of the candidates failed.   [JMB 1974]

12 Bag *A* contains 10 balls, of which 3 are red and 7 are blue. Bag *B* contains 10 balls of which 4 are red and 6 are blue.

A ball is drawn at random from each bag. Find the probability that (i) both are red,

(ii) at least one is blue.   [C 1974]

13 The probability of an event *A* happening is $\frac{1}{5}$ and the probability of an event *B* happening is $\frac{1}{4}$. Given that *A* and *B* are independent, calculate the probability that

(i) neither event happens,

(ii) just one of the two events happens.   [C 1975]

14 A man has a bunch of three keys, only one of which fits the lock of his front door. When he comes home in the dark he tries the keys at random until he finds the one that fits. Find the probability that

(a) on any one night, the first key he tries is a wrong one,

(b) in a week of five nights, he tries the right key first on at least one night.   [L 1972]

15 Balls are drawn at random from a bag containing 6 red and 4 green balls. Find the probability that

(a) the first ball drawn will be green,

(b) the first two balls drawn will both be green. (The first ball is not replaced before the second is drawn.)

The balls are all replaced and then more green balls are added, and it is now found that the probability of drawing a green ball is 2/3. Find how many more green balls have been added.

Another bag contains *r* red and *g* green balls. The probability of drawing a green ball at random is 3/7. Find a relation between *r* and *g*. If, in addition, the probability that when two balls are drawn both are green is 6/35, show that $5(g-1) = 2(r+g-1)$. (Again, the first ball is not replaced before the second is drawn.) Hence find the values of *r* and *g*.   [L 1975]

16 A bag contains two blue marbles and one red marble. If two marbles are taken together and at random from the bag, what is the probability that they are of different colours?   [JMB 1973]

17 An analysis was made of the numbers of goals scored by winning, losing and drawing teams in football matches played on a certain day. The results are as shown in the following table, except that three of the entries are replaced by the letters *x*, *y* and *z*.

Goals	0	1	2	3	4	5	6 or more
Winning teams	*x*	10	11	13	3	1	0
Losing teams	22	12	*y*	0	0	0	0
Drawing teams	10	22	*z*	2	0	0	0

(i) (a) Explain why *x* = 0.

(b) State what number is denoted by *y*.

(c) z was erroneously given as 13. Explain why this must be wrong.

(ii) Calculate the mean number of goals scored by winning teams.

(iii) Two of the teams are called A and B. It is known that A scored 1 goal and that B scored 3 goals. Calculate the probability

    (a) that A won,

    (b) that B drew,

    (c) that A won and B drew.   [L   1978]

18   In a game between two players, A and B, the probability that the player with the first move will win is $\frac{5}{9}$ and the probability that the other player will win is $\frac{4}{9}$. They play three games, tossing an unbiased coin to decide who has first move in the first game. Subsequently the winner of any game has first move in the next game.

  (i) Show that the probability that A wins the toss and then wins all three games is $\frac{125}{1458}$.

 (ii) If A has won the toss, show that the probability that he will then win precisely two games is $\frac{260}{729}$.

(iii) If A 'has lost the toss, find the probability that he will win precisely two games.   [O   1976]

19   The number x is chosen at random from the set $\{0, 3, 6, 9\}$ and the number y is chosen at random from the set $\{0, 2, 4, 6, 8\}$.

Calculate the probability of each of the following separate events.

  (i) $x > 6$,   (ii) $x + y = 11$,   (iii) $x > y$,

(iv) $xy = 0$,   (v) $10x + y = 34$.   [JMB   1975]

20   I am a heavy sleeper and, without the aid of the alarm clock, I never wake before 7.30 a.m. The probability then that I arrive punctually at school is $\frac{1}{5}$. If the alarm clock has been set the previous night it rings at 7.00 a.m. which gives me ample time but the probability that it wakes me is only $\frac{4}{5}$. I am also forgetful and the probability that I remember to set the alarm is $\frac{1}{3}$.

    Calculate the probabilities that on any morning

  (i) I am awakened at 7.00 a.m. by the alarm;

 (ii) I forgot to set the alarm but reach school punctually;

(iii) I set the alarm but it fails to wake me and yet I still reach school punctually;

(iv) I am late for school.   [O   1978]

Answers to exercises

Chapter 1

Exercise 1.1

1 $4\frac{1}{2}$ **2** $2\frac{11}{20}$ **3** $2\frac{1}{2}$ **4** $\frac{13}{15}$ **5** $5\frac{1}{4}$ **6** $2\frac{2}{3}$
7 $-\frac{2}{3}$ **8** 1 **9** $4\frac{3}{4}$ **10** $11\frac{7}{12}$
11 $\frac{3}{10}$ **12** 6 **13** $3\frac{1}{3}$ **14** $\frac{3}{4}$ **15** 3 **16** $\frac{1}{3}$ **17** $1\frac{1}{3}$ **18** $1\frac{1}{20}$
19 $1\frac{2}{3}$ **20** $4\frac{4}{5}$ **21** $4\frac{4}{5}$ **22** $2\frac{1}{24}$ **23** $\frac{27}{32}$ **24** $1\frac{1}{3}$ **25** $3\frac{19}{27}$ **26** 7
27 $3\frac{1}{2}$ **28** $\frac{2}{9}$ **29** $\frac{5}{9}$ **30** $-\frac{3}{10}$ **31** $\frac{21}{100}$ **32** $7\frac{5}{21}$ **33** $1\frac{1}{2}$
34 $\frac{7}{12}$ **35** $-7\frac{1}{5}$ **36** $2\frac{2}{5}$ **37** £8, £6 **38** $1\frac{1}{2}$ km **39** $1\frac{7}{9}$ **40** $\frac{2}{9}, \frac{1}{126}$

Exercise 1.2

1 14.2 **2** 3.723 **3** 18.9 **4** 0.022 **5** 17.3 **6** 2.53 **7** 19.13 **8** 3
9 8.6 **10** 2.1 **11** 19.1°C **12** 20.7 km **13** 89.5 min **14** 7.8 cm
15 4.18 cm **16** 31.2 **17** 0.81 **18** 29.946 **19** 0.1078 **20** 0.000 006
21 75 **22** 0.228 25 **23** 5.37 **24** 0.2355 **25** 8576 **26** 11.25
27 1.8 **28** 0.875 **29** $\frac{13}{20}$ **30** 0.0053 **31** 18 km/h **32** 2.01 cm
33 (a) 29 p, (b) £83.52 **34** 0.176 **35** 400 **36** (a) 398, (b) 397.7
37 (a) 7.51, (b) 7.5 **38** (a) 400 000, (b) 400 400.7 **39** (a) 8.01, (b) 8.0
40 (a) 0.0390, (b) 0.0 **41** 3.3×10^2 **42** 9.1×10^2 **43** 5.5×10^{-1}
44 3.523×10^{-2} **45** 3.6×10^2 **46** 3.811×10^9 **47** 7.35×10^4
48 2.13×10^{-2} **49** 1.764×10^{-1} **50** 9×10^1 **51** (a) 26, 30 cm,
(b) 38.25, 52.25 cm² **52** (a) 3; 6, (b) $1\frac{3}{4}$; 3 **54** 9.431, 9.617 m/s **55** 48 536

Exercise 1.3

1 $27_{10}, 52_{10}, 15_{10}, 89_{10}, 65_{10}, 37_{10}, 62_{10}, 721_{10}$ **2** (a) (i) 52_8, (ii) 101_8, (iii) 144_8,
(iv) 3700_8; (b) (i) 101010_2, (ii) 1000001_2, (iii) 1100100_2,
(iv) 11111000000_2 **3** (a) 1110_3, (b) 124_5, (c) 54_7 **4** 251_9, $110\ 101\ 111\ 010_2$
5 (a) 13000_5, (b) 1750_8 **6** (a) $5\frac{5}{9}$, (b) $4\frac{1}{4}$, (c) $14\frac{3}{4}$, (d) $9\frac{23}{36}$

Exercise 1.4

1 10000_2 **2** 1121_8 **3** 2_3 **4** 1314_5 **5** 4_6 **6** 102_4 **7** 113_9
8 20_7 **9** 1000001_2 **10** 1404_5 **11** 11417_8 **12** 30_9 **13** 523_6
14 11010010_2 **15** 120202_3

Chapter 2

Exercise 2.1

1 (a) 1:3, (b) 3:2, (c) 3:20, (d) 7:200, (e) 3:10 **2** (a) 250 km/h, (b) 30 p/kg,
(c) 30 p/dozen, (d) 5.5 km/l (e) £12.50/week **3** (a) 45%, (b) 59%, (c) 150%,

(d) 60%   **4** (a) $\frac{3}{4}$, 0.75, (b) $\frac{9}{20}$, 0.45, (c) $1\frac{2}{5}$, 1.4, (d) $\frac{1}{40}$, 0.025   **5** (a) 3:4, (b) 9:20,
(c) 7:5, (d) 1:40   **6** (a) 10p, (b) 170g, (c) 8.4m, (d) 30cm
7 5000:1   **8** (a) 6:5, (b) 24:19   **9** 33:40, £115.50
10 £84000   **11** 5:56, £43.75
12 70   **13** £1500   **14** (a) 0.12, (b) £7.20, (c) £8500   **15** (a) £32,
(b) £2100   **16** £194.88   **17** £4920   **18** (a) £166.50,
(b) £11.25   **19** 1:20000   **20** 8m by 6.4m

Exercise 2.2

1 (a) 150, (b) 60.3, (c) 286.2, (d) 8   **2** (a) $18\frac{2}{3}$, (b) 60, (c) 480, (d) 38   **3** (a) 3/2,
(b) $\frac{1}{3}$, (c) 5/3, (d) $\frac{5}{6}$ **4** 26p   **5** £87.50   **6** 9 hours   **7** 4 days
8 5   **9** $22\frac{2}{9}$ **10** 58.5kg, 24kg, 1.5kg   **11** 25cm, 30cm, 45cm
12 324kg   **13** £150, £250, £600   **14** £625, £875, £1250
15 £285   **16** 1200   **17** £14, £$23\frac{1}{3}$, £$32\frac{2}{3}$, £42
18 £400   **19** (a) £52, (b) £48, (c) £35.84, (d) £108.80   **20** (a) loss 12.5%,
(b) gain $33\frac{1}{3}$%, (c) loss $18\frac{3}{4}$%, (d) gain 15%, (e) 16%, (f) $44\frac{2}{9}$%, (g) $30\frac{10}{13}$%, (h) $16\frac{2}{3}$%
21 (a) £$16\frac{2}{3}$, (b) £70, (c) 50p, (d) £780
22 70%   **23** £2465   **24** £1.20   **25** £20   **26** $16\frac{2}{3}$%
27 40%   **28** (a) £399.50, (b) £900   **29** $45\frac{5}{11}$%   **30** £2250

Exercise 2.3

1 £120, £620   **2** £113.40, £437.40   **3** 5 years   **4** 2 years 9 months
5 5%   **6** $2\frac{2}{3}$%   **7** £600   **8** £355   **9** £1200   **10** £470   **11** £585
12 £20.44   **14** $4\frac{1}{2}$ years
15 £356   **16** £870   **17** £2.98   **18** £304.35   **19** 5%
20 $3\frac{1}{2}$ years   **21** £110.34   **22** (a) £828.82, (b) £1515.11
23 £400   **25** £6925   **26** £35.50   **27** 57245000
29 23.7%   **30** 7.18%

Chapter 3

Exercise 3.1

1 17.86m²   **2** 0.25m²   **3** 4.8m   **4** 1.645h   **5** 185m   **6** 6.9m²
7 1200   **8** 31.5m²; 4m   **9** 2.8cm   **10** 51cm²; 15cm
11 33.5cm²   **12** 48cm²   **13** 7.2cm   **14** 104m²
15 (a) 16cm, (b) 96cm²   **17** (a) 16m, (b) 17m   **18** (a) 5cm, (b) 7.5cm

Exercise 3.2

1 15.3m³, 15300l   **2** 2.236m, 1.7m
3 15000l   **4** 0.84m³   **5** 1080kg   **6** 560kg   **7** 396cm³
8 1.092kg   **9** 7875m³   **10** 134cm³   **11** 24.36l, 1616cm³
12 0.952cm/s   **13** 14080kg   **14** 2.8cm³   **15** 2.76m³
16 1.1cm   **17** 2.739cm   **18** 8.25cm

Exercise 3.3

1 (a) (i) 31.42cm, (ii) 78.54cm², (b) (i) 213.6m, (ii) 3632m² (c) (i) 2.513mm,
(ii) 0.5027mm²   **2** (a) (i) 15.92m, (ii) 796.2m², (b) (i) 4.456,
(ii) 62.38cm², (c) (i) 270.6m, (ii) 230000m²   **3** (a) (i) 1.262km,
(ii) 7.929km, (b) (i) 4cm, (ii) 25.13cm, (c) (i) 79.79m, (ii) 501.3m

4 (a) 84 m, (b) 1.126 h   **5** 678.1 m²   **6** 15 mm   **7** (a) (i) 1885 cm³,
(ii) 377 cm²,   (b) (i) 236 m³, (ii) 138.9 m²   (c) (i) 0.985 cm³,
(ii) 0.3519 cm²   **8** (a) 184.7 l, (b) 1.32 m²   **9** (a) 38.98 cm (b) 934.1 cm²
10 127.2 cm³   **11** 5.42 cm, 0.923 : 1
12 96 cm²   **13** (a) (i) 8796 cm³, (ii) 29 cm, (iii) 1822 cm²
(b) (i) 37.7 m³, (ii) 5 m, (iii) 47.12 m²   (c) (i) 1047 mm³, (ii) 14.14 mm, (iii) 444.3 mm²
14 (a) 503 cm², (b) 804 cm³   **15** 157 cm², 227 cm³
16 3 m   **17** (a) 1283 cm³, (b) 642.3 cm²   **18** (a) (i) 33.51 cm³, (ii) 50.27 cm²
(b) (i) 20.58 m³, (ii) 36.32 m²   **19** (a) 2094 cm³,
(b) 942.5 cm²   **20** 0.492 m   **21** 523.6 cm³   **22** 65.45 cm³   **23** 0.2 cm
24 (a) 754 cm³, (b) 415 cm²   **25** 2094 cm³, 628 cm²   **26** (a) 189 cm³,
(b) 5 cm   **27** 12 cm   **28** 83.8 %   **29** 31.5 cm   **30** 9.158 cm²

Miscellaneous Exercises A

1 £42.28   **2** $1\frac{5}{14}$ **3** $2\frac{4}{5}$ **4** £900   **5** $4\frac{1}{2}$ hours
6 £16   **7** £15.60   **8** (i) 2.7 s (ii) 6.75 s (iii) 66 km/h   **9** (i) £2222 (ii) £3700
(iii) £5525; $1500 + \frac{2}{5}(x - 5000) = \frac{x}{3}$, $x = 7500$ **10** (i) 1.2×10^{14} (ii) 7.5×10^{-2}
11 £1.65   **12** £105, £215.25, £331.01$\frac{1}{4}$; £514   **13** (i) 85$\frac{1}{2}$p (ii) £180
(iii) £10.15; 56.5 %   **14** 8, 12, 24; 4141, 2831, 1721   **15** (a) 100101 1; (b) (i) $p = 1$,
$q = 4, r = 3$ (ii) $p = 2, q = 1, r = 7$; (c) 2.45 cm³   **16** £102000   **17** (a) 2.807 cm³
(b) 9 594 cm² (c) 3.51 mm (d) 6837   **18** 25   **19** 83 kg   **20** 20π cm;
300π cm²; (a) $r = 10$ cm (b) $h = 28.28$ cm (c) 942$\frac{2}{3}$π cm²   **21** 210 m³; 24 min
22 (a) £1280 (b) £21; 7$\frac{7}{9}$ %   **23** (a) 110, (b) 170, (c) $(3a + 2)(a - 4)$, (d) $3^2 \times 7^4$;
$3 \times 7^2 = 147$ **24** £5.95, 134%; £48   **25** 4.806 cm ($\sqrt{60/\pi} + 4$)

Chapter 4

Exercise 4.1

1 (b), (c), (e).   **2** (a) square numbers, (b) even numbers from 10 to 18, inclusive,
(c) first 10 multiples of 5, (d) proper factors of 12, (e) Presidents of the USA since 1960,
(f) coins in current usage in England.   **3** (a) {10, 15, 20},
(b) {1, 2, 3, 5, 6, 10, 15, 30}, (c) {(1, 1), (4, 2), (9, 3), (16, 4), (25, 5), (36, 6),(49, 7)}
(d) {29, 31, 37}   **4** e.g. $A_1 = \{x : x$ is an M.P. who is a member of the Liberal party$\}$,
5 e.g. $a = 19, b = 23$,   **6** $\overline{A} = \{\varnothing, \{u\}\}, \overline{B} = \{\varnothing, \{u\}, \{v\}, \{u, v\}\}$,
$\overline{C} = \{\varnothing, \{u\}, \{v\}, \{w\}, \{u, v\}, \{u, w\}, \{v, w\}, \{u, v, w\}\}$; $n(A) = 1, n(\overline{A}) = 2$; $n(B) = 2$,
$n(\overline{B}) = 4$; $n(C) = 3, n(\overline{C}) = 8$ Number of subsets = 16; 14 are proper.

Exercise 4.2

1 (a) $A \cap B = \{2\}, A \cup B = \{1, 2\}$; (b) $A \cap B = \{1, 2\}, A \cup B = \{1, 2, 3\}$; (c) $A \cap B$
$= \{2\}, A \cup B = \{2, 3, 4, 5, 6, 7, 8, 11, 13, 17, 19\}$; (d) $A \cap B = B, A \cup B = A$;
(e) $A \cap B = \{2, 4, 6, 8\}, A \cup B = \{1, 2, 3, 4, 5, 6, 8, 10, 12, 15, 20, 24, 30, 40, 60, 120\}$;
(f) $A \cap B = \{2, 3, 4, 5, 6\}, A \cup B = \{1, 2, 3, 4, 5, 6, 7, 8, 9, 10, 11, 12\}$ **2** (a) {4},
(b) {1, 2, 4, 6, 8, 9, 10, 16} (c) {2, 6, 8, 10} (d) {1, 9, 16}   **3** (a) 0, (b) 14,
(c) 64   **4** $A = \{$January, March, May, July, August, October, December$\}$,
$B = \{$January, June, July$\}, A \cap B = \{$January, July$\}, A' \cap B' = \{$February, April, September,
November$\}$.   **5** (a) H.C.F. = 2, L.C.M. = 1368; (b) H.C.F. = 22, L.C.M. = 462;
(c) H.C.F. = 9, L.C.M. = 630   **6** $A = \{$Chelsea, Arsenal, Leeds, Sunderland,
Liverpool, West Ham$\}$; $B = \{$Everton, Arsenal, Derby, Liverpool, Leeds$\}$; $A \cap B$
$= \{$Arsenal, Liverpool, Leeds$\}$ $A \cup B = $ set $A + $ Everton and Derby.
7 ∞, 1, 0   **8** $A \triangle B = \{a, e, f, g\}$ **9** $A = \{3, 6, 9, 12, 15, 18, 21, 24, 27\}$,

$B = \{2, 3, 5, 7, 11, 13, 17, 19, 23, 29\}$, $C = \{1, 4, 9, 16, 25\}$. (a) False, e.g.
$3 \notin A'$, (b) False, $3 \in \{A \cap B\}$, (c) True, (d) False, $n(A) = 9$, (e) True, (f) False, e.g.
$6 \in \{B' \cap C'\}$ **10** (a) All the boys are wearing trousers, (b) not all children are wearing trousers, (c) all the foreign children are girls who are not wearing trousers.

Exercise 4.3

1

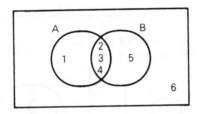

(a) $\{5, 6\}$,   (b) $\{1, 6\}$,   (c) $\{2, 3, 4\}$,   (d) $\{1, 2, 3, 4, 5\}$,   (e) $\{1, 5, 6\}$,
(f) $\{6\}$,   (g) $\{6\}$,   (h) $\{1, 5, 6\}$,
2

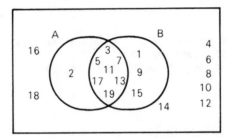

(a) $\{3, 5, 7, 11, 13, 17, 19\}$,   (b) $\{1, 2, 4, 6, 8, 9, 10, 12, 14, 15, 16, 18\}$,   (c) $\{2\}$
3

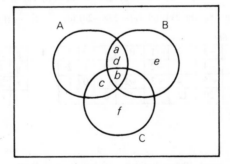

(a) $\{b\}$, (b) $\{a, b, c, d, e\}$, (c) $\{a, b, c, d, f\}$, (d) $\{a, b, c, d\}$, (e) $\{a, b, c, d\}$,
(f) $\{a, b, c, d, e, f\}$, (g) $\{a, b, c, d, e, f\}$.
4 (a), (d), (e), (f)

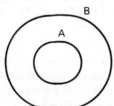

(b), (c)

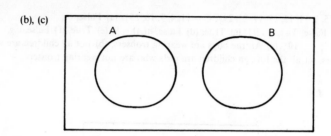

5 (a) $\varnothing$, (b) A, (c) A, (d) A, (e) $A \cup B$, (f) A, (g) A

7 Dual: $A \cap B = (A \cup B) \cap (A \cup B') \cap (A' \cup B)$.

8

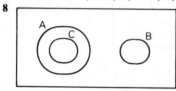

9

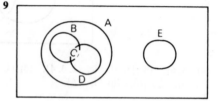

Exercise 4.4

1 (a) 3, (b) 29   **2** 60; 160   **3** 3   **4** (a) $n(A \cup B)' = n(A' \cap B') = 5$

(b) $35 \leqslant n(A \cup B) \leqslant 52, 0 \leqslant n(A \cap B) \leqslant 17$

5 2   **6** 33   **7** 36   **8** (a) 30, (b) 8   **9** 2; 3

Chapter 5

Exercise 5.1

1 (a) 0, (b) 6, (c) -5, (d) 4, (e) 12, (f) 9, (g) -6, (h) 0, (i) 18, (j) 25, (k) 6,

(l) 11   **2** (a) $7p - 8q$, (b) $2xy$, (c) $2ef - 2de - 2df$ (d) $\dfrac{7a}{12}$, (e) $\dfrac{x}{21}$, (f) $1\frac{1}{6}$, (g) $a^2 - ab$,

(h) $-4a^2 + 14ab - 6b^2$

3

x	-3	-2	-1	0	1	2	3
$x - 1$	-4	-3	-2	-1	0	1	2
$x - 2$	-5	-4	-3	-2	-1	0	1
$(x-1)(x-2)$	20	12	6	2	0	0	2

4

p	3	5	$-2\frac{1}{2}$	16
q	4	7	2	-4.25
r	2	3	12	-4.5
A	6	20	25	4

5 4, $2\frac{7}{8}$, 2, 4, 16, $27\frac{5}{8}$

Exercise 5.2

1 (a) (i) 4, (ii) 4; closed (b) (i) 8, (ii) 9; not closed, e.g. $-3\frac{1}{2} \notin \mathbb{R}$ (c) (i) 12,

(ii) 15; closed. (d) (i) 12, (ii) 3; not closed, e.g. $\sqrt{2x - 2} \notin \mathbb{R}$ (e) (i) 2,

(ii) 2; closed, (f) (i) 4, (ii) 1; closed.   **2** All closed except (a) (iii) e.g. $\frac{3}{5} \notin \mathbb{Z}$;

(d) (i) $3 \times 2 \notin P$, (ii) $7 - 3 \notin P$, (iii) $7 + 3 \notin P$; (e) (ii) $\frac{5}{6} \notin A$; (g) $2 * 6 \notin D + \quad$;

(h) $1 * 1\frac{1}{2} \notin J$.

Exercise 5.3

1 (a) All commutative except (b) and (e); (b) Not associative:

(b) e.g. $(2 * 2) * 3 = 2^2 * 3 = 4^3 = 64, 2 * (2 * 3) = 2 * 8 = 2^8 = 256$;

(d) e.g. $(2 * 8) * 16 = 4 * 16 = 8, 2 * (8 * 16) = 2 * 12 = \sqrt{24}$;

(e) e.g. $(1 * 2) * 3 = 4 * 3 = 96, 1 * (2 * 3) = 1 * 24 = 48.$ **2** (a) (i) $3 - 2 \neq 2 - 3$,
(ii) $\dfrac{3}{2} \neq \dfrac{2}{3}$; (b) $2 * 5 = \frac{7}{5}, 5 * 2 = \frac{7}{2}$; (c) $1 * 2 = -4, 2 * 1 = 1$ **3** (a) 0, (b) -42,
(c) -8, (d) -1; $8 * k = 6 \Rightarrow k = 2$; none.   **4** (a) none,
(b) none, (c) none, (d) all, (e) commutative, (f) none.   **5** (a) 86, (b) 26, (c) 18,
(d) 8, (e) $14\frac{5}{12}$, (f) $4\frac{5}{12}$; not associative.

Exercise 5.4

1 (a) (i) $\frac{1}{3}$, (ii) $1\frac{5}{7}$, (iii) $\frac{2}{3}$, (iv) $-1\frac{1}{6}$; (b) $1\frac{2}{7}$ **2** (i) (a) $\frac{1}{3}$ and 5,
(b) -5 and 5; (ii) (a) $-\frac{1}{2}$ and -2, (b) 2 and -2 (iii) (a) $1\frac{2}{3}$ and $\frac{3}{5}$,
(b) $-\frac{3}{5}$ and $\frac{3}{5}$.   **3** (a) identity is 1, (i) $2^{-1} = \frac{1}{2}$, (ii) $-1^{-1} = -1$;
(b) identity is -3, (i) $2^{-1} = -8$, (ii) $-1^{-1} = -5$ (c) identity is 0, (i) no inverse,
(ii) $-1^{-1} = \frac{2}{3}$; (d) no identity   (e) identity is 0, (i) $2^{-1} = 2$, (ii) $-1^{-1} = \frac{1}{2}$;
(f) identity is 0; (i) $2^{-1} = -\frac{2}{3}$, (ii) no inverse

Exercise 5.5

1 (a)

$*$	E	O
E	E	E
O	E	O

(b) (i)

$\cap$	A	A'
A	A	$\varnothing$
A'	$\varnothing$	A'

(ii)

$\cup$	A	A'
A	A	$\mathscr{E}$
A'	$\mathscr{E}$	A'

closed; commutative;   not closed; commutative;   not closed; commutative;
no identity   no identity   no identity

(c) (i)

$*$	-1	0	1
-1	2	1	2
0	1	0	1
1	2	1	2

(ii)

$*$	-1	0	1
-1	0	1	0
0	-1	0	-1
1	0	1	0

(d)

$*$	$\mathbf{I}$	$\mathbf{X}$
$\mathbf{I}$	$\mathbf{I}$	$\mathbf{X}$
$\mathbf{X}$	$\mathbf{X}$	$\mathbf{I}$

not closed; commutative;   closed; not commutative;   closed; commutative;
no identity   no identity   identity is $\mathbf{I}$;

$\mathbf{I}^{-1} = \mathbf{I}$;
$\mathbf{X}^{-1} = \mathbf{X}$

(e)

$*$	0	1	2	3
0	0	1	2	3
1	1	2	3	0
2	2	3	0	1
3	3	0	1	2

(f)

$*$	1	2	3
1	1	2	3
2	2	0	2
3	3	2	1

closed; commutative;   closed; commutative;
identity is 0;   identity is 1;
$0^{-1} = 0; 1^{-1} = 3;$ $1^{-1} = 1, 3^{-1} = 3,$
$2^{-1} = 2; 3^{-1} = 1.$ no inverse for 2.

2 (a) e.g. remainder when $x.y$ divided by 3,   (b) remainder when $x + y$ divided by 3,
(c) remainder when $x + y$ is divided by 12,   (d) remainder when xy divided by 12,
(e) see **1**(d)   (f) $\{0, 1, 2\}$, $x * y$ is remainder when $x + y$ divided by 3.

Exercise 5.6

1 All sets are closed under addition (mod n); possess symmetry about leading diagonal.
2 The sets are closed when $n = 3, 5, 7$; these possess same symmetry as in **1**. All sets
have an identity element 1. Inverses are given where they exist:
$n = 3: 1^{-1} = 1, 2^{-1} = 2; n = 4: 1^{-1} = 1, 3^{-1} = 3; n = 5: 1^{-1} = 1, 2^{-1} = 3, 3^{-1} = 2,$
$4^{-1} = 4; n = 6: 1^{-1} = 1, 5^{-1} = 5; n = 7: 1^{-1} = 1, 2^{-1} = 4, 3^{-1} = 5,$

$4^{-1} = 2, 5^{-1} = 3, 6^{-1} = 6$; $n = 8$: $1^{-1} = 1, 3^{-1} = 3, 5^{-1} = 5, 7^{-1} = 7$.
When n is prime.
3 (a) 4, (b) 2, (c) 3, (d) 3, (e) 2 or 3, (f) no solution.

Exercise 5.7

3 all   4 $n = 3, 5, 7$ 5 not all matrices have inverses   6 no identity.

Exercise 5.8

1 (a) 8; 4 lines of symmetry and 4 rotations about centre of square ($= 90k°$, $k = 1, 2, 3, 4$). (b) 4; reflections in diagonals and 2 rotations about centre ($= 180k°$, $k = 1, 2$) (c) 10; 5 reflections and 5 rotations about centre ($= 72k°$, $k = 1, 2, 3, 4, 5$) (d) 2; 180° and 360° rotation about centre.

2 (a)

	I	X
I	I	X
X	X	I

(b)

	I	X	Y	Z	R_1	R_2
I	I	X	Y	Z	R_1	R_2
X	X	I	R_1	R_2	Y	Z
Y	Y	R_2	I	R_1	Z	X
Z	Z	R_1	R_2	I	X	Y
R_1	R_1	Z	X	Y	R_2	I
R_2	R_2	Y	Z	X	I	R_1

(c)

	I	H
I	I	H
H	H	I

(d)

	I	H
I	I	H
H	H	I

(a), (c), (d) are isomorphic.

Exercise 5.9

1 RBG, RGB, BRG, BGR, GBR, GRB. Define $P_1 \ldots P_6$ as $P_1 = \begin{Bmatrix} R & B & G \\ R & B & G \end{Bmatrix}, \ldots$
$P_6 = \begin{Bmatrix} R & B & G \\ G & R & B \end{Bmatrix}$ Form a group of order 6 isomorphic to set $\{0, 1, 2, 3, 4, 5\}$ under addition (mod 6).

2 (a)

	I	P_1
I	I	P_1
P_1	P_1	I

(b)

	0	1
0	0	1
1	1	0

(c)

	E	O
E	E	O
O	O	E

(d)

	1	2
1	1	2
2	2	1

(e)

	1	4
1	1	4
4	4	1

(f)

	I	A
I	I	A
A	A	I

; yes.

3 (a)

	0	1	2
0	0	1	2
1	1	2	0
2	2	0	1

(b)

	I	R_1	R_2
I	I	R_1	R_2
R_1	R_1	R_2	I
R_2	R_2	I	R_1

(c)

	1	w	w^2
1	1	w	w^2
w	w	w^2	1
w^2	w^2	1	w

4

	a	b	c
a	a	b	c
b	b	c	a
c	c	a	b

Abelian $b^2 = c$, $b^3 = a$

5 (a)

	0	1	2	3
0	0	1	2	3
1	1	2	3	0
2	2	3	0	1
3	3	0	1	2

(b)

	1	2	3	4
1	1	2	3	4
2	2	4	1	3
3	3	1	4	2
4	4	3	2	1

(c)

	I	A	B	C
I	I	A	B	C
A	A	I	C	B
B	B	C	I	A
C	C	B	A	I

(d)

	1	5	7	11
1	1	5	7	11
5	5	1	11	7
7	7	11	1	5
11	11	7	5	1

(c) and (d) are isomorphic to the set $\{f_1, f_2, f_3, f_4\}$ under 'follows'.

6 (a)

	a	b	c	d
a	a	b	c	d
b	b	a	d	c
c	c	d	a	b
d	d	c	b	a

and (b)

	a	b	c	d
a	a	b	c	d
b	b	c	d	a
c	c	d	a	b
d	d	a	b	c

a is assumed to be the identity.
(a) is Klein 4   (b) is cyclic

Exercise 5.10

1 $x = 2$ **2** $x = 1$ **3** $x = f_3$ **4** $x = f_4$ **5** $x = H$
6 $x = Y$ **7** (a) d,   (b) d,   (c) c,   (d) a.

Exercise 5.11

2 (a) (i) 4, (ii) 4; yes (b) (i) 0, (ii) 0; yes
3 (a) 13,   (b) 2200,   (c) 578,   (d) 158,   (e) 4,   (f) 12.

Chapter 6

Exercise 6.1

1 $5x + 10$ **2** $3x - 21$ **3** $4x + 8y$ **4** $-x^2 + 5x$ **5** $3x^2 + x$
6 $x^3 + xy$ **7** $3x - 16$ **8** $-5x + 9$ **9** $x^2 + 13x + 40$
10 $-2x^2 + 3x + 5$ **11** $2x^2 + 11x + 5$ **12** $2x^2 - 13x - 24$ **13** $12x^2 - x - 1$
14 $12x^2 + 16x - 3$ **15** $x^2 + 16x + 64$ **16** $4x^2 + 12x + 9$ **17** $x^2 - 10x + 25$
18 $x^2 - 1$ **19** $4x^2 - 9$ **20** $16x^2 - 81$ **21** $x^4 - 1$
22 $x^3 + 5x^2 + 11x + 10$ **23** $x^3 + 3x^2 + 2x$ **24** $x^3 - x$

Exercise 6.2

1 $2(x + 2)$ **2** $3(x - 2)$ **3** $x(x - 1)$ **4** $7(3 - x)$ **5** $x(y - x)$
6 $p^2(p - q)$ **7** $2y(1 + 6y)$ **8** $3x^2(2x^2 - 1)$ **9** $x^2(1 + x + x^2)$
10 $5x(x - 2)$ **11** $3x(1 + 2x)$ **12** $x(1 + 2x^2 - x^4)$ **13** $ab^2c(c^2 + a^2)$
14 $2(x^2 + 2y^2)$ **15** $x(x + 2)$ **16** $(x - 1)(x - 2)$

Exercise 6.3

1 (a) $(x-2)(x+2)$, (b) $(y-1)(y+1)$, (c) $(p-7)(p+7)$, (d) $(10-q)(10+q)$,
(e) $(a-b)(a+b)$, (f) $(8x+1)(8x-1)$, (g) $(2x+1)(2x-1)$, (h) $(2x+3y)(2x-3y)$,
(i) $(2+5x)(2-5x)$, (j) $(5y+3)(5y-3)$, (k) $(3p+4q)(3p-4q)$, (l) $(4a+1)(4a-1)$,
(m) $3(3x+1)(3x-1)$, (n) $2(2x+5y)(2x-5y)$, (o) $13(x+2)(x-2)$,
(p) $p^2(1+q)(1-q)$, (q) $(x^2+1)(x-1)(x+1)$, (r) $p^2(1+p)(1-p)$, (s) $\pi(R+r)(R-r)$,
(t) $k(a+b)(a-b)$, (u) $2x+3$, (v) $4x$, (w) $(x+5)(x-3)$, (x) $(7+2x)(1-2x)$
2 (a) $100 \times 52 = 5200$, (b) $200 \times 198 = 39\,600$, (c) $9 \times 0.6 = 5.4$,
(d) $10 \times 2.8 = 28$ 3   (a) $\pi(5.24)(1) = 5.24\pi$, (b) $\pi(10)(8.16) = 81.6\pi$,
(c) $\pi(5)(0.7) = 3.5\pi$ 4 $BC^2 = 25^2 - 24^2 = (49)(1) \Rightarrow BC = 7$

Exercise 6.4

1 $(x-4)(x-1)$ 2 $(x+3)(x+2)$ 3 $(x-9)(x-3)$ 4 $(x+3)(x+4)$
5 $(x-1)(x-5)$ 6 $(x+8)(x+5)$ 7 $(y-6)(y+2)$ 8 $(y-4)(y+3)$
9 $(y-7)(y+6)$ 10 $(y-5)(y+3)$ 11 $(y+7)(y-2)$ 12 $(y-9)(y+2)$
13 $(1+3x)(1+2x)$ 14 $(1-3y)(1+y)$ 15 $(1+9x)(1+3x)$
16 $(p+12)(p-7)$ 17 $(p-12)(p+9)$ 18 $(p+13q)(p-2q)$
19 $5(t+2)(t-1)$ 20 $3(t-2)(t-3)$ 21 $2(t+5)(t-3)$ 22 $(x^2-3)(x^2+1)$
23 $x^2(x-5)(x-1)$ 24 $y(x-1)(x-4)$

Exercise 6.5

1 $(2x+1)(x-5)$ 2 $(3x-1)(x+3)$ 3 $(2x+1)(x-7)$
4 $(3x+2)(2x+1)$ 5 $(5x+1)(x+5)$ 6 $(3x-7)(2x+1)$ 7 $(7x-1)(x+2)$
8 $(5x+2)(x+2)$ 9 $(4x-3)(x-1)$ 10 $(2x-1)(x-11)$ 11 $(3x-2)(3x+1)$
12 $(6x+1)(2x-5)$ 13 $(3x-2)(2x+1)$ 14 $(7x+1)(2x-3)$
15 $(4-5x)(2-x)$ 16 $(5x-2)(3x+1)$ 17 $(2x-3)(x+9)$
18 $(5x+2)(2x+3)$ 19 $(3+2x)(2-x)$ 20 $(2-x)(1+7x)$
21 $(3x+2)(2x+5)$ 22 $2(2x+1)(x-5)$ 23 $4(3x-5)(x+9)$
24 $x(2x+1)(x-5)$

Exercise 6.6

1 $(x+y)(a+1)$ 2 $(x+2y)(3+a)$ 3 $(a+x)(b+x)$
4 $(x-y)(x+1)$ 5 $(x-2y)(x+3)$ 6 $(x+2)(y+3)$ 7 $(x-y)(x^2+xy+1)$
8 $(x+y)(x-y+1)$ 9 $(x-2y+1)(x-2y-1)$ 10 $(x-1+y)(x-1-y)$
11 $(3-x+2y)(3-x-2y)$ 12 $(w-x+y)(w+x-y)$ 13 $(x+6)(2x+y)$
14 $(x+2y)(x-y-5)$ 15 $(x+y)(x+10y-5)$

Exercise 6.7

1 $\frac{1}{2}$ 2 $\frac{1}{3}$ 3 2   4 -1 5 $2x-1$ 6 $\frac{x+1}{x}$ 7 $-x$

8 $x-1$ 9 $\frac{1}{2x-3y}$ 10 $\frac{x^2+y^2}{x+y}$ 11 $\frac{x-4}{x-1}$

12 $x+5$ 13 $\frac{x+1}{x+2}$ 14 $\frac{x-1}{x+4}$ 15 $\frac{2x+5}{3(x-2)}$ 16 $\frac{3x-1}{x-1}$ 17 $\frac{3x+2}{x+4}$

18 -1 19 $2(x+1)$ 20 $\frac{x-1}{2}$ 21 $\frac{4-x}{x-2}$

Exercise 6.8

1 $\frac{9x}{14}$ 2 $\frac{-x}{20}$ 3 $\frac{x+7}{6}$ 4 $\frac{3x+5}{x^2}$ 5 $\frac{-(5x+7)}{x(x+1)}$ 6 $\frac{3x^2+6x+2}{x(x+1)(x+2)}$

7 $\dfrac{2(x-2)}{(x-3)(x-1)}$ **8** $\dfrac{1}{3x}$ **9** $\dfrac{x+2}{x(x+1)}$ **10** $\dfrac{3x-1}{1-x^2}$ **11** $\dfrac{-(2x+3)}{(x+1)(x+2)}$

12 $\dfrac{2x-1}{(x-1)^2}$ **13** $\dfrac{(x+6)(x-2)}{x(x+1)}$ **14** $\dfrac{7x-3}{(x^2-1)(x+4)}$ **15** $\dfrac{x+4}{(x-3)(x+1)(2x+1)}$

16 $\dfrac{4}{(x+1)(x+5)}$ **17** $\dfrac{-1}{x(x+1)}$ **18** $\dfrac{-1}{5(x+1)(2x+3)}$

Chapter 7

Exercise 7.1

1 3   **2** -1 **3** 2   **4** $2\frac{2}{5}$ **5** $\frac{5}{12}$ **6** $8\frac{1}{3}$ **7** $\frac{3}{4}$ **8** $-\frac{1}{2}$
9 -3 **10** 10   **11** -1 **12** -2 **13** -4 **14** -5 **15** 0
16 -15

Exercise 7.2

1 4   **2** $-\frac{3}{22}$ **3** 0   **4** 1   **5** $1\frac{2}{7}$ **6** $1\frac{2}{7}$ **7** 1   **8** $1\frac{5}{9}$ **9** 7
10 5   **11** $2\frac{2}{3}$ **12** $3\frac{1}{3}$ **13** $\frac{8}{9}$ **14** $\frac{16}{45}$ **15** $\frac{2}{5}$ **16** $\frac{1}{6}$ **17** $3\frac{4}{7}$
18 15   **19** $3\frac{9}{13}$ **20** $\frac{12}{19}$

Exercise 7.3

1 10   **2** 9   **3** -49 **4** $1\frac{1}{7}$ **5** $\frac{7}{8}$ **6** $-1\frac{1}{3}$ **7** $\frac{2}{15}$ **8** $1\frac{6}{11}$
9 0   **10** $7\frac{1}{2}$ **11** 4   **12** $-28\frac{1}{2}$ **13** 5   **14** $-3\frac{4}{11}$
15 $2\frac{7}{8}$ **16** $-\frac{3}{10}$ **17** $1\frac{2}{5}$ **18** 7   **19** -3 **20** $-\frac{1}{3}$

Exercise 7.4

1 (a) $\{x:x > -2\frac{1}{2}\}$, (b) $\{x:x > 1\frac{1}{2}\}$, (c) $\{x:x > -\frac{1}{2}\}$, (d) $\{x:x \geqslant 5\}$,
(e) $\{x:x > 2\}$, (f) $\{x:x \leqslant -9\}$, (g) $\{x:x > 1\frac{1}{2}\}$, (h) $\{x:x < -2\frac{1}{3}\}$ **2** (a) -3,
(b) -13, (c) 0, (d) 3, (e) 1, (f) 22, (g) 1.

3

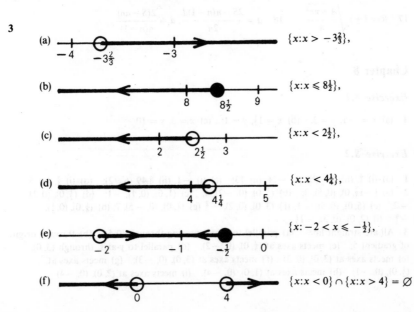

(a) $\{x:x > -3\frac{2}{3}\}$,

(b) $\{x:x \leqslant 8\frac{1}{2}\}$,

(c) $\{x:x < 2\frac{1}{2}\}$,

(d) $\{x:x < 4\frac{1}{4}\}$,

(e) $\{x:-2 < x \leqslant -\frac{1}{2}\}$,

(f) $\{x:x < 0\} \cap \{x:x > 4\} = \varnothing$

Exercise 7.5

1 (a) $\dfrac{3p}{25}$, (b) $\dfrac{9p}{25}$, (c) $\dfrac{3gp}{25}$, **2** $(110-4x)°$ **3** $P=(4x+4)\,\text{cm}$,

$A=(x^2+2x)\,\text{cm}^2$ **4** mn; integer part of $\dfrac{p-mn}{n}$; (a) $(n-2d)\,\text{cm}$,

(b) $m(n-2d)\,\text{cm}$ **5** (a) xy, (b) $100xy$ **6** (a) $2x+5y$, (b) $dx+fy$

7 $(12-x)$ years old. **8** $\dfrac{100-4x}{3}$ pence **9** 1 h 20 min; (a) $\dfrac{y}{x}$, (b) $\dfrac{y}{x}+\dfrac{1}{6}$.

(c) $\dfrac{y}{x}+\dfrac{z}{60}$ **10** $\dfrac{xz}{y}$ **11** $\dfrac{x+y}{5}$ **12** $7\left/\left(\dfrac{2}{x}+\dfrac{5}{y}\right)\right.$ or $\dfrac{7xy}{2y+5x}$

Exercise 7.6

1 23:5 **2** man is 36, wife is 32 **3** 108 **4** £18.50 **5** $3\frac{1}{2}$ cm
6 87 **7** 60 lb of tea, 44 lb of coffee **8** 6 **9** 18
10 5 **11** 1 h 55 min; $84\frac{1}{3}$ km from Bristol, $99\frac{2}{3}$ km from London. **12** $11\frac{1}{9}$ m
13 11 km/h, 14 km/h **14** $2\frac{1}{2}$ cm, $6\frac{1}{2}$ cm **15** 64 km

Exercise 7.7

1 $b=\dfrac{V}{ac}$ **2** $h=\dfrac{3V}{\pi r^2}$; $r=(\pm)\sqrt{\dfrac{3V}{\pi h}}$ **3** $u=\dfrac{2S-at^2}{2t}$; $a=\dfrac{2(S-ut)}{t^2}$

4 $F=\dfrac{9C+160}{5}$ **5** $l=\dfrac{T^2g}{4}$; $g=\dfrac{4l}{T^2}$ **6** $x=\pm\sqrt{9-y^2}$

7 $y=\pm\dfrac{5\sqrt{4-x^2}}{2}$ **8** $x=\dfrac{y}{4y-1}$ **9** $b=a+\dfrac{1}{c^2}$ **10** $x=\dfrac{ad-bc}{b+c-a-d}$

11 $m=\dfrac{n(f+g)}{g-f}$ **12** $x=\dfrac{y-1}{y+1}$ **13** $m=\dfrac{P-Mf}{f}$

14 $u=\dfrac{vw}{w+2v}$; $w=\dfrac{2uv}{v-u}$ **15** $x=\dfrac{1}{y-1}$ **16** $b=\dfrac{a}{\sqrt{c+d}}$; $c=\dfrac{a^2-b^2d}{b^2}$

17 $R=(\pm)\sqrt{\dfrac{A+\pi r^2}{\pi}}$ **18** $a=\dfrac{2S-n(n-1)d}{2n}$; $d=\dfrac{2(S-an)}{n(n-1)}$

Chapter 8

Exercise 8.1

4 (a) $x=-1,\ y=3$; (b) $x=1\frac{1}{2},\ y=1$; (c) $x=3,\ y=10$

Exercise 8.2

1 (a) (i) $\frac{4}{3}$, (ii) 5; (b) (i) $-2\frac{2}{5}$, (ii) 13; (c) (i) -1, (ii) 8.49 $(6\sqrt{2})$; (d) (i) $\frac{3}{4}$, (ii) 5
2 (a) $(-1\frac{2}{3},0)$, $(0,5)$, 3; (b) $(\frac{1}{2},0)$, $(0,-2)$, 4; (c) $(1,0)$, $(0,1)$, -1; (d) $(\frac{1}{2},0)$, $(0,1)$,
-2; (e) $(5,0)$, $(0,5)$, -1; (f) $(3,0)$, $(0,2)$, $-\frac{2}{3}$ (g) $(\frac{5}{7},0)$, $(0,-5)$, 7; (h) $(\frac{1}{4},0)$, $(0,\frac{1}{3})$,
$-\frac{4}{3}$; (i) $(2,0)$, $(0,3)$, $-1\frac{1}{2}$
3 All are straight lines (a) parallel to x-axis passing through $(0,5)$; (b) through origin
of gradient 5; (c) meets axes at $(\frac{2}{3},0)$, $(0,-2)$; (d) parallel to y-axis, through $(3,0)$;
(e) meets axes at $(3,0)$, $(0,3)$ (f) meets axes at $(3,0)$, $(0,-3)$; (g) meets axes at
$(\frac{1}{2},0)$, $(0,-1)$ (h) meets axes at $(1,0)$, $(0,-4)$; (i) meets axes at $(2,0)$, $(0,-4)$

Exercise 8.3

1 (a) $y = 3x + 4$; (b) $y = -2x + 1$; (c) $y = 4(x + 1)$ (d) $y + x = 9$;
(e) $y = 6x + 9$; (f) $2y = x + 4$
2 (a) $y = 2x - 1$ (b) $x + y = 7$ (c) $y = 4$ (d) $4x + y = 4$ (e) $5x - 3y = 15$
(f) $y + 2x + 2 = 0$
3 $y = 2x - 1$ **4** $x + y = 6$ **5** $y = 0$; $2y = 5x$; $y = 5$; $5x + 8y = 60$
6 All are straight lines passing through (a) $(-3\frac{1}{2}, 0)$, $(0, 7)$; (b) $(8, 0)$, $(0, 8)$;
(c) $(3, 0)$, $(0, 2)$; (d) $(2, 0)$, $(0, 8)$; (e) $(5, 0)$, $(0, -2)$ (f) $(1\frac{1}{2}, 0)$, $(0, 2\frac{2}{3})$

Exercise 8.4

1 $x = 4\frac{5}{7}$, $y = -2\frac{3}{7}$ **2** $x = -11\frac{1}{2}$, $y = 6\frac{1}{2}$ **3** no solution; parallel lines
4 $x = 2$, $y = 0$ **5** $x = 5$, $y = 4$ **6** $x = 1\frac{1}{2}$, $y = 2\frac{1}{2}$ **7** infinite set of solutions;
same line **8** $x = 7$, $y = 2$ **9** $x = 5$, $y = 3\frac{1}{3}$ **10** $x = 0$, $y = 5\frac{1}{7}$

Exercise 8.5

1 (a) $x = 2$, $y = 3$; (b) $x = 3$, $y = 2$; (c) $x = 2$, $y = 3$ (d) $x = -\frac{1}{7}$, $y = 3\frac{1}{2}$;
(e) $x = \frac{25}{56}$, $y = 1\frac{1}{14}$; (f) $x = 1\frac{1}{28}$, $y = \frac{9}{14}$; (g) $x = 1$, $y = \frac{1}{2}$; (h) $x = 1\frac{26}{43}$, $y = -\frac{4}{43}$
2 (a) $(6, 19)$; (b) $(\frac{3}{4}, 5)$; (c) $(\frac{2}{3}, 3\frac{2}{3})$;
(d) $(-13, -19)$; (e) $(1\frac{1}{3}, 5\frac{2}{3})$; (f) $(\frac{17}{25}, \frac{22}{25})$ **3** $(0, 2)$, $(\frac{3}{4}, 0)$, $(5, 17)$, $(8, 17)$, $(11\frac{2}{3}, 0)$

Exercise 8.6

1 (i) 54p, (ii) £10.80 **2** 450 (300 stalls, 15 circle) **3** 3 years old and
15 years old **4** $x = 15$, $y = 8$ **5** 50 large, 20 small **6** $2\frac{1}{2}$ km **7** 76
8 50p and 42p **9** 98p **10** $x = 100$, $y = 70$ **11** £1.40
12 84 (24 adults, 60 children)

Exercise 8.7

1 (a)

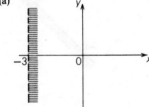

(b)

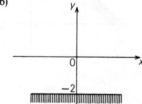

(c)

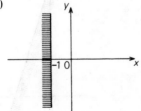

(d)

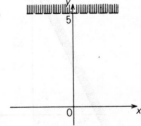

413

(e)

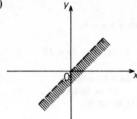

(f)

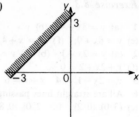

(g)

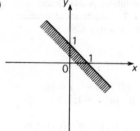

(h)

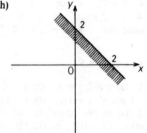

(i)

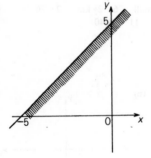

(j)

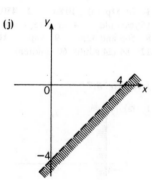

(k)

(l)

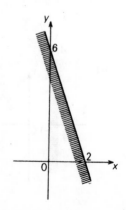

2 _(a)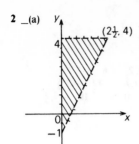

(b)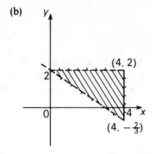

(c)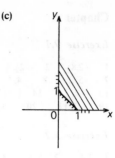

(d)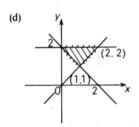

(e)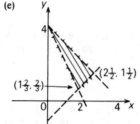

(f)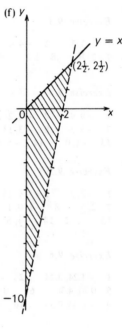

(g)

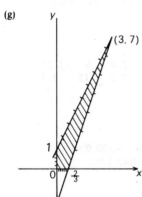

3 (a) $x \geq 0$, $y \geq 0$, $\dfrac{x}{3} + \dfrac{y}{4} < 1$; (b) $y \geq 0$, $y \leq x$, $x \leq 4$; (c) $y \geq 0$, $y \leq 3x$, $y \leq 3$,

$5y \geq 3(x-1)$; (d) $x \leq 2$, $y+x \geq 0$, $x+2y < 4$; (e) $y \leq 2$, $y \geq x-1$, $y+x+1 \geq 0$;

(f) $x+y \leq 2$, $x+y \geq -2$, $y \leq x+2$, $y \geq x-2$ **4** (a) (0, 0), (0, 1), (0, 2),

(0, 3), (1, 0), (1, 1), (1, 2), (2, 0). (2, 1). (i) (0, 3), (1, 2), (2, 1); (ii) (2, 0); (iii) (2, 0),

(2, 1); (b) (0, 0), (2, 1), (4, 2); (c) (i) 9 when $x = 6$, $y = 3$; (ii) 1 when $x = 1$,

$y = 3$ (d) 6 when $x = -3$, $y = 3$ (e) $-4 < x \leq 2$, $-2 \leq y < 4$

Exercise 8.8

1 £1500; 14 skilled, 6 apprentices **2** 21

3 £26,600; no, he uses 49 plots **4** 60 type α, 20 type β

5 6 American, 7 English (profit = £41.50); 6 m² remains.

6 91 when $x = 32$, $y = 59$ **7** 26; £4.76 **8** £420; either 18A, 10B or

19A, 9B or 20A, 8B **9** 17 type A, 3 type B; profit = £330

Chapter 9

Exercise 9.1

1 $-2, 8$ **2** $-2\frac{1}{2}, \frac{1}{3}$ **3** $0, 5$ **4** $-5, 6\frac{1}{2}$ **5** $-1, 2$ **6** $3, 5$
7 $-5, 2$ **8** $-4, 5$ **9** $-7, -8$ **10** $0, 8$ **11** $1, 6$ **12** $-7, \frac{1}{2}$
13 $-\frac{2}{5}, 1$ **14** $\frac{1}{3}, 3\frac{1}{2}$ **15** $1, 2$ **16** $-\frac{2}{3}, -7$ **17** $0, 3\frac{3}{4}$ **18** $-\frac{2}{7}, \frac{1}{2}$
19 $-2, 11$ **20** $-1, 3$

Exercise 9.2

1 $2, 4$ **2** $\frac{1}{3}, 4$ **3** $0, 2$ **4** $-7, 3$ **5** $3, 5$ **6** $-3, 7$
7 $-\frac{2}{3}, 2\frac{1}{2}$ **8** $-1\frac{1}{3}, \frac{2}{3}$ **9** $-\frac{1}{7}, \frac{1}{2}$ **10** $-2, 8$ **11** $0, 1\frac{1}{3}$ **12** $0, \frac{1}{2}$

Exercise 9.3

1 $-3, 3$ **2** $-4, 4$ **3** $-4, 3$ **4** $-3, 1$ **5** $\frac{1}{3}, 3$ **6** $-1, 4$
7 $2, 2\frac{2}{3}$ **8** $2, 2$ **9** $-\frac{1}{2}, 1$ **10** $-\frac{1}{2}, 5$ **11** $-\frac{2}{3}, 4$ **12** $-3, 1$

Exercise 9.4

1 $-9, 9$ **2** $-2, 2$ **3** $-5, 5$ **4** $-\frac{1}{2}, \frac{1}{2}$ **5** $-4, 4$ **6** $-5, 5$
7 $-5, 3$ **8** $-3, 13$ **9** $-2, 4$ **10** $1, 3$ **11** $1, 6$ **12** $-\frac{4}{5}, 0$
13 $-\frac{2}{3}, 0$ **14** $-5, 3$ **15** $-1\frac{1}{2}, \frac{1}{2}$

Exercise 9.5

1 $-2, 7$ **2** $-\frac{1}{2}, 1\frac{2}{3}$ **3** $-2, 2$ **4** $0, 3$ **5** $-12, 0$ **6** $-\frac{1}{2}, 7$
7 $2, 5$ **8** $-1, 0, 1$ **9** $-8, 2$ **10** $2, 3$ **11** $-3, 5$ **12** $-3, 4$
13 $-3, 2$ **14** $-\frac{1}{2}, 5$ **15** $-8, 9$

Exercise 9.6

1 $-1.24, 3.24$ **2** $-5.24, -0.76$ **3** $1.38, 3.62$ **4** $-3.30, 0.30$
5 $0.70, 4.30$ **6** $-0.16, 3.16$ **7** $-1.35, 1.85$ **8** $0.42, 1.58$
9 $-0.64, 0.39$ **10** $-1.12, 0.72$

Exercise 9.7

1 $-0.79, 3.79$ **2** $-3.45, 1.45$ **3** $0.27, 3.73$ **4** $-0.81, 0.53$ **5** $-2.78,$
-0.72 **6** $-1.17, 0.17$ **7** $-0.73, 2.73$ **8** $-6.37, -0.63$
9 $-0.61, 4.11$ **10** $-0.68, 0.88$ **11** $-1.43, -0.23$ **12** $-0.39, 0.64$

Exercise 9.8

1 $0, 5$ **2** $-4, +4$ **3** $-4.90, 4.90$ **4** $0, 8$ **5** $-7, 1$
6 $-5, \frac{1}{2}$ **7** $\frac{2}{3}, 1\frac{1}{2}$ **8** $-0.62, 1.62$ **9** $0.38, 2.62$ **10** $-2.28, -0.22$
11 $-1.47, 1.14$ **12** $-\frac{1}{2}, 7$ **13** $2, 5$ **14** $-8, \frac{1}{13}$ **15** $2, 3$
16 $-1.83, 3.83$ **17** $-\frac{1}{7}, 4$ **18** $-2, 1$

Exercise 9.9

1 $5\frac{1}{4}$, if $3(x+1)$ is hypotenuse; 7, if $4x-3$ is hypotenuse.   **2** 9 cm, 13 cm
3 32 m   **4** 14 and 30   **5** 25 and 48   **6** 9 km/h   **7** 20 min,
25 min   **8** 20   **9** 9   **10** 500   **11** 18   **12** 40 km/h
13 2   **14** 3 km/h

Exercise 9.10

1 (a) $\{x : x < -3\} \cup \{x : x > 5\}$ (b) $\{x : 0 \leqslant x \leqslant 5\}$
(c) $\{x : x \leqslant -2\} \cup \{x : x \geqslant 2\}$ (d) $\{x : -5 < x < 1\frac{2}{3}\}$ (e) $\{x : x < -\frac{3}{4}\} \cup \{x : x > 4\frac{1}{2}\}$
(f) $\{x : x \leqslant -\frac{1}{2}\} \cup \{x : x \geqslant 0\}$ (g) $\{x : 2 < x < 8\}$ (h) $\{x : x < -6\} \cup \{x : x > 7\}$
(i) $\{x : x \leqslant -\frac{1}{2}\} \cup \{x : x \geqslant 5\}$
(j) $\{x : -1 \leqslant x \leqslant 2\frac{1}{3}\}$ **2** (a) $\{x : x < -2\} \cup \{x : x > 8\}$ (b) $\{x : -5 < x < -1\}$;
$\{x : -5 < x < -2\} \cup \{x : -1 < x < 8\}$

Exercise 9.11

1 (a) 0; $x = -2$ (b) -33; $x = -5$ (c) $+6$; $x = +1$ (d) -29; $x = +6$
(e) $-\frac{1}{2}$; $x = -1\frac{1}{4}$ (f) $+\frac{7}{8}$, $x = +\frac{1}{4}$ **2** 3 **3** (a) $6\frac{1}{4}$, (b) $\frac{1}{4}$, (c) $6\frac{1}{8}$
4 0; $x = -3$
5 $a = 1$, $b = 4$; min 4 when $x = -1$

Exercise 9.12

1 $(\frac{1}{2}, -12\frac{1}{4})$ **2** (a) $b^2 - 4ac = -7$, number of intercepts $= 0$
(b) 36; 2 (c) 0; 1 (d) 4; 2 (e) -4; 0 (f) -8; 0
3
(a) Min$(-1\frac{1}{2}, 1\frac{3}{4})$ (b) Min$(3, -9)$

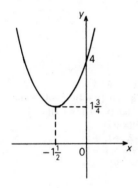

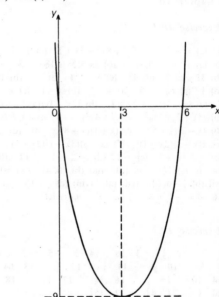

(c) Min$(2, 0)$

417

(d) Max$(0, 1)$ **(e)** Min$(-2, 1)$ **(f)** Min$(1, 1)$

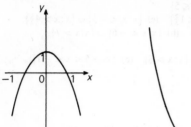

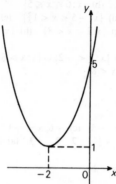

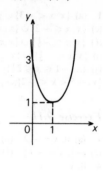

4 (a) $\{x : x < -3\} \cup \{x : x > 9\}$ (b) true for all x except 1
(c) $\{x : -5 \leqslant x \leqslant -2\}$ **5** $x^2 + 8x + 17 = (x + 4)^2 + 1 \geqslant 1$

Chapter 10

Exercise 10.1

1 (a) $x^3 - 1$ (b) $4x^3 + 8x^2 - 7x + 1$ (c) $1 - 8x^2 + 4x^3 + 3x^4$
2 (a) $x^2 + x - 4$; $+2$ (b) $2x + 5$; $+18$ **3** (a) 13
(b) 31   (c) 7   (d) 43   (e) 1   **4** (a) 71   (b) 19   (c) $-\frac{1}{4}$
(d) 1   (e) $6\frac{7}{9}$ **5** (a) $x - 2$ (b) $x - 1$ (c) $x - 1$ (d) $x + 1$ **6** $k = 2$
7 (a) $(x - 2)(x^2 + 2x + 4)$ (b) $(2x - 3y)(4x^2 + 6xy + 9y^2)$ **8** (a) $(x + 4)(x^2 - 4x + 16)$
(b) $(5x + 2y)(25x^2 - 10xy + 4y^2)$ **9** $a = 4, b = -2$ **10** (a) $(x - 1)(2x + 1)(x - 8)$
(b) $(x - 2)(x + 5)^2$ (c) $(x + 1)(x + 8)(x - 8)$ (d) $(x - 1)(2x - 3)(x + 2)$
(e) $x(x - 1)(2x - 1)^2$ (f) $(x - 3)(3x + 1)(2x + 5)$ **11** (a) $-2, +1, +5$
(b) $-2, 0, +1$ (c) -1 (d) $-2, \frac{1}{3}, 1$ **12** 1016   **13** $a = 5, k = 25$
14 (i) (c); $\{\frac{2}{3}\}$;   (ii) (d);   (iii) (b), $\{0, 4\}$ (iv) (a);   (v) (b), $\{-3, 9\}$
(vi) (b), $\{-6, 0\}$;   (vii) (a);   (viii) (d)   **15** (a) 2,   (b) -2
16 $a = -1, n = -1$ $[a = 0 = n$, trivial$]$

Exercise 10.2

1 7   **2** $\frac{1}{2}$ **3** 16   **4** 5   **5** -2 **6** $\frac{1}{16}$ **7** 1   **8** $\frac{1}{8}$
9 $\frac{1}{25}$ **10** $\frac{1}{81}$ **11** $\frac{1}{4}$ **12** $\frac{1}{4}$ **13** 64
14 10   **15** $\frac{3}{4}$ **16** $1\frac{1}{5}$ **17** $1\frac{9}{16}$ **18** $1\frac{1}{7}$ **19** $\frac{2197}{1331}$
20 $\frac{2}{3}$ **21** $4\frac{3}{4}$ **22** $15\frac{1}{2}$

Exercise 10.3

1 2   **2** -1 **3** -2 **4** 2   **5** -1 **6** 3   **7** 0.5
8 0   **9** -3 **10** -2 **11** 5   **12** 1.5

Exercise 10.4

1 2   **2** 1   **3** -1 **4** 3.5   **5** 3   **6** 1   **7** 1.5   **8** 2   **9** 2
10 1   **11** 1   **12** -3

Exercise 10.5

1 (a) 1.661 (b) 3.322 (c) 0.6990   **2** (a) 1.404 (b) 3.170
(c) -0.431 **3** (a) 2.0334 (b) 0.9031 (c) 0.5927   **4** (a) $\log 100x \sqrt[3]{y}$
(b) $\log 4$ **5** 1.893   **6** (a) 0.712 (b) -2

7 $\dfrac{1}{y^3 - 1}$ **8** $10x^2$ **9** $36 \log 2 = 10.836$ **10** 10

Exercise 10.6

1 $2n$ **2** $4n-1$ **3** $5n-9$ **4** $3n-3$ **5** $\frac{1}{2}n+1$
6 $18-5n$ **7** 2^n **8** 3^n **9** 2^{n+1} **10** $3(1\frac{1}{2})^n$
11 $(-2)^n$ **12** $5\left(\frac{1}{2}\right)^{n-1}$ **13** n^2+1 **14** $\frac{1}{2}(n^3-2)$
15 $26-n$ **16** $\dfrac{n}{2^n}$

Exercise 10.7

1 (a) 82 (b) 158   **2** (a) $66\frac{1}{4}$ (b) 297   **3** 1225
4 $\frac{1}{2}n(n+1)$ **5** (a) 208 (b) 203 (c) -390
(d) 418.6   **6** (a) 13 (b) 14 (c) 13 (d) 26   **7** (a) 588
(b) -4680 **8** $a=-47\frac{1}{3}$, $b=-18\frac{2}{3}$ **9** $2\frac{1}{2}, 5\frac{1}{2}, 8\frac{1}{2}$ **10** 2; 222

Exercise 10.8

1 (a) 5^6 (b) $-8(-3)^4 = -648$ (c) $\frac{1}{3}(\frac{1}{3})^5$ (d) $16(-\frac{1}{2})^{11}$
(e) $13(\frac{1}{5})^7$ (f) $4(2)^8$ **2** (a) $\frac{1}{4}(5^7-1)$
(b) $2\{(-3)^5-1\}$ (c) $\frac{3}{14}\{1-(\frac{1}{3})^6\}$ (d) $\frac{32}{3}\{1-(-\frac{1}{2})^{12}\}$ (e) $\frac{65}{4}\{1-(\frac{1}{5})^8\}$
(f) $4(2^9-1)$ **3** (a) 16 (b) 14   **4** $1\frac{1}{2}, 4\frac{1}{2}, 13\frac{1}{2}$ **5** $(x^5-1)/(x-1)$; $x-1$
and $x^4+x^3+x^2+x+1$ **6** $r=-3 \Rightarrow 3, -9, 27, -81, 243$; $r=4 \Rightarrow 3, 12, 48, 192, 768$;
a may be any value.   **7** -2 **8** $-4\frac{1}{2}$ and $+4\frac{1}{2}$ **9** $\frac{2}{9}, \frac{2}{3}, 2$; $S_n = \frac{1}{9}(3^n-1)$
10 $(2^{20}-1)$ p $= £10485.75$ **11** 247.9639 cm

Exercise 10.9

1 (a) $x=3, y=-1$ (b) $x=0, y=2$ or $x=-2, y=0$ (c) $x=5, y=-3$ or $x=11$,
$y=-7$ (d) $x=2, y=3$ or $x=3, y=2$ (e) $x=-4\frac{2}{3}, y=3$ or $x=7, y=-4$
(f) $x=2, y=-3$ or $x=19, y=31$ **2** (a) $x=1, y=1, z=1$ (b) $x=1$,
$y=-1, z=4$ (c) $x=3, y=\frac{1}{2}, z=-1$ (d) $x=0, y=2, z=3$ **3** $a=7$,
$b=-2, c=5$ **4** $a=16, b=-13, c=-3$; $4x+3$

Miscellaneous Exercises B

1 (i) $\{3, 4, 9\}$ (ii) $\{2, 4, 5, 6, 7, 9\}$ (iii) 2   **2** (i) 30, 60, 90 (ii) 9, 27, 45, 63, 81,
99 (iii) (a) M_6, (b) M_4, (c) M_{12}, (iv) 13
3 (d)   **4** (i) $n(A)=42, n(B)=22$; (ii) all are true   **5** 3   **6** (i) 4,
(ii) ± 5 **7** (i) 3, (iv) $\{-2, +4\}$, (v) $y=\dfrac{a}{a-1}$ **8** (i) $2\frac{1}{6}, 2\frac{121}{312}, 2\frac{1}{90}$
(ii) $x=1$, (iv) $x=2$ **9** (i) $2*2=0$ (ii) 1 (iii) 1, 3   **10** $(P, *)$ is not a group
as 5 has no inverse; $\{1, 3, 7, 9\}$ **11** (i) true, (ii) true, (iii) false, e.g. $3*(6+12)=3$;
$(3*6)+(3*12)=6$ (iv) true, (v) true, (vi) false   **12** (i) $(2x-3)(x+2)$
(ii) $\dfrac{2x-3}{x-2}$ **13** (a) $(p+q)(x+2y)$, (b) $\dfrac{2x+17}{(2x-5)(x+3)}$ **14** (i) $(2x+3)(3x-5)$,

(ii) $x = -1\frac{3}{5}$, (iii) $x = \pm\sqrt{\dfrac{4a-b^2}{3}}$ **15** (i) $(1000-308x)$p (ii) $x = 3$,

$y = -2$ (iii) $\dfrac{x+y}{12}$ **16** (i) (a), $x = \frac{1}{3}$; (ii) (c); (iii) (b), $x = -6$ or 0; (iv) (b),

$x = -3$ or 9   **17** (a) $x = -3$ or 4 (b) $\{x:x \leqslant -3\} \cup \{x:x \geqslant 4\}$ **18** (i) 14,
(ii) $-2, 3$, (iii) $-2 < x < 3$ **19** (a) $x < 1$, (b) $-3 < x < 3$; $\{x: -3 < x < 1\}$

20 (i) $x = 4.35, -0.35$; $y = 0.23, -2.90$ $\left(y = \dfrac{1}{x}\right)$ (ii) $\dfrac{x^2}{x+2}$ **21** $A = 2\frac{1}{2}$,

$B = -\frac{1}{2}$ **22** (a) $5:1$, (b) (i) 48, (ii) $28(-28)$ **23** $-\frac{2}{3}; 0, 2; a = -2$
24 $a = 0, b = 1, c = 4$ **25** $t = 5, y = 3x+5$ **26** $y = 2x+3; x = 1$,
$y = 5; 13$ **27** 97   **28** (i) $x = 0, y = 1$ or $x = -2, y = -3$

(ii) $a = 1, b = -5$ **29** (i) $£\dfrac{50}{x}$ (ii) $£\dfrac{60}{x+5}$ (iii) $x = 25$

(v) $(x+25)(x-10) = 0 \Rightarrow x = 10$ **30** (i) $\dfrac{40}{v}$h (ii) $\dfrac{60}{v+3}$h (iii) 15   **31** (a) $(3x-1)$

and $(x+2)$, (b) $2(x+2)(x-2)$, (c) $x = 9$ **32** (a) (iii), $d = -2\frac{1}{2}$; (b) (i), $r = -\frac{1}{4}$;

(c) -435, (d) -47 (e) $\dfrac{2-x}{-\frac{1}{2}-x} = \dfrac{-\frac{1}{2}-x}{1-x}\left[x = +\dfrac{7}{16}\right]\left[r = -\dfrac{3}{5}\right]$

33 (a) $3+x, 3+2x$, (b) x, x^2, (c) $x = -2, 4$ (d) 3240 (e) 11
34 (a) $x+y \leqslant 14$, (b) $x+7y \leqslant 49$; (i) $x = 10, y = 4$, (ii) $x = 7, y = 6$
35 (a) $4x+3y \leqslant 36, 2x+7y \leqslant 35$; 6.6 acres of cabbage, 3.1 acres of lettuce

Chapter 11

Exercise 11.1

1 $X \times Y = \{a, c), (a, d), (b, c), (b, d)\}$ $Y \times X = \{(c, a), (c, b), (d, a), (d, b)\}$ **2** $X \times Y$
$= \{(1, 2), (2, 2), (3, 2)\}$; $Y \times X = \{(2, 1), (2, 2), (2, 3)\}$ **3** Set of prints of the plane
contained in (including sides) the rectangle defined by the lines $x = 0$, $x = 2$, $y = 0$ and
$y = 1$ **4** $X^2 = \{(1, 1), (1, 2), (1, 3), (2, 1), (2, 2), (2, 3), (3, 1), (3, 2), (3, 3)\}$;
$n(X^2) = 9$ **5** $X \times Y = \{$(John, Austin), (John, B.M.W), (John, Citroen),
(Dave, Austin), (Dave, B.M.W.), (Dave, Citroen), (Fred, Austin), (Fred, B.M.W.), (Fred, Citroen)$\}$,
6 $X \times Y = \{$(Aston Villa, Birmingham), (Aston Villa, London), (Tottenham Hotspur,
Birmingham), (Tottenham Hotspur, London), (Arsenal, Birmingham). (Arsenal London)$\}$;
largest subset: $\{$(Aston Villa, Birmingham), (Tottenham Hotspur, London), (Arsenal,
London)$\}$; relationship: first entry is a soccer club in the city shown by second entry.

Exercise 11.2

1 Relations are: (a), (b), (c), (e), (f), (h), (i)   **2** e.g. 'is married to', 'is younger than',
'has the same nationality as'   **3** (a) 'is associated with the sport of'; $\{$(Boycott,
cricket), (Capes, athletics), (Hunt, motor car racing), (Ovett athletics), (Piggott, horse
racing)$\}$ (b) 'is the author of'; $\{$(Dickens, David Copperfield), (Orwell, 1984), (Orwell,
Animal Farm), (Austin, Pride and Prejudice)$\}$; (c) 'is the venue for international matches
in the sport of'; $\{$(Cardiff Arms Park, rugby), (The Oval, cricket), (Twickenham, rugby),
(Wembly, soccer), (Trent Bridge, cricket)$\}$ (d) 'is the capital of'; $\{$(Paris, France), (Oslo,
Norway), (Helsinki, Finland), (Rome, Italy)$\}$

Exercise 11.3

1 $\{0, 1\}$; into; **2** $\{y:y \geqslant 1\}$, into; **3** $\{1, 2, 3\}$, into; **4** $\{1, 2\}$, onto;
5 $\{11, 12, 20, 21, 30\}$, into; **6** $\{10, 11, 12, 20, 21, 30\}$, into; **7** $\{3, 4, 5, 6\}$, onto;
8 $\{y:0 \leqslant y < 3\}$, into; **9** $\{$Risk, Three Men in a Boat, A Tale of Two Cities,

Persuasion}; into; **10** {William Shakespeare, J. Conrad, Agatha Christie},
into; **12** {France, Japan, Italy, England}, into; **13** Y; onto; **13** {Newton,
Napoleon, Charles I, Milton, Pascal}, into;

Exercise 11.4

1 One–one; 2, 3, 9, 12 (if answered as in Ex. 11.3); one–many; 5, 6, 7, 8, 13; many–one: 1,
10; many–many: 4, 11, 14   **2** (a) one-one; (b) many-many; (c) many-one;
(d) hopefully one-one, but other possibilities; (e) many–many   **3** (a) $\mathbb{R}$; one-one;
(b) non-negative real numbers; many-one; (c) $\mathbb{R}$; one-one; (d) $\{x:x \geqslant 1\}$; many-one
4   many–many   **5** many–many

Exercise 11.5

1 (c)   **2** (a), (c)   **3** (a), (b), (c)   **4** (a), (b), (c)   **5** (a), (b), (c)   **6** (a),
(c)   **7** (a), (b), (c)   **8** (b)   **9** (a), (b), (c) [open to discussion: could be England
players, for example, but not in same league team]   **10** (a), (b), (c) [practically
(c) unlikely; if measured to the nearest cm, for example]   **11** (a), (b), (c) [Christians];
(c) may not be true   **12** (a), (b), (c)   **13** (a), (b), (c)   **14** (a), (b), (c)
equivalence relations: 3, 4, 5, 7, 9, 10, 11, 12, 13, 14

Exercise 11.6

1 (a) $r_1, r_2, r_4, r_5, r_7, r_8, r_9$,   (b) Dylan Thomas; 4; St. Andrews; France   (c) all are
many valued except r_9 where $x = $ Oslo   **2** (a) $\mathbb{R}$, (b) $\mathbb{R}$, (c) $\mathbb{R}$, (d) $\{x:x \geqslant 0\}$
(e) $\{x:x \in \mathbb{R}, x \neq 1\}$ (f) $\{x:x > 0\}$ **3**   (a) $\{3, 5, 7, 9\}$, $\{f_2(x): -9 \leqslant f_2(x) \leqslant 5\}$,
$\{f_3(x): 0 \leqslant f_3(x) \leqslant 18\}$, $\{f_4(x): -1 \leqslant f_4(x) \leqslant 1\}$ $\{f_5(x): 0 \leqslant f_5(x) \leqslant \frac{1}{2}\}$ $\{f_6(x) \geqslant 0\}$, $\mathbb{Z}$,
$\{f_8(x): 0 \leqslant f_8(x) < 1\}$ $\{f_9(x): -1 \leqslant f_9(x) \leqslant 2\}$ (b) (i) $f_2(\frac{1}{4}) = -1$, $f_4(45) = 0.7071$,
$f_5(1.5) = \frac{1}{3}$, $f_8(2\frac{1}{4}) = 0.25$; (ii) -2 or $+2$, 1, $\{x:5 \leqslant x < 6\}$
4 (a) $X = \{x: -\frac{9}{4} < x < \frac{3}{4}\}$; (b) $X = \{x:1 \leqslant x \leqslant 2\}$ or $\{x: -2 \leqslant x \leqslant -1\}$;
(c) $X = \{x:\alpha \leqslant x \leqslant 2, -2 \leqslant \alpha \leqslant 0\}$ or $\{x: -2 \leqslant x \leqslant \beta, 0 \leqslant \beta \leqslant 2\}$
(d) $X = \{x:1 \leqslant x \leqslant 100\}$

Exercise 11.7

1 $fg(5) = 43$, $fg(\frac{4}{5}) = 1$, $gf(0) = 1$, $gf(5) = 51$; $fg:x \to 10x - 7$; $gf:x \to 10x + 1$
2 $fg(1) = -4$, $gf(1) = 16$; $fg:x \to x^2 - 5$; $gf:x \to (x - 5)^2$ **3** $4x = x^2 \Rightarrow x = 0$ or $x = 4$;
$4x^2 = 16x^2 \Rightarrow x = 0$ **5** $fg(4) = -59$, $gf(4) = -59$; $fg:x \to -20x + 21$;
$gf:x \to -20x + 21$ **7** $fg:x \to \dfrac{1}{x^2 - 1}$; $gf:x \to \dfrac{1}{(x - 1)^2}$; no values   **8** $fg(\frac{1}{90}) = 1$,
$gf(90) = 1$, $gf(-90) = -1$, $gf(270) = -1$; $\{x:0 < x < 180\}$ **9**   When $a = 2$, $fg(x) = gf(x)$ when
$x = 1$ or $x = -1$ **10** $f_2 f_3 f_4 :x \to x$, $f_3 f_2 f_4 :x \to x$, $f_4 f_2 f_3 :x \to x$ **11** f_1, f_4, f_5, f_6 self inverse;
$f_2^{-1} = f_3$, $f_3^{-1} = f_2$ **12**   (a) $\{41, 62, 83\}$ (b) (i) $\{10, 26, 50\}$, (ii) $\{x:1 \leqslant x \leqslant 50\}$
(c) (i) $\{\frac{1}{9}, \frac{1}{6}, \frac{1}{3}\}$ (ii) $\{x:\frac{1}{9} \leqslant x \leqslant \frac{1}{3}\}$ (d) (i) $\{5, 7, 13\}$ (ii) $x:x \geqslant 5\}$
13 All composite functions are equivalent to the identity mapping: $x \to x$
14 (a) $g:x \to \frac{1}{2}x$ (b) $g:x \to 7x$ (c) $g:x \to x - 5$

Exercise 11.8

1 (a) $x \to \dfrac{x + 5}{2}$, (b) $x \to 3x - 2$ (c) $x \to \frac{1}{3}(x + 4)$ (d) $x \to -5(x - 4)$

(e) $x \to -\frac{1}{3}(x - 1)$ (f) $x \to \dfrac{x}{2}$ (g) $x \to \dfrac{1 - x}{x}$ (h) $x \to \dfrac{1}{x - 1}$ (i) $x \to \dfrac{5 - x}{4 - x}$

(j) $x \to x^2 - 1$ (k) $x \to 3\sqrt{\dfrac{x}{2}}$ (l) $x \to \dfrac{3x + 2}{1 - x}$ (m) $x \to \dfrac{2x - 1}{x - 2}$ (n) $x \to \sqrt{x - 2}$

2 (a), (b) $\{x:x \geqslant 0\}$ or $\{x:x \leqslant 0\}$ are the largest subsets. (c) $\{x:x \geqslant 1\}$ or $\{x:x \leqslant 1\}$

(d) $\{x:90 \leqslant x \leqslant 270\}$ **3**   (a) $f^{-1}:x \to 2(x-1)$, $g^{-1}:x \to \frac{1}{2}(1-x)$, $(fg)^{-1}:x \to \dfrac{3-2x}{2}$

(b) $f^{-1}:x \to \dfrac{x-2}{7}$, $g^{-1}:x \to 7x+2$, $(fg)^{-1}:x \to x$; (c) $f^{-1}:x \to \sqrt[3]{x}$, $g^{-1}:x \to x-1$,

$(fg)^{-1}:x \to \sqrt[3]{x}-1$; (d) $f^{-1}:x \to \sqrt{x}$, $g^{-1}:x \to \dfrac{x-2}{5}$, $(fg)^{-1}:x \to \dfrac{\sqrt{x}-2}{5}$

Exercise 11.9

1 $f^{-1}:x \to 2(x-1)$, $X = \{x: -\frac{1}{2} \leqslant x \leqslant 2\frac{1}{2}\}$ **2** $f^{-1}:x \to 3-x$,

$X = \{x:0 \leqslant x \leqslant 6\}$;   **3** $f^{-1}:x \to \sqrt{x}-3$, $X = \{x:0 \leqslant x \leqslant 9\}$;

4 $f^{-1}:x \to \dfrac{x^2}{9}$, $X = \{x:0 \leqslant x \leqslant 6\}$

Chapter 12

Exercise 12.1

1 (a) V varies as r^3 (b) T varies as the square root of l (c) A varies as x^2
2 (a) $C = kr^2$ (b) $W = kr^3$ (c) $d = k\sqrt{h}$ (d) $r = kn$
3 (a) $\frac{3}{32}$ (b) 3   (c) 96   **4** (a) new radius: old radius $= 1:\sqrt{2}$
(b) new vol: old vol $= 9:1$ (c) new vol: old vol $= 27:1$

5

	x	1	2	3	4	
(a)	y	7	14	21	28	$n = 1$
(b)	y	4	$4\sqrt{2}$	$4\sqrt{3}$	8	$n = \frac{1}{2}$
(c)	y	$\frac{1}{2}$	8	$40\frac{1}{2}$	128	$n = 4$

6 (a) 32 km   (b) 40 km; $h = 5$ m   **7** $\sqrt{3}(1.73)$s, 16 m

8 38.4 m; $20\sqrt{2}$ (28.28) km/h   **9**   24 or -24 **10** $\dfrac{32}{3}\pi$

Exercise 12.2

1 (a) $\frac{1}{8}$ (b) $\frac{8}{25}$ (c) 1 or -1 **2**   (a) $4\frac{1}{6}$ (b) 25   (c) $12\frac{1}{2}$

3

	x	1	2	$2\frac{1}{2}$	4	
(a)	y	48	12	$7\frac{17}{25}$	3	$n = 2$
(b)	y	1	0.5	0.4	0.25	$n = 1$
(c)	y	64	8	$4\frac{12}{125}$	1	$n = 3$

4 new radius: old radius $= 1:\sqrt{2}$; $3\frac{1}{3}$ cm   **5**   720   **6**   54
7 20.48 kg.f; 50 kg.f   **8** $\frac{1}{2}$(or $-\frac{1}{2}$)   **9** $1\frac{4}{5}$ **10**   10

Exercise 12.3

1 (a) 3125; 64   (b) scaled up by a factor $\sqrt{2}$ **2**   10   **3**   180 kJ
4 2.875 l (2875 cm³)   **5**   100 W $(l_1:l_2 = 15:16)$ **6**   £2.10
7 £726.67 (£726$\frac{2}{3}$)   **8** $S = \frac{1}{2}n(n+1)$; 1275   **9**   6000   **10**   130.5 m; 12 s

Chapter 13

Exercise 13.1

1 (b) $y = (x-1)^2 - 1$; lowest point is $(1, -1)$
(c) $y = (x + 1\frac{1}{2})^2 - 6\frac{1}{4}$; lowest point is $(-1\frac{1}{2}, -6\frac{1}{4})$ 2 $x = 0$, $(0, 0)$; $x = 1\frac{1}{4}$,
$(1\frac{1}{4}, -1\frac{1}{8})$; Min value is $-1\frac{1}{8}$
3 Max value is $2\frac{1}{4}$; translation $\begin{pmatrix} -\frac{1}{2} \\ 2\frac{1}{4} \end{pmatrix}$; $\{x: -\frac{1}{2} < x(\leqslant 3)\}$
4 (a) 2, (b) -2; $(2, -4)$; $\{x: -0.24 < x \leqslant 4\}$
5 (a) 0, (b) 1, (c) 2   6 (a) 1, (b) 3, (c) 1; gradient is 6
7 -16

Exercise 13.2

1 (a) $y = 0$ (x-axis), (b) $y = -1$, (c) $y = 2$ (d) $y = -6$, (e) $y = x - 2$,
(f) $y = 2 - 2x$; $y = -6$ and $y = x^2 - 5x + 2$ do not intersect.   2 (a) $y = 0$
(b) $y = -1$ (c) $y = 1$ (d) $y = x - 1$ (e) $2y = x$ (f) $y = x + 2$ 3 $x = 0$
and $x = 1\frac{1}{2}$ are solutions of $2x^2 - 3x = 0 [-x^2 + 2x = \frac{1}{2}x]$; $x > 1$
4 (a) 0.67, 1.19($\frac{2}{3}$, $1\frac{5}{27}$); (b) ≈ 0.33, 1.4, 2.3; (c) $0.33 \leqslant x \leqslant 1.4$, $x \geqslant 2.3$
5 (a) -2 and 3 (b) $-2 < x < 3$ 6 (a) -1, 4 $[y = 0]$ (b) -1.37, 7.37 $[y = 2]$
(c) 0.27, 3.73 $[y = x - 5]$ (d) -1.24, 3.24 $[y = -x]$
7 (a) -2.39, $1.89 [y = 4]$, (b) -2.16, $1.16 [y = -x]$, (c) -2.64, 1.89;
(d) $(-1.35, -2.7)$ and $(1.85, 3.7)$ $[2y = -x + 10]$ 8 (a) $(-1.6, 0.378)$,
$(2.38, 0.18)$; $x^3 - 6x^2 + 20 = 0$
(b) $110y = 5x + 33$; ≈ -6, -2.2, 1.6

9

x	0.5	1	1.5	2	3	4	5	6
y	0.5	-1	-1.17	-1	-0.33	0.5	1.4	2.33

(a) 0.72, 2.78; (b) 0.92

10 $A = (0, 2)$, $B = (0, 4)$, $C = (0, 3)$, $D = (0, 4)$ In (d) $k = 2$; in (e) $k = -1$
(a) 2, (b) 0, (c) 0, (d) 2, (e) 0, (f) 2

Exercise 13.3

1 About 12.42 h, 95 km from Bristol.   2 Meet at 13.04 h, 56 km from
Cambridge   3 The walker by 9 min   4 45 min   5 (a) almost
10.34 h, (b) $60 < \text{speed} < 100$ (c) 10.41 h   6 About 4.7 km   7 38 km;
5 km   8 21 min   9 12.12 h, about 4.2 km from Birmingham   10 60 km/h and
90 km/h

Exercise 13.4

1 (a) 36.7 (b) 149 (c) 22 (d) at -40 2 (a) 14.20 h (b) 14.57 h   3 Malton
to Pickering; about 3 km past Pickering   4 (a) about 8.15 m/s (b) about
2 m/s^2 (c) about 6 h 9 min   5 (a) about 21.1 km (b) about 49 m   6 (a) just
under 1.3s (b) 5 m (c) after 2.73 s   7 (a) 0.9 cm (b) 0.15–0.2 and
1.9–2.0   8 (a) -1.3, -1, 2.3 (c) $-1.3 < x < -1$ and $0 < x < 2.3$ 9 about
15.9   10 $d^2 = 45$ when $t = 4$ 11 (a) $13\frac{1}{3}\pi$ (b) 1.89

12

x	0.5	0.75	1	1.5	2	3
y	3.25	3.4	4	5.92	8.5	15.33

(a) $x = 1$ (b) ≈ 4.5

Chapter 14

Exercise 14.1

1 (a) 4, (b) 3, (c) 2.2, (d) 2.02, (e) 2.002, (f) $2+2h$ 2 (a) 0, (b) 1, (c) 1.8,
(d) 1.98, (e) 1.998, (f) $2-2h$ 4 $-\frac{1}{2}$ 5 (a) 0, (b) 0, (c) -2, (d) $6x$, (e) $4x^3$,
(f) $-\dfrac{2}{x^3}$ (g) $15x^2$, (h) $-3x^{-4}$, (i) $-5x^{-2}$, (j) $-8x^{-5}$ 6 (a) 96 m/s, (b) 150 m/s,
(c) 2.5, (d) 54 7 (a) 108 m, (b) 36 m/s 8 (a) 640 m, (b) 270 m/s,
(c) 370 m 9 (a) 33, (b) 2, (c) $-8\frac{1}{4}$, (d) -4, (e) -11, (f) 0 10 (a) 9,
(b) $-\frac{1}{27}$, (c) -5

Exercise 14.2

1 (a) $4x-y-4=0$, (b) $9x-y-36=0$, (c) $4x-y+6=0$ (d) $x+y-3=0$,
(e) $x-y-1=0$ 2 $(3,9)$, $x+12y-111=0$ 4 $27x+8y-72=0$
5 $4x-y-6=0$, $x+4y-10=0$, 8.5 6 (a) $(2,-1)$ min; (b) $(-\frac{1}{2}, 2\frac{1}{4})$ max,
(c) $(-1,1)$ min (d) $(-1,2)$ max, $(1,-2)$ min; (e) $(2,4)$ min, $(-2,-4)$ max
7 $12x-y-3=0$; $2x+24y-73=0$; 3/8, 55.5 8 $-6\frac{1}{8}$ 12 3
14 10.84 cm, 5.42 cm 15 2040, 14.7 16 $p=2x+24/x$; $2\sqrt{3}$
17 24.3 18 19 m/s 19 1.92π cm^2/s 20 2.7π cm^2/s
21 $\dfrac{16\pi}{3}$ cm^2/s, $\dfrac{16\pi}{3}$ cm^2/s 22 31.6 cm^2/s

Chapter 15

Exercise 15.1

1 (b) 52 m 2 35 m 3 128 m, 32 m/s 4 18 m/s^2, 138 m
6 $\dfrac{dy}{dx}=2$, $y=2x-14$ 7 $y=c-x^2$, $y=20-x^2$ 8 $6x^5$, $y=\dfrac{4x^6}{3}+C$
9 $-6x^{-7}$, $y=\dfrac{4x^{-6}}{3}+C$ 10 $S=7t-5t^2+4$ 11 $y=\dfrac{4}{x}-5$
12 $y=\dfrac{x^2}{2}+\dfrac{1}{2x^2}+3$ 13 x^4-x^2-9 14 $\dfrac{3x^4}{2}+C$ 15 $C-x^{-1}$
16 x^2-5x+C 17 $\dfrac{x^4}{4}-x^3+C$ 18 $\dfrac{x^3}{3}-x^2+x+C$
19 $3x-x^{-2}+C$ 20 $C-3x^{-1}-\dfrac{x^2}{2}$

Exercise 15.2

1 (a) 18, (b) 52, (c) $\frac{1}{2}$, (d) $-\frac{3}{8}$, (e) 0, (f) $13\frac{11}{15}$ (g) $1\frac{1}{3}$,
(h) $2\frac{2}{5}$ 2 10.5 3 (a) $8\frac{2}{3}$, (b) 60, (c) -18, (d) $-\frac{3}{4}$, (e) $\dfrac{64\sqrt{2}}{15}$ 4 (a) $20\frac{5}{6}$,
(b) $-13\frac{1}{2}$, (c) $\frac{1}{6}$, (d) $-21\frac{1}{6}$ 5 (a) $1\frac{1}{2}$, (b) $2\frac{1}{2}$, (c) 4 6 3 7 (a) 36,
(b) -36 8 $1\frac{1}{3}$ 9 $\frac{5}{6}$ 10 $22\frac{1}{2}$ 11 $\dfrac{1023\pi}{5}$ 12 24π 13 (a) $\dfrac{3\pi}{4}$,
(b) $\dfrac{8\pi}{15}$, (c) $\dfrac{26\pi}{9}$, (d) $\dfrac{65\pi}{2}$ 15 $\dfrac{625\pi}{3}$ cm^3

Exercise 15.3

2 620 m 3 (a) 122, (b) 102.5 4 13.8 5 1.6

Miscellaneous Exercises C

1 (i) $\{5, 0, -3\}$ (ii) $\{0, 1, 3, 4\}$ **2** $b = 4$; (i) $2 < x < 3$ (ii) $x = 1$
3 $gf: x \to 18x^2 - 24x + 9$; $a = 1$, $b = 1$; $fgh(-2) = 7$; $-3, 1$
4 (a) $f^{-1} = \{(1, 3), (2, 2), (3, 1)\}$, $g^{-1} = \{(1, 2), (2, 1), (3, 3)\}$ $fog = \{(1, 2), (2, 3), (3, 1)\}$,
$gof = \{(1, 3), (2, 1), (3, 2)\}$ (b) $R \times T = \{(2, 60), (2, 90), (5, 60), (5, 90)\}$; $(2, 60)$ and

$(2, 90)$; 1.04 cm **5** (a) (i) $f\{g(x)\}: x \to \dfrac{x^2}{2} + 1$, (ii) $g\{f(x)\}: x \to \dfrac{x^2}{4} + x + 1$; $0 \le x \le 4$

(iii) $f^{-1}: x \to 2(x - 1)$; $0 \le f(x) \le 2$, $0 \le g(x) \le 4$, $-6 \le f^{-1}(x) \le 2$ (b) A, C, E, B, D

6 (i)

x	1	2	3	4	5	...	20	21
$f(x)$	7	7	8	8	8		13	14

(ii) (a) 9, 10, 11 (b) no solution (iii) 9, 10, 11 (iv) 15, 16, 17, 18, 19, 20, 21

(v) 10 **7** 4 **8** $D = \dfrac{kv^2}{R}$; (i) 88, (ii) 9600, (iii) 46 **9** Missing entries:

$-14, -5, 1, -5, -9$; $x \approx -1.6, 2.35$; $a = 4$, $b = -3$, $c = -15$ **10** 4, -4;
(i) $\approx 0.7, 3.4$; $-1.5, 4.2$ (ii) 10 **11** (a) 20.7 (b) $1.61 < x < 5.36$ (c) ≈ 24.3 cm^3
(d) 3.65 **12** $2x^2 - 9x + 8 = 0$, $x \approx 1.22, 3.28$ **13** Missing entries for y:3.5, 2.67, 3.2,
3.83 (a) $x \approx 3.3(2)$, min $\approx 2.6(3)$, (b) 1.76, 6.24; ≈ 0.55 **14** (i) $83\frac{1}{8}$
(ii) 82.83 **15** (i) $5\frac{1}{3}$ (ii) 14.14 **16** 64 cm^3
17 (a) 2, (b) 3, (c) $14\frac{2}{3}$ **18** (i) $a = \frac{1}{4}$, $b = 4$, R is $(\frac{7}{8}, 2\frac{1}{8})$;
(ii) $1:4$ **19** $(-2, 0)$, $(2, 0)$, $(0, 4)$ (a) $10\frac{2}{3}$ (b) $8\pi(25.136)$ **20** (i) -9.15
(ii) $1\frac{1}{2}$ (iii) $14\frac{3}{4}$ (iv) 14 **21** (i) 6.3 (ii) 90 **22** (i) $a = -2$, $b = 4$,

(ii) $\frac{1}{6}$ **23** $y = 2x - \dfrac{1}{x} + 1$ **24** (a) 2 cm/s (b) $2\frac{1}{2}$s (c) -7 cm/s^2
(d) $3\frac{1}{8}$ cm/s (e) $4\frac{2}{3}$ cm **25** (i) 3 m/s^2 (ii) $13\frac{1}{4}$ m/s
(iii) $13\frac{1}{6}$ m

Chapter 16

Exercise 16.1

1 (a) 58°, (b) 47°, (c) $22\frac{1}{2}°$ **2** (a) 133°, (b) 67° (c) $112\frac{1}{2}°$ **3** 96°,
84° **4** 37°, 143° **5** 113°, 38° **6** QRN, NAS, KQR **7** 139°, 41°,
41° **8** (a) 60°, (b) 100°, (c) 15° **9** (a) 180°, (b) 30°, (c) 342°,
(d) 600° **10** $65\frac{5}{11}$ **12** 133°, 113°

Exercise 16.2

1 30° **2** 82°, 53° **3** 048° **4** 189° **5** 112°, 37° **6** 58°, 23°

Exercise 16.3

1 71°, 32°, 77° **2** 30°, 60°, 90° **3** $x = 19$; 64°, 41°, 75°
4 25 **5** 120° **6** 2340° **7** 18°, 162°
8 24 **9** 8 **10** 120 **12** 9, $x = 105$, $y = 157\frac{1}{2}$
13 7 **14** (a) 10, (b) 42 **15** 20, 24.

Chapter 17

Exercise 17.1

1 $A = 48.5°$, $B = 93°$, $C = 38.5°$ **2** no triangle since $AB + BC = CA$
3 $A = 50°$, $AC = 4.6$ cm, $BC = 4.1$ cm **4** $BC = 5.96$ cm, $B = 93.5°$,

$C = 38.5°$ **5** $A = 50°$; triangles similar   **6** $AC = 4.5$ cm, $B = 48°$,
$C = 42°$ **7**   no triangle possible   **8** $BC = 6.4$ cm, $B = 51.5°$,
$C = 38.5°$ **9**   two triangles possible $AB_1 = 9.6$ cm, $B_1 = 44.5°$, $C_1 = 105.5°$
$AB_2 = 2.5$ cm, $B_2 = 135.5°$, $C_2 = 14.5°$ **10**   no triangle possible
11 $AB = 6.1$ cm, $B = 90°$, $C = 60°$ **12**   no triangle possible.

Exercise 17.2

4 $BC = QR$, $A\hat{B}C = P\hat{Q}R$, $A\hat{C}B = P\hat{R}Q:80°$

Exercise 17.3

1 $108°, 138°$ **2** $133°$ **3** $64°$ **4** $42°$ **8** $150°$
9 48 cm², 9.6 cm   **15** $5(\sqrt{5}-1)$ cm

Exercise 17.4

1 2 cm   **2** 2 cm   **3** $4\frac{1}{2}$ cm, $6\frac{2}{3}$ cm   **4** 16 cm, 14.4 cm
5 26 cm, 19.5 cm   **7** $4\frac{2}{3}$ cm   **8** 6 cm   **10** $6\frac{1}{4}$ cm

Exercise 17.5

1 $3\frac{1}{3}$ cm, 10 cm   **2** 4 cm, 12 cm   **3** 3.6 cm, 20 cm   **4** 6 cm, 2.4 cm

Chapter 18

Exercise 18.1

1 15 cm   **2** 12.7 cm   **3** 6 cm   **4** 5.77 cm   **5** 16 cm   **6** 8.5 cm
7 4.5 cm   **11** 12.5 cm   **13** 21 cm   **14** $(4, -3)$

Exercise 18.2

1 $A = 70°, B = 50°, C = 60°$ **2** $59°, 121°$
3 $58°$ **4** $53°, 37°$ **5** $50°, 110°$
8 $A = 93°, B = 127°, C = 87°, D = 53°$
9 $24, 44$ **13** $81°, 41°$ **14** $120°$ **15** $45°, 135°$
16 $72°, 36°, 18°$ **21**   (a) rectangle,   (b) square

Exercise 18.3

1 $62°$ **2** $55°, 125°$ **3** $148°$ **4** $140°, 140°$ **5** $57°, 64°, 123°$
6 $138°, 71°$ **7** $37°$ **9** 12 cm   **10** 34 cm   **12** 5 cm   **15** 30 cm
16 2 cm   **17** $P = 65°, Q = 58°, R = 57°$ **18** $A = 80°, B = 60°, C = 40°$
19 4 cm   **20** $P = 113°, Q = 37°, R = 30°$ **21** $A = 32°, B = 80°, C = 68°$
22 $P = 98\frac{1}{2}°, Q = 82\frac{1}{2}°, R = 81\frac{1}{2}°, S = 97\frac{1}{2}°$ **24** $35°, 20°$ **28** 12 cm
29 19.1 cm, 12 cm

Exercise 18.4

1 8.1 cm   **2** 11 cm   **3** 7 cm   **4** 3.75 cm   **5** 7.83 cm   **6** 5 cm
7 $2, 6$ **8** 7 cm   **9** $3\sqrt{2}$ cm   **10** 24 cm   **11** $5\frac{7}{18}$ cm   **12** 6 m

Chapter 19

Exercise 19.1

1 Mediator of AB   **2** Two lines parallel to AB at a distance 3 cm from AB   **3** A line parallel to given lines, $2\frac{1}{2}$ cm from each   **4** The internal and external angle bisectors of the acute angle between the given lines   **5** Constant angle locus (see Figure 19.14)   **6** Two concentric circles, centre C of radii 3 cm and 5 cm   **7** Mediator of AB

8   **9**   **10**

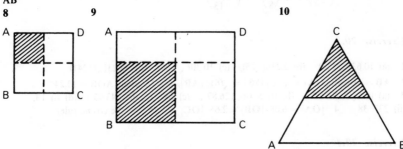

11 (a) plane perpendicular to AB through mid-point of AB (b) two planes through 0, perpendicular to the angle bisectors   **12** The surface of a solid consisting of a cylinder, radius 3 cm and length 5 cm, enclosed at each end by hemispheres, centres A and B, each of radius 3 cm   **13** Line perpendicular to plane ABCD through centre of square   **14** Line perpendicular to plane ABC through circumcentre of triangle ABC   **15** Circle of radius 6 cm. Curved surface of a cone of height 8 cm and base radius 6 cm.

Exercise 19.2

3 (a) 4.1 cm, (b) 5 cm, (c) 5.1 cm   **4** (a) 1.9 cm, (b) 2 cm, (c) 1.8 cm
5 6.2 cm   **11** 3.75 cm   **14** 3.4 cm   **15** 7.8 cm

Miscellaneous Exercises D

1 66°   **2** 30°   **4** $\hat{Q} = 124°, \hat{X} = 28°, \hat{Y} = 28°$ **5** 72°,
72°, 72°, 144°   **6** 15   **7** 100°, 50°   **8** ≈ 41.9 m   **11** (a) Perpendicular bisector of line XY (b) pair of lines parallel to XY, each distance 3 cm from XY
13 (a) (i) 4 cm (ii) 25 : 16; AE $= 2\frac{1}{2}$ cm   **14** ≈ 4.4 cm
18 PQ = 3 cm, QC $= 4\frac{1}{2}$ cm   **19** 36°   **20** 39°, 24°
21 (i) 106° (ii) 74° (iii) 70°   **22** 121°   **24** 4.2 cm, 8.2 cm
25 $AC^2 : BD^2$; $AD^2 : BC^2$

Chapter 20

Exercise 20.1

1 (a) boys and girls (b) no (c) 59 (d) 69 (e) s_1 and s_3
(f) $s_1 = 17b + 15g, s_2 = 18b + 13g$ **3** (a) 16 (b) $7a + 3b + 11c + d$

Exercise 20.2

1 (a) $3\mathbf{a}+8\mathbf{b}$ (b) $3\mathbf{a}+8\mathbf{b}$ (c) $7\mathbf{a}-2\mathbf{b}$ (d) $7\mathbf{a}-2\mathbf{b}$ (e) $\begin{pmatrix}12\\10\end{pmatrix}$ (f) $\begin{pmatrix}7\\2\end{pmatrix}$

(g) $5\mathbf{a}-2\mathbf{b}$ (h) $5\mathbf{a}-2\mathbf{b}$ 2 (a) $-\mathbf{a}+7\mathbf{b}$ (b) $\mathbf{a}-7\mathbf{b}$ (c) $2\mathbf{b}$

(d) $-2\mathbf{b}$ (e) $\begin{pmatrix}3\\3\end{pmatrix}$ (f) $\begin{pmatrix}5\\-3\end{pmatrix}$ 3 (a) $30\mathbf{a}+10\mathbf{b}$ (b) $3\mathbf{a}-3\mathbf{b}$

(c) $5\mathbf{a}+\mathbf{b}$ (d) $\begin{pmatrix}4\\-8\end{pmatrix}$ (e) $\begin{pmatrix}9\\8\end{pmatrix}$ (f) $\begin{pmatrix}-10\\13\end{pmatrix}$

Exercise 20.3

1 (a) $10.63(\sqrt{113})$, (b) $2.236(\sqrt{5})$, (c) $10.30(\sqrt{106})$ (d) $35.23(\sqrt{1241})$
2 $\mathbf{AB}=4\mathbf{i}+4\mathbf{j}$; $|\mathbf{OA}|=\sqrt{5}$, $|\mathbf{OB}|=\sqrt{61}$, $|\mathbf{AB}|=\sqrt{32}$; angle AOB $=13.24°$
3 (a) (i) $\sqrt{2}$, (ii) $45°$; (b) (i) 5, (ii) $126.87°$; (c) (i) $\sqrt{5}$, (ii) $243.43°$; (d) (i) 13,
(ii) $337°\,38'$ 4 $|\mathbf{OA}|=6.08$, $|\mathbf{OB}|=2.65$, $|\mathbf{OC}|=3.46$ (use the cosine rule)

Exercise 20.4

1 $\mathbf{a}$ is parallel to $3\mathbf{a}$ and $|\mathbf{a}|=\frac{1}{3}|3\mathbf{a}|$ 2 $\begin{pmatrix}c\\d\end{pmatrix}=k\begin{pmatrix}a\\b\end{pmatrix}$ 3 $\mathbf{a}=-\mathbf{b}$

4 parallel (in opposite direction) 5 $\mathbf{AB}=\begin{pmatrix}-1\\-6\end{pmatrix}$; $\mathbf{OM}=\begin{pmatrix}1\frac{1}{2}\\1\end{pmatrix}$; $\mathbf{AC}=\begin{pmatrix}-\frac{2}{3}\\-4\end{pmatrix}$; yes;

2:1. 6 no 7 $\mathbf{OE}=\dfrac{\mathbf{a}+\mathbf{b}}{2}$, $\mathbf{OF}=\dfrac{\mathbf{b}+\mathbf{c}}{2}$, $\mathbf{OG}=\dfrac{\mathbf{c}+\mathbf{d}}{2}$; $\dfrac{\mathbf{a}+\mathbf{b}+\mathbf{c}+\mathbf{d}}{4}$ 8 (a) $\mathbf{b}-\mathbf{a}$

(b) $\mathbf{c}-\mathbf{b}$ (c) $\mathbf{d}-\mathbf{c}$ (d) $\mathbf{a}-\mathbf{b}$ (e) $\mathbf{d}-\mathbf{a}$ (f) $-\mathbf{d}$ (g) $\mathbf{b}-\mathbf{d}$;
$\mathbf{OA}+\mathbf{AB}+\mathbf{BC}+\mathbf{CD}=\mathbf{OD}=\mathbf{d}$,
$\mathbf{BE}=\frac{1}{2}(\mathbf{c}-\mathbf{b})$, $\mathbf{CE}=\frac{1}{2}(\mathbf{b}-\mathbf{c})$, $\mathbf{OE}=\frac{1}{2}(\mathbf{b}+\mathbf{c})$, $\mathbf{FD}=\mathbf{d}-\frac{3}{4}\mathbf{c}$
9 $\mathbf{BC}=\mathbf{b}-\mathbf{a}$; $\mathbf{AD}=3\mathbf{b}-2\mathbf{a}$ 10 (a) $4\mathbf{i}+9\mathbf{j}$ (b) $-\mathbf{i}-16\mathbf{j}$

Exercise 20.5

1 (a) $k=3$, (b) $m=2$, (c) no value of n 3 (a) $\mathbf{b}$, (b) $-\mathbf{a}$, (c) $2\mathbf{b}$,
(d) $\mathbf{a}+\mathbf{b}$, (e) $\mathbf{b}-\mathbf{a}$ 4 $h=-3$, $k=-3$ 5 $h=1\frac{7}{13}$, $k=-\frac{3}{13}$
6 $\mathbf{c}=\frac{1}{12}\mathbf{a}$; $|\mathbf{a}|:|\mathbf{c}|=12:1$ 8 (a) rectangle, (b) rhombus 9 (a) $\mathbf{a}$,
(b) $2\mathbf{b}-2\mathbf{a}$, (c) $-\mathbf{b}$, (d) $\mathbf{a}-2\mathbf{b}$; area OBCD$=\frac{3}{4}$area OAB 11 DC$=5$BA; area
trapezium BDCA: area triangle OBA $=24:1$ 12 $\mathbf{AB}=\mathbf{b}-\mathbf{a}$, $\mathbf{AC}=\frac{5}{8}(\mathbf{b}-\mathbf{a})$,
$\mathbf{OC}=\frac{1}{8}(5\mathbf{b}+3\mathbf{a})$; $\mathbf{DC}=\frac{1}{8}\{3\mathbf{a}+(5-8\lambda)\mathbf{b}\}$; (a) $\lambda=\frac{5}{8}$, (b) $\lambda=\frac{1}{4}$ 13 $\mathbf{DB}=\frac{1}{3}(\mathbf{b}-\mathbf{a})$,
$\mathbf{BE}=\frac{1}{2}\mathbf{a}$, $\mathbf{DE}=\frac{1}{6}\mathbf{a}+\frac{1}{3}\mathbf{b}$; $\mathbf{OF}=2(\mathbf{a}+\mathbf{b})$; AF:DE $=6:1$ 14 (a) 3, (b) 5.196;
(a) 2.572, (b) 6.587 15 5 units: circle, centre O, radius 5 units; the defined
circle. 16 Circle, centre A, radius 2 units; perpendicular bisector of the line joining A and
B.

Exercise 20.6

1 (a) $28\frac{4}{7}$s, (b) 200 s 2 240 s; average speed $=1\frac{3}{4}$ m/s 3 4.878 h
4 (a) G.S. $=224$ k, track $=350°$; (b) G.S. $=212$ k, track $=302°$;
(c) W.V. $=33.6$ k, $219°$; (d) W.V. $=34.6$ k, $299°$; (e) course $=032°$, G.S. $=223$ k;
(f) Course $=247°$, G.S. $=277$ k 5 (a) $66.4°$ to upward bank; 4.58 m; 43.6 s
(b) 80 m; (c) $\approx 84.4°$ to bank; (d) straight across 6 (a) drift $=39°$,
(b) drift $=21.6°$ 7 $029.9°$ 8 56.6 min; $025.5°$ 9 $008.5°$; 607 n.m.
10 $198°$ 11 AB: $345.5°$; BC: $090°$; CD: $194.5°$; DA: $270°$; time $=79$ min
12 63.4 k from $037°$ 13 48 n.m.

Chapter 21

Exercise 21.1

1 (a) $\begin{pmatrix} 19 & 23 \\ 19 & -5 \end{pmatrix}$ (b) $\begin{pmatrix} 21 & 14 \\ 11 & 7 \end{pmatrix}$ (c) $\begin{pmatrix} 3 & -3 \\ -1 & 4 \end{pmatrix}$ (d) $\begin{pmatrix} -1 & 8 \\ -3 & 4 \end{pmatrix}$

(e) $\begin{pmatrix} 10 & 11 \\ 8 & 0 \end{pmatrix}$ (f) $\begin{pmatrix} 18 & 17 \\ 12 & 3 \end{pmatrix}$ (g) $\begin{pmatrix} -3 & 3 \\ 1 & -4 \end{pmatrix}$ (h) $\begin{pmatrix} 8 & 6 \\ 4 & 3 \end{pmatrix}$

Exercise 21.2

1 (a) $\begin{pmatrix} 10 \\ 16 \end{pmatrix}$ (b) $\begin{pmatrix} 10 \\ 24 \end{pmatrix}$ (c) (15) (d) $\begin{pmatrix} 15 & 27 & 54 \\ 12 & 19 & 29 \end{pmatrix}$ (e) $(17 \quad 50)$ (f) $\begin{pmatrix} 3 & 4 \\ 5 & 6 \end{pmatrix}$

(g) $\begin{pmatrix} 15 & 35 \\ 6 & 14 \end{pmatrix}$ (h) $\begin{pmatrix} 17 & 34 \\ 14 & 10 \end{pmatrix}$ (i) $\begin{pmatrix} 29 & 31 \\ 8 & -2 \end{pmatrix}$ 2 (a) $\begin{pmatrix} 13 & 20 \\ 5 & 8 \end{pmatrix}$

(b) $\begin{pmatrix} 31 & 12 \\ 18 & 7 \end{pmatrix}$ (c) $\begin{pmatrix} 88 & 66 \\ 44 & 33 \end{pmatrix}$ (d) $\begin{pmatrix} 27 & 10 \\ 11 & 4 \end{pmatrix}$ (e) $\begin{pmatrix} 17 & 24 \\ 10 & 14 \end{pmatrix}$ (f) $\begin{pmatrix} 88 & 66 \\ 44 & 33 \end{pmatrix}$

(g) $\begin{pmatrix} 98 & 52 \\ 45 & 23 \end{pmatrix}$ (h) $\begin{pmatrix} -18 & 8 \\ -13 & 1 \end{pmatrix}$ 4 (b) $\begin{pmatrix} 10 & 6 \\ 30 & 19 \\ 6 & 1 \end{pmatrix}$ (c) $\begin{pmatrix} 6 & -24 \\ 15 & -60 \end{pmatrix}$

(d) (-54) (e) $\begin{pmatrix} 22 & -6 \\ -36 & 10 \end{pmatrix}$ (f) $\begin{pmatrix} 4 & -1 \\ -6 & 2 \end{pmatrix}$

(g) $\begin{pmatrix} 4 & -1 \\ -6 & 2 \end{pmatrix}$ (h) $\begin{pmatrix} 2 & 0 \\ 0 & 2 \end{pmatrix}$ (i) $\begin{pmatrix} 2 & 0 \\ 0 & 2 \end{pmatrix}$ (j) $(-66 \quad -45)$ (k) $\begin{pmatrix} 9 & 12 & 11 \\ 34 & 44 & 42 \end{pmatrix}$

(l) $(-381 \quad -492 \quad -471)$ (m) $(-381 \quad -492 \quad -471)$ 5 (a) $\begin{pmatrix} 2 & -11 \\ -1 & 6 \end{pmatrix}$

(b) $\begin{pmatrix} 2 & -11 \\ -1 & 6 \end{pmatrix}$ 6 (a) $\begin{pmatrix} 0 & 0 \\ 0 & 0 \end{pmatrix}$ (b) $\begin{pmatrix} 0 & 0 \\ 0 & 0 \end{pmatrix}$; no, (see (a) and (b))

Exercise 21.3

1 (a) 1, (b) 1, (c) -1, (d) 1, (e) -1, (f) -1, (g) 15, (h) -6

Inverses: (a) $\begin{pmatrix} 4 & -3 \\ -1 & 1 \end{pmatrix}$ (b) $\begin{pmatrix} 5 & -6 \\ -4 & 5 \end{pmatrix}$ (c) $\begin{pmatrix} -1 & 0 \\ 0 & 1 \end{pmatrix}$ (d) $\begin{pmatrix} 1 & 0 \\ 0 & 1 \end{pmatrix}$

(e) $\begin{pmatrix} 0 & 1 \\ 1 & 0 \end{pmatrix}$ (f) $\begin{pmatrix} 1 & 0 \\ 0 & -1 \end{pmatrix}$ (g) $\begin{pmatrix} \frac{2}{15} & \frac{1}{5} \\ -\frac{1}{15} & \frac{2}{5} \end{pmatrix}$ (h) $\begin{pmatrix} 0 & \frac{1}{2} \\ \frac{1}{3} & -1 \end{pmatrix}$ 2 (a) $\begin{pmatrix} 8 & -3 \\ -13 & 5 \end{pmatrix}$

(b) $\begin{pmatrix} \frac{1}{2} & 0 \\ 0 & \frac{1}{2} \end{pmatrix}$ (c) $\begin{pmatrix} 1 & -3 \\ -2 & 7 \end{pmatrix}$ (d) $\begin{pmatrix} 2\frac{1}{2} & -2 \\ 1\frac{1}{2} & -1 \end{pmatrix}$ (e) $\begin{pmatrix} 2 & -1 \\ -1\frac{1}{2} & \frac{1}{2} \end{pmatrix}$ 3 (a) (i) $\begin{pmatrix} 11 \\ 22 \end{pmatrix}$

(ii) $\begin{pmatrix} 11 \\ 22 \end{pmatrix}$ (iii) $\begin{pmatrix} -21 \\ -7 \end{pmatrix}$ (iv) $\begin{pmatrix} -21 \\ -7 \end{pmatrix}$ (b) (i) $\begin{pmatrix} 11 & 10 \\ 22 & 20 \end{pmatrix}$

(ii) $\begin{pmatrix} 11 & 10 \\ 22 & 20 \end{pmatrix}$ (iii) $\begin{pmatrix} -21 & 15 \\ -7 & 5 \end{pmatrix}$ (iv) $\begin{pmatrix} -21 & 15 \\ -7 & 5 \end{pmatrix}$ $\mathbf{AB = AC} \Rightarrow \mathbf{A = 0}$

or $\mathbf{B = C}$ or $\mathbf{A}$ is singular   4 (b), (c) and (e) are singular;

Inverses: (a) $\begin{pmatrix} \frac{1}{2} & -\frac{1}{2} \\ \frac{1}{4} & \frac{1}{4} \end{pmatrix}$ (d) $\begin{pmatrix} 1 & 0 \\ 0 & 1 \end{pmatrix}$ (f) $\begin{pmatrix} \frac{1}{3} & -1 \\ 0 & \frac{1}{2} \end{pmatrix}$.

Exercise 21.4

1 $x = 3, y = 2$ 2 $x = 3, y = -2$ 3 $x = -1, y = 4$
4 $x = 7, y = 5$ 5 $x = 1\frac{1}{2}, y = -2$ 6 $x = 2, y = -1$ 7 $a = -\frac{3}{4}, b = 13$
8 $x = -\frac{1}{3}, k = \frac{4}{9}$ 9 $x = -4, k = -3\frac{1}{2}; x = 2, k = -\frac{1}{2}$ 10 $x = 1, y = -1$

11 $x = -\frac{1}{2}$ or $+5$; $k = -23$ **12** $x = -2, y = 4$; $x = \frac{1}{3}, y = 11$ **13** $+17$

14 $+2$ or -2 **15**   (a) $x = 1\frac{5}{19}, y = \frac{2}{19}$ (c) $x = 1\frac{1}{7}, y = \frac{9}{14}$

Exercise 21.5

1
$$
\begin{pmatrix} 20 & 10 & 35 & 0 \\ 10 & 20 & 30 & 6 \\ 30 & 20 & 50 & 10 \end{pmatrix}
\begin{pmatrix} 3 \\ 5 \\ 2 \\ 20 \end{pmatrix} =
\begin{array}{l} \text{Cost in p} \\ \begin{pmatrix} 180 \\ 310 \\ 490 \end{pmatrix} \end{array}
\begin{array}{l} A \\ B \\ C \end{array}
$$

2 (i)
$$
\begin{pmatrix} 77 & 59 & 102 \\ 65 & 54 & 25 \\ 57 & 117 & 69 \\ 84 & 96 & 34 \end{pmatrix}
\begin{pmatrix} 10 \\ 20 \\ 40 \end{pmatrix} =
\begin{array}{l} \text{Cost in p} \\ \begin{pmatrix} 6030 \\ 2730 \\ 5670 \\ 4120 \end{pmatrix} \end{array}
\begin{array}{l} \text{Tomato} \\ \text{Chicken} \\ \text{Vegetable} \\ \text{Consomme} \end{array}
$$

(ii) Total cash: $(10 \quad 20 \quad 40) \begin{pmatrix} 283 \\ 326 \\ 230 \end{pmatrix} = 18550\text{p}$ ($£185.50$)

3 (a)   (b)

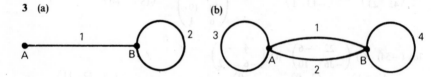

(c)   (d)

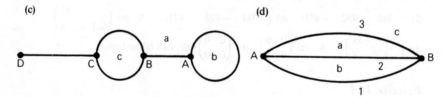

4 (a) $\mathbf{R} = \begin{pmatrix} 2 & 2 & 1 \\ 2 & 0 & 1 \\ 1 & 1 & 0 \end{pmatrix}$ $\mathbf{R}^2 = \begin{pmatrix} 9 & 5 & 4 \\ 5 & 5 & 2 \\ 4 & 2 & 2 \end{pmatrix} = \mathbf{T}$

(b) $\mathbf{R} = \begin{pmatrix} 0 & 2 & 1 & 0 \\ 2 & 0 & 2 & 0 \\ 1 & 2 & 0 & 1 \\ 0 & 0 & 1 & 0 \end{pmatrix}$ $\mathbf{R}^2 = \begin{pmatrix} 5 & 2 & 4 & 1 \\ 2 & 8 & 2 & 2 \\ 4 & 2 & 6 & 0 \\ 1 & 2 & 0 & 1 \end{pmatrix} = \mathbf{T}$

(c) $\mathbf{R} = \begin{pmatrix} 0 & 2 & 1 & 1 & 0 \\ 2 & 0 & 1 & 0 & 1 \\ 1 & 1 & 0 & 1 & 0 \\ 1 & 0 & 1 & 0 & 1 \\ 0 & 1 & 0 & 1 & 0 \end{pmatrix}$ $\mathbf{R}^2 = \begin{pmatrix} 6 & 1 & 3 & 1 & 3 \\ 1 & 6 & 2 & 4 & 0 \\ 3 & 2 & 3 & 1 & 2 \\ 1 & 4 & 1 & 3 & 0 \\ 3 & 0 & 2 & 0 & 2 \end{pmatrix} = \mathbf{T}$

5 (a) $\mathbf{R} = \begin{pmatrix} 0 & 1 & 1 & 1 & 0 \\ 1 & 0 & 1 & 0 & 0 \\ 0 & 1 & 0 & 0 & 0 \\ 1 & 0 & 1 & 0 & 1 \\ 0 & 0 & 0 & 1 & 0 \end{pmatrix}$ $\mathbf{R}^2 = \begin{pmatrix} 2 & 1 & 2 & 0 & 1 \\ 0 & 2 & 1 & 1 & 0 \\ 1 & 0 & 1 & 0 & 0 \\ 0 & 2 & 1 & 2 & 0 \\ 1 & 0 & 1 & 0 & 1 \end{pmatrix} = \mathbf{T}$

(b) $\mathbf{R} = \begin{pmatrix} 0 & 2 & 1 & 0 \\ 1 & 0 & 1 & 0 \\ 0 & 0 & 0 & 1 \\ 0 & 1 & 2 & 0 \end{pmatrix}$ $\mathbf{R}^2 = \begin{pmatrix} 2 & 0 & 2 & 1 \\ 0 & 2 & 1 & 1 \\ 0 & 1 & 2 & 0 \\ 1 & 0 & 1 & 2 \end{pmatrix} = \mathbf{T}$

(c) $\mathbf{R} = \begin{pmatrix} 1 & 2 & 0 & 0 \\ 1 & 0 & 1 & 0 \\ 1 & 1 & 0 & 1 \\ 0 & 0 & 1 & 0 \end{pmatrix}$ $\mathbf{R}^2 = \begin{pmatrix} 3 & 2 & 2 & 0 \\ 2 & 3 & 0 & 1 \\ 2 & 2 & 2 & 0 \\ 1 & 1 & 0 & 1 \end{pmatrix} = \mathbf{T}$

6 (a) (i) $\mathbf{X} = \begin{array}{c} \\ A \\ B \\ C \\ D \end{array}\begin{array}{c} \begin{array}{ccccc} 1 & 2 & 3 & 4 & 5 \end{array} \\ \begin{pmatrix} 1 & 0 & 0 & 1 & 0 \\ 0 & 0 & 1 & 1 & 1 \\ 0 & 1 & 1 & 0 & 0 \\ 1 & 1 & 0 & 0 & 1 \end{pmatrix}\end{array}$ $\mathbf{Y} = \begin{array}{c} \\ 1 \\ 2 \\ 3 \\ 4 \\ 5 \end{array}\begin{array}{c} \begin{array}{ccc} a & b & c \end{array} \\ \begin{pmatrix} 1 & 0 & 1 \\ 1 & 1 & 0 \\ 1 & 1 & 0 \\ 1 & 0 & 1 \\ 0 & 1 & 1 \end{pmatrix}\end{array}$ $\mathbf{Z} = \begin{array}{c} \\ A \\ B \\ C \\ D \end{array}\begin{array}{c} \begin{array}{ccc} a & b & c \end{array} \\ \begin{pmatrix} 1 & 0 & 1 \\ 1 & 1 & 1 \\ 1 & 1 & 0 \\ 1 & 1 & 1 \end{pmatrix}\end{array}$

(ii) $\mathbf{X} = \begin{array}{c} \\ A \\ B \\ C \\ D \\ E \end{array}\begin{array}{c} \begin{array}{cccccc} 1 & 2 & 3 & 4 & 5 & 6 \end{array} \\ \begin{pmatrix} 1 & 1 & 0 & 0 & 0 & 1 \\ 0 & 0 & 0 & 0 & 1 & 1 \\ 0 & 0 & 0 & 1 & 1 & 0 \\ 1 & 0 & 1 & 1 & 0 & 0 \\ 0 & 1 & 1 & 0 & 0 & 0 \end{pmatrix}\end{array}$ $\mathbf{Y} = \begin{array}{c} \\ 1 \\ 2 \\ 3 \\ 4 \\ 5 \\ 6 \end{array}\begin{array}{c} \begin{array}{ccc} a & b & c \end{array} \\ \begin{pmatrix} 1 & 0 & 1 \\ 0 & 1 & 1 \\ 0 & 1 & 1 \\ 1 & 1 & 0 \\ 1 & 1 & 0 \\ 1 & 1 & 0 \end{pmatrix}\end{array}$ $\mathbf{Z} = \begin{array}{c} \\ A \\ B \\ C \\ D \\ E \end{array}\begin{array}{c} \begin{array}{ccc} a & b & c \end{array} \\ \begin{pmatrix} 1 & 1 & 1 \\ 1 & 1 & 0 \\ 1 & 1 & 0 \\ 1 & 1 & 1 \\ 0 & 1 & 1 \end{pmatrix}\end{array}$

(iii) $\mathbf{X} = \begin{array}{c} \\ A \\ B \\ C \\ D \\ E \\ F \end{array}\begin{array}{c} \begin{array}{cccccc} 1 & 2 & 3 & 4 & 5 & 6 \end{array} \\ \begin{pmatrix} 1 & 0 & 0 & 0 & 0 & 0 \\ 1 & 1 & 0 & 0 & 0 & 0 \\ 0 & 1 & 1 & 0 & 1 & 0 \\ 0 & 0 & 1 & 1 & 0 & 0 \\ 0 & 0 & 0 & 1 & 0 & 0 \\ 0 & 0 & 0 & 0 & 1 & 2 \end{pmatrix}\end{array}$ $\mathbf{Y} = \begin{array}{c} \\ 1 \\ 2 \\ 3 \\ 4 \\ 5 \\ 6 \end{array}\begin{array}{c} \begin{array}{cc} a & b \end{array} \\ \begin{pmatrix} 2 & 0 \\ 2 & 0 \\ 2 & 0 \\ 2 & 0 \\ 2 & 0 \\ 1 & 1 \end{pmatrix}\end{array}$ $\mathbf{Z} = \begin{array}{c} \\ A \\ B \\ C \\ D \\ E \\ F \end{array}\begin{array}{c} \begin{array}{cc} a & b \end{array} \\ \begin{pmatrix} 1 & 0 \\ 2 & 0 \\ 3 & 0 \\ 2 & 0 \\ 1 & 0 \\ 2 & 1 \end{pmatrix}\end{array}$

(c) (i) $\mathbf{XY} = \begin{pmatrix} 2 & 0 & 2 \\ 2 & 2 & 2 \\ 2 & 2 & 0 \\ 2 & 2 & 2 \end{pmatrix} = 2\mathbf{Z}$ (ii) $\mathbf{XY} = \begin{pmatrix} 2 & 2 & 2 \\ 2 & 2 & 0 \\ 2 & 2 & 0 \\ 2 & 2 & 2 \\ 0 & 2 & 2 \end{pmatrix} = 2\mathbf{Z}$

(iii) $\mathbf{XY} = \begin{pmatrix} 2 & 0 \\ 4 & 0 \\ 6 & 0 \\ 4 & 0 \\ 2 & 0 \\ 4 & 2 \end{pmatrix} = 2\mathbf{Z}$

(d) (i) $\mathbf{Y'X'} = \begin{pmatrix} 2 & 2 & 2 & 2 \\ 0 & 2 & 2 & 2 \\ 2 & 2 & 0 & 2 \end{pmatrix} = 2\mathbf{Z'}$ (ii) $\mathbf{Y'X'} = \begin{pmatrix} 2 & 2 & 2 & 2 & 0 \\ 2 & 2 & 2 & 2 & 2 \\ 2 & 0 & 0 & 2 & 2 \end{pmatrix} = 2\mathbf{Z'}$

(iii) $\mathbf{Y'X'} = \begin{pmatrix} 2 & 4 & 6 & 4 & 2 & 4 \\ 0 & 0 & 0 & 0 & 0 & 2 \end{pmatrix} = 2\mathbf{Z'}$

(e) (i) $\mathbf{XX'} = \begin{pmatrix} 2 & 1 & 0 & 1 \\ 1 & 3 & 1 & 1 \\ 0 & 1 & 2 & 1 \\ 1 & 1 & 1 & 3 \end{pmatrix}$ $\mathbf{R} = \begin{pmatrix} 0 & 1 & 0 & 1 \\ 1 & 0 & 1 & 1 \\ 0 & 1 & 0 & 1 \\ 1 & 1 & 1 & 0 \end{pmatrix}$

(ii) $\mathbf{XX'} = \begin{pmatrix} 3 & 1 & 0 & 1 & 1 \\ 1 & 2 & 1 & 0 & 0 \\ 0 & 1 & 2 & 1 & 0 \\ 1 & 0 & 1 & 3 & 1 \\ 1 & 0 & 0 & 1 & 2 \end{pmatrix}$ $\mathbf{R} = \begin{pmatrix} 0 & 1 & 0 & 1 & 1 \\ 1 & 0 & 1 & 0 & 0 \\ 0 & 1 & 0 & 1 & 0 \\ 1 & 0 & 1 & 0 & 1 \\ 1 & 0 & 0 & 1 & 0 \end{pmatrix}$

(iii) $\mathbf{XX'} = \begin{pmatrix} 1 & 1 & 0 & 0 & 0 & 0 \\ 1 & 2 & 1 & 0 & 0 & 0 \\ 0 & 1 & 3 & 1 & 0 & 1 \\ 0 & 0 & 1 & 2 & 1 & 0 \\ 0 & 0 & 0 & 1 & 1 & 0 \\ 0 & 0 & 1 & 0 & 0 & 5 \end{pmatrix}$ $\mathbf{R} = \begin{pmatrix} 0 & 1 & 0 & 0 & 0 & 0 \\ 1 & 0 & 1 & 0 & 0 & 0 \\ 0 & 1 & 0 & 1 & 0 & 1 \\ 0 & 0 & 1 & 0 & 1 & 0 \\ 0 & 0 & 0 & 1 & 0 & 0 \\ 0 & 0 & 1 & 0 & 0 & 2 \end{pmatrix}$

$$\mathbf{R} = \begin{array}{c} \\ C \\ L \\ N \end{array} \begin{array}{c} \begin{array}{ccc} C & L & N \end{array} \\ \begin{pmatrix} 0 & 1 & 2 \\ 1 & 0 & 1 \\ 2 & 1 & 0 \end{pmatrix} \end{array}$$

(a) $\mathbf{T} = \mathbf{R}^2 = \begin{pmatrix} 5 & 2 & 1 \\ 2 & 2 & 2 \\ 1 & 2 & 5 \end{pmatrix}$ (b) $\mathbf{R}^3 = \begin{pmatrix} 4 & 6 & 12 \\ 6 & 4 & 6 \\ 12 & 6 & 4 \end{pmatrix}$

Chapter 22

Exercise 22.1

2 (a) $P' = (7, 0)$, $PP' = \sqrt{20}(4.47)$ (b) $P' = (1, 5)$, $PP' = \sqrt{97}(9.85)$
(c) $P' = (-7, -8)$, $PP' = \sqrt{72}(8.49)$ (d) $P' = (12, 21)$, $PP' = 5$ **3** $(1, 13)$
4 $(-2, 4)$, $(1, 1)$, $(-1, 3)$ **5** $(1, 5)$

Exercise 22.2

1 (a) $\begin{pmatrix} 9 & 3 \\ -13 & 0 \end{pmatrix}$ (b) $\begin{pmatrix} 3 & 2 \\ 4 & 8 \end{pmatrix}$ (c) $\begin{pmatrix} 1 & 2 \\ -11 & 6 \end{pmatrix}$ (d) $\begin{pmatrix} -3 & 9\frac{1}{2} \\ -4 & 16\frac{1}{2} \end{pmatrix}$

(e) $\begin{pmatrix} -\frac{4}{7} & \frac{3}{7} \\ \frac{5}{7} & -\frac{2}{7} \end{pmatrix}$ (f) $\begin{pmatrix} 1\frac{1}{2} & 1\frac{1}{4} \\ \frac{1}{2} & -\frac{1}{4} \end{pmatrix}$ (g) $\begin{pmatrix} 2 & 2 \\ 1 & 1 \end{pmatrix}$ (g) is a singular matrix; all points of

plane are mapped onto line $y = \frac{1}{2}x$ **2** $\begin{pmatrix} 7 & 2 \\ 6 & 5 \end{pmatrix}$; $\begin{pmatrix} \frac{5}{23} & -\frac{2}{23} \\ -\frac{6}{23} & \frac{7}{23} \end{pmatrix}$ inverse **3** Area
$= 30$ square units; determinant $= 30$ **4** 2:1 (16:8); determinant $= 2$ **5** Area $= 0$,
images lie on line $3y = x$; determinant $= 0$ **6** (a) half turn about the origin; (b) maps all
points onto line $4y = x$ (c) enlargement, centre origin, scale factor 3 (d) reflection in the line
$y = x$ **7** area OA'C'B' $= 13$ sq. units $[30 - 2(1\frac{1}{2} + 5 + 2)]$

Exercise 22.3

1 (a) $(-3, 4)$ (b) $(-2, -5)$ (c) $(3, 3)$ (d) $(5, -4)$ (e) $(4, 0)$ (f) $(-11, 4)$
(g) $(-2, -5)$ (h) $(0, 1)$ **2** $(-2, 0)$, $(-4, 0)$, $(-4, 1)$, $(-2, 1)$ **3** $x = 1$;

$A' = (-1, 0)$, $B' = (-1, 4)$ **4** (a) $x = 0$, (b) $y = 0$, (c) $y = -x$, (d) $y = 4\frac{1}{2}$, (e) $y = x$
(f) $y = -x$, (g) $x = 6$, (h) $y = -1$ **5** (a) $(-4, -7)$ (b) $(2, -5)$ (c) $(5, -5)$
(d) $(-5, 5)$ **6** (a), (d)   **7** $4\frac{1}{2}$ m   **8** $(1, 0)$, $(3, 1)$, $(7, 3)$; $m = \frac{1}{2}$, $c = -\frac{1}{2}$
9 $x = y^2$

Exercise 22.4

1 (a) $(1, 3)$, (b) $(0, 8)$, (c) $(2, 3)$, (d) $(-2, 0)$ (e) $(5, 2)$ (f) $(3, 4)$
2 (a) $(1, 1)$ (b) $36°8'$ **3** $(0, \frac{1}{2})$, (half turn)   **4** $(-3, 4)$, $(-4, -3)$, $(3, -4)$
5 (a) $(0, 5)$, (b) $(-3, 0)$, (c) $(-3, -4)$, (d) $(-7, -1)$
6 $(-4, 6)$, $(-6, 6)$, $(-5\frac{1}{2}, 5)$, $(-5, 6)$ **7** $\begin{pmatrix} -1 \\ \sqrt{3} \end{pmatrix}$ and $\begin{pmatrix} -1 \\ -\sqrt{3} \end{pmatrix}$
8 $(2, 2\sqrt{3})$, $(-2, 2\sqrt{3})$, $(-4, 0)$, $(-2, -2\sqrt{3})$, $(2, -2\sqrt{3})$

Exercise 22.5

1 (a) 3 axes; order 3, (b) 1; 1, (c) 0; 2, (d) 2; 2 (e) 1; 1, (f) 1; 1, (g) 4; 4,
(h) 2; 2 (i) infinite; infinite, (j) 5; 5 (k) 2; 2, (l) 1; 1   **2** (a) e.g. isosceles triangle
or trapezium, kite, arrowhead   (b) e.g. rectangle, rhombus, ellipse
(c) e.g. kite, arrowhead   (d) e.g. trapezium, parallelogram, scalene triangle

Exercise 22.6

1 (a) $(9, 6)$, (b) $(-2, 3\frac{1}{2})$, (c) $(-5, 22)$, (d) $(14, 4)$ (e) $(4, -13)$, (f) $(4, 3)$,
(g) $(3, -10)$ **2** (a) $\begin{pmatrix} 5 & 0 \\ 0 & 5 \end{pmatrix}$ (b) $\begin{pmatrix} 1 & 5 \\ 0 & 1 \end{pmatrix}$ (c) $\begin{pmatrix} 2 & 0 \\ 0 & 1 \end{pmatrix}$ (d) $\begin{pmatrix} -1 & 0 \\ 0 & -1 \end{pmatrix}$;
half turn about O   **5** (a) enlargement, scale factor $\frac{1}{2}$, centre 0 (b) stretch, y-axis invariant, $(1, 0) \rightarrow (5, 0)$ (c) shear, x-axis invariant, $(0, 1) \rightarrow (4, 1)$
(d) half turn about 0 (e) reflection in line $y = -x$ (f) reflection in line $y = x$
(g) shear, y-axis invariant, $(1, 0) \rightarrow (1, -2)$
(h) maps all points of plane onto line $2x = 3y$ **6** (a) $\begin{pmatrix} -\frac{1}{2} & 0 \\ 0 & -\frac{1}{2} \end{pmatrix}$
(b) $\begin{pmatrix} 1 & -2 \\ 0 & 1 \end{pmatrix}$ (c) $\begin{pmatrix} \frac{2}{11} & \frac{1}{11} \\ -\frac{3}{11} & \frac{4}{11} \end{pmatrix}$ (d) no inverse

Exercise 22.7

1 (a) $\begin{pmatrix} -1 & 0 \\ 0 & -1 \end{pmatrix} = \mathbf{H}$ (b) $\begin{pmatrix} 0 & 1 \\ 1 & 0 \end{pmatrix} = \mathbf{P}$ (c) $\begin{pmatrix} -1 & -3 \\ 0 & -1 \end{pmatrix}$ (d) $\begin{pmatrix} 2 & 0 \\ 4 & 2 \end{pmatrix}$
(e) $\begin{pmatrix} 0 & -1 \\ 1 & 3 \end{pmatrix}$ (f) $\begin{pmatrix} 1 & 0 \\ 0 & 1 \end{pmatrix} = \mathbf{I}$ (g) $\begin{pmatrix} -1 & 0 \\ 0 & -1 \end{pmatrix} = \mathbf{H}$ (h) $\begin{pmatrix} -1 & 0 \\ 0 & -1 \end{pmatrix} = \mathbf{H}$
(i) (j) no 2 × 2 matrices   **2** (a) $\begin{pmatrix} -1 & 0 \\ 0 & -1 \end{pmatrix} = \mathbf{H}$
(b) $\begin{pmatrix} 0 & -1 \\ -1 & 0 \end{pmatrix} = \mathbf{Q}$ (c) $\begin{pmatrix} -1 & -3 \\ 0 & -1 \end{pmatrix}$ (d) $\begin{pmatrix} 2 & 0 \\ 4 & 2 \end{pmatrix}$ (e) $\begin{pmatrix} 3 & -1 \\ 1 & 0 \end{pmatrix}$
(f) $\begin{pmatrix} 1 & 0 \\ 0 & 1 \end{pmatrix} = \mathbf{I}$ (g) $\begin{pmatrix} -1 & 0 \\ 0 & -1 \end{pmatrix} = \mathbf{H}$ (h) $\begin{pmatrix} -1 & 0 \\ 0 & -1 \end{pmatrix} = \mathbf{H}$ (a), (c), (d), (g) are
commutative   **3** (a) $(5, 2)$ (b) $(2, 5)$ (c) $2, 0)$ (d) $(1, -2)$ **5** The matrices
equivalent to $\mathbf{B\dot{A}}$ are: (a) $\begin{pmatrix} 0 & 1 \\ 1 & 3 \end{pmatrix}$ (b) $\begin{pmatrix} 5 & 0 \\ 0 & -5 \end{pmatrix}$ (c) $\begin{pmatrix} 0 & 2 \\ 2 & 0 \end{pmatrix}$ (d) $\begin{pmatrix} 1 & 0 \\ 0 & -1 \end{pmatrix}$

6 $S = \begin{pmatrix} 1 & -3 \\ 0 & 1 \end{pmatrix}$, $S^5 = \begin{pmatrix} 1 & -15 \\ 0 & 1 \end{pmatrix}$; area remains 10 cm² S(P) = (−9, 4), $S^5(P) = (-57, 4)$

7 $R_- = \begin{pmatrix} 0 & 1 \\ -1 & 0 \end{pmatrix}$, $R_-^5 = \begin{pmatrix} 0 & 1 \\ -1 & 0 \end{pmatrix}$, $R_-^{12} = \begin{pmatrix} 1 & 0 \\ 0 & 1 \end{pmatrix}$ $[R_-^4 = I]$

8 $P = \begin{pmatrix} 0 & 1 \\ 1 & 0 \end{pmatrix}$ $P^5 = \begin{pmatrix} 0 & 1 \\ 1 & 0 \end{pmatrix}$ $P^{12} = \begin{pmatrix} 1 & 0 \\ 0 & 1 \end{pmatrix}$ $[P^2 = I]$

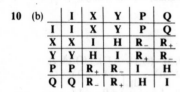

9

	I	X	Y	H
I	I	X	Y	H
X	X	I	H	Y
Y	Y	H	I	X
H	H	Y	X	I

(Klein 4-group)

10 (a)

	I	R₊	R₋	H
I	I	R₊	R₋	H
R₊	R₊	H	I	R₋
R₋	R₋	I	H	R₊
H	H	R₋	R₊	I

(closed, commutative−cyclic group)

10 (b)

	I	X	Y	P	Q
I	I	X	Y	P	Q
X	X	I	H	R₋	R₊
Y	Y	H	I	R₊	R₋
P	P	R₊	R₋	I	H
Q	Q	R₋	R₊	H	I

(not closed, not commutative)

10 (c)

	I	P	Q	X	Y	H
I	I	P	Q	X	Y	H
P	P	I	H	R₊	R₋	Q
Q	Q	H	I	R₋	R₊	P
X	X	R₋	R₊	I	H	Y
Y	Y	R₊	R₋	H	I	X
H	H	Q	P	Y	X	I

(not closed, not commutative)

Chapter 23

Exercise 23.1

1 7.279 cm **2** 27.61 cm **3** 13.62 m, 26.73 m **4** 21.09 m, 12.67 m
5 13 cm, 22°37′ **6** 48 m, 73°44′ **7** 6.036 cm, 13.18 cm **8** 19.31 m,
29.58 m **9** 3.911 m, 17.15 m **10** 58.29 cm, 58°35′ **11** 15 cm,
61°56 **12** 16 cm, 73°44′, 106°16′ **13** 26.01 m **14** 62°39′ **15** 6.928 m

Exercise 23.2

1 85.8 m **2** 38°40′ **3** 49.4 m, 45°26′ **4** 14°56′, 7°36′
5 6.403 km, 231.3° **6** (a) 20.92 km, 6.798 km **7** 51.44 km, 57.23 km,
318° **8** 111.9 m **9** (a) 32.8°, (b) 80.7 m **10** (a) 12.07 km, (b) 7.82 km,
(c) 211°, 303° **11** (a) 38.7°, 31.6° (b) 82 m, (c) 232.4°
12 (a) 39.8°, 30.5° (b) 15.6 m, 19.7 m

Exercise 23.3

1 (a) 3 cm, (b) $\frac{4}{5}$, (c) $\frac{4}{3}$, (d) $\frac{3}{5}$, (e) $\frac{4}{3}$ **2** (a) 25 m, (b) $\frac{7}{24}$, (c) $\frac{7}{25}$, (d) $\frac{7}{25}$,
(e) $\frac{24}{25}$ **3** (b) $\frac{15}{8}$, (c) $\frac{8}{17}$, (d) $\frac{15}{17}$, (e) 60 cm², (f) 7.06 cm **4** (a) 13 cm,
(b) 6.25 cm, (c) $\frac{4}{5}$, (d) $\frac{12}{13}$, (e) 39.375 cm² **5** (a) 20 cm,
(b) 210 cm², (c) $\frac{15}{17}$, (d) $\frac{4}{5}$

6 (c) $\dfrac{3}{\sqrt{10}}$ (d) $\dfrac{1}{\sqrt{10}}$ **7** (a) $2\sqrt{3}$ cm (b) $\sqrt{7}$ cm **8** (a) 10 cm (b) $8\sqrt{5}$ cm
10 (a) ± 41.4 (b) 9.85 **11** (a) 63.4, -63.4
(b) (i) (38, 0.78), (ii) 0.028 **12** (a) 4.5 (b) 0.60 (c) 0.07

Chapter 24

Exercise 24.1 (all units in cm)

1 15.76, 15.04 **2** 8.17, 5.31 **3** 11.61, 7.73 **4** 12.75, 13.24 **5** 26.67,
15.60 **6** 10.03, 13.05 **7** 10.54, 7.60 **8** 15.12, 25.43 **11** 8, 4.13, 8.51
12 17.32, 12.86, 19.70

Exercise 24.2 (angle values given in degrees and decimals of a degree)

2 40.51° **3** 70.87°, 109.13° **4** 37.47°, 16.16 cm
5 56.76, 123.24°; 11.82 cm, 3.05 cm **6** 36.44°
7 66.82°, 113.18°; 13.13 cm, 5.26 cm **8** (a) 6.89 cm, (b) 59.52°, 120.48°, (c) 35.07°

Exercise 24.3

1 4.36 cm **2** 14.11 cm **3** 14.14 cm **4** 7 cm **5** 22.45 cm **6** 55.77°
7 41.75° **8** 74.85° **9** 44.42°, 57.12°, 78.46° **10** 44.07°, 59.08°,
76.85° **11** 13.5 cm² **12** 66.5 cm² **13** 1630 m²
14 11.98 cm² **15** 18 cm² **16** 26.66 cm² **17** 65.48 cm²
18 (a) 34.8 cm² (b) 9.95 cm (c) 88.3° **19** (a) 80.26° (b) 64.06 cm²
20 (a) 923 m² (b) 95.3 m

Exercise 24.4

1 (a) 8 km (b) 060° **2** 32.84 km **3** (a) 0.5 m (b) 0.36 m (c) 0.61 m
4 2.41 km, 14.91 km **5** 2.78 km, 7.04 km **6** 16.32 km,
346.5° **7** 294.9 m **8** 109.3 km **9** 48.89 m **10** 120°
11 9.47 km **12** (a) 55.77° (b) 82.82° (c) 39.69 cm²

Exercise 24.5

1 35.3° **2** (a) 9.6° (b) 5.3° **3** 82.7° **4** (a) 22.6 m (b) 20.6°
5 (a) 9.3° (b) 59.3° **6** (a) 33.7° (b) 21.8° (c) 17.7° (d) 20.1 m
7 (a) 33.7° (b) 25.2° (c) 43.3° **8** (a) 5.77 cm (b) 8.17 cm (c) 54.7° (d) 70.5°
9 (a) 36.9° (b) 40.9° (c) 56.3° **10** 3 cm, (a) 41.8° (b) 19.5°
14 (a) 4.1 cm (b) 43.3 cm² **15** (a) 35.5° (b) 51° (b) 32° (d) 55°
16 (a) 17° (b) 24° **17** 7.3 cm **18** 9.8 cm

Chapter 25

Exercise 25.1

1 (a) $\dfrac{\sqrt{3}}{2}$ (b) $-\dfrac{\sqrt{3}}{2}$ (c) $-\dfrac{\sqrt{3}}{2}$ (d) $\dfrac{\sqrt{3}}{2}$ **2** (a) 1 (b) -1

(c) 1 (d) -1 **3** (a) $\frac{1}{2}$ (b) $-\dfrac{\sqrt{3}}{2}$ (c) $-\dfrac{\sqrt{3}}{2}$ (d) 0
4 (a) 0.788 (b) -0.788 (c) 0.788 (d) 0.788

5 (a) -0.6 (b) 0.6 (c) 0.6 (d) $\frac{5}{3}$ **6** (a) $\frac{\pi}{3}$ (b) $\frac{\pi}{4}$

(c) $\frac{5\pi}{12}$ (d) $\frac{5\pi}{6}$ (e) $\frac{3\pi}{2}$ (f) $\frac{5\pi}{3}$ **7** (a) 0.977 (b) 0.349 (c) 1.52

(d) 2.39 (e) 0.604 (f) 1.37 **8** (a) 36 (b) 120 (c) 150
(d) 480 (e) 468 **9** (a) 68.8 (b) 31.5 (c) 4.58

(d) 132 (e) 286 **10** $10\,\text{cm},\,25\,\text{cm}^2$ **11** (a) $\dfrac{\pi}{6}\,\text{cm}$

(b) $\dfrac{16\pi}{3}\,\text{cm}^2$ **12** (a) $10\,\text{cm}$ (b) $60\,\text{cm}^2$ **13** (a) $-\dfrac{4}{5}$

(b) $-\dfrac{3}{4}$ **14** (a) $-\dfrac{5}{12}$ (b) $-\dfrac{5}{13}$ **15** (a) $\frac{1}{2}$ (b) -1

(c) $\frac{1}{2}$ **16** $1.8\,\text{m/s}$ **17** $1\frac{2}{3}\,\text{rad/s}$ **18** (a) $3.8\,\text{rad/s}$
(b) $1.65\,\text{s}$ (c) $7.6\,\text{m/s}$ **19** $9.86\,\text{cm}$ **20** $288°$

Exercise 25.2

1 (a) $3090\,\text{n.m.}$ (b) $7440\,\text{n.m.}$ (c) $1200\,\text{n.m.}$ (d) $7140\,\text{n.m.}$
     $5723\,\text{km}$ $13\,780\,\text{km}$ $2222\,\text{km}$ $13\,220\,\text{km}$
   (e) $10\,320\,\text{n.m.}$
     $19\,110\,\text{km}$

2 (a) $206.5\,\text{n.m.}$ (b) $1811\,\text{n.m.}$ (c) $4758\,\text{n.m.}$ (d) $6456\,\text{n.m.}$
     $382.4\,\text{km}$ $3353\,\text{km}$ $8811\,\text{km}$ $11\,960\,\text{km}$
   (e) $1846\,\text{n.m.}$
     $3419\,\text{km}$

3 $45°\,\text{N},\,18°\,\text{W}$ **4** $13°\,\text{S},\,42.6°\,\text{E}$ **5** $5334\,\text{km}$
6 $34°\,\text{N},\,3°\,\text{W}$ **7** (a) $104.9°\text{W},\,4050\,\text{n.m.}$ **8** $12°\,\text{N},\,20.4°\,\text{E}$
9 $15\,000\,\text{km}$ **10** $60°$ **11** (a) 1900 (b) $1\frac{1}{3}°\,\text{S}$ **12** (a) $12\,\text{hours}$ (b) $6480\,\text{n.m}$
(c) $8737\,\text{n.m.}$

Miscellaneous Exercises E

1 (i) $\mathbf{b}-2\mathbf{a}$ (ii) $\frac{3}{4}\mathbf{b}-\frac{3}{2}\mathbf{a}$ (iii) $\frac{3}{4}\mathbf{b}+\frac{3}{2}\mathbf{a}$ (iv) $\mathbf{b}+2\mathbf{a}$; $\overrightarrow{OP}=\frac{3}{4}\overrightarrow{OB}$; O, P, B are collinear, P
divides OB in ratio $3:1$ **2** (i) (a) $\sqrt{13}\,(3.61)$ (b) 2.05 **3** (i) Trapezium;
$\mathbf{r}=\mathbf{q}-\mathbf{p}$ (ii) $\overrightarrow{OX}=\frac{1}{3}(\mathbf{a}+2\mathbf{b})$, $k=\frac{3}{2}$, $h=\frac{1}{4}$, $\overrightarrow{OZ}=\frac{1}{4}\mathbf{a}$ **4** (i) $(2,3)$ and $(4,0)$,
(ii) $(-1,-1)$, (iii) $(7,4)$ and $(1,-4)$ (iv) $(1\frac{2}{3},\frac{2}{3})$ **5** (i) $\begin{pmatrix}1\\0\end{pmatrix}$ (ii) $p=5$, $q=2$;

$\begin{pmatrix}4\\1\end{pmatrix},\begin{pmatrix}7\\2\end{pmatrix},\begin{pmatrix}4&7\\1&2\end{pmatrix}$ **6** (ii) $\begin{pmatrix}9\\12\end{pmatrix}$, (iii) $\frac{1}{3}\begin{pmatrix}3&-2\\0&1\end{pmatrix}$

7 $a=1\frac{1}{2}$, $b=0$, $c=1\frac{1}{3}$ **8** $\mathbf{A}^{-1}=\begin{pmatrix}2&-1\\-5&3\end{pmatrix}$ $\mathbf{B}^{-1}=\frac{1}{2}\begin{pmatrix}1&0\\1&2\end{pmatrix}$

$\mathbf{P}=\begin{pmatrix}5&-1\\-13&3\end{pmatrix}$ $\mathbf{Q}=\begin{pmatrix}1\frac{1}{2}&\frac{1}{2}\\6\frac{1}{2}&2\frac{1}{2}\end{pmatrix}$ (i) $\frac{1}{2}\begin{pmatrix}2&-1\\-8&5\end{pmatrix}$ (ii) $\frac{1}{2}\begin{pmatrix}1&-2\\-2&6\end{pmatrix}$

(iii) $\frac{1}{2}\begin{pmatrix}1&-2\\-2&6\end{pmatrix}$ **9** N singular, $\mathbf{M}^{-1}=\begin{pmatrix}-1-a&a\\a&1-a\end{pmatrix}$;

$\mathbf{M}-\mathbf{N}=\begin{pmatrix}0&1+a-a^2\\a-1&0\end{pmatrix}$ **10** (iv) $p=11$, $q=7$ **11** $\begin{pmatrix}3&2\\1&1\end{pmatrix}$; shear,

x-axis invariant, $(0,1)\to(2,1)$; $x=1$, $y=3$; $\mathbf{B}'=(13,5)$, $\mathbf{D}=(1,3)$;

area $=6$ **12** (i) $\begin{pmatrix}1&3\\2&-1\end{pmatrix}$ (ii) the x-axis, origin is invariant

13 $\overrightarrow{OA'}=\begin{pmatrix}1\\\frac{1}{2}\end{pmatrix}$, $\overrightarrow{OB'}=\begin{pmatrix}1\frac{1}{2}\\1\frac{1}{2}\end{pmatrix}$, $\overrightarrow{OC'}=\begin{pmatrix}\frac{1}{2}\\1\end{pmatrix}$; (i) $\frac{3}{4}$ (iii) $18.43°$

14 M is s shear, $y = -x$ invariant, area $= 2$; $\begin{pmatrix} 1 & -1 \\ 1 & 1 \end{pmatrix}$; $\begin{pmatrix} \frac{1}{2} & \frac{1}{2} \\ \frac{1}{2} & 1\frac{1}{2} \end{pmatrix}$

15 $P = \begin{pmatrix} 5 & 3 & 2 & 1 \\ 4 & 2 & 2 & 1 \end{pmatrix}$ $Q = \begin{pmatrix} 4 & 6 \\ 8 & 2 \\ 4 & 6 \\ 4 & 6 \end{pmatrix}$ $PQ = \begin{pmatrix} 56 & 54 \\ 44 & 46 \end{pmatrix}$ **16** (i) 27.55°,

(ii) 10.5 cm (iii) 6.22 cm² **17** PN $= 0.7002x$ ($x \tan 35°$),
$P\hat{R}Q = 19.30°$ **18** (i) 3.866 cm (ii) 7.482 cm
(iii) 22.58 cm² **19** (i) 9.063 cm (ii) 14.10 cm (iii) 26.50 cm
(iv) 29.13 cm **20** (a) AB $= 107$ m, AC $= 87$ m,
BC $= 138$ m, (b) 43° **21** (i) 56.31° (ii) 38.66°
(iii) 35.22° **22** (i) 14.04° (ii) 77.47°
(iii) 0.994 cm **23** BD $= 3.67$ cm, (a) 550.5 m
(b) 62550 m² (c) 250 m **24** (i) 10 km (ii) 34.64 km
(iii) 14.14 km **25** (i) 5.11 cm (ii) 55.91° **26** (i) 26.57° (ii) 50 cm
(iii) 60 cm **27** (30, 0.5), (270, 0), (225, −0.707)
28 (a) **29** $v = 5$ knots; track 126° 52'; course 13° 03' or 76° 57'
30 097°, 25 n.m. **31** 21600 n.m., 3438 n.m.; (i) 3885 n.m. (ii) 205.9 n.m.
32 (i) 17694 n.m. or 32841 km (ii) 2359 n.m. or 4379 km
(iii) 0.819:1 (iv) 60°N or 60°S **33** (a) 2548.5 km (b) 5337.6 km; 2430 km
35 $\simeq 3.54$ cm

Chapter 26

Exercise 26.1

1 (i) (a), (f), (i), (ii) discrete (b), (d), (g), (j); continuous (c), (e), (h)
7 144° **8** 9 cm, 3 cm, 3 cm

Exercise 26.2

1 (a) 7, (b) 16, (c) 49 **2** 1 **3** 31 kg, 37 kg
4 £77 **5** 353 **6** 9 **7** 11 **8** 15 **9** 58
10 288, 12 **11** 58 min **12** 100.2 p **13** 24.55 kg **14** 47.9

Exercise 26.3

1 (a) 2, 4 (b) 10, $9\frac{1}{2}$ (c) 9, 7 (d) 23, $24\frac{1}{2}$ **2** 6, $5\frac{1}{2}$
3 (a) $2\frac{5}{12}$ (b) 3 (c) 2 **4** (a) 12 (b) 10. I.Q.R. $= 3$ **5** class A : 2.2, 2, 2;
class B 4.1, 1, 3.5 **6** 14.6, 14, 15 **7** (a) 502.6 (b) 502.5 **8** 8.5, 8, 8. 11
9 $43\frac{1}{3}$ km/h, 250 km **10** (a) £4280 (b) £1530 **11** (a) 176 cm, 66 kg
(b) 170 cm, 16.5 cm; 61 kg, 11 kg **12** (a) 41 km/h (b) 13 cars

Chapter 27

Exercise 27.1

1 (a) $\frac{3}{5}$ (b) $\frac{3}{5}$ (c) $\frac{2}{5}$

2

Score	2	3	4	5	6	7	8	9	10
Probability	$\frac{1}{25}$	$\frac{2}{25}$	$\frac{3}{25}$	$\frac{4}{25}$	$\frac{5}{25}$	$\frac{4}{25}$	$\frac{3}{25}$	$\frac{2}{25}$	$\frac{1}{25}$

3 (a) $\frac{3}{5}$ (b) $\frac{18}{25}$ **4** $\frac{17}{30}$, 39 **5** 35 **6** (a) $\frac{9}{20}$ (b) $\frac{3}{10}$
(c) $\frac{3}{5}$ (d) $\frac{3}{20}$ **7** (a) $\frac{1}{13}$ (b) $\frac{1}{4}$ (c) $\frac{1}{2}$ (d) $\frac{7}{13}$ **8** (a) $\frac{1}{4}$ (b) $\frac{7}{12}$ (c) $\frac{5}{12}$ **9** $\frac{1}{2}$
10 $\frac{3}{4}$ **11** (a) $\frac{1}{4}$ (b) $\frac{5}{12}$ (c) 0 **12** (a) $\frac{1}{4}$ (b) $\frac{3}{7}$
13 $\frac{2}{5}$ **14** (a) 0.17 (b) 0.06

Exercise 27.2

1 (a) $\frac{4}{7}$ (b) $\frac{3}{7}$ (c) 1 (d) $\frac{1}{7}$ **2** (a) $\frac{3}{8}$ (b) $\frac{1}{8}$ (c) $\frac{5}{8}$ (d) $\frac{3}{4}$; (b) and (c)
3 (a) $\frac{1}{6}$ (b) $\frac{1}{4}$ (c) $\frac{1}{2}$; (b) and (c) **4** (a) $\frac{1}{2}$ (b) $\frac{1}{2}$ (c) $\frac{7}{13}$; $\frac{7}{26}$
5 (a) $\frac{1}{4}$ (b) $\frac{3}{7}$ (c) $\frac{19}{28}$ **6** (a) $\frac{4}{7}$ (b) $\frac{9}{28}$
7 $\frac{2}{15}, \frac{2}{5}, \frac{13}{15}$, 1. A' and B' not mutually exclusive
8 $\frac{5}{12}$ **9** $\frac{5}{12}$ **10** $\frac{22}{60}$ **11** $\frac{3}{5}$ **12** $\frac{1}{7}$
13 $\frac{1}{2}, \frac{7}{16}, \frac{1}{2}, \frac{13}{16}, \frac{1}{2}, 1, 0, \frac{5}{16}, 0$ **14** (a) $\frac{1}{4}$ (b) $\frac{5}{9}$ (c) $\frac{5}{36}$ (d) $\frac{2}{3}$
15 (a) $\frac{50}{99}$ (b) $\frac{20}{99}$ (c) $\frac{10}{99}$ (d) $\frac{50}{99}$

Exercise 27.3

1 $\frac{1}{4}$ **2** $\frac{4}{25}$ **3** $\frac{4}{45}$ **4** $\frac{1}{1110}$ **5** (a) $\frac{4}{5}$ (b) $\frac{7}{15}$ **6** (a) $\frac{1}{3}$ (b) $\frac{1}{3}$
7 $\frac{2}{7}$ (b) $\frac{5}{14}$ (c) $\frac{1}{2}$ **8** (a) $\frac{21}{100}$ (b) $\frac{14}{57}$ **9** (a) $\frac{1}{8}$ (b) $\frac{7}{8}$ **10** $\frac{99}{400}$
11 (a) $\frac{28}{435}$ (b) $\frac{77}{145}$ (c) $\frac{39}{145}$ **12** (a) $\frac{2}{13}$ (b) $\frac{1}{4}$ (c) $\frac{1}{26}$ (d) $\frac{19}{52}$ **13** (a) $\frac{1}{16}$
(b) $\frac{1}{169}$ (c) $\frac{36}{169}$ **14** $\frac{2}{27}, \frac{211}{243}$ **15** (a) $\frac{2}{15}$ (b) $\frac{1}{10}$

Miscellaneous Exercises F

1 7 **2** (i) −4 (ii) $12\frac{1}{2}\%$ **3** 9, 10, 11, 12, 13 **5** (i) £3 (ii) £6; £18
6 3.86; 22.67; 3.28; 245 **7** 3 (made), 4, 3.7 (mean); $\frac{2}{33}$ **8** (i) 5
(ii) any $y > 12$ (iii) 10 **9** (iii) 3.84 kg, (iv) 91 **10** (ii) 27.52; 27.73
11 45 **12** (i) $\frac{3}{25}$, (ii) $\frac{22}{25}$ **13** (i) $\frac{6}{10}$ (ii) $\frac{7}{20}$
14 (a) $\frac{2}{3}$ (b) $\frac{211}{243}$ **15** (a) $\frac{2}{3}$ (b) $\frac{2}{15}$; 8; 4 $g = 3r$; $g = 9, r = 12$
16 $\frac{2}{3}$ **17** (i) (a) a team cannot win if it does not score a goal
(b) 4 (c) there must be an even number of teams that draw (ii) 2.316 $(2\frac{6}{19})$
(iii) (a) $\frac{5}{22}(\frac{10}{44})$ (b) $\frac{2}{15}$ (c) $\frac{1}{33}$ **18** (iii) $\frac{244}{729}$
19 (i) $\frac{1}{4}$ (ii) $\frac{1}{10}$ (iii) $\frac{1}{2}$ (iv) $\frac{2}{3}$ (v) $\frac{1}{20}$ **20** (i) $\frac{4}{15}$ (ii) $\frac{2}{15}$
(iii) $\frac{1}{75}$ (iv) $\frac{44}{75}$

C000152655

EVOLUTION
AND
INTELLIGENT DESIGN
IN
THE SECRET DOCTRINE

$17.00

Other Theosophy Trust Books

The Secret Doctrine - Vols. I & II
by H.P. Blavatsky
compiled by The Editorial Board of Theosophy Trust

Meditation and Self-Study
by Raghavan Iyer

The Origins of Self-Consciousness
in *The Secret Doctrine*
by H.P. Blavatsky
compiled by The Editorial Board of Theosophy Trust

Wisdom in Action
Essays on the Spiritual Life
Raghavan Iyer

The Dawning of Wisdom
Essays on Walking the Path
Raghavan Iyer

Teachers of the Eternal Doctrine
From Tsong-Ka-Pa to Nostradamus
by Elton Hall

Symbols of the Eternal Doctrine
From Shamballa to Paradise
by Helen Valborg

The Key to Theosophy
An Exposition of the
Ethics, Science, and Philosophy
by H. P. Blavatsky

EVOLUTION
AND
INTELLIGENT DESIGN
IN
THE SECRET DOCTRINE

THE SYNTHESIS OF

SCIENCE, RELIGION, AND PHILOSOPHY

BY

HP BLAVATSKY

COMPILED BY
THE EDITORIAL BOARD OF THEOSOPHY TRUST

THEOSOPHY TRUST BOOKS
WASHINGTON, D.C.

Evolution and Intelligent Design in
The Secret Doctrine

Copyright © September 21, 2011 by Theosophy Trust

All rights reserved. No part of this book may be used or
reproduced by any means -graphic, electronic, or mechanical -
including photocopying, recording, taping or by any information
storage retrieval system without the written permission of the
publisher, except in the case of brief quotations embodied in critical
articles and reviews.

Theosophy Trust books may be ordered through
Amazon.com, Barnes & Noble, Smashwords,
and other booksellers, or by visiting:

http://www.theosophytrust.org/online_books.php

ISBN 978-0-9832220-2-6
ISBN 0-9832220-2-9

Library of Congress Control Number 2011928188

Printed in the United States of America

"Between degrading superstition and still more degrading brutal materialism, the White Dove of Truth has hardly room whereon to rest her weary unwelcome feet.

It is time that Theosophy should enter the arena."

Lucifer, August, 1896

Contents

vii

INTRODUCTION

In December 2005, Middle District of Pennsylvania District Court Judge John E. Jones III ruled in Kitzmiller vs. Dover Area School District that the doctrine called "Intelligent Design" is not science, and therefore cannot be taught as an alternative explanation to scientific evolution theory. During the preceding year, the Dover Area School District board had approved a statement to be read in ninth grade biology classes that indicated there are flaws in the current theory of evolution, and that a textbook on intelligent design could be consulted in the school library. In resolving the ensuing litigation, Judge Jones found that intelligent design is not science, that, as presented in the textbook, it is disguised biblical creationism, that it is not a theory for which scientific evidence was gathered, and that showing that contemporary evolution theory is incomplete does not in itself constitute an alternative scientific theory. Judge Jones wisely refrained from asserting the truth of either evolution or intelligent design. He had no objection to teaching biblically rooted intelligent design in a philosophy class or elsewhere, but he barred its teaching in science classes.

Judge Jones was especially concerned about the insistence by proponents of biblical intelligent design theories of the following either/or proposition: that either the modern version of Darwinian evolution is true, or biblical intelligent design is true. He flatly rejected this utterly false dichotomy, noting in his decision that there are other alternatives to both views. The compilation in the present volume presents a sweeping alternative to both contemporary evolutionary theory, with its insistence upon an ancestor common to the ape and the human race, and contemporary Christian creationism, with its insistence upon a special creation of each soul by a personal god. These highly philosophical views were first expressed in detail in The Secret Doctrine by H.P. Blavatsky, just as Darwinian theory was emerging as a serious rival to the mainstream Christian theology of 19th Century

Europe and America. Needless to say, these topics quickly began to dominate the public discourse of that long-gone era.

Contemporary science seems to regard the belief that a personal god created the heavens and earth within the past 10,000 years as a deliberate surrendering of the intellect to superstition, and is justifiably indignant. In their eyes, it is mind boggling that, in the year 2006, 45% of the American population claims to hold such a belief in the face of the tremendous body of undeniable scientific facts about the age of this earth and its diverse fauna and flora that have existed upon it for millions of years. Many adherents of evolutionary theory regard this not as a triumph of faith, but as a failure of education.

A large portion of the Christian community does not see it quite so – they see their own views as a rejection of an unwarranted intrusion by science upon their spiritual intuitions. These Christians are indignant that evolutionary science is based upon the idea that chance is the supreme guiding principle behind the manifold diversity and ingenious intelligence that is so evident throughout this earth, as "chance" is most definitely a slap aimed directly at their deity's cheek. They are equally horrified at the scientific proposition that the human race is descended from an animal ancestor also common to the anthropoid and pithecoid apes.

Christians are not alone in having this feeling. Something in the intuitions of men and women of every tradition very rightly rejects this provenance for Humanity. There is just too much evidence testifying to the noble origins of humanity. One simply has to think of all the examples of heroic self-sacrifice and devotion to duty that populate one's own local mental horizon to cast serious doubt upon the proposition that "man is nothing but a higher animal."

But the possibility that Man has both an animal and a divine origin is one that neither contemporary science nor conventional Christianity cares to seriously consider.

To some astute thinkers, it is as likely that the higher apes are descended from humans as vice-versa. That some members of early humanity were guilty of unnatural couplings with animals of lower forms, and produced an offspring that – over several millions of years – resulted in the higher apes, is a possibility not incompatible with the scientific evidence of genetic homology between humans and apes. There are enough gaps in this area of evolutionary "theory" – and at this level, it is indeed a "theory" – to allow one reasonably to not believe in ape-like ancestors for humans. However we formulate our views, we must keep alive our intuitions that there is something grander and nobler to life in the human form than merely promoting one's individual existence, perpetuating the species, or serving as the helpless agent of all-powerful chance.

Science is quite right in fighting against the idea of the intervention of a supposed personal god, and Christianity is quite right in fighting against the assumption of meaningless chance and ape ancestors for humans in evolutionary science. Clearly, what is needed is a synthesis of the truths of science and religion, not more either-or false dichotomies.

Is there any middle ground in this debate?

If there is a middle ground, it lies in the indestructible intuitions of human beings that there is some kind of guiding intelligence behind all of Nature (of which humans are a part). Whether it is one being, a trinity of beings, or perhaps galaxies of myriads of intelligent spiritual beings, they do not act by chance; they act with purpose throughout all of invisible Nature, they act hierarchically, and they act harmonically, in accord with universal law in guiding evolution. They are not visible to most of us ordinary humans; rather, they are the invisible agents who propel evolution forward in accordance with some overarching plan within the mind of Nature, what some of the ancients (pagans, mostly) called "universal mind," and whom they viewed as the real "intelligent designer." Theosophically, we human beings are evolved from these same spiritual ancestors; that is why those ancients considered us to be both divine and animal, divine beings in animal bodies.

In her exposition of the Theosophical philosophy, H.P. Blavatsky taught that spirit and matter are two aspects of a single reality, thereby rejecting both Cartesian dualism and crude reductionism. The universe is unitary, and no fundamental feature of it arises as an epiphenomenon at some stage in its development. Fact and value, spirit and matter, form and consciousness, all are present in some important way from the very beginning of the cosmos and evolve with it at every point. This teaching has some very practical implications that differ widely from contemporary scientific evolutionary theory – with its postulate of blind chance as the driving force behind evolution – and from contemporary Christian theology – with its postulate of a special creation by a personal deity of every human soul. Theosophically, Man is a divine being, and integral to the evolution of the universe in which he finds himself.

In rejecting reductionism, H.P. Blavatsky pointed to the limits of science as then and now conceived. Many scientists today reject any simple-minded form of reductionism. As mathematician Ian Stewart and reproductive biologist Jack Cohen show in their book *Figments of Reality: The Evolution of the Curious Mind*, such reductionism is inadequate to the task of providing complete explanations in science. Huston Smith in *Why Religion Matters* and Tenzin Gyatso, the XIVth Dalai Lama, in *The Universe in a Single Atom*, agree in quite different ways that the problem in modern science is not science itself, but the metaphysical assumptions that scientists too easily make: (1) how science discovers truth is the only way to discover truth, and (2) what empirical science explores, the material world, is all there is to explore. For his part, the Dalai Lama embraces the findings of empirical science, but notes that much that is not objectively empirical is worthy of deep study, *e.g.* the discoveries about consciousness that occur in deep meditative states. He supports a confluence of objective and subjective methods as mutually beneficial ways to discern truth.

H. P. Blavatsky taught that the evolution of the universe and the evolution of man form a seamless whole. Because spirit and matter constitute a continuum, the evolution of man and his real nature must be studied within the context of the nature, structure, and evolution of the universe. This comprehensive approach, refusing to fall prey to scientific compartmentalization or sectarian exclusivity, requires a radically revised anthropology. Additionally, she held that all religions contain a core of truth, but, being subjected to the limited understanding of generations upon generations of human beings, that truth is largely buried within an obscure system of allegory and symbolism, and has to be teased out of the encrusted religious traditions vying for the world's allegiance. "There is no religion higher than Truth" was the motto she picked for the Theosophical quest for truth, and that motto puts both science and religion in a distinctive perspective.

H.P. Blavatsky clearly set the false dichotomy between Darwinian evolution and biblical intelligent design within the historical framework and human mind sets in which it arose, and she offered Theosophy as a liberating and truth-oriented alternative. She wrote:

> The pendulum of thought oscillates between extremes. Having now finally emancipated herself from the shackles of theology, Science has embraced the opposite fallacy; and in the attempt to interpret Nature on purely materialistic lines, she has built up that most extravagant theory of the ages – the derivation of man from a ferocious and brutal ape. So rooted has this doctrine, in one form or another, now become, that the most Herculean efforts will be needed to bring about its final rejection. The Darwinian anthropology is the incubus of the ethnologist, a sturdy child of modern Materialism, which has grown up and acquired increasing vigour, as the ineptitude of the theological legend of Man's "creation" became more and more apparent. It has thriven on account of the strange delusion that – as a scientist of repute puts it – "All hypotheses and theories with respect to the rise of man can be reduced to two (the Evolutionist and the Biblical exoteric account). There is no other hypothesis conceivable..."!! The anthropology of the secret volumes is, however, the best possible answer to such a worthless contention.

The Secret Doctrine, II, 689

The human eye sees only part of the electromagnetic spectrum, that part called "visible light." X-rays, radio waves, infrared and ultraviolet light and much else fall outside that scope. To deny their existence because we can't see them would be bad common sense and bad science. Similarly, to divide the world into 'spiritual' and 'material' would be to fail to understand that both those terms cover wide ranges of subjective and objective phenomena. H.P. Blavatsky's writings explore the rainbow of phenomena that constitutes our universe and ourselves, and in so doing, she redefines science and spirituality, showing that we and the universe are simultaneously more subtle and complex than any simple dichotomies and dogmas can begin to encompass.

A careful reading of the following passages will open up perspectives that profoundly aid a vastly deeper understanding of the inextricable links between the evolution of the universe and humankind; the remarkable philosophy behind them will certainly provoke a perplexity which only its deeper realization may at last relieve.

Prof. Elton. A. Hall
Boise, Idaho
January 2006

Editor's Preface

All of the quotations included in the present volume come from H. P. Blavatsky's monumental work, *The Secret Doctrine,* the Original Edition of which was published in 1888. Students of Theosophy know well the origins of *The Secret Doctrine;* H.P.B. (as she is known to students) alludes to a group of ancient texts – the Stanzas of Dzyan – that are inconceivably old, have been kept secret and away from the prying eyes of the profane world, and were only made known to the world in general in the last quarter of the 19th Century. These Stanzas, along with a series of "Commentaries" that are based upon them – also unknown in the West and forming the key to understanding the Stanzas themselves – are ancient records that describe the evolutionary development of both the Cosmos and Man. They form the principal subject matter of *The Secret Doctrine.*

Newcomers to the Theosophical philosophy may find that a number of very interesting and worthwhile questions about the original *Stanzas* and the Commentaries (those interested may look further into these matters by consulting *The Secret Doctrine* itself, where an extensive treatment of these question can be found – see www.theosophytrust. org) naturally arise, but these may be set aside temporarily in reading the current work, as most of its themes and arguments stand on the firm ground of logic and true scientific impartiality, without reliance upon any "authority" other than the integrity and logic of the arguments set forth.

The present work can be comprehended by any person who is impartial enough in approaching the ongoing debate between Evolution and Intelligent Design to take on a very different third perspective, one that gives credit and some sympathy to each of the two principal sides in the debate - where they are clearly warranted - but takes an uncompromising stand in a third position that rejects both the materialistic assumptions of the Evolutionists and the illogic of the Creationists. The Theosophical philosophy provides a solid middle ground for a perspective that is both religious and rational.

Readers may judge for themselves how well this work establishes that perspective.

A judicious selection of passages dealing specifically with the subject under consideration - the scientific evolutionary theory and the Christian theory of Intelligent Design (or Creationism) - has been chosen from the approximately 1500+ pages of *The Secret Doctrine* for inclusion in this volume. Another person or group of editors might have included other passages not found herein, and might not have included some that are contained in this book. There is room for debate on the matters of inclusion and exclusion; however, that discussion need not take away from the fact that the philosophy expounded in *The Secret Doctrine* offers a valuable and much-needed fresh voice in an on-going debate that has become a stand-off, with neither side willing to concede either truth or logic to the opposing point of view for fear of losing the argument altogether.

As a passage from *The Great Master's Letter* (as it is known to Theosophists) says, "It is time that Theosophy should enter the arena."

Much of the scientific terminology has changed over the 118 years since the publication of *The Secret Doctrine*, and many of the authors and their works referred to – other than Darwin and his *The Descent of Man* – are now quite unknown by most of the public at large and many researchers themselves in the fields of anthropology, paleontology, and biology; in addition, the basic theories, discoveries, and developments in these fields have undergone enormous change, so much so that the reader acquainted with modern science might be tempted to dismiss altogether the arguments and facts alluded to by H.P.B. in these passage as being hopelessly outdated, if not merely quaint. To take this attitude would be a serious mistake, as the arguments and evidence posed by H.P.B. are as powerful and pertinent to the debate now as they were in the 19th Century. The underlying assumptions behind science – whether that of the 19th or the 21st centuries – have not altered significantly, and those assumptions are what H.P.B.'s arguments are directed toward, as they form the framework that supports the entire edifice of scientific evolutionary theory.

Readers who find the numerous Sanskrit and other non-English terms used in these passage a serious obstacle to understanding the writing can turn to a very excellent work titled "*The Theosophical Glossary*" for help; this work is available at www.theosophy.org and other Internet sites. The *Glossary* was written by H. P. Blavatsky to help the earnest enquirer gain a broader understanding of crucial terms used in her explanations of the Theosophical philosophy. Those who want to read more of the entire source book for the present work, *The Secret Doctrine*, can either purchase it online or download it in MOBI, ePUB, or PDF from *www.theosophytrust.org.*

The selections in this book reflect the original as closely as possible, except for the italicizing and the capitalization and heading conventions, the application of which has been applied with more rigor. Some of the typesetting conventions of the 19th Century book publishers and printers – such as the use of italics, bold, all caps, small caps, semi-colons, colons, and final periods – varied considerably with each publisher or printer. Modern, large publishing houses employing well-trained copy editors working from style sheets can achieve a high level of consistency; such publishers were not so numerous in the 19th Century as they are today. Very frequently a book was taken to a print shop for publication, and the application of style conventions would vary with the experience, taste, and predilections of the typesetter. Hence, a large number of irregularities in the use of those conventions can be seen in a printed work like the Original Edition of *The Secret Doctrine.*

This present book has tried to correct some of the more glaring style irregularities and to be more consistent in punctuation and the application of style conventions, while retaining those unusual styles that HPB applied principally for emphasis and effect. Nothing has been altered from the original that might detract from her original intent, as far as we can discern that intent.

This book is published with the high hope that the clash between the opposing viewpoints of Evolution vs. Intelligent Design may be tempered by the middle ground of an ancient perspective, one vast enough to both protect the innate religious perception of human beings everywhere that Humanity has a divine origin, and accommodate the bewildering array of empirical anthropological evidence of the many links that bind diverse life forms into one interconnected whole.

The Editorial Board of Theosophy Trust

Selection 1

NEITHER OCCULTISM NOR THEOSOPHY HAS EVER SUPPORTED THE WILD THEORIES OF THE PRESENT DARWINISTS

It is really with surprise that we have ascertained the fact that *"Esoteric Buddhism"* was so little understood by some Theosophists, as to have led them into the belief that it thoroughly supported Darwinian evolution, and especially the theory of the descent of man from a pithecoid ancestor. As one member writes: "I suppose you realise that three-fourths of Theosophists and even outsiders imagine that, as far as the evolution of man is concerned, Darwinism and Theosophy kiss one another." Nothing of the kind was ever realised, nor is there any great warrant for it, so far as we know, in *"Esoteric Buddhism."* It has been repeatedly stated that evolution as taught by Manu and Kapila was the groundwork of the modern teachings, but – least of all the descent of man from an ape. Of this, more hereafter. But one has only to turn to p. 47 of *"Esoteric Buddhism,"* 5th Ed., to find there the statement that "Man belongs to a kingdom distinctly separate from that of the animals." With such a plain and unequivocal statement before him, it is very strange that any careful student should have been so misled unless he is prepared to charge the author with a gross contradiction.

Every Round repeats on a higher scale the evolutionary work of the preceding Round. With the exception of some higher anthropoids, as just mentioned, the Monadic inflow, or inner evolution, is at an end till the next *Manvantara.* It can never be too often repeated, that the full-blown human Monads have to be first disposed of, before the new crop of candidates appears on this Globe at the beginning of the next cycle. Thus there is a lull; and this is why, during the Fourth Round, man appears on Earth earlier than any animal creation, as will be described.

But it is still urged that the author of *"Esoteric Buddhism"* has "preached Darwinism" all along. Certain passages would undoubtedly seem to lend countenance to this inference. Besides which the Occultists themselves are ready to concede *partial* correctness to the Darwinian hypothesis in later details, bye-laws of Evolution, and after the midway point of the Fourth Race. Of that which has taken place, physical science can really know nothing, for such matters lie entirely outside of its sphere of investigation. But what the Occultists have never admitted, nor will they ever admit, is that man was *an ape in this or in any other Round*; or that he ever could be one, however much he may have been "ape-like." This is vouched for by the very authority from whom the author of "*Esoteric Buddhism*" got his information.

Thus to those who confront the Occultists with these lines from the above-named volume: "It is enough to show that we may as reasonably – and that we must, if we would talk about these matters at all – conceive a life-impulse giving birth to mineral form, as of the same sort of impulse concerned to *raise a race of apes into a race of rudimentary men*." To those who bring this passage forward as showing "decided Darwinism," the Occultists answer by pointing to the explanation of the Master (Mr. Sinnett's "teacher") which would contradict these lines, were they written in the spirit attributed to them. A copy of this letter was sent to the writer, together with others, two years ago (1886), with additional marginal remarks, to quote from, in the "*Secret Doctrine*." It begins by considering the difficulty experienced by the Western student, in reconciling some facts, previously given, with the evolution of man from the animal, *i.e.* from the mineral, vegetable and animal kingdoms, and advises the student to hold to the doctrine of analogy and correspondences. Then it touches upon the mystery of the *Devas*, and even Gods, having to pass through states which it was agreed to refer to as "Immetallization, Inherbation, Inzoonization and finally Incarnation," and explains this by hinting at the necessity of failures even in the ethereal races of *Dhyan Chohans*. Concerning this it says:

"Still, as these 'failures' are too far progressed and spiritualized to be thrown back forcibly from Dhyan Chohanship into the vortex of a new primordial evolution through the lower kingdoms. . . . ." After which only a hint is given about the mystery contained in the allegory of the fallen *Asuras*, which will be expanded and explained in Book II. When Karma has reached them at the stage of human evolution, "they will have to drink it to the last drop in the bitter cup of retribution. Then they become an active force and commingle with the Elementals, the progressed entities of the pure animal kingdom, to develop little by little the full type of humanity."

These *Dhyan Chohans*, as we see, do not pass through the three kingdoms as do the lower *Pitris*; nor do they incarnate in man until the Third Root Race. Thus, as the teaching stands:

A Master's Letter

"*Man in the First Round and First Race on Globe D, our Earth, was an ethereal being (a Lunar Dhyani, as man), non-intelligent but super-spiritual; and correspondingly, on the law of analogy, in the First Race of the Fourth Round. In each of the subsequent races and sub-races . . . he grows more and more into an encased or incarnate being, but still preponderatingly ethereal. . . . He is sexless, and, like the animal and vegetable, he develops monstrous bodies correspondential with his coarser surroundings.*

"*II. Round. He (Man) is still gigantic and ethereal but growing firmer and more condensed in body, a more physical man. Yet still less intelligent than spiritual (1), for mind is a slower and more difficult evolution than is the physical frame . . .*

"*III. Round. He has now a perfectly concrete or compacted body, at first the form of a giant-ape, and now more intelligent, or rather cunning, than spiritual. For, on the downward arc, he has now reached a point where his primordial spirituality is eclipsed and overshadowed by nascent mentality (2). In the last half of the Third Round his gigantic stature decreases, and his body improves in texture, and he becomes a more rational being, though still more an ape than a Deva. . . . (All this is almost exactly repeated in the third Root-Race of the Fourth Round.)*

"*IV. Round. Intellect has an enormous development in this Round. The (hitherto) dumb races acquire our (present) human speech on this globe, on which, from the Fourth Race, language is perfected and knowledge increases. At this half-way point of the Fourth Round (as of the Fourth Root, or Atlantean, race) humanity passes the axial point of the minor Manvantara cycle. . . . the world teeming with the results of intellectual activity and spiritual decrease . .*"

This is from the authentic letter; what follows are the later remarks and additional explanations traced by the same hand in the form of footnotes.. ."

(1.) "*. . . The original letter contained general teaching – a 'bird's-eye view' – and particularized nothing. . . . To speak of 'physical man' while limiting the statement to the early Rounds would be drifting back to the miraculous and instantaneous 'coats of skin.'. . . The first 'Nature,' the first 'body,' the first 'mind'* *on the first plane of perception, on the first Globe in the first Round, is what was meant. For Karma and evolution have –*

> ' . . . centred in our make such strange extremes!
> From different Natures marvellously mixed . . .'

(2.) "*Restore: he has now reached the point (by analogy, and as the Third Root Race in the Fourth Round) where his ("the angel"- man's) primordial spirituality is eclipsed and overshadowed by nascent human mentality, and you have the true version on your thumb-nail.*"

These are the words of the Teacher – text, words and sentences in brackets, and explanatory footnotes. It stands to reason that there must be an enormous difference in such terms as "objectivity" and "subjectivity," "materiality" and "spirituality," when the same terms are applied to different planes of being and perception. All this must be taken in its relative sense. And therefore there is little to be wondered at, if, left to his own speculations, an author, however eager to learn, yet quite inexperienced in these abstruse teachings, has fallen into an error. Neither was the difference between the "Rounds" and the "Races" sufficiently defined in the letters received, nor was there anything of the kind required before, as the ordinary Eastern disciple would have found out the difference in a moment. Moreover, to quote from a letter of the Master's (188-), "the teachings were imparted under protest. . . . They were, so to say, smuggled goods . . . and when I remained face to face with only one correspondent, the other, Mr. – – – , had so far tossed all the cards into confusion, that little remained to be said without trespassing upon law." Theosophists, "whom it may concern," will understand what is meant.

Third Race "Men" Created that Missing Link which Became the Remote Ancestor of the Real Ape

The outcome of all this is that nothing had ever been said in the letters" to warrant the assurance that the Occult doctrine has ever taught, or any Adept believed in, the preposterous modern theory of the descent of man from a common ancestor with the ape – an anthropoid of the actual animal kind, unless metaphorically. To this day the world is more full of "ape-like men" than the woods are of "men-like apes." The ape is sacred in India because its origin is well known to the Initiates, though concealed under a thick veil of allegory. Hanuman is the son of Pavana (Vayu, "the god of the wind") by Anjana, a monster called Kesarî, though his genealogy varies. The reader who bears this in mind will find in Book II *passim*, the whole explanation of this ingenious allegory. The "Men" of the Third Race (who separated) were "Gods" by their spirituality and purity, though senseless, and as yet destitute of mind, as men.

These "Men" of the Third Race – the ancestors of the Atlanteans – were just such ape-like, intellectually senseless giants as were those beings, who, during the Third Round, represented Humanity. Morally irresponsible, it was these third Race "men" who, through promiscuous connection with animal species lower than themselves, created that missing link which became ages later (in the tertiary period only) the remote ancestor of the real ape as we find it now in the pithecoid family.[1]

The Preliminary Creation Of Man

Thus the earlier teachings, however unsatisfactory, vague and fragmentary, did not teach the evolution of "man" from the "ape." Nor does the author of "*Esoteric Buddhism*" assert it anywhere in his work in so many words; but, owing to his inclination towards modern science, he uses language which might perhaps justify such an inference. The man who preceded the Fourth, the Atlantean race, however much he may have looked physically like a "gigantic ape" – "the counterfeit of man who hath not the life of a man" – was still a thinking and already a speaking man. The "Lemuro-Atlantean" was a highly civilized race, and if one accepts tradition, which is better history than the speculative fiction which now passes under that name, he was higher than we are with all our sciences and the degraded civilization of the day: at any rate, the Lemuro-Atlantean of the closing Third Race was so.

---

1 And if this is found clashing with that other statement which shows the animal later than man, then the reader is asked to bear in mind that the placental mammal only is meant. In those days there were animals of which zoology does not even dream in our own; and the modes of reproduction were not identical with the notions which modern physiology has upon the subject. It is not altogether convenient to touch upon such questions in public, but there is no contradiction or impossibility in this whatever.

THE MAN, OR THE APE; WHICH THE FIRST?

The last human Monad incarnated before the beginning of the 5th Root-Race. [2] The cycle of metempsychosis for the human monad is closed, for we are in the Fourth Round and the Fifth Root-Race. The reader will have to bear in mind – at any rate one who has made himself acquainted with "*Esoteric Buddhism*" – that the Stanzas which follow in this Book and Book II speak of the evolution in our Fourth Round only. The latter is the cycle of the turning-point, after which, matter, having reached its lowest depths, begins to strive onward

---

2 Such anthropoids form an exception because they were not intended by Nature, but are the direct product and creation of "senseless" man. The Hindus give a divine origin to the apes and monkeys because the men of the Third Race were gods from another plane who had become "senseless" mortals. This subject had already been touched upon in "*Isis Unveiled*" twelve years ago as plainly as was then possible. On pp. 278-279, the reader is referred "to the Brahmins, if he would know the reason of the regard they have for the monkeys. For then he (the reader) would perhaps learn–were the Brahman to judge him worthy of an explanation–that the Hindu sees in the ape but what Manu desired he should: the transformation of species most directly connected with that of the human family, a bastard branch engrafted on their own stock before the final perfection of the latter. He might learn, further, that in the eyes of the educated 'heathen' the spiritual or inner man is one thing, and his terrestrial physical casket another. That physical nature, the great combination of physical correlations of forces, ever creeping onward towards perfection, has to avail herself of the material at hand; she models and remodels as she proceeds, and finishing her crowning work in man, presents him alone as a fit tabernacle for the overshadowing of the divine Spirit."

Moreover, a German scientific work is mentioned in a footnote on the same page. It says that a Hanoverian scientist had recently published a Book entitled "*Ueber die Auflosung der Arten durch Naturliche Zucht-wahl*," in which he shows, with great ingenuity, that Darwin was wholly mistaken in tracing man back to the ape. On the contrary, he maintains that it is the ape which is evolved from man. He shows that, in the beginning, mankind were morally and physically the types and prototypes of our present Race, and of our human dignity, by their beauty of form, regularity of feature, cranial development, nobility of sentiments, heroic impulses, and grandeur of ideal conception. This is a purely Brahmanic, Buddhistic and Kabalistic philosophy. The Book is copiously illustrated with diagrams, tables, etc. It asserts that the gradual debasement and degradation of man, morally and physically, can be readily traced throughout the ethnological transformation down to our time. And, as one portion has already degenerated into apes, so the civilized man of the present day will at last, under the action of the inevitable law of necessity, be also succeeded by like descendants. If we may judge of the future by the actual Present, it certainly does seem possible that so unspiritual and materialistic a body should end as Simia rather than as Seraphs. But though the apes descend from man, it is certainly not the fact that the human Monad, which has once reached the level of humanity, ever incarnates again in the form of an animal.

and to get spiritualized with every new Race and with every fresh cycle. Therefore the student must take care not to see contradiction where there is none, as in *"Esoteric Buddhism"* Rounds are spoken of in general, while here only the Fourth, or our present Round, is meant. Then it was the work of formation; now it is that of reformation and evolutionary perfection.

The Secret Doctrine, i 184–191

Selection 2

The Hierarchy Commissioned to "Create" Men

The group of the hierarchy which is commissioned to "create"[3] men is a special group, then; yet it evolved shadowy man in this cycle just as a higher and still more spiritual group evolved him in the Third Round. But as it is the Sixth – on the downward scale of Spirituality – the last and seventh being the terrestrial Spirits (elementals) which gradually form, build, and condense his physical body – this Sixth group evolves no more than the future man's shadowy form, a filmy, hardly visible transparent copy of themselves. It becomes the task of the fifth Hierarchy – the mysterious beings that preside over the constellation Capricornus, Makara, or "Crocodile" in India as in Egypt – to inform the empty and ethereal animal form and make of it the Rational Man. This is one of those subjects upon which very little may be said to the general public. It is a MYSTERY, truly but only to him who is prepared to reject the existence of intellectual and conscious spiritual Beings in the Universe, limiting full Consciousness to man alone, and that only as a "function of the Brain." Many are those among the Spiritual Entities, who have incarnated bodily in man, since the beginning of his appearance, and who, for all that, still exist as independently as they did before, in the infinitudes of Space. . . .

What Incarnates in Animal Man?

To put it more clearly: the invisible Entity may be bodily present on earth without abandoning, however, its status and functions in the supersensuous regions. If this needs explanation, we can do no better than remind the reader of like cases in Spiritualism, though such cases

---

3 Creation is an incorrect word to use, as no religion, not even the sect of the Visishta Adwaitees in India—one which anthropomorphises even Parabrahmam—believes in creation out of *nihil* as Christians and Jews do, but in evolution out of preexisting materials.

8

are very rare, at least as regards the nature of the Entity incarnating,[4] or taking temporary possession of a medium. Just as certain persons – men and women, reverting to parallel cases among living persons – whether by virtue of a peculiar organization, or through the power of acquired mystic knowledge, can be seen in their "double" in one place, while the body is many miles away; so the same thing can occur in the case of superior Beings.

Man, philosophically considered, is, in his outward form, simply an animal, hardly more perfect than his pithecoid-like ancestor of the third round. He is a living body, not a living being, since the realisation of existence, the "Ego-Sum," necessitates self-consciousness, and an animal can only have direct consciousness, or instinct. This was so well understood by the Ancients that the Kabalist even made of soul and body two lives, independent of each other.[5] The soul, whose body vehicle is the Astral, ethero-substantial envelope, could die and man be still living on earth – *i.e.* the soul could free itself from and quit the tabernacle for various reasons – such as insanity, spiritual and physical depravity, etc.[6] Therefore, that which living men (Initiates) can do,

---

4 The so-called "Spirits" that may occasionally possess themselves of the bodies of mediums are not the Monads or Higher Principles of disembodied personalities. Such a "Spirit" can only be either an Elementary, or—a *Nirmânakâya*.

5 On pp. 340–351 (*Genesis of the Soul*) in the "*New Aspects of Life*," the Author states the Kabalistic teaching: "They held that, functionally, Spirit and Matter of corresponding opacity and density tended to coalesce; and that the resultant created Spirits, in the disembodied state, were constituted on a scale in which the differing opacities and transparencies of Elemental or uncreated Spirit were reproduced, and that these Spirits in the disembodied state attracted, appropriated, digested and assimilated Elemental Spirit and Elemental Matter whose condition was conformed to their own." "They therefore taught that there was a wide difference in the condition of created Spirits; and that in the intimate association between the Spirit-world and the world of Matter, the more opaque Spirits in the disembodied state were drawn towards the more dense parts of the material world, and therefore tended towards the centre of the Earth, where they found the conditions most suited to their state; while the more transparent Spirits passed into the surrounding aura of the planet, the most rarified finding their home in its satellite."

This relates exclusively to our Elementary Spirits, and has naught to do with either the Planetary, Sidereal, Cosmic or Inter-Etheric Intelligent Forces or "Angels" as they are termed by the Roman Church. The Jewish Kabalists, especially the practical Occultists who dealt with ceremonial magic, busied themselves solely with the spirits of the Planets and the "Elementals" so-called. Therefore this covers only a portion of the Esoteric Teaching.

the *Dhyanis*, who have no physical body to hamper them, can do still better. This was the belief of the Antediluvians, and it is fast becoming that of modern intellectual society, in Spiritualism, besides the Greek and Roman Churches, which teach the ubiquity of their angels. The Zoroastrians regarded their *Amshaspends* as dual entities (*Ferouers*), applying this duality – in esoteric philosophy, at any rate – to all the spiritual and invisible denizens of the numberless worlds in space which are visible to our eye. In a note of Damascius (sixth century) on the Chaldean oracles, we have a triple evidence of the universality of this doctrine, for he says: "In these oracles the seven *Cosmocratores* of the world, ('*The World-Pillars*') mentioned likewise by St. Paul, are double – one set being commissioned to rule the superior worlds the spiritual and the sidereal, and the other to guide and watch over the worlds of matter." Such is also the opinion of Iamblichus, who makes an evident distinction between the archangels and the "*Archontes.*" (See "*De Mysteriis,*" Sec. II., Ch. 3.) The above may be applied, of course, to the distinction made between the degrees or orders of spiritual beings, and it is in this sense that the Roman Catholic Church tries to interpret and teach the difference; for while the archangels are in her teaching divine and holy, their doubles are denounced by her as devils.[7] But the word "*ferouer*" is not to be understood in this sense, for it means simply the reverse or the opposite side of some attribute or quality. Thus when the Occultist says that the "Demon is the lining of God" (evil, the reverse

---

6 The possibility of the "Soul" (*i.e.* the eternal Spiritual Ego) dwelling in the unseen worlds, while its body goes on living on Earth, is a pre-eminently occult doctrine, especially in Chinese and *Buddhist* philosophy. See "*Isis Unveiled,*" Vol. I, p. 602, for an illustration. Many are the *Soulless* men among us, for the occurrence is found to take place in wicked materialists as well as in persons "who advance in holiness and never turn back." (See *Ibid* and also "*Isis Unveiled,*" Vol. II, p. 369.)

7 This identity between the Spirit and its material "double" (in man it is the reverse) explains still better the confusion, alluded to already in this work, made in the names and individualities, as well as the numbers, of the *Rishis* and the *Prajâpatis*, especially between those of the *Satya yuga* and the Mahabhâratan period. It also throws additional light on what the Secret Doctrine teaches with regard to the Root and the Seed *Manus* (see Book II, "On the primitive *Manus* of humanity"). Not only those progenitors of our mankind, but every human being, we are taught, has its prototype in the Spiritual Spheres, which prototype is the highest essence of his seventh principle. Thus the seven *Manus* become 14, the Root *Manu* being the Prime Cause, and the "Seed-*Manu*" its effect, and when the latter reach from *Satya yuga* (the first stage) to the heroic period, these *Manus* or *Rishis* become 21 in number.

of the medal), he does not mean two separate actualities, but the two aspects or facets of the same Unity. Now the best man living would appear, side by side with an Archangel – as described in Theology – a fiend. Hence a certain reason to depreciate a lower "double," immersed far deeper in matter than its original. But there is still as little cause to regard them as devils, and this is precisely what the Roman Catholics maintain against all reason and logic.

THE ARCHAIC DOCTRINE: MAN IS SEVEN-FOLD IN HIS CONSTITUTION

The concluding sentence of this *sloka* shows how archaic is the belief and the doctrine that man is seven-fold in his constitution. The thread of being which animates man and passes through all his personalities, or rebirths on this Earth (an allusion to *Sutratma*), the thread on which moreover all his "Spirits" are strung – is spun from the essence of the "threefold," the "fourfold" and the "fivefold"; which contain all the preceding. *Panchâsikha*, agreeably to *Bhâgavata Purâna* (V. XX. 25 – 28), is one of the seven *Kumâras* who go to Sveta-Dvipa to worship Vishnu. We shall see further on, what connection there is between the "celibate" and chaste sons of Brahmâ, who refuse "to multiply," and terrestrial mortals. Meanwhile it is evident that "the Man-Plant," *Saptaparna*, thus refers to the seven principles, and man is compared to the seven-leaved plant of this name so sacred among Buddhists.

The Secret Doctrine, i 233-236

Selection 3

THE INFORMING VITAL SOUL OF THE PLANETS AND OUR EARTH

... (our Esoteric Doctrine) teaches that it is this original, primordial *prima materia*, divine and intelligent, the direct emanation of the Universal Mind – the *DaiviPrakriti* (the divine light emanating from the *Logos*[8]) – which formed the nuclei of all the "self-moving" orbs in *Kosmos*. It is the informing, ever-present moving-power and life-principle, the vital soul of the suns, moons, planets, and even of our Earth. The former latent: the last one active – the invisible Ruler and guide of the gross body attached to, and connected with, its Soul, which is the spiritual emanation, after all, of these respective planetary Spirits.

Another quite occult doctrine is the theory of Kant, that the matter of which the inhabitants and the animals of other planets are formed is of *a lighter and more subtle nature and of a more perfect conformation in proportion to their distance from the Sun*. The latter is too full of Vital Electricity, of the physical, life-giving principle. Therefore, the men on Mars are more ethereal than we are, while those of Venus are more gross, though far more intelligent, if less spiritual.

The last doctrine is not quite ours – yet those Kantian theories are as metaphysical, and as transcendental as any occult doctrines; and more than one man of Science would, if he but *dared* speak his mind, accept them as Wolf does. From this Kantian mind and soul of the Suns and Stars to the MAHAT (mind) and *Prakriti* of the *Purânas*, there is but a step. After all, the admission of this by Science would be only the admission of a natural cause, whether it would or would not stretch its belief to such metaphysical heights. But then *Mahat*, the MIND, is a "God," and physiology admits "mind" only as a temporary function of the material brain, and no more.

---

8 Which "Light" we call *Fohat*.

SOME SCIENTISTS ACCEPT VIEWS SIMILAR TO THE OCCULTISTS

The Satan of Materialism now laughs at all alike, and denies the visible as well as the invisible. Seeing in light, heat, electricity, and even in the *phenomenon of life*, only properties inherent in matter, it laughs whenever life is called VITAL PRINCIPLE, and derides the idea of its being independent of and distinct from the organism.

But here again scientific opinions differ as in everything else, and there are several men of science who accept views very similar to ours. Consider, for instance, what Dr. Richardson, F.R.S. (elsewhere quoted at length) says of that "Vital principle," which he calls "nervous ether" ("*Popular Science Review,*" Vol. 10):

"I speak only of a veritable *material agent*, refined, it may be, to the world at large, but *actual and substantial*: an agent having quality of weight and of volume, an agent susceptible of chemical combination, and thereby of change of physical state and condition, an agent passive in its action, moved always, that is to say, by influences apart from itself,[9] obeying other influences, an agent possessing no initiative power, no *vis* or *energia naturæ*,[10] but still playing a most important, if not a primary part in the production of the phenomena resulting from the action of the *energeia* upon visible matter" (p. 379).

As biology and physiology now deny, *in toto*, the existence of a "vital principle," this extract, together with de Quatrefages' admission, is a clear confirmation that there are men of science who take the same views about "things occult" as Theosophists and occultists do. These recognise a distinct vital principle independent of the organism – material, of course, *as physical force cannot be divorced from matter*, but of a substance existing in a state unknown to Science. *Life for them is something more than the mere interaction of molecules and atoms. There is a vital principle without which no molecular combinations could ever have resulted in a living organism, least of all in the so-called "inorganic" matter of our plane of consciousness.*

---

9 This is a mistake, which implies a material agent, distinct from the influences which move it, i.e. blind matter and perhaps "God" again, whereas this ONE Life is the very God and Gods "Itself."

10 The same error.

By "molecular combinations" is meant, of course, those of the matter of our present illusive perceptions, which matter energises only on this, our plane. And this is the chief point at issue.[11]

Thus the Occultists are not alone in their beliefs. Nor are they so foolish, after all, in rejecting even the "gravity" of modern Science along with other *physical* laws, and in accepting instead *attraction* and *repulsion*. They see, moreover, in these two opposite Forces only the two *aspects* of the universal unit, called "Manifesting Mind"; in which aspects, Occultism, through its great Seers, perceives an innumerable Host of operative Beings: Cosmic *Dhyan Chohans*, Entities, whose essence, in its *dual* nature, is the Cause of all terrestrial phenomena. For that essence is co-substantial with the universal Electric Ocean, which is Life; and being dual, as said – positive and negative – it is the emanations of that duality that act now on earth under the name of "modes of motion"; even *Force* having now become objectionable as a word, for fear it should lead someone, even in thought, to separate it from matter! It is, as Occultism says, the dual *effects* of that dual essence, which have now been called centripetal and centrifugal forces, negative and positive poles, or polarity, heat and cold, light and darkness, etc., etc.

And it is maintained that even the Greek and Roman Catholic Christians are wiser in believing, as they do – even if blindly connecting and tracing them all to an anthropomorphic god – in Angels, Archangels, Archons, Seraphs, and Morning Stars: in all those theological *Deliciæ humani generis*, in short, that rule the cosmic elements, than Science is, in disbelieving in them altogether, and advocating its mechanical Forces. For these act very often with more than human intelligence and pertinency. Nevertheless, that intelligence

---

11 "Is the *Jiva* a myth, as science says, or is it not?" ask some Theosophists, wavering between materialistic and idealistic Science. The difficulty of really grasping esoteric problems concerning the "ultimate state of matter" is again the old crux of the *objective* and the *subjective*. What is matter? Is the matter of our present objective consciousness anything but our SENSATIONS? True, the sensations we receive come *from without*, but can we really (except in terms of phenomena) speak of the "gross matter" of this plane as an entity apart from and independent of us? To all such arguments Occultism answers: True, in *reality* matter is not independent of, or existent outside, our perceptions. Man is an *illusion*: granted. But the existence and actuality of other, still more illusive, but not less *actual*, entities than we are, is not a claim which is lessened, but rather strengthened by this doctrine of Vedantic and even Kantian Idealism.

is denied and attributed to blind chance. But, as De Maîstre was right in calling the law of gravitation merely a word which replaced "the thing unknown" (Soirées), so are we right in applying the same remark to all the other Forces of Science. And if it is objected that the Count was an ardent Roman Catholic, then we may cite Le Couturier, as ardent a materialist, who said the same thing, as also did Herschell and many others. (*Vide Musée des Sciences*, August, 1856.)

From *Gods* to *men*, from Worlds to atoms, from a star to a rush-light, from the Sun to the vital heat of the meanest organic being – the world of Form and Existence is an immense chain, whose links are all connected. The law of Analogy is the first key to the world-problem, and these links have to be studied co-ordinately in their occult relations to each other.

When, therefore, the Secret Doctrine – postulating that conditioned or limited space (location) has no real being except in this world of illusion, or, in other words, in our perceptive faculties – teaches that every one of the higher, as of the lower worlds, is interblended with our own objective world; that millions of things and beings are, in point of localization, around and *in* us, as we are around, with, and in them; it is no metaphysical figure of speech, but a sober fact in Nature, however incomprehensible to our senses.

The Secret Doctrine, i 602–605

Selection 4

PHYSICAL MAN WAS ORIGINALLY A COLOSSAL PRE-TERTIARY GIANT

The claim that physical man was originally a colossal pre-tertiary giant, and that he existed 18,000,000 years ago, must of course appear preposterous to admirers of, and believers in, modern learning. The whole *posse comitatus* of biologists will turn away from the conception of this third race Titan of the Secondary age, a being fit to fight as successfully with the then gigantic monsters of the air, sea, and land, as his forefathers – the ethereal prototype of the Atlantean – had little need to fear that which could not hurt him. The modern anthropologist is quite welcome to laugh at our Titans, as he laughs at the Biblical Adam, and as the theologian laughs at his pithecoid ancestor. The Occultists and their severe critics may feel that they have pretty well mutually squared their accounts by this time. Occult sciences claim less and give more, at all events, than either Darwinian anthropology or Biblical theology.

Nor ought the Esoteric Chronology to frighten any one; for, with regard to figures, the greatest authorities of the day are as fickle and as uncertain as the Mediterranean wave. As regards the duration of the geological periods alone, the learned men of the Royal Society are all hopelessly at sea, and jump from one million to five hundred millions of years with the utmost ease, as will be seen more than once during this comparison.

Take one instance for our present purpose – the calculations of Mr. Croll. Whether, according to this authority, 2,500,000 years represent the time since the beginning of the tertiary age, or the Eocene period, as an American geologist makes him say;[12] or whether again Mr. Croll "allows fifteen millions since the beginning of the Eocene period," as

---

12 A. Winchell, Professor of Geology, *"World-Life,"* p. 369.

quoted by an English geologist,[13] both sets of figures cover the claims made by the Secret Doctrine.[14] For assigning as the latter does from four to five million years between the incipient and the final evolution of the Fourth Root-Race, on the Lemuro-Atlantean Continents; one million years for the Fifth, or Aryan Race, to the present date; and about 850,000 since the submersion of the last large peninsula of the great Atlantis – all this may have easily taken place within the 15,000,000 years conceded by Mr. Croll to the Tertiary Age. But, *chronologically* speaking, the duration of the period is of secondary importance, as we have, after all, certain American scientists to fall back upon. These gentlemen, unmoved by the fact that their assertions are called not only dubious but absurd, yet maintain that man existed so far back as in the Secondary Age. They have found human footprints on rocks of that formation; and furthermore, M. de Quatrefages finds no valid *scientific* reason why man should not have existed during the Secondary Age.

The Secret Doctrine, ii 9-10

---

13 Mr. Charles Gould, late Geological surveyor of Tasmania, in *"Mythical Monsters,"* p. 84.

14 Sir Charles Lyell, who is credited with having "happily invented the terms Eocene, Miocene, and Pliocene," to mark the three divisions of the Tertiary age, ought really to have settled upon some approximate age for his "Mind-offspring." Having left the duration of these periods, however, to the speculations of specialists, the greatest confusion and perplexity are the result of that happy thought. It seems like a hopeless task to quote one set of figures from one work, without the risk of finding it contradicted by the same Author in an earlier or a subsequent volume. Sir W. Thomson, one of the most eminent among the modern authorities, has changed about half-a-dozen times his opinion upon the age of the Sun and the date of the consolidation of the Earth's crust. In Thomson and Tait's *"Natural Philosophy,"* one finds only ten million years allowed since the time when the temperature of the Earth permitted vegetable life to appear on it; (*App. D et seq.*; also *Trans. Roy. Soc. Edin.* XXIII, Pt. 1, 157, 1862, where 847 is cancelled). Mr. Darwin gives Sir W. Thomson's estimate as "a minimum of 98 and a maximum of 200 millions of years since the consolidation of the crust" (See Ch. Gould). In the same work *"Natural Philosophy,"* 80 millions are given from the time of incipient incrustation to the present state of the world. And in his last lecture, as shown elsewhere, Sir W. Thomson declares (1887) that the Sun is not older than 15 millions of years! Meanwhile, basing his arguments as to the limits to the age of the Sun's heat on figures previously established by Sir W. Thomson, Mr. Croll allows 60 millions of years since the beginning of the Cambrian period. This is hopeful for the lovers of exact knowledge. Thus, whatever figures are given by Occult Science, they are sure to be corroborated by those of some one among the modern men of Science who are considered as authorities.

Selection 5

On The Identity And Differences Of The Incarnating Powers

THE Progenitors of Man, called in India "Fathers," *Pitara* or *Pitris*, are the creators of our bodies and lower principles. They are ourselves, as the first personalities, and we are they. Primeval man would be "the bone of their bone and the flesh of their flesh," if they had body and flesh. As stated, they were "lunar Beings."

The Endowers of man with his conscious, immortal EGO, are the "Solar Angels"— whether so regarded metaphorically or literally. The mysteries of the Conscious EGO or human Soul are great. The esoteric name of these "Solar Angels" is, literally, the "Lords" (Nath) of "persevering ceaseless devotion" (*pranidhâna*). Therefore they of the fifth principle (*Manas*) seem to be connected with, or to have originated the system of the *Yogis* who make of *pranidhâna* their fifth observance (see *Yoga* Shastra, II., 32.) It has already been explained why the trans-Himalayan Occultists regard them as evidently identical with those who in India are termed *Kumâras, Agnishwattas*, and the *Barhishads*.

How precise and true is Plato's expression, how profound and philosophical his remark on the (human) soul or EGO, when he defined it as "a compound of the same and the other." And yet how little this hint has been understood, since the world took it to mean that the soul was the breath of God, of Jehovah. It is "the same and the other," as the great Initiate-Philosopher said; for the EGO (the "Higher Self" when merged with and in the Divine Monad) is Man, and yet the same as the "OTHER," the Angel in him incarnated, as the same with the universal MAHAT. The great classics and philosophers felt this truth, when saying that "there must be something within us which produces our thoughts. Something very subtle; it is a breath; it is fire; it is ether; it is quintessence; it is a slender likeness; it is an intellection; it is a number; it is harmony. . . . . " (Voltaire).

All these are the *Manasam* and *Rajasas*: the *Kumâras, Asuras*, and other rulers and *Pitris*, who incarnated in the Third Race, and in this and various other ways endowed mankind with Mind.

There are seven classes of *Pitris*, as shown below, three incorporeal and four corporeal; and two kinds, the *Agnishwatta* and the *Barhishad*. And we may add that, as there are two kinds of *Pitris*, so there is a double and a triple set of *Barhishad* and *Agnishwatta*. The former, having given birth to their astral doubles, are reborn as Sons of Atri, and are the "*Pitris* of the Demons," or corporeal beings, on the authority of *Manu* (III., 196); while the *Agnishwatta* are reborn as Sons of Marichi (a son of Brahmâ), and are the *Pitris* of the Gods (*Manu* again, *Matsya* and *Padma Purânas* and Kulluka in the *Laws of the Manavas*, III., 195). [15] Moreover, the *Vayu Purâna* declares all the seven orders to have originally been the first gods, the *Vairajas*, whom Brahmâ "with the eye of *Yoga*, beheld in the eternal spheres, and who are the gods of gods"; and the *Matsya* adds that the Gods worshipped them; while the *Harivansa* (S. 1, 935) distinguishes the *Virâjas* as one class of the *Pitris* only — a statement corroborated in the Secret Teachings, which, however, identify the *Virâjas* with the elder *Agnishwattas* [16] and the *Rajasas*, or *Abhuta Rajasas*, who are incorporeal without even an astral phantom. Vishnu is said, in most of the MSS., to have incarnated in and through them. "In the *Raivata Manvantara*, again, Hari, best of gods, was born of Sambhuti, as the divine *Manasas* — originating with the deities called *Rajasas*." Sambhuti was a daughter of Daksha, and wife of Marichi, the father of the *Agnishwatta*, who, along with the *Rajasas*, are ever associated with *Manasas*. As remarked by a far more able Sanskritist than Wilson, Mr. Fitzedward Hall, "*Manasa* is no inappropriate name for a deity associated with the *Rajasas*. We appear to have in it *Manasam* — the same as *Manas* — with the change of termination required to express male personification" (*Vishnu Purâna* Bk. III., ch. I., p. 17 footnote). All the sons of Virâja are *Manasa*, says Nilakantha. And Virâja is Brahmâ, and, therefore, the incorporeal *Pitris* are called *Vairâjas* from being the sons of Virâja, says *Vayu Purâna*.

We could multiply our proofs *ad infinitum*, but it is useless. The

---

15 We are quite aware that the *Yayu* and *Matsya Purânas* identify (agreeably to Western interpretation) the *Agnishwatta* with the seasons, and the *Barhishad Pitris* with the months; adding a fourth class — the *Kavyas* — cyclic years. But do not Christian, Roman Catholics identify their Angels with planets, and are not the seven *Rishis* become the *Saptarshi* — a constellation? They are deities presiding over all the cyclic divisions.

16 The *Vayu Purâna* shows the region called Virâja-loka inhabited by the *Agnishwattas*.

wise will understand our meaning, the unwise are not required to. There are thirty-three *crores*, or 330 millions, of gods in India. But, as remarked by the learned lecturer on the *Bhagavad Gîtâ*, "they may be all *devas*, but are by no means all 'gods', in the high spiritual sense one attributes to the term." "This is an unfortunate blunder," he remarks, "generally committed by Europeans. *Deva* is a kind of spiritual being, and because the same word is used in ordinary parlance to mean god, it by no means follows that we have to worship thirty-three *crores* of gods." And he adds suggestively: "These beings, as may be naturally inferred have a certain affinity with one of the three component *Upadhis* (basic principles) into which we have divided man."—(Vide *Theosophist*, Feb., 1887, *et seq.*)

The names of the deities of a certain mystic class change with every *Manvantara*. Thus the twelve great gods, *Jayas*, created by Brahmâ to assist him in the work of creation in the very beginning of the *Kalpa*, and who, lost in *Samadhi*, neglected to create — whereupon they were cursed to be repeatedly born in each *Manvantara* till the seventh — are respectively called *Ajitas*, *Tushitas*, *Satyas*, *Haris*, *Vaikunthas*, *Sadhyas*, and *Adityas*: they are *Tushitas* (in the second *Kalpa*), and *Adityas* in this *Vaivasvata* period (see *Vayu Purâna*), besides other names for each age. But they are identical with the *Manasa* or *Rajasas*, and these with our incarnating *Dhyan Chohans*. They are all classes of the *Gnana-devas*.

Yes; besides those beings, who, like the *Yakshas*, *Gandharvas*, *Kinaras*, etc., etc., taken in their individualities, inhabit the astral plane, there are real *Devagnanams*, and to these classes of *Devas* belong the *Adityas*, the *Vairâjas*, the *Kumaras*, the *Asuras*, and all those high celestial beings whom Occult teaching calls *Manaswin*, the Wise, foremost of all, and who would have made all men the self-conscious spiritually intellectual beings they will be, had they not been "cursed" to fall into generation, and to be reborn themselves as mortals for their neglect of duty.

SEVEN CLASSES OF *PITRIS*

STANZA IV. — (Continued.)

15. SEVEN TIMES SEVEN SHADOWS (*chhayas*) OF FUTURE MEN (or *Amanasas*) (a) WERE (thus) BORN, EACH OF HIS OWN COLOUR (complexion) AND KIND (b). EACH (also) INFERIOR TO HIS FATHER (creator). THE FATHERS, THE BONELESS, COULD GIVE NO LIFE TO

BEINGS WITH BONES. THEIR PROGENY WERE BHUTA (phantoms) WITH NEITHER FORM NOR MIND, THEREFORE THEY WERE CALLED THE CHHAYA (image or shadow) RACE (c).

(*a*) *Manu*, as already remarked, comes from the root "man" to think, hence "a thinker." It is from this Sanskrit word very likely that sprung the Latin "mens," mind, the Egyptian *"Menes,"* the "Master-Mind," the Pythagorean *Monas*, or conscious "thinking unit," mind also, and even our *"Manas"* or mind, the fifth principle in man. Hence these shadows are called *amanasa*, "mindless."

With the Brahmins the *Pitris* are very sacred, because they are the Progenitors, [17] or ancestors of men — the first *Manushya* on this Earth — and offerings are made to them by the Brahmin when a son is born unto him. They are more honoured and their ritual is more important than the worship of the gods (See the *"Laws of Manu,"* Bk. III., p. 203).

May we not now search for a philosophical meaning in this dual group of progenitors?

The *Pitris* being divided into seven classes, we have here the mystic number again. Nearly all the *Purânas* agree that three of these are *arupa*, formless, while four are corporeal; the former being intellectual and spiritual, the latter material and devoid of intellect. Esoterically, it is the *Asuras* who form the first three classes of *Pitris* — "born in the body of night" — whereas the other four were produced from the body of twilight. Their fathers, the gods, were doomed to be born fools on Earth, according to *Vayu Purâna*. The legends are purposely mixed up and made very hazy: the *Pitris* being in one the sons of the gods, and, in another those of Brahmâ; while a third makes them instructors of their own fathers. It is the Hosts of the four material classes who create men simultaneously on the seven zones.

Now, with regard to the seven classes of *Pitris*, each of which is again divided into seven, a word to students and a query to the profane. That class of the "Fire *Dhyanis*," which we identify on undeniable grounds

---

17 This was hinted at in *Isis Unveiled*, Vol. I., p. xxxviii., though the full explanation could not then be given: "The *Pitris* are not the ancestors of the present living men, but those of the first human kind or Adamic race; the spirits of human races, which, on the great scale of descending evolution, preceded our races of men, and were physically as well as spiritually, far superior to our modem pigmies. In *Manava-Dharma-Sastra* they are called the Lunar ancestors."

with the *Agnishwattas,* is called in our school the "Heart" of the Dhyan-Chohanic Body; and it is said to have incarnated in the third race of men and made them perfect. The esoteric Mystagogy speaks of the mysterious relation existing between the hebdomadic essence or substance of this angelic Heart and that of man, whose every physical organ, and psychic, and spiritual function, is a reflection, so to say, a copy on the terrestrial plane of the model or prototype above. Why, it is asked, should there be such a strange repetition of the number seven in the anatomical structure of man? Why should the heart have four lower "cavities and three higher divisions," answering so strangely to the septenary division of the human principles, separated into two groups, the higher and the lower; and why should the same division be found in the various classes of *Pitris,* and especially our Fire *Dhyanis?* For, as already stated, these Beings fall into four corporeal (or grosser) and three incorporeal (or subtler) "principles," or call them by any other name you please. Why do the seven nervous plexuses of the body radiate seven rays? Why are there these seven plexuses, and why seven distinct layers in the human skin?

"Having projected their shadows and made men of one element (ether), the progenitors re-ascend to *Maha-loka,* whence they descend periodically, when the world is renewed, to give birth to new men.

"The subtle bodies remain without understanding (*Manas*) until the advent of the *Suras* (Gods) now called *Asuras* (not Gods)," says the Commentary.

"Not-gods," for the Brahmins, perhaps, but the highest Breaths, for the Occultist; since those progenitors (*Pitar*), the formless and the intellectual, refuse to build man, but endow him with mind; the four corporeal classes creating only his body.

This is very plainly shown in various texts of the *Rig Veda* — the highest authority for a Hindu of any sect whatever. Therein *Asura* means "spiritual divine," and the word is used as a synonym for Supreme Spirit, while in the sense of a "God," the term "*Asura*" is applied to Varuna and Indra and pre-eminently to Agni — the three having been in days of old the three highest gods, before Brahmanical Theo-Mythology distorted the true meaning of almost everything in the Archaic Scriptures. But, as the key is now lost, the *Asuras* are hardly mentioned.

In the *Zend Avesta* the same is found. In the Mazdean, or Magian, religion, "*Asura*" is the lord *Asura VisvaVedas*, the "all-knowing" or "omniscient Lord"; and *Asura-Mazdha*, become later *Ahura-Mazdha*, is, as Benfey shows, "the Lord who bestows Intelligence" — *Asura-Medha* and *Ahura-Mazdao*. Elsewhere in this work it is shown, on equally good authority, that the Indo-Iranian *Asura* was always regarded as sevenfold. This fact, combined with the name *Mazdha*, as above, which makes of the sevenfold *Asura* the "Lord," or "Lords" collectively "who bestow Intelligence," connects the *Amshaspends* with the *Asuras* and with our incarnating *Dhyan Chohans*, as well as with the *Elohim*, and the seven informing gods of Egypt, Chaldea, and every other country.

Why these "gods" refused to create men is not, as stated in exoteric accounts, because their pride was too great to share the celestial power of their essence with the children of Earth, but for reasons already suggested. However, allegory has indulged in endless fancies and theology taken advantage thereof in every country to make out its case against these first-born, or the logoi, and to impress it as a truth on the minds of the ignorant and credulous. (Compare also what is said about Makara and the *Kumâras* in connection with the Zodiac.)

The Christian system is not the only one which has degraded them into demons. Zoroastrianism and even Brahmanism have profited thereby to obtain hold over the people's mind. Even in Chaldean exotericism, Beings who refuse to create, i.e., who are said to oppose thereby the *Demiurgos*, are also denounced as the Spirits of Darkness. The *Suras*, who win their intellectual independence, fight the *Suras* who are devoid thereof, who are shown as passing their lives in profitless ceremonial worship based on blind faith — a hint now ignored by the orthodox Brahmins — and forthwith the former become *A-Suras*. The first and mind-born Sons of the Deity refuse to create progeny, and are cursed by Brahmâ to be born as men. They are hurled down to Earth, which, later on, is transformed, in theological dogma, into the infernal regions. Ahriman destroys the Bull created by Ormazd — which is the emblem of terrestrial illusive life, the "germ of sorrow" — and, forgetting that the perishing finite seed must die, in order that the plant of immortality, the plant of spiritual, eternal life, should sprout and live, Ahriman is proclaimed the enemy, the opposing power, the devil. Typhon cuts Osiris into fourteen pieces, in order to prevent his peopling the world and thus creating misery; and Typhon becomes, in the exoteric, theological teaching, the Power of Darkness. But all this is the exoteric shell. It is the worshippers of the latter who attribute to disobedience and rebellion the effort and self-sacrifice of those who would help men to their original status of divinity through self-conscious efforts; and it is these worshippers of Form who have made demons of the Angels of Light.

Esoteric philosophy, however, teaches that one third [18] of the *Dhyanis* — i.e., the three classes of the *Arupa Pitris*, endowed with intelligence, "which is a formless breath, composed of intellectual not elementary substances" (see *Harivamsa*, 932) — was simply doomed by the law of Karma and evolution to be reborn (or incarnated) on Earth. [19] Some of these were *Nirmanakayas* from other *Manvantaras*. Hence we see them, in all the *Purânas*, reappearing on this globe, in the third *Manvantara*, as Kings, *Rishis* and heroes (read Third Root-Race). This tenet, being too philosophical and metaphysical to be grasped by the multitudes, was, as already stated, disfigured by the priesthood for the purpose of preserving a hold over them through superstitious fear.

The supposed "rebels," then, were simply those who, compelled by Karmic law to drink the cup of gall to its last bitter drop, had to incarnate anew, and thus make responsible thinking entities of the astral statues projected by their inferior brethren. Some are said to

---

18 Whence the subsequent assertions of St. John's vision, referred to in his Apocalypse, about "the great red Dragon having seven heads and ten horns, and seven crowns upon his heads," whose "tail drew the third part of the stars of heaven and did cast them to the earth" (ch. xii.).

19 The verse "did cast them to the Earth," plainly shows its origin in the grandest and oldest allegory of the Aryan mystics, who, after the destruction of the Atlantean giants and sorcerers, concealed the truth — astronomical, physical, and divine, as it is a page out of pre-cosmic theogony — under various allegories. Its esoteric, true interpretation is a veritable Theodice of the "Fallen Angels," so called; the willing and the unwilling, the creators and those who refused to create, being now mixed up most perplexingly by Christian Catholics, who forget that their highest Archangel, St. Michael, who is shown to conquer (to master and to assimilate) the DRAGON OF WISDOM and of divine Self-sacrifice (now miscalled and calumniated as Satan), WAS THE FIRST TO REFUSE TO CREATE! This led to endless confusion. So little does Christian theology understand the paradoxical language of the East and its symbolism, that it even explains, in its dead letter sense, the Chinese *Buddhist* and Hindu exoteric rite of raising a noise during certain eclipses to scare away the "great red Dragon," which laid a plot to carry away the light! But here "Light" means esoteric Wisdom, and we have sufficiently explained the secret meaning of the terms Dragon, Serpent, etc., etc., all of which refer to Adepts and Initiates.

have refused, because they had not in them the requisite materials — i.e., an astral body — since they were *Arupa*. The refusal of others had reference to their having been Adepts and *Yogis* of long past preceding *Manvantaras*; another mystery. But, later on, as *Nirmanakayas*, they sacrificed themselves for the good and salvation of the Monads which were waiting for their turn, and which otherwise would have had to linger for countless ages in irresponsible, animal-like, though in appearance human, forms. It may be a parable and an allegory within an allegory. Its solution is left to the intuition of the student, if he only reads that which follows with his spiritual eye.

As to their fashioners or "Ancestors" — those Angels who, in the exoteric legends, obeyed the law — they must be identical with the *Barhishad Pitris*, or the *Pitar-Devata*, i.e., those possessed of the physical creative fire. They could only create, or rather clothe, the human Monads with their own astral Selves, but they could not make man in their image and likeness. "Man must not be like one of us," say the creative gods, entrusted with the fabrication of the lower animal but higher; (see Gen. and Plato's *Timæus*). Their creating the semblance of men out of their own divine Essence means, esoterically, that it is they who became the first Race, and thus shared its destiny and further evolution. They would not, simply because they could not, give to man that sacred spark which burns and expands into the flower of human reason and self-consciousness, for they had it not to give. This was left to that class of *Devas* who became symbolised in Greece under the name of Prometheus, to those who had nought to do with the physical body, yet everything with the purely spiritual man. (See Part II of this volume, "The Fallen Angels"; also "The Gods of Light proceed from the Gods of Darkness.")

WHAT PROMETHEUS SYMBOLIZED

Each class of Creators endows man with what it has to give: the one builds his external form; the other gives him its essence, which later on becomes the Human Higher Self owing to the personal exertion of the individual; but they could not make men as they were themselves — perfect, because sinless; sinless, because having only the first, pale shadowy outlines of attributes, and these all perfect — from the human standpoint — white, pure and cold as the virgin snow. Where there is no struggle, there is no merit. Humanity, "of the Earth earthy," was not destined to be created by the angels of the first divine Breath: therefore they are said to have refused to do so, and man had to be formed by more material creators, [20] who, in their turn, could give only what they had in their own natures, and no more. Subservient to eternal law, the pure gods could only project out of themselves shadowy men, a little less ethereal and spiritual, less divine and perfect than themselves — shadows still. The first humanity, therefore, was a pale copy of its progenitors; too material, even in its ethereality, to be a hierarchy of gods; too spiritual and pure to be MEN, endowed as it is with every negative (*Nirguna*) perfection. Perfection, to be fully such, must be born out of imperfection, the incorruptible must grow out of the corruptible, having the latter as its vehicle and basis and contrast. Absolute light is absolute darkness, and vice versa. In fact, there is neither light nor darkness in the realms of truth. Good and Evil are twins, the progeny of Space and Time, under the sway of *Maya*. Separate them, by cutting off one from the other, and they will both die. Neither exists per se, since each has to be generated and created out of the other, in order to come into being; both must be known and appreciated before becoming objects of perception, hence, in mortal mind, they must be divided.

Nevertheless, as the illusionary distinction exists, it requires a lower order of creative angels to "create" inhabited globes — especially ours — or to deal with matter on this earthly plane. The philosophical

---

20 In spite of all efforts to the contrary, Christian theology — having burdened itself with the Hebrew esoteric account of the creation of man, which is understood literally — cannot find any reasonable excuse for its "God, the Creator," who produces a man devoid of mind and sense; nor can it justify the punishment following an act, for which Adam and Eve might plead non compos. For if the couple is admitted to be ignorant of good and evil before the eating of the forbidden fruit, how could it be expected to know that disobedience was evil? If primeval man was meant to remain a half-witted, or rather witless, being, then his creation was aimless and even cruel, if produced by an omnipotent and perfect God. But Adam and Eve are shown, even in *Genesis*, to be created by a class of lower divine Beings, the *Elohim*, who are so jealous of their personal prerogatives as reasonable and intelligent creatures, that they will not allow man to become "as one of us." This is plain, even from the dead-letter meaning of the *Bible*. The Gnostics, then, were right in regarding the Jewish God as belonging to a class of lower, material and not very holy denizens of the invisible World.

Gnostics were the first to think so, in the historical period, and to invent various systems upon this theory. Therefore in their schemes of creation, one always finds their Creators occupying a place at the very foot of the ladder of spiritual Being. With them, those who created our earth and its mortals were placed on the very limit of mayavic matter, and their followers were taught to think — to the great disgust of the Church Fathers — that for the creation of those wretched races, in a spiritual and moral sense, which grace our globe, no high divinity could be made responsible, but only angels of a low hierarchy, [21] to which class they relegated the Jewish God, Jehovah.

Mankinds different from the present are mentioned in all the ancient Cosmogonies. Plato speaks, in the *Phædrus*, of a winged race of men. Aristophanes (in Plato's *Banquet*), speaks of a race androgynous and with round bodies. In Pymander, all the animal kingdom even is double-sexed. Thus in § 18, it is said: "The circuit having been accomplished, the knot was loosened. . . . and all the animals, which were equally androgynous, were untied (separated) together with man. . . . ." for. . . . "the causes had to produce effects on earth." [22] Again, in the ancient Quiche *Manu*script, the *Popol Vuh* — published by the late Abbé Brasseur de Bourbourg — the first men are described as a race "whose sight was unlimited, and who knew all things at once": thus showing the divine knowledge of Gods, not mortals. The Secret Doctrine, correcting the unavoidable exaggerations of popular fancy, gives the facts as they are recorded in the Archaic symbols.

The Secret Doctrine, ii 88-96

---

21 In *Isis Unveiled* several of these Gnostic systems are given. One is taken from the *Codex Nazaræus*, the Scriptures of the Nazarenes, who, although they existed long before the days of Christ, and even before the laws of Moses, were Gnostics, and many of them Initiates. They held their "Mysteries of Life" in Nazara (ancient and modern Nazareth), and their doctrines are a faithful echo of the teachings of the Secret Doctrine — some of which we are now endeavouring to explain.

22 See the translation from the Greek by Francois, Monsieur de Foix, Evesque d'Ayre: the work dedicated to Marguerite de France, Reine de Navarre. Edition of 1579, Bordeaux.

Selection 6

The Evolution of the Sexless Second Race

STANZA 18. The first (*Race*) were the Sons of Yoga. Their sons, the children of the Yellow Father and the White Mother.

In the later *Commentary*, the sentence is translated:

"*The Sons of the Sun and of the Moon, the nursling of ether* (or the wind)

(*a*) . . . . . "*They were the shadows of the shadows of the Lords* (*b*). *They* (the shadows) *expanded. The Spirits of the Earth clothed them; the solar Lhas warmed them* (i.e. preserved the vital fire in the nascent physical forms). *The Breaths had life, but had no understanding. They had no fire nor water of their own* (*c*).

(*a*) Remember in this connection the *Tabula Smaragdina* of Hermes, the esoteric meaning of which has seven keys to it. The Astro-Chemical is well known to students, the anthropological may be given now. The "One thing" mentioned in it is MAN. It is said: "The Father of THAT ONE ONLY THING is the Sun; its Mother the Moon; the Wind carries it in his bosom, and its nurse is the Spirituous Earth." In the occult rendering of the same it is added: "and *Spiritual* Fire is its instructor (*Guru*)."

The Spirits of the Earth Clothed the Shadows and Expanded Them

This fire is the higher Self, the Spiritual Ego, or that which is eternally reincarnating under the influence of its lower personal Selves, changing with every re-birth, full of *Tanha* or desire to live. It is a strange law of Nature that, on this plane, the higher (Spiritual) Nature should be, so to say, in bondage to the lower. Unless the Ego takes refuge in the *Atman*, the ALL-SPIRIT, and merges entirely into the essence thereof, the personal Ego may goad it to the bitter end. This cannot be thoroughly understood unless the student makes himself

28

familiar with the mystery of evolution, which proceeds on triple lines – spiritual, psychic and physical.

That which propels towards, and forces evolution, *i.e.* compels the growth and development of Man towards perfection, is (*a*) the MONAD, or that which acts in it unconsciously through a force inherent in itself; and (*b*) the lower astral body or the *personal* SELF. The former, whether imprisoned in a vegetable or an animal body, is endowed with, is indeed itself, that force. Owing to its identity with the ALL-FORCE, which, as said, is inherent in the Monad, it is all-potent on the *Arupa*, or formless plane. On our plane, its essence being too pure, it remains all-potential, but individually becomes inactive: *e.g.* the rays of the Sun, which contribute to the growth of vegetation, do not select this or that plant to shine upon. Uproot the plant and transfer it to a piece of soil where the sunbeam cannot reach it, and the latter will not follow it. So with the *Atman*: unless the higher Self or EGO gravitates towards its Sun – the Monad – the lower *Ego*, or *personal* Self, will have the upper hand in every case. For it is this Ego, with its fierce Selfishness and animal desire to live a Senseless life (*Tanha*), which is "the maker of the tabernacle," as Buddha calls it in *Dhammapada* (153 and 154). Hence the expression, "the Spirits of the Earth clothed the shadows and expanded them." To these "Spirits" belong temporarily the human astral selves; and it is they who give, or build, the physical tabernacle of man, for the Monad and its conscious principle, *Manas*, to dwell in. But the "Solar" *Lhas*, Spirits, warm them, the shadows. This is physically and literally true; metaphysically, or on the psychic and spiritual plane, it is equally true that the *Atman* alone *warms* the inner man; *i.e.* it enlightens it with the ray of divine life and alone is able to impart to the inner man, or the reincarnating Ego, its immortality. Thus, as we shall find, for the first three and a half Root-Races, up to the middle or turning point, it is the astral shadows of the "progenitors," the lunar *Pitris*, which are the formative powers in the Races, and which build and gradually force the evolution of the physical form towards perfection – this, at the cost of a proportionate loss of spirituality. Then, from the turning point, it is the Higher Ego, or incarnating principle, the *nous* or *Mind*, which reigns over the animal Ego, and rules it whenever it is not carried down by the latter. In short, Spirituality is on its ascending arc, and the animal or physical impedes it from steadily progressing on the path of its evolution only when the selfishness of the *personality* has so strongly infected the real inner man with its lethal virus, that the upward attraction has lost all its power on the thinking reasonable man. In sober truth, vice and wickedness are an *abnormal, unnatural* manifestation, at this period of our human evolution – at least they ought to be so. The fact that mankind was never more selfish and vicious than it is now, civilized nations having succeeded in making of the first an ethical characteristic, of the second an art, is an additional proof of the exceptional nature of the phenomenon.

The entire scheme is in the "*Chaldean Book of Numbers*," and even in the *Zohar*, if one only understood the meaning of the apocalyptic hints. First comes En-Soph, the "Concealed of the Concealed," then the *Point, Sephira* and the later *Sephiroth*; then the *Atzilatic* World, a *World of Emanations* that gives birth to three other worlds – called the Throne, the abode of pure Spirits; the second, the *World of Formation*, or Jetzira, the habitat of the Angels who sent forth the Third, or World of Action, the Asiatic *World*, which is the Earth or *our* World; and yet it is said of it that this world, also called *Kliphoth*, containing the (six other) Spheres, כלכלים, and matter, is the residence of the "Prince of Darkness." This is as clearly stated as can be; for *Metatron*, the Angel of the second or *Briatic* World, means Messenger, ἄγελος , Angel, called the great Teacher, and under him are the Angels of the third World, *Jetzira*, whose ten and seven classes are the *Sephiroth*,[23] of whom it is said that "they inhabit and vivify this world as Essential *Entities* and *Intelligences*, whose *correlatives* and *contraries* inhabit the third or "*Asiatic World*." These "Contraries" are called "the *Shells*," כליסדה, or *demons*,[24] who inhabit the seven habitations called *Sheba Hachaloth*, which are simply the seven zones of our globe. Their prince is called in the *Kabala* Samael, the Angel of Death, who is also the seducing serpent Satan; but that Satan is also Lucifer, the bright angel of Light, the *Light* and *Life-bringer*, the "Soul" alienated from the HOLY Ones, the other angels, and for a period, *anticipating the time* when they would have descended on Earth to incarnate in their turn.

---

23 See Vol. I. Part III., "*Gods, Monads and Atoms*." It is symbolised in the Pythagorean Triangle, the 10 dots within, and the seven points of the Triangle and the Cube.

24 Whence the Kabalistic name of *Shells* given to the astral form, the body called *Kama Rupa*, left behind by the higher angels in the shape of the higher *Manas*, when the latter leaves for *Devachan*, forsaking its residue.

IN THE "SOUL" IS THE REAL MAN, I.E. THE EGO AND THE CONSCIOUS I AM

"The *Souls* (Monads) are pre-existent in the world of Emanations," ("*Book of Wisdom*," VIII, p. 20); and the *Zohar* teaches that in the "Soul" "is the *real man*, i.e. the Ego and the conscious I AM: '*Manas*'. "

"They descend from the pure air to be *chained to bodies*," says Josephus, repeating the belief of the Essenes (*De Bello Judæo*, 11, 12). "The air is full of Souls," states Philo, "*they descend, to be tied to mortal bodies, being desirous to live in them*." (*De Gignat*, 222 C.; *De Somniis*, p.455)[25]; because through, and in, the human form they will become *progressive* beings, whereas the nature of the angel is purely *intransitive*, therefore man has in him the potency of transcending the faculties of the Angels. Hence the Initiates in India say that it is the Brahmin, the twice-born, who rules the gods or *devas*; and Paul repeated it in I *Corinthians* vi., 3: "Know ye not that we (the Initiates) shall judge angels"?

Finally, it is shown in every ancient scripture and Cosmogony that man evolved primarily as a *luminous incorporeal form*, over which, like the molten brass round the clay model of the sculptor, the physical frame of his body was built by, through, and from, the lower forms and types of animal terrestrial life. "The Soul and the *Form* when descending on Earth put on an earthly garment," says the *Zohar*. His protoplastic body was not formed of that matter of which our mortal frames are fashioned. "When Adam dwelt in the garden of Eden, he was clothed in the celestial garment, which is the garment of heavenly light. . . . *light of that light which was used in the garden of Eden*," (*Zohar* II. 229 B). "Man (the heavenly Adam) *was created* by the ten *Sephiroth* of the Jetziric world, and by the common power they (the seven angels of a still lower world) *engendered the earthly Adam* . . . . First Samael fell, and then *deceiving* (?) man, caused his fall also."

(*b*) The sentence: "They were the shadows of the shadows of the Lords," *i.e.* the progenitors created man out of their own astral bodies, explains an universal belief. The *Devas* are credited in the East with having no shadows of their own. "The *devas* cast no shadows," and this is the sure sign of a *good holy Spirit*.

---

25 Which shows that the Essenes believed in re-birth and many reincarnations on Earth, as Jesus himself did, a fact we can prove from the *New Testament* itself.

Why had they "no fire or water of their own"?[26] Because:

(c) That which Hydrogen is to the elements and gases on the objective plane, its noumenon is in the world of mental or subjective phenomena; since its trinitarian latent nature is mirrored in its three active emanations from the three higher principles in man, namely, "Spirit, Soul, and Mind," or *Atma, Buddhi,* and *Manas.* It is the spiritual and also the material human basis. Rudimentary man, having been nursed by the "air" or the "wind," becomes the perfect man later on; when, with the development of "Spiritual fire," the *noumenon* of the "Three in One" within his Self, he acquires from his inner Self, or Instructor, the Wisdom of Self-Consciousness, which he does not possess in the beginning. Thus here again divine Spirit is symbolised by the Sun or Fire; divine Soul by Water and the Moon, both standing for the Father and Mother of *Pneuma,* human Soul, or Mind, symbolised by the Wind or air, for *Pneuma,* means "breath."

The Secret Doctrine, ii 109-113

---

26 It is corroborated, however, as we have shown, by the esotericism of *Genesis.* Not only are the animals created therein after the "Adam of Dust," but vegetation is shown in the Earth before "the heavens and the Earth were created." "Every plant of the field before it (the day that the heavens and the Earth were made, v. 4) was in the Earth" (v. 5). Now, unless the Occult interpretation is accepted, which shows that in this 4th Round the Globe was covered with vegetation, and the first (*astral*) humanity was produced before almost anything could grow and develop thereon, what can the dead letter mean? Simply that the grass was in the earth of the Globe before that Globe was created? And yet the meaning of verse 6, which says that "there went up a mist from the Earth" and watered the whole face of the Earth before it rained, and caused the trees, etc., to grow, is plain enough. It shows also in what geological period it occurred, and further what is meant by "Heaven and Earth." It meant the firmament and dry *incrustated* land, separated and ridden of its vapours and exhalations. Moreover, the student must bear in mind that, as Adam Kadmon, "the male and female being" of *Genesis,* ch. I., is no physical human being but the host of the *Elohim,* among which was Jehovah himself—so the animals mentioned in that chapter as "created" before man in the dead letter text, were no animals, but the Zodiacal signs and other sidereal bodies.

Selection 7

THE FIRST RACE OF MEN WERE THE IMAGES OF THEIR FATHERS

The first race of men were, then, simply the images, the astral doubles, of their Fathers, who were the pioneers, or the most progressed Entities from a preceding though *lower* sphere, the shell of which is now our Moon. But even this shell is all-potential, for, having generated the Earth, it is the *phantom* of the Moon which, attracted by magnetic affinity, sought to form its first inhabitants, the pre-human monsters, (*vide supra*, Stanza 2.). To assure himself of this, the student has again to turn to the Chaldean Fragments, and read what Berosus says. Berosus obtained his information, he tells us, from Ea, the male-female deity of Wisdom. While the gods were generated in its androgynous bosom (Svâbhâvat, Mother-space) its (the Wisdom's) reflections became on Earth the woman Omoroka, who is the Chaldean Thavatth, or the Greek Thalassa, the Deep or the Sea, which esoterically and even exoterically is *the Moon*. It was the Moon (Omoroka) who presided over the monstrous creation of nondescript beings which were slain by the *Dhyanis*. (*Vide Hibbert Lectures*, p. 370 *et seq.*; also in Part II, Adam-Adami.")

Evolutionary law compelled the lunar "Fathers" to pass, in their monadic condition, through all the forms of life and being on this globe; but at the end of the Third Round, they were already human in their divine nature, and were thus called upon to become the creators of the forms destined to fashion the tabernacles of the less progressed Monads, whose turn it was to incarnate. These "Forms" are called "Sons of Yoga," because *Yoga* (union with Brahmâ exoterically) is the supreme condition of the passive infinite deity, since it contains all the divine energies and is the essence of Brahmâ, who is said (as Brahmâ) to create everything through *Yoga* power. Brahmâ, Vishnu and Siva are the most powerful energies of God, Brahma, the Neuter, says a Purânic text. *Yoga* here is the same as Dhyâna, which word is again synonymous with *Yoga* in the Tibetan text, where the "Sons of Yoga" are called "Sons of *Dhyâna*," or of that abstract meditation through which the *Dhyani-Buddhas* create their celestial sons, the *Dhyani-Bodhisattvas*. All the creatures in the world have each a superior above. "This superior, whose inner pleasure it is *to emanate into them*, cannot impart efflux until they have adored" – *i.e.* meditated as during *Yoga*. (*Sepher M'bo Sha-arim*, translated by Isaac Myer, "*Qabbalah*," pp. 109 – 111)

STANZA 19. THE SECOND RACE (*was*) THE PRODUCT BY BUDDING AND EXPANSION; THE A-SEXUAL (*form*) FROM THE SEXLESS (*shadow*). THUS WAS, O LANOO, THE SECOND RACE PRODUCED (*a*).

THE TWO MODES OF PROCREATION OF THE 2ND AND 3RD RACES

(*a*) What will be most contested by scientific authorities is this a-sexual Race, the Second, the fathers of the "Sweat-born" so-called, and perhaps still more the Third Race, the "Egg-born" androgynes. These two modes of procreation are the most difficult to comprehend, especially for the Western mind. It is evident that no explanation can be attempted for those who are not students of Occult metaphysics. European language has no words to express things which Nature repeats no more at this stage of evolution, things which therefore can have no meaning for the materialist. But there are analogies. It is not denied that in the beginning of physical evolution there must have been processes in Nature, spontaneous generation, for instance, now extinct, which are repeated in other forms. Thus we are told that microscopic research shows no permanence of any particular mode of reproducing life. For "it shows that the same organism may run through various metamorphoses in the course of its life-cycle, during some of which it may be *sexual*, and in others *a-sexual*; *i.e.* it may reproduce itself alternately by the co-operation of two beings of opposite sex, and also by fissure or budding from one being only, which is of no sex."[27] "*Budding*" is the very word used in the Stanza. How could these *Chhayas* reproduce themselves otherwise; viz., procreate the Second Race, since they were ethereal, a-sexual, and even devoid, as yet, of the vehicle of desire, or *Kama Rupa*, which evolved only in the Third

---

27 See Laing's "*Modern Science and Modern Thought*," p. 90.

Race? They evolved the Second Race unconsciously, as do some plants. Or, perhaps, as the *Amœba*, only on a more ethereal, impressive, and larger scale. If, indeed, the cell-theory applies equally to Botany and Zoology, and extends to Morphology, as well as to the Physiology of organisms, and if the microscopic cells are looked upon by physical science as independent living beings – just as Occultism regards the "fiery"[28] – there is no difficulty in the conception of the primitive process procreation.

Consider the first stages of the development of a germ-cell. Its *nucleus* grows, changes, and forms a double cone or spindle, thus, $\times$, *within* the cell. This spindle approaches the surface of the cell, and one half of it is *extruded* in the form of what are called the "*polar cells*." These polar cells now die, and the embryo develops from the growth and segmentation of the remaining part of the nucleus which is *nourished* by the substance of the cell. Then why could not beings have lived thus, and been created in this way – at the very beginning of *human and* mammalian *evolution*?

This may, perhaps, serve as an analogy to give some idea of the process by which the Second Race was formed from the First.

The astral form clothing the Monad was surrounded, as it still is, by its egg-shaped sphere of *aura*, which here corresponds to the substance of the germ-cell or *ovum*. The astral form itself is the nucleus, now, as then, instinct with the principle of life.

When the season of reproduction arrives, the *sub*-astral "*extrudes*" a miniature of itself from the egg of surrounding aura. This germ grows and feeds on the aura till it becomes fully developed, when it gradually separates from its parent, carrying with it its own sphere of aura; just as we see living cells reproducing their like by growth and subsequent division into two.

The analogy with the "*polar cells*" would seem to hold good, since their death would *now* correspond to the change introduced by the separation of the sexes, when gestation *in utero, i.e. within the cell*, became the rule.

"*The early Second* (Root) *Race were the Fathers of the 'Sweat-born'; the*

28 See Book I, Part I, Stanza VII, *Commentary* 10.

later Second (Root) *Race were 'Sweat-born' themselves."*

This passage from the *Commentary* refers to the work of evolution from the beginning of a Race to its close. The "Sons of Yoga," or the primitive astral race, had seven stages of evolution *racially*, or collectively; as every individual Being in it had, and has now. It is not Shakespeare only who divided the ages of man into a series of seven, but Nature herself. Thus the first sub-races of the Second Race were born at first by the process described on the law of analogy; while the last began gradually, *pari passu* with the evolution of the human body, to be formed otherwise. The process of reproduction had seven stages also in each Race, each covering æons of time. What physiologist or biologist could tell whether the present mode of generation, with all its phases of gestation, is older than half a million, or at most on million of years, since their cycle of observation began hardly half a century ago.

PRIMEVAL HUMAN HERMAPHRODITES ARE A FACT IN NATURE

Primeval human hermaphrodites are a fact in Nature well known to the ancients, and form one of Darwin's greatest perplexities. Yet there is certainly no impossibility, but, on the contrary, a great probability that hermaphroditism existed in the evolution of the early races; while on the grounds of analogy, and on that of the existence of one universal law in physical evolution, acting indifferently in the construction of plant, animal, and man, it must be so. The mistaken theories of monogenesis, and the descent of man from the mammals instead of the reverse, are fatal to the completeness of evolution as taught in modern schools on Darwinian lines, and they will have to be abandoned in view of the insuperable difficulties which they encounter. Occult tradition – if the terms Science and Knowledge are denied in this particular to antiquity – can alone reconcile the inconsistencies and fill the gap. "If thou wilt know the invisible, open thine eye wide on the visible," says a Talmudic axiom.

In the *"Descent of Man"*[29] occurs the following passage; which shows how near Darwin came to the acceptance of this ancient teaching.

---

29 Second Edition, p. 161.

It has been known that in the vertebrate kingdom one sex bears rudiments of various accessory parts appertaining to the reproductive system, which properly belong to the opposite sex. . . . Some remote progenitor of the whole vertebrate kingdom appears to have been hermaphrodite or androgynous[30] . . . But here we encounter a *singular difficulty*. In the mammalian *class the males possess rudiments of a uterus with the adjacent passages in the Vesiculæ prostaticæ; they bear also rudiments of mammæ, and some male marsupials have traces of a marsupial sac*. Other analogous facts could be added. Are we then to suppose that some extremely ancient mammal continued androgynous after it had acquired the chief distinctions of its class, and therefore after it had diverged from the lower classes of the vertebrate kingdom? This seems very improbable,[31] for *we have to look to fishes, the lowest of all the classes, to find any still existent androgynous forms.*"

Mr. Darwin is evidently strongly disinclined to adopt the hypothesis which the facts so forcibly suggest, viz., that of a primeval androgynous stem from which the *mammalia* sprang. His explanation runs: "The fact that various accessory organs proper to each sex, are found in a rudimentary condition in the opposite sex may be explained by such organs having been gradually acquired by the one sex and then transmitted in a more or less imperfect condition to the other." He instances the case of "spurs, plumes, and brilliant colours, acquired for battle or for ornament by male birds" and only *partially* inherited by their female descendants. In the problem to be dealt with, however, the need of a more satisfactory explanation is evident, the facts being of so much more prominent and important a character than the mere superficial details with which they are compared by Darwin. Why not candidly admit the argument in favour of the hermaphroditism which characterises the old fauna? Occultism proposes a solution which embraces the facts in a most comprehensive and simple manner. These relics of a prior androgyne stock must be placed in the same category as the pineal gland, and other organs as mysterious, which afford us silent testimony as to the reality of functions which have long since become atrophied in the course of animal and human progress, but

---

30 And why not all the progenitive first Races, human as well as animal; and why *one* "remote progenitor"?

31 Obviously so, on the lines of Evolutionism, which traces the *mammalia* to some *Amphibia*n ancestor.

which once played a signal part in the general economy of primeval life.

The occult doctrine, anyhow, can be advantageously compared with that of the most liberal men of science, who have theorised upon the origin of the first man.

THE CHHAYA CONTAINS WITHIN ITSELF THE POTENTIALITY OF ALL FORMS

Long before Darwin, Naudin, who gave the name of *Blastema* to that which the Darwinists call protoplasm, put forward a theory half occult and half scientifico-materialistic. He made Adam, the *a-sexual*, spring suddenly from the *clay*, as it is called in the *Bible*, the *Blastema* of Science. "It is from this larval form of mankind that the evolutive force effected the completion of species. For the accomplishment of this great phenomenon, Adam had to pass through a phase of immobility and unconsciousness, very analogous to the nymphal state of animals undergoing metamorphosis," explains Naudin. For the eminent botanist, Adam was not one man, however, but *mankind*, "which remained concealed within a temporary organism . . . . distinct from all others and never contracting alliance with any of these." He shows the differentiation of sexes accomplished by "a process of germination similar to that of Medusæ and Ascidians." Mankind, thus constituted physiologically, "would retain a sufficient evolutive force for the rapid production of the various great human races."

De Quatrefages criticises this position in the *"Human Species."* It is *unscientific,* he says, or, properly speaking, Naudin's ideas "do not form a scientific theory," inasmuch as primordial *Blastema* is connected in his theory with the *First Cause,* which is credited with having made potentially in the Blastema all past, present, and future beings, and thus of having in reality *created* these beings *en masse;* moreover, Naudin does not even consider the *secondary* Causes, or their action in this evolution of the organic world. Science, which is only occupied with Secondary Causes, has thus "nothing to say to the theory of Naudin" (p. 125).

Nor will it have any more to say to the occult teachings, which are to some extent approached by Naudin. For if we but see in his "primordial

Blastema" the Dhyan-Chohanic essence, the *Chhaya* or double of the *Pitris*, which contains within itself the potentiality of all forms, we are quite in accord. But there are two real and vital differences between our teachings. M. Naudin declares that evolution has progressed by sudden leaps and bounds, instead of extending slowly over millions of years; and his primordial Blastema is endowed only with blind instincts – a kind of *unconscious* First Cause in the *manifested Kosmos* – which is an absurdity. Whereas it is our *Dhyan Chohanic* essence – the *causality* of the *primal cause* which creates *physical man* – which is the living, active and potential matter, pregnant *per se* with that animal consciousness of a superior kind, such as is found in the ant and the beaver, which produces the long series of physiological differentiations. Apart from this his "ancient and general process of creation" from *proto-organisms* is as occult as any theory of Paracelsus or Khunrath could be.

Moreover, the Kabalistic works are full of the proof of this. The *Zohar*, for instance, says that every type in the visible has its prototype in the invisible Universe. "All that which is in the lower (our) world is found in the upper. The Lower and the Upper act and react upon each other." (*Zohar*, fol. 186.) *Vide infra*, Part II., "*Esoteric Tenets corroborated in every Scripture.*"

STANZA 20. THEIR FATHERS WERE THE SELF-BORN. THE SELF-BORN, THE *CHHAYA* FROM THE BRILLIANT BODIES OF THE LORDS, THE FATHERS, THE SONS OF TWILIGHT (*a*).

(*a*) The "shadows," or *Chhayas*, are called the sons of the "self-born," as the latter name is applied to all the gods and Beings born through the WILL, whether of Deity or Adept. The *Homunculi* of Paracelsus would, perhaps, be also given this name, though the latter process is on a far more material plane. The name "Sons of Twilight" shows that the "Self-born" progenitors of our doctrine are identical with the *Pitris* of the Brahmanical system, as the title is a reference to their mode of birth, these *Pitris* being stated to have issued from Brahmâ's body of twilight." (See the *Purânas*.)

The Secret Doctrine, ii 115-121

Selection 8

THE DIVINE HERMAPHRODITE

An impenetrable veil of secrecy was thrown over the occult and religious mysteries taught, after the submersion of the last remnant of the Atlantean race, some 12,000 years ago, lest they should be shared by the unworthy, and so desecrated. Of these sciences several have now become exoteric – such as Astronomy, for instance, in its purely mathematical and physical aspect. Hence their dogmas and tenets, being all symbolised and left to the sole guardianship of parable and allegory, have been forgotten, and their meaning has become perverted. Nevertheless, one finds the hermaphrodite in the scriptures and traditions of almost every nation; and why such unanimous agreement if the statement is only a fiction?

It is this secrecy which led the Fifth Race to the establishment, or rather the re-establishment of the religious mysteries, in which ancient truths might be taught to the coming generations under the veil of allegory and symbolism. Behold the imperishable witness to the evolution of the human races from the divine, and especially from the androgynous Race – the Egyptian Sphinx, that riddle of the Ages! Divine wisdom incarnating on earth, and forced to taste of the bitter fruit of personal experience of pain and suffering, generated under the shade of the tree of the knowledge of Good and Evil – a secret first known only to the *Elohim*, the SELF-INITIATED, "higher gods" – on earth only. [32]

In the *Book of Enoch* we have Adam, [33] the first divine androgyne, separating into man and woman, and becoming *JAH-HEVA* in one

---

32 See "*Book of Enoch.*"

33 Adam (*Kadmon*) is, like Brahmâ and Mars, the symbol of the generative and creative power typifying Water and Earth – an alchemical secret. "It takes Earth and Water to create a human soul," said Moses. Mars is the Hindu *Mangala*, the planet Mars, identical with *Kartikeya*, the "War-God," born of Gharma-ja (Siva's sweat) and of the Earth. He is *Lokita*, the red, like Brahmâ also and Adam. The Hindu Mars is, like Adam, born from no woman and mother. With the Egyptians, Mars was the primeval generative Principle, and so are Brahmâ, in exoteric teaching, and Adam, in the *Kabala*.

form, or Race, and Cain and Abel [34] (male and female) in its other form or Race – the double-sexed *Jehovah* [35] – an echo of its Aryan prototype, Brahmâ-Vâch. After which come the Third and Fourth Root-Races of mankind [36] – that is to say, Races of men and women, or individuals of opposite sexes, no longer sexless semi-spirits and androgynes, as were the two Races which precede them. This fact is hinted at in every Anthropogony. It is found in fable and allegory, in myth and revealed Scriptures, in legend and tradition. Because, of all the great Mysteries, inherited by Initiates from hoary antiquity, this is one of the greatest. It accounts for the bi-sexual element found in every creative deity, in Brahmâ-Virâj-Vâch, as in Adam-*Jehovah*-*Eve*, also in "*Cain-Jehovah-Abel*." For "The Book of the Generations of Adam" does not even mention Cain and Abel, but says only: "Male and female created he them. . . and called their name Adam" (ch. v. 5). Then it proceeds to say: "And Adam begat a son in his own likeness, after his image, and called his name Seth" (v. 3); after which he begets other sons and daughters, thus proving that Cain and Abel are his own allegorical permutations. Adam stands for the primitive human race, especially in its cosmo-sidereal sense. Not so, however, in its theo-anthropological meaning. The compound name of *Jehovah*, or *Jah-Hovah*, meaning male life and female life – first androgynous, then separated into sexes – is used in this sense in *Genesis* from ch. v. onwards. As the author of "*The Source of Measures*" says (p. 159): "The two words of which *Jehovah* is composed make up the original idea of male-female, as the birth originators"; for the Hebrew letter *Jod* was the *membrum virile* and *Hovah* was Eve, the mother of all living, or the procreatrix, Earth and Nature. The author believes, therefore, that "It is seen that the perfect one" (the perfect female circle or *Yoni*, 20612, numerically), "as originator of measures, takes also the form of birth-origin, as Hermaphrodite one; hence the phallic form and use."

Precisely; only "the phallic form and use" came long ages later; and the first and original meaning of Enos, the son of Seth, was the First Race born in the present usual way from man and woman – for Seth is no man, but a race. Before him humanity was hermaphrodite.

---

34 Abel is *Chebel*, meaning "Pains of Birth," conception.

35 See "*Isis Unveiled*," Vol. II, p. 398, where Jehovah is shown to be Adam and Eve blended, and Hevah, and Abel, the feminine serpent.

36 See "*Isis Unveiled*," Vol. I., 305: "The union of the two create a third Race, etc."

While Seth is the first result (physiologically) after the FALL, he is also the first man; hence his son Enos is referred to as the "Son of man." (Vide *infra*.) Seth represents the later Third Race.

To screen the real mystery name of *AIN-SOPH* – the Boundless and Endless No-Thing – the Kabalists have brought forward the compound attribute-appellation of one of the personal creative *Elohim*, whose name was Yak and Jab, the letters i or j or y being interchangeable, or *Jah-Hovah*, i.e. male and female; [37] *Jah-Eve* an hermaphrodite, or the first form of humanity, the original Adam of Earth, not even *Adam Kadmon*, whose " mind-born son" is the earthly *Jah-Hovah*, mystically. And knowing this, the crafty Rabbin-Kabalist has made of it a name so secret, that he could not divulge it later on without exposing the whole scheme; and thus he was obliged to make it sacred.

How close is the identity between *Brahmâ-Prajâpati* and *Jehovah-Sephiroth*, between *Brahmâ-Virâj* and *Jehovah-Adam*, the *Bible* and the *Purânas* compared can alone show. Analysed and read in the same light, they afford cogent evidence that they are two copies of the same original – made at two periods far distant from each other. Compare once more in relation to this subject *Genesis* ch. 4. verses 1 and 26 and Manu I., and they will both yield their meaning. In *Manu* (Book I. 32) Brahmâ, who is also both man and god, and divides his body into male and female, stands in his esoteric meaning, as does *Jehovah* or Adam in the *Bible*, for the symbolical personification of creative and generative power, both divine and human. The *Zohar* affords still more convincing proof of identity, while some Rabbins repeat word for word certain original Purânic expressions; e.g., the "creation" of the world is generally considered in the Brahmanical books to be the Lila, delight or sport, the amusement of the Supreme Creator, "Vishnu being thus discrete and indiscrete substance, spirit, and time, sports like a playful boy in frolics." (*Vishnu Purâna*, Book I., ch. ii.) Now compare this with what is said in the Book, "Nobeleth' *Hokhmah*": "The Kabalists say that the entering into existence of the worlds happens through delight, in that *Ain-Soph* (? !) rejoiced in Itself, and flashed and beamed from

---

37 *Jod* in the *Kabala* has for symbol the hand, the forefinger and the *lingham*, while numerically it is the perfect one; but it is also the number 10, male and female, when divided.

Itself to Itself . . . . which are all called delight," etc. (Quoted in Myer's "*Qabbalah*," p. 110). Thus it is not a "curious idea of the Qabbalists," as the author just quoted remarks, but a purely Purânic, Aryan idea. Only, why make of *Ain-Soph* a Creator?

The "Divine Hermaphrodite" is then *Brahmâ-Vâch-Virâj*; and that of the Semites, or rather of the Jews, is Jehovah-Cain-Abel. Only the "Heathen" were, and are, more sincere and frank than were the later Israelites and Rabbis, who undeniably knew the real meaning of their exoteric deity. The Jews regard the name given to them – the *Yah-oudi* – as an insult. Yet they have, or would have if they only wished it, as undeniable a right to call themselves the ancient *Yah-oudi,* "*Jah-hovians,*" as the Brahmins have to call themselves Brahmins, after their national deity. For *Jah-hovah* is the generic name of that group or hierarchy of creative planetary angels, under whose star their nation has evolved. He is one of the planetary *Elohim* of the regent group of Saturn. Verse 26 of *Genesis*, ch. iv., when read correctly, would alone give them such a right, for it calls the new race of men sprung from Seth and Enos, *Jehovah*, something quite different from the translation adopted in the *Bible*: – "To him also, was born a son, Enos; then began men to call themselves *Jah* or *Yah-hovah*," to with men and women, the "lords of creation." One has but to read the above-mentioned verse in the original Hebrew text and by the light of the *Kabala*, to find that, instead of the words as they now stand translated, it is: "Then began men to call themselves *Jehovah*," which is the correct translation, and not "Then began men to call upon the name of the Lord"; the latter being a mistranslation, whether deliberate or not. Again the well-known passage: "I have gotten a man from the Lord," should read: "I have gotten a man, even *Jehovah*." [38] Luther translated the passage one way, the Roman Catholics quite differently. Bishop Wordsworth renders it: "Cain – I have gotten *Kain*, from *Kânithi*, "I have gotten." Luther: "I have gotten a man O – even the Lord" (*Jehovah*); and the author of "*The Source of Measures*": "I have measured a man, even *Jehovah*." The last is the correct rendering, because (*a*) a famous Rabbin, a Kabalist, explained the passage to the writer in precisely this way, and (*b*) because this rendering is identical with that in the Secret Doctrine of the East with

---

38 See "*Source of Measures*," p. 227. † Vol. II., p. 264, et seq.

regard to Brahmâ. In *"Isis Unveiled,"* [39] it was explained by the writer that "Cain . . . is the son of the 'Lord' not of Adam (*Genesis* iv. I)" The "Lord" is *Adam Kadmon*, the "father" of *Yodcheva*, "Adam-Eve," or *Jehovah*, the son of sinful thought, not the progeny of flesh and blood. Seth, on the other hand, is the leader and the progenitor of the Races of the Earth; for he is the son of Adam, exoterically, but esoterically he is the progeny of Cain and Abel, since Abel or Hebel is a female, the counterpart and female half of the male Cain, and Adam is the collective name for man and woman: "male and female (*Zachar va Nakobeh*) created he them . . . and called their name Adam." The verses in *Genesis* from Chs. i. to v., are purposely mixed up for Kabalistic reasons. After MAN of *Genesis* Ch. i. 26 and Enos, Son of Man of ch. iv. v. 26, after Adam, the first androgyne, after *Adam Kadmon*, the sexless (the first) *Logos*, Adam and Eve once separated, come finally *Jehovah-Eve* and *Cain-Jehovah*. These represent distinct Root-Races, for millions of years elapsed between them.

The Secret Doctrine, ii 124–128

---

39 Vol. II., p. 264, et seq.

Selection 9

The Evolution of the "Sweat-born"

STANZA 22. Then the Second evolved the Sweat-Born, the third (*Race*). The sweat grew, its drops grew, and the drops became hard and round. The Sun warmed it; the Moon cooled and shaped it; the Wind fed it until its ripeness. The white swan from the starry vault (*the Moon*), overshadowed the big drop. The egg of the future race, the Man-Swan (*Hamsa*) of the later Third (*a*). First Male-Female, then Man and Woman (*b*).

(*a*) The text of the Stanza clearly implies that the human embryo was nourished *ab extra* by Cosmic forces, and that the "Father-Mother" furnished apparently the germ that ripened: in all probability a "sweat-born egg," to be hatched out, in some mysterious way, disconnected from the "double" parent. It is comparatively easy to conceive of an oviparous humanity, since even now man is, in one sense, "egg-born." Magendie, moreover, in his *Précis Elémentaire de Physiologie*, citing "a case where the umbilical cord was ruptured and perfectly cicatrized," yet the infant was born alive, pertinently asks, "How was the circulation carried on in this organ?" On the next page he says: "Nothing is at present known respecting the use of digestion in the fœtus;" and respecting its nutrition, propounds this query: "What, then, can we say of the nutrition of the fœtus? Physiological works contain only *vague conjectures* on this point." "Ah, but," the sceptic may urge, "Magendie's book belongs to the last generation, and Science has since made such strides that his stigma of ignorance can no longer be fixed upon the profession." Indeed; then let us turn to a very great authority upon Physiology, viz., Sir M. Foster ("*Text-Book of Physiology*," 3rd Ed., 1879, p. 623); and to the disadvantage of modern Science we shall find him saying, "Concerning the rise and development of the functional activities of the embryo, our knowledge is almost a blank. We know scarcely anything about the various steps by which the primary fundamental qualities of the protoplasm of the *ovum* are differentiated into the complex phenomena which we have attempted in this book to explain." The students of Trin. Coll. Cantab. will now kindly draw a veil before the statue of Hygeia and bandage the eyes of the busts of Galen and Hippocrates, lest they look reproachfully at their degenerate descendants. One further fact we must note. Sir M. Foster is discreetly silent about the case of the ruptured umbilical cord cited by his great French *confrère*.

THE SEPARATION OF SEXES OCCURRED IN THE THIRD RACE

This is a very curious statement as explained in the Commentaries. To make it clear: The First Race having created the Second by "budding," as just explained, the Second Race gives birth to the Third – which itself is separated into three distinct divisions, consisting of men differently procreated. The first two of these are produced by an oviparous method, presumably unknown to modern Natural History. While the early sub-races of the Third Humanity procreated their species by a kind of exudation of moisture or vital fluid, the drops of which coalescing formed an oviform ball – or shall we say egg? – which served as an extraneous vehicle for the generation therein of a *fœtus* and child, the mode of procreation by the later races changed, in its results at all events. The little ones of the earlier races were entirely sexless – shapeless even for all one knows[40]; but those of the later races were born androgynous. It is in the Third Race that the separation of sexes occurred. From being previously a-sexual, Humanity became distinctly hermaphrodite or bi-sexual; and finally the man-bearing eggs began to give birth, gradually and almost imperceptibly in their evolutionary development, first, to Beings in which one sex predominated over the other, and, finally, to distinct men and women. And now let us search for corroboration of these statements in the religious legends of East and West. Let us take the "Egg-born Race" first. Think of Kasyapa, the Vedic sage, and the most prolific of creators. He was the son of Marichi, Brahmâ's mind-born son; and he is made to become the father of the *Nagas*, or Serpents, among other beings. Exoterically, the *Nagas* are semi-divine beings which have a human face and the tail of a serpent. Yet there was a race of *Nagas*, said to be a thousand in number only, born or rather sprung from Kadra, Kasyapa's wife, *for the purpose of peopling Pâtâla*, which is undeniably America, as will be shown; and there was a *NAGA-Dwipa*, one of the seven divisions of *Bhârata-Varsha*,

---

40 See the "*Timæus*."

India, inhabited by a people bearing the same name, who are allowed, even by some Orientalists, to be *historical*, and to have left many a trace behind them to this day.

BI-SEXUAL REPRODUCTION

Now the point most insisted upon at present is that, whatever origin be claimed for man, his evolution took place in this order: (1) Sexless, as all the earlier forms are; (2) then, by a natural transition, he became, "a solitary hermaphrodite," a bi-sexual being; and (3) finally separated and became what he is now. Science teaches us that all the primitive forms, though sexless, "still retained the power of undergoing the processes of A-Sexual multiplication;" why, then, should man be excluded from that law of Nature? Bi-sexual reproduction is an evolution, a specialized and perfected form on the scale of matter of the fissiparous act of reproduction. Occult teachings are pre-eminently panspermic, and the early history of humanity is hidden only "from ordinary mortals;" nor is the history of the primitive Races buried from the Initiates in the tomb of time, as it is for profane science. Therefore, supported on the one hand by that science which shows to us progressive development and an internal cause for every external modification, as a law in Nature; and, on the other hand, by an implicit faith in the wisdom – we may say pansophia even – of the universal traditions gathered and preserved by the Initiates, who have perfected them into an almost faultless system – thus supported, we venture to state the doctrine clearly.

In an able article, written some fifteen years ago, our learned and respected friend Prof. Alex. Wilder, of New York, shows the absolute logic and necessity of believing "The Primeval Race Double-Sexed," and gives a number of scientific reasons for it.[41] He argues firstly, "that a large part of the vegetable creation exhibits the phenomenon of bisexuality . . . the Linnaean classification enumerating thus almost all plants. This is the case in the superior families of the vegetable kingdoms as much as in the lower forms, from the Hemp to the Lombardy Poplar and Ailanthus. In the animal kingdom, in insect life, the moth generates a worm, as in the *Mysteries* the great secret was expressed: "*Taurus Draconem genuit, et Taurum Draco.*" The coral-producing family, which, according to Agassiz, 'has spent many hundreds of thousands of years,

---

41 See Extracts from that Essay in "*The Theosophist*" of February, 1883.

during the present geological period, in building out the peninsula of Florida . .produce their offspring from themselves like the buds and ramifications in a tree.' Bees are somewhat in the same line . . . . The Aphides or plant lice keep house like Amazons, and *virgin parents* perpetuate the Race for ten successive generations."

What say the old sages, the philosopher-teachers of antiquity. Aristophanes speaks thus on the subject in Plato's "*Banquet*": Our nature of old was not the same as it is now. It was *androgynous*, the form and name partaking of, and being common to both the male and female. . . . Their bodies were round, and the manner of their running circular.[42] They were terrible in force and strength and had prodigious ambition. Hence Zeus *divided each of them into two*, making them weaker; Apollo, under his direction, closed up the skin."

Meshia and Meshiane were but a single individual with the old Persians. "They also taught that man was the product of the tree of life, growing in androgynous pairs, till they were separated at a subsequent modification of the human form."[43]

The Elohim (Gods) Brought Forth from Themselves Man in Their Image

In the *Toleduth* (generation) of Adam, the verse "God created (*bara*, brought forth) man in his image, in the image of God created he him, male and female created he them," if read esoterically will yield the true sense, viz.: "The *Elohim* (Gods) brought forth from themselves (by modification) man in their image . . . . created they *him* (collective humanity, or *Adam*), male and female created *he* (collective deity) them."[44] This will show the esoteric point. The *sexless* Race was their first

---

42 Compare Ezekiel's vision (chap. i.) of the four divine beings who "had the likeness of a man" and yet had the appearance of a wheel, "when they went they went upon their four sides . . . . for the spirit of the living creature was in the wheel."

43 See Prof. Wilder's Essay "*The Primeval Race Double-Sexed*.

44 Eugibinus, a Christian, and the Rabbis Samuel, *Manas*seh ben Israel, and Maimonides taught that "Adam had *two* faces and *one* person, and from the beginning he was both male and female—male on one side and female on the other (like Manu's Brahmâ), but afterwards the parts were separated." The one hundred and thirty-ninth Psalm of David recited by Rabbi Jeremiah ben Eliazar is evidence of this. "Thou hast *fashioned* me behind and before," not *beset* as in the *Bible*, which is absurd and meaningless, and this shows, as Prof. Wilder thinks, "that the primeval form of mankind was androgynous."

production, a modification *of* and *from* themselves, the pure spiritual existences; and this was Adam *solus*. Thence came the *second* Race: Adam-Eve or *Jod-Heva*, inactive androgynes; and finally the *Third*, or the "*Separating* Hermaphrodite," Cain and Abel, who produce the Fourth, Seth-Enos, etc. It is that Third, the last semi-spiritual *race*, which was also the last vehicle of the divine and innate Wisdom, ingenerate in the Enochs, the Seers of that Mankind. The *Fourth*, which had tasted from the fruit of the Tree of Good and Evil – Wisdom united already to earthy, and therefore *impure*, intelligence[45] – had consequently to acquire that Wisdom by initiation and great struggle. And the union of Wisdom and Intelligence, the former *ruling* the latter, is called in the Hermetic books "the God possessing the double fecundity of the two sexes." Mystically Jesus was held to be man-woman. See also in the Orphic *hymns*, sung during the Mysteries, we find: "Zeus is a male, Zeus is an immortal maid." The Egyptian Ammon was the goddess Neïth, in his other half. Jupiter has female breasts, Venus is bearded in some of her statues, and Ila, the goddess, is also Su-Dyumna, the god, as *Vaivasvata's* progeny.

"The name *Adam*," says Professor A. Wilder, "or man, itself implies this double form of existence. It is identical with *Athamas*, or *Thomas* (Tamil *Tam*), which is rendered by the Greek *Didumos*, a twin; if, therefore, the first woman was formed subsequently to the first man, she must, as a logical necessity, be 'taken out of man' . . . and the side which the *Elohim* had taken from man, 'made he a woman' (*Gen. ii.*). The Hebrew word here used is *Tzala*, which bears the translation we have given. It is easy to trace the legend in Berosus, who says that *Thalatth* (the *Omoroca*, or Lady of Urka) was the beginning of creation. She was also Melita, the queen of the Moon. . . . The two twin births of *Genesis*, that of Cain and Abel, and of Esau and Jacob, shadow the same idea. *The name 'Hebel' is the same as Eve*, and its characteristic seems to be feminine," continues the author. "Unto thee shall be his desire," said the Lord God to Cain, "and thou shalt rule over him." The same language had been uttered to Eve: "Thy desire shall be to thy husband, and he shall rule over thee."

---

45 See the union of *Chochmah*, Wisdom, with *Binah*, Intelligence, or Jehovah, the *Demiurge*, called *Understanding* in the *Proverbs of Solomon*, ch. vii. Unto men *Wisdom* (divine occult Wisdom) crieth: "Oh, ye simple, understand Wisdom; and ye *fools*, be *of an understanding heart*." It is *spirit* and *matter*, the *nous* and the *psyche*; of the latter of which St. James says that it is "earthly, sensual, and devilish."

The Pristine Bi-Sexual Unity of the Human Third Root-Race

Thus the pristine bi-sexual unity of the human *Third* Root-Race is an axiom in the Secret Doctrine. Its virgin individuals were raised to "Gods," because that Race represented their "divine Dynasty." The moderns are satisfied with worshipping the male heroes of the Fourth Race, who created gods after their own sexual image, whereas the gods of primeval mankind were "male and female."

As stated in Book I, the humanities developed coördinately, and on parallel lines with the four Elements, every new Race being physiologically adapted to meet the additional element. Our Fifth Race is rapidly approaching the Fifth Element – call it interstellar ether, if you will – which has more to do, however, with psychology than with physics. We men have learned to live in every climate, whether frigid or tropical, but the first two Races had nought to do with climate, nor were they subservient to any temperature or change therein. And thus, we are taught, men lived down to the close of the Third Root-Race, when eternal spring reigned over the whole globe, such as is now enjoyed by the inhabitants of Jupiter; a "world," says M. Flammarion, "which is not subject like our own to the vicissitudes of seasons nor to abrupt alternations of temperature, but which is enriched with all the treasures of eternal spring." ("*Pluralité des Mondes*," p. 69.) Those astronomers who maintain that Jupiter is in a molten condition, in our sense of the term, are invited to settle their dispute with this learned French Astronomer.[46] It must, however, be always borne in mind that

---

46 An hypothesis evolved in 1881 by Mr. Mattieu Williams seems to have impressed Astronomers but little. Says the author of "*The Fuel of the Sun*," in *Knowledge*, Dec. 23, 1881: "Applying now the researches of Dr. Andrews to the conditions of Solar existence . . . I conclude that the sun has *no nucleus*, either solid, liquid, or gaseous, but is composed of dissociated matter in the critical state, surrounded, first, by a flaming envelope, due to the recombination of the dissociated matter, and outside of this, by another envelope of vapours due to this combination."

This is a novel theory to be added to other hypotheses, *all scientific and orthodox*. The meaning of the "*critical state*" is explained by Mr. M. Williams in the same journal (Dec. 9, 1881), in an article on "Solids, Liquids, and Gases." Speaking of an experiment by Dr, Andrews on carbonic acid, the scientist says that "when 88° is reached, the boundary between liquid and gas vanished; *liquid and gas have blended into one mysterious intermediate fluid; an indefinite fluctuating something is there filling the whole of the tube—an etherealised liquid or a visible gas.* Hold a red-hot poker between your eye and the light; you will see an upflowing wave of movement of what appears like liquid air. The appearance of the *hybrid* fluid in the tube resembles this, but is sensibly denser, and evidently stands

the "eternal spring" referred to is only a condition *cognised as such by the Jovians*. It is not "spring" *as we know it*. In this reservation is to be found the reconciliation between the two theories here cited. Both embrace *partial* truths.

It is thus a universal tradition that mankind has evolved gradually into its present shape from an almost transparent condition of texture, and neither by miracle nor by sexual intercourse. Moreover, this is in full accord with the ancient philosophies; from those of Egypt and India with their Divine Dynasties down to that of Plato. And all these universal beliefs must be classed with the "presentiments" and

between the liquid and gaseous states of matter, as pitch or treacle stands between solid and liquid."

The *temperature at which this occurs has been named by Dr. Andrews the "critical temperature"*: here the gaseous and the liquid states are "continuous," and it is probable that *all other substances capable of existing* in both states have their own particular critical temperatures.

Speculating further upon this "critical" state, Mr. Mattieu Williams emits some quite *occult* theories about Jupiter and other planets. He says: "*Our notions of solids, liquids, and gases are derived from our experiences of the state of matter here upon this Earth. Could we be removed to another planet, they would be curiously changed.* On Mercury water would rank as one of the condensible gases; on Mars, as a fusible solid; but what on Jupiter?"

"Recent observations justify us in regarding this as a miniature sun, with an external envelope of cloudy matter, apparently of partially-condensed water, but red-hot, or probably still hotter within. His vaporous atmosphere is evidently of enormous depth, and the force of gravitation being on his visible outer surface two-and-a-half times greater than that on our Earth's surface, the atmospheric pressure, in descending below this visible surface, must soon reach that at which the vapour of water would be brought to its critical condition. Therefore we may infer that *the oceans of Jupiter are neither of frozen, liquid, nor gaseous water, but are oceans or atmospheres of critical water. If any fish or birds swim or fly therein, they must be very critically organized.*"

As the whole mass of Jupiter is 300 times greater than that of the Earth and its compressing energy towards the centre proportional to this, its materials, if similar to those of the Earth, and no hotter, would be considerably more dense and the whole planet would have a higher specific gravity; but we know by the movement of its satellites that, instead of this, its specific gravity is less than a fourth of that of the Earth. This justifies the conclusion that it is intensely hot, for even hydrogen, if cold, would become denser than Jupiter under such pressure.

"As all elementary substances may exist as solids, liquids, or gases, or, critically, according to the conditions of temperature and pressure, I am justified in hypothetically concluding that *Jupiter is neither a solid, a liquid, nor a gaseous planet, but a critical planet, or an orb composed internally of associated elements in the critical state, and surrounded by a dense atmosphere of their vapour*s and those of some of their compounds such as water. The same reasoning applies to Saturn and other large and rarified planets."

It is gratifying to see how *scientific imagination* approaches every year more closely to the borderland of our occult teachings.

"obstinate conceptions," some of them ineradicable, in popular faiths. Such beliefs, as remarked by Louis Figuier, are "frequently the outcome of the wisdom and observation of an infinite number of generations of men." For, "*a tradition which has an uniform and universal existence, has all the weight of scientific testimony*."[47] And there is more than one such tradition in the Purânic allegories, as has been shown. Moreover, the doctrine that the first Race of mankind was formed out of the *chhayas* (astral images) of the *Pitris*, is fully corroborated in the *Zohar*. "In the *Tzalam* (shadow image) of *Elohim* (the *Pitris*) was made Adam (man). (Cremona, Ed. iii, 76a; Brody, Ed. iii, 159a; "*Qabbalah*," Isaac Myer, p. 420)

STANZA 23. THE SELF-BORN WERE THE CHHAYAS, THE SHADOWS FROM THE BODIES OF THE SONS OF TWILIGHT. NEITHER WATER NOR FIRE COULD DESTROY THEM. THEIR SONS WERE (*so destroyed*) (*a*).

(*a*) This verse cannot be understood without the help of the Commentaries. It means that the First Root-Race, the "Shadows" of the Progenitors, could not be injured or destroyed by death. Being so ethereal and so little human in constitution, they could not be affected by any element – flood or fire. But their "Sons," the Second Root-Race, could be and were so destroyed. As the "progenitors" merged wholly in their own astral bodies, which were their progeny, so that progeny was absorbed in its descendants, the "Sweat-born." These were the second Humanity – composed of the most heterogeneous gigantic semi-human monsters – the first attempts of material nature at building human bodies. The ever-blooming lands of the Second Continent (Greenland, among others) were transformed, in order, from Edens with their eternal spring, into hyperborean Hades. This transformation was due to the displacement of the great waters of the globe, to oceans changing their beds, and the bulk of the Second Race perished in this first great throe of the evolution and consolidation of the globe during the human period. Of such great cataclysms there have already been four,[48] and we may expect a fifth for ourselves in due course of time.

The Secret Doctrine, ii 131-138

---

47 "*The Day After Death*," p. 23.

48 The first occurred when what is now the North Pole was separated from the later Continents.

Selection 10

Could Men Have Existed 18,000,000 Years Ago?

To this Occultism answers in the affirmative, notwithstanding all scientific objectors. Moreover, this duration covers only the *Vaivasvata-Manu* Man, i.e., the male and female entity already separated into distinct sexes. The two and a half Races that preceded that event may have lived 300,000,000 years ago for all that science can tell. For the geological and physical difficulties in the way of the theory could not exist for the primeval, ethereal man of the Occult teachings. The whole issue of the quarrel between the profane and the esoteric sciences depends upon the belief in, and demonstration of, the existence of an astral body within the physical, the former independent of the latter. Paul d'Assier, the Positivist, seems to have proven the fact pretty plainly, [49] not to speak of the accumulated testimony of the ages, and that of the modern spiritualists and mystics. It will be found difficult to reject this fact in our age of proofs, tests, and ocular demonstrations.

The Secret Doctrine maintains that, notwithstanding the general cataclysms and disturbances of our globe, which – owing to its being the period of its greatest physical development, for the Fourth Round is the middle-point of the life allotted to it – were far more terrible and intense than during any of the three preceding Rounds (the cycles of its earlier psychic and spiritual life and of its semi-ethereal conditions) physical Humanity has existed upon it for the last 18,000,000 years. [50] This period was preceded by 300,000,000 years of the mineral and vegetable development. To this, all those who refuse to accept the theory of a "boneless," purely ethereal, man, will object. Science, which

---

49 *"Posthumous Humanity"* — translated by H. S. Olcott, London, 1887.

50 Professor Newcomb says: "The heat evolved by contraction would last only 18,000,000 years" (*"Popular Astronomy,"* p. 500); but "a temperature permitting the existence of water could not be reached earlier than 10,000,000 years ago" (Winchell's *"World-Life,"* p. 356). But Sir W. Thomson says that the whole age of the incrustation of the Earth is 18,000,000 years, though, this year, he has again altered his opinion and allows only 15,000,000 years as the age of the Sun. As will be shown in the Addenda, the divergence of scientific opinions is so great that no reliance can ever be placed upon scientific speculation.

knows only of physical organisms, will feel indignant; and materialistic theology still more so. The first will object on logical and reasonable grounds, based on the preconception that all animate organisms have always existed on the same plane of materiality in all the ages; the last on a tissue of most absurd fictions. The ridiculous claim usually brought forward by theologians, is based on the virtual assumption that mankind (read Christians) on this planet have the honour of being the only human beings in the whole *Kosmos*, who dwell on a globe, and that they are consequently, the best of their kind. [51]

The Secret Doctrine, ii, 148-150

---

[51] The essay on "*The Plurality of Worlds*" (1853) — an anonymous work, yet well known to have been the production of Dr. Whewell — is a good proof of this. No Christian ought to believe in either the plurality of worlds or the geological age of the globe, argues the Author; because, if it is asserted that this world is only one among the many of its kind, which are all the work of God, as it is itself; that all are the seat of life, all the realm and dwelling of intelligent creatures endowed with will, subject to law and capable of free-will; then, it would become extravagant to think that our world should have been the subject of God's favours and His special interference, of His communications and His personal visit. . . . . . . Can the Earth presume to be considered the centre of the moral and religious Universe, he asks, if it has not the slightest distinction to rely upon in the physical Universe? Is it not as absurd to uphold such an assertion (of the plurality of inhabited worlds), as it would be to-day to uphold the old hypothesis of Ptolemy, who placed Earth in the centre of our system? . . . The above is quoted from memory, yet almost textually. The author fails to see that he is bursting his own soap-bubble with such a defence.

Selection 11

THE MONADS DESTINED TO ANIMATE FUTURE RACES WERE READY FOR THE NEW TRANSFORMATION

The Occultists, who believe firmly in the teachings of the mother-philosophy, repel the objections of both theologians and scientists. They maintain, on their side, that, during those periods when there must have been insufferable heat, even at the two poles, successive floods, upheaval of the valleys and constant shifting of the great waters and seas, none of these circumstances could form an impediment to human life and organization, such as is *assigned by them to the early mankind.* Neither the heterogeneity of ambient regions, full of deleterious gases, nor the perils of a crust hardly consolidated, could prevent the First and Second Races from making their appearance even during the Carboniferous, or the Silurian age itself.

Thus the *Monads* destined to animate future Races were ready for the new transformation. They had passed their phases of immetalization, of plant and animal life, from the lowest to the highest, and were waiting for their human, more intelligent form. Yet, what could the plastic modellers do but follow the laws of evolutionary Nature? Could they, as claimed by the Biblical dead-letter, form "Lord-God"-like, or as Pygmalion in the Greek allegory, Adam-Galatea out of volcanic dust, and breathe a *living* soul into Man? No, because the soul was already there, latent in its *Monad,* and needed but a *coating.* Pygmalion, who fails to *animate his statue,* and Bahak-Zivo of the Nazarean Gnostics, who fails to construct "a human soul in the creature," are, as conceptions, far more philosophical and scientific than Adam, taken in the dead-letter sense, or the Biblical *Elohim*-Creators. Esoteric philosophy, which teaches spontaneous generation – after the *Sishta* and *Prajâpati* have thrown the seed of life on the Earth – shows the lower angels able to *construct physical* man only, even with the help of Nature, after having evolved the ethereal form out of themselves, and leaving the physical form to evolve gradually from its ethereal, or what would now be called, *protoplasmic* model.

Is "Spontaneous Generation" Possible under Different Conditions?

This will again be objected to: "Spontaneous Generation" is an exploded theory, we shall be told. Pasteur's experiments disposed of it twenty years ago, and Professor Tyndall is against it. Well, suppose he is? He ought to know that, should spontaneous generation be indeed proven impossible in our present world – period and actual conditions – which the Occultists deny – still it would be no demonstration that it could not have taken place under different cosmic conditions, not only in the seas of the Laurentian period, but even on the then convulsed Earth. It would be interesting to know how Science could ever account for the appearance of species and life on Earth, especially of *Man*, once that she rejects both the Biblical teachings and spontaneous generation. Pasteur's observations, however, are far from being perfect or proven. Blanchard and Dr. Lutaud reject their importance and show that they have none. The question is so far left *sub judice,* as well as that other one, "when, at what period, life appeared on the Earth?" As to the idea that Hæckel's *Moneron* – a pinch of salt! – has solved the problem of the origin of life, it is simply absurd. Those materialists, who feel inclined to pooh-pooh the theory of the "Self-existent," the "Self-born heavenly man," represented as an ethereal, astral man, must excuse even a tyro in Occultism laughing, in his turn, at some speculations of modern thought. After proving most learnedly that the primitive speck of *protoplasm (Moneron)* is neither animal nor plant, but both, and that it *has no ancestors* among either of these, since it is that *Moneron* which serves as a point of departure for all organized existence, we are finally told that *the Monera are their own ancestors.* This may be very scientific, but it is very metaphysical also; too much so, even for the Occultist.

If spontaneous generation has changed its methods now, owing perhaps to accumulated material on hand, so as to almost escape detection, it was in full swing in the genesis of terrestrial life. Even the simple physical form and the evolution of species show how Nature proceeds. The scale-bound, gigantic *sauria,* the winged *pterodactyl,* the *Megalosaurus,* and the hundred-feet long *Iguanodon* of the later period, are the transformations of the earliest representatives of the animal kingdom found in the sediments of the primary epoch. There was a time when all those above enumerated "antediluvian" monsters appeared as filamentoid infusoria without shell or crust, with neither nerves, muscles, organs nor sex, and reproduced their kind by gemmation, as do microscopical animals also, the architects and builders of our mountain ranges, agreeably to the teachings of science. Why not man in this case? Why should he not have followed the same law in his growth, *i.e.* gradual condensation? Every unprejudiced person would prefer to believe that primeval humanity had at first an ethereal – or, if so preferred, a huge filamentoid, jelly-like form, evolved by gods or natural "forces," which grew, condensed throughout millions of ages, and became gigantic in its physical impulse and tendency, until it settled into the huge, physical form of the Fourth Race Man, – rather than believe him created of the dust of the Earth (literally), or from some unknown anthropoid ancestor.

Nor does our esoteric theory clash with scientific data, except on first appearance, as Dr. A. Wilson, F.R.S., says, in a letter to "*Knowledge*," (Dec. 23, 1881). "Evolution – rather Nature, in the light of evolution – has only been studied for some *twenty-five years or so*. That is, of course, a mere fractional space in the history of human thought." And just because of that we do not lose all hope that materialistic science will amend its ways, and will gradually accept the esoteric teachings – if even at first divorced from their (to science) too metaphysical elements.

Has the last word on the subject of human evolution yet been said? "Each . . . . answer to the great Question (Man's Real Place in Nature), invariably asserted by the followers of its propounder, if not by himself, to be *complete and final*, remains in high authority and esteem, *it may be for one century*, it may be for twenty," writes Prof. Huxley; "but, as invariably, time proves each reply to have been a *mere approximation to the truth – tolerable chiefly on account of the ignorance of those by whom it was accepted, and wholly intolerable when tested by the larger knowledge of their successors*"!! Will this eminent Darwinian admit the possibility of his *pithecoid ancestry* being assignable to the list of "wholly intolerable beliefs," in the "larger knowledge" of Occultists? *But whence the savage*? Mere "rising to the civilized state" does not account for the evolution of form.

In the same letter, *"The Evolution of Man,"* Dr. Wilson makes other strange confessions. Thus, he observes, in answer to the queries put to *"Knowledge"* by "G. M.":

> "'Has evolution effected any change in man? If so, what change? If not, why not?' . . . If we refuse to admit (as science does) that man was created a perfect being, and then became degraded, there exists only another supposition – that of evolution. If man has arisen from a savage to a civilized state, that surely is evolution. *We do not yet know, because such knowledge is difficult to acquire, if the human frame is subject to the same influences as those of lower animals.* But there is little doubt that elevation from savagery to civilized life means and implies 'evolution,' and that of considerable extent. Mentally, man's evolution cannot be doubted; the ever-widening sphere of thought has sprung from small and rude beginnings, like language itself. But man's ways of life, his power of adaptation to his surroundings, and countless other circumstances, have made the facts and course of his 'evolution' very difficult to trace."

DARWIN'S EVOLUTION BEGINS AT THE MIDDLE POINT, INSTEAD OF COMMENCING FOR MAN FROM UNIVERSALS

This very difficulty ought to make the Evolutionists more cautious in their affirmations. But why is evolution *impossible*, if "man was created a perfect being, and then became degraded?" At best it can only apply to the *outward, physical man.* As remarked in *"Isis Unveiled,"* Darwin's evolution begins at the middle point, instead of commencing for man, as for everything else, from the universals. The Aristotle-Baconian method may have its advantages, but it has undeniably already demonstrated its defects. Pythagoras and Plato, who proceeded from the Universals downwards, are now shown more learned, in the light of modern science, than was Aristotle. For he opposed and denounced the idea of the revolution of the earth and even of its rotundity. "Almost all those," he wrote, "who affirm that they have studied heaven in its uniformity, claim that the earth is in the centre, but those of the Italian School, otherwise called the Pythagoreans, teach entirely the contrary. . . ." Because (*a*) the Pythagoreans were Initiates, and (*b*) they followed the deductive method. Whereas, Aristotle, the father of the inductive system, complained of those who taught that the centre of our system was occupied by the Sun, and the earth was only a star, which by a rotatory motion around the same centre, produces night and day" (*Vide "De Cœlo,"* Book II, Chp. 13.) The same with regard to man. The theory taught in the Secret Doctrine, and now expounded, is the only one, which can – without falling into the absurdity of a "miraculous" man created out of the dust of the Earth, or the still greater fallacy of man evolving from a pinch of lime-salt, (the ex-protoplasmic *Moneron*) – account for his appearance on Earth.

Analogy is the guiding law in Nature, the only true Ariadne's thread that can lead us, through the inextricable paths of her domain, toward her primal and final mysteries. Nature, as a creative potency, is infinite, and no generation of physical scientists can ever boast of having exhausted the list of her ways and methods, however uniform the laws upon which she proceeds. If we can conceive of a ball of Fire-mist becoming gradually – as it rolls through æons of time in the interstellar spaces – a planet, a self-luminous globe, to settle into a *man-bearing* world or Earth, thus having passed from a soft plastic body into a rockbound globe; and if we see on it everything evolving from the non-nucleated jelly-speck that becomes the sarcode[52] of the *Moneron*, then passes from its *protistic* state[53] into the form of an animal, to grow into a gigantic reptilian monster of the Mesozoic times; then dwindles again into the (comparatively) dwarfish crocodile, now confined solely to tropical regions, and the universally common lizard[54] – how can man alone escape the general law? "There were giants on earth in those days," says *Genesis*, repeating the statement of all the other Eastern Scriptures, and the Titans are founded on anthropological and physiological fact.

---

52 Or what is more generally known as *Protoplasm*. This substance received its name of "*Sarcode*" from Prof. Dujardin Beaumetz far earlier.

53 The *Monera* are indeed *Protista*. They are neither animals "nor plants," writes Hæckel; ". . . the whole body of the *Moneron* represents nothing more than a single thoroughly homogeneous particle of albumen in a firmly adhesive condition." ("*Journal of Microscopical Science,*" Jan. 1869, p. 28.)

54 Behold the Iguanodon of the Mesozoic ages—the monster 100 feet long—now transformed into the small Iguana lizard of South America. Popular traditions about giants in days of old, and their mention in every mythology, including the *Bible*, may some day be shown to be founded on fact. In nature, the logic of analogy alone ought to make us accept these traditions as scientific verities.

And, as the hard-shelled crustacean was once upon a time a jelly-speck, "a thoroughly homogeneous particle of albumen in a firmly adhesive condition," so was the outward covering of primitive man, his early "coat of skin," *plus* an immortal spiritual monad, and a psychic temporary form and body within that shell. The modern, hard, muscular man, almost impervious to any climate, was, perhaps, some 25,000,000 years ago, just what the Hæckelian *Moneron* is, strictly "an organism without organs," an entirely homogeneous substance with a structureless albumen body within, and a human form only outwardly.

The Secret Doctrine, ii 150-154

Selection 12

A Stanza Containing the Whole Key to the Mysteries of Evil, the So-called Fall of the Angels

STANZA 24. The Sons of Wisdom, the Sons of Night (*issued from the body of Brahmâ when it became night*), ready for re-birth, came down. They saw the (*intellectually*) vile forms of the first third (*still race*) (*a*). "We can choose," said the Lords, "we have wisdom." Some entered the Chhayas. Some projected a spark. Some deferred till the Fourth (*race*). From their own essence they filled (*intensified*) the Kama (*the vehicle of desire*). Those who received but a spark remained destitute of (*higher*) knowledge. The spark burnt low (*b*). The Third remained mindless. Their Jivas (*monads*) were not ready. These were set apart among the Seven (*primitive human species*). They (*became the*) narrow-headed. The third were ready. In these shall we dwell, said the Lords of the Flame and of the Dark Wisdom (*c*).

This Stanza contains, in itself, the whole key to the mysteries of evil, the so-called Fall of the angels, and the many problems that have puzzled the brains of the philosophers from the time that the memory of man began. It solves the secret of the subsequent inequalities of intellectual capacity, of birth or social position, and gives a logical explanation to the incomprehensible Karmic course throughout the æons which followed. The best explanation which can be given, in view of the difficulties of the subject, shall now be attempted.

(*a*) Up to the Fourth Round, and even to the later part of the Third Race in this Round, *Man* – if the ever-changing forms that clothed the Monads during the first three Rounds and the first two and a half races of the present one can be given that misleading name – is, so far, only an animal intellectually. It is only in the actual *midway* Round that he develops in himself entirely the fourth principle as a fit vehicle for the fifth. But *Manas* will be relatively *fully* developed only in the following Round, when it will have an opportunity of becoming entirely divine until the end of the Rounds. As Christian Schœttgen says in *Horæ Hebraicæ*, etc., the first terrestrial Adam "had only the breath of life," *Nephesh, but not the living Soul.*

(*b*) Here the inferior Races, of which there are still some analogues left – as the Australians (now fast dying out) and some African and Oceanic tribes – are meant. "They were not ready" signifies that the Karmic development of these Monads had not yet fitted them to occupy the forms of men destined for incarnation in higher intellectual Races. But this is explained later on.

(*c*) The *Zohar* speaks of "Black Fire," which is *Absolute* Light-Wisdom. To those who, prompted by old theological prejudice, may say: "But the *Asuras* are the rebel *Devas*, the *opponents of the Gods* – hence devils, and the spirits of Evil," it is answered: Esoteric philosophy admits neither good nor evil *per se*, as existing independently in nature. The cause for both is found, as regards the *Kosmos*, in the necessity of contraries or contrasts, and with respect to man, in his human nature, his ignorance and passions. There is no *devil* or the utterly depraved, as there are no Angels absolutely perfect, though there may be spirits of Light and of Darkness; thus LUCIFER – the spirit of Intellectual Enlightenment and Freedom of Thought – is metaphorically the guiding beacon, which helps man to find his way through the rocks and sandbanks of Life, for Lucifer is the *Logos* in his highest, and the "Adversary" in his lowest, aspect – both of which are reflected in our *Ego*. Lactantius, speaking of the Nature of Christ, makes the *Logos*, the *Word*, *"the first-born brother of Satan*, the *"first of all creatures."* (*Inst. div.* Book II, Chp. VIII, "*Qabbalah*," 116.)

The *Vishnu Purâna* describes these primeval creatures (the *Arvaksrota*) with *crooked* digestive canals: They were "endowed with inward manifestations, but mutually in ignorance about *their kind and nature*." The twenty-eight kinds of *Badha*, or imperfections, do not apply, as Wilson thought, to the animals now known and specified by him,[55] for these did not exist in those geological periods. This is quite plain in the said work, in which the first created (on this globe) are the "five-fold immovable creation," minerals and vegetables; then come those fabulous animals, *Tiryaksrota*, (the monsters of the abyss slain by the "Lords," see Stanzas 2 and 3.); then the *Urdhwasrotas*, the happy celestial beings, which feed on ambrosia; then lastly, the *Arvaksrotas*, human beings – Brahmâ's seventh creation so-called. But these "creations," including the latter, did not occur on this globe,

---

55 See Book I, Chp. V, p. 71.

wherever else they may have taken place. It is not Brahmâ who creates things and men on this Earth, but the chief and Lord of the *Prajâpati,* the Lords of Being and terrestrial Creation.[56] Obeying the command of Brahmâ, Daksha (the synthesis, or the aggregate, of the terrestrial creators and progenitors, *Pitris* included) made superior and inferior (*vara* and *avara*) things referring to "*putra*" progeny, and "*bipeds* and *quadrupeds*, and subsequently by his will (the Sons of Will and Yoga) made females," *i.e.* separated the androgynes. Here again, we have "bipeds" or men, created before the "quadrupeds" as in the esoteric teachings. (*Vide supra* and Stanza 12 as explained.)

Since, in the exoteric accounts, the *Asuras* are the first beings created from the "body of night," while the *Pitris* issue from that of *Twilight,* the "gods" being placed by Parâsara (*Vishnu Purâna*) between the two, and shown to evolve from the "body of the day," it is easy to discover a determined purpose to veil the order of creation. Man is the *Arvaksrota* coming from the "Body of the Dawn ; and elsewhere, man is again referred to, when the creator of the world, Brahmâ, is shown "creating fierce beings, denominated Bhûtas and eaters of flesh," or as the text has it, "fiends frightful from being monkey-coloured and carnivorous."[57] Whereas the *Râkshasas* are generally translated by "Evil Spirits" and the "enemies of the gods," which identifies them with the *Asuras*. In the *Ramâyana,* when Hanuman is reconnoitering the enemy in Lanka, he finds there *Râkshasas,* some hideous, "while some were beautiful to look upon," and, in *Vishnu Purâna,* there is a direct reference to their becoming the Saviours of "Humanity," or of Brahmâ.

AN INGENIOUS ALLEGORY

The allegory is very ingenious. Great intellect and too much knowledge are a two-edged weapon in life, and instruments for evil as well as for good. When combined with Selfishness, they will make of the whole of Humanity a footstool for the elevation of him who possesses them, and a means for the attainment of his objects; while, applied to altruistic humanitarian purposes, they may become the means of the salvation of many. At all events, the absence of self-consciousness and intellect will make of man an idiot, a brute in human form. Brahmâ is

---

56 "*Vishnu Purâna,*" Book B, Chp. XV of Vol. 2.
57 *Ibid.,* Book 1., chap. v.

Mahat – the universal Mind – hence the too-selfish among the *Râkshasas* showing the desire to become possessed of it all – to "devour" *Mahat*. The allegory is transparent.

At any rate, esoteric philosophy identifies the pre-Brahmanical *Asuras*, *Rudras*,[58] *Râkshasas* and all the "Adversaries" of the Gods in the allegories, with the Egos, which, by incarnating in the still witless man of the Third Race, made him *consciously* immortal. They are, then, during the cycle of Incarnations, the true *dual Logos* – the conflicting and two-faced divine Principle in Man. The *Commentary* that follows, and the next Stanzas may, no doubt, throw more light on this very difficult tenet, but the writer does not feel competent to give it out fully. Of the succession of Races, however, they say:

"First come the SELF-EXISTENT on this Earth. They are the 'Spiritual Lives' projected by the absolute WILL and LAW, at the dawn of every rebirth of the worlds. These LIVES are the divine 'Sishta,' (the seed – Manus, or the Prajâpati and the Pitris)."

From these proceed –

1. *The First Race, the "Self-born," which are the* (astral) *shadows of their Progenitors.*[59] *The body was devoid of all understanding* (mind, intelligence, and will). *The inner being* (the higher self or Monad), *though within the earthly frame, was unconnected with it. The link, the Manas, was not there as yet.*

2. *From the First* (race) *emanated the second, called the "Sweat-born"*[60],

---

58 Whom Manu calls "our paternal grandfathers" (III., 284). The *Rudras* are the seven manifestations of Rudra-Siva, "the destroying god," and *also* the grand *Yogi* and ascetic.

59 See § II., §§ I, *Commentary*.

60 To speak of *life* as having arisen, and of the human race as having originated, in this *absurdly unscientific* way, in the face of the modern Pedigrees of Man, is to court instantaneous annihilation. The esoteric doctrine risks the danger, nevertheless, and even goes so far as to ask the impartial reader to compare the above hypothesis (if it is one) with Hæckel's theory—now fast becoming an axiom with science—which is quoted verbatim:—

". . . How did life, the living world of organisms, arise? And, secondly, the special question: How did the human race originate? The first of these two inquiries, that as to the first appearance of living beings, can only be decided empirically (!!) by proof of the so-called *Archebiosis*, or equivocal generation, or the spontaneous production of organisms of the simplest conceivable kind. Such are the *Monera* (Protogenes,

and the "Boneless." This is the Second Root-Race, endowed by the preservers (*Râkshasas*)[61] *and the incarnating gods* (*Asuras* and the *Kumâras*) *with the first primitive and weak spark* (the germ of intelligence) . . . . *And from these in turn proceeds*:

~~Protamoeba, etc)~~, exceedingly simple microscopic masses of protoplasm without structure or organisation, which take in nutrient and *reproduce themselves by division*. Such a *Moneron* as that primordial organism *discovered* by the renowned English zoologist Huxley, and named *Bathybius Hæckelii*, appears as a continuous thick protoplasmic covering at the greatest depths of the ocean, between 3,000 and 30,000 feet. *It is true that the first appearance of such Monera has not up to the present moment been actually observed*; but there is nothing intrinsically improbable in such an evolution." (The "*Pedigree of Man*," Aveling's translation, p. 33.)

The Bathybius protoplasm having recently turned out to be no organic substance at all, there remains little to be said. Nor, after reading this, does one need to consume further time in refuting the further assertion that . . . . "in that case man also has *beyond a doubt* (to the minds of Hæckel and his like) arisen from the lower *mammalia*, apes and the earlier simian creatures, the still earlier *Marsupialia, Amphibia*, Pisces, by progressive transformations," all produced by "a series of *natural forces working blindly, . . without aim, without design*" (p. 36).

The above-quoted passage bears its criticism on its own face. Science is made to teach that which, up to the present time, "*has never been actually observed*." She is made to deny the phenomenon of an intelligent nature and a vital force independent of form and matter, and to find it more scientific to teach the miraculous performance of "natural forces *working blindly without aim or design*." If so, then we are led to think that the *physico-mechanical* forces of the brains of certain eminent Scientists are leading them on as blindly to sacrifice logic and common sense on the altar of mutual admiration. Why should the protoplasmic *Moneron* producing the first living creature through *self-division* be held as a very scientific hypothesis, and an ethereal *pre-human* race generating the primeval men in the same fashion be tabooed as *unscientific* superstition? Or has materialism obtained a sole monopoly in Science?

61   The *Râkshasas*, regarded in Indian popular theology as demons, are called the "Preservers" beyond the Himalayas. This double and contradictory meaning has its origin in a philosophical allegory, which is variously rendered in the *Purânas*. It is that when Brahmâ created the demons, *Yakshas* (from *Yaksh*, to eat) and the *Râkshasas*, both of which kinds of demons, as soon as born, wished to devour their creator, those among them that called out "Not so! oh, let him be saved (preserved)" were named *Râkshasas* (*Vishnu Purâna*, Book I. ch. v.). The *Bhâgavata Purâna* (III, 19-21) renders the allegory differently. Brahmâ transformed himself into night (or ignorance) invested with a body, upon which the *Yakshas* and *Râkshasas* seized, exclaiming "Do not spare it; devour it." Brahmâ then cried out, "Do not devour me, spare me." This has an inner meaning of course. The body of Night is the darkness of ignorance, and it is the darkness of silence and secrecy. Now the *Râkshasas* are shown in almost every case to be *Yogis*, pious Saddhus and Initiates, a rather unusual occupation for *demons*. The meaning then is that while we have power to dispel the darkness of ignorance, "*devour it*," we have to preserve the sacred truth from profanation. "Brahmâ is for the Brahmins alone," says that proud caste. The moral of the *fable* is evident.

3. The Third Root-Race, the "Two-fold" (Androgynes). The first Races hereof are shells, till the last is "inhabited" (i.e. informed) *by the Dhyanis.*

The Second Race, as stated above, being also sexless, evolved out of itself, at its beginning, the Third Androgyne Race by an analogous but already more complicated process. As described in the *Commentary,* the very earliest of that race were:

"The 'Sons of Passive Yoga.'[62] *They issued from the second Manushyas* (human race) *and became oviparous.* "The emanations that came out of their bodies during the seasons of procreation were ovulary; the small spheroidal nuclei developing into a large soft, egg-like vehicle, gradually hardened, when, after a period of gestation, it broke and the young human animal issued from it unaided, as the fowls do in our race."

THE PROGRESSIVE ORDER OF THE METHODS OF REPRODUCTION, AS UNVEILED BY SCIENCE, IS A BRILLIANT CONFIRMATION OF ESOTERIC ETHNOLOGY

This must seem to the reader ludicrously absurd. Nevertheless, it is strictly on the lines of evolutionary analogy, which science perceives in the development of the living animal species. First the *Moneron-*like procreation by self-division (*vide* Hæckel); then, after a few stages, the oviparous, as in the case of the reptiles, which are followed by the birds; then, finally, the mammals with their *ovoviviparous* modes of producing their young ones.

If the term *ovoviviparous* is applied to some fish and reptiles, which hatch their eggs within their bodies, why should it not be applied to female mammalians, including woman? The ovule, in which, after impregnation, the development of the foetus takes place, is an egg.

At all events, this conception is more philosophical than that of Eve with a suddenly created placenta giving birth to Cain, because of

---

62 The gradual evolution of man in the Secret Doctrine shows that all the later (to the profane the earliest) Races have their *physical* origin in the early Fourth Race. But it is the sub-race which preceded the one that separated sexually that is to be regarded as the *spiritual* ancestors of our present generations, and especially of the Eastern Aryan Races. Weber's idea that the Indo-Germanic Race preceded the Aryan *Vedic* Race is, to the Occultist, grotesque to the last degree.

the Apple, when even the marsupial, the earliest of mammals, *is not placental yet.*

Moreover, the *progressive* order of the methods of reproduction, as unveiled by science, is a brilliant confirmation of esoteric Ethnology. It is only necessary to tabulate the data in order to prove our assertion. (*Cf.* especially Schmidt's "*Doctrine of Descent and Darwinism*," p. 39, *et seq.*, and Laing's "*A Modern Zoroastrian*," pp. 102 – 111.)

I. *Fission*:

(*a*) As seen in the division of the homogeneous speck of protoplasm, known as *Moneron* or Amœba, into two.

(*b*) As seen in the division of the nucleated cell, in which the cell-nucleus splits into two sub-nuclei, which either develop within the original cell-wall or burst it, and multiply outside as independent entities. (*Cf.*, the First Root-Race.)

II. *Budding:*A small portion of the parent structure swells out at the surface and finally parts company, growing to the size of the original organism, *e.g.* many vegetables, the sea-anemone, etc. (*Cf.*, the Second Root-Race.)[63]

III. *Spores:*A single cell thrown off by the parent organism, which develops into a multicellular organism reproducing the features of the latter, *e.g.* bacteria and mosses.

IV. *Intermediate Hermaphroditism:*Male and female organs inhering in the same individual, *e.g.* the majority of plants, worms, and snails, etc.; allied to budding. (*Cf. Second and early Third Root-Races.*)

V. *True sexual union:*(*Cf.*, later Third Root-Race.)

THE DOUBLE EVOLUTION OF THE HUMAN RACE

We now come to an important point with regard to the double evolution of the human race. The Sons of Wisdom, or the *spiritual Dhyanis*, had become "intellectual" through their contact with matter, because they had already reached, during previous cycles of incarnation, that

---

63 Every process of healing and cicatrisation in the higher animal groups—even in the case of reproduction of mutilated limbs with the *Amphibians*—is effected by *fission* and *gemmation* of the elementary morphological elements.

degree of intellect which enabled them to become independent and self-conscious entities, *on this plane of matter*. They were reborn only by reason of Karmic effects. They *entered* those who were "ready," and became the *Arhats*, or *sages*, alluded to above. This needs explanation.

It does not mean that *Monads* entered forms in which other Monads already were. They were "Essences," "Intelligences," and *conscious spirits*, entities seeking to become still more conscious by uniting with more developed matter. Their essence was too pure to be distinct from the universal essence. but their "Egos," or *Manas* (since they are called *Manasaputra*, born of "*Mahat*," or Brahmâ) had to pass through earthly human experiences to become *all-wise*, and be able to start on the returning ascending cycle. The *Monads* are not *discrete* principles, limited or conditioned, but rays from that one universal *absolute* Principle. The entrance into a dark room through the same aperture of one ray of sunlight following another will not constitute *two* rays, but one ray intensified. It is not in the course of natural law that man should become a perfect septenary being before the seventh race in the seventh Round. Yet he has all these principles latent in him from his birth. Nor is it part of the evolutionary law that the Fifth principle (*Manas*) should receive its complete development before the Fifth Round. All such prematurely developed intellects (on the spiritual plane) in our Race are abnormal; they are those whom we call the "Fifth-Rounders." Even in the coming seventh Race, at the close of this Fourth Round, while our four lower principles will be fully developed, that of *Manas* will be only proportionately so. This limitation, however, refers solely to the spiritual development. The intellectual, on the physical plane, was reached during the Fourth Root-Race. Thus, those who were "half ready," who received "but a spark," constitute the average humanity which has to acquire its intellectuality during the present Manvantaric evolution, after which they will be ready in the next for the full reception of the "Sons of Wisdom." While those which "were not ready" at all, the latest Monads, which had hardly evolved from their last transitional and lower animal forms at the close of the Third Round, remained the "narrow-brained" of the Stanza. This explains the otherwise unaccountable degrees of intellectuality among the various races of men – the savage Bushman and the European – even now. Those tribes of savages, whose reasoning powers are very little above the level of the animals, are not the unjustly disinherited, or the *unfavoured*, as some may think – nothing of the kind. They are simply those *latest arrivals* among the human Monads, which *were not ready*: which have to evolve during the present Round, as on the three remaining globes (hence on four different planes of being) so as to arrive at the level of the average class when they reach the Fifth Round. One remark may prove useful, as food for thought to the student in this connection. The MONADS of the lowest specimens of humanity (the "narrow-brained"[64] savage South-Sea Islander, the African, the Australian) *had no Karma to work out when first born as men, as their more favoured brethren in intelligence had.* The former are spinning out Karma only now; the latter are burdened with past, present, and future Karma. In this respect the poor savage is more fortunate than the greatest genius of *civilised countries.*

Let us pause before giving any more such strange teachings. Let us try and find out how far any ancient Scriptures, and even Science, permit the possibility of, or even distinctly corroborate, such wild notions as are found in our Anthropogenesis.

Recapitulating that which has been said we find: That the Secret Doctrine claims for man, (1) a polygenetic origin; (2) a variety of modes of procreation before humanity fell into the ordinary method of generation; (3) that the evolution of animals – of the mammalians at any rate – follows that of man instead of preceding it. And this is diametrically opposed to the now generally accepted theories of evolution and the descent of man from an animal ancestor.

The Chances for the Polygenetic Theory among the Men of Science

Let us, by giving to Cæsar what is Cæsar's, examine, first of all, the chances for the polygenetic theory among the men of science.

---

64 The term here means neither the *dolicho-cephalic* nor the *brachyo-cephalic*, nor yet skulls of a smaller volume, but simply brains devoid of intellect generally. The theory which would judge of the intellectual capacity of a man according to his cranial capacity seems absurdly illogical to one who has studied the subject. The skulls of the stone period, as well as those of African Races (Bushmen included), show that the first are above rather than below the average of the brain capacity of the modern man, and the skulls of the last are on the whole (as in the case of Papuans and Polynesians generally) larger by one cubic inch than that of the average Frenchman. Again, the cranial capacity of the Parisian of today represents an average of 1437 cubic centimeters compared to 1523 of the Auvergnat.

Now the majority of the Darwinian evolutionists incline to a polygenetic explanation of the origin of Races. On this particular question, however, scientists are, as in many other cases, at sixes and sevens; they agree to disagree.

"Does man descend from one *single couple* or from *several groups* – monogenism or polygenism? As far as one can venture to pronounce on what in the absence of witnesses (?) will never be known (?), the second hypothesis is far the most probable."[65] Abel Hovelacque, in his *"Science of Language,"* comes to a similar conclusion, arguing from the evidence available to a linguistic enquirer.

In an address delivered before the British Association, Professor W. H. Flower remarked on this question:

"The view which appears best to accord with what is now known of the characters and distribution of the races of man . . . . is a modification of the monogenistic hypothesis (!). Without entering into the difficult question of the method of man's first appearance upon the world, we must assume for it a vast antiquity, at all events as measured by any historical standard. *If we had any approach to a complete palæontological record, the history of Man could be re-constructed, but nothing of the kind is forthcoming.*"

Such an admission must be regarded as fatal to the dogmatism of the physical Evolutionists, and as opening a wide margin to occult speculations. The opponents of the Darwinian theory were, and still remain, polygenists. Such "intellectual giants" as John Crawford and James Hunt discussed the problem and favoured polygenesis, and in their day there was a far stronger feeling in favour of than against this theory. It is only in 1864 that Darwinians began to be wedded to the theory of unity, of which Messrs. Huxley and Lubbock became the first *coryphæi.*

As regards that other question, of the priority of man to the animals in the order of evolution, the answer is as promptly given. If man is really the Microcosm of the Macrocosm, then the teaching has nothing so very impossible in it, and is but logical. For, man becomes that Macrocosm for the three lower kingdoms under him. Arguing from a physical standpoint, all the lower kingdoms, save the mineral

---

65 A. Lefèvre, *"Philosophy,"* p. 498.

– which is light itself, crystallised and immetallised – from plants to the creatures which preceded the first mammalians, all have been consolidated in their physical structures by means of the "cast-off dust" of those minerals, and *the refuse of the human matter, whether from living or dead bodies, on which they fed and which gave them their outer bodies.* In his turn, man grew more physical, by re-absorbing into his system that which he had given out, and which became transformed in the living anima crucibles through which it had passed, owing to Nature's alchemical transmutations. There were animals in those days of which our modern naturalists have never dreamed, and the stronger became physical material man, the giants of those times, the more powerful were his emanations. Once that Androgyne "humanity" separated into sexes, transformed by Nature into child-bearing engines, it ceased to procreate its like through drops of vital energy oozing out of the body. But while man was still ignorant of his procreative powers on the human plane (before his Fall, as a believer in Adam would say), all this vital energy, scattered far and wide from him, was used by Nature for the production of the first mammal-animal forms. Evolution is *an eternal cycle of becoming*, we are taught, and nature never leaves an atom unused. Moreover, from the beginning of the Round, all in Nature tends to become Man. All the impulses of the dual, centripetal and centrifugal Force are directed towards one point – MAN. The progress in the succession of beings, says Agassiz, "consists in an increasing similarity of the living fauna, and among the vertebrates especially, in the increasing resemblance to man. Man is the end towards which all *animal* creation has tended from the first appearance of the first palæozoic "fishes."[66]

Just so, but "the palæozoic fishes" being at the lower curve of the arc of the evolution of *forms*, this Round began with astral man, the *reflection of the Dhyan Chohans, called the "Builders."* Man *is the alpha and the omega of objective creation.* As said in *"Isis Unveiled,"* all things had their origin in spirit – evolution having originally begun from above and proceeding downwards, instead of the reverse, as taught in the Darwinian theory."[67] Therefore, the tendency spoken of by the eminent naturalist above quoted, is one inherent in every atom. Only, were one to apply it to both sides of the evolution, the observations made would

66 *"Principles of Zoology,"* p. 206.
67 Vol. I, p. 154.

greatly interfere with the modern theory, which has now almost become (Darwinian) law.

But in citing the passage from Agassiz' work with approval, it must not be understood that the occultists are making *any concession* to the theory, which derives man from the animal kingdom. The fact that in this Round he preceded the *mammalia* is obviously not impugned by the consideration that the latter (*mammalia*) follow in the wake of man.

THE REFUSAL BY THE MANASA TO INCARNATE IN HALF-READY PHYSICAL BODIES

STANZA 25. How did the Manâsa, the Sons of Wisdom act? They rejected the Self-born, (*the boneless*). They are not ready. They spurned the (*First*) Sweat-born.[68] They are not quite ready. They would not enter the (*First*) egg-born.[69]

To a Theist or a Christian this verse would suggest a rather theological idea: that of the Fall of the Angels through Pride. In the Secret Doctrine, however, the reasons for the refusal to incarnate in *half-ready* physical bodies seem to be more connected with physiological than metaphysical reasons. Not all the organisms were sufficiently ready. The incarnating powers chose the ripest fruits and spurned the rest.[70]

By a curious coincidence, when selecting a familiar name for the continent on which the first androgynes, the Third Root-Race, separated, the writer chose, on geographical considerations, that of "Lemuria," invented by Mr. P. L. Sclater. It is only later, that reading Hæckel's "*Pedigree of Man*," it was found that the German "Animalist" had chosen the name for his late continent. He traces, properly enough, the centre of human evolution to "Lemuria," but with a slight scientific

---

68 This is explained in the Selection which follows this series of Stanzas in the allegory from the *Purânas* concerning Kandu, the holy sage, and Pramlochâ, the nymph alleged to have hypnotised him (*Vide* §§ II., *Commentary* after St. I.); a suggestive allegory, scientifically, as the drops of perspiration, which she exuded, are the symbols of the spores of science (*Vide infra*).

69 This will be explained as we proceed. This unwillingness to fashion men, or create, is symbolized in the *Purânas* by Daksha having to deal with his opponent Narada, the "strife-making ascetic."

70 *Vide* Verse 24.

variation. Speaking of it as that "cradle of mankind," he pictures the gradual transformation of the anthropoid mammal into the primeval savage!! Vogt, again, holds that in America, Man sprang from a branch of the platyrrhine apes, *independently* of the origination of the African and Asian root-stocks from the old world *catarrhinians*. Anthropologists are, as usual, at loggerheads on this question, as on many others. We shall examine this claim in the light of esoteric philosophy in Stanza 8. Meanwhile, let us give a few moments of attention to the various consecutive modes of procreation according to the laws of Evolution.

Let us begin by the mode of reproduction of the later sub-races of the Third human race, by those who found themselves endowed with the *sacred fire* from the spark of higher and then independent Beings, who were the psychic and spiritual parents of Man, as the lower *Pitar Devata* (the *Pitris*) were the progenitors of his physical body. That Third and holy Race consisted of men who, at their zenith, were described as "towering giants of godly strength and beauty, and the depositaries of all the mysteries of Heaven and Earth." Have they likewise *fallen*, if, then, incarnation was the *Fall*?

Of this presently. The only thing now to be noted of these is, that the chief gods and heroes of the Fourth and Fifth Races, as of later antiquity, are the *deified images of these men of the Third*. The days of their physiological purity, and those of their so-called Fall, have equally survived in the hearts and memories of their descendants. Hence, the dual nature shown in those gods, both virtue and sin being exalted to their highest degree, in the biographies composed by posterity. They were the *pre-Adamite* and the divine Races, with which even theology, in whose sight they are all "the accursed Cainite Races," now begins to busy itself.

But the action of "spiritual progenitors" of that Race has first to be disposed of. A very difficult and abstruse point has to be explained with regard to Stanzas 26 and 27. These say:

STANZA 26. When the Sweat-born produced the Egg-born, the Two-fold (*androgyne Third Race*)[71], the Mighty, the Powerful with Bones,

---

71 The evolutionist Professor Schmidt alludes to "the fact of the separation of sexes, as to the derivation of which from species *once hermaphrodite* all (the believers in creation naturally excepted) are assuredly of one accord." Such indeed is the incontestable evidence drawn from the presence of rudimentary organs. (*Cf.* his "*Doctrine of Descent*

THE LORDS OF WISDOM SAID: "NOW SHALL WE CREATE" (*a*).

Why "now" – and not earlier? This the following *sloka* explains.

STANZA 27. (*Then*) THE THIRD (*race*) BECAME THE VAHAN (*vehicle*) OF THE LORDS OF WISDOM. IT CREATED SONS OF "WILL AND YOGA," BY *KRIYASAKTI* (*b*) IT CREATED THEM, THE HOLY FATHERS, ANCESTORS OF THE ARHATS. . . .

(a) How did they *create*, since the "Lords of Wisdom" are identical with the Hindu *Devas*, who refuse "to create"? Clearly they are the *Kumâras* of the Hindu Pantheon and *Purânas*, those elder sons of Brahmâ, "Sanandana and the other sons of *Vedhas*," who, previously created by him "without desire or passion, remained chaste, full of holy wisdom and undesirous of progeny?"[72]

THE SONS OF WILL AND YOGA WERE CREATED, NOT BEGOTTEN

The power by which they first created is just that which has since caused them to be degraded from their high status to the position of evil spirits, of Satan and his Host, created in their turn by the unclean fancy of exoteric creeds. It was by *Kriyasakti*, that mysterious and divine power latent in the will of every man, and which, if not called to life, quickened and developed by *Yogi*-training, remains dormant in 999,999 men out of a million, and gets atrophied. This power is explained in the "*Twelve Signs of the Zodiac*,"[73] as follows:

(b) *Kriyasakti* – the mysterious power of thought which enables it to produce external, perceptible, phenomenal results by its own inherent energy. The ancients held that any idea will manifest itself externally, if one's attention (and Will) is deeply concentrated upon it; similarly, an intense volition will be followed by the desired result. A *Yogi* generally performs his wonders by means of *Itchasakti* (Will-power)

and Darwinism," p. 159.) Apart from such palpable traces of a primeval hermaphroditism, the fact may be noted that, as Laing writes, "a study of embryology, . . . shows that in the *human higher animal* species the distinction of sex is not developed until a *considerable progress* has been made in the growth of the embryo." ("*A Modern Zoroastrian*," p. 106.) The Law of Retardation—operative alike in the case of human races, animal species, etc., when a higher type has once been evolved—still preserves hermaphroditism as the reproductive method of the majority of plants and many lower animals.

72 See "*Vishnu Purâna*." Book I., ch. 7, para. I.

73 See "*Five Years of Theosophy*," p. 777.

and *Kriyasakti*."

The Third Race had thus created the so-called SONS OF WILL AND YOGA, or the "ancestors" (the *spiritual* forefathers) of all the subsequent and present *Arhats*, or *Mahatmas*, in a truly *immaculate* way. They were indeed *created*, not *begotten*, as were their brethren of the Fourth Race, who were generated sexually after the separation of sexes, the *Fall of Man*. For creation is but the result of will acting on phenomenal matter, the calling forth out of it the primordial divine *Light* and eternal *Life*. They were the "holy seed-grain" of the future Saviours of Humanity.

Here we have to make again a break, in order to explain certain difficult points, of which there are so many. It is almost impossible to avoid such interruptions. For explanations and a philosophical account of the nature of those beings, which are now viewed as the "Evil" and rebellious Spirits, the creators by *Kriyasakti*, the reader is referred to the chapters on "The Fallen Angels" and "The Mystic Dragons," in Part II. of this Volume.

The order of the evolution of the human Races stands thus in the Fifth Book of the Commentaries, and was already given:

The First men were Chhayas (1); *the second, the* "*Sweat-born*" (2); *the Third,* "*Egg-born,*" *and the holy Fathers born by the power of Kriyasakti* (3); *the Fourth were the children of the Padmapani* (Chenresi) (4).

Of course such primeval modes of procreation – by the evolution of one's image, through drops of perspiration, after that by *Yoga*, and then by what people will regard as magic (*Kriyasakti*) – are doomed beforehand to be regarded as fairy-tales. Nevertheless, beginning with the first and ending with the last, there is really nothing miraculous in them, nor anything which could not be shown natural. This must be proven.

1. *Chhaya-birth*, or that primeval mode of *sexless* procreation, the first Race having *oozed out*, so to say, from the bodies of the *Pitris*, is hinted at in a Cosmic allegory in the *Purânas*.[74] It is the beautiful allegory and story of Sanjnâ, the daughter of Viswakarman – married to the Sun, who, "unable to endure the fervours of her lord," gave him her *chhaya* (shadow, image, or *astral body*), while she herself repaired to the

----

74 *Vide* "*Vishnu-Purâna*" Book III, Chp. 2.

jungle to perform religious devotions, or *Tapas*. The Sun, supposing the *"chhaya"* to be his wife begat by her children, like Adam with Lilith – an *ethereal shadow* also, as in the legend, though an actual living female monster millions of years ago.

But, perhaps, this instance proves little except the exuberant fancy of the Purânic authors. We have another proof ready. If the materialised forms, which are sometimes seen oozing out of the bodies of certain mediums could, instead of vanishing, be fixed and made solid – the *creation* of the first Race would become quite comprehensible. This kind of procreation cannot fail to be suggestive to the student. Neither the mystery nor the *impossibility* of such a mode is certainly any greater – while it is far more comprehensible to the mind of the true metaphysical thinker – than the mystery of the conception of the foetus, its gestation and birth as a child, as we now know it.

Now to the curious and little understood corroboration in the *Purânas* about the "Sweat-born."

2. Kandu is a sage and a *Yogi*, eminent in holy wisdom and pious austerities, which finally awaken the jealousy of the gods, who are represented in the Hindu Scriptures as being in never-ending strife with the ascetics. Indra, the "King of the Gods,"[75] finally sends one of his female *Apsarasas* to tempt the sage. This is no worse than Jehovah sending Sarah, Abraham's wife, to tempt Pharoah; but in truth it is those gods (and god) who are ever trying to disturb ascetics and thus make them lose the fruit of their austerities, who ought to be regarded as "tempting demons," instead of applying the term to the *Rudras, Kumâras*, and *Asuras*, whose great sanctity and chastity seem a standing reproach to the Don Juanic gods of the Pantheon. But it is the reverse that we find in all the Purânic allegories, and not without good esoteric reason.

The king of the gods (or Indra) sends a beautiful *Apsarasas* (nymph) named Pramlochâ to seduce Kandu and disturb his penance. She succeeds in her unholy purpose and "907 years six months and three days"[76] spent in her company seem to the sage as one day. When this

---

75 In the oldest MS. of *"Vishnu-Purâna"* in the possession of an Initiate in Southern India, the god is not Indra, but *Kama*, the god of love and desire. See text further on.

76 These are the exoteric figures given in a purposely reversed and distorted way, being the figure of the duration of the cycle between the first and second human race.

psychological or hypnotic state ends, the *Muni* curses bitterly the creature who seduced him, thus disturbing his devotions. "Depart, begone!" he cries, "vile bundle of illusions!" . . . And Pramlochâ, terrified, flies away, *wiping the perspiration from her body* with the leaves of the trees as she passes through the air. She went from tree to tree, and as with the dusky shoots that crowned their summits she dried her limbs, the child she had conceived by the *Rishi* came forth from the pores of her skin in drops of perspiration. The trees received the living dews, and the winds collected them into one mass. "This," said Soma (the Moon), "I matured by my rays, and gradually it increased in size, till the exhalation that had rested on the tree tops became the lovely girl named Mârishâ."[77]

Now Kandu stands here for the *First Race.* He is a son of the *Pitris,* hence one *devoid of mind,* which is hinted at by his being unable to discern a period of nearly one thousand years from one day; therefore he is shown to be so easily deluded and blinded. Here is a variant of the allegory in *Genesis,* of Adam, born an image of clay, into which the "Lord-god" breathes the *breath of life* but not of intellect and discrimination, which are developed only after he had tasted of the fruit of the Tree of Knowledge; in other words when he has acquired the first development of Mind and had implanted in him *Manas,* whose terrestrial aspect is of the Earth earthy, though its highest faculties connect it with Spirit and the *divine Soul.* Pramlochâ is the Hindu Lilith of the Aryan Adam; and Mârishâ, the daughter born of the perspiration from her pores, is the "sweat-born," and stands as a symbol for the Second Race of Mankind.

As remarked in the footnote (*vide supra*), it is not Indra, who now figures in the *Purânas,* but *Kama Deva,* the god of love and desire, who sends Pramlochâ on Earth. Logic, besides the esoteric doctrine, shows that it must be so. For *Kama* is the king and lord of the *Apsarasas,* of whom Pramlochâ is one; and, therefore, when Kandu, in cursing her, exclaims "Thou hast performed the office assigned by the monarch of the gods, go!" he must mean by that monarch *Kama* and not Indra, to whom the *Apsarasas* are not subservient. For *Kama,* again, is in the *Rig*

All Orientalists to the contrary, there is not a word in any of the *Purânas* that has not a special esoteric meaning.

77 "*Vishnu Purâna,*" Book I., ch, 15. *Cf.* also Vivien's temptation of Merlin (Tennyson), the same legend in Irish tradition.

Veda (x. 129) the personification of that feeling which leads and propels to creation. He was the *first movement* that stirred the ONE, after its manifestation from the purely abstract principle, to create, "Desire first arose in It, which was the *primal germ of mind*; and which sages, searching with their intellect, have discovered to be the bond which connects Entity with Non-Entity." A hymn in the *Atharva Veda* exalts *Kama* into a supreme God and Creator, and says: "*Kama* was born the first. Him, neither gods nor fathers (*Pitara*) nor men have equalled." . . . . The *Atharva Veda* identifies him with Agni, but makes him superior to that god. The *Taittarîya Brâhmana* makes him allegorically the son of *Dharma* (moral religious duty, piety and justice) and of *Sraddha* (faith). Elsewhere *Kama* is born from the heart of Brahmâ; therefore he is *Atma-Bhu*, "Self-Existent," and *Aja*, the "unborn." His sending Pramlochâ has a deep philosophical meaning; sent by Indra – the narrative has none. As *Eros* was connected in early Greek mythology with the world's creation and only afterwards became the sexual Cupid, so was *Kama* in his original Vedic character (*Harivansa* making him a son of Lakshmi, who is Venus). The allegory, as said, shows the psychic element developing the physiological before the birth of *Daksha, the progenitor of real physical men*, made to be born from Mârishâ and before whose time living beings and men were procreated "by the will, by sight, by touch and by *Yoga*," as will be shown.

This, then, is the allegory built on the mode of procreation of the *Second* or the "Sweat-born." The same for the *Third Race* in its final development.

Mârishâ, through the exertions of Soma, the Moon, is taken to wife by the *Prachetasas*, the production of the "Mind-born" sons of Brahmâ also[78], from whom they beget the Patriarch Daksha, a son of Brahmâ

---

78 The text has: "From Brahmâ were born mind-engendered progeny, with forms and faculties derived from his corporeal nature, *embodied spirits* produced from the limbs (*gâtra*) of *Dhimat* (all-wise deity)." These beings were the abode of the three qualities of *deva-sarga* (divine creation, which, as the five-fold creation, is *devoid of clearness of perception, without reflection*, dull of nature). But as they *did not multiply themselves*, Brahmâ created other mind-born sons like "himself," namely, the Brahmâ-*Rishis*, or the *Prajâpati* (ten and seven). Sanandana and the other sons of Vedhas (Brahmâ) were previously created, but, as shown elsewhere, they were "*without desire or passion*, inspired with holy wisdom, estranged from the universe and undesirous of progeny (Book I., ch. 7). These Sanandana and other *Kumâras* are, then, the Gods, who after refusing to "create progeny" are forced to incarnate in senseless men. The reader must pardon unavoidable repetitions in view of the great number of the facts given.

also, in a former *Kalpa* or life, explain and add the *Purânas* in order to mislead, yet speaking the truth.

EARLY THIRD RACE HUMANITY: SWEAT-BORN AND ANDROGYNE

(3.) The early Third Race, then, is formed from drops of "sweat," which, after many a transformation, grow into human bodies. This is not more difficult to imagine or realise than the growth of the fœtus from an imperceptible germ, which fœtus develops into a child, and then into a strong, heavy man. But this race again changes its mode of procreation, according to the Commentaries. It is said to have emanated a *vis formativa*, which changed the drops of perspiration into greater drops, which grew, expanded, and became ovoid bodies – huge eggs. In these the human fœtus gestated for several years. In the *Purânas*, Mârishâ, the daughter of Kandu, the sage, becomes the wife of the *Prachetasas* and the mother of Daksha. Now Daksha is the father of the first *human-like* progenitors, having been born in this way. He is mentioned later on. The evolution of man, the microcosm, is analogous to that of the Universe, the macrocosm. His evolution stands between that of the latter and that of the animal, for which man, in his turn, is a macrocosm.

Then the race becomes:

(4.) The androgyne, or hermaphrodite. This process of men-bearing explains, perhaps, why Aristophanes[79] describes the nature of the old race as *androgynous*, the form of every individual being rounded, "having the back and sides as *in a circle*," whose "manner of running was circular . . . . terrible in force and strength and with prodigious ambition." Therefore, to make them weaker, "Zeus divided them (in the Third Root-Race) into two, and Apollo (the Sun), under his direction, closed up the skin." The Madagascans (the island belonged to Lemuria) have a tradition about the first man, who lived at first without eating, and, having indulged in food, a swelling appeared in his leg; this bursting, there emerged from it a female, who became the mother of their race. Truly . . . "We have our sciences of *Heterogenesis* and *Parthenogenesis*, showing that the field is yet open. . . . . The polyps . . . . produce their

---

79. See Plato's *"Banquet"*.

offspring from themselves, like the buds and ramifications of a tree. . . ." Why not the primitive *human* polyp? The very interesting polyp *Stauridium* passes alternately from gemmation into the sex method of reproduction. Curiously enough, though it grows merely as a polyp on a stalk, it produces gemmules, which ultimately develop into a sea-nettle or *Medusa*. The *Medusa* is utterly dissimilar to its parent-organism, the *Stauridium*. It also reproduces itself differently, by sexual method, and from the resulting eggs, *Stauridia* once more put in an appearance. This striking fact may assist many to understand that a form may be evolved – as in the sexual Lemurians from hermaphrodite parentage – quite unlike its immediate progenitors. It is moreover, unquestionable that in the case of human incarnations, the law of Karma, racial or individual, overrides the subordinate tendencies of "Heredity," its servant.

The Secret Doctrine, ii 161-178

Selection 13

EVOLUTION OF THE ANIMAL MAMMALIANS — THE FIRST FALL

§§ (28) How the first mammals were produced. (29) A quasi-Darwinian Evolution. (30) The animals get solid bodies. (31) Their separation into sexes. (32) The first sin of the mindless men.

28. FROM THE DROPS OF SWEAT (a); FROM THE RESIDUE OF THE SUBSTANCE; MATTER FROM DEAD BODIES AND ANIMALS OF THE WHEEL BEFORE (previous, Third Round); AND FROM CAST-OFF DUST; THE FIRST ANIMALS (of this Round) WERE PRODUCED.

(a) The Occult doctrine maintains that, in this Round, the mammalians were a later work of evolution than man. Evolution proceeds in cycles. The great Manvantaric cycle of Seven Rounds, beginning in the First Round with mineral, vegetable, and animal, brings its evolutionary work on the descending arc to a dead stop in the middle of the Fourth Race, at the close of the first half of the Fourth Round. It is on our Earth, then, (the Fourth sphere and the lowest) and in the present Round, that this middle point has been reached. And since the Monad has passed, after its "first inmetallization" on Globe A, through the mineral, vegetable, and animal worlds in every degree of the three states of matter, except the last degree of the third or solid state, which it reached only at the "mid-point of evolution" it is but logical and natural that at the beginning of the Fourth Round on Globe D, Man should be the first to appear; and also that his frame should be of the most tenuous matter that is compatible with objectivity. To make it still clearer: if the Monad begins its cycle of incarnations through the three objective kingdoms on the descending curved line, it has necessarily to enter on the re-ascending curved line of the sphere as a man also. On the descending arc it is the spiritual which is gradually transformed into the material. On the middle line of the base, Spirit and Matter are equilibrized in Man. On the ascending arc, Spirit is slowly re-asserting itself at the expense of the physical, or matter, so that, at the close of the seventh Race of the Seventh Round, the Monad will find itself as free from matter and all its qualities as it was in the beginning; having gained in addition the experience and wisdom, the fruition of all its personal lives, without their evil and temptations.

MEN, THE PROGENITORS OF ANIMALS

This order of evolution is found also in *Genesis* (ch. 1 and 2) if one reads it in its true esoteric sense, for chapter i. contains the history of the first Three Rounds, as well as that of the first Three Races of the Fourth, up to that moment when Man is called to conscious life by the *Elohim* of Wisdom. In the first chapter, animals, whales and fowls of the air, are created before the androgyne Adam. [80]

In the second, Adam (the sexless) comes first, and the animals only appear after him. Even the state of mental torpor and unconsciousness of the first two races, and of the first half of the Third Race, is symbolized, in the second chapter of *Genesis*, by the deep sleep of Adam. It was the dreamless sleep of mental inaction, the slumber of the Soul and Mind, which was meant by that "sleep," and not at all the physiological process of differentiation of sexes, as a learned French theorist (M. Naudin) imagined.

The *Purânas*, the Chaldean and Egyptian fragments, and also the Chinese traditions, all show an agreement with the Secret Doctrine as to the process and order of evolution. We find in them the corroboration of almost all our teaching. For instance: the statement concerning the oviparous mode of procreation of the Third Race, and even a hint at a less innocent mode of the procreation of the first mammal forms, "gigantic, transparent, dumb and monstrous they were," says the Commentary. Study the stories of the several *Rishis* and their multifarious progeny; e.g., Pulastya is the father of all the Serpents and *Nagas* — the oviparous brood; Kasyapa was grandsire, through his wife Tamra, of the birds and of Garuda, king of the feathered tribe; while by his wife Surabhi, he was the parent of cows and buffaloes, etc., etc.

In the Secret Doctrine, the first *Nagas* — beings wiser than Serpents — are the "Sons of Will and Yoga," born before the complete separation

---

80 An allegorical reference to the "Sacred Animals" of the Zodiac and other heavenly bodies. Some Kabalists see in them the prototypes of the animals.

of the sexes, "matured in the man-bearing eggs [81] produced by the power (*Kriyasakti*) of the holy sages" of the early Third Race. [82]

". . . . . In these were incarnated the Lords of the three (upper) worlds, the various classes of *Rudras*, who had been *Tushitas*, who had been *Jayas*, who are *Adityas*;" for, as explained by Parâsara, "There are a hundred appellations of the immeasurably mighty *Rudras*."

Some of the descendants of the primitive *Nagas*, the Serpents of Wisdom, peopled America, when its continent arose during the palmy days of the great Atlantis, (America being the Pâtâla or Antipodes of Jambu-Dwipa, not of Bharata-Varsha). Otherwise, whence the traditions and legends — the latter always more true than history, as says Augustin Thierry — and even the identity in the names of certain "medicine men" and priests, who exist to this day in Mexico? We shall have to say something of the Nargals and the Nagals and also of Nagalism, called "devil-worship" by the Missionaries.

In almost all the *Purânas*, the story of the "Sacrifice of Daksha" is given, the oldest account of which is to be found in *Vayu Purâna*. Allegorical as it is, there is more meaning and biological revelation in it to a Naturalist, than in all the pseudo-scientific vagaries, which are regarded as learned theories and hypotheses.

Daksha, who is regarded as the Chief Progenitor, is, moreover, pointed out as the creator of physical man in the "fable," which makes him lose his head from his body in the general strife between the gods

---

81 In "Hesiod," Zeus creates his third race of men out of ash-trees. In the "*Popol Vuh*" the Third Race of men is created out of the tree Tzita and the marrow of the reed called *Sibac*. But *Sibac* means "egg" in the mystery language of the *Artufas* (or Initiation caves). In a report sent in 1812 to the Cortes by Don Baptista Pino it is said: "All the Pueblos have their *Artufas* — so the natives call subterranean rooms with only a single door where they (secretly) assemble. . . . . These are impenetrable temples . . . . and the doors are always closed to the Spaniards. . . . . They adore the Sun and Moon . . . . fire and the great SNAKE (the creative power), whose eggs are called *Sibac*."

82 There is a notable difference esoterically between the words *Sarpa* and *Naga*, though they are both used indiscriminately. *Sarpa* (serpent) is from the root Srip, serpo to creep; and they are called "Ahi," from Ha, to abandon. "The sarpa was produced from Brahmâ's hair, which, owing to his fright at beholding the *Yakshas*, whom he had created horrible to behold, fell off from the head, each hair becoming a serpent. They are called *Sarpa* from their creeping and Ahi because they had deserted the head" (Wilson). But the *Nagas*, their serpent's tail notwithstanding, do not creep, but manage to walk, run and fight in the allegories.

and the Raumas. This head, being burnt in the fire, is replaced by the head of a ram (Kasi-Khanda). Now the ram's head and horns are ever the symbol of generating power and of reproductive force, and are phallic. As we have shown, it is Daksha who establishes the era of men engendered by sexual intercourse. But this mode of procreation did not occur suddenly, as one may think, and required long ages before it became the one "natural" way. Therefore, his sacrifice to the gods is shown as interfered with by Siva, the destroying deity, evolution and PROGRESS personified, who is the regenerator at the same time; who destroys things under one form but to recall them to life under another more perfect type. Siva-Rudra creates the terrible Virabhadra (born of his breath) the "thousand-headed, thousand-armed" (etc.) monster, and commissions him to destroy the sacrifice prepared by Daksha. Then Virabhadra, "abiding in the region of the ghosts (ethereal men). . . . created from the pores of the skin (Romakupas), powerful Raumas, [83] (or Raumyas)." Now, however mythical the allegory, the Mahabhârata, which is history as much as is the Iliad, shows [84] the Raumyas and other races, as springing in the same manner from the Romakupas, hair or skin pores. This allegorical description of the "sacrifice" is full of significance to the students of the Secret Doctrine who know of the "Sweat-born."

In the *Vayu Purâna*'s account of Daksha's sacrifice, moreover, it is said to have taken place in the presence of creatures born from the egg, from the vapour, vegetation, pores of the skin, and, finally only, from the womb.

Daksha typifies the early Third Race, holy and pure, still devoid of an individual Ego, and having merely the passive capacities. Brahmâ, therefore, commands him to create (in the exoteric texts); when, obeying the command, he made "inferior and superior" (*avara* and *vara*) progeny (*putra*), bipeds and quadrupeds; and by his will, gave birth to females . . . . to the gods, the *Daityas* (giants of the Fourth Race), the snake-gods, animals, cattle and the *Danavas* (Titans and demon Magicians) and other beings."

. . . . "From that period forward, living creatures were engendered

---

83 *"Doctrine of Descent and Darwinism,"* pp. 186-7. The "Unknown Ancestry" referred to are the primeval astral prototypes. Cf. § II., p. 260 (a).

84 See verse 24.

by sexual intercourse. Before the time of Daksha, they were variously propagated — by the will, by sight, by touch, and by *Yoga*-power." [85] And now comes the simply zoological teaching.

29. ANIMALS WITH BONES, DRAGONS OF THE DEEP AND FLYING SARPAS (*serpents*) WERE ADDED TO THE CREEPING THINGS. THEY THAT CREEP ON THE GROUND GOT WINGS. THEY OF THE LONG NECKS IN THE WATER, BECAME THE PROGENITORS OF THE FOWLS OF THE AIR (*a*).

(*a*) This is a point on which the teachings and modern biological speculation are in perfect accord. The missing links representing this transition process between reptile and bird are apparent to the veriest bigot, especially in the *ornithoscelidæ, hesperornis*, and the archæopteryx of Vogt.

30. DURING THE THIRD (*Race*), THE BONELESS ANIMALS GREW AND CHANGED: THEY BECAME ANIMALS WITH BONES (a), THEIR CHHAYAS BECAME SOLID (*also*).

31. THE ANIMALS SEPARATED THE FIRST (*into male and female*) (*b*).

(*a*) Vertebrates, and after that mammalians. Before that the animals were also ethereal proto-organisms, just as man was.

(*b*) The fact of former hermaphrodite mammals and the subsequent separation of sexes is now indisputable, even from the stand-point of Biology. As Prof. Oscar Schmidt, an avowed Darwinist, shows: "Use and disuse combined with selection elucidate (?) the separation of the sexes, and the existence, totally incomprehensible, of rudimentary sexual organs. In the *Vertebrata* especially, each sex possesses such distinct traces of the reproductive apparatus characteristic of the other, that even antiquity assumed hermaphroditism as a natural primeval form of mankind. . . . The tenacity with which the rudiments of sexual organs are inherited is remarkable. In the class of mammals, actual hermaphroditism is unheard of, although through the whole period of their development they drag along with them these residues born by their unknown ancestry, no one can say how long ago." [86]

---

85 These "animals," or monsters, are not the anthropoid or any other apes, but verily what the Anthropologists might call the "missing link," the primitive lower man; see *infra*.

86 Wilson translates the word as "demigods" (See his *Vishnu Purâna*, p. 130); but Raurnas

31. . . . . THEY (*the animals*) BEGAN TO BREED. THE TWO-FOLD MAN (*then*) SEPARATED ALSO. HE (man), SAID "LET US AS THEY; LET US UNITE AND MAKE CREATURES." THEY DID. . . .

32. AND THOSE WHICH HAD NO SPARK (the "narrow-brained" [87] TOOK HUGE SHE-ANIMALS UNTO THEM (*a*). THEY BEGAT UPON THEM DUMB RACES. DUMB THEY WERE (the "narrow-brained") THEMSELVES. BUT THEIR TONGUES UNTIED (*b*). THE TONGUES OF THEIR PROGENY REMAINED STILL. MONSTERS THEY BRED. A RACE OF CROOKED, RED-HAIR-COVERED MONSTERS, GOING ON ALL FOURS. [88] A DUMB RACE, TO KEEP THE SHAME UNTOLD. [89]

(*a*) The animals "separated the first," says Stanza 31. Bear in mind that at that period men were different, even physiologically, from what they are now, having passed the middle point of the Fifth Race. We are not told what the "huge she-animals" were; but they certainly were as different from any we know now, as were the men.

This was the first physical "fall into matter" of some of the then existing and lower races. Bear in mind Stanza 24. The "Sons of Wisdom" had spurned the early Third Race, i.e., the non-developed, and are shown incarnating in, and thereby endowing with intellect, the later Third Race. Thus the sin of the brainless or "mindless" Races, who had no "spark" and were irresponsible, fell upon those who failed to do by them their Karmic duty.

(*b*) See later on concerning the beginning of human speech.

The Secret Doctrine, ii 180-184

---

or *Raumyas* are simply a race, a tribe.

87 See verse 24.

88 "*Vishnu Purâna*"

89 The shame of their animal origin which our modern scientists would emphasize if they could.

Selection 14

Occultism Rejects the Idea that Nature Developed Man from the Ape, or Even from an Ancestor Common to Both

Thus Occultism rejects the idea that Nature developed man from the ape, or even from an ancestor common to both, but traces, on the contrary, some of the most anthropoid species to the Third Race man of the early Atlantean period. As this proposition will be maintained and defended elsewhere, a few words more are all that are needed at present. For greater clearness, however, we shall repeat in brief what was said previously in Book I, Stanza 6.

Our teachings show that, while it is quite correct to say that nature had built, at one time, around the human astral form an *ape-like external* shape, yet it is as correct that this shape was no more that of the "missing link," than were the coverings of that astral form during the course of its natural evolution through all the kingdoms of nature. Nor was it, as shown in the proper place, on this Fourth Round planet that such evolution took place, but only during the First, Second, and Third Rounds, when Man was, in turn, "a stone, a plant, and an animal," until he became what he was in the First Root-Race of present humanity. The real line of evolution differs from the Darwinian, and the two systems are irreconcilable, except when the latter is divorced from the dogma of "Natural Selection" and the like. Indeed, between the *Monera* of Hæckel and the *Sarisripa* of Manu, there lies an impassable chasm in the shape of the *Jiva*; for the "human" Monad, whether *immetallised* in the stone-atom, or *invegetallised* in the plant, or *inanimalised* in the animal, is still and ever a divine, hence also, a HUMAN Monad. It ceases to be human only when it becomes *absolutely divine*. The terms "mineral," "vegetable," and "animal" *monad* are meant to create a superficial distinction: there is no such thing as a Monad (*jiva*) other than divine, and consequently having been, or having to become, human. And the latter term has to remain meaningless unless the difference is well understood. The Monad is a drop out of the shoreless Ocean beyond, or, to be correct, *within* the plane primeval differentiation. It is divine in its higher and *human* in its lower condition – the adjectives "higher" and "lower" being used for lack of better words – and a monad it remains at all times, save in the Nirvanic state, under whatever conditions, or whatever external forms. As the *Logos* reflects the Universe in the Divine Mind, and the manifested Universe reflects itself in each of its Monads, as Leibniz put it, repeating an Eastern teaching, so the Monad has, during the cycle of its incarnations, to reflect in itself every *root-form* of each kingdom. Therefore, the Kabalists say correctly that "Man becomes a stone, a plant, an animal, a man, a Spirit, and finally God. Thus accomplishing his cycle or circuit and returning to the point from which he had started as the *heavenly* Man." But by "Man," the divine Monad is meant, and not the thinking Entity, much less his physical body. While rejecting the immortal Soul, the men of Science now try to trace the latter through a series of animal forms from the lowest to the highest; whereas, in truth, all the present fauna are the descendants of those primordial monsters of which the Stanzas speak. The animals – the creeping beasts and those in the waters that preceded man in this Fourth Round, as well as those contemporary with the Third Race, and again the *mammalia* that are posterior to the Third and Fourth Races – all are either directly or indirectly the mutual and correlative product (physically) of man. It is correct to say that the man of this *Manvantara, i.e.* during the three preceding Rounds, has passed through all the kingdoms of nature. That he was "a stone, a plant, an animal." But (*a*) these stones, plants, and animals were the prototypes, the filmy presentiments of those of the Fourth Round; and (*b*) even those at the beginning of the Fourth Round were the astral shadows of the present, as the Occultists express it. And finally, the forms and *genera* of neither man, animal, nor plant were what they became later. Thus the astral prototypes of the lower beings of the animal kingdom of the Fourth Round, which *preceded* (the *chhayas* of) *Men*, were the consolidated, though still very ethereal *sheaths* of the still more ethereal forms or models produced at the close of the Third Round on Globe D.[90] "Produced from the residue of the substance matter; from dead bodies of men and (other *extinct*) animals of the wheel before," or the previous *Third* Round – as Stanza 24 tells us. Hence, while the nondescript "animals" that preceded the astral man at the beginning of this life-cycle on our Earth were still, so to speak, the progeny of the man of the Third Round, the mammalians of this Round owe their existence, in a great measure, to man again.

---

90 *Vide "Esoteric Buddhism."*

Moreover, the "ancestor" of the present anthropoid animal, the ape, is the direct production of the yet mindless *Man*, who desecrated his human dignity by putting himself physically on the level of an animal.

The above accounts for some of the alleged physiological proofs, brought forward by the anthropologists as a demonstration of the descent of man from the animals.

THE MYSTERIOUS DEVELOPMENT OF THE HUMAN EMBRYO HOLDS THE SECRET OF THE METEMPSYCHOSIS OF THE HUMAN RACE

The point most insisted upon by the Evolutionists is that, "the history of the embryo is an epitome of that of the race." That "every organism, in its development from the egg, runs through a series of forms, through which, in like succession, its ancestors have passed in the long course of Earth's history.[91] The history of the embryo . . . . is a picture in little, and outline of that of the race. *This conception forms the gist of our fundamental biogenetic law, which we are obliged to place at the head of the study of the fundamental law of organic development.*"[92]

This modern theory was known as a fact to, and far more philosophically expressed by, the Sages and Occultists from the remotest ages. A passage from "*Isis Unveiled*" may here be cited to furnish a few points of comparison. In Vol. I, pp. 388 – 9, it was asked why, with all their great learning, physiologists were unable to explain teratological

---

91 "A very strong argument in favour of variability is supplied by the science of Embryology. Is not a man in the uterus . . . a simple cell, a vegetable with three or four leaflets, a tadpole with branchiæ, a mammal with a tail, lastly a primate (?) and a biped? It is scarcely possible not to recognise in the embryonic evolution a rapid sketch, a faithful summary, of the entire organic series." (Lefèvre, "*Philosophy*," p. 484).

The summary alluded to is, however, only that of the *store of types* hoarded up in man, the microcosm. This simple explanation meets all such objections, as the presence of the rudimentary tail in the foetus—a fact triumphantly paraded by Hæckel and Darwin as conclusively in favour of the Ape-Ancestor theory. *It may also be pointed out that the presence of a vegetable with leaflets* in the embryonic stages is *not explained* on ordinary evolutionist principles. Darwinists have not traced man through the vegetable, but Occultists have. *Why then this feature in the embryo,* and how do the former explain it?

92 "*The Proofs of Evolution*," a lecture by Hæckel.

phenomena? Any anatomist who has made the development and growth of the embryo "a subject of special study," can tell, without much brain-work, what daily experience and the evidence of his own eyes show him, viz., that up to a certain period, the human embryo is a facsimile of a young batrachian in its first remove from the spawn – a tadpole. But no physiologist or anatomist seems to have had the idea of applying to the development of the human being – from the first instant of its physical appearance as a germ to its ultimate formation and birth – the Pythagorean esoteric doctrine of metempsychosis, so erroneously interpreted by critics. The meaning of the axiom: "A stone becomes a plant; a plant, a beast; a beast, a man, etc." was mentioned in another place in relation to the spiritual and physical evolution of men on this Earth. We will now add a few more words to make the matter clearer.

What is the primitive shape of the future man? A grain, a corpuscle, say some physiologists; a molecule, an *ovum* of the *ovum*, say others. If it could be analysed – by the microscope or otherwise – of what ought we to expect to find it composed? Analogically, we should say, of a nucleus of inorganic matter, deposited from the circulation at the germinating point, and united with a deposit of organic matter. In other words, this infinitesimal nucleus of the future man is composed of the same elements as a stone – of the same elements as the Earth, which the man is destined to inhabit. Moses is cited by the Kabalists as authority for the remark that it required earth and water to make a living being, and thus it may be said that man first appears as a stone.

At the end of three or four weeks, the *ovum* has assumed a plant-like appearance, one extremity having become spheroidal and the other tapering like a carrot. Upon dissection it is found to be composed, like an onion, of very delicate *laminæ* or coats, enclosing a liquid. The *laminæ* approach each other at the lower end, and the embryo hangs from the root of the umbilicus almost like the fruit from the bough. The stone has now become changed, by "metempsychosis," into a plant. Then the embryonic creature begins to shoot out, from the inside outward, its limbs, and develops its features. The eyes are visible as two black dots; the ears, nose, and mouth form depressions, like the points of a pineapple, before they begin to project. The embryo develops into an animal-like fœtus – the shape of a tadpole – and, like an amphibious reptile, lives in water and develops from it. Its Monad has not yet become either human or immortal, for the Kabalists tells us that this only occurs at the "fourth hour." One by one the fœtus assumes the characteristics of the human being, the first flutter of the immortal breath passes through its being; it moves; and the divine essence settles in the infant frame, which it will inhabit until the moment of physical death, when man becomes a spirit.

This mysterious process of a nine-months' formation, the Kabalists call the completion of the "individual cycle of evolution." As the fœtus develops amidst the *liquor amnii* in the womb, so the Earths germinate in the universal ether, or astral fluid, in the womb of the Universe. These cosmic children, like their pigmy inhabitants, are at first nuclei, then ovules, then gradually mature; and becoming mothers, in their turn, develop mineral, vegetable, animal, and human forms. From centre to circumference, from the imperceptible vesicle to the uttermost conceivable bounds of the *Kosmos*, those glorious thinkers, the Occultists, trace cycle merging into cycle, containing and contained in an endless series. The embryo evolving in its pre-natal sphere, the individual in his family, the family in the state, the state in mankind, the Earth in our system, that system in its central universe, the universe in the *Kosmos*, and the *Kosmos* in the ONE CAUSE . . . thus runs *their* philosophy of evolution, differing as we see, from that of Hæckel:

> "All are but parts of one stupendous whole,
> Whose body Nature is, and (*Parabrahm*) the soul . . ."

These are the proofs of Occultism, and they are rejected by Science. But how is the chasm between the mind of man and animal to be bridged in this case? How, if the anthropoid and *Homo primigenius* had, *argumenti gratiâ*, a common ancestor (in the way modern speculation puts it), did the two groups diverge so widely from one another as regards mental capacity? True, the Occultist may be told that in every case, Occultism does what Science repeats: it gives a *common* ancestor to ape and man, since it makes the former issue from primeval man. Aye, but that "primeval man" was *man* only in external form. He was *mindless* and *soulless* at the time he begot, with a female animal monster, the forefather of a series of apes. This speculation – if speculation it be – is at least logical, and fills the chasm between the mind of man and animal. Thus it accounts for and explains the hitherto unaccountable and inexplicable. The fact that, in the present stage of evolution, Science is almost certain that no issue can follow from the union of man and animal, is considered and explained elsewhere.

Now what is the fundamental difference between the accepted (or nearly so) conclusions, as enunciated in "*The Pedigree of Man*," viz., that man and ape have a common ancestor; and the teachings of Occultism, which deny this conclusion and accept the fact that all things and all living beings have originated from one common source? Materialistic science makes man evolve gradually to what *he is now*, and, starting from the first protoplasmic speck called *Moneron* (which we are told has, like the rest, "originated in the course of immeasurable ages from a few, or from one simple, *spontaneously arising* original form, that has obeyed one law of evolution), pass through "unknown and unknowable" types up to the ape, and thence to the human being. Where the transitional shapes are discoverable we are not told, for the simple reason that no "missing links" between man and the apes have ever yet been found, though this fact in no way prevents men like Hæckel from inventing them *ad libitum*.

Nor will they ever be met with; simply, again, because that link which unites man with his real ancestry is searched for on the objective plane and in the material world of forms, whereas it is safely hidden from the microscope and dissecting knife *within* the animal tabernacle of man himself. We repeat what we have said in *Isis Unveiled*:

". . . . All things had their origin in spirit – evolution having originally begun from above and proceeded downward, instead of the reverse, as taught in the Darwinian theory. In other words, there has been a gradual materialization of forms until a fixed ultimate of debasement is reached. This point is that at which the doctrine of modern evolution enters into the arena of speculative hypothesis. Arrived at this period we will find it easier to understand Hæckel's *Anthropogeny*, which traces the pedigree of man 'from its proto-plasmic root, sodden in the mud of seas which existed before the oldest of the fossiliferous rocks were deposited,' according to Professor Huxley's exposition. We may believe the man (of the Third Round) evolved 'by gradual modification of an (astral) mammal of ape-like organization – still easier when we remember that (though in a more condensed and less elegant, but still as comprehensible, phraseology) the same theory was said by Berosus to have been taught many thousands of years before his time by the man-fish Oannes or Dagon, the semi-demon of Babylonia[93] (though on somewhat modified lines).

"But what lies back of the Darwinian line of descent? So far as he is concerned nothing but 'unverifiable hypotheses.' For, as he puts it, he views all beings 'as the lineal descendants of some few beings which lived long before the first bed of the Silurian system was deposited.'[94] He does not attempt to show us who these 'few beings' were. But it answers our purpose quite as well, for, in the admission of their existence at all, resort to the ancients for corroboration and elaboration of the idea receives the stamp of scientific approbation. . . ."

Truly, as also said in our first work: "If we accept Darwin's theory of the development of species, we find that his starting point is placed in front of an open door. We are at liberty with him, to either remain within, or cross the threshold, beyond which lies the limitless and the incomprehensible, or rather the *Unutterable*. If our mortal language is inadequate to express what our spirit dimly foresees in the great '*Beyond*' – while on this earth – it *must* realize it at some point in the timeless Eternity." But what lies "beyond" Hæckel's theory? Why *Bathybius Hæckelii*, and no more!

A further answer is given in Part III, *Addenda*.

The Secret Doctrine, ii 185-190

---

93 Cory, *"Ancient Fragments."*
94 *"Origin of Species,"* pp. 448–9, first edition.

Selection 15

THE "FALL" OF MANKIND

The "Fall" occurred, according to the testimony of ancient Wisdom and the old records, as soon as Daksha (the reincarnated Creator of men and things in the early Third Race) disappeared to make room for that portion of mankind which had "separated." This is how the *Commentary* explains the details that preceded the "Fall":

In the initial period of man's Fourth evolution, the human kingdom branched off in several and various directions. The outward shape of its first specimens was not uniform, for the vehicles (the egg-like, external shells, in which the future fully physical man gestated) *were often tampered with, before they hardened, by huge animals, of species now unknown, and which belonged to the tentative efforts of Nature. The result was that intermediate races of monsters, half animals, half men, were produced. But as they were failures, they were not allowed to breathe long and live, though the intrinsically paramount power of psychic over physical nature being yet very weak, and hardly established, the 'Egg-Born' Sons had taken several of their females unto themselves as mates, and bred other human monsters. Later, animal species and human races becoming gradually equilibrized, they separated and mated no longer. Man created no more – he begot. But he also begot animals, as well as men, in days of old. Therefore the Sages* (or wise men), *who speak of males who had no more will-begotten offspring, but begat various animals along with Danavas* (giants) *on females of other species – animals being as (or in a manner of) Sons putative to them; and they* (the human males) *refusing in time to be regarded as* (putative) *fathers of dumb creatures – spoke truthfully and wisely. Upon seeing this* (state of things), *the kings and Lords of the Last Races* (of the Third and the Fourth) *placed the seal of prohibition upon the sinful intercourse. It interfered with Karma, it developed new (Karma).*[95] *They* (the divine Kings) *struck the culprits with sterility. They destroyed the Red and Blue Races.*[96]

---

95 It is next to impossible to translate verbally some of these old Commentaries. We are often obliged to give the meaning only, and thus retranslate the verbatim translations.

96 Rudra, as a *Kumâra*, is *Lilalohita*—red and blue.

In another we find:

"*There were blue and red-faced animal-men even in later times; not from actual intercourse* (between the human and animal species), *but by descent.*"

And still another passage mentions:

"*Red-haired, swarthy men going on all-fours, who bend and unbend* (stand erect and fall on their hands again) *who speak as their forefathers, and run on their hands as their giant fore-mothers.*"

MAN HAS NOT ONE DROP OF PITHECOID BLOOD IN HIS VEINS

Perchance in these specimens, Hæckelians might recognize, not the *Homo primigenius*, but some of the lower tribes, such as some tribes of the Australian savages. Nevertheless, even these are not descended from the anthropoid apes, but from human fathers and semi-human mothers, or, to speak more correctly, from human monsters – those "failures" mentioned in the first *Commentary*. The real anthropoids, Hæckel's *Catarrhini* and *Platyrrhini*, came far later, in the closing times of Atlantis. The orang-outang, the gorilla, the chimpanzee and *cynocephalus* are the latest and purely physical evolutions from lower anthropoid mammalians. They have a spark of the purely human essence in them; man on the other hand, has not one drop of pithecoid[97]

---

97 This, regardless of modern materialistic evolution, which speculates in this wise: "The primitive human form, whence as we think all human species sprang, has perished this long time." (This we deny; it has only decreased in size and changed in texture.) "But many facts point to the conclusion that it was hairy and *dolichocephalic.*" (African races are even now *dolichocephalic* in a great measure, but the Palæolithic Neanderthal skull, the oldest we know of, is of a large size, and no nearer to the capacity of the gorilla's cranium than that of any other now-living man). "Let us, for the time being, call this hypothetical species *Homo primigenius. . . .* This first species, or the Ape-man, the ancestor of all the others, PROBABLY arose in the *tropical regions* of the old world from ANTHROPOID APES." Asked for proofs, the evolutionist, not the least daunted, replies: "Of these NO FOSSIL REMAINS ARE AS YET KNOWN TO US, BUT THEY WERE *probably* AKIN TO THE GORILLA AND ORANG OF THE PRESENT DAY." And then the Papuan negro is mentioned as the probable descendant in the first line ("*Pedigree of Man,*" p. 80).

Hæckel holds fast to Lemuria, which with East Africa and South Asia also, he mentions as the possible cradle of the primitive Ape-men, and so do many geologists. Mr. A. R. Wallace admits its reality, though in a rather modified sense, in his "*Geographical*

blood in his veins. Thus saith old Wisdom and universal tradition.

How Was the Separation of Sexes Effected?

How was the separation of sexes effected?", it is asked. Are we to believe in the old Jewish fable of the rib of Adam yielding Eve? Even such belief is more logical and reasonable than the descent of man from the Quadrumana without any reservation, as the former hides an esoteric truth under a fabulous version, while the latter conceals no deeper fact than a desire to force upon mankind a materialistic fiction. The rib is bone, and when we read in *Genesis* that Eve was made out of the rib, it only means that the *Race with bones* was produced out of a previous Race and Races, which were "boneless." This is an esoteric tenet spread far and wide, as it is almost universal under its various forms. A Tahitian tradition states that man was created out of *Aræa*, "red Earth." Taaroa, the creative power, the chief god, "put man to sleep for long years, for several lives," which means racial periods, and is a reference to his *mental sleep*, as shown elsewhere. During that time the deity pulled an *Ivi* (bone) out of man and she became a woman.[98]

Nevertheless, whatever the allegory may mean, even its exoteric meaning necessitates a *divine* Builder of man, a "Progenitor." Do we then believe in such "supernatural" beings? We say, No. Occultism has never believed in anything, whether animate or inanimate, *outside* nature. Nor are we Cosmolators or Polytheists for believing in "Heavenly Man" and divine men, for we have the accumulated testimony of the ages, with its unvarying evidence on every essential point, to support us in this, the Wisdom of the Ancients and UNIVERSAL

Distribution of Animals." But let not Evolutionists speak so lightly of the comparative size of the brains of man and the ape, for this is very *unscientific*, especially when they pretend to see no difference between the two, or very little at any rate. For Vogt himself showed that, while the highest of the Apes, the gorilla, has a brain of only 30 to 51 cubic inches, the brain of the lowest of the Australian aborigines amounts to 99.35 cubic inches. The former is thus "not half of the size of the brain of a new-born babe," says Pfaff.

98 *"Polynesian Researches,"* Ellis, Vol. II, p. 38.
Missionaries seem to have pounced upon this name *Ivi* and made of it *Eve*. But, as shown by Professor Max Müller, Eve is not the Hebrew name but an European transformation of chavah, "life," or "mother of all living," while the Tahitian *Ivi* and the Maori *Wheva* meant bone and bone only." (*"False Analogies"*)

tradition. We reject, however, every groundless and baseless tradition, which, having outgrown strict allegory and symbolism, has found acceptance in exoteric creeds. But that which is preserved in *unanimous* traditions, only the willfully blind could reject. Hence we believe in races of beings other than our own in far remote geological periods; in races of ethereal, following *incorporeal, "Arupa,"* men, with form but no solid substance, giants who preceded us pigmies; in dynasties of divine beings, those Kings and Instructors of the Third Race in arts and sciences, compared with which our little modern science stands less chance than elementary arithmetic with geometry.

No, certainly not. We do not believe in the *supernatural,* but only in the *superhuman,* or rather *interhuman,* intelligences. One may easily appreciate the feeling of reluctance that an educated person would have to being classed with the superstitious and ignorant, and even realize the great truth uttered by Renan when he says that, "The supernatural has become like the original sin, a blemish that every one seems ashamed of – even those most religious persons who refuse in our day to accept even a *minimum* of *Bible* miracles in all their crudeness, and who, seeking to reduce them to the *minimum,* hide and conceal it in the furthermost corners of the past."[99]

But the "supernatural" of Renan belongs to dogma and its dead letter. It has nought to do with its Spirit nor with the reality of facts in Nature. If theology asks us to believe that four or five thousand years ago men lived 900 years and more, that a portion of mankind, the enemies of the people of Israel exclusively, was composed of giants and monsters, we decline to believe that such a thing existed in Nature 5,000 *years back.* For Nature never proceeds by jumps and starts, and logic and common sense, besides geology, anthropology, and ethnology have justly rebelled against such assertions. But if that same theology, giving up her fantastic chronology, had claimed that men lived 969 years – the age of Methuselah – five million years ago, we would have nothing to say against the claim. For in those days the physical frame of men was, compared to the present human body, as that of a *Megalosaurus* to a common lizard.

---

99 *"Chaire d'Hébreu au collège de France,"* p. 20.

FOURTH RACE HUMANITY BEGOT OFFSPRING FROM FEMALES OF A SEMI-HUMAN NOT QUITE ANIMAL RACE

A naturalist suggests another difficulty. The human is the only species which, however unequal in its races, can breed together. "There is no question of selection between *human races*," say the anti-Darwinists, and no evolutionist can deny the argument – one which very triumphantly proves *specific unity*. How then can Occultism insist that a portion of the Fourth Race humanity begot young ones from females of another, only *semi-human*, if not quite an animal, race, the hybrids resulting from which union not only bred freely but produced the ancestors of the modern anthropoid apes? Esoteric science replies to this that it was in the very beginnings of physical man. Since then, Nature has changed her ways, and sterility is the only result of the crime of man's bestiality. But we have to this day proofs of this. The Secret Doctrine teaches that the *specific unity of mankind* is not without exceptions even now. For there are, or rather still were a few years ago, descendants of these half-animal tribes or races, both of remote Lemurian and Lemuro-Atlantean origin. The world knows them as Tasmanians (now extinct), Australians, Andaman Islanders, etc. The descent of the Tasmanians can be almost proved by a fact, which struck Darwin a good deal, without his being able to make anything of it. This fact deserves notice.

Now de Quatrefages and other naturalists, who seek to prove Monogenesis by the very fact of every race of mankind being capable of crossing with every other, have left out of their calculations *exceptions*, which do not in this case confirm the rule. Human crossing may have been a general rule from the time of the separation of sexes, and yet that other law may assert itself, *viz.*, sterility between two human races, just as between two animal species of various kinds, in those rare cases when a European, condescending to see in a female of a savage tribe a mate, happens to chose a member of such mixed tribes.[100] Darwin notes

---

100 Of such semi-animal creatures, the sole remnants known to Ethnology were the Tasmanians, a *portion* of the Australians and a mountain tribe in China, the men and women of which are entirely covered with hair. They were the last descendants in a *direct* line of the semi-animal latter-day Lemurians referred to. There are, however, considerable numbers of the mixed Lemuro-Atlantean peoples produced by various crossings with such semi-human stocks—*e.g.* the wild men of Borneo, the Veddhas of Ceylon, classed by Prof. Flower among Aryans (!), most of the remaining Australians, Bushmen, Negritos, Andaman Islanders, etc.

such a case in a Tasmanian tribe, whose women were suddenly struck with sterility, *en masse*, some time after the arrival among them of the European colonists. The great naturalist tried to explain this fact by change of diet, food, conditions, etc., but finally gave up the solution of the mystery. For the Occultist it is a very evident one. "Crossing," as it is called, of Europeans with Tasmanian women – *i.e.* the representatives of a race, whose progenitors were a "soulless"[101] and mindless monster and a real human, though still as mindless a man – brought on sterility. This, not alone as a consequence of a physiological law, but also as a decree of *Karmic* evolution in the question of further survival of the abnormal race. In no one point of the above is Science prepared to believe *as yet* – but it will have to in the long run. Esoteric philosophy, let us remember, only fills the gaps made by science and corrects her false premises.

Yet, in this particular, geology and even botany and zoology support the esoteric teachings. It has been suggested by many geologists that the Australian native – co-existing as he does with an *archaic fauna and flora* – must date back to an enormous antiquity. The whole environment of this mysterious race, about whose origin ethnology is silent, is a testimony to the truth of the esoteric position.

"It is a very curious fact," says Jukes,[102] that not only these marsupial animals (the mammals found in the Oxfordshire stone-field slates), but several of the shells – as for instance, the *Trigonias* and even some of the plants found fossil in the Oölitic rocks – much more nearly resemble those now living in Australia than the living forms of any other part of the globe. This might be explained on the supposition that, since the Oölitic (Jurassic) period, *less change has taken place in Australia than*

The Australians of the Gulf of St. Vincent and the neighbourhood of Adelaide are *very hairy*, and the brown down on the skin of boys of five or six years of age assumes a *furry appearance*. They are, however, degraded *men*—not the closest approximation to the "*pithecoid* man," as Hæckel so sweepingly affirms. Only a portion of these men are a Lemurian relic. (*Cf.* "*Esoteric Buddhism,*" p. 55.)

101 In calling the animal "Soulless," it is not depriving the beast, from the humblest to the highest species, of a "soul," but only of a conscious surviving *Ego-soul, i.e.* that principle which survives after a man and reincarnates in a like man. The animal has an astral body that survives the physical form for a short period, but its (animal) Monad does not re-incarnate in the same, but in a higher species, and has no "*Deva*chan" of course. It has the *seeds* of all the human principles in itself, but they are *latent*.

102 "*Manual of Geology,*" p. 302.

elsewhere, and that the Australian flora and fauna consequently retain something of the Oölitic type, *while it had been altogether supplanted and replaced on the rest of the Globe.*" (!!)

Now why has less change taken place in Australia than elsewhere? Where is the *raison d'être* for such a "curse of retardation"? It is simply because the nature of the environment develops *pari passu* with the race concerned. Correspondences rule in every quarter. The survivors of those later Lemurians, who escaped the destruction of their fellows when the main continent was submerged, became the ancestors of a portion of the present native tribes. Being a very low sub-race, begotten originally of animals, of monsters, whose very fossils are now resting miles under the sea floors, their stock has since existed in an environment strongly subjected to the *law of retardation*. Australia is one of the oldest lands now above the waters, and in the senile decrepitude of old age, its "*virgin* soil" notwithstanding. It can produce no new forms, unless helped by new and fresh races, and artificial cultivation and breeding.

THIRD RACE HUMANITY WAS ALMOST SEXLESS AND BECAME ANDROGYNOUS

To return, however, once more to the history of the Third Race, the "Sweat-Born," the "Egg-bearing," and the "Androgyne." Almost sexless in its early beginnings, it became bisexual or androgynous, very gradually of course. The passage from the former to the latter transformation required numberless generations, during which the simple cell that issued from the earliest parent (the two in one) first developed into a bisexual being, and then the cell, becoming a regular egg, gave forth a unisexual creature. The Third Race mankind is the most mysterious of all the hitherto developed five Races. The mystery of the "How" of the generation of the distinct sexes must, of course, be very obscure here, as it is the business of an embryologist and a specialist, the present work giving only faint outlines of the process. But it is evident that the units of the Third Race humanity began to separate in their pre-natal shells, or eggs,[103] and to issue out of them as

---

103 The "fables" and "myths" about Leda and Jupiter, and such like, could never have sprung up in people's fancy, had not the allegory rested on a fact in nature. Evolution, gradually transforming man into a mammal, did in his case only what it did in that of

distinct male and female babes, ages after the appearance of its early progenitors. And as time rolled on its geological periods, the newly born sub-races began to lose their natal capacities. Toward the end of the fourth *sub-race*, the babe lost its faculty of walking as soon as liberated from its shell, and by the end of the fifth, mankind was born under the same conditions and by the same identical process as our historical generations. This required, of course, millions of years. The reader has been made acquainted with the approximate figures, at least of the exoteric calculations, in Stanza 2.

We are approaching the turning-point of the evolution of the Races. Let us see what occult philosophy says on the origin of language.

The Development of Speech Occurred during the Early Third Race to the Fourth Race Humanity

The Commentaries explain that the first Race – the ethereal or astral Sons of Yoga, also called "Self-born" – was, in our sense, speechless, as it was devoid of mind on our plane. The Second Race had a "Sound-language," to wit, chant-like sounds composed of vowels alone. The Third Race developed in the beginning a kind of language which was only a slight improvement on the various sounds in Nature, on the cry of gigantic insects and of the first animals, which, however, were hardly nascent in the day of the "Sweat-born" (the *early* Third Race). In its second half, when the "Sweat-born" gave birth to the "Egg-born," (the *middle* Third Race); and when these, instead of "hatching out" (may the reader pardon the rather ridiculous expression when applied to human beings in our age) as androgynous beings, began to evolve into separate males and females; and when the same law of evolution led them to reproduce their kind sexually, an act which forced the creative gods, compelled by Karmic law, to incarnate in *mindless* men; then only was speech developed. But even then it was still no better than a tentative effort. The whole human race was at that time of "one language and of one lip." This did not prevent the last two Sub-Races of the Third Race[104] from building cities, and sowing far and

other animals. But this does not prevent man from having always stood at the head of the animal world and other organic species, and from having preceded the former.

104 To avoid confusion, let the reader remember that the term Root-Race applies to one of the seven great Races, sub-Race to one of its great Branches, and Family-Race to one

wide the first seeds of civilization under the guidance of their divine instructors[105] and their own already awakened minds. Let the reader also bear in mind that, as each of the seven races is divided into four ages – the Golden, Silver, Bronze, and Iron Age – so is every smallest division of such races.[106] Speech then developed, according to occult teaching, in the following order:

I. Monosyllabic speech: that of the first approximately fully developed human beings at the close of the Third Root-Race, the "golden-coloured," yellow-complexioned men, after their separation into sexes, and the full awakening of their minds. Before that, they communicated through what would now be called "thought-transference," though, with the exception of the Race called the "Sons of Will and Yoga" – the first in whom the "Sons of Wisdom" had incarnated – thought was but very little developed in nascent physical man, and never soared above a low terrestrial level. Their physical bodies belonging to the Earth, their Monads remained on a higher plane altogether. Language could not be well developed before the full acquisition and development of their reasoning faculties. This monosyllabic speech was the vowel parent, so to speak, of the monosyllabic languages mixed with hard consonants, still in use amongst the yellow races which are known to the anthropologist.[107]

II. These linguistic characteristics developed into the agglutinative languages. The latter were spoken by some Atlantean races, while other parent stocks of the Fourth Race preserved the mother language. And as languages have their cyclic evolution, their childhood, purity, growth, *fall into matter*, admixture with other languages, maturity, decay, and finally death,[108] so the primitive

of the sub-divisions, which include nations and large tribes.

105 In the Selection on the Divine Dynasties, the nature of these "Instructors" is explained.

106 *Vide* Selection attached to the "Divisions into *Yugas*."

107 The present yellow races are the descendants, however, of the early branches of the Fourth Race. Of the third, the only *pure and direct* descendants are, as said above, a portion of the fallen and degenerated Australians, whose far distant ancestors belonged to a division of the seventh Sub-race of the Third. The rest are of mixed Lemuro-Atlantean descent. They have since then entirely changed in stature and intellectual capacities.

108 *Language* is certainly coeval with reason and could never have been developed before men became one with the informing principles in them—those who fructified

speech of the most civilized Atlantean races – that language, which is referred to as "Râkshasi Bhasa," in old Sanskrit works – decayed and almost died out. While the "cream" of the Fourth Race gravitated more and more toward the apex of physical and intellectual evolution, thus leaving as an heirloom to the nascent Fifth (the Aryan) Race the inflectional, highly developed languages, the agglutinative decayed and remained as a fragmentary fossil idiom, scattered now, and nearly limited to the aboriginal tribes of America.

III. The inflectional speech – the root of the Sanskrit, very erroneously called "the elder sister" of the Greek, instead of its mother – was the first language (now the mystery tongue of the Initiates, of the Fifth Race). At any rate, the "Semitic" languages are the bastard descendants of the first phonetic corruptions of the eldest children of the early Sanskrit. The occult doctrine admits of no such divisions as the Aryan and the Semite, accepting even the Turanian with ample reservations. The Semites, especially the Arabs, are later Aryans – degenerate in spirituality and perfected in materiality. To these belong all the Jews and the Arabs. The former are a tribe descended from the Tchandalas of India, the outcasts, many of them ex-Brahmins, who sought refuge in Chaldea, in Scinde, and Aria (Iran), and were truly born from their father *A-bram* (No Brahmin) some 8,000 years B.C. The latter, the Arabs, are the descendants of those Aryans who would not go into India at the time of the dispersion of nations, some of whom remained on the borderlands thereof, in Afghanistan and Kabul,[109] and

---

and awoke to life the manasic element dormant in primitive man. For, as Professor Max Müller tells us in his "*Science of Thought*," "Thought and language are identical." Yet to add to this the reflection that *thoughts which are too deep for words do not really exist at all*, is rather risky, as thought impressed upon the astral tablets exists in eternity whether expressed or not. *Logos* is both reason and speech. But language, proceeding in cycles, is not always adequate to express *spiritual* thoughts. Moreover, in one sense, the Greek *Logos* is the equivalent of the Sanskrit *Vâch*, "the immortal (intellectual) ray of spirit." And the fact that *Vâch* (as *Devasena*, an *aspect* of Saraswati, the goddess of hidden Wisdom) is the spouse of the eternal celibate *Kumâra*, unveils a suggestive, though veiled, reference to the *Kumâras*, those "who refused to create," but who were compelled later on to complete *divine* Man by incarnating in him. All this will be fully explained in the Selections that follow.

109 Ptolemy, speaking in his ninth table of the *Kabolitæ* (Kabul tribes), calls them Ἀριστόφυλοι, *Aristophyli*, the aristocratic or *noble tribes*. The Afghans call themselves *Ben-Issrael* (children of Is(*sa*)rael), from *Issa*, "woman and also earth," Sons of Mother Earth. But if you call an Afghan *Yahoudi* (*Jew*), he will kill you. The subject is fully treated elsewhere. The names of the supposed twelve tribes and the names of the real

along the Oxus, while others penetrated into and invaded Arabia.

THE TRANSFORMATION OF THE EARTH

But this was when Africa had already been raised as a continent. We have meanwhile to follow, as closely as limited space will permit, the gradual evolution of the now truly human species. It is in the suddenly arrested evolution of certain sub-races, and their forced and violent diversion into the purely animal line by artificial cross-breeding, truly analogous to the hybridization, which we have now learned to utilize in the vegetable and animal kingdoms, that we have to look for the origin of the anthropoids.

In these red-haired and hair-covered monsters, the fruit of the unnatural connection between men and animals, the "Lords of Wisdom" did not incarnate, as we see. Thus by a long series of transformations due to unnatural cross-breeding (unnatural "sexual selection") originated in due course of time the lowest specimens of humanity, while further bestiality and the fruit of their first animal efforts of reproduction begat a species which developed into mammalian apes ages later.[110]

As to the separation of sexes, it did not occur suddenly, as one may

---

tribes, the same in number, of the Afghans, are the same. The Afghans being far older (at any rate, their Arabic stock) than the Israelites, no one need be surprised to find such tribal names among them as *Youssoufzic*, "Sons of Joseph" in Punjcaure and Boonere; the *Zablistanee* (Zebulon); Ben-manasseh (sons of *Manas*seh) among the Khojar Tartars; Isaguri, or Issachar (now Ashnagor in Afghanistan), etc., etc. The whole twelve names of the so-called twelve tribes are names of the signs of the Zodiac, as is now well proven. At any rate, the names of the oldest Arabic tribes, re-transliterated, yield the names of the zodiacal signs and of the mythical sons of Jacob likewise. Where are the traces of the Jewish twelve tribes? Nowhere. But there is a trace, and a good one, that the Jews have tried to deceive people with the help of those names. For, see what happens *ages after the ten tribes* had wholly disappeared from Babylon. Ptolemy Philadelphus, desiring to have the Hebrew Law translated for him into Greek (the famous *Septuagint*), wrote to the high priest of the Jews, Eleazar, to *send him six men from each of the twelve tribes*; and the *seventy-two representatives* (of whom sixty were ghosts apparently) came to the king in Egypt and translated the Law amid miracles and wonders. See Butler's *"Horæ Biblicæ,"* Josephus, and Philo Judæus.

110 The *Commentary* explains that the apes are the only species, among the animals, which has gradually and with every generation and variety tended more and more to return to the original type of its male forefather—the dark gigantic Lemurian and Atlantean.

think. Nature proceeds slowly in whatever she does.

STANZA 37. THE ONE (*androgyne*) BECAME TWO; ALSO ALL THE LIVING AND CREEPING THINGS, THAT WERE STILL ONE, GIANT-FISH, BIRDS, AND SERPENTS WITH SHELL-HEADS (*a*).

This relates evidently to the so-called age of the amphibious reptiles, during which ages science maintains that *no man existed*! But what could the ancients know of antediluvian prehistoric animals and monsters! Nevertheless, in Book VI of the Commentaries is found a passage which says, freely translated:

"*When the Third separated and fell into sin by breeding men-animals, these* (the animals) *became ferocious, and men and they mutually destructive. Till then, there was no sin, no life taken. After* (the separation) *the Satya (Yuga) was at an end. The eternal spring became constant change and seasons succeeded. Cold forced men to build shelters and devise clothing. Then man appealed to the superior Fathers* (the higher gods or angels). *The Nirmânakaya of the Nâgas, the wise Serpents and Dragons of Light came, and the precursors of the Enlightened* (Buddhas). *Divine Kings descended and taught men sciences and arts, for man could live no longer in the first land* (Adi-Varsha, the Eden of the first Races), *which had turned into a white frozen corpse.*"

The above is suggestive. We will see what can be inferred from this brief statement. Some may incline to think that there is more in it than is apparent at first sight.

The Secret Doctrine, ii 192–201

Selection 16

Many of the So-Called Mythical Animals Were Creatures that Really Once Existed

Thus opens the introduction to a recent (1886) and most interesting work by Mr. Charles Gould, called "*Mythical Monsters*," He boldly states his belief in most of these monsters. He submits that, "Many of the so-called mythical animals, which, throughout long ages and in all nations, have been the fertile subjects of fiction and fable, come legitimately within the scope of plain matter-of-fact natural history; and that they may be considered, not as the outcome of exuberant fancy, but as creatures which really once existed, and of which, unfortunately, only imperfect and inaccurate descriptions have filtered down to us, probably very much refracted, through the mists of time. . . . Traditions of creatures *once co-existing with man, some of which are so weird and terrible as to appear at first sight to be impossible*. For me the major part of those creatures are not chimeras but objects of rational study. The dragon, in place of being a creature evolved out of the imagination of an Aryan man by the contemplation of lightning flashing through the caverns which he tenanted, as is held by some mythologists, is an animal which once lived and dragged its ponderous coils and perhaps flew. . . . . To me the specific existence of the Unicorn seems not incredible, and in fact, more probable than that theory which assigns its origin to a lunar myth[111] . . . For my part I doubt the general derivation of myths from 'the contemplation of the visible workings of external nature.' It seems to me easier to suppose that the palsy of time has enfeebled the utterance of these oft-told tales until their original appearance is almost unrecognisable, than that *uncultured savages should possess powers of imagination and poetical invention far beyond those enjoyed by the most instructed nations of the present day*; less hard to believe that these wonderful stories of gods and demigods, of giants and dwarfs, of dragons and monsters of all descriptions are *transformations than to believe* them to be inventions."[112]

---

111 "*The Unicorn: A Mythological Investigation*," Robert Brown, jun., F.S.A.
112 Pp. 3–4, Introduction to "*Mythical Monsters*."

MAN CO-EXISTED WITH ANIMALS WHICH HAVE LONG SINCE BECOME EXTINCT

It is shown by the same geologist that man, "successively traced to periods *variously estimated from thirty thousand to one million years . . . . . .* co-existed with animals which have long since become extinct (p. 20)." These animals, "weird and terrible," were, to give a few instances: (1) "Of the genus *Cidastes*, whose huge bones and vertebræ show them to have attained a length of nearly two hundred feet . . . . . ." The remains of such monsters, no less than ten in number, were seen by Professor Marsh in the Mauvaises Terres of Colorado, strewn upon the plains; (2) The *Titanosaurus montanus*, reaching fifty or sixty feet in length; (3) the *Dinosaurians* (in the Jurassic beds of the Rocky Mountains), of still more gigantic proportions; and (4) the *Atlanto-Saurus immanis*, a femur of which alone is over six feet in length, and which would be thus over one hundred feet in length! But even yet the line has not been reached, and we hear of the discovery of remains of such titanic proportions as to possess a thigh-bone over twelve feet in length (p. 37). Then we read of the monstrous *Sivatherium* in the Himalayas, the four-horned stag, as large as an elephant, and exceeding the latter in height; of the gigantic *Megatherium*; of colossal flying lizards, *Pterodactyli*, with crocodile jaws on a duck's head, etc., etc. *All these were co-existent with man, most probably attacked man, as man attacked them,* and we are asked to believe that the said man was no larger then than he is now! Is it possible to conceive that, surrounded in Nature with such monstrous creatures, man, unless himself a colossal giant, could have survived, while all his foes have perished? Is it with his stone hatchet that he had the best of a *Sivatherium* or a gigantic flying saurian? Let us always bear in mind that at least one great man of science, de Quatrefages, sees no good scientific reasons why man should not have been "contemporaneous with the earliest *mammalia* and go back as *far as the Secondary Period.*"[113]

"It appears," writes the very conservative Professor Jukes, "that the flying dragons of romance had something like a real existence in "former ages of the world."[114] "Does the written history of man," the author goes on to ask, "comprising a few thousand years, embrace the whole

---

113 *"The Human Species,"* p. 52.
114 *"Manual of Geology,"* p. 301.

course of his intelligent existence? Or have we in the long mythical eras, extending over hundreds of thousands of years, and recorded in the chronologies of Chaldea and China, shadowy mementoes of prehistoric man, handed down by tradition, and perhaps transported by a few survivors to existing lands, from others which, like the fabled Atlantis of Plato, may have been submerged, or the scene of some great catastrophe which destroyed them with all their civilization" (p. 17).

The few remaining giant animals, such as elephants, themselves smaller than their ancestors, the Mastodons, and *Hippopotami*, are the only surviving relics, and tend to disappear more entirely with every day. Even they have already had a few pioneers of their future genus, and have decreased in size in the same proportion as men did. For the remains of a pigmy elephant were found (*E. Falconeri*) in the cave deposits of Malta, and the same author asserts that they were associated with the remains of pigmy *Hippopotami*, the former being "only two feet six inches high; or the still – existing *Hippopotamus* (*Chœropsis*) *Liberiensis*, which M. Milne-Edwards figures as little more than two feet in height."[115]

Sceptics may smile and denounce our work as full of nonsense or fairy-tales. But by so doing they only justify the wisdom of the Chinese philosopher Chuang, who said that "the things that men do know can in no way be compared, numerically speaking, to the things that are unknown,"[116] and thus they laugh only at their own ignorance.

The Secret Doctrine, ii 217-219

---

115 "*Recherches sur les Mammifères*," plate I.
116 Preface to "*Wonders by Land and Sea*," (Shan Hai King).

Selection 17

THE GODS BECAME NO-GODS

STANZA 38. THUS TWO BY TWO, ON THE SEVEN ZONES, THE THIRD (*Race*) GAVE BIRTH TO THE FOURTH (*Race men*). THE GODS BECAME NO-GODS (*Sura became a-Sura*) (*a*).

STANZA 39. THE FIRST (*Race*) ON EVERY ZONE WAS MOON-COLOURED (*yellow white*); THE SECOND, YELLOW, LIKE GOLD; THE THIRD, RED; THE FOURTH, BROWN, WHICH BECAME BLACK WITH SIN.[117] THE FIRST SEVEN (*human*) SHOOTS WERE ALL OF ONE COMPLEXION IN THE BEGINNING. THE NEXT (*seven, the sub-races*) BEGAN MIXING THEIR COLOURS (*b*).

(*a*) To understand this verse 38, it must be read together with the three verses of Stanza 9. Up to this point of evolution man belongs more to metaphysical than physical nature. It is only after the so-called FALL that the races began to develop rapidly into a purely human shape. And in order that he may correctly comprehend the full meaning of the Fall, so mystic and transcendental is it in its real significance, the student must be told at once the details which preceded this event, of which event modern theology has formed a pivot on which its most pernicious and absurd dogmas and beliefs are made to turn.

SOME EGOS REFUSED TO INCARNATE INTO THE THIRD RACE HUMANITY - THEIR LATER KARMIC PUNISHMENT

---

117 Strictly speaking, it is only from the time of the Atlantean, brown and yellow giant Races, that one ought to speak of MAN, since it was the Fourth race only which was the first *completely human species*, however much larger in size than we are now. In "Man" (by two *chelas*), all that is said of the Atlanteans is quite correct. It is chiefly that race which became "black with sin" that brought the divine names of the *Asuras*, the *Râkshasas*, and the *Daityas* into disrepute and passed them on to posterity as the names of fiends. For, as said, the *Suras* (gods) or *Devas*, having incarnated in the wise men of Atlantis, the names of *Asuras* and *Râkshasas* were given to the Atlanteans; which names, owing to their incessant conflicts with the last remnants of the Third Race and the "Sons of Will and Yoga," have led to the later allegories about them in the *Purânas*. "*Asura* was the generic appellation of all the Atlanteans who were the enemies of the spiritual heroes of the Aryans (gods)." ("*Man*," p. 97.)

The archaic commentaries explain, as the reader must remember, that, of the Host of *Dhyanis*, whose turn it was to incarnate as the Egos of the immortal, but, *on this plane, senseless* monads – that some "obeyed" (the law of evolution) immediately when the men of the Third Race became physiologically and physically ready, *i.e.* when they had separated into sexes. These were those early conscious Beings who, now adding conscious knowledge and will to their inherent Divine purity, *created by Kriyasakti* the semi-Divine man, who became the seed on earth for future adepts. Those, on the other hand, who, jealous of their intellectual freedom (unfettered as it then was by the bonds of matter), said, "We can choose . . . we have wisdom" (see verse 24) and incarnated far later – these had their first Karmic punishment prepared for them. They got bodies (physiologically) inferior to their astral models, because their *chhayas* had belonged to progenitors of an inferior degree in the seven classes. As to those "Sons of Wisdom" who had "deferred" their incarnation till the Fourth Race, which was already tainted (physiologically) with sin and impurity, they produced a terrible cause, the Karmic result of which weighs on them to this day. It was produced in themselves, and they became the carriers of that seed of iniquity for æons to come, because the bodies they had to inform had become defiled through their own procrastination. (See verses 32, 36.)

This was the "Fall of the angels," because of their rebellion against Karmic Law. The "fall of *man*" was no fall, *for he was irresponsible.* But "Creation" having been invented on the dualistic system as the "prerogative of God alone," the legitimate *attribute* patented by theology in the name of an *infinite* deity of their own making, this power had to be regarded as "Satanic," and as an usurpation of divine rights. Thus, the foregoing, in the light of such narrow views, must naturally be considered as a terrible slander on man, "created in the image of God," a still more dreadful blasphemy in the face of the dead-letter dogma. "Your doctrine," the Occultists were already told, "makes of man, created out of dust in the likeness of his God, a vehicle of the Devil, from the first." "Why did you make of your god a devil – both, moreover, created *in your own image*?" is our reply. The *esoteric* interpretation of the *Bible*, however, sufficiently refutes this slanderous invention of theology; the Secret Doctrine must some day become the just Karma of the Churches – more anti-Christian than the representative assemblies of the most confirmed Materialists and Atheists.

THE OLD DOCTRINE ABOUT THE TRUE MEANING OF THE "FALLEN ANGELS" EXPLAINS THE BIBLE

The old doctrine about the true meaning of the "Fallen Angels," in its anthropological and evolutionary sense, is contained in the *Kabala* and explains the *Bible*. It is found pre-eminently in *Genesis* when the latter is read in a spirit of research for truth, with no eye to dogma, and in no mood of preconception. This is easily proven. In *Genesis* (vi.) the "Sons of God" – *B'ne Aleim* – become enamoured of the daughters of men, marry, and reveal to their wives the mysteries unlawfully learnt by them in heaven, according to Enoch; and this is the "Fall of Angels."[118] But what is, in reality, the "*Book of Enoch*" itself, from which the author of *Revelation* and even the St. John of the *Fourth Gospel* have so profusely quoted? (*e.g.* verse 8, in Chp. 10, about all who have come

---

118 In general, the so-called *orthodox* Christian conceptions about the "fallen" angels or Satan, are as remarkable as they are absurd. About a dozen could be cited, of the most various character as to details, and all from the pen of educated lay authors, "University graduates" of the present quarter of our century. Thus, the author of "Earth's Earliest Ages," J. H. Pember, M.A., devotes a thick volume to proving Theosophists, Spiritualists, Metaphysicians, Agnostics, Mystics, poets, and every contemporary author on oriental speculations, to be the devoted servants of the "Prince of the Air," and irretrievably damned. He describes Satan and his Antichrist in this wise:

"Satan is the Anointed Cherub' of old. . . . God created Satan, the fairest and wisest of all his creatures in this part of His Universe, and made him Prince of the World, and of the Power of the Air. . . . He was placed in an Eden, which was both far anterior to the Eden of *Genesis*. . . . and of an altogether different and more substantial character, resembling the New Jerusalem. Thus, Satan being perfect in wisdom, and beauty, His vast empire is our earth, if not the whole solar system. . . . Certainly no other angelic power of greater or even equal dignity has been revealed to us. The *Archangel Michael himself is quoted by Jude as preserving towards the Prince of Darkness the respect due to a superior, however wicked he may be, until God has formally commanded* his deposition." Then we are informed that "Satan was from the moment of his creation *surrounded by the insignia of royalty*" (!!): that he "awoke to consciousness to find the air filled with the rejoicing music of those whom God had appointed . . . ." Then the Devil "*passes from the royalty to his priestly dignity*" (!!!) "Satan *was also a priest of the Most High*," etc., etc. And now—"Antichrist will be Satan incarnate" (pp. 56–59). The Pioneers of the coming Apollyon have already appeared—they are the Theosophists, the Occultists, the authors of the "*Perfect Way*," of "*Isis Unveiled*," of the "*Mystery of the Ages*," and even of the "LIGHT OF ASIA"!! The author notes the "*avowed origin*" (of Theosophy) *from the "descending angels*," from the "*Nephilim*," or the angels of the 6th Chp. of *Genesis*, and the Giants. He ought to note his own descent from them also, as the present Secret Doctrine endeavours to show—unless he refuses to belong to the present humanity.

before Jesus, being "thieves and robbers.") Simply a *Book of Initiation*, giving out in allegory and cautious phraseology the programme of certain archaic mysteries performed in the *inner* temples. The author of the "*Sacred Mysteries among the Mayas and Quichés*" very justly suggests that the so-called "*Visions*" of Enoch relate to his (Enoch's) experience at initiation and what he learned in the mysteries, while he very erroneously states his opinion that Enoch had learned them before being converted to Christianity (!!); furthermore, he believes that this book was written "at the beginning of the Christian era, when . . . the customs and religion of the Egyptians fell into decadency"! This is hardly possible, since Jude quotes in his epistle from the "*Book of Enoch*" (verse 14); and, therefore, as Archbishop Laurence, the translator of the *Book of Enoch* from the Ethiopic version, remarks, it "could not have been the production of a writer who lived after . . . or was even coeval with" the writers of the *New Testament*, unless, indeed, Jude and the Gospels, and all that follows, was also a production of the already established Church – which, some critics say, is not impossible. But we are now concerned with the "Fallen Angels" of Enoch, rather than with Enoch himself.

In Indian exotericism, these angels (*Asuras*) are also denounced as "the enemies of the gods," those who oppose sacrificial worship offered to the latter. In Christian theology they are broadly referred to as the "Fallen Spirits," the heroes of various conflicting and contradictory legends about them, gathered from Pagan sources. The *coluber tortuosus*, "the tortuous snake," a qualification said to have originated with the Jews, had quite another meaning before the Roman Church distorted it: among others, *a purely astronomical meaning*.

The "Serpent" fallen from on high, "*deorsum fluens*," was credited with the possession of the Keys of the Empire of the Dead, τοῦ θανάτου ἀρχή, to that day, when Jesus saw it "falling like lightning from heaven" (*Luke* x. 17, 18), the Roman Catholic interpretation of *cadebat ut fulgur* to the contrary, notwithstanding; and it means indeed that even "the devils are subject" to the *Logos* – who is Wisdom, but who, as the opponent of ignorance, is Satan or Lucifer at the same time. This remark refers to divine Wisdom falling like lightning on, and quickening the intellects of those who fight the devils of ignorance and superstition. Up to the time when Wisdom, in the shape of the incarnating Spirits of MAHAT, descended from on high to animate and call the Third Race to real conscious life, humanity – if it can be so called in its animal, senseless state – was of course doomed to *moral* as well as to physical death. The Angels *fallen into generation* are referred to metaphorically as *Serpents* and *Dragons of Wisdom*. On the other hand, regarded in the light of the LOGOS, the Christian Saviour, like Krishna, whether as man or *Logos*, may be said to have saved those who believed in the secret teachings from "eternal death," to have conquered the Kingdom of Darkness, or Hell, as every Initiate does. This in the human, terrestrial form of the Initiates, and also because the *Logos* is *Christos*, that principle of our inner nature which develops in us into the Spiritual Ego – the Higher-Self – being formed of the indissoluble union of *Buddhi* (the sixth) and the spiritual efflorescence of *Manas*, the fifth principle.[119] "The *Logos* is passive Wisdom in Heaven and Conscious, Self-Active Wisdom on Earth," we are taught. It is the Marriage of "Heavenly man" with the "Virgin of the World" – Nature, as described in *Pymander*, the result of which is their progeny – immortal man. It is this which is called in St. John's *Revelation* the marriage of the lamb with his bride. (xix. 7.) That "wife" is now identified with the Church of Rome owing to the arbitrary interpretations of her votaries. But they seem to forget that her *linen* may be fine and white *outwardly* (like the "whitened sepulchre"), but that the rottenness she is inwardly filled with is not "the righteousness of Saints" (v. 8, *ibid*), but rather the blood of the Saints she has "slain upon the earth" (Chp. xviii, 24.) Thus the remark made by the great Initiate (in *Luke* x, 18) – one that referred allegorically to the ray of Enlightenment and reason, *falling like lightning* from on high into the hearts and *minds* of the converts to that old wisdom-religion then presented in a new form by the wise Galilean Adept[120] – was distorted

---

119 It is not correct to refer to Christ—as some Theosophists do—as the sixth principle in man—*Buddhi*. The latter *per se* is a passive and latent principle, the spiritual vehicle of *Atman*, inseparable from the manifested Universal Soul. It is only in union and in conjunction with *Self-consciousness* that *Buddhi* becomes the Higher Self and the divine, discriminating Soul. *Christos* is the seventh principle, if anything.

120 To make it plainer, any one who reads that passage in *Luke*, will see that the remark follows the report of the *seventy*, who rejoice that "even the devils (the spirit of controversy and reasoning, or the opposing power, since Satan means simply *"adversary"* or *opponent*) are subject unto us through thy name." (*Luke* x, 17) Now, "thy

out of recognition (as was his own personality), and made to fit in with one of the most cruel as the most pernicious of all theological dogmas. (*Vide* at the end of Stanza 11, "Satanic Myths.")

But if Western theology alone holds the patent for, and copyright of Satan – in all the dogmatic horror of that fiction – other nationalities and religions have committed equal errors in their misinterpretation of this tenet, which is one of the most profoundly philosophical and ideal conceptions of ancient thought. For they have both disfigured and hinted at the correct meaning of it in their numerous allegories touching the subject. Nor have the semi-esoteric dogmas of Purânic Hinduism failed to evolve very suggestive symbols and allegories concerning the rebellious and fallen gods. The *Purânas* teem with them, and we find a direct hint at the truth in the frequent allusions of Parâsara (*Vishnu Purâna*) to all those *Rudras, Rishis, Asuras, Kumâras,* and *Munis,* having *to be born in every age,* to re-incarnate in every *Manvantara.* This (esoterically) is equivalent to saying that the FLAMES born of the Universal Mind (*Mahat*), owing to the mysterious workings of Karmic Will and an impulse of Evolutionary Law, had, as in Pymander – without any gradual transition – landed on this Earth, having *broken through the seven Circles of fire,* or the seven intermediate Worlds, in short.

There is an eternal cyclic law of re-births, and the series is headed at every new Manvantaric dawn by those who had enjoyed their rest from re-incarnations in previous *Kalpas* for incalculable *Æons* – by the

name" means the name of *Christos,* or *Logos,* or the spirit of true divine wisdom, as distinct from the spirit of intellectual or mere materialistic reasoning—the HIGHER SELF in short. And when Jesus remarks to this that he has "beheld Satan as lightning fall from heaven," it is a mere statement of his clairvoyant powers, notifying then that he already knew it, and a reference to the incarnation of the divine ray (the gods or angels) which *falls into generation.* For not all men, by any means, benefit by that incarnation, and with some the power remains latent and dead during the whole life. Truly "No man knoweth who the Son is, but the Father; and who the Father is, but the Son" as added by Jesus then and there (*Ibid* v. 22)—the Church "of Christ" less than any one else. The Initiates alone understood the secret meaning of the term "Father and the Son," and knew that it referred to Spirit and Soul on the Earth. For the teachings of Christ were occult teachings, which could only be explained at the initiation. They were never intended for the masses, for Jesus forbade the twelve to go to the Gentiles and the Samaritans (*Matt.* x, 8), and repeated to his disciples that the "mysteries of Heaven" were for them alone, not for the multitudes (*Mark* iv, II).

highest and the earliest *Nirvanees*. It was the turn of those "Gods" to incarnate in the present *Manvantara*; hence their presence on Earth, and the ensuing allegories; hence, also, the perversion of the original meaning.[121] The Gods who had *fallen* into generation, whose mission it was to complete *divine* man, are found represented later on as Demons, evil Spirits, and fiends, at feud and war with Gods, or the irresponsible agents of the one Eternal law. But no conception of such creatures as the devils and Satan of the Christian, Jewish, and Mahomedan religions was ever intended under those thousand and one Aryan allegories.[122] (See *"The Fallen Angels"* and *"The Mystic Dragons"* in Part II.)

The Secret Doctrine, ii 227–232

---

121 So, for instance, in the *Purânas*, "Pulastya," a *Prajâpati*, or son of Brahmâ—the progenitor of the *Râkshasas*, and the grandfather of Ravana, the Great King of Lanka (see *Ramayana*)—had, *in a former birth*, a son named Dattoli, "who is now known as the sage Agastya"—says *Vishnu Purâna*. This name of Dattoli alone, has six more variants to it, or seven meanings. He is called respectively, Dattoi, Dattâli, Dattotti, Dattotri, Dattobhri, Dambhobhi and Dambholi—which seven variants have each a secret sense, and refer in the esoteric comments to various ethnological classifications, and also to physiological and anthropological mysteries of the primitive races. For, surely, the *Râkshasas* are not *demons*, but simply the primitive and ferocious giants, the Atlanteans, who were scattered on the face of the globe as the Fifth Race is now. Va*Sishta* is a warrant to this, if his words addressed to Parâsara, who attempted a bit of JADOO (sorcery), which he calls "sacrifice," for the destruction of the *Râkshasas*, mean anything. For he says, "Let no more of *these unoffending 'Spirits of Darkness'* be destroyed" (see for details *Adiparvan*, s. 176, *Mahabhârata*; also the *Linga Purâna "Purvârdha,"* s. 64.)

122 We have a passage from a Master's letter which has a direct bearing upon these incarnating angels. Says the letter: "Now there are, and there must be, failures in the ethereal races of the many classes of *Dhyan Chohans*, or *Devas (progressed entities of a previous* planetary period), as well as among men. But still, as the *failures* are too far progressed and spiritualized to be thrown back forcibly from Dhyan-Chohanship into the vortex of a new primordial evolution through the lower Kingdoms, this then happens. Where a new solar system has to be evolved, these *Dhyan Chohans* are borne in by influx 'ahead' of the Elementals (Entities . . . to be developed into humanity at a future time) and remain as a latent or inactive spiritual force, in the aura of a nascent world . . . until the stage of human evolution is reached. . . . Then they *become an active force* and commingle with the Elementals, to *develop little by little the full type of humanity."* That is to say, to develop in, and endow man with his Self-conscious mind, or *Manas.*

Selection 18

MAN, THE PALE SHADOW OF GOD

Now, as everything proceeds cyclically, the evolution of man like everything else, the order in which he is generated is described fully in the Eastern teachings, whereas it is only hinted at in the *Kabala*. Says the *Book of Dzyan* with regard to primeval man when first projected by the "Boneless," the incorporeal Creator: "First, the Breath, then *Buddhi*, and the Shadow-Son (the Body) were 'CREATED.' But where was the pivot (the middle principle, *Manas*)? Man is doomed. When alone, the indiscrete (undifferentiated Element) and the *Vahan* (*Buddhi*) — the cause of the causeless — break asunder from manifested life" — "unless cemented and held together by the middle principle, the vehicle of the personal consciousness of JIVA"; explains the Commentary. In other words, the two higher principles can have no individuality on Earth, cannot be man, unless there is (*a*) the Mind, the *Manas*-Ego, to cognize itself, and (*b*) the terrestrial false personality, or the body of egotistical desires and personal Will, to cement the whole, as if round a pivot (which it is, truly), to the physical form of man. It is the Fifth and the Fourth principles [123] — *Manas* and *Kama Rupa* — that contain the dual personality: the real immortal Ego (if it assimilates itself to the two higher) and the false and transitory personality, the mayavi or astral body, so-called, or the animal-human Soul — the two having to be closely blended for purposes of a full terrestrial existence. Incarnate the Spiritual Monad of a Newton grafted on that of the greatest saint on earth — in a physical body the most perfect you can think of — i.e., in a two or even a three-principled body composed of its *Sthula Sarira*, *prana* (life principle), and *linga sarira* — and, if it lacks its middle and fifth principles, you will have created an idiot — at best a beautiful, soul-less, empty and unconscious appearance. "*Cogito — ergo sum*" — can find no room in the brain of such a creature, not on this plane, at any rate.

There are students, however, who have long ago understood the

---

123 The Fourth, and the Fifth from below beginning by the physical body; the Third and the Fourth, if we reckon from *Atma*.

philosophical meaning underlying the allegory — so tortured and disfigured by the Roman Church — of the Fallen Angels. "The Kingdom of Spirits and spiritual action which flows from and is the product of Spirit Volition, is outside and contrasted with and in contradiction to the Kingdom of (divine) Souls and divine action." [124] As said in the text:

> "Like produces like and no more at the *Genesis* of being, and evolution with its limited conditioned laws comes later. The Self-Existent [125] are called CREATIONS, for they appear in the Spirit Ray, manifested through the potency inherent in its UNBORN Nature, which is beyond time and (limited or conditioned) Space. Terrene products, animate and inanimate, including mankind, are falsely called creation and creatures: they are the development (evolution) of the discrete elements." (Com. xiv.)

Again:

> "The Heavenly *rupa* (*Dhyan Chohan*) creates (man) in his own form; it is a spiritual ideation consequent on the first differentiation and awakening of the universal (manifested) Substance; that form is the ideal shadow of Itself: and this is THE MAN OF THE FIRST RACE."

To express it in still clearer form, limiting the explanation to this earth only, it was the duty of the first "differentiated Egos" — the Church calls them Archangels — to imbue primordial matter with the evolutionary impulse and guide its formative powers in the fashioning of its productions. This it is which is referred to in the sentences both in the Eastern and Western tradition —"the Angels were commanded to create." After the Earth had been made ready by the lower and more material powers, and its three Kingdoms fairly started on their way to be "fruitful and multiply," the higher powers, the Archangels or *Dhyanis*, were compelled by the evolutionary Law to descend on Earth, in order to construct the crown of its evolution — MAN. Thus the "Self-created" and the "Self-existent" projected their pale shadows; but group the Third, the Fire-Angels, rebelled and refused to join their Fellow *Devas*.

---

124 *"New Aspects of Life."*

125 Angelic, Spiritual Essences, immortal in their being because unconditioned in Eternity; periodical and conditioned in their Manvantaric manifestations.

Hindu exotericism represents them all as *Yogins*, whose piety inspired them to refuse creating, as they desired to remain eternally *Kumâras*, "Virgin Youths," in order to, if possible, anticipate their fellows in progress towards *Nirvana* — the final liberation. But, agreeably to esoteric interpretation, it was a self-sacrifice for the benefit of mankind. The "Rebels" would not create will-less irresponsible men, as the "obedient" angels did; nor could they endow human beings with only the temporary reflections of their own attributes; for even the latter, belonging to another and a so-much higher plane of consciousness, would leave man still irresponsible, hence interfere with any possibility of a higher progress. No spiritual and psychic evolution is possible on earth — the lowest and most material plane — for one who on that plane, at all events, is inherently perfect and cannot accumulate either merit or demerit. Man remaining the pale shadow of the inert, immutable, and motionless perfection, the one negative and passive attribute of the real I am that I am, would have been doomed to pass through life on earth as in a heavy dreamless sleep; hence a failure on this plane. The Beings, or the Being, collectively called *Elohim*, who first (if ever) pronounced the cruel words, "Behold, the man is become as one of us, to know good and evil; and now, lest he put forth his hand and take also of the tree of life and eat and live for ever . . . " must have been indeed the *Ilda-baoth*, the *Demiurge* of the Nazarenes, filled with rage and envy against his own creature, whose reflection created *Ophiomorphos*. In this case it is but natural — even from the dead letter standpoint — to view Satan, the Serpent of *Genesis*, as the real creator and benefactor, the Father of Spiritual mankind. For it is he who was the "Harbinger of Light," bright radiant Lucifer, who opened the eyes of the automaton created by *Jehovah*, as alleged; and he who was the first to whisper: "in the day ye eat thereof ye shall be as *Elohim*, knowing good and evil" — can only be regarded in the light of a Saviour. An "adversary" to *Jehovah* the "personating spirit," he still remains in esoteric truth the ever-loving "Messenger" (the angel), the *Seraphim* and *Cherubim* who both knew well, and loved still more, and who conferred on us spiritual, instead of physical immortality — the latter a kind of static immortality that would have transformed man into an undying "Wandering Jew."

As narrated in King's "*Gnostics*," "*Ilda-Baoth*, whom several sects regarded as the God of Moses, was not a pure spirit, he was ambitious and proud, and rejecting the spiritual light of the middle space offered him by his mother *Sophia-Achamoth*, he set himself to create a world of his own. Aided by his sons, the six planetary *genii*, he fabricated man, but this one proved a failure. It was a monster, soulless, ignorant, and crawling on all fours on the ground like a material beast. *Ilda-Baoth* was forced to implore the help of his spiritual mother. She communicated to him a ray of her divine light, and so animated man and endowed him with a soul. And now began the animosity of *Ilda-Baoth* toward his own creature. Following the impulse of the divine light, man soared higher and higher in his aspirations; very soon he began presenting not the image of his creator *Ilda-Baoth* but rather that of the Supreme Being, the 'primitive man,' *Ennoia*. Then the *Demiurgos* was filled with rage and envy; and fixing his jealous eye on the abyss of matter, his looks envenomed with passion were suddenly reflected as in a mirror; the reflection became animate, and there arose out of the abyss Satan, serpent, *Ophiomorphos* — 'the embodiment of envy and cunning. He is the union of all that is most base in matter, with the hate, envy, and craft of a spiritual intelligence.' " This is the exoteric rendering of the Gnostics, and the allegory, though a sectarian version, is suggestive, and seems true to life. It is the natural deduction from the dead letter text of chapter iii. of *Genesis*.

Hence the allegory of Prometheus, who steals the divine fire so as to allow men to proceed consciously on the path of spiritual evolution, thus transforming the most perfect of animals on earth into a potential god, and making him free to "take the kingdom of heaven by violence." Hence also, the curse pronounced by Zeus against Prometheus, and by *Jehovah-Il-da-Baoth* against his "rebellious son," Satan. The cold, pure snows of the Caucasian mountain and the never-dying, singeing fire and flames of an extinguishable hell. Two poles, yet the same idea; the dual aspect of a refined torture: a fire producer — the personified emblem of *"phosphoros"* of the astral fire and light in the *anima mundi* — (that element of which the German materialist philosopher Moleschott said: *"ohne phosphor kein gedanke,"* i.e., without phosphorus no thought), burning in the fierce flames of his terrestrial passions; the conflagration fired by his Thought, discerning as it now does good from evil, and yet a slave to the passions of its earthly Adam; feeling the vulture of doubt and full consciousness gnawing at its heart — a Prometheus indeed, because a conscious, hence a responsible entity. [126] The curse

---

126 The history of Prometheus, Karma, and human consciousness, is found further on.

of life is great, yet how few are those men, outside some Hindu and Sufi mystics, who would exchange all the tortures of conscious life, all the evils of a responsible existence, for the unconscious perfection of a passive (objectively) incorporeal being, or even the universal static Inertia personified in Brahmâ during his "night's" rest. For, to quote from an able article by one [127] who, confusing the planes of existence and consciousness, fell a victim to it:

"Satan, or Lucifer, represents the active, or, as M. Jules Baissac calls it, the 'Centrifugal Energy of the Universe' in a cosmic sense. He is Fire, Light, Life, Struggle, Effort, Thought, Consciousness, Progress, Civilization, Liberty, Independence. At the same time he is pain, which is the Re-action of the pleasure of action, and death — which is the revolution of life — Satan, burning in his own hell, produced by the fury of his own momentum — the expansive disintegration of the nebulæ which is to concentrate into new worlds. And fitly is he again and again baffled by the eternal Inertia of the passive energy of the *Kosmos* — the inexorable 'I AM' — the flint from which the sparks are beaten out. Fitly is he . . . and his adherents . . . consigned to the 'sea of fire,' because it is the Sun (in one sense only in the Cosmic allegory), the fount of life in our system, where they are purified (disintegrated) and churned up to re-arrange them for another life (the resurrection); that Sun which, as the origin of the active principle of our Earth, is at once the Home and the Source of the Mundane Satan. . ." To demonstrate furthermore the accuracy of Baissac's general theory (in *Le Diable et Satan*) cold is known to have a 'Centripetal' effect. "Under the influence of cold everything contracts. . . . Under it life hybernates, or dies out, thought congeals, and fire is extinguished. Satan is immortal in his own Fire-Sea — it is only in the '*Nifl-heim*' (the cold Hell of the Scandinavian *Eddas*) of the 'I AM' that he cannot exist. But for all that there is a kind of Immortal

---

127   By an Englishman whose erratic genius killed him. The son of a Protestant clergyman, he became a Mahomedan, then a rabid atheist, and after meeting with a master, a *Guru*, he became a mystic; then a theosophist who doubted, despaired; threw up white for black magic, went insane and joined the Roman Church. Then again turning round, anathematized her, re-became an atheist, and died cursing humanity, knowledge, and God, in whom he had ceased to believe. Furnished with all the esoteric data to write his "War in Heaven," he made a semi-political article out of it, mixing Malthus with Satan, and Darwin with the astral light. Peace be to his – Shell. He is a warning to the *chelas* who fail. His forgotten tomb may now be seen in the Mussulman burial ground of the Joonagad, Kathiawar, in India.

Existence in the *Nifl-heim*, and that existence must be painless and peaceful, because it is Unconscious and Inactive. In the Kingdom of *Jehovah* (if this God were all that the Jews and Christians claim for him) there is no Misery, no War, no marrying and giving in marriage, no change, no Individual Consciousness. [128] All is absorbed in the spirit of the most Powerful. It is emphatically a kingdom of Peace and loyal Submission as that of the 'Arch-Rebel' is one of War and Revolution. . . It (the former) is in fact what Theosophy calls *Nirvana*. But then Theosophy teaches that separation from the Primal Source having once occurred, Re-union can only be achieved by Will Effort — which is distinctly Satanic in the sense of this essay."

It is "Satanic" from the standpoint of orthodox Romanism, for it is owing to the prototype of that which became in time the Christian Devil — to the Radiant Archangels, *Dhyan-Chohans*, who refused to create, because they wanted Man to become his own creator and an immortal god — that men can reach *Nirvana* and the haven of heavenly divine Peace.

To close this rather lengthy comment, the Secret Doctrine teaches that the Fire-*Devas*, the *Rudras*, and the *Kumâras*, the "Virgin-Angels," (to whom Michael and Gabriel, the Archangels, both belong), the divine "Rebels" — called by the all-materializing and positive Jews, the *Nahash* or "Deprived" — preferred the curse of incarnation and the long cycles of terrestrial existence and rebirths, to seeing the misery (even if unconscious) of the beings (evolved as shadows out of their Brethren) through the semi-passive energy of their too spiritual Creators. If "man's uses of life should be such as neither to animalize nor to spiritualize, but to humanize Self," [129] before he can do so, he

---

128 The author talks of the active, fighting, damning *Jehovah* as though he were a synonym of *Parabrahm*! We have quoted from this article to show where it dissents from theosophic teachings; otherwise it would be quoted some day against us, as everything published in the *Theosophist* generally is.

129 Explaining the *Kabala*, Dr. H. Pratt says, "Spirit was to man (to the Jewish Rabbin, rather?) a bodiless, disembodied, or deprived, and degraded being, and hence was termed by the ideograph *Nahash* 'Deprived;' represented as appearing to and seducing the human race – men through the Woman. . . . In the picture from this *Nahash*, this spirit was represented by a serpent, because from its destitution of bodily members, the Serpent was looked upon as a deprived and depraved and degraded creature" ("*New Aspects*," p. 235). Symbol for symbol there are those who would prefer that of the serpent – the symbol of wisdom and eternity, deprived of limbs as it is – to the *Jod* – the poetical

must be born human not angelic. Hence, tradition shows the celestial *Yogis* offering themselves as voluntary victims in order to redeem Humanity — created god-like and perfect at first — and to endow him with human affections and aspirations. To do this they had to give up their natural status and, descending on our globe, take up their abode on it for the whole cycle of the *Mahayuga*, thus exchanging their impersonal individualities for individual personalities — the bliss of sidereal existence for the curse of terrestrial life. This voluntary sacrifice of the Fiery Angels, whose nature was Knowledge and Love, was construed by the exoteric theologies into a statement that shows "the rebel angels hurled down from heaven into the darkness of Hell" — our Earth. Hindu philosophy hints at the truth by teaching that the *Asuras* hurled down by Siva, are only in an intermediate state in which they prepare for higher degrees of purification and redemption from their wretched condition; but Christian theology, claiming to be based on the rock of divine love, charity, and justice of him it appeals to as its Saviour — has invented, to enforce that claim paradoxically, the dreary dogma of hell, that Archimedean lever of Roman Catholic philosophy.

As to Rabbinical Wisdom — than which there is none more positive, materialistic, or grossly terrestrial, as it brings everything down to physiological mysteries — it calls these Beings, the "Evil One;" and the Kabalists — *Nahash*, "Deprived," as just said, and the Souls, that have thrown themselves, after having been alienated in Heaven from the Holy One, into an abyss at the dawn of their very existence, and have anticipated the time when they are to descend on earth. (*Zohar* iii., 61, C.)

And let me explain at once that our quarrel is not with the *Zohar* and the *Kabala* in their right interpretation — for the latter is ours — but only with the gross, pseudo-esoteric explanations of the later, and especially those of the Christian Kabalists.

The Secret Doctrine, ii 241–247

ideograph of Jehovah in the *Kabala* – the god of the male symbol of generation.

Selection 19

THE HINDU PURÂNAS ARE QUITE IN ACCORDANCE WITH PHYSICAL SCIENCE

The writer cannot give *too much* proof that the system of Cosmogony and Anthropogeny as described actually existed, that its records *are* preserved, and that it is found mirrored even in the modern versions of ancient Scriptures.

The *Purânas* on the one hand, and the Jewish Scriptures on the other, are based on the same scheme of evolution, which, read esoterically and expressed in modern language, would be found to be quite as scientific as much of what now passes current as the final word of recent discovery. The only difference between the two schemes is, that the *Purânas*, giving as much and perhaps more attention to the causes than to the effects, allude to the pre-Cosmic and pre-Genetic periods rather than to those of so-called Creation, whereas the *Bible*, saying only a few words of the former period, plunges forthwith into material genesis, and, while nearly skipping the *pre-Adamic* races, proceeds with its allegories concerning the Fifth Race.

Now, whatever the onslaught made on the Order of creation in *Genesis*, and its dead letter account certainly lends itself admirably to criticism,[130] he who reads the Hindu *Purânas* – its allegorical

---

130 Mr. Gladstone's unfortunate attempt to reconcile the Genetic account with science (see "*Nineteenth Century*," "Dawn of Creation," and the "Proem to *Genesis*," 1886) has brought upon him the Jovian thunderbolt hurled by Mr. Huxley. The dead-letter account warranted no such attempt, and his fourfold order, or division of animated creation, has turned into the stone which, instead of killing the fly on the sleeping friend's brow, killed the man instead. Mr. Gladstone killed *Genesis* for ever. But this does not prove that there is no esotericism in the latter. The fact that the Jews and all the Christians, the modern as well as the early sects, have accepted the narrative literally for two thousand years, shows only their ignorance, and shows the great ingenuity and constructive ability of the initiated Rabbis, who have built the two accounts— the Elohistic and the Jehovistic—esoterically, and have purposely confused the meaning by the vowelless glyphs or word-signs in the original text. The six days (*yom*) of creation do mean six periods of evolution, and the seventh that of culmination of perfection (not of rest), and refer to the seven Rounds and

exaggerations notwithstanding – will find them quite in accordance with physical Science.

Even what appears to be the, on the face of it, perfectly nonsensical allegory of Brahmâ assuming the form of a Boar to rescue the Earth from under the waters, finds in the Secret Commentaries a perfectly scientific explanation, relating as it does to the many risings and sinkings, and the constant alternation of water and land from the earliest to the latest geological periods of our globe; for Science teaches us now that nine-tenths of the stratified formations of the earth's crust have been gradually constructed beneath water, at the bottom of the seas. The ancient Aryans are credited with having known nothing whatever of natural history, geology, and so on. The Jewish race is, on the other hand, proclaimed even by its severest critic, an uncompromising opponent of the *Bible* (see "*Modern Science and Modern Thought,*" p. 337), to have the merit of having conceived the idea of monotheism "earlier, and retained it more firmly, than any of the *less philosophical* and *more immoral religions* (! !) of the "ancient world." Only, while we find in Biblical esotericism physiological sexual mysteries symbolised, and very little more (*something for which very little real philosophy is requisite*), in the *Purânas* one may find the most scientific and philosophical "dawn of creation," which, if impartially analyzed and rendered into plain language from its fairy tale-like allegories, would show that modern zoology, geology, astronomy, and nearly all the branches of modern knowledge, have been anticipated in the ancient Science, and were known to the philosophers in their general features, if not in such detail as at present!

Purânic astronomy, with all its deliberate concealment and confusion for the purpose of leading the profane off the real track, was shown even by Bentley to be a real science, and those who are versed in the mysteries of Hindu astronomical treatises will prove that the modern theories of the progressive condensation of nebulæ, nebulous stars, and suns, with the most minute details about the cyclic progress

---

the seven Races with a distinct "creation" in each; though the use of the words *boker*, dawn or morning, and *crib*, evening twilight—which have esoterically the same meaning as *sandhya*, twilight, in Sanskrit—have led to a charge of the most crass ignorance of the order of evolution.

of asterisms – far more correct than Europeans have even now – for chronological and other purposes, were known in India to perfection.

In the Present Round, Man Was on Earth from the Beginning and Preceded the Mammals

If we turn to geology and zoology we find the same. What are all the myths and endless genealogies of the seven *Prajâpati* and their sons, the seven *Rishis* or *Manus*, and of their wives, sons and progeny, but a vast detailed account of the progressive development and evolution of animal creation, one species after the other? Were the highly philosophical and metaphysical Aryans – the authors of the most perfect philosophical systems of transcendental psychology, of Codes of Ethics, and such a grammar as Pânini's, of the *Sankhya* and *Vedanta* systems, and a moral code (Buddhism), proclaimed by Max Müller the most perfect on earth – such fools, or children, as to lose their time in writing *fairy tales*, such tales as the *Purânas* now seem to be in the eyes of those who have not the remotest idea of their secret meaning? What is the *fable*, the genealogy and origin of Kasyapa, with his twelve wives, by whom he had a numerous and diversified progeny of *nagas* (serpents), reptiles, birds, and all kinds of living things, and who was thus the *father* of all kinds of animals, but a *veiled* record of the order of evolution in this round? So far, we do not see that any Orientalist ever had the remotest conception of the truths concealed under the allegories and personifications. "The *Satapatha Brâhmana*," says one, "gives *a not very intelligible* account of Kasyapa's origin. . . He was the son of Marîchi, the Son of Brahmâ, the father of Vivasvat, the father of Manu, the progenitor of mankind. . . . Having assumed the form of a tortoise, *Prajâpati* created offspring. That which he created he made *akarot*, hence the word *kûrma* (tortoise). Kasyapa means tortoise; hence men say, 'All creatures are descendants of Kasyapa,' etc., etc. (*Hindu Classical Dictionary*).

He was all this; he was also the father of Garuda, the bird, the "King of the feathered tribe," who descends *from,* and is of one stock *with the reptiles,* the *nagas,* and who becomes their mortal enemy *subsequently* – as *he is also a cycle, a period of time, when in the course of evolution the birds which developed from reptiles in their "struggle for life," – "survival of the fittest," etc., etc., turned in preference on those they issued from, to devour them* – perhaps prompted by natural law, in order to make room for other and more perfect species. (*Vide* Part II, "Symbolism.")

In that admirable epitome of "*Modern Science and Modern Thought*," a lesson in natural history is offered to Mr. Gladstone, showing the utter variance with it of the *Bible*. The author remarks that Geology, commencing with –

> ". . . the earliest known fossil, the Eozoon Canadense of the Laurentian, continued in a chain, every link of which is firmly welded, through the Silurian, with its abundance of molluscous, crustacean, and vermiform life and first indication of fishes; the Devonian, with its predominance of fish and first appearance of reptiles; the Mesozoic with its batrachians (or frog family); the Secondary formations, in which reptiles of the sea, land and air preponderated, and the first humble forms of vertebrate land animals began to appear; and finally, the Tertiary, in which mammalian life has become abundant, and type succeeding to type and species to species, are gradually differentiated and specialized, through the Eocene, Miocene, and Pliocene periods, until we arrive at the Glacial and Pre-historic periods, and at positive proof of the existence of man."

The same order, *plus* the description of animals unknown to modern science, is found in the commentaries on the *Purânas* in general, and in the *Book of Dzyan* – especially. The only difference, a grave one, no doubt – as implying a spiritual and divine nature of man independent of his physical body in this illusionary world, in which the *false personality* and its cerebral basis alone is known to orthodox psychology – is as follows. Having been in all the so-called "Seven creations," allegorizing the seven evolutionary changes, or the *sub-races*, we may call them, *of the First Root-Race of Mankind* – MAN was on earth in this Round from the beginning. Having passed through all the kingdoms of nature in the previous *three Rounds*,[131] his *physical*

---

131 "Follow the law of analogy"— the Masters teach *Atma-Buddhi* is dual and *Manas* is triple, inasmuch as the former has two aspects, and the latter three, *i.e.* as a principle *per se*, which gravitates, in its higher aspect, to *Atma-Buddhi*, and follows, in its lower nature, *Kama*, the seat of terrestrial and animal desires and passions. Now compare the evolution of the Races, the First and the Second, which are of the nature of *Atma-Buddhi*,

frame – one adapted to the thermal conditions of those early periods – was ready to receive the *divine Pilgrim* at the first dawn of human life, *i.e.* 18,000,000 years ago. It is only at the mid-point of the 3rd Root Race that man was endowed with *Manas*. Once united, the *two* and then the *three* made one; for though the lower animals, from the amoeba to man, received *their* monads, in which all the higher qualities are potential, all have to remain dormant till each reaches its human form, before which stage *Manas* (mind) has no development in them.[132] In the animals every principle is paralysed, and in a foetus-like state, save the second (vital) and the third (the astral) and the rudiments of the fourth (*Kama*, which is desire, instinct), whose intensity and development varies and changes with the species. To the materialist wedded to the Darwinian theory, this will read like a fairy-tale, a mystification; to the believer in the inner, spiritual man, the statement will have nothing unnatural in it.

Now the writer is certain to meet what will be termed insuperable objections. We shall be told that the line of embryology, the gradual development of every individual life, and the progress of what is known to take place in the order of progressive stages of specialization – that all this is opposed to the idea of man preceding mammals. Man begins as the humblest and most primitive vermiform creature, "from the primitive speck of protoplasm and the nucleated cell in which all life originates," and "is developed through stages undistinguishable from those of fish, reptile and mammal, until the cell finally attains the highly specialized development of *the quadrumanous*, and *last of all, of the human type*." (Laing, *op cit*, p. 335.)

This is perfectly scientific, and we have nothing against *that*, for

their passive Spiritual progeny, and the Third Root-Race, which shows three distinct divisions or aspects physiologically and psychically: the earliest, sinless, the middle portions awakening to intelligence, and the third and last decidedly animal, *i.e. Manas* succumbs to the temptations of *Kama*.

132 Men are made complete only during their third, toward the fourth cycle (race). They are made "gods" for good and evil, and responsible only when the two arcs meet (after 3½ rounds towards the fifth Race). They are made so by the *Nirmânakaya* (spiritual or astral remains) of the Rudra-*Kumâras*, "cursed to be reborn on earth again, meaning—doomed in their natural turn to reincarnation in the higher ascending arc of the terrestrial cycle." (*Commentary* IX)

all this relates to the *shell* of man – his body, which in its growth is subject, of course, like every other (once called) morphological unit, to such metamorphoses. It is not those who teach the transformation of the mineral atom through crystallization – which is the same function, and bears the same relation to its *inorganic* (so-called) *upadhi* (or basis) as the formation of *cells* to their organic *nuclei*, through plant, insect, and animal into man – it is not they who will reject this theory, as it will finally lead to the recognition of a Universal Deity in nature, ever-present and as ever invisible, and unknowable, and of *intra*-Cosmic gods, who all were men.[133]

But we would ask, what does science and its exact and now axiomatic discoveries prove against *our* Occult theory? Those who believe in the law of Evolution and gradual progressive development from a cell (which from a *vital* has become a morphological cell, until it awoke as protoplasm pure and simple) – these can surely never limit their belief to one line of evolution. The types of life are innumerable, and the progress of evolution, moreover, does not go at the same rate in every kind of species. The constitution of primordial matter in the Silurian age – we mean "primordial" *matter* of science – is the same in every essential particular, save its degree of present grossness, as the primordial *living* matter of today. Nor do we find that which ought to be found, if the now orthodox theory of Evolution were *quite* correct, namely, a constant, ever-flowing progress in every species of being. Instead of that, what does one see? While the intermediate groups of animal being all tend toward a higher type, and while specializations, now of one type and now of another, develop through the geological ages, change forms, assume new shapes, appear and disappear with a kaleidoscopic rapidity in the description of palæontologists from one period to another, the two solitary exceptions to the general rule are those at the two opposite poles of life and type, namely – MAN *and the lower genera of being!*

"Certain well-marked forms of living beings have existed through enormous epochs, surviving not only the changes of physical

---

133 The whole trouble is this: neither physiologists nor pathologists will recognize that the cell-germinating substance (the *cytoblastema*) and the mother-lye from which crystals originate, are one and the same essence, save in differentiation for purposes.

conditions, *but persisting comparatively unaltered,* while other forms of life have appeared and disappeared. Such forms may be termed 'persistent types' of life, and examples of them are abundant enough in both the animal and the vegetable worlds" (Huxley, *"Proc. of R. Inst.,"* Vol. III, p. 151).

Nevertheless, we are not given any good reason why Darwin links together reptiles, birds, amphibians, fishes, mollusca, etc., etc., as off-shoots of a moneric ancestry. Nor are we told whether reptiles, for instance, are direct descendants of the amphibia, the latter of fishes, and fishes of lower forms – which they certainly are. For the Monads have passed through all these forms of being up to man, on every planet, in the Three *preceding* Rounds; every Round, as well as every subsequent Globe, from A to G, having been, and still having to be the arena of the same evolution, only repeated each time on a more solid material basis. Therefore the question, "What relation is there between the Third Round astral prototypes and ordinary physical development in the course of the origination of pre-mammalian organic species?" is easily answered. One is the shadowy prototype of the other, the preliminary, hardly defined, and evanescent sketch on the canvas of objects which are destined to receive the final and vivid form under the brush of the painter. The fish evolved into an amphibian – a frog – in the *shadows* of ponds, and man passed through all his metamorphoses on this Globe in the Third Round as he did in this, his Fourth Cycle. The Third Round types contributed to the formation of the types in this one. On strict analogy, the cycle of Seven Rounds in their work of the gradual formation of man through every kingdom of Nature are repeated on a microscopical scale in the first seven months of gestation of a future human being. Let the student think over and work out this analogy. As the seven months' old unborn baby, though quite ready, yet needs two months more in which to acquire strength and consolidate, so man, having perfected his evolution during seven Rounds, remains two periods more in the womb of mother-Nature before he is born, or rather reborn a *Dhyani,* still more perfect than he was before he launched forth as a Monad on the newly built chain of worlds. Let the student ponder over this mystery, and then he will easily convince himself that, as there are also physical links between many classes, so there are precise domains wherein the astral merges into physical evolution. Of this Science breathes not one word. Man has evolved with and from the monkey, it says. But now see the contradiction.

THE CONTRADICTIONS OF SCIENCE

Huxley proceeds to point out plants, ferns, club mosses, some of them generically identical with those now living, which are met with in the carboniferous epoch, for "The cone of the oolitic *Araucaria* is hardly distinguishable from that of existing species. . . . . Sub-kingdoms of animals yield the same instances. The *globigerina* of the Atlantic soundings is identical with the cretaceous species of the same genus . . . the tabulate corals of the Silurian epoch are wonderfully like the millepores of our own seas. . . . The *arachnida*, the highest group of which, the scorpions, is represented in the coal by a genus differing only from its living congeners only in . . . the eyes," etc., etc., all of which may be closed with Dr. Carpenter's authoritative statement about the *Foraminifera*. "There is no evidence," he says, "of any fundamental modification or advance in the Foraminiferous type from the palæozoic period to the present time. . . . The Foraminiferous Fauna of our own series probably present a greater range of variety than existed at any previous period; but *there is no indication of any tendency to elevation towards a higher type.*" ("*Introduction to the Study of the Foraminifera,*" p. xi.)

Now, if there is no indication of change in the *Foraminifera*, a *protozoon* of the lowest type of life, mouthless and eyeless, except its greater variety now than before, man, who is on the uppermost rung of the ladder of being, indicates still less change, as we have seen, the skeleton of his Palæolithic ancestor being even found superior in some respects to his present frame. Where is, then, the claimed uniformity of law, the *absolute rule* for one species shading off into another, and, by insensible gradations, into higher types? We see Sir William Thomson admitting as much as 400,000,000 of years in the earth's history, since the surface of the globe became sufficiently cool to permit of the presence of living things;[134] and during that enormous lapse of time in the Oolitic period

---

134   "*Trans. of Geolog. Soc. of Glasgow,*" Vol. III. Very strangely, however, he has just

alone, the so-called "age of reptiles," we find a most extraordinary variety and abundance of Saurian forms, the Amphibian type reaching *its highest developments.* We learn of *Ichthyosauri* and *Plesiosauri* in the lakes and rivers, and of winged crocodiles or lizards flying in the air. After which, in the Tertiary period "we find the Mammalian type exhibiting remarkable divergences from previously existing forms . . . . Mastodons, Megatheriums, and other unwieldy denizens of the ancient forests and plains; and subsequently," are notified of "*the gradual modification of one of the ramifications* of the Quadrumanous order, *into those beings from whom primeval man himself may claim to have been evolved.*" ("*The Beginnings of Life*")

He *may;* but no one, except materialists, can see why he should, as there is not the slightest necessity for it, nor is such an evolution warranted by facts, for those most interested in the proofs thereof confess their utter failure to find one single fact to support their theory. There is no need for the numberless types of life to represent the members of one progressive series. They are "the products of various and different evolutional divergences, taking place now in one direction and now in another." Therefore it is far more justifiable to say that the monkey evolved into the Quadrumanous order, than that primeval man, who has *remained stationary in his human specialization ever since his fossil is found in the oldest strata,* and of whom no variety is found save in colour and facial type has developed from a common ancestor together with the ape.

IDENTITY OF HUMAN AND ANIMAL EMBRYOS

That man originates like other animals in a cell and develops "through stages undistinguishable from those of fish, reptile, and mammal until the cell attains the highly specialized development of the quadrumanous and *at last the human type,*" is an Occult axiom thousands of years old. The Kabalistic axiom: "A stone becomes a plant; a plant a beast; a beast a man; a man a God," holds good throughout the ages. Hæckel, in his *Shöpfungsgeschichte,* shows a double drawing representing two embryos – that of a dog six weeks old, and that of a

changed his opinion. The sun, he says, is only 15,000,000 old.

man, eight weeks. The two, except the slight difference in the head, larger and wider about the brain in the man, are undistinguishable. "In fact, we may say that every human being passes through the stage of fish and reptile before arriving at that of mammal and finally of man. If we take him up at the more advanced stage where the embryo has already passed the reptilian form . . . for a considerable time, the line of development remains the same as that of other *mammalia*. The rudimentary limbs are exactly similar, the five fingers and toes develop in the same way, and the resemblance after the first four weeks' growth *between the embryo of a man and a dog is such that it is scarcely possible to distinguish them*. Even at the age of eight weeks the embryo man is an animal with a tail hardly to be distinguished from an embryo puppy" ("*Modern Science and Modern Thought*," p. 171).

Why, then, not make man and dog evolve from a common ancestor, or from a reptile – *a Naga*, instead of coupling man with the quadrumana? This would be just as logical as the other, and more so. The shape and the stages of the human embryo have not changed since historical times, and these metamorphoses were known to Æsculapius and Hippocrates as well as to Mr. Huxley. Therefore, since the Kabalists had remarked it since prehistoric times, it is no new discovery. In "*Isis Unveiled*," Vol. I, p. 389, it is noticed and half explained.

The Secret Doctrine, ii 251 – 259

Selection 20

THE EMBRYO OF MAN CONTAINS IN ITSELF THE TOTALITY OF THE KINGDOMS OF NATURE

As the embryo of man has no more of the ape in it than of any other mammal, but *contains in itself the totality of the kingdoms of nature*, and since it seems to be "a persistent type" of life, far more so than even the *Foraminifera*, it seems as illogical to make him evolve from the ape as it would be to trace his origin to the frog or the dog. Both Occult and Eastern philosophies believe in evolution, which Manu and Kapila[135] give with far more clearness than any scientist does at present. No need to repeat that which was fully debated in *Isis Unveiled*, as the reader may find all these arguments and the description of the basis on which all the Eastern doctrines of Evolution rested, in our earlier books.[136] But no Occultist can accept the unreasonable proposition that all the now existing forms, "from the structureless Amœba to man," are the direct lineal descendants of organisms which lived millions and millions of years before the birth of man, in the pre-Silurian epochs, in the sea or land-mud.

The Occultists believe in *an inherent law* of progressive *development*.[137] Mr. Darwin never did, and says so himself.

On page 145 of the "*Origin of Species*" we find him stating that, since *there can be no advantage* "to the infusorian animalcule or an intestinal worm . . . to become highly organized," therefore, "natural selection,"

---

135 Hence the philosophy in the allegory of the 7, 10, and finally 21 *Prajâpati, Rishis, Munis*, etc., who all are made the fathers of various things and beings. The order of the seven classes or orders of plants, animals, and even inanimate things, given at random in the *Purânas*, is found in several commentaries in the correct rotation. Thus, Prithu is the father of the Earth. He milks her, and makes her bear every kind of grain and vegetable, all enumerated and specified. Kasyapa is the father of all the reptiles, snakes, demons, etc., etc.

136 See Vol. I, p. 151, *et seq.*, about the tree of evolution, the "Mundane Tree."

137 Checked and modified, however, by the Law of Retardation, which imposes restriction on the advance of all species when a Higher Type makes its appearance.

not including necessarily progressive development – leaves the animalcule and the worm (the "persistent types") quiet.

There does not appear much *uniform* law in such behaviour of Nature, and it looks more like the discriminative action of some *Super*-Natural selection, perhaps that aspect of *Karma*, which Eastern Occultists would call the "Law of Retardation," may have something to do with it.

But there is every reason to doubt whether Mr. Darwin himself ever gave such an importance to *his* law – as is given to it now by his atheistic followers. The knowledge of the various living forms in the geological periods that have gone by is very meagre. The reasons given for this by Dr. Bastian are very suggestive: (1) On account of the imperfect manner in which the several forms may be represented in the strata pertaining to the period; (2) on account of the extremely limited nature of the explorations which have been made in these imperfectly representative strata; and (3) because so many parts of the record are absolutely inaccessible to us – nearly all beneath the Silurian system having been blotted out by time, whilst those two-thirds of the earth's surface in which the remaining strata are to be found are now covered over by seas." Hence Mr. Darwin says himself:

"For my part, following out Lyell's metaphor, I look at the geological record as a history of the world imperfectly kept, and written in a changing dialect; *of this history we possess the last volume alone*, relating only to two or three countries. Of this volume, *only here and there a short chapter has been preserved*, and of each page *only here and there a few lines.*"

A "Missing Link" that Will Prove the Existing Theory Will Never Be Found by Palæontologists

It is not on such meagre data, certainly, that the last word of Science can be said. Nor is it on any ground of human pride or unreasonable belief in man's representing even here on earth – (in *our* period, perhaps) – the highest type of life, that Occultism denies that all the preceding forms of human life belonged to types lower than our own, for it is not so. But simply because the "missing link," such as to prove the existing theory undeniably, will never be found by palæontologists. Believing as we do that man has evolved from, and passed through (during the preceding Rounds), the lowest forms of every life, vegetable and animal, on earth, there is nothing very degrading in the idea of having the orang-outang as an ancestor of our physical form. Quite the reverse; as it would forward the Occult doctrine with regard to the final evolution of everything in terrestrial nature into man, most irresistibly. One may even enquire how it is that biologists and anthropologists, having once firmly accepted the theory of the descent of man from the ape – how it is that they have hitherto left untouched the future evolution of the existing apes into man? This is only a logical sequence of the first theory, unless Science would make of man a privileged being and his evolution a *non*-precedent in nature, quite a *special* and unique case. And that is what all this leads physical Science to. The reason, however, why the Occultists reject the Darwinian, and especially the Hæckelian, hypothesis is because it is the ape which is, in sober truth, a special and unique instance, not man. The pithecoid is *an accidental creation*, a forced growth, the result of an unnatural process.

The occult doctrine is, we think, more logical. It teaches a cyclic, never varying law in nature, the latter having no personal "special design," but acting on a uniform plan that prevails through the whole manvantaric period and deals with the land worm as it deals with man. Neither the one nor the other have sought to come into being, hence both are under the same evolutionary law, and both have to progress according to Karmic law. Both have started from the same neutral centre of Life and both have to re-merge into it at the consummation of the cycle.

It is not denied that in the preceding Round man was a gigantic ape-like creature; and when we say "man" we ought perhaps to say, the rough mould that was developing for the use of man in this Round only – the middle, or the transition point of which we have hardly reached. Nor was man what he is now during the first two and a half Root-Races. That point he reached, as said before, only 18,000,000 years ago, during the secondary period, as we claim.

Till then he was, according to tradition and Occult teaching, "a god on earth who had fallen into matter," or generation. This may or may not be accepted, since the Secret Doctrine does not impose itself as an infallible dogma; and since, whether its prehistoric records are accepted or rejected, it has nothing to do with the question of the *actual* man and his inner nature, the Fall mentioned above having left no original sin on Humanity. But all this has been sufficiently dealt with.

Furthermore, we are taught that the transformations through which man passed on the descending arc – which is centrifugal for spirit and centripetal for matter – and those he prepares to go through, henceforward, on his ascending path, which will reverse the direction of the two forces – *viz.* matter will become centrifugal and spirit centripetal – that all such transformations *are next in store for the anthropoid ape also*, all those, at any rate, who have reached the remove next to man in this Round – and these will all be men in the Fifth Round, as present men inhabited ape-like forms in the Third, the preceding Round.

Behold, then, in the modern denizens of the great forests of Sumatra the degraded and *dwarfed examples* – "blurred copies," as Mr. Huxley has it – of ourselves, as we (the majority of mankind) were in the earliest sub-races of the Fourth Root-Race during the period of what is called the "Fall into generation." The ape we know is not the product of natural evolution but an *accident*, a cross-breed between an animal being, or form, and man. As has been shown in the present volume (Anthropogenesis), it is the speechless animal that first started sexual connection, having been the first to separate into males and females. Nor was it intended by Nature that man should follow the bestial example – as shown by the comparatively painless procreation of their species by the animals, and the terrible suffering and danger of the same in the woman. The Ape is, indeed, as remarked in *Isis Unveiled* (Vol. II, p. 278) "a transformation of species most directly connected with that of the human family – *a hybrid branch engrafted on their own stock before the final perfection of the latter*" – or man. The apes are millions of years later than the speaking human being, and are the latest contemporaries of our Fifth Race. Thus, it is most important to remember that the *Egos* of the apes are entities compelled by their Karma to incarnate in the animal forms, which resulted from the bestiality of the *latest* Third and the earliest Fourth Race men. They are entities who had already reached the "human stage" before this Round. Consequently, they form an exception to the general rule. The numberless traditions about

Satyrs are no fables, but represent an extinct race of animal men. The animal "Eves" were their foremothers, and the human "Adams" their forefathers; *hence the Kabalistic allegory of Lilith or Lilatu*, Adam's *first* wife, whom the Talmud describes as a *charming* woman, *with long wavy hair*, *i.e.* a female hairy animal of a character now unknown, still a female animal, who in the Kabalistic and Talmudic allegories is called the female reflection of Samael, Samael-Lilith, or man-animal united, a being called *Hayo Bischat*, the Beast or Evil Beast (*Zohar*). It is from this unnatural union that the present apes descended. The latter are truly "speechless men," and will become speaking animals (or men of a lower order) in the Fifth Round, while the adepts of a certain school hope that some of the Egos of the apes of a higher intelligence will reappear at the close of the Sixth Root-Race. What their form will be is of secondary consideration. The form means nothing. Species and genera of the flora, fauna, and the highest animal, its crown – man, change and vary according to the environments and climatic variations, not only with every Round, but every Root-Race likewise, as well as after every geological cataclysm that puts an end to, or produces a turning point in the latter. In the Sixth Root-Race, the fossils of the Orang, the Gorilla, and the Chimpanzee will be those of extinct quadrumanous mammals, and new forms – though fewer and ever wider apart as ages pass on and the close of the *Manvantara* approaches – will develop from the "cast off" types of the human races as they revert once again to astral, out of the mire of physical, life. There were none before man, and they will be extinct before the Seventh Race develops. Karma will lead on the monads of the unprogressed men of our race and lodge them in the newly evolved human frames of the thus physiologically regenerated baboon. (But see Part III, *Addenda*.)

This will take place, of course, millions of years hence. But the picture of this cyclic precession of all that lives and breathes now on earth, of each species in its turn, is a true one, and needs no "special creation" or miraculous formation of man, beast, and plant *ex nihilo*.

This is how Occult Science explains the absence of any link between ape and man, and shows the former evolving from the latter.

The Secret Doctrine, ii 259 – 263

Selection 21

THEN THE THIRD EYE ACTED NO LONGER

STANZA X - (Cont'd)

40. THEN THE THIRD AND FOURTH (races) BECAME TALL WITH PRIDE. WE ARE THE KINGS, WE ARE THE GODS (*a*).

41. THEY TOOK WIVES FAIR TO LOOK AT. WIVES FROM THE "MINDLESS," THE NARROW-HEADED. THEY BRED MONSTERS, WICKED DEMONS, MALE AND FEMALE. ALSO KHADO (*Dakini*) WITH LITTLE MINDS (*b*).

42. THEY BUILT TEMPLES FOR HUMAN BODY. MALE AND FEMALE THEY WORSHIPPED (*c*). THEN THE THIRD EYE ACTED NO LONGER (*d*).

(*a*) Such were the first truly physical men, whose first characteristic was - pride! It is the Third Race and the gigantic Atlanteans, the memory of whom lingered from one generation and race to another generation and race down to the days of Moses, and which found an objective form in those antediluvian giants, those terrible sorcerers and magicians, of whom the Roman Church has preserved such vivid and at the same time distorted legends. One who has read and studied the Commentaries on the archaic doctrine, will easily recognise in some Atlanteans, the prototypes of the Nimrods, the Builders of the Tower of Babel, the Hamites, and all these *tutti quanti* of "accursed memory," as theological literature expresses it: of those, in short, who have furnished posterity with the orthodox types of Satan. And this leads us naturally to inquire into the religious ethics of these early races, mythical as these may be.

What was the religion of the Third and Fourth Races? In the common acceptation of the term, neither the Lemurians, nor yet their progeny, the Lemuro-Atlanteans, had any, as they knew no dogma, nor had they to believe on faith. No sooner had the mental eye of man been opened to understanding, than the Third Race felt itself one with the ever-present as the ever to be unknown and invisible ALL, the One

138

Universal Deity. Endowed with divine powers, and feeling in himself his inner God, each felt he was a Man-God in his nature, though an animal in his physical Self. The struggle between the two began from the very day they tasted of the fruit of the Tree of Wisdom; a struggle for life between the spiritual and the psychic, the psychic and the physical. Those who conquered the lower principles by obtaining mastery over the body, joined the "Sons of Light." Those who fell victims to their lower natures, became the slaves of Matter. From "Sons of Light and Wisdom" they ended by becoming the "Sons of Darkness." They had fallen in the battle of mortal life with Life immortal, and all those so fallen became the seed of the future generations of Atlanteans. [138]

At the dawn of his consciousness, the man of the Third Root Race had thus no beliefs that could be called religion. That is to say, he was equally as ignorant of "gay religions, full of pomp and gold" as of any system of faith or outward worship. But if the term is to be defined as the binding together of the masses in one form of reverence paid to those we feel higher than ourselves, of piety - as a feeling expressed by a child toward a loved parent - then even the earliest Lemurians had a religion - and a most beautiful one - from the very beginning of their intellectual life. Had they not their bright gods of the elements around them, and even within themselves? [139] Was not their childhood passed with, nursed and tendered by those who had given them life and called them forth to intelligent, conscious life? We are assured it was so, and we believe it. For the evolution of Spirit into matter could never have been achieved; nor would it have received its first impulse, had not the bright Spirits sacrificed their own respective super-ethereal essences to animate the man of clay, by endowing each of his inner principles with a portion, or rather, a reflection of that essence. The *Dhyanis* of the Seven Heavens (the seven planes of Being) are the NOUMENOI of the actual and the future Elements, just as the Angels of the Seven Powers of nature - the grosser effects of which are perceived by us in what Science is pleased to call the "modes of motion" - the imponderable forces and what not - are the still higher noumenoi of still higher Hierarchies.

---

138 The name is used here in the sense of, and as a synonym of "sorcerers." The Atlantean races were many, and lasted in their evolution for millions of years: all were not bad. They became so toward their end, as we (the fifth) are fast becoming now.

139 The "Gods of the Elements" are by no means the Elementals. The latter are at best used by them as vehicles and materials in which to clothe themselves. . ..

THE GOLDEN AGE

It was the "Golden Age" in those days of old, the age when the "gods walked the earth, and mixed freely with the mortals." Since then, the gods departed (i.e., became invisible), and later generations ended by worshipping their kingdoms - the Elements.

It was the Atlanteans, the first progeny of semi-divine man after his separation into sexes - hence the first-begotten and humanly-born mortals - who became the first "Sacrificers" to the god of matter. They stand in the far-away dim past, in ages more than prehistoric, as the prototype on which the great symbol of Cain was built, [140] as the first anthropomorphists who worshipped form and matter. That worship degenerated very soon into self-worship, thence led to phallicism, or that which reigns supreme to this day in the symbolisms of every exoteric religion of ritual, dogma, and form. Adam and Eve became matter, or furnished the soil, Cain and Abel - the latter the life-bearing soil, the former "the tiller of that ground or field."

Thus the first Atlantean races, born on the Lemurian Continent, separated from their earliest tribes into the righteous and the unrighteous; into those who worshipped the one unseen Spirit of Nature, the ray of which man feels within himself - or the Pantheists, and those who offered fanatical worship to the Spirits of the Earth, the dark Cosmic, anthropomorphic Powers, with whom they made alliance. These were the earliest *Gibborim*, "the mighty men of renown in those days" (*Gen.* vi.); who become with the Fifth Race the *Kabirim*: *Kabiri* with the Egyptians and the Phœnicians, Titans with the Greeks, and *Râkshasas* and *Daityas* with the Indian races.

Such was the secret and mysterious origin of all the subsequent and modern religions, especially of the worship of the later Hebrews for their tribal god. At the same time this sexual religion was closely allied to, based upon and blended, so to say, with astronomical phenomena. The Lemurians gravitated toward the North Pole, or the Heaven of their

---

140 Cain was the sacrificer, as shown at first in chap. iv. of *Genesis*, of "the fruit of the ground," of which he was first tiller, while Abel "brought of the firstlings of his flock" to the Lord. Cain is the symbol of the first male, Abel of the first female humanity, Adam and Eve being the types of the third race. (See "*The Mystery of Cain and Abel*.") The "murdering" is blood-shedding, but not taking life.

Progenitors (the Hyperborean Continent); the Atlanteans, toward the Southern Pole, the pit, cosmically and terrestrially - whence breathe the hot passions blown into hurricanes by the cosmic Elementals, whose abode it is. The two poles were denominated, by the ancients, Dragons and Serpents - hence good and bad Dragons and Serpents, and also the names given to the "Sons of God" (Sons of Spirit and Matter): the good and bad Magicians. This is the origin of this dual and triple nature in man. The legend of the "Fallen Angels" in its esoteric signification, contains the key to the manifold contradictions of human character; it points to the secret of man's self-consciousness; it is the angle-iron on which hinges his entire life-cycle; - the history of his evolution and growth.

On a firm grasp of this doctrine depends the correct understanding of esoteric anthropogenesis. It gives a clue to the vexed question of the Origin of Evil; and shows how man himself is the separator of the ONE into various contrasted aspects.

The reader, therefore, will not be surprised if so considerable space is devoted in each case to an attempt to elucidate this difficult and obscure subject. A good deal must necessarily be said on its symbological aspect; because, by so doing, hints are given to the thoughtful student for his own investigations, and more light can thus be suggested than it is possible to convey in the technical phrases of a more formal, philosophical exposition. The "Fallen Angels," so-called, are Humanity itself. The Demon of Pride, Lust, Rebellion, and Hatred, has never had any being before the appearance of physical conscious man. It is man who has begotten, nurtured, and allowed the fiend to develop in his heart; he, again, who has contaminated the indwelling god in himself, by linking the pure spirit with the impure demon of matter. And, if the Kabalistic saying, *"Demon est Deus inversus"* finds its metaphysical and theoretical corroboration in dual manifested nature, its practical application is found in Mankind alone.

No Devils Outside Humanity

Thus it has now become self-evident that postulating as we do (*a*) the appearance of man before that of other *mammalia*, and even before the ages of the huge reptiles; (*b*) periodical deluges and glacial periods owing to the karmic disturbance of the axis; and chiefly (*c*) the birth of man from a Superior Being, or what materialism would call a supernatural Being, though it is only super-human - it is evident that our teachings have very few chances of an impartial hearing. Add to it the claim that a portion of the Mankind in the Third Race - all those Monads of men who had reached the highest point of Merit and Karma in the preceding *Manvantara* - owed their psychic and rational natures to divine Beings hypostasizing into their fifth principles, and the Secret Doctrine must lose caste in the eyes of not only Materialism but even of dogmatic Christianity. For, no sooner will the latter have learned that those angels are identical with their "Fallen" Spirits, than the esoteric tenet will be proclaimed most terribly heretical and pernicious. [141] The divine man dwelt in the animal, and, therefore, when the physiological separation took place in the natural course of evolution - when also "all the animal creation was untied," and males were attracted to females - that race fell: not because they had eaten of the fruit of Knowledge and knew good from evil, but because they knew no better. Propelled by the sexless creative instinct, the early sub-races had evolved an intermediate race in which, as hinted in the Stanzas, the higher *Dhyan Chohans* had incarnated. [142] "When we have ascertained the extent of the Universe and learnt to know all that there is in it, we will multiply our race," answer the Sons of Will and Yoga to their brethren of the same race, who invite them to do as they do. This means that the great Adepts and Initiated ascetics will "multiply," i.e., once more produce Mind-born immaculate Sons - in the Seventh Root-Race.

It is so stated in the *Purânas*; in *Adi Parvan* (p. 115) and *Brahmâ Purâna*, etc. In one portion of the *Pushkara Mahatmya*, moreover, the separation of the sexes is allegorized by Daksha, who, seeing that his will-born progeny (the "Sons of passive Yoga"), will not create men, "converts half

---

141 It is, perhaps, with an eye to this degradation of the highest and purest Spirits, who broke through the intermediate planes of lower consciousness (the "Seven circles of fire" of Pymander), that St. James is made to say that "this Wisdom (psüche in the original) descended not from above, but is earthly, sensual, devilish"; and Psüche is *Manas*, the "human soul," the Spiritual Wisdom or Soul being *Buddhi*. Yet *Buddhi* per se, being so near the Absolute, is only latent consciousness.

142 This is the "undying race" as it is called in Esotericism, and exoterically the fruitless generation of the first progeny of Daksha, who curses Narada, the divine *Rishi*, alleged to have dissuaded the Haryaswas and the Sabalâswas, the sons of Daksha, from procreating their species, by saying "Be born in the womb; there shall not be a resting place for thee in all these regions"; after this Narada, the representative of that race of fruitless ascetics, is said, as soon as he dies in one body, to be reborn in another.

himself into a female by whom he begets daughters," the future females of the Third Race which begat the giants of Atlantis, the Fourth Race, so called. In the *Vishnu Purâna* it is simply said that Daksha, the father of mankind, established sexual intercourse as the means of peopling the world.

Happily for the human race the "Elect Race" had already become the vehicle of incarnation of the (intellectually and spiritually) highest *Dhyanis* before Humanity had become quite material. When the last sub-races - save some lowest - of the Third Race had perished with the great Lemurian Continent, "the seeds of the Trinity of Wisdom" had already acquired the secret of immortality on Earth, that gift which allows the same great personality to step *ad libitum* from one worn-out body into another.

(*b*) The first war that earth knew, the first human gore shed, was the result of man's eyes and senses being opened; which made him see that the daughters of his Brethren were fairer than his own, and their wives also. There were rapes committed before that of the Sabines, and Menelauses robbed of their Helens before the Fifth Race was born. Titans or giants were the stronger; their adversaries, the wiser. This took place during the Fourth Race - that of the giants.

For "there were giants" in the days of old, indeed [143] and the evolutionary series of the animal world is a warrant that the same thing took place within the human races. Lower still in the order of creation we find witnesses for the same in the flora going *pari passu* with the fauna in respect of size. The pretty ferns we collect and dry among the leaves of our favourite volumes are the descendants of the gigantic ferns which grew during the carboniferous period.

Scriptures, and fragments of philosophical and scientific works - in short, almost every record that has come down to us from antiquity -

---

143   The traditions of every country and nation point to this fact. Donnelly quotes from Father Duran's *Historia Antigua de la Nueva Espana* of 1885, in which a native of Cholula, a centenarian, accounts for the building of the great pyramid of Cholula, by saying as follows: "In the beginning, before the light of the Sun had been created, this land (Cholula) was in obscurity and darkness . . . but immediately after the light of the Sun arose in the East, there appeared gigantic men . . .who built the said pyramid, its builders being scattered after that to all parts of the Earth."

"A great deal of the Central American history is taken up with the doings of an ancient race of giants called Quinanes," says the author of *"Atlantis"* (p. 204.)

contain references to giants. No one can fail to recognize the Atlanteans of the Secret Doctrine in the *Râkshasas* of Lanka - the opponents conquered by Rama. Are these accounts no better than the production of empty fancy? Let us give the subject a few moments of attention.

ARE GIANTS A FICTION?

Here, again, we come into collision with Science. The latter denies, so far, that man has ever been much larger than the average of the tall and powerful men one meets with occasionally now. Dr. Henry Gregor denounces such traditions as resting upon ill-digested facts. Instances of mistaken judgments are brought forward. Thus, in 1613, in a locality called from time immemorial the "Field of Giants" in the Lower Dauphine (France, four miles from St. Romans) enormous bones were found deeply buried in the sandy soil. They were attributed to human remains, and even to Teutobochus, the Teuton chief slain by Marius. But Cuvier's later research proved them to be the fossil remains of the *Dinotherium giganteum* of the family of tapirs, 18 feet long. Ancient buildings are pointed to as an evidence that our earliest ancestors were not much larger than we are, the entrance doors being of no larger size then than they are now. The tallest man of antiquity known to us was the Roman Emperor Maximus, we are told, whose height was only seven and a half feet. Nevertheless, in our modern day we see every year men taller than this. The Hungarian who exhibited himself in the London Pavilion was nearly 9 feet high. In America a giant was shown 9 ½ feet tall; the Montenegrin Danilo was 8 feet 7 inches. In Russia and Germany one often sees men in the lower classes above 7 feet. And as the ape-theorists are told by Mr. Darwin that the species of animals which result from cross breeding "always betray a tendency to revert to the original type," they ought to apply the same law to men. Had there been no giants as a rule in ancient days, there would be none now.

All this applies only to the historic period. And if the skeletons of the prehistoric ages have failed so far (which is positively denied) to prove undeniably in the opinion of science the claim here advanced, it is but a question of time. Moreover, as already stated, human stature is little changed since the last racial cycle. The Giants of old are all buried under the Oceans, and hundreds of thousands of years of constant friction by water would reduce to dust and pulverize a brazen, far more a human skeleton. But whence the testimony of well-known classical writers, of philosophers and men who, otherwise, never had the reputation for lying? Let us bear in mind, furthermore, that before the year 1847, when Boucher de Perthes forced it upon the attention of Science, almost nothing was known of fossil man, for archæology complacently ignored his existence. Of Giants who were "in the earth in those days" of old, the *Bible* alone had spoken to the wise men of the West, the Zodiac being the solitary witness called upon to corroborate the statement in the persons of Atlas or Orion, whose mighty shoulders are said to support the world.

Nevertheless, even the "Giants" have not been left without their witnesses, and one may as well examine both sides of the question. The three Sciences - Geological, Sidereal and Scriptural (the latter in its Universal character) - may furnish us with the needed proofs. To begin with geology; it has already confessed that the older the excavated skeletons, the larger, taller and the more powerful their structure. This is already a certain proof in hand. "All those bones" writes Frederic de Rougemont - who, though believing too piously in Noah's ark and the *Bible*, is none the less a Scientific witness - "all those skeletons found in the Departments of the Gard, in Austria, Liege, etc., etc. . . those skulls which remind all of the negro type. . . and which by reason of that type might be mistaken for animals, have all belonged to men of very high stature". . . ("*Histoire de la Terre,*" p. 154) The same is repeated by Lartet, an authority, who attributes a tall stature to those who were submerged in the deluge (not necessarily "Noah's") and a smaller stature to the races which lived subsequently.

As for the evidence furnished by ancient writers, we need not stop at that of Tertullian, who assures us that in his day a number of giants were found at Carthage - for, before his testimony can be accepted, his own identity [144] and actual existence would have to be proven. But we may turn to the scientific journals of 1858, which spoke of a sarcophagus of giants found that year on the site of that same city. As

---

144 There are critics who, finding no evidence about the existence of Tertullian save in the writings of Eusebius "the veracious," are inclined to doubt it.

to the ancient pagan writers - we have the evidence of Philostratus, who speaks of a giant skeleton twenty-two cubits long, as well as of another of twelve cubits, seen by himself at Sigeus. This skeleton may perhaps not have belonged, as believed by Protesilaus, to the giant killed by Apollo at the siege of Troy; nevertheless, it was that of a giant, as well as that other one discovered by Messecrates of Stire, at Lemnos - "horrible to behold," according to Philostratus (*Heroica*, p. 35). Is it possible that prejudice would carry Science so far as to class all these men as either fools or liars?

Pliny speaks of a giant in whom he thought he recognised Orion, the son of Ephialtes (*Nat. Hist.*, vol. VII, ch. xvi.). Plutarch declares that Sertorius saw the tomb of Antæus, the giant; and Pausanias vouches for the actual existence of the tombs of Asterius and of Geryon, or Hillus, son of Hercules - all giants, Titans and mighty men. Finally the Abbé Pègues (cited in de Mirville's *Pneumatologie*) affirms in his curious work on "The Volcanoes of Greece" that "in the neighbourhood of the volcanoes of the isle of Thera, giants with enormous skulls were found laid out under colossal stones, the erection of which must have necessitated everywhere the use of titanic powers, and which tradition associates in all countries with the ideas about giants, volcanoes and magic." (Page 48.)

In the same work above cited of the Abbé Pègues, the author wonders why in *Bible* and tradition the *Gibborim*, (Giants, the mighty ones) the *Rephaim*, or the spectres (Phantoms), the *Nephilim*, or the fallen ones - (*irruentes*) - are shown "as if identical, though they are all men, since the *Bible* calls them the primitive and the mighty ones" - e.g., Nimrod. The "Doctrine" explains the secret. These names, which belong by right only to the four preceding races and the earliest beginning of the Fifth, allude very clearly to the first two Phantom (astral) races; to the fallen one - the Third; and to the race of the Atlantean Giants - the Fourth, after which "men began to decrease in stature."

Bossuet (*Elevations*, p. 56) sees the cause of subsequent universal idolatry in the "original sin." "Ye shall be as gods," says the serpent of *Genesis* to Eve, thus laying the first germ of the worship of false divinities. Hence, he thinks, came idolatry, or the cult and adoration of images, of anthropomorphized or human figures. But, if it is the latter that idolatry is made to rest upon, then the two Churches, the Greek and the Latin especially, are as idolatrous and pagan as any other religion. [145] It is only in the Fourth Race that men, who had lost all right to be considered divine, resorted to body worship, in other words to phallicism. Till then, they had been truly gods, as pure and as divine as their progenitors, and the expression of the allegorical serpent does not, as sufficiently shown in the preceding pages, refer at all to the physiological fall of men, but to their acquiring the knowledge of good and evil, which knowledge comes to them prior to their fall. It must not be forgotten that it is only after his forced expulsion from Eden that "Adam knew Eve his wife" (*Genesis*, iv.). It is not, however, by the dead-letter of the Hebrew *Bible* that we shall check the tenets of the Secret Doctrine; but point out, rather, the great similarities between the two in their esoteric meaning.

It is only after his defection from the Neo-Platonists, that Clement of Alexandria began to translate *gigantes* by *serpentes*, explaining that "Serpents and Giants signify Demons." (*Genesis*, chapter v.) [146]

---

145 And that, notwithstanding the formal prohibition at the great Church Council of Elyrus in A.D. 303, when it was declared that "the form of God, which is immaterial and invisible, shall not be limited by figure or shape." In 692, the council of Constantinople had similarly prohibited "to paint or represent Jesus as a lamb," as also "to bow the knee in praying, as it is the act of idolatry." But the council of Nicæa (787) brought this idolatry back, while that of Rome (883) excommunicated John, the Patriarch of Constantinople, for his showing himself a declared enemy of image worship.

146 Treating of the Chinese Dragon and the literature of China, Mr. Ch. Gould writes in his "*Mythical Monsters*" on p. 212: - "Its mythologies, histories, religions, popular stories and proverbs, all teem with references to a mysterious being who has a physical nature and spiritual attributes. Gifted with an accepted form, which he has the supernatural power of casting off for the assumption of others, he has the power of influencing the weather, producing droughts or fertilizing rains at pleasure, of raising tempests and allaying them. Volumes could be compiled from the scattered legends which everywhere abound relating to this subject. . . "
This "mysterious being" is the mythical Dragon, i.e., the symbol of the historical, actual Adept, the master and professor of occult sciences of old. It is stated already elsewhere, that the great "magicians" of the Fourth and Fifth Races were generally called the "Serpents" and the "Dragons" after their progenitors. All these belonged to the hierarchy of the so-called "Fiery Dragons of Wisdom," the *Dhyan Chohans*, answering to the *Agnishwatta Pitris*, the *Maruts* and *Rudras* generally, as the issue of Rudra their father, identified with the god of fire. More is said in the text. Now Clement, an initiated Neo-Platonist, knew, of course, the origin of the word "Dragon," and why the initiated Adepts were so-called, as he knew the secret of *Agathodæmon*, the Christ, the seven-vowelled Serpent of the Gnostics. He knew that the dogma of his new faith required the transformation of all the rivals of Jehovah, the angels supposed to have rebelled against that *Elohim* as the Titan-Prometheus rebelled against Zeus, the usurper of his father's kingdom; and that "Dragon" was the mystic appellation of the "Sons of Wisdom"; from

We may be told that, before we draw parallels between our tenets and those of the *Bible*, we have to show better evidence of the existence of the giants of the Fourth Race than the reference to them found in *Genesis*. We answer, that the proofs we give are more satisfactory, at any rate they belong to a more literary and scientific evidence, than those of Noah's Deluge will ever be. Even the historical works of China are full of such reminiscences about the Fourth Race. In Shoo-King (4th part, chap. XXVII, p. 291), anyone can read in the French translation, "When the Mao-tse" ("that antediluvian and perverted race," explains the Annotator, "which had retired in the days of old to the rocky caves, and the descendants of whom are said to be still found in the neighbourhood of Canton"), [147] "according to our ancient documents, had, owing to the beguilements of Tchy-Yeoo, troubled all the earth, it became full of brigands." The Lord Chang-ty (a king of the divine dynasty) saw that his people had lost the last vestiges of virtue. Then he commanded Tehong and Lhy (two lower *Dhyan Chohans*) to cut away every communication between heaven and earth. Since then, there was no more going up and down!" [148]

"Going up and down" means an untrammelled communication and intercourse between the two worlds. Not being in a position to give out a full and detailed history of the Third and Fourth Races, as many isolated facts concerning them as are permitted must be now collated together; especially those corroborated by direct as well as by inferential evidence found in ancient literature and history. As the

this knowledge came his definition, as cruel as it was arbitrary, "Serpents and Giants signify Demons," i.e., not "Spirits," but Devils, in Church parlance.

147 "What would you say to our affirmation that the Chinese - I speak of the inland, the true Chinaman, not of the hybrid mixture between the Fourth and Fifth Races now occupying the throne, the aborigines who belong in their unallied nationality wholly to the highest and last branch of the Fourth Race - reached their highest civilization when the Fifth had hardly appeared in Asia" (*Esoteric Buddhism*, p. 67). And this handful of the inland Chinese are all of a very high stature. Could the most ancient MSS. in the Lolo language (that of the aborigines of China) be got at and translated correctly, many a priceless piece of evidence would be found. But they are as rare as their language is unintelligible. So far, one or two European archæologists only have been able to procure such priceless works.

148 Remember the same statement in the *Book of Enoch*, as also the ladder seen by Jacob in his dream. The "two worlds" mean of course the "two planes of Consciousness and Being." A seer can commune with beings of a higher plane than the earth, without quitting his arm-chair.

"coats of skin" of men thickened, and they fell more and more into physical sin, the intercourse between physical and ethereal divine man was stopped. The veil of matter between the two planes became too dense for even the inner man to penetrate. The mysteries of Heaven and Earth, revealed to the Third Race by their celestial teachers in the days of their purity, became a great focus of light, the rays from which became necessarily weakened as they were diffused and shed upon an uncongenial, because too material soil. With the masses they degenerated into Sorcery, taking later on the shape of exoteric religions, of idolatry full of superstitions, and man-, or hero-worship. Alone a handful of primitive men - in whom the spark of divine Wisdom burnt bright, and only strengthened in its intensity as it got dimmer and dimmer with every age in those who turned it to bad purposes - remained the elect custodians of the Mysteries revealed to mankind by the divine Teachers. There were those among them, who remained in their Kumâric condition from the beginning; and tradition whispers, what the secret teachings affirm, namely, that these Elect were the germ of a Hierarchy which never died since that period:

"The inner man of the first * * * only changes his body from time to time; he is ever the same, knowing neither rest nor *Nirvana*, spurning *Devachan* and remaining constantly on Earth for the salvation of mankind.. . ." "Out of the seven virgin-men (*Kumâra* [149]) four sacrificed themselves for the sins of the world and the instruction of the ignorant, to remain till the end of the present *Manvantara*. Though unseen, they are ever present. When people say of one of them, "He is dead"; behold, he is alive and under another form. These are the Head, the Heart, the Soul, and the Seed of undying knowledge (*Gnyana*). Thou shalt never speak, O Lanoo, of these great ones (*Maha* . . .) before a multitude, mentioning them by their names. The wise alone will understand." . . (*Catechism of the Inner Schools.*)

The Secret Doctrine, ii 271 – 282

---

[149] *Vide supra* the Commentary on the Four Races - and on the "Sons of Will and Yoga," the immaculate progeny of the Androgynous Third Race.

Selection 22

Neither the Human Atlantean Giants nor the "Animals" Were the Physiologically Perfect Men and Mammalians that Are Now Known to Us

Yet the "Lemurians" and the Atlanteans, "those children of Heaven and Earth," were indeed marked with a character of SORCERY, for the Esoteric doctrine charges them precisely with that, which, if believed, would put an end to the difficulties of science with regard to the origin of man, or rather, his anatomical similarities to the *Anthropoid Ape*. It accuses them of having committed the (to us) abominable crime of breeding with so-called "animals," and thus producing a truly pithecoid species, now extinct. Of course, as in the question of spontaneous generation – in which Esoteric Science believes, and which it teaches – the possibility of such a cross-breed between man and an animal of any kind will be denied. But apart from the consideration that in those early days, as already remarked, neither the human Atlantean giants, nor yet the "animals," were the physiologically perfect men and mammalians that are now known to us, the modern notions upon this subject – those of the physiologists included – are too uncertain and fluctuating to permit them an absolute denial *a priori* of such a fact.

A careful perusal of the Commentaries would make one think that the Being that the new *"incarnate"* bred with, was called an "animal," not because he was no human being, but rather because he was so dissimilar physically and mentally to the more perfect races, which had developed physiologically at an earlier period. Remember Stanza 7 and what is said in its first verse (24th), that when the "Sons of Wisdom" came to incarnate the first time, some of them incarnated fully, others projected into the forms only *a spark*, while some of the shadows were left over from being *filled* and perfected, till the Fourth Race. Those races, then, which "remained destitute of knowledge," or those again which were left "mindless," remained as they were, even after the natural separation of the sexes. It is these who committed the first crossbreeding, so to speak, and bred monsters, and it is from the descendants of these that the Atlanteans chose their wives. Adam and Eve were supposed, with Cain and Abel, to be the only *human* family on Earth. Yet we see Cain going to the land of Nod and taking there a wife. Evidently one race only was supposed perfect enough to be called human, and, even in our own day, while the Singhalese regard the Veddhas of their jungles as *speaking animals* and no more, some British people believe firmly, in their arrogance, that every other human family – especially the dark Indians – is an *inferior* race. Moreover there are naturalists who have sincerely considered the problem whether some savage tribes – like the Bushmen for instance – can be regarded as men at all. The *Commentary* says, in describing that species (or race) of animals "fair to look at" as a biped, "*Having human shape, but having the lower extremities, from the waist down, covered with hair.*" Hence the race of the *satyrs*, perhaps.

If men existed two million years ago, they must have been – just as the animals were – quite different physically and anatomically from what they have become; and they were nearer then to the type of pure mammalian animal than they are now. Anyhow, we learn that the animal world breeds strictly *inter se, i.e.* in accordance with genus and species – only since the appearance *on this earth* of the Atlantean race. As demonstrated by the author of that able work, "*Modern Science and Modern Thought*," this idea of the refusal to breed with another species, or that sterility is the only result of such breeding, "appears to be a *primâ facie* deduction rather than an absolute law" even now. He shows that "different species, do, in fact, often breed together, as may be seen in the familiar instance of the horse and ass. It is true that in this case the mule is sterile. . . . but this rule is not universal, and recently one new hybrid race, that of the leporine, or hare-rabbit, has been created which is perfectly fertile." The progeny of wolf and dog is also instanced, as that of several other domestic animals (p. 101), "like foxes and dogs again, and the modern Swiss cattle shown by Rutimeyer as descended from three distinct species of fossil-oxen, the *Bos primigenius, Bos longifrons and Bos frontosus.*" *Yet some of those species, as the ape family, which so clearly resembles man in physical structure,* contain, we are told, "numerous branches, which graduate into one another, but the extremes of which differ more widely than man does from the highest of the ape series" – the gorilla and chimpanzee, for instance (see *Addenda*).

Thus Mr. Darwin's remark – or shall we say the remark of Linnæus? – *natura non facit saltum*, is not only corroborated by Esoteric Science but would – were there any chance of the real doctrine being accepted by any others than its direct votaries – reconcile in more than one way, if not entirely, the modern Evolution theory with facts, as also with the absolute failure of the anthropologists to meet with the "missing link" in our Fourth Round geological formations.

We will show elsewhere that, however unconsciously to itself, modern Science pleads our case upon its own admissions, and that de Quatrefages is perfectly right, when he suggests in his last work, that it is far more likely that the anthropoid ape should be discovered to be *the descendant of man*, than that these two types should have a common, fantastic and nowhere-to-be-found ancestor. Thus the wisdom of the compilers of the old Stanzas is vindicated by at least one eminent man of Science, and the Occultist prefers to believe as he ever did that –

"Man was the first and highest (mammalian) *animal that appeared in this* (Fourth Round) *creation. Then came still huger animals; and last of all the dumb man who walks on all fours." For, the Râkshasas* (giant-demons) *and Daityas* (Titans) *of the "White Dwipa"* (continent) *spoiled his* (the dumb man's) *Sires." (Commentary)*

Furthermore, as we see, there are anthropologists who have traced man back to an epoch which goes far to break down the apparent barrier that exists between the chronologies of modern science and the Archaic Doctrine. It is true that English scientists generally have declined to commit themselves to the sanction of the hypothesis of even a Tertiary Man. They, each and all, measure the antiquity of *Homo primigenius* by their own lights and prejudices. Huxley, indeed, ventures to speculate on a possible Pliocene or Miocene Man. Prof. Seeman and Mr. Grant Allen have relegated his advent to the Eocene, but speaking generally, English scientists consider that we cannot safely go beyond the Quaternary. Unfortunately, the facts do not accommodate the too cautious reserve of these latter. The French school of anthropology, basing their views on the discoveries of l'Abbé Bourgeois, Capellini, and others, has accepted, almost without exception, the doctrine that the traces of our ancestors are certainly to be found in the Miocene, while M. de Quatrefages now inclines to postulate a Secondary-Age Man. Further on we shall compare such estimates with the figures given in the Brahminical exoteric books which approximate to the esoteric teaching.

The Secret Doctrine, ii 286 – 288

Selection 23

It Was the Belief of Entire Antiquity, Pagan and Christian, that the Earliest Mankind Was a Race of Giants

It was the belief of entire antiquity, Pagan and Christian, that the earliest mankind was a race of giants. Certain excavations in America in mounds and in caves, have already yielded in isolated cases groups of skeletons of nine and twelve feet high.[150] These belong to tribes of the early Fifth Race, now degenerated to an average size of between five and six feet. But we can easily believe that the Titans and Cyclopes of old really belonged to the Fourth (Atlantean) Race, and that all the subsequent legends and allegories found in the Hindu *Purânas* and the Greek Hesiod and Homer were based on the hazy reminiscences of real Titans – men of a superhuman tremendous physical power, which enabled them to defend themselves, and hold at bay the gigantic monsters of the Mesozoic and early Cenozoic times – and of actual Cyclopes – three-eyed mortals.

It has been often remarked by observant writers that the "origin of nearly every popular myth and legend could be traced invariably to a fact in Nature."

In these fantastic creations of an exuberant subjectivism, there is always an element of the objective and real. The imagination of the masses, disorderly and ill-regulated as it may be, could never have conceived and fabricated *ex nihilo* so many monstrous figures, such a wealth of extraordinary tales, had it not had, to serve it as a central nucleus, those floating reminiscences, obscure and vague, which unite the broken links of the chain of time to form with them the mysterious,

---

150 Darwinian Evolutionists who are so wont to refer to the evidence of *reversion to type*—the full meaning of which, in the case of human monsters, is embraced in the esoteric solution of the embryological problem—as proof of their arguments, would do well to inquire into those instances of *modern giants* who are often 8, 9, and even 11 feet high. Such *reversions* are imperfect, yet undeniable reproductions of the original towering man of primeval times.

dream foundation of our collective consciousness.[151]

The evidence for the Cyclopes – a race of giants – will be pointed out in forthcoming Sections, in the Cyclopean remnants, so called to this day. An indication that, during its evolution and before the final adjustment of the human organism – which became perfect and symmetrical only in the Fifth Race – the early Fourth Race may have been three-eyed, without having necessarily a third eye in the middle of the brow, like the legendary Cyclops, is also furnished by Science.

To the Occultists who believe that spiritual and psychic *involution* proceeds on parallel lines with physical *evolution*; that the *inner* senses – innate in the first human races – atrophied during racial growth and the material development of the outer senses; to the student of Esoteric symbology, finally, this statement is no conjecture or possibility, but simply *a phase of the law of growth, a proven fact* in short. They understand the meaning of this passage in the *Commentaries* which says:

"*There were four-armed human creatures in those early days of the male-females* (hermaphrodites); *with one head yet three eyes. They could see before them and behind them.*[152] A KALPA *later* (after the separation of the sexes) *men having fallen into matter, their spiritual vision became dim, and coördinately the third eye commenced to lose its power.* . . . *When the Fourth* (Race) *arrived at its middle age, the inner vision had to be awakened and acquired by artificial stimuli, the process of which was known to the old sages.*[153] . . . *The third eye likewise, getting gradually* PETRIFIED[154], SOON

---

151 See "*Mythical Monsters,*" by Ch. Gould, from whose interesting and scientific volume a few passages are quoted further on. See in Mr. Sinnett's "*Occult World*" the description of a cavern in the Himalayas filled with relics of human and animal giant bones.

152 *Viz.* the third eye was at the back of the head. The statement that the latest hermaphrodite humanity was "four-armed" unriddles probably the mystery of all the representations and idols of the exoteric gods of India. On the Acropolis of Argos, there was a ξόvov, a rudely carved wooden statue (attributed to Dædalus), representing a three-eyed colossus, which was consecrated to Zeus *Triopas* (three-eyed). The head of the " god" has two eyes in its face and one above on the top of the forehead. It is considered the most archaic of all the ancient statues (*Schol. Vatic. ad Eurip. Troad.* 14).

153 The *Inner sight* could henceforth be acquired only through training and initiation, save in the cases of "natural and born magicians," sensitives and mediums, as they are called now.

154 This expression "petrified" instead of "ossified" is curious. The "back eye," which is of course the *pineal gland*, now so-called, the small pea-like mass of grey nervous matter attached to the back of the third ventricle of the brain, is said to almost invariably

DISAPPEARED. THE DOUBLE-FACED BECAME THE ONE-FACED, AND THE EYE WAS DRAWN DEEP INTO THE HEAD AND IS NOW BURIED UNDER THE HAIR. DURING THE ACTIVITY OF THE INNER MAN (DURING TRANCES AND SPIRITUAL VISIONS) THE EYE SWELLS AND EXPANDS. THE ARHAT SEES AND FEELS IT AND REGULATES HIS ACTION ACCORDINGLY . . . THE UNDEFILED LANOO (DISCIPLE, CHELA) NEED FEAR NO DANGER; HE WHO KEEPS HIMSELF NOT IN PURITY (WHO IS NOT CHASTE) WILL RECEIVE NO HELP FROM THE 'DEVA EYE.'"

THE THIRD EYE IS DEAD AND ACTS NO LONGER, BUT IT HAS LEFT BEHIND A WITNESS TO ITS EXISTENCE

Unfortunately not. The "deva-eye" exists no more for the majority of mankind. The *third eye is dead,* and acts no longer, but it has left behind a witness to its existence. This witness is now the PINEAL GLAND. As for the "four-armed" men, it is they who become the prototypes of the four-armed Hindu gods, as shown in a preceding footnote.

Such is the mystery of the human eye that, in their vain endeavours to explain and account for all the difficulties surrounding its action, some scientists have been forced to resort to occult explanations. The development of the *Human eye* gives more support to the occult anthropology than to that of the materialistic physiologists. "The eyes in the human embryo *grow from within without*" out of the brain, instead of being part of the skin, as in the insects and cuttlefish. Professor Lankester, thinking the brain a queer place for the eye, and attempting to explain the phenomenon on *Darwinian lines*, suggests the curious view that "our" earliest vertebrate ancestor was a *transparent* creature and hence did not mind where the eye was! And so was man "a transparent creature" once upon a time, we are taught; hence our theory holds good. But how does the Lankester hypothesis square with the Haeckelian view that the vertebrate eye originated by changes *in the epidermis*? If it started *inside*, the theory goes into the wastebasket. This seems to be proved by embryology. Moreover, Professor Lankester's extraordinary suggestion – or shall we say admission? – is rendered perhaps necessary by evolutionist necessities. Occultism with its teaching as to the gradual development of senses "FROM WITHIN WITHOUT," from astral

---

contain *mineral concretions* and *sand*, and "nothing more." (*Vide Infra.*)

prototypes, is far more satisfactory: The *third eye retreated inwards* when its course was run – another point in favour of Occultism.

The allegorical expression of the Hindu mystics when speaking of the "eye of Siva," the *Tri-bochana* ("three-eyed"), thus receives its justification and *raison d'être* – the transference of the pineal gland (once that "third eye") to the forehead, being an exoteric licence. This throws also a light on the mystery – incomprehensible to some – of the connection between *abnormal*, or Spiritual Seership, and the physiological purity of the Seer. The question is often asked, " Why should celibacy and chastity be a *sine quâ non* rule and condition of regular *chelaship*, or the development of psychic and occult powers? The answer is contained in the *Commentary*. When we learn that the "third eye" was once a physiological organ, and that later on, owing to the gradual disappearance of spirituality and increase of materiality (Spiritual nature being extinguished by the physical), it became an atrophied organ, as little understood now by physiologists as the spleen is; when we learn this, the connection will become clear. During human life the greatest impediment in the way of spiritual development, and especially to the acquirement of *Yoga* powers, is the activity of our physiological senses. Sexual action being closely connected, by interaction, with the spinal cord and the grey matter of the brain, it is useless to give any longer explanation. Of course, the normal and abnormal state of the brain and the degree of active work in the *medulla oblongata* reacts powerfully on the pineal gland, for, owing to the number of "centres" in that region, which controls by far the greater majority of the physiological actions of the animal economy, and also owing to the close and intimate neighbourhood of the two, there must be exerted a very powerful "inductive" action by the *medulla* on the pineal gland.

All this is quite plain to the Occultist, but is very vague in the sight of the general reader. The latter must then be shown the possibility of a three-eyed man in nature, in those periods when his formation was yet in a comparatively chaotic state. Such a possibility may be inferred from anatomical and zoological knowledge, first of all, then it may rest on the assumptions of materialistic science itself.

It is asserted upon the authority of Science, and upon evidence, which is not merely a fiction of theoretical speculation this time, that many of the animals – especially among the lower orders of the *vertebrata* – *have* a third eye, now atrophied, but necessarily active in its origin.[155] The *Hatteria* species, a lizard of the order *Lacertilia*, recently discovered in New Zealand (*a part of ancient Lemuria so called, mark well*), presents this peculiarity in a most extraordinary manner, and not only the *Hatteria punctata*, but the chameleon, certain reptiles, and even fishes. It was thought, at first, that it was no more than the prolongation of the brain ending with a small protuberance, called *epiphysis*, a little bone separated from the main bone by a cartilage, and found in every animal. But it was soon found to be more than this. It offered – as its development and anatomical structure showed – such an analogy with that of the eye, that it was found impossible to see in it anything else. There were and are palaeontologists who feel convinced to this day that this "third eye" has functioned in its origin, and they are certainly right. For this is what is said of the pineal gland in *Quain's Anatomy* (Vol. II, 9th Ed., pp. 830 – 851, "*Thalamencephalon*" Interbrain):

> "It is from this part, constituting at first the whole and subsequently the hinder part of the anterior primary encephalic vesicle, that the optic vesicles are developed in the earliest period, and the fore part is that in connection with which the cerebral hemispheres and accompanying parts are formed. The *thalamus opticus* of each side is formed by a lateral thickening of the medullary wall, while the interval between, descending towards the base, constitutes the cavity of the third ventricle with its prolongation in the *infundibulum*. The grey commissure afterwards stretches across the ventricular cavity. .
> . . . The hinder part of the roof is developed by a peculiar process, to be noticed later, into the pineal gland, which remains united on each side by its pedicles to the *thalamus*, and behind these a transverse

---

155 "Deeply placed within the head, covered by thick skin and muscles, true eyes that cannot see are found in certain animals." Also, says Hæckel, "Vertebrate . . . blind moles and field mice, blind snakes and lizards. . . . They shun daylight . . . dwelling under the ground. They were not originally blind but have evolved from ancestors that lived in the light and had well-developed eyes. The atrophied eye beneath the opaque skin may be found in these blind beings in every stage of reversion." ("*Sense Organs*," Hæckel.) And if two eyes could become so atrophied in lower animals, why not one eye—the pineal gland—in man, who is but a higher animal in his physical aspect?

band is formed as posterior commissure.

"The *lamina terminalis* (*lamina cinerea*) continues to close the third ventricle in front, below it the optic commissure forms the floor of the ventricle, and further back the infundibulum descends to be united in the *sella turcica* with the tissue adjoining the posterior lobe of the pituitary body.

"The two *optic thalami* formed from the posterior and outer part of the anterior vesicle, consist at first of a single hollow sac of nervous matter, the cavity of which communicates on each side in front with that of the commencing cerebra hemispheres, and behind with that of the middle cephalic vesicle (*corpora quadrigemina*). Soon, however, by increased deposit taking place in their interior, behind, below, and at the sides, the thalami become solid, and at the same time a cleft or fissure appears between them above, and penetrates down to the internal cavity, which continues open at the back part opposite the entrance of the Sylvian aqueduct. This cleft or fissure is the *third ventricle*. Behind, the two thalami continue united by the *posterior commissure*, which is distinguishable about the end of the third month, and also by the peduncles of the pineal gland. . . . .

"At an early period the *optic tracts* may be recognised as hollow prolongations from the outer part of the wall of the *thalami* while they are still vesicular. At the fourth month these tracts are distinctly formed. They subsequently are prolonged backwards into connection with the *corpora quadrigemina*.

"The formation of the pineal gland and pituitary body presents some of the most interesting phenomena which are connected with the development of the *Thalamencephalon*."

The Cyclops Is No Myth

The above is specially interesting when it is remembered that, were it not for the development of the hinder part of the cerebral hemispheres backwards, the pineal gland would be perfectly visible on the removal of the parietal bones. It is very interesting also to note the obvious connection to be traced between the (originally) hollow optic tracts and the eyes anteriorly, the pineal gland and its peduncles behind, and all of these with the optic thalami. So that the recent discoveries in connection with the third eye of *Hatteria punctata* have a very important bearing on the developmental history of the human senses, and on the occult assertions in the text.

It is well known (and also regarded as a fiction now, by those who have ceased to believe in the existence of an immortal principle in man) that Descartes saw in the pineal gland the *Seat of the Soul*. Although it is joined to every part of the body, he said, there is one special portion of it in which the Soul exercises its functions more specially than in any other. And, as neither the heart, nor yet the brain could be that "special" locality, he concluded that it was that little gland tied to the brain, yet having an action independent of it, as it could easily be put into a kind of swinging motion "*by the animal Spirits*[156] *which, cross* the cavities of the skull in every sense."

Unscientific as this may appear in our day of exact learning, Descartes was yet far nearer the occult truth than is any Hæckel. For the pineal gland, as shown, is far more connected with Soul and Spirit than with the physiological senses of man. Had the leading Scientists a glimmer of the *real* processes employed by the Evolutionary Impulse, and the winding *cyclic* course of this great law, they would *know* instead of conjecturing, and feel as certain of the future physical transformations of the human kind by the knowledge of its past forms. Then, would they see the fallacy and all the absurdity of their modern "blind-force" and mechanical processes of nature, realizing, in consequence of such knowledge, that the said pineal gland, for instance, could not but be disabled for *physical* use at this stage of our cycle. If the odd "eye" in man is now atrophied, it is a proof that, as in the lower animal, it has once been active, for nature never creates the smallest, the most insignificant form without some definite purpose and use. It was an *active* organ, we say, at that stage of evolution when the spiritual element in man reigned supreme over the hardly nascent intellectual and psychic elements. And, as the cycle ran down toward

---

156 The "Nervous Ether" of Dr. B.W. Richardson. F.R.S.—the nerve-aura of occultism. The "animal spirits" (?) are equivalent to the currents of nerve-auric compound circulation.

that point when the physiological senses were developed by, and went *pari passu* with, the growth and consolidation of the physical man, the interminable and complex vicissitudes and tribulations of zoological development, that median "eye" ended by atrophying along with the early spiritual and purely psychic characteristics in man. The eye is the mirror and also the window of the soul, says popular wisdom,[157] and *Vox populi Vox Dei*.

The Evolution of the Eye

In the beginning, every class and family of living species was hermaphrodite and objectively one-eyed. In the animal, whose form was as ethereal (astrally) as that of man, before the bodies of both began to evolve their coats of skin, *viz.* to evolve *from within without* the thick coating of physical substance or matter with its internal physiological mechanism, the third eye was primarily, as in man, the only seeing organ. The two physical front eyes developed[158] later on in both brute and man, whose organ of physical sight was, at the commencement of the Third Race, in the same position as that of some of the blind *vertebrata*, in our day, *i.e.* beneath an opaque skin.[159] Only the stages

---

157 Let us remember that the *First* Race is shown in Occult sciences as spiritual within and ethereal without; the *Second*, psycho-spiritual mentally, and ethero-physical bodily; the *Third*, still bereft of intellect in its beginning, is astro-physical in its body, and lives an inner life, in which the psycho-spiritual element is in no way interfered with as yet by the hardly nascent physiological senses. Its two front eyes look before them without seeing either past or future. But the "third eye" *"embraces ETERNITY."*

158 But in a very different manner to that pictured by Hæckel as an *"evolution by natural selection in the struggle for existence"* (*"Pedigree of Man,"* Sense Organs, p. 335). The mere "thermal sensibility of the skin," to hypothetical light-waves, is absurdly incompetent to account for the beautiful combination of adaptations present in the eye. It has, moreover, been previously shown that "natural Selection" is a pure myth when credited with the *origination* of variations (*vide infra*, Part III, on Darwinian mechanical causation), as the "survival of the fittest" can only take place after useful variations have sprung up, together with improved organisms. Whence came the "useful variations," which developed the eye? Only from " blind forces . . . without aim, without design?" The argument is puerile. The true solution of the mystery is to be found in the impersonal Divine Wisdom, in its IDEATION—reflected through matter.

159 Palæontology has ascertained that in the animals of the Cenozoic age—the Saurians especially, such as the antediluvian *Labyrinthodon*, whose fossil skull exhibits a perforation otherwise inexplicable—the third, or odd eye must have been much developed. Several naturalists, among others E. Korscheldt, feel convinced that

of the *odd*, or primeval eye, in man and brute, are now inverted, as the former has already passed that animal *non-rational* stage in the Third Round, and is ahead of mere brute creation by a whole plane of consciousness. Therefore, while the "Cyclopean" eye was, and still *is*, in man the organ of *spiritual* sight, in the animal it was that of objective vision. And this eye, having performed its function, was replaced, in the course of physical evolution from the simple to the complex, by two eyes, and thus was stored and laid aside by nature for further use in Æons to come.

This explains why the pineal gland reached its highest development proportionately with the lowest physical development. It is the *vertebrata* in which it is the most prominent and objective, and in man it is most carefully hidden and inaccessible, except to the anatomist. No less light is thrown thereby on the future physical, spiritual, and intellectual state of mankind, in periods corresponding on parallel lines with other past periods, and always on the lines of ascending and descending cyclic evolution and development. Thus, a few centuries before the *Kali yuga* – the black age which began nearly 5,000 years ago – it was said (paraphrased into comprehensible sentences):

"*We* (the Fifth Root-Race) *in our first half* (of duration) *onward* (on the now ASCENDING arc of the cycle) *are on the mid point of* (or between) *the First and the Second Races – falling downward* (*i.e.* the races were then on the descending arc of the cycle). . . . *Calculate for thyself, Lanoo, and see.*" (*Commentary* XX.).

Calculating as advised, we find that during that transitional period – namely, in the second half of the First Spiritual ethero-astral race – nascent mankind was devoid of the intellectual brain element. As it was on its *descending* line, and as we are parallel to it, on the *ascending*, we are, therefore, devoid of the Spiritual element, which is now replaced by the intellectual. For, remember well, as we are in the *Manasa* period of our cycle of races, or in the Fifth, we have, therefore, crossed the meridian point of the perfect adjustment of Spirit and Matter – or that

whereas, notwithstanding the opaque skin covering it, such an eye in the reptiles of the present period can only distinguish light from darkness (as the human eyes do when bound with a handkerchief, or even tightly closed), in the now extinct animals that eye functioned and was a real organ of vision.

equilibrium between brain intellect and Spiritual perception. One important point has, however, to be borne in mind.

EVOLUTION OF ROOT RACES IN THE FOURTH ROUND

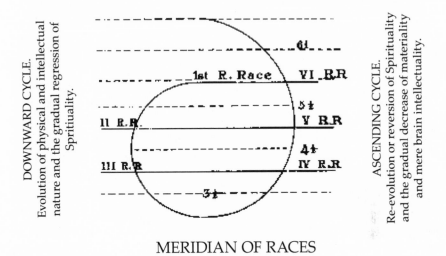

MERIDIAN OF RACES

THE "ODD EYE" HAS BEEN GRADUALLY TRANSFORMED INTO A SIMPLE GLAND

We are only in the Fourth Round, and it is in the Fifth that the full development of *Manas*, as a direct ray from the Universal MAHAT – a ray unimpeded by matter – will be finally reached. Nevertheless, as every sub-race and nation have their cycles and stages of developmental evolution repeated on a smaller scale, it must be the more so in the case of a Root-Race. Our race then has, as a Root-Race, crossed the equatorial line and is cycling onward on the Spiritual side, but some of our sub-races still find themselves on the shadowy descending arc of their respective national cycles, while others again – the oldest – having crossed their crucial point, which alone decides whether a race, a nation, or a tribe will live or perish, are at the apex of spiritual development as sub-races.

It becomes comprehensible now why the "odd eye" has been

gradually transformed into a simple gland, after the physical Fall of those we have agreed to call the "Lemurians."

It is a curious fact that it is especially in human beings that the cerebral hemispheres and the lateral ventricles have been developed, and that the *optic thalami, corpora quadrigemina,* and *corpora striata* are the principal parts which are developed in the mammalian brain. Moreover it is asserted that the intellect of any man may to some extent be gauged by the development of the central convolutions and the fore part of the cerebral hemispheres. It would seem a natural corollary that if the development and increased size of the pineal gland may be considered to be an index of the astral capacities and spiritual proclivities of any man, there will be a corresponding development of that part of the cranium, or an increase in the size of the pineal gland at the expense of the hinder part of the cerebral hemispheres. It is a curious speculation which would receive a confirmation in this case. We should see, below and behind, the cerebellum which has been held to be the seat of all the animal proclivities of a human being, and which is allowed by science to be the great centre for all the physiologically coordinated movements of the body, such as walking, eating, etc., etc., in front, the fore-part of the brain – the cerebral hemispheres – the part especially connected with the development of the intellectual powers in man, and in the middle, dominating them both, and especially the animal functions, the developed pineal gland, in connection with the more highly evolved, or spiritual man.

It must be remembered that these are only physical correspondences, just as the ordinary human brain is the registering organ of memory, but not memory itself.

This is, then, the organ which gave rise to so many legends and traditions, among others to that of man with one head but two faces. These may be found in several Chinese works, besides being referred to in the Chaldean fragments. Apart from the work already cited – the Shan Hai King, compiled by King Chia from engravings on nine urns made 2,255 B.C. by the Emperor Yü. They may be found in another work, called the "*Bamboo Books*," and in a third one, the "*Rh Ya*" – "initiated according to tradition by Chow Kung, uncle of Wu Wang, the first Emperor of the Chow Dynasty, B.C. 1,122" – says Mr. Ch. Gould in his "*Mythical Monsters*." The *Bamboo Books* contain the ancient annals of China, found A.D. 279 at the opening of the grave of King Seang of Wai, who died B.C. 295. Both these works mention men with two faces on one head – one in front and one behind (p. 27).

Now that which the students of Occultism ought to know is that THE "THIRD EYE" IS INDISSOLUBLY CONNECTED WITH KARMA. The tenet is so mysterious that very few have heard of it.

The "eye of Siva" did not become entirely atrophied before the close of the Fourth Race. When spirituality and all the divine powers and attributes of the deva-man of the Third had been made the hand-maidens of the newly-awakened physiological and psychic passions of the physical man, instead of the reverse, the eye lost its powers. But such was the law of Evolution, and it was, in strict accuracy, no FALL. The sin was not in using those newly-developed powers, but in *misusing* them, in making of the tabernacle, designed to contain a god, the fane of every *spiritual* iniquity. And if we say "sin," it is merely that everyone should understand our meaning, as the term *Karma*[160] *would be the right one to use in this case; while the reader who would feel perplexed at the use of the term "spiritual" instead of "physical" iniquity is reminded of the fact that there can be no physical iniquity. The body is simply the irresponsible organ, the tool of the psychic, if not of the "Spiritual man."* While in the case of the Atlanteans, it was precisely the Spiritual being which sinned, the Spirit element being still the "Master" principle in man, in those days. Thus it is in those days that the heaviest Karma of the Fifth Race was generated by our Monads.

As this sentence may again be found puzzling, it is better that it should be explained for the benefit of those who are ignorant of the Theosophical teachings.

---

160 Karma is a word of many meanings, and has a special term for almost every one of its aspects. It means, as a synonym of sin, the performance of some action for the attainment of an object of *worldly*, hence *selfish*, desire, which cannot fail to be hurtful to somebody else. Karma is action, the Cause; and Karma again is "the law of ethical causation," the *effect* of an act produced egotistically, when the great law of harmony depends on altruism.

THE NUMBER OF MONADS IS LIMITED

Questions with regard to *Karma* and *re-births* are constantly offered, and a great confusion seems to exist upon this subject. Those who are born and bred in the Christian faith, and have been trained in the idea that a new soul is created by God for every newly-born infant, are among the most perplexed. They ask whether in such case the number of incarnating Monads on earth is limited, to which they are answered in the affirmative. For, however countless, in our conceptions, the number of the incarnating monads – even if we take into account the fact that ever since the Second Race, when their respective seven groups were furnished with bodies, several births and deaths may be allowed for every second of time in the aeons already passed – still, there must be a limit. It was stated that Karma-Nemesis, whose bond-maid is Nature, adjusted everything in the most harmonious manner, and that, therefore, the fresh pouring-in, or arrival of new Monads, had ceased as soon as Humanity had reached its full physical development. No fresh Monads have incarnated since the middle-point of the Atlanteans. Hence, remembering that, save in the case of young children and of individuals whose lives were violently cut off by some accident, no Spiritual Entity can re-incarnate before a period of many centuries has elapsed, such gaps alone must show that the number of Monads is necessarily finite and limited. Moreover, a reasonable time must be given to other animals for their evolutionary progress.

Hence the assertion that many of us are now working off the effects of the evil Karmic causes produced by us in Atlantean bodies. The Law of KARMA is inextricably interwoven with that of Re-incarnation.

It is only the knowledge of the constant re-births of one and the same individuality throughout the life-cycle, the assurance that the same MONADS – among whom are many *Dhyan Chohans*, or the "Gods" themselves – have to pass through the "Circle of Necessity," rewarded or punished by such rebirth for the suffering endured or crimes committed in the former life, that those very Monads, which entered the empty, senseless shells, or astral figures of the First Race emanated by the *Pitris*, are the same who are now amongst us – nay, ourselves, perchance; it is only this doctrine, we say, that can explain to us the mysterious problem of Good and Evil, and reconcile man to the terrible and *apparent* injustice of life. Nothing but such certainty can quiet our revolted sense of justice. For, when one unacquainted with the noble doctrine looks around him and observes the inequalities of birth and fortune, of intellect and capacities; when one sees honour paid fools and profligates, on whom fortune has heaped her favours by mere privilege of birth, and their nearest neighbour, with all his intellect and noble virtues – far more deserving in every way – perishing of want and for lack of sympathy; when one sees all this and has to turn away, helpless to relieve the undeserved suffering, one's ears ringing and heart aching with the cries of pain around him – that blessed knowledge of Karma alone prevents him from cursing life and men, as well as their supposed Creator.[161]

Of all the terrible blasphemies and accusations virtually thrown on their God by the Monotheists, none is greater or more unpardonable than that (almost always) false humility which makes the presumably "pious" Christian assert, in connection with every evil and undeserved blow, that "such *is the will of God.*"

Dolts and hypocrites! Blasphemers and impious Pharisees, who speak in the same breath of the endless merciful love and care of their God and creator for helpless man, and of that God *scourging the good, the very best of his creatures, bleeding them to death like an insatiable Moloch*! Shall we be answered to this, in Congreve's words:

"But who shall dare to tax Eternal Justice?" *Logic and simple common sense*, we answer: if we are made to believe in the "original Sin," in *one* life, on this Earth only, for every Soul, and in an anthropomorphic Deity, who seems to have created some men only for the pleasure of condemning them to eternal hell-fire (and this whether they are good or bad, says the Predestinarian),[162] why should not every man endowed

---

161 Objectors to the doctrine of Karma should recall the fact that it is absolutely *out of the question* to attempt a reply to the Pessimists on other data. A firm grasp of the principles of Karmic Law knocks away the whole basis of the imposing fabric reared by the disciples of Schopenhauer and Von Hartmann.

162 The doctrine and theology of Calvinists. "The purpose of God *from eternity* respecting all events" (which becomes *fatalism* and kills free will, or any attempt of exerting it for good). . . . . "It is the pre-assignment or allotment of men to everlasting

with reasoning powers condemn in his turn such a villainous Deity? Life would become unbearable, if one had to believe in the God created by man's unclean fancy. Luckily he exists only in human dogmas, and in the unhealthy imagination of some poets, who believe they have solved the problem by addressing him as –

> "Thou great Mysterious Power, who hast *involved*
> The pride of human wisdom, *to confound*
> The daring scrutiny and prove *the faith*
> Of thy *presuming* creatures!

Truly a robust "faith" is required to believe that it is "presumption" to question the justice of one who creates helpless little man but to "perplex" him and to test a "faith" with which that "Power," moreover, may have forgotten, if not neglected, to endow him, as happens sometimes.

Karma-Nemesis, or the Law of Retribution, Predestines Nothing and No One

Compare this blind faith with the philosophical belief, based on every reasonable evidence and life-experience, in Karma-Nemesis, or the Law of Retribution. This Law – whether Conscious or Unconscious – predestines nothing and no one. It exists from and in Eternity, truly, for it is Eternity itself; and as such, since no act can be co-equal with eternity, it cannot be said to act, for it is action itself. It is not the Wave which drowns a man, but the *personal* action of the wretch, who goes deliberately and places himself under the *impersonal* action of the laws that govern the Ocean's motion. Karma creates nothing, nor does it design. It is man who plans and creates causes, and Karmic law adjusts the effects, which adjustment is not an act, but universal harmony, tending ever to resume its original position, like a bough, which, bent down too forcibly, rebounds with corresponding vigour. If it happen to dislocate the arm that tried to bend it out of its natural position, shall we say that it is the bough which broke our arm, or that our own folly has brought us to grief? Karma has never sought to destroy intellectual

happiness or misery." (*Catechism*) A noble and encouraging Doctrine this!

and individual liberty, like the God invented by the Monotheists. It has not involved its decrees in darkness purposely to perplex man, nor shall it punish him who dares to scrutinise its mysteries. On the contrary, he who unveils through study and meditation its intricate paths, and throws light on those dark ways, in the windings of which so many men perish owing to their ignorance of the labyrinth of life, is working for the good of his fellow-men. KARMA is an Absolute and Eternal law in the World of manifestation; and as there can only be one Absolute, as One eternal ever present Cause, believers in Karma cannot be regarded as Atheists or materialists – still less as fatalists,[163] for Karma is one with the Unknowable, of which it is an aspect in its effects in the phenomenal world.

Intimately, or rather indissolubly, connected with Karma, then, is the law of re-birth, or of the re-incarnation of the same spiritual individuality in a long, almost interminable, series of personalities. The latter are like the various costumes and characters played by the same actor, with each of which that actor identifies himself and is identified

---

163 Some Theosophists, in order to make Karma more comprehensible to the Western mind, as being better acquainted with the Greek than with Aryan philosophy, have made an attempt to translate it by *Nemesis*. Had the latter been known to the profane in antiquity, as it was understood by the Initiate, this translation of the term would be unobjectionable. As it is, it has been too much anthropomorphised by Greek fancy to permit our using it without an elaborate explanation. With the early Greeks, "from Homer to Herodotus, she was no goddess, but a *moral feeling* rather," says Decharme, the barrier to evil and immorality. He who transgresses it, commits a sacrilege in the eyes of the gods and is pursued by Nemesis. But, with time, that "feeling" was deified, and its personification became an ever-fatal and punishing goddess. Therefore, if we would connect Karma with Nemesis, it has to be done in the triple character of the latter, *viz.* as Nemesis, Adrasteia, and Themis. For, while the latter is the goddess of Universal Order and Harmony, who, like Nemesis, is commissioned to repress every excess and keep man within the limits of Nature and righteousness under severe penalty, *Adrasteia*—"the inevitable"—represents Nemesis as the immutable effect of causes created by man himself. Nemesis, as the daughter of *Dikè*, is the equitable goddess reserving her wrath for those alone who are maddened with pride, egoism, and impiety. (See *Mesomed. Hymn. Nemes.*, Vol. 2, *Brunck, Analecta II*, p. 292; *Mythol. de la Grèce Antique*, p. 304.) In short, while Nemesis is a mythological, exoteric goddess, or Power, personified and anthropomorphised in its various aspects, *Karma* is a highly philosophical truth, a most divine noble expression of the primitive intuition of man concerning Deity. It is a doctrine which explains the origin of Evil, and ennobles our conceptions of what divine immutable Justice ought to be, instead of degrading the unknown and unknowable Deity by making it the whimsical, cruel tyrant, which we call Providence.

by the public, for the space of a few hours. The *inner,* or real man, who personates those characters, knows the whole time that he is Hamlet for the brief space of a few acts, which represent, however, on the plane of human illusion the whole life of Hamlet. And he knows that he was, the night before, King Lear, the transformation in his turn of the Othello of a still earlier preceding night; but the outer, visible character is supposed to be ignorant of the fact. In actual life that ignorance is, unfortunately, but too real. Nevertheless, the *permanent* individuality is fully aware of the fact, though, through the atrophy of the "spiritual" eye in the physical body, that knowledge is unable to impress itself on the consciousness of the false personality.

The possession of a physical *third* eye, we are told, was enjoyed by the men of the Third Root-Race down to nearly the middle period of Third Sub-race of the Fourth Root-Race, when the consolidation and perfection of the human frame made it disappear from the outward anatomy of man. Psychically and spiritually, however, its mental and visual perceptions lasted till nearly the end of the Fourth Race, when its functions, owing to the materiality and depraved condition of mankind, died out altogether before the submersion of the bulk of the Atlantean continent. And now we may return to the Deluges and their many "Noahs."

The student has to bear in mind that there were many such deluges as that mentioned in *Genesis,* and three far more important ones, which will be mentioned and described in the Section devoted to the subject of pre-historic continents. To avoid erroneous conjectures, however, with regard to the claim that the esoteric doctrine has much in it of the legends contained in the Hindu Scriptures; that, again, the chronology of the latter is almost that of the former, only explained and made clear; and that finally the belief that "*Vaivasvata Manu*" – a generic name indeed! – was the Noah of the Aryans and his prototype; all this, which is also the belief of the Occultists, necessitates at this juncture a new explanation. (*Vide* Part III, "*Submerged Continents.*")

The Secret Doctrine, ii 293 – 306

Selection 24

SCIENCE IS AS INCONSISTENT AS WAS ANCIENT AND MEDIÆVAL THEOLOGY IN THEIR INTERPRETATIONS OF THE SO-CALLED REVELATION

It is just what we can never repeat too often, though the voices of both Occultists and Roman Catholics are raised in the desert. Nevertheless, no one can fail to see that Science is as inconsistent, to say the least, in its modern speculations, as was ancient and mediæval theology in *its* interpretations of the so-called *Revelation*. Science would have men descend from the pithecoid ape – a transformation requiring millions of years – and yet fears to make mankind older than 100,000 years! Science teaches the gradual transformation of species, natural selection, and evolution from the lowest form to the highest, from mollusc to fish, from reptile to bird and mammalian. Yet it refuses to man, who physiologically is only a higher mammal and animal, such transformation of his external form. But if the monstrous iguanodon of the Wealden may have been the ancestor of the diminutive iguana of today, why could not the monstrous man of the Secret Doctrine have become the modern man – the link between Animal and Angel? Is there anything more unscientific in *this* "theory," than in that of refusing to man any spiritual immortal Ego, making of him an automaton, and ranking him, at the same time, *as a distinct genus* in the system of Nature? Occult Sciences may be less scientific than the present exact Sciences, they are withal more logical and consistent in their teachings. Physical forces, and natural affinities of atoms may be sufficient as factors to transform a plant into an animal, but it requires more than a mere interplay between certain material aggregates and their environment to call to life *a fully conscious man*, even though he were no more indeed than a ramification between two "poor cousins" of the Quadrumanous order. Occult Sciences admit with Hæckel that (objective) life on our globe "is a logical postulate of Scientific natural history," but add that the rejection of alike *Spiritual* involution, from *within without*, of invisible subjective Spirit-life – eternal and a Principle

171

in Nature – is more illogical, if possible, than to say that the Universe and all in it has been gradually built by blind forces inherent in matter, without any *external* help.

Suppose an Occultist were to claim that the first grand organ of a cathedral had come originally into being in the following manner. First, there was a progressive and gradual elaboration in Space of an organizable material, which resulted in the production of a state of matter named *organic* PROTEIN. Then, under the influence of incident forces, those states having been thrown into a phase of unstable equilibrium, they slowly and majestically evolved into and resulted in new combinations of carved and polished wood, of brass pins and staples, of leather and ivory, wind-pipes and bellows. After which, having adapted all its parts into one harmonious and symmetrical machine, the organ suddenly pealed forth Mozart's *Requiem*. This was followed by a Sonata of Beethoven, etc. *ad infinitum*, its keys playing of themselves and the wind blowing into the pipes by its own inherent force and fancy. . . . . What would Science say to such a theory? Yet, it is precisely in such wise that the materialistic *savants* tell us that the Universe was formed, with its millions of beings, and man, its spiritual crown.

IT TAKES A GOD TO BECOME A MAN

Whatever may have been the real inner thought of Mr. Herbert Spencer, when writing on the subject of the gradual transformation of species, what he says in it applies to our doctrine. "Construed in terms of evolution, every kind of being is conceived as a product of modifications wrought by insensible gradations *on a pre-existing kind of being.*" ("*Essays on Physiology,*" p. 144.) Then why, in this case, should not historical man be the product of a modification on a pre-existent and pre-historical kind of man, even supposing for argument's sake that there is nothing within him to last longer than, or live independently of, his physical structure? But this is not so! For, when we are told that "organic matters are produced in the laboratory by what we may literally call *artificial evolution* (Appendix to "*Principles of Biology,*" p. 482), we answer the distinguished English philosopher that Alchemists and great adepts have done as much, and, indeed, far more, before the chemists ever attempted to "build out of dissociated elements complex combinations." The *Homunculi* of Paracelsus are a fact in Alchemy, and will become one in Chemistry very likely, and then Mrs. Shelley's Frankenstein will have to be regarded as a prophecy. But no chemist, or Alchemist either, will ever endow such a "Frankenstein's Monster" with more than animal instinct, unless indeed he does that which the "Progenitors" are credited with, namely, if he leaves his own physical body, and incarnates in the "empty form." But even this would be an *artificial*, not a natural man, for our "Progenitors" had, in the course of eternal evolution, to become *gods* before they became men.

The above digression, if one, is an attempt at justification before the few thinking men of the coming century who may read this. But this accounts also for the reason why the best and most spiritual men of our present day can no longer be satisfied with either Science or theology, and why they prefer any such "psychic craze" to the dogmatic assertions of both, neither of the two having anything better to offer than *blind* faith in their respective infallibility. *Universal* tradition is indeed the far safer guide in life. And universal tradition shows primitive man living for ages together with his Creators and first instructors – the *Elohim* – in the World's "Garden of Eden," or "Delight." We shall treat of the Divine Instructors in Stanza 12.

The Secret Doctrine, ii 347 – 349

Selection 25

A Genealogical Tree of the Human Family

Let the reader remember well that which is said of the divisions of Root Races and the evolution of Humanity in this work, and stated clearly and concisely in Mr. Sinnett's *"Esoteric Buddhism."* 1. There are seven ROUNDS in every *Manvantara*; this one is the Fourth, and we are in the Fifth Root-Race, at present. 2. Each Root-Race has seven sub-races. 3. Each sub-race has, in its turn, seven ramifications, which may be called Branch or "Family" races. 4. The little tribes, shoots, and offshoots of the last-named are countless and depend on Karmic action. Examine the "genealogical tree" hereto appended, and you will understand. The illustration is purely diagrammatic, and is only intended to assist the reader in obtaining a slight grasp of the subject, amidst the confusion which exists between the terms which have been used at different times for the divisions of Humanity. It is also here attempted to express in figures – but only within approximate limits, for the sake of comparison – the duration of time through which it is possible to definitely distinguish one division from another. It would only lead to hopeless confusion if any attempt were made to give accurate dates to a few, for the Races, Sub-Races, etc., etc., down to their smallest ramifications, overlap and are entangled with each other until it is nearly impossible to separate them.

The human Race has been compared to a tree, and this serves admirably as an illustration.

The main stem of a tree may be compared to the ROOT-RACE (A). Its larger limbs to the various SUB-RACES; seven in number (B^1, B^2).

On each of these limbs are seven BRANCHES, OR FAMILY-RACES (C).

After this, the cactus-plant is a better illustration, for its fleshy "leaves" are covered with sharp spines, each of which may be compared to a nation or tribe of human beings.

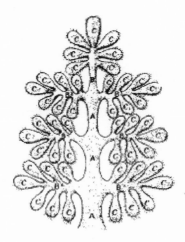

The European "Family Race" Has Many Thousands of Years Yet to Run

Now our Fifth Root-Race has already been in existence – as a race *sui generis* and quite free from its parent stem – about 1,000,000 years; therefore it must be inferred that each of the four preceding Sub-Races has lived approximately 210,000 years; thus each Family-Race has an average existence of about 30,000 years. Thus the European "Family Race" has still a good many thousand years to run, although the nations or the innumerable spines upon it, vary with each succeeding "season" of three or four thousand years. It is somewhat curious to mark the comparative approximation of duration between the lives of a "Family-Race" and a "Sidereal year."

The knowledge of the foregoing, and the accurately correct division, formed part and parcel of the Mysteries, where these Sciences were taught to the disciples, and where they were transmitted by one hierophant to another. Everyone is aware that the European astronomers assign (arbitrarily enough) the date of the invention of the Egyptian Zodiac to the years 2000 or 2400 B.C. (*Proctor*), and insist that this invention coincides in its date with that of the erection of the Great Pyramid. This, to an Occultist and Eastern astronomer, must appear quite absurd. The year of the *Kaliyuga* is said to have begun between the 17th and 18th of February in the year 3102 B.C. Now the Hindus claim that in the year 20,400 before *Kaliyugam*, the origin of their Zodiac coincided with the spring equinox – there being at the time a conjunction of the Sun and Moon – and Bailly proved by a lengthy and careful computation of that date, that, even if fictitious, the epoch from which they had started to establish the beginning of their *Kaliyug* was very real. That "epoch is the year 3102 before our era," he writes. (See Part III, Book I, *"Hindu Astronomy defended by an Academician".*) The lunar eclipse arriving just a fortnight after the beginning of the black Age – it took place in a point situated between the Wheat Ear of Virgo and the star θ (*θ*) of the same constellation. One of their most esoteric Cycles is based upon certain conjunctions and respective positions of Virgo and the Pleiades (*Krittika*). Hence, as the Egyptians brought their Zodiac from Southern India and Lanka,[164] the esoteric meaning was evidently identical. The three "Virgins," or Virgo in three different positions, meant, with both, the record of the first three "divine or astronomical Dynasties," who taught the Third Root-Race, and after having abandoned the Atlanteans to their doom, returned (or redescended, rather) during the third Sub-Race of the Fifth, in order to reveal to saved humanity the mysteries of their birth-place – the sidereal Heavens. The same symbolical record of the human races and the three Dynasties (Gods, Manes – semi-divine astrals of the Third and Fourth – and the "Heroes" of the Fifth Race), which preceded the purely human kings, was found in the distribution of the tiers and passages of the Egyptian Labyrinth. As the three inversions of the Poles of course changed the face of the Zodiac, a new one had to be constructed each time. In Mackey's *"Sphinxiad"* the speculations of the bold author must have horrified the orthodox portion of the population of Norwich, as he says, fantastically enough:

The Egyptian Zodiac Is between 75 – 80,000 Years Old

"But, after all, the greatest length of time recorded by those monuments (the Labyrinth, the Pyramids, and the Zodiacs) *does not*

---

164   Ceylon.

exceed five millions of years (which is not so)[165], which falls short of the records given us both by the (esoteric) Chinese and Hindus, which latter nation has registered a knowledge of time for seven or eight millions of years[166], which I have seen upon a talisman of porcelain.
. . ."

The Egyptian priests had the Zodiacs of the Atlantean *Asura-Maya,* as the modern Hindus still have. As stated in "*Esoteric Buddhism,*" the Egyptians, as well as the Greeks and "Romans" some thousand years ago, were "remnants of the Atlanto-Aryans," *i.e.* the former, of the older, or the Ruta Atlanteans; the last-named, the descendants of the last race of that island, whose sudden disappearance was narrated to Solon by the Egyptian Initiates. The *human* Dynasty of the older Egyptians, beginning, with *Menes,* had all the *knowledge* of the Atlanteans, though there was no more Atlantean blood in their veins. Nevertheless, they had preserved all their Archaic records. All this has been shown long ago.[167] And it is just because the Egyptian Zodiac is between 75 and 80,000 years old that the Zodiac of the Greeks is far later. Volney has correctly pointed out in his "Ruins of Empires" (p. 360) that it is only 16,984 years old, or up to the present date 17,082.[168]

The Secret Doctrine, ii 434 – 436

---

165 The forefathers of the Aryan Brahmins had their Zodiacal calculations and Zodiac from those born by *Kriyasakti* power, the "Sons of Yoga", the Egyptians from the Atlanteans of Ruta.

166 The former, therefore, may have registered time for seven or eight millions of years, but the Egyptians could not.

167 This question was amply challenged, and as amply discussed and answered. See "*Five Years of Theosophy.*" (Article "*Mr. Sinnett's Esoteric Buddhism,*" pp. 325–46).

168 Volney says that, as Aries was in its 15th degree 1447 B.C., it follows that the first degree of "Libra" could not have coincided with the vernal equinox more lately than 15,194 years B.C., to which if you add 1790 since Christ, when Volney wrote this, it appears that 16,984 years have elapsed since the (Greek or rather Hellenic) origin of the Zodiac.

Selection 26

SCIENCE CANNOT EXPLAIN THE MYSTERIOUS NATURE OF CONSCIOUSNESS, OF SOUL, SPIRIT IN MAN

It is this divergence among men of Science, their mutual, and often their *self*-contradictions, that gave the writer of the present volumes the courage to bring to light other and older teachings, if only as hypotheses for *future* scientific appreciation. Though not in any way very learned in modern sciences, so evident, even to the humble recorder of this archaic clearing, are the said scientific fallacies and gaps, that she determined to touch upon all these, in order to place the two teachings on parallel lines. For Occultism, it is a question of self-defence, and nothing more.

So far, the "Secret Doctrine" has concerned itself with metaphysics, pure and simple. It has now landed on Earth, and finds itself within the domain of physical science and practical anthropology, or those branches of study which materialistic Naturalists claim as their rightful domain, coolly asserting, furthermore, that the higher and more perfect the working of the Soul, the more amenable it is to the analysis and explanations *of the zoologist and the physiologist alone*. (Hæckel on "*Cell-Souls and Soul-Cells*.") This stupendous pretension comes from one, who, to prove his pithecoid descent, has not hesitated to include among the ancestors of man the *Lemuridæ*, which have been promoted by him to the rank of *Prosimiæ, indeciduate mammals*, to which he very incorrectly attributes a *decidua* and a discoidal placenta.[169] For this Hæckel was taken severely to task by de Quatrefages and criticised by his own brother materialists and agnostics, as great, if not greater, authorities than himself, namely, by Virchow and du Bois-Reymond.[170]

---

169 *Vide infra*, M. de Quatrefages' *exposé* of Hæckel, in § II, "The Ancestors Mankind is offered by Science."

170 Strictly speaking du Bois-Reymond is an *agnostic*, and not a materialist. He has protested most vehemently against the materialistic doctrine, which affirms mental phenomena to be merely the product of molecular motion. The most accurate *physiological* knowledge of the structure of the brain leaves us "nothing but matter in

Such opposition notwithstanding, Hæckel's wild theories are, to this day, called scientific and logical by some. The mysterious nature of Consciousness, of Soul, Spirit in Man being now explained as a mere advance on the functions of the protoplasmic molecules of the lively *Protista*, and the gradual evolution and growth of human mind and "social instincts" toward civilization having to be traced back to their origin in the civilization of ants, bees, and other creatures, the chances left for an impartial hearing of the doctrines of archaic Wisdom, are few indeed. The *educated* profane is told that "the social instincts of the lower animals have, of late, been regarded *as being clearly the origin of morals,* even of those of man" (!) and that our divine consciousness, our soul, intellect, and aspirations have "worked their way up from the lower stages of the simple cell-soul" of the gelatinous Bathybius (see Hæckel's *"Present Position of Evolution"* Notes), and he seems to believe it. For such men, the metaphysics of Occultism must produce the effect that our grandest orchestral and vocal oratorios produce on the Chinaman: a sound that jars upon their nerves.

PHYSICAL EVOLUTION, AS MODERN SCIENCE TEACHES IT, IS A SUBJECT FOR OPEN CONTROVERSY

Yet, are our esoteric teachings about "angels," the first three pre-animal human Races, and the downfall of the Fourth, *on a lower level of fiction and self-delusion* than the Hæckelian "plastidular," or the inorganic "molecular Souls of the *Protista*"? Between the evolution of the spiritual nature of man from the above Amœbian Souls, and the alleged development of his physical frame from the protoplastic dweller in the Ocean slime, there is an abyss which will not be easily crossed by any man in the *full* possession of his intellectual faculties. Physical evolution, as modern Science teaches it, is a subject for open controversy; spiritual and moral development on the same lines is the insane dream of a crass materialism.

Furthermore, past as well as present daily experience teaches that no truth has ever been accepted by the learned bodies unless it dovetailed with the habitual preconceived ideas of their professors. "The crown

motion," he asserts: *"we must go further,* and admit the utterly incomprehensible nature of the psychical principle which it is *impossible to regard* as a mere outcome of material causes."

of the innovator is a crown of thorns", said G. St. Hilaire. It is only that which fits in with popular hobbies and accepted notions that, as a general rule, gains ground. Hence the triumph of the Hæckelian ideas, notwithstanding their being proclaimed by Virchow, du Bois Reymond, and others as the "*testimonium paupertatis* of natural Science."

Diametrically opposed as may be the materialism of the German Evolutionists to the spiritual conceptions of Esoteric philosophy, radically inconsistent as is their accepted anthropological system with the real facts of nature, the pseudo-idealistic bias now colouring English thought is almost more pernicious. The pure materialistic doctrine admits of a direct refutation and appeal to the logic of facts. The idealism of the present day not only contrives to absorb, on the one hand, the basic negations of Atheism, but lands its votaries in a tangle of *unreality*, which culminates in a practical Nihilism. Argument with such writers is almost out of the question. Idealists, therefore, will be still more antagonistic to the Occult teachings now given than even the Materialists. But as no worse fate can befall the exponents of Esoteric Anthropo-Genesis than being openly called by their foes by their old and time-honoured names of "lunatics" and "ignoramuses," the present archaic theories may be safely added to the many modern speculations, and bide their time for their full or even partial recognition. Only, as the existence itself of these "archaic theories" will probably be denied, we have to give our best proofs and stand by them to the bitter end.

In our race and generation the one "temple in the Universe" is in rare cases – *within* us; but our body and mind have been too defiled by both Sin and Science to be outwardly now anything better than a fane of iniquity and error. And here our mutual position – that of Occultism and Modern Science – ought to be once for all defined.

We, Theosophists, would willingly bow before such men of learning as the late Prof. Balfour Stewart, Messrs. Crookes, Quatrefages, Wallace, Agassiz, Butlerof, and several others, though we may not agree, from the stand-point of esoteric philosophy, with all they say. But nothing could make us consent to even a show of respect for the opinions of other men of science, such as Hæckel, Carl Vogt, or Ludwig Büchner, in Germany; or even of Mr. Huxley and his co-thinkers in materialism in England, the colossal erudition of the first named, notwithstanding.

Such men are simply the intellectual and moral murderers of future generations; especially Hæckel, whose crass materialism often rises to the height of idiotic *naivetés* in his reasonings. One has but to read his *"Pedigree of Man, and Other Essays"* (Aveling's translation) to feel a desire, in the words of Job, that his remembrance should perish from the earth, and that he "shall have no name in the streets." Hear him deriding the idea of the origin of the human race "as a supernatural (?) phenomenon," as one "that could not result from *simple mechanical causes, from physical and chemical forces,* but requires the direct intervention of a creative personality. . ."

. . . . "Now the central point of Darwin's teaching," . . goes on the creator of the mythical *Sozura,* "lies in this, that it demonstrates the simplest mechanical causes, purely physico-chemical phenomena of nature, as wholly sufficient to explain the highest and most difficult problems. Darwin puts in the place of *a conscious creative force,* building and arranging the organic bodies of animals and plants on a designed plan, *a series of natural forces working blindly (or we say) without aim, without design.* In place of an arbitrary act of operation, we have a necessary law of Evolution . . . ." (So had Manu and Kapila, and, at the same time, guiding, conscious and intelligent Powers). . . "Darwin had very wisely . . . put on one side the question as to the first appearance of life. But very soon that consequence, so full of meaning, so wide reaching, was openly discussed by able and brave scientific men, such as Huxley, Carl Vogt, Ludwig Büchner. *A mechanical origin of the earliest living form,* was held as the necessary sequence to Darwin's teaching. . . and we are at present concerned with a single consequence of the theory, *the natural* origin of the human race through ALMIGHTY EVOLUTION (pp. 34, 37).

To which, unabashed by this scientific farrago, Occultism replies: In the course of Evolution, when the physical triumphed over, and nearly crushed under its weight, spiritual and mental evolutions, the great gift of *Kriyasakti*[171] *remained the heirloom of only a few elect men in every age* . . . . *Spirit strove vainly to manifest itself in its fullness in purely organic forms* (as has been explained in Part I of this Volume), and the

---

171 For explanation of the term *Kriyasakti,* see *Commentary* 2 in Stanza 26.

faculty, which had been a natural attribute in the early humanity of the Third Race, became one of the class regarded as simply phenomenal by the Spiritualists and Occultists, and as *scientifically impossible* by the materialists.

In our modern day the mere assertion that there exists a power which can create human forms – ready-made *sheaths* for the "conscious monads" or *Nirmânakâyas* of past *Manvantaras* to incarnate within – is, of course, absurd, ridiculous! That which is regarded as quite natural, on the other hand, is the production of a Frankenstein's monster, *plus* moral consciousness, religious aspirations, genius, and a feeling of one's own immortal nature within one's self – by "physico-chemical forces, guided by blind Almighty Evolution" ("*Pedigree of Man*").

THE ESOTERIC TEACHING IS ABSOLUTELY OPPOSED TO THE DARWINIAN EVOLUTION AS APPLIED TO MAN

As to the origin of that man, not *ex nihilo*, cemented by a little red clay, but from a living divine Entity consolidating the astral body with surrounding materials – this conception is too absurd even to be mentioned in the opinion of the materialists. Nevertheless, Occultists and Theosophists are ready to have their claims and theories – however unscientific and superstitious at first glance – compared as to their intrinsic value and probability, with those of the modern evolutionists. Hence the esoteric teaching is absolutely opposed to the Darwinian evolution, *as applied to man, and partially* so with regard to other species.

It would be interesting to obtain a glimpse of the mental representation of Evolution in the Scientific brain of a materialist. What is EVOLUTION? If asked to define the full and *complete* meaning of the term, neither Huxley nor Hæckel will be able to do it any better than Webster does: "the act of unfolding; the process of growth, development; as the evolution of a flower from a bud, or an animal from the egg." Yet the bud must be traced through its parent-plant to the seed, and the egg to the animal or bird that laid it, or at any rate to the speck of protoplasm from which it expanded and grew. And both the *seed* and the *speck* must have the latent potentialities in them for the reproduction and gradual development, the unfolding of the thousand and one forms or phases of evolution, through which they must pass before the flower or the animal are fully developed? Hence, the future plan, if not a DESIGN, *must be there*. Moreover, that *seed has to be traced*, and its nature ascertained. Have the Darwinists been successful in this? Or will the *Moneron* be cast in our teeth? But this atom of the Watery Abysses is *not* homogeneous matter, and there must be something or somebody that had moulded and cast it into being.

Here Science is once more silent. But since there is no self-consciousness as yet in either speck, seed, or germ, according to both Materialists and Psychologists of the modern school – Occultists agreeing in this for once with their natural enemies – what is it that guides the force or forces so unerringly in this process of evolution? *Blind* force? As well call *blind* the brain which evolved in Hæckel his "*Pedigree of Man*" and other lucubrations. We can easily conceive that the said brain lacks an important centre or two. For, whoever knows anything of the anatomy of the human, or even of any animal, body, and is still an *atheist* and a *materialist*, must be "hopelessly insane," according to Lord Herbert, who rightly sees in the frame of man's body and the coherence of its parts, something so strange and paradoxical that he holds it "to be the greatest miracle of nature." *Blind* forces, and *no* design" in anything under the Sun; when no *sane* man of Science would hesitate to say that, even from the little he knows and has hitherto discovered of the forces at work in *Kosmos*, he sees very plainly that every part, every speck and atom are in harmony with their fellow atoms, and these with the whole, each having its distinct mission throughout the life-cycle. But, fortunately, the greatest, the most eminent thinkers and Scientists of the day are now beginning to rise against this "Pedigree," and even Darwin's *natural selection* theory, though its author had never, probably, contemplated such widely stretched conclusions. The remarkable work of the Russian Scientist N. T. Danilevsky – "*Darwinism, a Critical Investigation of the Theory*" – upsets it completely and without appeal, and so does de Quatrefages in his last work. Our readers are recommended to examine the learned paper by Dr. Bourges – read by its author, a member of the Paris Anthropological Society at a recent official meeting of the latter – called "*Evolutionary*

Psychology; the Evolution of Spirit, etc." in which he reconciles entirely the two teachings – namely those of the physical and spiritual evolutions. He explains the origin of the variety of organic forms, made to fit their environments with such evident intelligent design, by the existence and the mutual help and *interaction* of two principles in (manifest) nature, the inner Conscious Principle adapting itself to physical nature and the innate potentialities in the latter. Thus the French Scientist has to return to our old friend – *Archæus*, or the life-Principle – without naming it, as Dr. Richardson has done in England in his "Nerve-Force," etc. The same idea was recently developed in Germany by Baron Hellenbach, in his remarkable work, "*Individuality in the Light of Biology and Modern Philosophy.*"

We find the same conclusions arrived at in still another excellent volume of another Russian deep thinker, N. N. Strachof – who says in his "*Fundamental Conceptions of Psychology and Physiology,*" "The most clear, as the most familiar, type of development may be found in our own mental or physical evolution, which has served others as a model to follow . . . . If organisms are *entities* . . . then it is only just to conclude and assert that the organic life strives to beget psychic life; but it would be still more correct and in accordance with the spirit of these two categories of evolution to say, that *the true cause of organic life is the tendency of spirit to manifest in substantial forms, to clothe itself in substantial reality. It is the highest form which contains the complete explanation of the lowest, never the reverse.*" This is admitting, as Bourges does in the Mémoire above quoted, the identity of this mysterious, integrally acting and organizing Principle with the Self-Conscious and Inner Subject, which we call the EGO and the world at large – the Soul. Thus, gradually, all the best scientists and thinkers are approaching the Occultists in their general conclusions.

THE ONE UNPARDONABLE SIN

But such metaphysically inclined men of Science are out of court and will hardly be listened to. Schiller, in his magnificent poem on the Veil of Isis, makes the mortal youth who dared to lift the impenetrable covering fall down dead after beholding naked Truth in the face of the stern goddess. Have some of our Darwinians, so tenderly united in natural selection and affinity, also gazed at the Saitic Mother bereft of her veils? One might almost suspect it after reading their theories. Their great intellects must have collapsed while gauging too closely the uncovered face of Nature, leaving only the grey matter and ganglia in their brain, to respond to *blind* physico-chemical forces. At any rate, Shakespeare's lines apply admirably to our modern Evolutionist who symbolizes that "proud man," who –

> "Dress'd in a little brief authority;
> Most ignorant of what he's most assured
> His glassy essence – like an angry ape,
> Plays such fantastic tricks before high heaven,
> As make the Angels weep! . . . . "

These have nought to do with the "angels." Their only concern is the human ancestor, the pithecoid Noah who gave birth to three sons – the tailed Cynocephalus, the tailless Ape, and the "arboreal" Palæolithic man. On this point, they will not be contradicted. Every doubt expressed is immediately set down as an attempt to cripple scientific inquiry. The insuperable difficulty at the very foundation of the evolution theory, namely, that no Darwinian is able to give even an approximate definition of the period *at* which, and the form *in* which, the first man appeared, is smoothed down to a trifling impediment, which is "really of no account." Every branch of knowledge is in the same predicament, we are informed. The chemist bases his most abstruse calculations simply "upon a hypothesis of atoms and molecules, of which not one has ever been seen isolated, weighed, or defined. The electrician speaks of magnetic fluids which have never intangibly revealed themselves. No definite origin can be assigned either to molecules or magnetism. Science cannot and does not pretend to any knowledge of the beginnings of law, matter or life, . . ." etc., etc. (*Knowledge*, January, 1882.)

And, withal, to reject a *scientific hypothesis*, however absurd, is to commit the one unpardonable sin! We risk it.

The Secret Doctrine, ii 649 – 655

Selection 27

THE ANCESTORS MANKIND IS OFFERED BY SCIENCE

"The question of questions for mankind – the problem
which underlies all others and is more deeply
interesting than any other – is the ascertainment
of the place which man occupies in nature, and of
his relations to the universe of things." Huxley

The world stands divided this day, and hesitates between *divine* progenitors – be they Adam and Eve or the lunar *Pitris* – and *Bathybius Hæckelii*, the gelatinous hermit of the briny deep. Having explained the occult theory, it may now be compared with that of the modern Materialism. The reader is invited to choose between the two after having judged them on their respective merits.

We may derive some consolation for the rejection of our divine ancestors, in finding that the Hæckelian speculations receive no better treatment at the hands of strictly *exact* Science than do our own. Hæckel's *phylogenesis* is no less laughed at by the foes of his fantastic evolution, by other and greater Scientists, than our primeval races will be. As du Bois-Reymond puts it, we may believe him easily when he says that "ancestral trees of our race sketched in the 'Schöpfungsgeschichte' are of about as much value as are the pedigrees of the Homeric heroes in the eyes of the historical critic."

This settled, everyone will see that one hypothesis is as good as another. And as we find that German naturalist (Hæckel) himself confessing that neither geology (in its history of the past) nor the ancestral history of organisms will ever "rise to the position of a real exact Science,"[172] a large margin is thus left to Occult Science to make its annotations and lodge its protests. The world is left to choose between the teachings of Paracelsus, the "Father of Modern Chemistry," and

---

172 *"Pedigree of Man,"* The Proofs of Evolution, p. 273.

those of Hæckel, the Father of the mythical *Sozura*. We demand no more.

Without presuming to take part in the quarrel of such very learned naturalists as du Bois-Reymond and Hæckel *à propos* of our blood relationship to "those ancestors (of ours) which have led up from the unicellular classes, Vermes, Acrania, Pisces, Amphibia, Reptilia to the Aves," one may put in a few words, a question or two, for the information of our readers. Availing ourselves of the opportunity, and bearing in mind Darwin's theories of natural selection, etc., we would ask Science – with regard to the origin of the human and animal species – which theory of evolution of the two herewith described is the more scientific, or the more *unscientific*, if so preferred.

(1). Is it that of an Evolution which starts from the beginning with sexual propagation?

(2). Or that teaching which shows the gradual development of organs, their solidification, and the procreation of each species, at first by simple easy separation from one into two or even several individuals. Then follows a fresh development – the first step to a species of separate distinct sexes – the hermaphrodite condition; then again, a kind of Parthenogenesis, "virginal reproduction," when the egg-cells are formed within the body, issuing from it in atomic emanations and becoming matured outside of it; until, finally, after a definite separation into sexes, the human beings begin procreating through sexual connection?

Of these two, the former "theory" – rather, a *"revealed* fact" – is enunciated by all the *exoteric* Bibles (except the *Purânas*), preeminently by the Jewish Cosmogony. The last one, is that which is taught by the Occult philosophy, as explained all along. An answer is found to our question in a volume just published by Mr. S. Laing – the best lay exponent of Modern Science.[173] In Chp. VIII of his latest work, "A *Modern Zoroastrian*," the author begins by twitting "all ancient religions and philosophies" for "assuming a male and female principle for their gods." At first sight, he says "the distinction of sex appears as

---

173 Author of "*Modern Science and Modern Thought*."

fundamental as that of plant and animal.". . . "The Spirit of god brooding over Chaos and producing the world," he goes on to complain, "is only a later edition, revised according to monotheistic ideas, of the far older Chaldean legend which describes the creation of *Kosmos* out of Chaos by the co-operations of great gods, male and female . ." Thus, in the orthodox Christian creed, we are taught to repeat "begotten, not made," a phrase which is absolute nonsense, an instance of using words like counterfeit notes, which have no solid value of an idea behind them. For "begotten" is a very definite term which "implies the conjunction of two opposite sexes to produce a new individual."

However, we may agree with the learned author as to the inadvisability of using wrong words, and the terrible anthropomorphic and *phallic* element in the old Scriptures – especially in the orthodox Christian *Bible* – nevertheless, there may be two extenuating circumstances in the case. Firstly, all these "ancient philosophies" and "modern religions" are – as sufficiently shown in these two volumes – an exoteric veil thrown over the face of esoteric truth; and – as the direct result of this – they are allegorical, *i.e.* mythological in form; but still they are immensely more philosophical in essence than any of the new *scientific* theories, so-called. Secondly, from the Orphic theogony down to Ezra's last remodeling of the Pentateuch, every old Scripture having in its origin borrowed its facts from the East, it has been subjected to constant alterations by friend and foe, until of the original version there remained but the name, a dead shell from which the Spirit had been gradually eliminated.

This alone ought to show that no religious work now extant can be understood without the help of the Archaic wisdom, the primitive foundation on which they were all built.

SCIENCE MAKES SAD HAVOC WITH THIS IMPRESSION OF SEXUAL GENERATION BEING THE ORIGINAL AND ONLY MODE OF REPRODUCTION

But to return to the direct answer expected from Science to *our* direct question. It is given by the same author, when, following his train of thought on the unscientific euhemerization of the powers of Nature in ancient creeds, he pronounces a condemnatory verdict upon them in the following terms:

"Science, however, makes sad havoc with this impression *of sexual generation being the original and only mode of reproduction*,[174] and the microscope and dissecting knife of the naturalist introduce us to new and altogether unsuspected (?) worlds of life." So little *"unsuspected,"* indeed, that the *original* a-sexual "modes of reproduction" must have been known – to the ancient Hindus, at any rate – Mr. Laing's assertion to the contrary, notwithstanding. In view of the statement in the *Vishnu Purâna*, quoted by us elsewhere, that Daksha "established sexual intercourse as the means of multiplication," only after a series of other "modes," which are all enumerated therein, (Vol. II, p. 12, Wilson's Translation), it becomes difficult to deny the fact. This assertion, moreover, is found, note well, in an EXOTERIC work. Then, Mr. S. Laing goes on to tell us that:

> . . . . "By far the larger proportion of living forms, in number . . . . have come into existence, *without the aid of sexual* propagation." He then instances Hæckel's monera . . . . *"multiplying by self-division."* The next stage the author shows in the nucleated cell, "which does exactly the same thing." The following stage is that in "which the organism does not divide into two equal parts, but a *small portion of it swells out* . . . . *and finally parts company* and starts on separate existence, which grows to the size of the parent by its inherent faculty of manufacturing fresh protoplasm from surrounding inorganic materials."[175]

This is followed by a many-celled organism which is formed by *"germ-buds reduced to spores, or single cells, which are emitted from the parent"* . . . . when "we are at the threshold of that system of sexual propagation, which has (now) become the rule in all the higher families of animals" . . . . It is when an "organism, having advantages in the struggle for life, established itself permanently" . . . that special organs developed to meet the altered condition . . . . when a distinction "would be firmly established of a female organ or ovary containing the egg or

---

174 *Vide* Part I of this volume, page 183, Stanza VIII.

175 In this, as shown in Part I, Modern Science was again anticipated, far beyond its own speculations in this direction, by *Archaic* Science.

primitive cell from which the new being was to be developed.".... "This is confirmed by a study of embryology, *which shows that in the* HUMAN and higher animal species *the distinction of sex is not developed* until a considerable progress has been made in the growth of the embryo . . . ." In the great majority of plants, and in some lower families of animals . . . the male and female organs are developed within the same being . . . a hermaphrodite. Moreover, in the "virginal reproduction – germ-cells apparently similar in all respects to egg-cells, develop themselves into new individuals *without any fructifying element*," etc., etc. (pp. 103 – 107).

Of all which we are as perfectly well aware as of this – that the above was never applied by the very learned English popularizer of Huxleyo-Hæckelian theories to the genus *homo*. He limits this to specks of protoplasm, plants, bees, snails, and so on. But if he would be true to the theory of descent, he must be as true to ontogenesis, in which the fundamental biogenetic law, we are told, runs as follows: "the development of the embryo (ontogeny) is a condensed and abbreviated repetition *of the evolution of the race* (phylogeny). This repetition is the more complete, the more the true original order of evolution (palingenesis) has been retained by continual heredity. On the other hand, this repetition is the less complete, the more by varying adaptations the later spurious development (cænogenesis) has obtained." (*Anthropogeny*, 3rd Ed., p. 11.)

This shows to us that every living creature and thing on earth, including man, evolved from *one common primal form*. Physical man must have passed through the same stages of the evolutionary process in the various modes of procreation as other animals have: he must have *divided* himself; then, hermaphrodite, have given birth *parthenogenetically* (on the immaculate principle) to his young ones; the next stage would be the *oviparous* – at first "without any fructifying element," then "with the help of the fertilitary spore"; and only after the final and definite evolution of both sexes, would he become a distinct "male and female," when reproduction through sexual union would grow into universal law. So far, all this is scientifically proven. There remains but one thing to be ascertained: the plain and comprehensively described processes of such *ante*-sexual reproduction. This is done in the Occult books, a slight outline of which was attempted by the writer in Part I of this Volume.

MAN HAS A DISTINCTLY DUAL NATURE

Either this, or – man is a distinct being. Occult philosophy may call him that, because of his distinctly *dual* nature. Science cannot do so, once that it rejects every interference save *mechanical laws, and* admits of no principle outside matter. The former – the archaic Science – allows the human physical frame to have passed through every form, from the lowest to the very highest, its present one, or from the simple to the complex – to use the accepted terms. But it claims that in this cycle (the fourth), the frame having already existed among the types and models of nature from the preceding Rounds – that it was quite ready for man from the beginning of *this Round*.[176] The Monad had but to step into the astral body of the progenitors, in order that the work of physical consolidation should begin around the shadowy prototype.[177]

What would Science say to this? It would answer, of course, that as man appeared on earth as the latest of the mammalians, he had no need, no more than those mammals, to pass through the primitive stages of procreation as above described. His mode of procreation was already established on Earth when he appeared. In this case, we may reply: since to this day not the remotest sign of a link between man and the animal has yet been found, then (if the Occultist doctrine is to be repudiated) he must have sprung *miraculously* in nature, like a fully armed Minerva from Jupiter's brain. And in such case the *Bible* is right,

---

176 Theosophists will remember that, according to Occult teaching, Cyclic *pralayas* so-called are but *obscurations*, during which periods Nature, *i.e.* everything visible and *invisible* on a resting planet, remains *in statu quo*. Nature rests and slumbers, no work of destruction going on on the globe even if no active work is done. All forms, as well as their astral types, remain as they were at the last moment of its activity. The "night" of a planet has hardly any twilight preceding it. It is caught like a huge mammoth by an avalanche, and remains slumbering and frozen till the next dawn of its new day – a very short one indeed in comparison to the "Day of Brahmâ."

177 This will be pooh-poohed, because it will not be understood by our modern men of science, but every Occultist and Theosophist will easily realize the process. There can be *no objective* form on Earth (nor in the Universe either) without its astral prototype being first formed in Space. From Phidias down to the humblest workman in the ceramic art—a sculptor has had to create first of all a model in his mind, then sketch it in one and two dimensional lines, and then only can he reproduce it in a three dimensional or objective figure. And if human mind is a living demonstration of such successive stages in the process of evolution—how can it be otherwise when NATURE'S MIND and creative powers are concerned?

along with other national "revelations." Hence the scientific scorn, so freely lavished by the author of *"A Modern Zoroastrian"* upon ancient philosophies and *exoteric* creeds, becomes premature and uncalled for. Nor would the sudden discovery of a "missing-link"-like fossil mend matters at all. For neither one such solitary specimen nor the *scientific conclusions* thereupon, could insure its being the long-sought-for relic, *i.e.* that of an undeveloped, still a once *speaking* MAN. Something more would be required as a final proof (*vide infra*, Note). Besides which, even *Genesis* takes up man, her Adam of dust, only where the Secret Doctrine leaves her "Sons of God and Wisdom" and picks up the physical man of the THIRD Race. Eve is *not* "begotten," but is extracted out of Adam on the manner of "Amœba A," contracting in the middle and splitting into Amœba B – by division. (See p. 103, in *"The Modern Zoroastrian."*) Nor has human speech developed from the various animal sounds.

WHERE ARE THE "MISSING LINKS"?

Hæckel's theory that "speech arose gradually from a few simple, crude animal sounds . . . ." as such "speech still remains amongst a few races of lower rank" (Darwinian theory in *"Pedigree of Man,"* p. 22) is altogether unsound, as argued by Professor Max Müller, among others. He contends that no plausible explanation has yet been given as to how the "roots" of language came into existence. A *human* brain is necessary for *human* speech. And figures relating to the size of the respective brains of man and ape show how deep is the gulf which separates the two. Vogt says that the brain of the largest ape, the gorilla, measures no more than 30.51 cubic inches, while the average brains of the flat-headed Australian natives – the lowest now in the human races – amount to 99.35 cubic inches! Figures are awkward witnesses and cannot lie. Therefore, as truly observed by Dr. F. Pfaff, whose premises are as sound and correct as his biblical conclusions are silly: "The brain of the apes most like man, does not amount to quite a third of the brain of the lowest races *of men: it is not half the size of the brain of a new-born child.*" (*"The Age and Origin of Man."*) From the foregoing it is thus very easy to perceive that in order to prove the Huxley-Hæckelian theories of the descent of man, it is not *one*, but a great number of *"missing links"* – a true ladder of progressive evolutionary steps – that would have to be first found and then presented by Science to thinking and reasoning humanity, before it would abandon belief in gods and the immortal Soul for the worship of Quadrumanic ancestors. Mere myths are now greeted as "axiomatic truths." Even Alfred Russel Wallace maintains with Hæckel that primitive man was a speechless ape-creature. To this Joly answers, "Man never was, in my opinion, this *pithecanthropus alalus* whose portrait Hæckel has drawn *as if he had seen and known him,* whose *singular* and *completely hypothetical* genealogy he has even given, from the mere mass of living protoplasm to the man endowed with speech and a civilization analogous to that of the Australians and Papuans." ("*Man before Metals,*" p. 320, *N. Joly. Inter. Scient. Series*)

Hæckel, among other things, often comes into direct conflict with the Science of languages. In the course of his attack on Evolutionism ("*Mr. Darwin's Philosophy of Language,*" 1873), Prof. Max Müller stigmatized the Darwinian theory as "vulnerable at the beginning and at the end." The fact is, that only the partial truth of many of the *secondary* "laws" of Darwinism is beyond question – M. de Quatrefages evidently accepting "Natural Selection," the "struggle for existence" and transformation within species, as proven not once and for ever, but *pro tem.* But it may not be amiss, perhaps, to condense the linguistic case against the "Ape ancestor" theory.

Languages have their phases of growth, etc., like all else in nature. It is almost certain that the great linguistic families pass through three stages.

(1) All words are roots and merely placed in juxtaposition (Radical languages).

(2) One One root defines the other, and becomes merely a determinative element (Agglutinative).

(3) The determinative element (the determinating meaning of which has longed lapsed) unites into a whole with the formative element (Inflected).

The problem then is: Whence these ROOTS? Max Müller argues that the existence of these *ready-made materials of speech* is a proof that man cannot be the crown of a long organic series. This *potentiality of forming roots* is the great crux which materialists almost invariably avoid.

Von Hartmann explains it as a manifestation of the "Unconscious," and admits its cogency *versus* mechanical Atheism. Hartmann is a fair representative of the Metaphysician and Idealist of the present age.

The argument has never been met by the non-pantheistic Evolutionists. To say with Schmidt, "Forsooth are we to halt before the origin of language?", is an avowal of dogmatism and of speedy defeat. (*Cf.* his "*Doctrine of Descent and Darwinism,*" p. 304.)

We respect those men of science who, wise in their generation, say: "Prehistoric Past being utterly beyond our powers of direct observation, we are too honest, too devoted to the truth – or what we regard as truth – to speculate upon the unknown, giving out our unproven theories along with facts absolutely established in modern Science." . . . . "The borderland of (metaphysical) knowledge is best left to time, which is the best test as to truth" ("*A Modern Zoroastrian,*" p. 136).

Proofs of Humanity's "Noble Descent"

This is a wise and an honest sentence in the mouth of a materialist. But when a Hæckel, after just saying that "*historical* events of past time. . ." having "occurred *many millions of years ago*,[178] . . . are for ever removed from direct observation," and that neither geology nor phylogeny[179] can or will "rise to the position of a real *exact* science," then *insists* on the development of *all* organisms – "from the lowest vertebrate to the highest, from Amphioxus to man" – we ask for a weightier proof than he can give. Mere "*empirical* sources of knowledge," so extolled by the author of "*Anthropogeny*" – when he has to be satisfied with the qualification for his own views – are not competent to settle problems lying beyond their domain, nor is it the province of exact science to

---

178 It thus appears that in its anxiety to prove our noble descent from the catarrhine "baboon," Hæckel's school has pushed the times of pre-historic man millions of years back. (See "*Pedigree of Man,*" p. 273.) Occultists render thanks to science for such corroboration of our claims!

179 This seems a poor compliment to pay Geology, which is not a speculative but as exact a science as astronomy—save, perhaps its too risky chronological speculations. It is mainly a "Descriptive" as opposed to an "Abstract" Science.

place any reliance on them.[180] If "empirical" – and Hæckel declares so himself repeatedly – then they are no better, nor any more reliable, in the sight of *exact* research, when extended into the remote past, than our Occult teachings of the East, both having to be placed on quite the same level. Nor are his *phylogenetic* and *palingenetic* speculations treated in any better way by the real scientists, than are our cyclic repetitions of the evolution of the Great in the minor races, and the original order of evolutions. For the province of exact, real Science, materialistic though it be, is to carefully avoid anything like guess-work, speculation which *cannot be* verified, in short, all *suppressio veri* and all *suggestio falsi*. The business of the man of exact Science is to observe, each in his chosen department, the phenomena of nature, to record, tabulate, compare and classify the facts, down to the smallest minutiæ which a*re presented to the observation of the senses with the help of all the exquisite mechanism that modern invention supplies, not by the aid of metaphysical flights of fancy.* All that he has a legitimate right to do, is to correct by the assistance of physical instruments the defects or illusions of his own coarser vision, auditory powers, and other senses. He has no right to trespass on the grounds of metaphysics and psychology. His duty is to verify and to rectify all the facts that *fall under his direct* observation, to profit by the experiences and mistakes of the Past in endeavouring to trace the working of a certain concatenation of cause and effects, which, but only by its constant and unvarying repetition, may be called a Law. This it is which a man of science is expected to do, if he would become a teacher of men and remain true to his original programme of natural or physical sciences. Any sideway path from this royal road becomes *speculation*.

---

180 Such newly-coined words as "*perigenesis of plastids*," "plastidule Souls" (!), and others less comely, invented by Hæckel, may be very learned and correct in so far as they may express very graphically the ideas in his own vivid fancy. As a *fact*, however, they remain for his less imaginative colleagues painfully *cænogenetic*—to use his own terminology; *i.e.* for *true* Science they are *spurious* speculations so long as they are derived from "empirical sources." Therefore, when he seeks to prove that "the origin of man from other mammals, and most directly from the catarrhine ape, is a *deductive law* that follows necessarily from *the inductive* law of the theory of descent" ("*Anthropogeny*," p. 392)—his no less learned foes (du Bois Reymond—for one) have a right to see in this sentence a *mere jugglery of words*; a "*testimonium paupertatis* of natural science"—as he himself complains, calling them, in return, *ignoramuses* (see "*Pedigree of Man*," Notes).

SOME SCIENTISTS DEMAND THEIR WILD THEORIES BE TAKEN ON BLIND FAITH AS THE OUTCOME OF SCIENCE.

Instead of keeping to this, what does many a so-called man of science do in these days? He rushes into the domains of pure metaphysics, while deriding it. He delights in rash conclusions and calls it "a *deductive* law from the *inductive* law" of a theory based upon and drawn out of the depths of his own consciousness, that consciousness being perverted by, and honeycombed with, one-sided materialism. He attempts to explain the "origin" of things, which are yet embosomed only in his own conceptions. He attacks spiritual beliefs and religious traditions millenniums old, and denounces everything, save his own hobbies, as superstition. He suggests theories of the Universe, a Cosmogony developed by blind, mechanical forces of nature alone, far more *miraculous and impossible* than even one based upon the assumption of *fiat lux* out of *nihil* – and tries to astonish the world by such a wild theory; which, being known to emanate from a scientific brain, is taken on *blind faith* as very scientific and the outcome of SCIENCE.

Are those the opponents Occultism would dread? Most decidedly not. For such theories are no better treated by *real* (not empirical) Science than our own. Hæckel, hurt in his vanity by du Bois Reymond, never tires of complaining publicly of the latter's onslaught on his fantastic theory of descent. Rhapsodizing on "the exceedingly rich storehouse of empirical evidence," he calls those "recognised physiologists" who oppose every speculation of his drawn from the said "storehouse" – *ignorant* men. "If many men," he declares – "and among them even some scientists of repute – hold that the whole of phylogeny is a castle in the air, and genealogical trees (from monkeys?) are empty plays of phantasy, they only in speaking thus demonstrate their ignorance of that wealth of *empirical sources of knowledge* to which reference has already been made" ("*Pedigree of Man*," p. 273).

We open Webster's Dictionary and read the definitions of the word "empirical": "Depending upon experience or observation alone, *without due regard to modern science and theory.*" This applies to the Occultists, Spiritualists, Mystics, etc., etc. Again, "an *Empiric*: "One who confines himself to applying the results of his own observations" (only) (which is Hæckel's case); "one *wanting Science* . . . . an ignorant and unlicensed practitioner; a quack; a CHARLATAN."

No Occultist or "magician," has ever been treated to any worse epithets. Yet the Occultist remains on his own metaphysical grounds, and does not endeavour to rank *his knowledge,* the fruits of *his* personal observation and experience, among the *exact* sciences of modern learning. He keeps within his legitimate sphere, where he is master. But what is one to think of a rank materialist, whose duty is clearly traced before him, who uses such an expression as this:

"The origin of man from other mammals, and most directly from the catarrhine ape, *is a deductive law, that follows necessarily from the inductive law of the* THEORY OF DESCENT. *("Anthropogeny,"* p. 392).

A "theory" is simply a hypothesis, a speculation, and *no law.* To say otherwise is only one of the many liberties taken now-a-days by scientists. They enunciate an absurdity, and then hide it behind the shield of Science. Any deduction from theoretical speculation is no better than *a speculation on a speculation.* Now Sir W. Hamilton has already shown that the word theory is now used "in a very loose and improper sense" .... "that it is convertible into *hypothesis,* and *hypothesis* is commonly used as another term for *conjecture,* whereas the terms 'theory' and 'theoretical' are properly used in opposition to the term *practice* and *practical."*

But modern Science puts an extinguisher on the latter statement, and mocks at the idea. Materialistic philosophers and Idealists of Europe and America may be agreed with the Evolutionists as to the physical origin of man – yet it will never become a general truth with the true metaphysician, and the latter defies the materialists to make good their arbitrary assumptions. That the ape-theory theme[181] of Vogt

---

181 The mental barrier between man and ape, characterized by Huxley as an *"enormous gap,* a distance *practically* immeasurable"! ! is, indeed, in itself conclusive. Certainly it constitutes a standing puzzle to the materialist, who relies on the frail reed of "natural selection." The physiological differences between Man and the Apes are in reality—despite a curious community of certain features—equally striking. Says Dr. Schweinfurth, one of the most cautious and experienced of naturalists:—

"In modern times there are no animals in creation that have attracted more attention from the scientific student than the great *quadrumana* (the anthropoids), bearing such a striking resemblance to the human form as to have justified the epithet of anthropomorphic being conferred on them. . . . But *all investigation at present only leads human intelligence to a confession of its insufficiency;* and nowhere is caution more to be advocated, *nowhere is premature judgment more to be deprecated than in the attempt to bridge*

and Darwin, on which the Huxley-Hæckelians have composed of late such extraordinary variations, is far less scientific – because clashing with the fundamental laws of that theme itself – than ours can ever be shown to be, is very easy of demonstration. Let the reader only turn to the excellent work on "*Human Species*" by the great French naturalist de Quatrefages, and our statement will at once be verified.

Moreover, between the esoteric teaching concerning the origin of man and Darwin's speculations, no man, unless he is a rank materialist, will hesitate. This is the description given by Mr. Darwin of "the earliest ancestors of man."

> "They were without doubt once covered with hair; both sexes having beards; their ears were pointed and capable of movement; *and their bodies were provided with a tail*, having the proper muscles. Their limbs and bodies were acted on by many muscles which now only occasionally reappear in man, but which are still normally present in the quadrumana. . . . The foot, judging from the condition of the great toe in the fœtus, was then prehensile, and our progenitors, no doubt, were *arboreal in their habits*, frequenting some warm forest-clad land, and the males were provided with canine teeth which served as formidable weapons. . . ." [182]

Darwin connects him with the type of the tailed catarrhines, "and consequently removes him a stage backward in the scale of evolution. The English naturalist is not satisfied to take his stand upon the ground of his own doctrines, and, like Hæckel, *on this point places himself in direct variance with one of the fundamental laws* which constitute the principal charm of Darwinism . . ." And then the learned French naturalist proceeds to show how this fundamental law is broken. "In fact," he says, "in the theory of Darwin, transmutations do not take place, either by chance or in every direction. They are ruled by certain laws which are due to the organization itself. If an organism is once modified in a given direction, it can undergo secondary or tertiary transmutations,

over the MYSTERIOUS CHASM which separates man and beast." "Heart of Africa" I, 520.

182 A ridiculous instance of evolutionist contradictions is afforded by Schmidt ("*Doctrine of Descent and Darwinism*," p. 292). He says, "Man's kinship with the apes is *not impugned* by the *bestial strength* of the teeth of the male orang or gorilla." Mr. Darwin, on the contrary, endows this fabulous being with teeth used as weapons!

but will still preserve the impress of the original. It is the law of *permanent characterization, which alone* permits Darwin to explain the filiation of groups, their characteristics, and their numerous relations. It is by virtue of this law that *all* the descendants of the first mollusc have been molluscs; all the descendants of the first vertebrate have been vertebrates. It is clear that this constitutes one of the foundations of the doctrine. . . . It follows that two beings belonging to two distinct types can be referred to *a common ancestor,* but the one cannot be the descendant of the other" (p. 106).

A WALKING ANIMAL CANNOT BE DESCENDED FROM A CLIMBING ONE

"Now man and ape present a very striking contrast in *respect to type.* Their organs. . . correspond almost exactly term for term, but these organs are arranged after a very different plan. In man they are so arranged that he is essentially a *walker,* while in apes they necessitate his being a *climber.* . . . There is here an anatomical and mechanical distinction. . . . A glance at the page where Huxley has figured side by side a human skeleton and the skeletons of the most highly developed apes is a sufficiently convincing proof."

The consequence of these facts, from the point of view of the logical application of the law of *permanent characterizations,* is that man cannot be descended from an ancestor who is already characterized as an ape, any more than a catarrhine tailless ape can be descended from a tailed catarrhine. A *walking animal* cannot be descended from a *climbing* one.

"Vogt, in placing man among the *primates,* declares without hesitation that *the lowest class of apes have passed the landmark* (the common ancestor), from which the different types of this family have originated and diverged." (This ancestor of the apes, Occult science sees in the lowest human group during the Atlantean period, as shown before.) . . . "We must, then, place the origin of man beyond the last apes," goes on de Quatrefages, thus corroborating our Doctrine, "if we would adhere to one of the laws most emphatically necessary to the Darwinian theory. We then come to the *prosimiæ* of Hæckel, the loris, indris, etc. But those animals also are climbers; we must go further, therefore, in search of our first direct ancestor. But the genealogy by Hæckel brings us from the latter to the marsupials. . . . From men to the Kangaroo, the distance is certainly great. Now neither living nor extinct fauna show the intermediate types which ought to serve as landmarks. This difficulty causes but slight embarrassment to Darwin.[183] We know that he considers the *want of information* upon similar questions *as a proof in his favour.* Hæckel doubtless is as little embarrassed. He admits the existence of an absolutely *theoretical pithecoid man.*"

"Thus, since it has been proved that, according to Darwinism itself, the origin of man must be placed beyond the eighteenth stage, and since it becomes, in consequence, *necessary* to fill up the gap between marsupials and man, will Hæckel admit the existence *of four unknown intermediate groups* instead of one?" asks de Quatrefages. "Will he complete his genealogy in this manner? It is not for me to answer." ("*The Human Species,*" p. 107 – 108.)

But see Hæckel's famous genealogy, in "*The Pedigree of Man,*" called by him "Ancestral Series of Man." In the "Second Division" (Eighteenth Stage) he describes "Prosimiæ, allied to the Loris (Stenops) and Makis (Lemur) as without marsupial bones and cloaca, but *with placenta.*" And now turn to de Quatrefages' "*The Human Species,*" pp. 109 – 110, and see his proofs, based on the latest discoveries, to show that "the prosimiae of Hæckel have no *decidua* and a diffuse placenta." They cannot be the ancestors of the apes even, let alone man, according to a fundamental law of Darwin himself, as the great French Naturalist shows. But this does not dismay the "animal theorists" in the least, for self-contradiction and paradoxes are the very soul of modern Darwinism. Witness – Mr. Huxley. Having himself shown, with regard to fossil man and the "missing link," that "neither in quaternary ages nor at the present time *does any intermediary being fill the gap* which separates man from the Troglodyte," and that to "deny the existence of this gap *would be as reprehensible as absurd,*" the great man of Science denies his own words *in actu* by supporting with all the weight of his scientific authority that

---

183 According even to a *fellow-thinker,* Professor Schmidt, Darwin has evolved "a certainly not flattering, and perhaps in *many points an incorrect,* portrait of our presumptive ancestors in the dawn of humanity." ("*Doctrine of Descent and Darwinism,*" p. 284.)

most "absurd" of all theories – the *descent of man from an ape!*

"This genealogy," says de Quatrefages, "*is wrong throughout,* and is founded on a material error." Indeed, Hæckel bases his descent of man on the 17th and 18th stages (See Aveling's "*Pedigree of Man,*" p. 77), the *marsupialia* and *prosimiæ* (genus *Hæckelii*?). Applying the latter term to the *Lemuridæ* – hence making of them animals with a *placenta* – *he commits* a zoological blunder. For after having himself divided mammals according to their anatomical differences into two groups, the *indeciduata,* which have no *decidua* (or special membrane uniting the placentæ), and the *deciduata,* those who possess it, he includes the *prosimiæ* in the latter group. Now we have shown elsewhere what other men of science had to say to this. As de Quatrefages says, "The anatomical investigations of . . . Milne Edwards and Grandidier upon these animals . . . place it beyond all doubt that the *prosimiæ* of Hæckel have no decidua and a diffuse placenta. They are *indeciduata.* Far from any possibility of their being the ancestors of the apes, according to the principles laid down by Hæckel himself, *they cannot be regarded even as the ancestors of the zonoplacental mammals . . .* and ought to be connected with the *pachydermata,* the *edentata,* and the *cetacea*" (p. 110). And yet Hæckel's inventions pass off with some as exact science!

AGREEMENT WITH THE DARWINIAN SCHOOL: THE LAW OF GRADUAL AND EXTREMELY SLOW EVOLUTION, EMBRACING MANY MILLIONS OF YEARS

The above mistake, if indeed, one, is not even hinted at in Hæckel's "*Pedigree of Man,*" translated by Aveling. If the excuse may stand good that at the time the famous "genealogies" were made, "the embryogenesis of the *prosimiæ* was not known," it is familiar now. We shall see whether the next edition of Aveling's translation will have this important error rectified, or if the 17th and 18th stages remain as they are to blind the profane, as one of the real intermediate links. But, as the French naturalist observes, "their (Darwin's and Hæckel's) process is always the same, considering the *unknown* as a proof in favour of their theory." (*Ibid*)

It comes to this. Grant to man an immortal Spirit and Soul; endow the whole animate and inanimate creation with the monadic principle gradually evolving from the latent and passive into active and positive polarity – and Hæckel will not have a leg to stand upon, whatever his admirers may say.

But there are important divergences even between Darwin and Hæckel. While the former makes us proceed from the *tailed* catarrhine, Hæckel traces our hypothetical ancestor to the *tailless* ape, though, at the same time, he places him in a hypothetical "stage" immediately preceding this, "*Menocerca with tails*" (19th stage).

Nevertheless, we have one thing in common with the Darwinian school: it is the law of gradual and extremely slow evolution, embracing many million years. The chief quarrel, it appears, is with regard to the nature of the primitive "Ancestor." We shall be told that the *Dhyan Chohan*, or the "progenitor" of Manu, is a hypothetical being unknown on *the physical plane*. We reply that it was believed in by the whole of antiquity, and by nine-tenths of the present humanity, whereas not only is the *pithecoid man*, or "ape-man," a purely hypothetical creature of Hæckel's creation, unknown and untraceable on this earth, but further its genealogy – as invented by him – clashes with scientific facts and all the known data of modern discovery in Zoology. It is simply absurd, even as a fiction. As de Quatrefages demonstrates in a few words, Hæckel "admits the existence of an *absolutely theoretical pithecoid man*" – a hundred times more difficult to accept than any *Deva* ancestor. And it is not the only instance in which he proceeds in a similar manner in order to complete his genealogical table; he admits very *naively* his inventions himself. Does he not confess the non-existence of his *sozura* (14th stage) – a creature entirely *unknown to science* – by confessing over his own signature, that, "The proof of its existence arises from the necessity of an intermediate type between the 13th and the 14th stages"!

If so, we might maintain with as much scientific right, that the proof of the existence of our three ethereal races, and the three-eyed men of the Third and Fourth Root-Races "arises also from the necessity of an intermediate type" between the *animal* and the gods. What reason would the Hæckelians have to protest in this special case?

Of course there is a ready answer: "Because we do not grant the presence of the monadic essence." The manifestation of the *Logos* as individual *consciousness* in the animal and human creation is not accepted by exact science, nor does it cover the whole ground, of course. But the failures of science and its arbitrary assumptions are far greater on the whole than* any "extravagant" esoteric doctrine can ever furnish. Even thinkers of the school of Von Hartmann have become tainted with the general epidemic. They accept the Darwinian anthropology (more or less), though they also postulate the individual Ego as a manifestation of the Unconscious (the Western presentation of the *Logos* or Primeval Divine Thought). They say the evolution of the physical man is from the animal, but that mind in its various phases is altogether a thing apart from material facts, though organism (as an *upadhi*) is necessary for ITS manifestation.

The Secret Doctrine, ii 656 – 670

Selection 28

THE FOSSIL RELICS OF MAN AND THE ANTHROPOID APE

The data derived from scientific research as to "primeval man" and the ape lend no countenance to theories deriving the former from the latter. "Where, then, must we look for primeval man?" still queries Mr. Huxley, after having vainly searched for him in the very depths of the quaternary strata. "Was the oldest *Homo sapiens* Pliocene or Miocene, or yet more ancient? In still older strata do the fossilized bones of *an ape more anthropoid,* or *a man more pithecoid* than any yet known, await the researches of some unborn palæontologist? Time will show . . . ." (*"Man's Place in Nature,"* p. 159).

It will – undeniably – and thus vindicate the anthropology of the Occultists. Meanwhile, in his eagerness to vindicate Mr. Darwin's *Descent of Man,* Mr. Boyd Dawkins believes he has all but found the "missing link" – in theory. It was due to theologians more than to geologists that, till nearly 1860, man had been considered a relic no older than the Adamic orthodox 6,000 years. As Karma would have it though, it was left to a French Abbé – l'abbé Bourgeois – to give this easy-going theory even a worse blow than had been given to it by the discoveries of Boucher de Perthes. Everyone knows that the Abbé discovered and brought to light good evidence that man already existed during the Miocene period, for flints of undeniably human making were excavated from Miocene strata. In the words of the author of *"Modern Science and Modern Thought"*:

"They must either have been chipped by man, or, as Mr. Boyd Dawkins supposes, by the *Dryopithecus* or some other anthropoid ape which had a dose of intelligence so much superior to the gorilla, or chimpanzee, as to be able to fabricate tools. But in this case the problem would be solved and the missing link discovered, for such an ape might well have been the *ancestor* of Palæolithic man."

Or – *the descendant of Eocene Man,* which is a variant offered to the theory. Meanwhile, the *Dryopithecus* with such fine mental endowments is yet to be discovered. On the other hand, Neolithic and even Palæolithic man having become an absolute certainty – and, as the same author justly observes: "If 100,000,000 years have elapsed since the earth became sufficiently solidified to support vegetable and animal life, the Tertiary period may have lasted for 5,000,000, or for 10,000,000 years, if the life-sustaining order of things has lasted, as Lyell supposes, for at least 200,000,000 years" – why should not another theory be tried? Let us carry man, as an hypothesis, to the close of Mesozoic times – admitting *argumenti causâ* that the (much more recent) higher apes then existed! This would allow ample time to man and the modern apes to have diverged from the mythical *"ape more anthropoid,"* and even for the latter to have degenerated into those that are found *mimicking* man in using "branches of trees as clubs, and cracking cocoa-nuts with hammer and stones."[184] Some savage tribes of hillmen in India build their abodes on trees, just as the gorillas build their dens. The question, which of the two, the beast or the man, has become the imitator of the other, is scarcely an open one, even granting Mr. Boyd Dawkins' theory. The fanciful character of his hypothesis, is, however, generally admitted. It is argued that, while in the Pliocene and Miocene periods, there were true apes and baboons, and man was undeniably contemporaneous with the former of those times – though as we see orthodox anthropology still hesitates in the teeth of facts to place him in the era of the *Dryopithecus,* which latter "has been considered by some anatomists as in some respects superior to the chimpanzee or the gorilla" – yet, in the Eocene there have been no other fossil *primates* unearthed and no pithecoid stocks found save a few extinct Lemurian forms. And we find it also *hinted* that the *Dryopithecus may have been* the "missing link," though the brain of the creature no more warrants the theory than does the brain of the modern gorilla. (*Vide* also Gaudry's speculations.)

---

184 This is the way *primitive man* must have acted? We do not know of men, not even of savages, in our age, who are known to have imitated the apes who live side by side with them in the forests of America and the islands. We do know of large apes who, tamed and living in houses, will mimic men to the length of donning hats and coats. The writer had personally a chimpanzee who, without being taught, opened a newspaper and pretended to read in it. It is the descending generations, the children, who mimic their parents—not the reverse.

Now we would ask who among the Scientists is ready to prove that *there was no man* in existence in the early Tertiary period? What is it that prevented his presence? Hardly thirty years ago his existence any farther back than 6,000 or 7,000 years was indignantly denied. Now he is refused admission into the Eocene age. Next century it may become a question whether man was not contemporary with the "flying Dragons," the pterodactyl, the plesiosaurus and iguanodon, etc., etc. Let us listen, however, to the echo of Science.

INSURMOUNTABLE DIFFICULTIES

"Now wherever anthropoid apes lived, it is clear that, whether as a question of anatomical structure, or of climate and surroundings, man, or *some creature which was the ancestor of man*, might have lived also. Anatomically speaking, apes and monkeys are as much special variations of the mammalian type as man, whom they resemble, bone for bone, and muscle for muscle, and the physical animal man is simply an instance of the quadrumanous type specialised for erect posture and a larger brain[185] . . . . If he could survive, as we know he did, the adverse conditions and extreme vicissitudes of the Glacial period, there is no reason why he might not have lived in the semi-tropical climate of the Miocene period, when a genial climate extended even to Greenland and Spitzbergen . . ." (*"Modern Science and Modern Thought,"* p. 152)

While most of the men of Science, who are uncompromising in their belief in the descent of man from an "extinct anthropoid mammal," will not accept even the bare tenability of any other theory than an ancestor common to man and the *Dryopithecus*, it is refreshing to find in a work of real scientific value such a margin for compromise. Indeed, it is as wide as it can be made under the circumstances, *i.e.* without immediate danger of getting knocked off one's feet by the tidal wave of "science-adulation." Believing that the difficulty of accounting "for the

---

185 It is asked, whether it would change one iota of the scientific truth and fact contained in the above sentence if it were to read, "the ape is simply an instance of the biped type specialized for going on all fours, generally, and a smaller brain." *Esoterically* speaking, this is the real truth, and not the reverse.

development of *intellect* and *morality* by evolution is *not so great as that presented by the difference as to physical structure*[186] between man and the highest animal," the same author says:

> "But it is not so easy to see how this difference of physical structure arose, and how a being came into existence which had such a brain and hand, and such undeveloped capabilities for an almost unlimited progress. The difficulty is this: the difference in structure between the lowest existing race of man and the highest existing ape is too great to admit of the possibility of one being the direct descendant of the other. The negro in some respects makes a slight approximation towards the Simian type. His skull is narrower, his brain less capacious, his muzzle more projecting, his arm longer than those of the average European man. Still he is essentially a man, and separated by a wide gulf from the chimpanzee or the gorilla. *Even the idiot or cretin,* whose brain is no larger and intelligence no greater than that of the chimpanzee, is *an arrested man, not an ape.*"

> "If, therefore, the Darwinian theory holds good in the case of man and ape, we must go back to some common ancestor from whom both may have originated . . . . But to establish this as a *fact* and not a *theory* we require to find that ancestral form, or, at any rate, some intermediate forms tending towards it . . . . in other words . . . . the missing link! Now it must be admitted that, hitherto, not only have no such missing links been discovered, but the oldest known

---

186 We cannot follow Mr. Laing here. When avowed Darwinists like Huxley point to "the *great gulf* which intervenes between the lowest ape and the highest man in *intellectual* power," the "*enormous gulf* . . . between them," the "*immeasurable and practically infinite* divergence of the Human from the Simian stirps" ("*Man's Place in Nature*," pp. 102–3); when even the physical basis of mind— the brain—so *vastly* exceeds in size that of the highest existing apes; when men like Wallace are forced to invoke the agency of extra-terrestrial intelligences in order to explain the rise of such a creature as the *Pithecanthropus alalus,* or speechless savage of Hæckel to the level of the large-brained and *moral* man of today—it is idle to dismiss Evolutionist puzzles so lightly. If the *structural* evidence is so unconvincing and, taken as a whole, so hostile to Darwinism, the difficulties as to the "how" of the Evolution of the human *mind* by natural selection are ten-fold greater.

human sculls and skeletons which date from the Glacial period, and are probably at least 100,000 years old, show no very decided approximation towards any such pre-human type. On the contrary, *one of the oldest types,* that of the men of the sepulchral cave of Cro-Magnon,[187] is *that of a fine race, tall in stature, large in brain, and on the whole superior to many of the existing races of mankind.* The reply of course is that the time is insufficient, *and if man and the ape had a common ancestor,* that as a highly developed anthropoid ape, certainly, and man, probably, already existed in the Miocene period, such ancestor must be sought still further back at a distance compared with which the whole Quaternary period sinks into insignificance. . . . It may well make us hesitate before we admit that man. . . is alone an exception. . . . This is more difficult to believe, as the ape family which man (?) so closely resembles . . . . contains numerous branches which graduate into one another, but the extremes of which differ more widely than man does from the highest of the ape series. If a special creation is required for man, *must there not have been special creations for the chimpanzee, the gorilla, the orang,* and for at least 100 different species of ape and monkeys which are all built on the same lines?" ("*Modern Science and Modern Thought*," p. 182)

Materialism Is Puzzled

There *was* a "special creation" for man, and a "special creation" for the ape, *his* progeny, only on other lines than ever bargained for by Science. Albert Gaudry and others give some weighty reasons why man cannot be regarded as the crown of an ape-stock. When one finds that not only was the "primeval savage" (?) a reality in the Miocene times, but that, as de Mortillet shows, the flint relics he has left behind him were splintered *by fire* in that remote epoch; when we learn that the *Dryopithecus, alone of the anthropoids,* appears in those strata, what is the natural inference? That the Darwinians are in a quandary. The

---

187 A race which MM. de Quatrefages and Hamy regard as a branch of the *same stock* whence the *Canary Island Guanches* sprung—offshoots of the Atlanteans, in short.

very manlike Gibbon is *still in the same low grade of development, as it was when it co-existed with Man at the close of the Glacial Period*. It has not appreciably altered since the Pliocene times. Now there is little to choose between the *Dryopithecus* and the existing anthropoids – gibbon, gorilla, etc. If, then, the Darwinian theory is all-sufficient, how are we to "explain" the evolution of this ape into Man during the first half of the Miocene? The time is far too short for such a theoretical transformation. The extreme slowness with which variation in species supervenes renders the thing inconceivable – more especially on the Natural Selection hypothesis. The enormous mental and structural gulf between a savage acquainted with fire and the mode of kindling it, and a brutal anthropoid, is too much to bridge even in idea, during so contracted a period. Let the Evolutionists push back the process into the preceding *Eocene*, if they prefer to do so; let them even trace both Man and *Dryopithecus* to a common ancestor; the unpleasant consideration has, nevertheless, to be faced that in Eocene strata the anthropoid fossils are as conspicuous by their absence, as is the fabulous *pithecanthropus* of Hæckel. Is an exit out of this *cul de sac* to be found by an appeal to the "unknown," and a reference with Darwin to the "imperfection of the geological record"? So be it; but the same right of appeal must be accorded equally to the Occultists, instead of remaining the monopoly of puzzled materialism. Physical man, we say, existed before the first bed of the Cretaceous rocks was deposited. In the early part of the Tertiary Age, the most brilliant civilization the world has ever known flourished at a period when the Hæckelian *man-ape* is conceived to have roamed through the primeval forests, and Mr. Grant Allen's putative ancestor to have swung himself from bough to bough with his hairy mates, the degenerated Liliths of the Third Race Adam. Yet there were no anthropoid apes in the brighter days of the civilization of the Fourth Race; but Karma is a mysterious law, and no respecter of persons. The monsters bred in sin and shame by the Atlantean giants, *"blurred copies"* of their bestial sires, and hence of modern man (Huxley), now mislead and overwhelm with error the speculative anthropologist of European Science.

The Secret Doctrine, ii 675 – 679

Selection 29

WHERE DID THE FIRST MEN LIVE?

Where did the first men live? Some Darwinists say in Western Africa, some in Southern Asia, others, again, believe in an independent origin of human stocks in Asia and America from a Simian ancestry (Vogt). Hæckel, however, advances gaily to the charge. Starting from his "*prosimiæ*" . . . "the ancestor common to all other *catarrhini*, including man" – a "link" now, however, disposed of for good by recent anatomical discoveries! – he endeavours to find a habitat for the primeval *Pithecanthropus alalus*. "In all probability it (the transformation of animal into man) occurred in Southern Asia, in which region many evidences are forthcoming that here was the original home of the different species of men. Probably Southern Asia itself was not the earliest cradle of the human race, but LEMURIA, *a continent that lay to the south of Asia, and sank later on beneath the surface of the Indian Ocean. (Vide infra,* "Scientific and geological proofs of the former existence of several submerged continents.") "The period during which the evolution of the anthropoid apes into apelike men took place was probably the last part of the tertiary period, the Pliocene Age, and perhaps the Miocene, its forerunner." ("*Pedigree of Man,*" p. 73)

Of the above speculations, the only one of any worth is that referring to Lemuria, which was the cradle of mankind – of the physical sexual creature who materialized through long æons out of the ethereal hermaphrodites. Only, if it is proved that *Easter Island* is an actual relic of Lemuria, we must believe that according to Hæckel the "*dumb ape-men,*" just removed from a brutal mammalian monster, built the gigantic portrait-statues, some of which are now in the British Museum. Critics are mistaken in terming Hæckelian doctrines "abominable, revolutionary, immoral" – though materialism is the legitimate outcome of the ape-ancestor myth – they are simply too absurd to demand disproof.

THE COMPARATIVE ANATOMY OF MAN AND ANTHROPOID IS NOT A CONFIRMATION OF DARWINISM

We are told that while every other heresy against modern science may be disregarded, this, our denial of the Darwinian theory as applied to Man, will be the one "unpardonable" sin. The Evolutionists stand firm as rock on the evidence of similarity of structure between the ape and the man. The anatomical evidence, it is urged, is quite overpowering in this case; it is *bone for bone*, and *muscle for muscle*, even the brain conformation being very much the same.

Well, what of that? All this was known before King Herod, and the writers of the *Ramayana*, the poets who sang the prowess and valour of Hanuman, the monkey-God, "whose feats were great and Wisdom never rivaled," must have known as much about his anatomy and brain as does any Hæckel or Huxley in our modern day. Volumes upon volumes were written upon this similarity, in antiquity as in more modern times. Therefore, there is nothing new whatever given to the world or to philosophy, in such volumes as Mivart's "*Man and Apes*," or Messrs. Fiske and Huxley's defence of Darwinism. But what are those *crucial* proofs of man's descent from a pithecoid ancestor? If the Darwinian theory *is not the true one* – we are told – if man and ape do not descend from a common ancestor, then we are called upon to explain the reason of:

(I.) The similarity of structure between the two; the fact that the higher animal world – man and beast – is physically of one type or pattern.

(II.) The presence of *rudimentary organs* in man, *i.e.* traces of former organs now atrophied by disuse. Some of these organs, it is asserted, could not have had any scope for employment, except for a semi-animal, semi-arboreal monster. Why, again, do we find in Man those "rudimentary" organs (as useless as its rudimentary wing is to the *Apteryx* of Australia), the vermiform appendix of the *cœcum*, the ear muscles,[188] the "rudimentary tail" (with which children are still sometimes born), etc., etc.?

---

188 Professor Owen believes that these muscles—the *attollens, retrahens,* and *attrahens aurem*—were actively functioning in men of the Stone Age. This may or may not be the case. The question falls under the ordinary "occult" explanation, and involves no postulate of an "animal progenitor" to solve it.

Such is the war cry; and the cackle of the smaller fry among the Darwinians is louder, if possible, than even that of the scientific Evolutionists themselves!

Furthermore, the latter themselves – with their great leader Mr. Huxley, and such eminent zoologists as Mr. Romanes and others – while defending the Darwinian theory, are the first to confess the almost insuperable difficulties in the way of its final demonstration. And there are as great men of science as the above-named, who deny, most emphatically, the uncalled-for assumption, and loudly denounce the unwarrantable exaggerations on the question of this supposed similarity. It is sufficient to glance at the works of Broca, Gratiolet, of Owen, Pruner-Bey, and finally, at the last great work of de Quatrefages, *"Introduction à l'Etude des Races humaines, Questions générales,"* to discover the fallacy of the Evolutionists. We may say more: the exaggerations concerning such similarity of structure between man and the anthropomorphous ape have become so glaring and absurd of late, that even Mr. Huxley found himself forced to protest against the too sanguine expectations. It was that great anatomist personally who called the "smaller fry" to order, by declaring in one of his articles that the differences in the structure of the human body and that of the highest anthropomorphous pithecoid, were not only *far from being trifling and unimportant,* but were, on the contrary, very great and suggestive: "each of the bones of the gorilla has its own specific impress on it that distinguishes it from a similar human bone." Among the existing creatures there is not one single intermediate form that could fill the gap between man and the ape. To ignore that gap, he added, "was *as uncalled-for as it was absurd*."[189]

---

189 Quoted in the Review of the *"Introduction à l'Etude des Races Humaines,"* by de Quatrefages. We have not Mr. Huxley's work at hand to quote from. Or to cite another good authority: "We find one of the most man-like apes (gibbon) in the *tertiary period,* and this species is *still in the same low grade,* and *side by side* with it at the end of the Ice-period, man is found in the same high grade as today, the ape not having approximated more nearly to the man, and modern man not having become further removed from the ape than the first (fossil) man. . . these facts contradict a theory of constant progressive development." (Pfaff.) When, according to Vogt, the average Australian brain = 99. 35 cubic inches, that of the gorilla 30. 51 cubic inches, and that of the chimpanzee only 25.45, the *giant gap* to be bridged by the advocate of "Natural" Selection becomes apparent.

Finally, the absurdity of such an *unnatural* descent of man is so palpable in the face of all the proofs and evidence of the skull of the pithecoid as compared to that of man, that even de Quatrefages resorted unconsciously to our esoteric theory by saying *that it is rather the apes that can claim descent from man* than *vice versâ*. As proven by Gratiolet, with regard to the cavities of the brain of the anthropoids, in which species that organ develops in an inverse ratio to what would be the case were the corresponding organs in man really the product of the development of the said organs in the apes – the size of the human skull and its brain, as well as the cavities, increase with the individual development of man. His intellect develops and increases with age, while his facial bones and jaws diminish and straighten, thus being more and more spiritualized: whereas with the ape it is the reverse. In its youth the anthropoid is far more intelligent and good-natured, while with age it becomes duller, and, as its skull recedes and seems to diminish as it grows, its facial bones and jaws develop, the brain being finally crushed, and thrown entirely back, to make with every day more room for the animal type. The organ of thought – the brain – recedes and diminishes, entirely conquered and replaced by that of the wild beast – the jaw apparatus.

Thus, as wittily remarked in the French work, a gorilla would have a perfect right to address an Evolutionist, claiming its right of descent from himself. It would say to him, "We, anthropoid apes, form a retrogressive departure from the human type, and therefore our development and evolution are expressed by a transition from a human-like to an animal-like structure of organism; but in what way could you, men, descend from us – how can you form a continuation of our genus? For, to make this possible, your organization would have to differ still more than ours does from the human structure, it would have to approach still closer to that of the beast than ours does, and in such a case justice demands that you should give up to us your place in nature. You are lower than we are, once that you insist on tracing your genealogy from our kind; for the structure of our organization and its development are such that we are unable to generate forms of a higher organization than our own.

MAN CANNOT DESCEND FROM EITHER AN APE OR AN ANCESTOR COMMON TO BOTH

This is where the Occult Sciences agree entirely with de Quatrefages. Owing to the very type of his development man *cannot descend* from either an ape or an ancestor common to both, but shows his origin from a type far superior to himself. And this type is the "Heavenly man" – the *Dhyan Chohans,* or the *Pitris* so-called, as shown in the first Part of this volume. On the other hand, the pithecoids, the orang-outang, the gorilla, and the chimpanzee can, and as the Occult Sciences teach, *do* descend from the animalized Fourth human Root-Race, being the product of man and an extinct species of mammal – whose *remote* ancestors were themselves the product of Lemurian bestiality – which lived in the Miocene age. The ancestry of this semi-human monster is explained in the Stanzas as originating in the sin of the "Mind-less" races of the middle Third Race period.

When it is borne in mind that all forms which now people the earth are so many variations on *basic types* originally thrown off by the MAN of the Third and Fourth Round, such an evolutionist argument as that insisting on the "unity of structural plan" characterising all vertebrates, loses its edge. The basic types referred to were very few in number in comparison with the multitude of organisms to which they ultimately gave rise, but a general unity of type has, nevertheless, been preserved throughout the ages. The economy of Nature does not sanction the co-existence of several utterly opposed "ground plans" of organic evolution on one planet. Once, however, that the general drift of the occult explanation is formulated, inference as to detail may well be left to the intuitive reader.

Similarly with the important question of the "rudimentary" organs discovered by anatomists in the human organism. Doubtless this line of argument, when wielded by Darwin and Hæckel against their European adversaries, proved of great weight. Anthropologists, who ventured to dispute the derivation of man from an animal ancestry, were sorely puzzled how to deal with the presence of gill-clefts, with the "tail" problem, and so on. Here again Occultism comes to our assistance with the necessary data.

The fact is that, as previously stated, the human type is the repertory of all potential organic forms, and the central point from which these latter radiate. In this postulate we find a true "*Evolution*" or "*unfolding*" – a sense which cannot be said to belong to the mechanical theory of natural selection. Criticising Darwin's inference from "rudiments," an able writer remarks, "Why is it not just as probably a true hypothesis to suppose that Man was *created with the rudimentary sketches in his organization, and that they became useful appendages in the lower animals into which man degenerated,* as to suppose that these parts existed in full development in the lower animals out of which man was generated? ("*Creation or Evolution?*", Geo. T. Curtis, p. 76.)

Read for "into which Man degenerated," "the prototypes which man shed in the course of his astral developments," and an aspect of the true esoteric solution is before us. But a wider generalization is now to be formulated.

So far as our present *Fourth Round* terrestrial period is concerned, the mammalian fauna are alone to be regarded as traceable to prototypes shed by Man. The amphibia, birds, reptiles, fishes, etc. are the resultants of the Third Round astral fossil forms stored up in the auric envelope of the Earth and projected into physical objectivity subsequent to the deposition of the first Laurentian rocks. "Evolution" has to deal with the progressive modifications, which palæontology shows to have affected the lower animal and vegetable kingdoms in the course of geological time. It does not, and from the nature of things cannot, touch on the subject of the pre-physical types which served as the basis for future differentiation. Tabulate the general laws controlling the development of physical organisms it certainly may, and to a certain extent it has acquitted itself ably of the task.

To return to the immediate subject of discussion. The *mammalia*, whose first traces are discovered in the marsupials of the Triassic rocks of the Secondary Period, were evolved from *purely* astral progenitors contemporary with the Second Race. They are thus *post-Human*, and, consequently, it is easy to account for the general resemblance between their embryonic stages and those of Man, who necessarily embraces in himself and epitomizes in his development the features of the group he originated. This explanation disposes of a portion of the Darwinist brief. "But how to account for the presence of the gill-clefts in the human fœtus, which represent the stage through which the branchiæ of the fish are developed;[190] for the pulsating vessel corresponding to the heart of the lower fishes, which constitutes the fœtal heart; for the entire analogy presented by the segmentation of the human *ovum*, the formation of the blastoderm, and the appearance of the 'gastrula' stage, with corresponding stages in lower vertebrate life and even among the sponges; "for the various types of lower animal life which the form of the future child shadows forth in the cycle of its growth?" "How comes it to pass that stages in the life of fishes, whose ancestors swam" – æons before the epoch of the First Root-Race – "in the seas of the Silurian period, as well as stages in that of the later amphibian, reptilian fauna, are mirrored in the 'epitomized history' of human fœtal development?"

The Secret Doctrine, ii 679 – 685

---

190 "At this period," writes Darwin, "the arteries run in arch-like branches, as if to carry the blood to branchiæ which are not present in the higher *vertebrata*, though the slits on the side of the neck still remain, marking their former (?) position."
It is noteworthy that, though gill-clefts are absolutely useless to all but *Amphibia* and fishes, *etc.* their appearance is regularly noted in the fœtal development of vertebrates. Even children are occasionally born with an opening in the neck corresponding to one of the clefts.

Selection 30

Reversion from the Wrong End

This plausible objection is met by the reply that the *Third Round* terrestrial animal forms were just as much referable to types thrown off by Third Round man, as that new importation into our planet's area – the mammalian stock – is to the Fourth Round Humanity of the Second Root-Race. The process of human fœtal growth epitomizes not only the general characteristics of the Fourth, but of the Third Round terrestrial life. The diapason of type is run through in brief. Occultists are thus at no loss to "account for" the birth of children with an actual caudal appendage, or for the fact that the tail in the human fœtus is, at one period, double the length of the nascent legs. The potentiality of every organ useful to animal life is locked up in Man – the microcosm of the Macrocosm – and abnormal conditions may not unfrequently result in the strange phenomena which Darwinists regard as "reversion to ancestral features."[191] Reversion, indeed, but scarcely in the sense contemplated by our present-day empiricists!

Darwinism and the Antiquity of Man: The Anthropoids and Their Ancestry

The public has been notified by more than one eminent modern geologist and man of science, that "all estimate of geological duration is not merely *impossible*, but necessarily imperfect; for we are ignorant of the causes, though they must have existed, which quickened or retarded the progress of the sedimentary deposits."[192] And now another man of Science, as well known (Croll), calculating that the tertiary

---

191 Those who, with Hæckel, regard the gill-clefts with their attendant phenomena as illustrative of an active function in our *Amphibia*n and piscine ancestors (*Vide* his XIIth and XIIIth stages) ought to explain why the "*Vegetable with leaflets*" (Lefèvre) represented in fœtal growth, does not appear in his 22 stages through which the *Monera* have passed in their ascent to Man. Hæckel does *not* postulate a *vegetable* ancestor. The embryological argument is thus a two-edged sword and here cuts its possessor.

192 "*Physiology*," Lefevre, p. 480.

age began either 15 or 2½ million of years ago – the former being a more correct calculation, according to Esoteric doctrine, than the latter – there seems in this case, at least, no very great disagreement. Exact Science, refusing to see in man "a special creation" (to a certain degree the Secret Sciences do the same), is at liberty to ignore the first three, or rather two-and-a-half Races – *the Spiritual, the semi-astral, and the semi-human* – of our teachings. But it can hardly do the same in the case of the Third at its closing period, the Fourth, and the Fifth Races, since it already divides mankind into Palæolithic and Neolithic man.[193] The geologists of France place man in the mid-Miocene age (Gabriel de Mortillet), and some even in the *Secondary* period, as de Quatrefages suggests, while the English *savants* do not generally accept such antiquity for their species. But they may know better some day. For "If we consider," says Sir Charles Lyell in *"Antiquity of Man"* (p. 246):

> "the absence or extreme scarcity of human bones and works of art in all strata, whether marine or fresh water, even in those formed in the immediate proximity of land inhabited by millions of human beings, we shall be prepared for the general dearth of human memorials in glacial formations, whether recent, Pleistocene, or of more ancient date. If there were a few wanderers over lands covered with glaciers, or over seas infested with icebergs, and if a few of them left their bones or weapons in moraines or in marine drifts, the chances, after the lapse of thousands of years, of a geologist meeting with one of them must be infinitesimally small."

193 We confess to not being able to see any good reasons for Mr. E. Clodd's certain statement in *Knowledge*. Speaking of the men of Neolithic times, "concerning whom Mr. Grant Allen has given . . . a vivid and accurate sketch," and who are "the direct ancestors of peoples of whom remnants yet lurk in out-of-the way corners of Europe, where they have been squeezed or stranded," he adds to this: "but the men of Palæolithic times can be identified with no existing races; they were savages of a more degraded type than any extant; tall, yet barely erect, with short legs and twisted knees, with prognathous, that is, projecting ape-like jaws, and small brains. Whence they come we cannot tell, and their 'grave knoweth no man to this day.'
Besides the possibility that there may be men who *know* whence they came and how they perished—it is not true to say that the Palæolithic men, or their fossils, are all found with "small brains." The oldest skull of all those hitherto found, the "Neanderthal skull," is of average capacity, and Mr. Huxley was compelled to confess that it was no real approximation whatever to that of the "missing link." There are aboriginal tribes in India whose brains are far smaller and nearer to that of the ape than any hitherto found among the skulls of Palæolithic man.

The men of Science avoid pinning themselves down to any definite statement concerning the age of man, as indeed they hardly could, and thus leave enormous latitude to bolder speculations. Nevertheless, while the majority of the anthropologists carry back the existence of man *only* into the period of the *post*-glacial drift, or what is called the Quaternary period, those of them who, as *Evolutionists, trace man to a common origin with that of the monkey,* do not show great consistency in their speculations. The Darwinian hypothesis demands, in reality, a far greater antiquity for man, than is even dimly suspected by superficial thinkers. This is proven by the greatest authorities on the question – Mr. Huxley, for instance. Those, therefore, who accept the Darwinian evolution *ipso facto* hold very tenaciously to an antiquity of man so very great, indeed, that it falls not so far short of the Occultist's estimate.[194]

The modest thousands of years of the *Encyclopædia Britannica* and the 100,000 years to which anthropology in general limits the age of Humanity seem quite microscopical when compared with the figures implied in Mr. Huxley's bold speculations. The former, indeed, makes of the original race of men ape-like cave-dwellers. The great English biologist, in his desire to prove man's pithecoid origin, insists that the transformation of the primordial ape into a human being must have occurred *millions of years back.* For in criticising the excellent average cranial capacity of the Neanderthal skull, notwithstanding his assertion that it is overlaid with "pithecoid bony walls," coupled with Mr. Grant Allen's assurances that this skull "possesses large bosses on the forehead, strikingly (?) suggestive of those which give the gorilla its peculiarly fierce appearance"[195] (*Fortnightly Review,* 1882), still Mr.

---

194 The actual time required for such a theoretical transformation is necessarily enormous. "If," says Professor Pfaff, "in the hundreds of thousands of years which you (the Evolutionists) accept between the rise of Palæolithic man and our own day, a greater distance of man from the brute is not demonstrable, (*the most ancient man was just as far removed from the brute as the now living man*), what reasonable ground can be advanced for believing that man has been developed from the brute, and has receded further from it by infinitely small gradations?" . . . . "*The longer the interval of time placed between our times and the so-called Palæolithic men, the more ominous and destructive for the theory of the gradual development of man from the animal kingdom is the result stated.*" Huxley states ("*Man's Place in Nature,*" p. 159) that the *most liberal* estimates for the antiquity of Man *must be still further* extended.

195 The baselessness of this assertion, as well as that of many other exaggerations of the imaginative Mr. Grant Allen, was ably exposed by the eminent anatomist, Professor R. Owen, in "*Longman's Magazine,*" No. 1. Must it be repeated, moreover, that the Cro-

Huxley is forced to admit that, in the said skull, his theory is once more defeated by the "completely human proportions of the accompanying limb-bones, together with the fair development of the Engis skull." In consequence of all this we are notified that those skulls, "clearly indicate that the first traces of the primordial stock whence man has proceeded, need no longer be sought by those who entertain any form of the doctrine of progressive development in the newest Tertiaries; but that they *may be looked for in an epoch more distant from the age of the* ELEPHAS PRIMIGENIUS *than that is from us*"[196] (Huxley).

An *untold* antiquity for man is thus, then, the scientific *sine quâ non* in the question of Darwinian Evolution, since the oldest Palæolithic man shows as yet no appreciable differentiation from his modern descendant. It is only of late that modern Science began to widen with every year the abyss that now separates her from old Science, that of the Plinys and Hippocrateses, none of whom would have derided the archaic teachings with respect to the evolution of the human races and animal species, as the present day Scientist – geologist or anthropologist – is sure to do.

Magnon Palæolithic type is superior to a very large number of existing races?

196 It thus stands to reason that science would never dream of a *pre*-tertiary man, and that de Quatrefages' *secondary* man makes every Academician and "F.R.S." faint with horror because, TO PRESERVE THE APE-THEORY, SCIENCE MUST MAKE MAN POST-SECONDARY. This is just what de Quatrefages has twitted the Darwinists with, adding, that on the whole, there were more scientific reasons to trace the ape from man than man from the anthropoid. With this exception, science has not one single valid argument to offer against the antiquity of man. But in this case modern Evolution demands far more than the fifteen million years of Croll for the Tertiary period, for two very simple but good reasons: (a) No anthropoid ape has been found before the Miocene period; (b) man's flint relics have been traced to the Pliocene and their presence *suspected*, if not accepted by all, in the Miocene strata. Again, where is the "missing link" in such case? And how could even a Palæolithic Savage, a "Man of Canstadt," evolve into thinking men from the brute *Dryopithecus* of the Miocene *in so short a time*. One sees now the reason why Darwin rejected the theory that only 60,000,000 years had elapsed since the Cambrian period. "He judges from the small amount of organic changes since the glacial epoch, and adds that the previous 140 million years can hardly be considered as sufficient for the development of the varied forms of life which certainly existed toward the close of the Cambrian period." (Ch. Gould.)

The Mammalian Type Was a Post-Human Fourth Round Product

Holding, as we do, that the mammalian type was a post-human Fourth Round product, the following diagram – as the writer understands the teaching – may make the process clear:

PRIMEVAL ASTRAL MAN

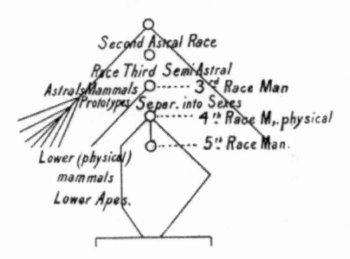

The unnatural union was *invariably* fertile, because the then mammalian types *were not remote enough* from their Root-type[197] – Primeval Astral Man – to develop the necessary barrier. Medical science records such cases of monsters, bred from human and animal parents, even in our own day. The possibility is, therefore, only one of *degree*, not of fact. Thus it is that Occultism solves one of the strangest problems presented to the consideration of the anthropologist.

The Incubus of Ethnology

The pendulum of thought oscillates between extremes. Having now

---

197 Let us remember in this connection the esoteric teaching which tells us of Man having had in the Third Round a GIGANTIC APE-LIKE FORM on the astral plane. And similarly at the close of the Third Race in this Round. Thus it accounts for the human features of the apes, especially of the later anthropoids—apart from the fact that these latter preserve by *Heredity* a resemblance to their Atlanto-Lemurian sires.

finally emancipated herself from the shackles of theology, Science has embraced the opposite fallacy; and in the attempt to interpret Nature on purely materialistic lines, she has built up that most extravagant theory of the ages – the derivation of man from a ferocious and brutal ape. So rooted has this doctrine, in one form or another, now become, that the most Herculean efforts will be needed to bring about its final rejection. The Darwinian anthropology is the incubus of the ethnologist, a sturdy child of modern Materialism, which has grown up and acquired increasing vigour, as the ineptitude of the theological legend of Man's "creation" became more and more apparent. It has thriven on account of the strange delusion that – as a scientist of repute puts it – "All hypotheses and theories with respect to the rise of man can be reduced to *two* (the Evolutionist and the Biblical exoteric account). . . There is no other hypothesis conceivable. . ."!! The anthropology of the secret volumes is, however, the best possible answer to such a worthless contention.

The anatomical resemblance between Man and the higher Ape, so frequently cited by Darwinists as pointing to some former ancestor common to both, presents an interesting problem, the proper solution of which is to be sought for in the esoteric explanation of the genesis of the pithecoid stocks. We have given it as far as was useful, by stating that the bestiality of the primeval mindless races resulted in the production of huge man-like monsters – the offspring of human and animal parents. As time rolled on, and the still semi-astral forms consolidated into the physical, the descendants of these creatures were modified by external conditions, until the breed, dwindling in size, culminated in the lower apes of the Miocene period. With these the later Atlanteans renewed the sin of the "Mindless" – this time with full responsibility. The resultants of their crime were the species of apes now known as Anthropoid.

It may be useful to compare this very simple theory – and we are willing to offer it even as a hypothesis to the unbelievers – with the Darwinian scheme, so full of insurmountable obstacles, that no sooner is one of these overcome by a more or less ingenious hypothesis, than ten worse difficulties are forthwith discovered behind the one disposed of.

Proofs for the Antiquity of the Human Race

Millions of years have dropped into Lethe, leaving no more recollection in the memory of the profane than the few millenniums of the orthodox Western chronology as to the origin of Man and the history of the primeval races.

All depends on the proofs found for the antiquity of the Human Race. If the still-debated man of the Pliocene or even the Miocene period was the *Homo primigenius*, then science may be right (*argumenti causâ*) in basing its present anthropology – as to the date and mode of origin of *Homo sapiens* – on the Darwinian theory.[198] But if the skeletons of man should, at any time, be discovered in the Eocene strata, but no fossil ape, thereby proving the existence of man prior to the anthropoid – then Darwinians will have to exercise their ingenuity in another direction. And it is said in well-informed quarters that the XXth century will be yet in its earliest teens, when such undeniable proof of Man's priority will be forthcoming.

Even now evidence is brought forward that the dates for the foundations of cities, civilizations, and various other historical events have been absurdly curtailed. This was done as a peace-offering to Biblical chronology. "No date," writes the well-known Palæontologist, Edward Lartet, "is to be found in *Genesis*, which assigns a time for the birth of primitive humanity," but chronologists have for fifteen centuries endeavoured to force the *Bible* facts into agreement with their systems. Thus, no less than one hundred and forty different opinions have been formed about the single date of "Creation", "and between the extreme variations there is a discrepancy of 3,194 years, in the reckoning of the period between the beginning of the world and the birth of Christ.

The Secret Doctrine, ii 685 – 690

---

198 It may here be remarked that those Darwinians, who with Mr. Grant Allen, place our "hairy arboreal" ancestors so far back as the *Eocene Age*, are landed in rather an awkward dilemma. No fossil anthropoid ape—much less the fabulous common ancestor assigned to Man and the Pithecoid—appears in Eocene strata. The first presentment of an anthropoid ape is Miocene.

Selection 31

SUPPLEMENTARY REMARKS ON ESOTERIC GEOLOGICAL CHRONOLOGY

It seems, however, possible to calculate the *approximate* duration of the geological periods from the combined data of Science and Occultism now before us. Geology is, of course, able to determine almost with certainty one thing – the thickness of the several deposits. Now, it also stands to reason that the time required for the deposition of any stratum on a sea-bottom must bear a strict proportion to the thickness of the mass thus formed. Doubtless the rate of erosion of land and the sorting out of matter on to ocean beds has varied from age to age, and cataclysmic changes of various kinds break the "uniformity" of ordinary geological processes. *Provided, however, we have some definite numerical basis on which to work,* our task is rendered less difficult than it might at first sight appear to be. Making due allowance for variations in the rate of deposit, Professor Lefèvre gives us the relative figures which sum up geological time. He does not attempt to calculate the lapse of years since the first bed of the Laurentian rocks was deposited, but postulating that time as = X, he presents us with the relative proportions in which the various periods stand to it. Let us premise our estimate by stating that, roughly speaking, the Primordial rocks are 70,000 ft., the Primary 42,000 ft., the Secondary 15,000 ft., the Tertiary 5,000 ft., and the Quaternary some 500 ft. in thickness:

"Dividing into a hundred parts the time, *whatever its actual length,* that has passed since the dawn of life on this earth (lower Laurentian strata), we shall be led to attribute to the primordial age more than half of the whole duration, say 53.5; to the Primary 32.2; to the Secondary 11. 5; to the Tertiary 2.3; to the Quaternary 0.5, or one-half per cent." ("*Philosophy,*" p. 481.)

Now, as it is certain, on occult data, that the time which has elapsed since the first sedimentary deposits = 320,000,000 years, we are able to infer that the:

ROUGH APPROXIMATIONS.

Primordial	Laurentian Cambrian Silurian	lasted 171,200,000 yrs.
Primary	Devonian Coal Permian	lasted 103,040,000 yrs.
Secondary	Triassic Jurassic Cretaceous	lasted 36,800,000 yrs.
Tertiary	Eocene Miocene Pliocene	lasted 7,360,000 yrs. (probably in excess).
Quaternary		lasted 1,600,000 yrs. (probably in excess).

Such estimates harmonise with the statements of Esoteric Ethnology in almost every particular. The *Tertiary* Atlantean part-cycle, from the "apex of glory" of that Race in the early Eocene to the great mid-Miocene cataclysm, would appear to have lasted some 3½ to four million years. If the duration of the Quaternary is not rather (as seems likely) overestimated, the sinking of Ruta and Daitya would be post-Tertiary. It is probable that the results here given allow somewhat too long a period to both the Tertiary and Quaternary, as the *Third Race* goes very far back into the Secondary Age. Nevertheless, the figures are most suggestive.

But the argument from *geological evidence* being only in favour of 100,000,000 years, let us compare our claims and teachings with those of exact science.

Mr. Edward Clodd,[199] in reviewing M. de Mortillet's work *"Materiaux pour l'Histoire de l'Homme,"* which places man in the mid-Miocene period,[200] remarks that "it would be in defiance of all that the doctrine

---

199 *Knowledge*, March 31, 1882.
200 And who yet, in another work, *"La Préhistorique Antiquité de l'Homme,"* some twenty years ago, generously allowed only 230,000 years to our mankind. Since we learn now that he places man "in the mid-Miocene period," we must say that the much respected

of evolution teaches, and moreover, win no support from believers in special creation and the fixity of species, to seek for so highly specialized a mammalian as man at an early stage in the life-history of the globe." To this, one could answer: (a) the doctrine of evolution, as inaugurated by Darwin and developed by later evolutionists, is not only the reverse of *infallible*, but it is repudiated by several great men of science, *e.g.* de Quatrefages, in France, and Dr. Weismann, an *ex*-evolutionist in Germany, and many others, the ranks of the *anti*-Darwinists growing stronger with every year;[201] and (b) truth to be worthy of its name, and remain truth and fact, hardly needs to beg for support from any class or sect. For were it to *win support* from believers in special creation, it would never gain the favour of the evolutionists, and *vice versâ*. Truth must rest upon its own firm foundations of facts, and take its chances for recognition, when every prejudice in the way is disposed of. Though the question has been already fully considered in its main aspects, it is, nevertheless, advisable to combat every so-called *"scientific"* objection as we go along, when making what are regarded as heretical and "anti-scientific" statements.

Divergences between Orthodox and Esoteric Science on the Question of the Age of the Globe and of Man

Let us briefly glance at the divergences between orthodox and esoteric science on the question of the age of the globe and of man. With the two respective synchronistic tables before him, the reader will be enabled to see at a glance the importance of these divergences and to perceive, at the same time, that it is not impossible – nay, it is most likely – that further discoveries in geology and the finding of fossil remains of man will force science to confess that it is esoteric philosophy which is right after all, or, at any rate, nearer to the truth.

Professor of Prehistoric Anthropology (in Paris) is somewhat contradictory and inconsistent, if not *naïf* in his views.

201   The root and basic idea of the origin and transformation of species—the *heredity* (of acquired faculties) seems to have found lately very serious opponents in Germany. Du Bois Raymond and Dr. Pflüger, the physiologists, besides other men of science as eminent as any, find insuperable difficulties and even impossibilities in the doctrine.

PARALLELISM OF LIFE

SCIENTIFIC HYPOTHESES	ESOTERIC THEORY
Science divides the period of the globe's history, since the beginning of life on earth (or the Azoic age), into five main divisions or periods, according to Hæckel.[1]	Leaving the classification of the geological periods to Western Science, esoteric philosophy divides only the life-periods on the globe. In the present *Manvantara*, the actual period is separated into seven *Kalpas* and seven great human races. Its first *Kalpa*, answering to the "Primordial Epoch," is the age of the

PRIMORDIAL Epoch	Laurentian Cambrian Silurian	*Deva* or Divine men, the "Creators" and Progenitors.[3]

The Primordial Epoch is, science tells us, by no means devoid of vegetable and animal life. In the Laurentian deposits are found specimens of the *Eozoon Canadense* – a chambered shell. In the Silurian are discovered sea-weeds (*algæ*), molluscs, crustacea, and lower marine organisms, also the first trace of fishes. The primordial Epoch shows algæ, molluscs, crustacea, polyps, and marine organisms, etc., etc. Science teaches, therefore, that marine life was present from the very beginnings of time, leaving us, however, to speculate for ourselves as to how life appeared on earth. If it rejects the Biblical "Creation" (as we do), why does it not give us another, approximately plausible hypothesis?	The Esoteric Philosophy agrees with the statement made by science (see parallel column), demurring, however, in one particular. The 300,000,000 years of vegetable life (see "Brahminical Chronology") preceded the "Divine Men," or Progenitors. Also, no teaching denies that there were traces of life *within* the Earth besides the *Eozoon Canadense* in the Primordial Epoch. Only, whereas the said vegetation belonged to this Round, the zoological relics now found in the Laurentian, Cambrian, and Silurian systems, so called, *are the relics of* the *Third* Round. At first *astral* like the rest, they consolidated and materialized *pari passu* with the NEW vegetation.

		Divine Progenitors, SECONDARY GROUPS, and the 2 1/2 races. "Fernforests, Sigillaria, Coniferæ, fishes, firsttraceofreptiles." Thus saith modern science; the esoteric doctrine repeats that which was said above. These are all relics of the preceding Round.[5] Once, however, the prototypes are projected out of the astral envelope of the earth, an indefinite amount of modification ensues.
PRIMARY	Devonian[4]	
	Coal	
	Permian	

According to every calculation, the Third Race had already made its appearance, as during the Triassic there were already a few mammals, and it must have separated.

Triassic
Jurassic
Chalk or
Cretaceous.

This is the age of Reptiles, of the gigantic Megalosauri, Ichthyosauri, Plesiosauri, etc., etc. Science denies the presence of man in that period. If so, it has to explain how men came to know of these monsters and describe them *before* the age of Cuvier? The old annals of China, India, Egypt, and even of Judea are full of them, as demonstrated elsewhere. In this period also appear the first (marsupial) mammals[6] – insectivorous, carnivorous, phytophagous, and (as Prof. Owen thinks) an herbivorous hoofed mammal.

Science does not admit the appearance of man before *the close* of the Tertiary period.[7] Why? Because man has to be shown younger than the higher mammals. But Esoteric philosophy teaches us the reverse. And as science is quite unable to come to anything like an approximate conclusion as to the age of man, or even the geological periods, therefore, even accepted only as a hypothesis, the occult teaching is more logical and reasonable.

This, then, is the age of the Third Race, in which the origins of the early Fourth may be perhaps also discoverable. We are, however, here left entirely to conjecture, as no definite data are yet given out by the Initiates. The analogy is but a poor one; still it may be argued that, as the early Mammalia and pre-*mammalia* are shown in their evolution merging from one kind into a higher one, anatomically, so are the human races in their procreative processes. A parallel might certainly be found among the Monotremata, the Didelphia (or Marsupialia), and the placental Mammals, divided in their turn into three orders[8] like the First, Second, and Third Root-Races of men.[9] But this would require more space than can be now allotted to the subject.

No man is yet allowed to have lived during this period:

		Eocene
[13]Tertiary		Miocene
		Pliocene

Says Mr. E. Clodd, in *Knowledge*: "Although the placenta mammals and the order of Primates to which man is related, appear in Tertiary times and the climate, tropical in the Eocene age, warm in the Miocene and temperate in the Pliocene, was favourable to his presence, the proofs of his existence *in Europe* before the close of the Tertiary epoch . . . . are not generally accepted here."

Tertiary

The Third Race has now almost utterly disappeared, carried away by the fearful geological cataclysms of the Secondary age, leaving behind it but a few hybrid races. The Fourth, born millions of years before[10] the said cataclysm took place, perishes during the Miocene period,[11] when the Fifth (our Aryan race) had one million years of independent existence. (See *"Esoteric Buddhism,"* 4th Ed., pp. 53 – 55) How much older it is from its origin -- who knows? As the "Historical" Period has begun, with the Indian Aryans, with their *Vedas*, for their multitudes,[12] and far earlier in the Esoteric Records, it is useless to establish here any parallels.

Geology has now divided the periods and placed man in the

		Palaeolithic man,
Quaternary		Neolithic man, and
		Historical Period.

If the Quaternary period is allowed 1,500,000 years, then only does our Fifth Race belong to it.

(*Footnotes to PARALLELISM OF LIFE*)

1 *"History of Creation,"* p. 20.

2 The same names are retained as those given by science, to make the parallels clearer. Our terms are quite different.

3 Let the student remember that the Doctrine teaches that there are seven degrees of *Devas* or "Progenitors," or seven classes, from the most perfect to the

less exalted.

4 It may be said that we are inconsistent in not introducing into this table a *Primary-Age Man*. The parallelism of Races and geological periods here adopted, is, so far as the origin of *1st* and *2nd* are concerned, purely tentative, no direct information being available. Having previously discussed the question of a possible Race in the *Carboniferous Age*, it is needless to renew the debate.

5 During the *interim* from one Round to another, the globe and everything on it remains *in statu quo*. Remember, vegetation began in its ethereal form before what is called the Primordial, running through the Primary, and condensing in it, and reaching its full physical life in the Secondary.

6 Geologists tell us that "in the Secondary epoch, the only mammals which have been (hitherto) discovered in *Europe* are the fossil remains of a small marsupial or pouch-bearer." ("*Knowledge*," March 31, 1882, p. 464.) Surely the marsupial or didelphis (the only surviving animal of the family of those who were on earth during the presence on it of androgyne man) cannot be the only animal that was then on earth? Its presence speaks loudly for that of other (though unknown) mammals, besides the monotremes and marsupials, and thus shows the appellation of "mammalian age" given only to the Tertiary period to be misleading and erroneous, as it allows one to infer that there were no mammals, but reptiles, birds, *Amphibia*ns, and fishes alone in the Mesozoic times—the Secondary.

7 Those who feel inclined to sneer at that doctrine of Esoteric Ethnology, which pre-supposes the existence of Man in the *Secondary* Age, will do well to note the fact that one of the most distinguished anthropologists of the day, M. de Quatrefages, seriously argues in that direction. He writes: "There is nothing impossible in the supposition that he (Man) may have appeared on the globe *with the first representatives of the type to which he belongs in virtue of his organism*." This statement approximates most closely to our fundamental assertion that man preceded the other *mammalia*.

Professor Lefèvre admits that the "labours of Boucher de Perthes, Lartet, Christy, Bourgeois, Desnoyers, Broca, de Mortillet, Hamy, Gaudry, Capellini, and a hundred others, have overcome all doubts and clearly established the progressive development of the human organism and industries from the *Miocene epoch of the Tertiary age*." ("*Philosophy*," p. 499, chapter on Organic Evolution.) Why does he reject the possibility of a Secondary-Age man? Simply because he is involved in the meshes of the Darwinian Anthropology!! "The origin of man is bound up with that of the higher mammals;" he appeared "only with the last types of his class"!! This is not argument, but dogmatism. *Theory* can never excommunicate *fact*! Must everything give place to the mere working-hypotheses of Western Evolutionists? Surely not.

8 These *Placentalia* of the third sub-class are divided, it appears, into Villiplacentalia (placenta composed of many separate scattered tufts), the

Zonoplacentalia (girdle-shaped placenta), and the discoplacentalia (or discoid). Hæckel sees in the *Marsupialia Didelphia,* one of the connecting links *genealogically* between man and the *Moneron*!!

9   This inclusion of the First Race in the Secondary is necessarily only a provisional working-hypothesis—the actual chronology of the First, Second, and Early Third Races being closely veiled by the Initiates. For all that can be said on the subject, the First Root-Race may have been Pre-Secondary, as is, indeed, taught. (*Vide supra.*)

10   Though we apply the term "*truly human,*" only to the Fourth Atlantean Root-Race, yet the Third Race is almost human in its latest portion, since it is during its fifth sub-race that mankind *separated* sexually, and that the *first man was born* according to the now normal process. This "first man" answers in the *Bible* (*Genesis*) to Enos or Henoch, son of Seth (Ch. IV).

11   Geology records the former existence of a universal ocean, sheets of marine sediments uniformly present everywhere testifying to it, but, it is not even the epoch referred to in the allegory of *Vaivasvata* Manu. The latter is a *Deva-Man* (or Manu) saving in an ark (the *female* principle) the germs of humanity, and also the seven *Rishis*—who stand here as the symbols for the seven human principles—of which allegory we have spoken elsewhere. The "Universal Deluge" is the watery abyss of the Primordial Principle of Berosus. (See Stanzas from 2 to 8 in Part I). How, if Croll allowed fifteen million years to have elapsed since the Eocene period (which we state on the authority of a Geologist, Mr. Ch. Gould), only 60 millions are assigned by him "since the beginning of the Cambrian period, in the *Primordial Age*", passes comprehension. The Secondary strata are twice the thickness of the Tertiary, and Geology thus shows the Secondary age alone to be of twice the length of the Tertiary. Shall we then accept only 15 million years for both the Primary and the Primordial? No wonder Darwin rejected the calculation.

12   We hope that we have furnished all the Scientific data for it elsewhere.

13   The above parallels stand good only if Professor Croll's earlier calculations are adopted, namely, 15,000,000 years since the beginning of the Eocene period (see Charles Gould's "*Mythical Monsters,*" p. 84), not those in his "*Climate and Time,*" which allow only 2½ million years', or at the utmost three million years' duration to the Tertiary age. This, however, would make the whole duration of the incrusted age of the world only 131,600,000 years according to Professor Winchell, whereas in the Esoteric doctrine, sedimentation began in *this Round* approximately over 320 million years ago. Yet his calculations do not clash much with ours with regard to the epochs of glacial periods in the Tertiary age, which is called in our Esoteric books the age of the "Pigmies." With regard to the 320 millions of years assigned to sedimentation, it must be noted that even a greater time elapsed during the preparation of this globe for the Fourth Round *previous to stratification.*   (*End of Footnotes*)

Yet, *mirabile dictu!* – while the *non-cannibal* Palæolithic man, who must have certainly antedated cannibal Neolithic man by hundreds of thousands of years[202], is shown to be a remarkable artist, Neolithic man is made out almost an abject savage, his lake dwellings notwithstanding.[203] For see what a learned geologist, Mr. Charles Gould, tells the reader in his *"Mythical Monsters"*:

> "Palæolithic men were unacquainted with pottery and the art of weaving, and apparently had no domesticated animals or system of cultivation, but the Neolithic lake-dwellers of Switzerland had looms, pottery, cereals, sheep, horses," etc., etc.

Yet, though "Implements of horn, bone, and wood were in common use among both races . . . those of the older are frequently distinguished *by their being sculptured with great ability, or ornamented with life-like engravings of the various animals living at the period,* whereas there appears to have been *a marked absence of any similar artistic ability*[204] on the part of *"Neolithic man."* Let us give the reasons for it.

(1) The oldest fossil man, the primitive cave-men of the old Palæolithic period, and of the Pre-glacial period (of whatever length, and however far

---

202 It is conceded by Geology to be "beyond doubt that a considerable period must have supervened after the departure of Palæolithic man and before the arrival of his Neolithic successor." (See James Geikie's *"Prehistoric Europe,"* and Ch. Gould's *"Mythical Monsters,"* p. 98.)

203 Resembling in a manner the *pile-villages* of Northern Borneo.

204 "The *most clever sculptor of modern times* would probably not succeed very much better, if his graver were a splinter of flint and stone and bone were the materials to be engraved"!! (Prof. Boyd Dawkins' *"Cave-Hunting,"* p. 344.) It is needless after such a concession to further insist on Huxley's, Schmidt's, Laing's, and others' statements to the effect that Palæolithic man cannot be considered to lead us back in any way to a pithecoid human race, thus demolishing the fantasies of many superficial evolutionists. The relic of artistic merit here *re-appearing* in the Chipped-Stone-Age men is traceable to their *Atlantean* ancestry. Neolithic man was a fore-runner of the great *Aryan* invasion, and immigrated from quite another quarter—Asia, and in a measure Northern Africa. (The tribes peopling the latter towards the North-West, were certainly of an Atlantean origin—dating back hundreds of thousands of years before the Neolithic Period in Europe—but they had so diverged from the parent type as to present no longer any marked characteristic peculiar to it.) As to the contrast between Neolithic and Palæolithic Man, it is *a remarkable fact that, as Carl Vogt remarks, the former was a cannibal, the much earlier man of the Mammoth era not.* Human manners and customs do not seem to improve with time, then? Not in this instance at any rate.

back), is always the same genus man, and there are no fossil remains proving for him "what the Hipparion and Anchitherium have proved for the genus horse – that is, gradual progressive specialization from a simple ancestral type to more complex existing forms" ("Modern Science," p. 181).

(2) As to the so-called Palæolithic *hâches* . . . "when placed side by side with the rudest forms of stone hatchets actually used by the Australian and other savages, it is difficult to detect any difference" (*Ibid*, p. 112) . This goes to prove that there have been savages *at all times*, and the inference would be that there might have been civilized people in those days as well, cultured nations contemporary with those rude savages. We see such a thing in Egypt 7,000 years ago.

(3) An obstacle which is the direct consequence of the two preceding: Man, if no older than the Palæolithic period, could not possibly have had the actual time to get transformed from the "missing link" into what he is known to have been even during that remote geological time, *i.e.* even *a finer specimen than many of the now existing races.*

SOME OF THE PRESENT DIFFICULTIES OF SCIENCE MIGHT BE EASILY MADE TO DISAPPEAR

The above lends itself naturally to the following syllogism: (1) The *primitive* man (known to Science) was, in some respects, even a finer man of his genus than he is now; (2) The earliest monkey known, the *lemur*, was *less* anthropoid than the modern pithecoid species; (3) *Conclusion*: even though a *missing link* were found, the balance of evidence would remain more in favour of the ape *being a degenerated man* made dumb by some fortuitous circumstances,[205] than tending to show that man descends from a pithecoid ancestor. The theory cuts both way.

On the other hand, if the existence of Atlantis is accepted, and the statement is believed that in the Eocene Age "even in its very first part, the great cycle of the Fourth Race men, the Atlanteans had already reached its highest point . . . ." ("*Esoteric Buddhism*," p. 64), then some of the present difficulties of science might be easily made to disappear.

---

205 On the data furnished by modern science, physiology, and natural selection, and without resorting to any miraculous creation, two negro human specimens of the lowest intelligence—say idiots born dumb—might by breeding produce a dumb *Pastrana* species, which would start a new modified race, and thus produce in the course of geological time the regular anthropoid ape.

The rude workmanship of the Palæolithic tools proves nothing against the idea that, side by side with their makers, there lived nations highly civilized. We are told that "only a very small portion of the earth's surface has been explored, and of this a very small portion consists of ancient land surfaces or fresh water formations, where alone we can expect to meet with traces of the higher forms of animal life," . . . and that "even these have been so imperfectly explored, that where we now meet with thousands and tens of thousands of undoubted human remains lying almost under our feet, it is only within the last thirty years that their existence has even been suspected" (*Ibid*, p. 98). It is very suggestive also that along with the rude *hâches* of the lowest savage, explorers meet with specimens of workmanship of such artistic merit as could hardly be found, or expected, in a modern peasant belonging to any European country – unless in exceptional cases. The "portrait" of the "Reindeer feeding," from the Thayngin grotto in Switzerland, and those of the man running, with two horse's heads sketched close to him – a work of the Reindeer period, *i.e. at least* 50,000 *years ago* – are pronounced by Mr. Laing not only exceedingly well done, but, especially the reindeer feeding, as one that "*would do credit to any modern animal painter*" – by no means exaggerated praise, as anyone may see (*vide infra*). Now, since side by side with the modern Esquimaux, who also have a tendency, like their Palæolithic ancestors of the Reindeer period, *the rude and savage human species*, to be constantly drawing with the point of their knives sketches of animals, scenes of the chase, etc., we have our greatest painters of Europe, why could not the same have happened in those days? Compared with the specimens of Egyptian drawing and sketching – "7,000 years ago" – the "*earliest* portraits" of men, horses' heads, and reindeer, made 50,000 years ago, *are certainly superior.* Nevertheless, the Egyptians of those periods are known to have been a highly civilized nation, whereas the Palæolithic men are called *savages* of the lower type. This is a small matter seemingly, yet extremely suggestive as showing that every new geological discovery is made to fit in with current theories, instead of the reverse. Yes, Mr. Huxley is right in saying, "Time will show." It will, and must vindicate Occultism.

Meanwhile, the most uncompromising materialists are driven by necessity into the most *occult-like* admissions. Strange to say, it is the most materialistic – those of the German school – who, with regard to *physical* development, come the nearest to the teachings of the Occultists. Thus, Professor Baumgärtner, who believes that "the germs for the higher animals could only be the eggs of the lower animals"; who thinks that "besides the advance of the vegetable and animal world in development, there occurred in that period the formation of *new original germs*," which formed the basis of new metamorphoses, etc.; thinks also that "the first men who proceeded from the germs of animals beneath them, lived first in a *larva* state."

Just so, in a *larva* state, we say, too, only from no "animal" germ, and that "larva" was the soulless astral form of the pre-physical Races. And we believe, as the German professor does, with several other men of Science in Europe now, that the human races "have not descended from one pair, but appeared immediately in numerous races" (*Anfänge zu einer Physiologischen Schöpfungs-geschichte der Pflanzen und Thierwelt*, 1885). Therefore, when we read "*Force and Matter*," and find that Emperor of Materialists, Büchner, repeating after Manu and Hermes, that the plant passes "imperceptibly into the animal, and the animal into man" (*Ibid*, p. 85), we need only add "and man into a spirit," to complete the Kabalistic axiom. The more so, since on page 82 of the same work we read the following admission: . . . "Produced in the way of spontaneous generation . . . it is by the aid of intense natural forces and *endless periods of time* (that) there has progressively arisen that rich and infinitely modified organic world by which we are at present surrounded." . . And (p. 84) "Spontaneous generation played, no doubt, *a more important part in the primeval epoch than at present; nor can it be denied that in this way beings of a higher organization* were produced than now,"[206] for this is the claim of Occultism.

THE ORIGIN AND THE DESCENT OF MAN IS STILL A GREAT PROBLEM FOR SCIENCE

The whole difference lies in this: Modern Science places her materialistic theory of primordial germs on earth, and the *last germ of* life on this globe, of man, and everything else, between *two voids*. Whence the *first* germ, if both spontaneous generation and the

---

206 "*Force and Matter*," by Dr. Louis Büchner, translated and edited by J. Frederick Collingwood, F.R.S., F.G.S., 1864.

interference of external forces, are absolutely rejected now? Germs of organic life, we are told, by Sir W. Thomson, *came to our earth in some meteor*? This helps in no way and only shifts the difficulty from this earth to the supposed meteor.

These are our agreements and disagreements with Science. About the *endless periods* we are, of course, at one even with materialistic speculation, for we believe in Evolution, though on different lines. Professor Huxley very wisely says: "If *any form* of progressive development is correct, we must extend by long epochs the most liberal estimate that has yet been made of the antiquity of man." But when we are told that this man is a product of the natural forces inherent *in* matter, *force*, according to modern views, being but a quality of matter, a "mode of motion," etc., and when we find Sir W. Thomson repeating in 1885 what was asserted by Büchner and his school thirty years ago, we fear all our reverence for real Science is vanishing into thin air! One can hardly help thinking that materialism is, in certain cases, a *disease*. For when men of Science, in the face of the magnetic phenomena and the attraction of iron particles through insulating substances, like glass, maintain that the said attraction is due to "molecular motion," or to the "rotation of the molecules of the magnet," then, whether the teaching comes from a "credulous" Theosophist innocent of any notion of physics, or from an eminent man of Science, it is equally ridiculous. The individual who asserts such a theory in the teeth of *fact*, is only one more proof that "When people have not a niche in their minds in which to shoot facts, so much the worse for the facts."

At present the dispute between the spontaneous generationists and their opponents is at rest, having ended in the provisional victory of the latter. But even they are forced to admit, as Büchner did, and Messrs. Tyndall and Huxley still do – that spontaneous generation *must have occurred once*, under "special thermal conditions." Virchow refuses even to argue the question; it must have taken place sometime in the history of our planet, and there's an end of it. This seems to look more natural than Sir W. Thomson's hypothesis just quoted, that the germs of organic life fell on our earth in some meteor, or that other *scientific* hypothesis coupled to the recently adopted belief that there exists no "Vital principle" whatever, but only vital phenomena, which can all be traced to the molecular forces of the original protoplasm. But this does not help Science to solve the still greater problem – the origin and *the descent* of Man, for here is a still worse plaint and lamentation.

"While we can trace the skeletons of Eocene mammals through several directions of specialization in succeeding Tertiary times, man presents the phenomenon of an *unspecialized* skeleton which cannot fairly be connected with any of these lines." ("*Origin of the World*," by Sir W. Dawson, LL.D., F.R.S., p. 39)

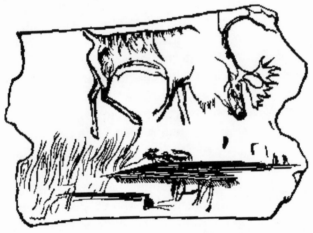

REINDEER ENGRAVED ON ANTLER BY PALÆOLITHIC MAN (After Geikie.)

The secret could be soon told, not only from the esoteric but even from the standpoint of every religion the world over, without mentioning the Occultists. The "specialized skeleton" is sought for in the wrong place, where it can never be found. It is expected to be discovered in the physical remains of man, in some pithecoid "missing link," with a skull larger than that of the ape's, and with a cranial capacity smaller than in man, *instead* of looking for that *specialization* in *the super-physical essence of his inner astral constitution, which can hardly be excavated from any geological strata*! Such a tenacious, hopeful clinging to a self-degrading theory is the most wonderful feature of the day.

Meanwhile, this is a specimen of an engraving made by a *Palæolithic* "savage", Palæolithic meaning the "earlier Stone-age" man, one supposed to have been as savage and brutal as the brutes he lived with.

Leaving the modern South Sea Islander, or even any Asiatic race, aside, we defy any grown-up schoolboy, or even a European youth, one who has never studied drawing, to execute such an engraving or even a pencil sketch. Here we have the true artistic *raccourci*, and correct lights and shadows without any *plane* model before the artist, who copied direct from nature, thus exhibiting a knowledge of anatomy and proportion. The artist who engraved this reindeer belonged, we are asked to believe, to the primitive "semi-animal" savages (contemporaneous with the mammoth and the woolly rhinoceros), whom some over-zealous Evolutionists once sought to picture to us as distinct approximations to the type of their hypothetical "pithecoid man"!

This engraved antler proves as eloquently as any fact can that the evolution of the races has ever proceeded in a series of rises and falls, that man, perhaps, is as old as incrustated Earth, and – if we can call his Divine ancestor "Man" – far older still.

Even de Mortillet himself seems to experience a vague distrust of the conclusions of modern archæologists, when he writes, "The prehistoric is a new science, *far, very far*, from having said its last word." (*"Prehistoric Antiquity of Man,"* 1883.) According to Lyell, one of the highest authorities on the subject, and the "Father" of Geology: "The expectation of always meeting with a lower type of human skull, the older the formation in which it occurs, *is based on the theory of progressive development*, and it *may* prove to be sound; nevertheless, we must remember that as yet, *we have no distinct geological evidence that the appearance of what are called the inferior races of mankind has always preceded in chronological order that of the higher races.*" (*"Antiquity of Man Historically Considered,"* p. 25) Nor has such evidence been found to this day. Science is thus offering for sale the skin of a bear, which has hitherto never been seen by mortal eye!

This concession of Lyell's reads most suggestively with the subjoined utterance of Professor Max Müller, whose attack on the Darwinian anthropology from the standpoint of LANGUAGE has, by the way, never been satisfactorily answered:

> "What do we know of savage tribes beyond the *last chapter of their history*?" (*cf.* this with the Esoteric view of the

Australians, Bushmen, as well as of Palæolithic European man, the Atlantean offshoots retaining a relic of a lost culture, which throve when the parent root-race was in its prime.) "Do we ever get an insight into their antecedents. . . . *How have they come to be what they are?* . . . . Their language proves, indeed, that these so-called heathens, with their complicated systems of mythology, their artificial customs, their unintelligible whims and savageries, are not the creatures of today or yesterday. unless we admit a special creation for these savages, they must be as old as the Hindus, the Greeks and Romans (far older). . . . They may have passed through ever so many vicissitudes, and *what we consider as primitive, may be, for all we know, a* relapse into savagery or a corruption of something that was more rational and intelligible in former stages." (*"India,"* 1883, F. Max Müller)

"The primeval savage is a familiar term in modern literature," remarks Professor Rawlinson, "but there is no evidence that the primeval savage ever existed. Rather, *all the evidence looks the other way.*" (*"Antiquity of Man Historically Considered"*) In his *"Origin of Nations,"* pp. 10 – 11, he rightly adds, *"The mythical traditions of almost all nations place at the beginning of human history a time of happiness and perfection, a* 'golden age' which has no features of savagery or barbarism, but many of civilization and refinement." How is the modern evolutionist to meet this consensus of evidence?

We repeat the question asked in *"Isis Unveiled"*: "Does the finding of the remains in the cave of Devon prove that there were no contemporary races then who were highly civilized? When the present population of the earth have disappeared, and some archæologist belonging to the 'coming race' of the distant future shall excavate the domestic implements of one of our Indian or Andaman Island tribes, will he be justified in concluding that mankind in the nineteenth century was 'just emerging from the Stone Age'?"

Another strange inconsistency in scientific knowledge is that *Neolithic* man is shown as being far more of a primitive savage than the Palæolithic one. Either Lubbock's *"Pre-historic Man,"* or Evans' *"Ancient*

Stone Implements" must be at fault, or – both. For this is what we learn from these works and others:

1) As we pass from Neolithic to Palæolithic Man, the stone implements become, from gracefully shaped and polished instruments, rude lumbering makeshifts. Pottery, etc., disappear as we descend the scale. And yet the latter could engrave such a reindeer!

2) Palæolithic Man lived in caves which he shared with hyænas and lions also,[207] whereas Neolithic man dwelt in lake-villages and buildings.

ENTRAPPED BY THE REINDEER

Every one who has followed even superficially the geological discoveries of our day, knows that a gradual improvement in workmanship is found, from the clumsy chipping and rude chopping of the early Palæolithic *hâches*, to the relatively graceful stone celts of that part of the Neolithic period immediately preceding the use of metals. But this *is in Europe*, a few portions only of which were barely rising from the waters in the days of the highest Atlantean civilizations. There were rude savages and highly civilized people then, as there are now. If 50,000 years hence, pigmy Bushmen are exhumed from some African cavern together with far earlier pigmy elephants, such as were found in the cave deposits of Malta by Milne Edwards, will that be a reason to maintain that in our age all men and all elephants were pigmies? Or if the weapons of the Veddhas of Ceylon are found, will our descendants be justified in setting us all down as Palæolithic savages? All the articles which geologists now excavate in Europe can certainly never date earlier than from the close of the Eocene age, since the lands of Europe were not even above water before that period. Nor can what we have said be in the least invalidated by theorists telling us that these quaint sketches of animals and men by Palæolithic man, were executed only *toward the close of the Reindeer period* – for this

207 In such a case, Palæolithic man must have been endowed in his day with thrice Herculean force and magic invulnerability, or else the lion was as weak as a lamb at that period, for both to share the same dwelling. We may as well be asked to believe next that it is that lion or hyæna which has engraved the deer on the antler, as be told that this bit of workmanship was done by a savage of such a kind.

explanation would be a very lame one indeed, in view of the geologists' ignorance of even the approximate duration of periods.

The Esoteric Doctrine teaches distinctly the *dogma* of the risings and falls of civilization, and now we learn that, "It is a remarkable fact that cannibalism seems to have become more frequent as man advanced in civilization, and that while its traces are frequent in *Neolithic* times they . . . . altogether disappear in the age of the mammoth and the reindeer." (*"Modern Science and Modern Thought,"* p. 164.)

Another evidence of the cyclic law and the truth of our teachings. Esoteric history teaches that idols and their worship died out with the Fourth Race, until the survivors of the hybrid races of the latter (Chinamen, African negroes, etc.) gradually brought the worship back. The *Vedas* countenance no idols; all the modern Hindu writings do.

"In the early Egyptian tombs, and in the remains of the pre-historic cities excavated by Dr. Schliemann, images of owl and ox-headed goddesses, and other symbolical figures, or idols, are found in abundance. But when we ascend into Neolithic times, such idols are no longer found . . . the only ones which may be said with some certainty to have been idols are one or two discovered by M. de Braye in some artificial caves of the Neolithic period . . . which appear to be intended for female figures of life size" . . . . (p. 199, *ibid*)

And these may have been simply statues. Anyhow, all this is one among the many proofs of the cyclic rise and fall of civilization and religion. The fact that no traces of human relics or skeletons are so far found beyond post-tertiary or "Quaternary" times – though Abbé Bourgeois' flints may serve as a warning[208] – seems to point to the truth of another esoteric statement, which runs thus: "Seek for the remains of thy forefathers in the high places. The vales have grown into mountains and the mountains have crumbled to the bottom of the seas." . . . Fourth Race mankind, thinned after the last cataclysm by two-thirds of its population, instead of settling on the new continents and islands that

---

208 More than twenty specimens of fossil monkeys have been found in one locality alone, in Miocene strata (Pikermi, near Athens). If man was not then, the period is too short for him to have been *transformed*—stretch it as you may. And if he was, and if no monkey is found earlier, what follows?

reappeared while their predecessors formed the floors of new Oceans – deserted that which is now Europe and parts of Asia and Africa for the summits of gigantic mountains, the seas that surrounded some of the latter having since "retreated" and made room for the table lands of Central Asia.

The most interesting example of this progressive march is perhaps afforded by the celebrated Kent's Cavern at Torquay. In that strange recess, excavated by water out of the Devonian limestone, we find a most curious record preserved for us in the geological memoirs of the earth. Under the blocks of limestone, which heaped the floor of the cavern, were discovered, embedded in a deposit of black earth, many implements of the Neolithic period of *fairly excellent workmanship*, with a few fragments of pottery – possibly traceable to the era of the Roman colonization. There is no trace of Palæolithic man here. No flints or traces of the extinct animals of the Quaternary period. When, however, we penetrate still deeper through the dense layer of stalagmite beneath the mould into the red earth, which, of course, itself once formed the pavement of the retreat, things assume a very different aspect. *Not one implement fit to bear* comparison *with the finely-chipped weapons found in the overlying stratum is to be seen;* only a host of the rude and lumbering little hatchets (with which the monstrous giants of the animal world were subdued and killed by little man, we have to think?) and scrapers of the Palæolithic age, mixed up confusedly with the bones of species now either extinct or emigrated, driven away by change of climate. It is the artificer of these ugly little hatchets, you see, who sculptured the reindeer over the brook, on the antler as shown above. In all cases we meet with the same evidence that, from historic to Neolithic and from Neolithic to Palæolithic man, things slope downwards on an inclined plane from the rudiments of civilization to the most abject barbarism – *in Europe again*. We are made also to face the "mammoth age" – the extreme or earliest division of the Palæolithic age – in which the great rudeness of implements reaches its maximum, and the *brutal* (?) appearance of contemporary skulls, such as the Neanderthal, point to a very low type of Humanity. But they may sometimes point also to something besides, to a race of men quite distinct from our (Fifth Race) Humanity.

Strange Confessions of Science

As said by an anthropologist in *"Modern Thought"* (article *"The Genesis of Man"*): "The theory, scientifically based or not, of Peyrère may be considered to be equivalent to that which divided man in two species. Broca, Virey, and a number of the French anthropologists have recognised that the lower race of man, comprising the Australian, Tasmanian, and Negro race, excluding the Kaffirs and the Northern Africans, *should be placed apart*. The fact that in this species, or rather sub-species, the third lower molars are usually larger than the second, and the squamosal and frontal bones are generally united by suture, places the *Homo Afer* on the level of being as good a distinct species as many of the kinds of finches. I shall abstain on the present occasion from mentioning the facts of hybridity, whereon the late Professor Broca has so exhaustively commented. The history, in the past ages of the world, of this race is peculiar. It has *never originated a system of architecture or a religion of its own*" (Dr. C. Carter Blake). It is peculiar, indeed, as we have shown in the case of the Tasmanians. However it may be, *fossil* man in Europe can neither prove nor disprove the antiquity of man on this Earth nor the age of his earliest civilizations.

It is time the Occultists should disregard any attempts to laugh at them, scorning the heavy guns of the satire of the men of science as much as the pop-guns of the profane, since it is impossible, so far, to obtain either proof or disproof, while their theories can stand the test better than the hypotheses of the Scientists at any rate. As to the proof for the antiquity which they claim for man, they have, moreover, Darwin himself and Lyell. The latter confesses that they (the naturalists) "have already obtained evidence of the existence of man at so remote a period that there has been time for many conspicuous *mammalia*, once his contemporaries, to die out, and *this even before the era of the earliest* historical records."[209] This is a statement made by one of England's great authorities upon the question. The two sentences that follow are as suggestive, and may well be remembered by the students of Occultism, for with all others he says: "In spite of the long lapse of prehistoric ages during which he (Man) must have flourished

---

209 *"Antiquity of Man,"* p. 530.

on Earth, *there is no proof of any perceptible change in his bodily structure.* If, therefore, he ever diverged from some unreasoning brute ancestor, we must suppose him to have existed at a far more distant epoch, *possibly on some continents or islands now submerged* beneath the Ocean."

Thus lost continents are officially suspected. That worlds (also Races) are periodically destroyed by fire (volcanoes and earthquakes) and water, in turn, and renewed, is a doctrine as old as man. Manu, Hermes, the Chaldees, all antiquity believed in this. Twice already has the face of the globe been changed by fire, and twice by water, since man appeared on it. As land needs rest and renovation, new forces, and a change for its soil, so does water. Thence arises a periodical redistribution of land and water, change of climates, etc., all brought on by geological revolution, and ending in a final change in the axis. Astronomers may pooh-pooh the idea of a periodical change in the behaviour of the globe's axis, and smile at the conversation given in the *Book of Enoch* between Noah and his "grandfather" Enoch; the allegory is, nevertheless, a geological and an astronomical fact: there is a secular change in the inclination of the earth's axis, and its appointed time is recorded in one of the great Secret Cycles. As in many other questions, Science is gradually moving toward our way of thinking. Dr. Henry Woodward, F.R.S., F.G.S., writes in the *Popular Science Review* (New Series in Vol. I, p. 115), article "*Evidences of the Age of Ice*": "If it be necessary to call in extramundane causes to explain the great increase of ice at this glacial period, I would prefer the theory propounded by Dr. Robert Hooke in 1688; since, by Sir Richard Phillips and others; and lastly by Mr. Thomas Belt, C.E., F.G.S.; namely, a slight increase in the present obliquity of the ecliptic, a proposal in perfect accord with other known astronomical facts, and the introduction of which is essential to our cosmical condition as a unit in the great solar system."

The following, quoted from a lecture by W. Pengelly, F.R.S., F.G.S., delivered in March, 1885, on "*The Extinct Lake of Bovey Tracey*" shows the hesitation, in the face of every evidence in favour of Atlantis, to accept the fact. It is a quotation in the body of the lecture:

"Evergreen Figs, Laurels, Palms, and Ferns having gigantic rhizomes have their existing congeners *in a sub-tropical climate, such, it cannot be doubted, as prevailed in Devonshire in Miocene times,* and are thus calculated to suggest caution when the *present climate* of any district is regarded as normal.

"When, moreover, Miocene plants are found in Disco Island, on the west coast of Greenland, lying between 69° 20' and 70°30' N. Lat.; when we learn that among them were two species found also at Bovey (*Sequoia couttsiæ, Quercus Lyelli*); when, to quote Professor Heer, we find that "the 'splendid evergreen' (*Magnolia Inglefieldi*) 'ripened its fruits so far north as on the parallel of 70°' " (*Phil. Trans.,* CLIX, p. 457, 1869); when also the number, variety, and luxuriance of the Greenland Miocene plants are found to have been such that, had land continued so far, some of them would in all probability have flourished at the Pole itself, the problem of changes of climate is brought prominently into view, but only to be dismissed apparently with the feeling that *the time for its solution has not yet arrived.*

"It seems to be admitted on all hands that the Miocene plants of Europe have their nearest and most numerous existing analogues in North America, and hence arises the question, How was the migration from one area to the other effected? Was there, as some have believed, an Atlantis? – a continent, or an archipelago of large islands, occupying the area of the North Atlantic. There is perhaps nothing unphilosophical in this hypothesis, for since, as geologists state, "the Alps have acquired 4,000, and even in some places more than 10,000 feet of their present altitude since the commencement of the Eocene period' (Lyell's *Principles,* 11th Ed., 1872, p. 256), a Post-Miocene (?) depression might have carried the hypothetical Atlantis into almost abysmal depths. But an Atlantis is apparently unnecessary and uncalled for. According to Professor Oliver, "A close and very peculiar analogy subsists between the Flora of Tertiary Central Europe and the recent Floras of the American States and of the Japanese region; an analogy much closer and more intimate than is to be traced between the Tertiary and Recent Floras of Europe. We find the Tertiary element of the Old World to be intensified towards its extreme eastern margin. . . . This accession of the Tertiary element is rather gradual and not abruptly assumed in the Japan islands only. Although it there attains a maximum, we may trace it from the Mediterranean, Levant, Caucasus, and Persia ... then along the Himalaya and through China. ... We learn also that during the Tertiary epoch, counterparts of Central European Miocene genera certainly grew in North-West America. . . . We note further that the present Atlantic Islands' Flora affords no substantial evidence of a former direct communication with the mainland of the New World. . . . The consideration of these facts leads me to the opinion that botanical evidence does not favour the hypothesis of an Atlantis. On the other hand, it strongly favours the view that at some period of the Tertiary epoch North-Eastern Asia was united to North-Western America, perhaps by the line where the Aleutian chain of islands now extends." (*Nat. Hist. Rev.*, II, p. 164, 1862.) See, however, "*Scientific and Geological Proofs of the Reality of Several Submerged Continents.*"

THERE IS NO "MISSING LINK" ANYWHERE

But nothing short of a pithecoid man will ever satisfy the luckless searchers after the thrice hypothetical "missing link." Yet, if beneath the vast floors of the Atlantic, from the Teneriffe Pic to Gibraltar, the ancient emplacement of the lost Atlantis, all the submarine strata were to be broken up miles deep, no such skull as would satisfy the Darwinists would be found. As Dr. C. R. Bree remarks ("*Fallacies of Darwinism*"), no missing links between man and ape having been discovered in various gravels and formations above the tertiaries, if they had gone down with the continents now covered with the sea, they might still be found "in those beds of contemporary geological strata which have *not* gone down to the bottom of the sea." Yet they are as fatally absent from the latter as from the former. Were not preconceptions to fasten vampire-like on man's mind, the author of "*Antiquity of Man*" would have found a clue to the difficulty in that same work of his, by going ten pages back (p. 530) and reading over a quotation of his own from Professor G. Rolleston's work. This physiologist, he says, suggests that as there is considerable plasticity in the human frame, not only in youth and during growth, but even in the adult, we ought not always to take for granted, as some advocates of the development theory seem to do, that each advance in physical power depends on an improvement in bodily structure, for why may not *the soul, or the higher intellectual and moral faculties, play the first instead of the second part in a progressive scheme*?

This hypothesis is made in relation to Evolution *not being entirely due to "natural selection"*, but it applies as well to our case in hand. For we, too, claim that it is the "Soul," or the *inner* man, that descends on Earth first, the psychic *astral*, the mould on which physical man is gradually built – his Spirit, intellectual and moral faculties awakening later on as that physical stature grows and develops.

"Thus incorporeal Spirits to smaller forms reduced their shapes immense," . . . and became the men of the Third and the Fourth Races. Still later, ages after, appeared the men of our Fifth Race, reduced from the still gigantic (in our modern sense) stature of their primeval ancestors, to about half of that size at present.

Man is certainly no special creation, and he is the product of Nature's gradual perfective work, like any other living unit on this Earth. But this is only with regard to the human tabernacle. That which lives and thinks in man and survives that frame, the masterpiece of evolution – is the "Eternal Pilgrim," the Protean differentiation in space and time of the One Absolute "Unknowable."

PALÆOLITHIC MAN, A CALIGRAPH!

In his *"Antiquity of Man,"* Sir C. Lyell quotes – perhaps in rather a mocking spirit – what Hallam says (in Vol. IV, p. 162) in his *"Introduction to the Literature of Europe"*:

> "If man was made in the image of God, he was also made in the image of an ape. The framework of the body of him who has weighed the stars and made the lightning his slave, approaches to that of a speechless brute who wanders in the forest of Sumatra. Thus standing on the frontier land between animal and angelic natures, what wonder that he should partake of both?"

An Occultist would have put it otherwise. He would say that man was indeed made in the image of a type projected by his progenitor, the creating *Angel-Force*, or *Dhyan Chohan*, while the wanderer of the forest of Sumatra was made *in the image of man*, since the framework of the ape, we say again, is the revival, the resuscitation by abnormal means, of the actual form of the Third-Round and of the Fourth-Round *Man* as well, later on. Nothing is lost in nature, *not an atom*: this latter is at least certain on scientific data. Analogy would appear to demand that *form* should be equally endowed with permanency.

And yet what do we find:

> "It is significant," says Sir W. Dawson, F.R.S., "that Professor Huxley in his lectures in New York, while resting his case as to the lower animals, mainly on the supposed genealogy of the horse, which has often been shown to amount to no certain evidence, *avoided altogether the discussion of the origin of men from the apes*, now obviously complicated with so many difficulties that both Wallace and Mivart are staggered by them. Professor Thomas in his recent lectures ("*Nature*," 1876), admits that there is no lower man known than the Australian, and that there is no known link of connection with the monkeys, and that Hæckel has to admit that the penultimate link in his phylogeny, the ape-like man, *is absolutely unknown* ('*History of Creation*') . . . . The so-called '*nallies*' found with the bones of Palæocosmic men in European caves, and illustrated in the admirable works of Christy and Lartet, show that the *rudiments even of writings were already in possession* of the oldest race of men known to archæology or geology." (See Wilson's "*Prehistoric Man*," Vol. II, p. 54; "*Origin of the World*," p. 393.)

Again in Dr. C. R. Bree's "*Fallacies of Darwinism*," on p. 160, we read:

> "Mr. Darwin justly says that the difference physically and, more especially mentally, between the lowest form of man and the highest anthropomorphous ape, is enormous. Therefore, *the time* – which in Darwinian evolution must be almost inconceivably slow – must have been *enormous* also during man's development from the monkey.[210] The chance, therefore, of some of these variations being found in the different gravels or fresh-water formations above the tertiaries, must be very great. And yet *not one single variation,*

---

210 And how much more "enormous" if we reverse the subjects and say during the monkey's development from the Third Race Man.

not one single specimen of a being between a monkey and a man has ever been found. Neither in the gravel, nor the drift-clay, nor the fresh-water beds, nor in the tertiaries below them has there ever been discovered the remains of any member of the missing families between the monkey and the man, as *assumed* to have existed by Mr. Darwin. Have they gone down with the depression of the earth's surface and are they now covered with the sea? If so, it is beyond all probability that they should not also be found in those beds of contemporary geological strata which have *not* gone down to the bottom of the sea; still more improbable that some portions should not be dredged from the ocean bed like the remains of the mammoth and the rhinoceros which are also found in fresh-water beds and gravels and drift!. . . . . . . the celebrated Neanderthal skull, about which so much has been said, belongs confessedly to this remote epoch (bronze and stone ages), and yet presents, although it may have been the skull of an idiot, immense differences from the highest known anthropomorphous ape."

Our globe being convulsed each time that it *reawakens* for a new period of activity, like a field which has to be ploughed and furrowed before fresh seed for its new crop is thrown into it – it does seem quite hopeless that fossils belonging to its previous Rounds should be found in the beds of either its oldest or its latest geological strata. Every new *Manvantara* brings along with it the renovation of forms, types, and species; every type of the preceding organic forms – vegetable, animal, and human – changes and is perfected in the next, even to the mineral, which has received in this Round its final opacity and hardness, its softer portions having formed the present vegetation, the astral relics of previous vegetation and fauna having been utilized in the formation of the lower animals, and determining the structure of the primeval Root-Types of the highest *mammalia*. And, finally, the form of the gigantic Ape-Man of the former Round has been reproduced in this one by human bestiality and transfigured into the *parent* form in the modern Anthropoid.

This doctrine, even imperfectly delineated as it is under our inefficient pen, is assuredly more logical, more consistent with facts, and *far more* probable than many "scientific" theories; that, for instance, of the first organic germ descending on a meteor to our Earth – like Ain Soph on his Vehicle, Adam Kadmon. Only, the latter descent is allegorical, as every one knows, and the Kabalists have never offered this figure of speech for acceptance in its dead-letter garb. But the germ on the meteor theory, as coming from such high scientific quarters, is an eligible candidate for axiomatic truth and law, a theory people are in honour bound to accept, if they would be on a right level with modern Science. What the next theory necessitated by the materialistic premises will be – no one can tell. Meanwhile, the *present* theories, as any one can see, clash together far more discordantly among themselves than even those of the Occultists outside the *sacred* precincts of learning. For what is there, next in order, now that exact Science has made even of the Life-principle an empty word, a meaningless term, and now insists that life is an effect *due to the molecular action of the primordial protoplasm!* The new doctrine of the Darwinists may be defined and summarized in a few words, in which Mr. Herbert Spencer has defined "special creation". . ."it is worthless. Worthless, by its derivation; worthless, in its intrinsic incoherence; worthless, as absolutely without evidence; worthless, as not supplying an intellectual need; worthless, as not satisfying a moral want. We must, therefore, *consider it as counting for nothing in opposition to any other hypothesis respecting the origin of organic beings.*" ("*Principles of Biology,*" Vol. I, p. 345.)

The Secret Doctrine, ii 709-730

Selection 32

THE GRADUAL DEVELOPMENT OF SPECIES IN ALL THE KINGDOMS OF NATURE WORKS BY UNIFORM LAWS

It is argued that the Universal Evolution, otherwise, the gradual development of species in all the kingdoms of nature, works by uniform laws. This is admitted, and the law enforced far more strictly in Esoteric than in modern Science. But we are told also, that it is equally a law that "development works from the less to the more perfect, and from the simpler to the more complicated, by incessant changes, small in themselves, but constantly accumulating in the required direction." It is from the infinitesimally small that the comparatively gigantic species are produced.

Esoteric Science agrees with it, but adds that this law applies only to what is known to it as the *Primary Creation* – the evolution of worlds from primordial atoms, and the *pre-primordial* ATOM, at the first differentiation of the former, and that during the period of cyclic evolution in space and time, this law is limited and works only in the lower kingdoms. It did so work during the first geological periods, from simple to complex, on the rough material surviving from the relics of the Third Round, which relics are projected into objectivity when terrestrial activity recommences.

NEITHER SCIENCE NOR ESOTERIC PHILOSOPHY ADMIT DESIGN OR "SPECIAL CREATION"

No more than Science, does esoteric philosophy admit *design* or "special creation." It rejects every claim to the "miraculous," and accepts nothing outside the uniform and immutable laws of Nature. But it teaches a cyclic law, a double stream of force (or spirit) and of matter, which, starting from the *neutral centre* of Being, develops in its cyclic progress and incessant transformations. The primitive germ from which all vertebrate life has developed throughout the ages, being distinct from the primitive germ from which the vegetable and the animal life have evolved, there are side laws whose work is determined by the conditions in which the materials to be worked upon are found by them, and of which Science – physiology and anthropology especially – seems to be little aware. Its votaries speak of that "primitive germ," and maintain that it is shown beyond any doubt that the "design" and the "*designer,*" if there be any, in the case of man, with the wonderful structure of his limbs, and his hand especially, "must be placed very much farther back, and (the design) is, in fact, involved in the primitive germ," from which not only all vertebrate life, but, "probably all life, animal and vegetable, have been slowly developed" ("*Modern Science and Modern Thought,*" p. 94).

This is as true of the "primitive germ" as it is false that that "germ" is only "very much farther back" than man is; for it is at an immeasurable and inconceivable distance (*in time,* though not in space) from the origin even of our Solar system. As the Hindu philosophy very justly teaches, the "*Aniyámsam Aniyâsam,*" can be known only through false notions. It is the "many" that proceed from the ONE – the living spiritual germs *or centres of forces* – each in a septenary form, which first generate, and then give the PRIMARY IMPULSE to the law of evolution and gradual slow development.

Limiting the teaching strictly to this, our earth, it may be shown that, as the ethereal forms of the first Men are first projected on seven zones by seven Dhyan-Chohanic *centres* of Force, so there are centres of creative power for every ROOT or parent species of the host of forms of vegetable and animal life. This is, again, no "special creation," nor is there any "Design," except in the general "ground-plan" worked out by the universal law. But there are certainly "designers," though these are neither omnipotent nor omniscient in the absolute sense of the term. They are simply *Builders,* or Masons, working under the impulse given them by the ever-to-be-unknown (on our plane) Master Mason – the ONE LIFE and Law. Belonging to this sphere, they have no hand in, or possibility of working on any other, during the present *Manvantara,* at any rate. That they work in cycles and on a strictly geometrical and mathematical scale of progression, is what the extinct animal species amply demonstrate; that they act by *design* in the details of minor lives (of side animal issues, etc.), is what natural history has sufficient evidence for. In the *creation* of new species, departing sometimes very widely from the Parent stock, as in the great variety of the genus *Felis* – like the lynx, the tiger, the cat, etc. – it is the "designers" who direct the new evolution by adding to, or depriving the species of certain appendages, either needed or becoming useless in the new environments. Thus, when we say that *Nature* provides for every animal and plant, whether large or small, we speak correctly. For, it is those terrestrial spirits of Nature, who form the aggregated Nature, which, if it fails occasionally in its design, is neither to be considered blind, nor to be taxed with the failure, since, belonging to *a differentiated* sum of qualities and attributes, it is in virtue of that alone *conditioned and imperfect*.

Were there no such thing as evolutionary cycles, an eternal spiral progress into matter with a proportionate *obscuration* of spirit – though the two are one – followed by an inverse ascent into spirit and the defeat of matter – active and passive by turn – how explain the discoveries of zoology and geology? How is it that, on the dictum of authoritative science, one can trace the animal life from the mollusc up to the great Sea Dragon, from the smallest land-worm up again to the gigantic animals of the Tertiary Period, and that the latter were once crossed is shown by the fact of all those species *decreasing, dwindling down, and being dwarfed*. If the seeming process of development working from the less to the more perfect, and from the simpler to the more complex, were a universal law indeed, instead of being a very imperfect generalization of a mere secondary nature in the great Cosmic process, and if there were no such cycles as those claimed, then the Mesozoic fauna and flora ought to change places with the latest Neolithic. It is the Plesiosauri and the Ichthyosauri that we ought to find developing from the present sea and river reptiles, instead of giving place to their dwarfed modern analogies. It is, again, our old friend, the good-tempered elephant, that would be the fossil antediluvian ancestor, and the mammoth of the Pliocene age who would be in the menagerie; the megalonyx and the gigantic megatherium would be found instead of the lazy sloth in the forests of South America, in which the colossal ferns of the carboniferous periods would take the place of moss and present trees – dwarfs, even the giants of California, in comparison with the Titan-trees of past geological periods. Surely the organisms of the megasthenian world of the Tertiary and the Mesozoic Ages must have been *more complex and perfect* than those of the microsthenian plants and animals of the present age? The *Dryopithecus*, for instance, is found more perfect anatomically, more fit for a greater development of brain power, than the modern gorilla or gibbon? How is this, then? Are we to believe that the constitution of all those colossal land and sea-dragons, of the gigantic flying reptiles, was not far more developed and complex than the anatomy of the lizards, turtles, crocodiles, and even of the whales – in short, all those animals we are acquainted with?

The "To Be or Not To Be" of Science

Let us admit, however, for argument's sake, that all those cycles, races, septenary forms of evolution and the *tutti quanti* of esoteric teaching, are no better than a delusion and a snare. Let us agree with Science and say that man, instead of being an imprisoned "Spirit," and his vehicle, the *shell* or body, a gradually perfected and now complete mechanism for material and terrestrial uses, as claimed by the Occultists – is simply a more developed animal, whose primal form emerged from one and the same primitive germ on this earth, as the flying dragon and the gnat, the whale and the amœba, the crocodile and the frog, etc., etc. In this case, he must have passed through the identical developments and through the same process of growth as all the other mammals? If man is an animal, *and nothing more*, a highly intellectual *ex-brute*, he should be privileged, at least, and allowed to have been a gigantic mammal of his kind, a *meganthropos* in his day. It is just this, that esoteric science shows as having taken place in the first three rounds, and in this, as in most other things, it is more logical and consistent than modern science. It classifies the human body with the brute creation, and maintains it in the path of animal evolution, from first to last, while science leaves man a parentless orphan born of sires unknown, an "unspecialized skeleton" truly! And this mistake is due to a stubborn rejection of the doctrine of cycles.

The Origin and Evolution of the Mammalia: Science and the Esoteric Phylogeny

Having dealt almost exclusively with the question of the origin of Man in the foregoing criticism of Western Evolutionism, it may not be amiss to define the position of the Occultists with regard to the differentiation of species. The *pre-human* fauna and flora have been already generally dealt with in the *Commentary* on the Stanzas, and the truth of much of modern biological speculation admitted, *e.g.* the derivation of birds from reptiles, the *partial* truth of "natural selection," and the transformation theory generally. It now remains to clear up the mystery of the origin of those first mammalian fauna which M. de Quatrefages so brilliantly endeavours to prove as contemporary with the *Homo primigenius* of the Secondary Age.

The somewhat complicated problem relating to the *"Origin of Species,"* – more especially of the varied groups of fossil or existing mammalian fauna – will be rendered less obscure by the aid of a diagram. It will then he apparent to what extent the "Factors of Organic Evolution," relied upon by Western biologists,[211] are to be considered as adequate to meet the facts. The line of demarcation between ethero-spiritual, astral, and physical evolution must be drawn. Perhaps, if Darwinians deigned to consider the possibility of the second process, they would no longer have to lament the fact that "we are *referred to conjecture and inference* for the origin of the Mammals"!! ("*The Doctrine of Descent and Darwinism*," by Professor O. Schmidt, p. 268) At present, the

---

211 The Darwinian theory has been so strained, that even Huxley was forced at one time to deprecate its occasional degeneration into "fanaticism." Oscar Schmidt presents a good instance of a thinker who unconsciously exaggerates the worth of an hypothesis. He admits (*"The Doctrine of Descent and Darwinism,"* p. 158) that "natural selection is in some cases . . . *inadequate, . . .* in others . . . not requisite, as the solution of the formation of species is found in other natural conditions." He also asserts the *"intermediate grades are . . . wanting,* which would entitle us to infer with certainty the direct transition from unplacental to placental mammals" (p. 271); that "we are referred *entirely to conjecture and inference* for the origin of the mammals" (p. 268), and the repeated failures of the framers of *"hypothetical pedigrees,"* more especially of Hæckel. Nevertheless, he asserts on p. 194 that "what we have gained by the Doctrine of Descent based on the theory of selection is the KNOWLEDGE of the connection of organisms as 'consanguineous beings.' " Knowledge in the face of the above-cited concessions, is, then, the synonym for conjecture and theory only?

admitted chasm between the systems of reproduction of the oviparous vertebrates and *mammalia* constitutes a hopeless crux to those thinkers who, with the Evolutionists, seek to link all existing organic forms in a continuous line of descent.

Let us take – *exempli gratiâ* – the case of the ungulate mammals. "In no other division," it is said, "do we possess such abundant fossil material." So much progress has been made in this direction, that in some instances the intermediate links between the modern and Eocene ungulates have been unearthed, a notable example being that of the complete proof of the derivation of the present one-toed horse from the three-toed Anchitherium of the old Tertiary. This standard of comparison between Western biology and the Eastern doctrine could not, therefore, be improved upon. The pedigree here utilized, as embodying the view, of scientists in general, is that of Schmidt based on the exhaustive researches of Rütimeyer. Its *approximate* accuracy – from the standpoint of evolutionism – leaves little to be desired:

UNGULATE MAMMALS

The midway point of evolution. Science comes to a standstill. "*The root to which these two families lead back* is UNKNOWN" (Schmidt).

THE "ROOT" ACCORDING TO OCCULTISM

ANOPLOTHERIDAE	PALAETHERIDAE

II.   One of the Seven primeval physico-astral and bisexual Root-types of the Mammalian Kingdom (animal). These were Contemporaries of the early Lemurian races – the "unknown roots" of Science.

No. I. represents the realm explored by Western Evolutionists, the area in which climatic influences, "natural selection," and all the other physical causes of organic differentiation are present. Biology and palæontology find their province here in investigating the many physical agencies which contribute so largely, as shown by Darwin, Spencer, and others, to the *segregation of species*. But even in this domain the sub-conscious workings of the *Dhyan-Chohanic wisdom* are at the root of all the "ceaseless striving towards perfection," though its influence is vastly modified by those purely material causes which de Quatrefages terms the "*milieux*" and Spencer the "Environment."

The "midway point of evolution" is that stage where the *astral* prototypes definitely begin to pass into the physical, and thus become subject to the differentiating agencies now operative around us. Physical causation supervenes immediately on the assumption of "coats of skin" – *i.e.* the physiological equipment in general. The forms of Men and *mammalia* previous to the separation of sexes[212] are woven out of astral matter and possess a structure utterly unlike that of the physical organisms, which eat, drink, digest, etc., etc., etc. The known physiological contrivances in organisms were almost entirely evolved subsequently to the incipient physicalization of the 7 Root-Types out of the astral – during the "midway halt" between the two planes of existence. Hardly had the "ground-plan" of evolution been limned out in these ancestral types, than the influence of the accessory terrestrial laws, familiar to us, supervened, resulting in the whole crop of mammalian species. Æons of slow differentiation were, however, required to effect this end.

---

212 Bear in mind, please, that though the animals—mammalians included—have all been evolved after and partially from man's cast-off tissues, still, as a far lower being, the mammalian animal became placental and separated far earlier than man.

THE UNITY OF TYPE

No. II. represents the domain of the purely astral prototypes previous to their descent into (gross) matter. Astral matter, it must be noted, is fourth-state matter, having, like our gross matter, its own "protyle." There are several "protyles" in Nature, corresponding to the various planes of matter. The two sub-physical elemental kingdoms, the plane of mind (*manas*, the fifth-state matter), as also that of *Buddhi* (sixth-state matter), are each and all evolved from one of the six "protyles" which constitute the basis of the Object-Universe. The three "states," so-called of our terrestrial matter, known as the "solid," "liquid," and "gaseous," are only, in strict accuracy, SUB-states. As to the former reality of the descent into the physical, which culminated in physiological man and animal, we have a palpable testimony in the fact of the so-called spiritualistic "materializations."

In all these instances a complete temporary mergence of the astral into the physical takes place. The evolution of physiological Man out of the astral races of *early* Lemurian age – the Jurassic age of Geology – is exactly paralleled by the "materialization" of "spirits" (?) in the séance-room. In the case of Professor Crookes' "Katie King," the presence of a *physiological* mechanism – heart, lungs, etc. – was indubitably demonstrated!!

This, in a way, is the ARCHETYPE of Goethe. Listen to his words: "Thus much we should have gained. . . all the nine perfect organic beings. . . (are) formed *according to an archetype* which merely fluctuates more or less in its very persistent parts and, moreover, day by day, completes and transforms itself by means of reproduction." This is a seemingly imperfect foreshadowing of the occult fact of the differentiation of species from the primal *astral root-types*. Whatever the whole *posse comitatus* of "natural selection," etc., etc., may effect, the *fundamental unity of structural plan* remains practically unaffected by all subsequent modifications. The "Unity of Type" common, in a sense, to all the animal and human kingdoms, is not, as Spencer and others appear to hold, a proof of the consanguinity of *all* organic forms, but a witness to the essential unity of the "ground-plan" Nature has followed in fashioning her creatures.

To sum up the case, we may again avail ourselves of a tabulation of the actual *factors* concerned in the differentiation of species. The stages of the process itself need no further comment here, being the basic principles underlying organic development, than to enter on the domain of the biological specialist.

FACTORS CONCERNED IN THE ORIGIN OF SPECIES, ANIMAL AND VEGETABLE

BASIC ASTRAL PROTOTYPES PASS INTO THE PHYSICAL

The *Dhyan Chohanic Impulse* constituting Lamarck's "inherent and necessary" law of development. It lies behind all minor agencies.

1. Variation transmitted by heredity.
2. Natural Selection.
3. Sexual Selection.
4. Physiological Selection.
5. Isolation.
6. Correlation of Growth.
7. Adaptation to Environment. (Intelligent as opposed to mechanical causation.)

| | | | |

SPECIES

Is Science against those who maintain that, down to the Quaternary period, the distribution of the human races was widely different from what it is now? Is Science against those who, further, maintain that the fossil men found in Europe – although having almost reached a plane of *sameness* and unity from the fundamental physiological and anthropological aspects which continues till this day – still differ, sometimes greatly, from the type of the now existing populations. The late Littré confesses it in an article published by him on the Memoir called *Antiquités Celtiques et Antediluviennes* by Boucher de Perthes (1849), in the *Revue des Deux Mondes* (March 1, 1859). He says in it (a) that in these periods when the Mammoths, exhumed with the hatchets in Picardy, lived in the latter region, there must have been an eternal spring reigning over all the terrestrial globe[213]; nature was the contrary

---

213 Scientists now admit that Europe enjoyed in the Miocene times a warm, in the Pliocene or later *Tertiary*, a temperate climate. Littré's contention as to the balmy spring of the *Quaternary*—to which deposits M. de Perthes' discoveries of flint implements

of what it is now – thus leaving an *enormous margin for the antiquity of those "periods"* and then adds (*b*) "Spring, professor of the Faculty of Medicine at Liège, found in a grotto near Namur, in the mountain of Chauvaux, numerous human bones '*of a race quite distinct from ours.*'"

Skulls exhumed in Austria offered a great analogy with those of African negro races, according to Littré, while others, discovered on the shores of the Danube and the Rhine, resembled the skulls of the Caribs and those of the ancient inhabitants of Peru and Chile. Still, the Deluge, whether Biblical or Atlantean, was denied. But further geological discoveries having made Gaudry write conclusively: "Our forefathers were positively contemporaneous with the *rhinoceros tichorrhinus*, the *hippopotamus major*", and add that the soil called *diluvial* in geology "was formed *partially* at least after man's apparition on earth" – Littré pronounced himself finally. He then showed the necessity, before "the resurrection of so many old witnesses," of *rehandling* all the origins, all the durations, and added that there was AN AGE hitherto unknown to study "either at the dawn of the actual epoch or, as I believe, at the beginning of the epoch *which preceded it.*"

The types of the skulls found in Europe are of two kinds, as is well known: the orthognathous and the prognathous, or the Caucasian and the negro types, such as are now found only in the African and the lower savage tribes. Professor Heer – who argues that the facts of botany necessitate the hypothesis of an Atlantis – has shown that the plants of the Neolithic lake-villagers are mainly of *African* origin. How did the latter come to be in Europe if there was no former point of union between Africa and Europe? How many thousand years ago did the seventeen men live whose skeletons were exhumed in the Department of the Haute Garonne, in a squatting posture near the remains of a coal fire, with some amulets and broken crockery around them, and in company with the bear *spelæus*, the *Elephas primigenius*, the *aurochs* (regarded by Cuvier as a distinct species), the *Megaceros hibernicus*

are traceable (since when the Somme has worn down its valley many scores of feet)— must be accepted with much reservation. The Somme-valley relics are *post-glacial*, and possibly point to the immigration of savages during one of the more temperate periods intervening between *minor* ages of Ice.

– all antediluvian mammals? Certainly at a most distant epoch, but not one which carries us further back than the Quaternary. A much greater antiquity for Man has yet to be proved. Dr. James Hunt, the late President of the Anthropological Society, makes it 9,000,000 years. This man of science, at any rate, makes some approach to our esoteric computation, if we leave the first two semi-human, ethereal races, and the early Third Race out of the computation.

The question, however, arises – who were these Palæolithic men of the European quaternary epoch? Were they aboriginal, or the outcome of some immigration dating back into the unknown past? The latter is the only tenable hypothesis, as all scientists agree in eliminating Europe from the category of possible "cradles of mankind." Whence, then, radiated the various successive streams of "primitive" men?

The earliest Palæolithic men in Europe – about whose origin Ethnology is silent, and whose very characteristics are but imperfectly known, though expatiated on as "ape-like" by imaginative writers such as Mr. Grant Allen – were of pure Atlantean and "Africo" Atlantean stocks.[214] (It must be borne in mind that by this time, the Atlantis continent itself was a dream of the past.) Europe in the Quaternary epoch was very different from the Europe of today, being then only in process of formation. It was united to N. Africa – or rather what is now N. Africa – by a neck of land running across the present Straits of Gibraltar – N. Africa thus constituting a species of extension of Spain, while a broad sea washed the great basin of the Sahara. Of the great Atlantis, the main bulk of which sank in the Miocene, there remained only Ruta and Daitya and a stray island or so. The Atlantean connections of the forefathers[215] of the Palæolithic cave-men are evidenced by the

---

214 "Whence they (the old cave-men) came, we *cannot tell*" (Grant Allen).
"*The Palæolithic hunters of the Somme Valley did not originate in that inhospitable climate, but moved into Europe from some more genial region.*" (Dr. Southall's "*Epoch of the Mammoth,*" p. 315)

215 The *pure* Atlantean stocks—of which the tall quaternary cave-men were, in part the direct descendants—immigrated into Europe long prior to the Glacial Period; in fact, as far back as the Pliocene and Miocene times in the Tertiary. *The worked Miocene, flints of Thenay, and the traces of Pliocene man discovered by Professor Capellini in Italy, are witnesses to the fact.* These colonists were portions of the once glorious race, whose cycle from the

upturning of fossil skulls (in Europe) reverting closely to the *West Indian* Carib and *ancient Peruvian* type – a mystery indeed to all those who refuse to sanction the "hypothesis" of a former Atlantic continent to bridge the ocean (*Cf.* "*Scientific and geological proofs of the reality of several submerged continents*"). What are we also to make of the fact that while de Quatrefages points to that "*magnificent race*," the TALL Cro-Magnon cave-men and the *Guanches* of the Canary Islands as representatives of one type – Virchow also allies the Basques with the latter in a similar way? Professor Retzius independently proves the relationship of the aboriginal *American* dolichocephalous tribes and these same *Guanches*. The several links in the chain of evidence are securely joined together. Legions of similar facts could be adduced. As to the African tribes – themselves diverging offshoots of Atlanteans modified by climate and conditions – they crossed into Europe over the peninsula which made the Mediterranean an inland sea. Fine races were many of these European cave-men; the Cro-Magnon, for instance. But, as was to be expected, *progress is almost non-existent* through the whole of the vast period allotted by Science to the Chipped Stone-Age.[216] *The cyclic impulse downwards* weighs heavily on the stocks thus transplanted – the incubus of the *Atlantean Karma* is upon them. Finally, Palæolithic man makes room for his successor – and disappears almost entirely from the scene. Professor Lefèvre asks in this connection:

"Has the Polished succeeded the Chipped Stone-Age by an imperceptible transition, or was it due to an invasion of brachycephalous Celts? But whether, again, the deterioration produced in the populations of La Vezère was the result of violent crossings, or of a general retreat northwards in the wake of the reindeer, is of little moment to us." He continues:

"Meantime the bed of the ocean has been upheaved, Europe is

Eocene downwards had been running down the scale.

216 The artistic skill displayed by the old cave-men renders the hypothesis which regards them as approximations to the "pithecanthropus alalus"—that very mythical Hæckelian monster—an absurdity requiring no Huxley or Schmidt to expose it. We see in their skill in engraving a *gleam* of Atlantean culture *atavistically* re-appearing." It will be remembered that Donnelly regards modern European as a *renaissance* of Atlantean civilization. ("*Atlantis*," pp. 237–264.)

now fully formed, her flora and fauna fixed. With the taming of the dog begins the pastoral life. *We enter on those polished stone and bronze periods,* which succeed each other at irregular intervals, which even overlap one another in the midst of ethnical fusions and migrations. . . . The primitive European populations are interrupted in their special evolution and, without perishing, become absorbed in other races, engulfed . . . by successive waves of migration overflowing from Africa, *possibly from a lost Atlantis* [? ? far too late by æons of years] and from prolific Asia . . .

all Forerunners Of The Great Aryan Invasion" (Fifth Race).

The Secret Doctrine, ii 731 – 741

Selection 33

THE DAY WHEN THE CHURCH WILL FIND THAT ITS ONLY SALVATION LIES IN THE OCCULT INTERPRETATION OF THE BIBLE MAY NOT BE FAR OFF

The day when the Church will find that its only salvation lies in the *occult* interpretation of the *Bible*, may not be so far off as some imagine. Already many an abbé and ecclesiastic has become an ardent Kabalist, and as many appear publicly in the arena, breaking a lance with Theosophists and Occultists in support of the metaphysical interpretation of the *Bible*. But they commence, unfortunately for them, from the wrong end. They are advised, before they begin to speculate upon the *metaphysical* in their Scriptures, to study and master that which relates to the purely *physical* – *e.g.* its geological and ethnological hints. For such allusions to the Septenary constitution of the Earth and Man, to the seven Rounds and Races, abound in the New as in the Old Testaments, and are as visible as the sun in the heavens to him who reads both symbolically. What do the laws in Chapter XXIII, v. 15, of *Leviticus* apply to? What is the philosophy of reason for all such *hebdomadic* offerings and symbolical calculations as: "ye shall count. . . . from the morrow after the Sabbath. . . . that ye brought the sheaf of the wave offering; *seven Sabbaths shall be completed*" (15); "And ye shall offer with the bread seven lambs without blemish" (18), etc. etc. We shall be contradicted, no doubt, when we say that all these "wave" and "peace" offerings were in commemoration of the *Seven* "Sabbaths" of the mysteries, which Sabbaths are seven *pralayas*, between seven *Manvantaras*, or what we call *Rounds* – for "Sabbath" *is* an elastic word, meaning a period of Rest of whatever nature, as explained elsewhere (Part II, "*Selections on the Septenary*.") And if this is not sufficiently conclusive, then we may turn to the verse which follows (16), and which adds, "even unto the morrow after the seventh Sabbath shall ye number fifty days" (forty-nine, 7 x 7, stages of activity, and forty-nine stages of *rest*, on the seven globes of the chain, and then comes the *rest* of Sabbath, the *fiftieth*); after which "ye shall offer *a new meat offering* unto the Lord," *i.e.* ye shall make an offering of your flesh or "coats of skin," and, divesting yourselves of your bodies, ye shall remain pure spirits. This law of offering, degraded and materialized with ages, was an institution that dated from the earliest Atlanteans; it came to the Hebrews *viâ* the "Chaldees," who were the "wise men" of a *caste*, not of a nation, a community of great adepts come from their "Serpent-holes," and who had settled in Babylonia ages before. And if this interpretation from Leviticus (full of the disfigured *Laws of Manu*) is found too far-fetched, then turn to *Revelation*. Whatever interpretation profane mystics may give to the famous Chapter XVII, with its riddle of the woman in purple and scarlet; whether Protestants nod at the Roman Catholics, when reading "MYSTERY, BABYLON THE GREAT, THE MOTHER OF HARLOTS AND ABOMINATIONS OF THE EARTH," or Roman Catholics glare at the Protestants, the Occultists pronounce, in their impartiality, that these words have applied from the first to all and every exoteric Churchianity, that which was the "ceremonial magic" of old, with its terrible effects, and is now the harmless (because distorted) farce of ritualistic worship. The "mystery" of the woman and of the beast, are the symbols of soul-killing Churchianity and of SUPERSTITION. "The beast that was, and is not, and yet is." "And here is the Mind which hath wisdom. The seven heads are seven mountains (seven continents and seven races) on which the woman sitteth," the symbol of all the exoteric, barbarous, idolatrous faiths which have covered that symbol "with the blood of the saints and the blood of the martyrs" who protested and do protest. "And there are *seven Kings* (seven races); five are fallen (our fifth race included), and one is (the fifth continues), and the other (the *sixth* and the *seventh* races) is not yet come. . . . And when he (the race "King") cometh, he must continue a short space" (v. 10). There are many such Apocalyptic allusions, but the student has to find them out for himself. These five Kings were mentioned before.

THE APE ARRIVED ON THE SCENE LATER THAN MAN

If the *Bible* combines with archæology and geology to show that human civilization has passed through three more or less distinct stages, in Europe at least; and if man, both in America and Europe, as much as in Asia, dates from geological epochs – why should not the statements of the Secret Doctrine be taken into consideration? Is it more philosophical or logical and scientific too, to *disbelieve*, with Mr. Albert Gaudry, in Miocene man, while believing that the famous Thenay flints[217] "were carved by the *Dryopithecus monkey*; or, with the Occultist, that the anthropomorphous monkey came ages after man? For if it is once conceded, and even scientifically demonstrated, that "there was not in the middle of the Miocene epoch a single species of mammal identical with species now extant" (*"Les Enchainements du monde animal dans les temps géologiques,"* by Albert Gaudry, p. 240); and that man was then just as he is now, only taller, and more athletic than we are,[218] then where is the difficulty? That they could hardly be the descendants of monkeys, which are themselves not traced before the Miocene epoch,[219] is, on the other hand, testified to by several eminent naturalists.

> "Thus, in the savage of quaternary ages who had to fight against the mammoth with stone weapons, we find all those craniological characters generally considered as the sign of great intellectual development" (de Quatrefages, *"The Human Species,"* p. 312.)

Unless man emerged spontaneously, endowed with all his intellect and wisdom, from his brainless catarrhine ancestor, he could not have acquired such brain within the limits of the Miocene period, if we are to believe the learned Abbé Bourgeois (*Vide infra*, footnote).

As to the matter of giants, though the tallest man hitherto found in Europe among fossils is the "Mentone man" (6 ft. 8 in.), others may yet be excavated. Nilsson, quoted by Lubbock, states that "in a tomb of the

---

217 "The flints of Thenay bear unmistakable trace of the work of human hands." (G. de Mortillet, *"Promenades au Musée de St. Germain,"* p. 76.)

218 Speaking of the reindeer hunters of Périgord, Joly says of them that "they were of *great height*, athletic, with a strongly built skeleton . . ." etc. (*"Man before Metals,"* 353).

219 "On the shores of the lake of Beauce," says the Abbé Bourgeois, "man lived in the midst of a fauna which completely disappeared (*Aceratherium, Tapir, Mastodon*) . With the fluviatile sands of Orléanais came the anthropomorphous monkey (*pliopithecus antiquus*); therefore, later than man." (See *Comptes Rendus* of the *"Prehistoric Congress"* of 1867 at Paris.)

Neolithic age . . . . a skeleton of extraordinary size was found in 1807," and that it was attributed to a king of Scotland, Albus McGaldus.

And if in our own day we occasionally find men and women from 7 ft. to even 9 ft. and 11 ft. high, this only proves – on the law of atavism, or the reappearance of ancestral features of character – that there was a time when 9 ft. and 10 ft. was the average height of humanity, even in our latest Indo-European race.

But as the subject was sufficiently treated elsewhere, we may pass on to the Lemurians and the Atlanteans, and see what the old Greeks knew of these early races and what the moderns know now.

The great nation mentioned by the Egyptian priests, from which descended the forefathers of the Greeks of the age of Troy, and which, as averred, had been destroyed by the Atlantic race, was then, as we see, assuredly no race of Palæolithic *savages*. Nevertheless, already in the days of Plato, with the exception of priests and Initiates, no one seems to have preserved any distinct recollection of the preceding races. The earliest Egyptians had been separated from the latest Atlanteans for ages upon ages; they were themselves descended from an *alien* race, and had settled in Egypt some 400,000 years before,[220] but their Initiates had preserved *all the records*. Even so late as the time of Herodotus, they had still in their possession the statues of 341 kings who had reigned over their little Atlanto-Aryan Sub-race (*Vide* about the latter "*Esoteric Buddhism*," 5th Ed., p. 66). If one allows only twenty years as an average figure for the reign of each King, the duration of the Egyptian Empire has to be pushed back, from the day of Herodotus, about 17,000 years.

Bunsen allowed the great Pyramid an antiquity of 20,000 years.

---

220 "In making soundings in the stony soil of the Nile Valley two baked bricks were discovered, one at the depth of 20, the other at 25 yards. If we estimate the thickness of the annual deposit formed by the river at 8 inches per century (more careful calculations have shown no more than from three to five per century), we must assign to the first of these bricks 12,000 years, and to the second 14,000 years. By means of analogous calculations, Burmeister supposes 72,000 years to have elapsed since the first appearance of man on the soil of Egypt, and Draper attributes to the European man, who witnessed the last glacial epoch, an antiquity of more than 250,000 years." ("*Man before Metals*," p. 183.) Egyptian Zodiacs show more than 75,000 years of observation! (See further.) Note well also that Burmeister speaks only of the Delta population.

More modern archæologists will not give it more than 5,000, or at the utmost 6,000 years, and generously concede to Thebes with its hundred gates, 7,000 years from the date of its foundation. And yet there are records which show Egyptian priests – Initiates – journeying in a North-Westerly direction, *by land, viâ* what became later the Straits of Gibraltar; turning North and traveling through the future Phœnician settlements of Southern Gaul; then still further North, until reaching Carnac (Morbihan), they turned to the West again and arrived, *still traveling by land*, on the North-Western promontory of the New Continent.[221]

What was the object of their long journey? And how far back must we place the date of such visits? The archaic records show the Initiates of the Second Sub-race of the Aryan family moving from one land to the other for the purpose of supervising the building of *menhirs* and dolmens, of colossal Zodiacs in stone, and places of sepulchre to serve as receptacles for the ashes of generations to come. When was it? The fact of their crossing from France to Great Britain by land may give an idea of the date when such a journey could have been performed on *terrâ firma*.

It was –

> "When the level of the Baltic and of the North Sea was 400 feet higher than it is now; when the valley of the Somme was not hollowed to the depth it has now attained; when Sicily was joined to Africa, Barbary to Spain," when Carthage, the Pyramids of Egypt, the palaces of Uxmal and Palenqué were not in existence, and the bold navigators of Tyre and Sidon, who at a later date were to undertake their perilous voyages along the coasts of Africa, were yet unborn. What we know with *certainty is that European man was contemporaneous with* the extinct species of the quaternary epoch. . . . that he witnessed the upheaval of the Alps[222] and the extension of

221 Or on what are now the British Islands, which were not yet detached from the main continent in those days. "The ancient inhabitant of Picardy could pass into Great Britain without crossing the Channel. The British Isles were united to Gaul by an isthmus which has since been submerged." (*"Man before Metals,"* p. 184.)

222 He witnessed and remembered it too, as "the final disappearance of the largest continent of Atlantis was an event coincident with the elevation of the Alps," a master

the glaciers, in a word that he lived for thousands of years before the dawn of the remotest *historical* traditions. . . . It is even possible that man was the contemporary of extinct *mammalia* of species yet more ancient. . . . of the *Elephas meridionalis* of the sands of St. Prest. . . and the *Elephas antiquus*, assumed to be prior to the *elephas primigenius*, since their bones are found in company with carved flints in several English caves, associated with those of the *Rhinoceros hemitæchus* and even of the *Machairodus latidens*, which is of still earlier date. . . . M. E. Lartet is of opinion that there is nothing really impossible in the existence of man as early as the "Tertiary period."[223]

DARWINIANS REJECT THE TRUTH

If "there is nothing impossible" scientifically in the idea, and it may be admitted that man lived already as early as the Tertiary period, then it is just as well to remind the reader that Mr. Croll places the beginning of that period 2,500,000 years back (See Croll's "*Climate and Time*"); but there was a time when he assigned to it 15,000,000 years.

And if all this may be said of *European man*, how great is the antiquity of the Lemuro-Atlantean and of the Atlanto-Aryan man? Every educated person who follows the progress of Science, knows how all vestiges of man during the Tertiary period are received. The calumnies that were poured on Desnoyers in 1863, when he made known to the Institute of France that he had made a discovery "in the undisturbed Pliocene sands of St. Prest near Chartres, proving the co-existence of man and the *Elephas meridionalis*" – were equal to the occasion. The later discovery (in 1867) by the Abbé Bourgeois, that man lived in the Miocene epoch, and the reception it was given at the Pre-historic Congress held at Brussels in 1872, proves that the average

writes (See "*Esoteric Buddhism,*" p. 70). *Pari passu,* as one portion of the dry land of our hemisphere disappeared, some land of the new continent emerged from the seas. It is on this colossal cataclysm, which lasted during a period of 150,000 years, that traditions of all the Deluges are built, the Jews building their version on an event which took place later in "Poseidonis."

223 The Antiquity of the Human Race, in "*Men before Metals,*" by M. Joly, Professor at the Science Faculty of Toulouse, p. 184.

man of Science will never see but *that which he wants to see.*[224]

The modern archæologist, though speculating *ad infinitum* upon the dolmens and their builders, knows, in fact, nothing of them or their origin. Yet, these weird, and often colossal monuments of unhewn stones – which consist generally of four or seven gigantic blocks placed together – are strewn over Asia, Europe, America, and Africa, in groups or rows. Stones of enormous size are found placed horizontally and variously upon two, three, four, and as in Poitou, upon six and seven blocks. People name them "devil's altars," druidic stones, and giant tombs. The stones of Carnac in the Morbihan, Brittany – nearly a mile in length and numbering 11,000 ranged in eleven rows – are twin sisters of those at Stonehenge. The Conical *menhir* of Loch-Maria-ker in Morbihan, measures twenty yards in length and nearly two yards across. The Menhir of Champ Dolent (near St. Malo) rises thirty feet above the ground, and is fifteen feet in depth below. Such dolmens and prehistoric monuments are met with in almost every latitude. They are found in the Mediterranean basin; in Denmark (among the local *tumuli* from twenty-seven to thirty-five feet in height); in Shetland, and in Sweden, where they are called *ganggriften* (or tombs with corridors); in Germany, where they are known as the giant tombs (Hünengräben); in Spain (see the dolmen of *Antiguera* near Malaga), and Africa; in Palestine and Algeria; in Sardinia (see the *Nuraghi* and *Sepolture dei giganti*, or tombs of giants); in Malabar, in India, where they are called the tombs of the *Daityas* (giants) and of the *Râkshasas*, the mendemons of *Lanka*; in Russia and Siberia, where they are known as the *Koorgan*; in Peru and Bolivia, where they are termed the *chulpas* or burial places, etc., etc., etc.

There is no country from which they are absent. Who built them? Why are they all connected with Serpents and Dragons, with Alligators and Crocodiles? Because remains of "Palæolithic man" were, it is thought, found in some of them, and because in the funeral mounds of America

---

224 The scientific "jury" disagreed, as usual; while de Quatrefages, de Mortillet, Worsaæ, Engelhardt, Waldemar, Schmidt, Capellini, Hamy, and Cartailhac, saw upon the flints the traces of human handiwork, Steenstrup, Virchow and Desor refused to do so. Still the majority, if we except some English Scientists, are for Bourgeois.

bodies of later races were discovered with the usual paraphernalia of bone necklaces, weapons, stone and copper urns, etc., hence they are declared ancient *tombs*. But surely the two famous mounds – one in the Mississippi valley and the other in Ohio – known respectively as "the Alligator Mound" and "the Great Serpent Mound," were never meant for tombs [225] (*Vide infra*). Yet one is told authoritatively that the Mounds, and the Mound or Dolmen Builders, are all "Pelasgic" in Europe, antecedent to the Incas, in America, yet of "not extremely distant times." They are built by "*no* race of Dolmen Builders," which *never existed* (opinion of De Mortillet, Bastian, and Westropp) save in the earlier archæological fancy. Finally Virchow's opinion of the giant tombs of Germany is now accepted as an axiom:"The tombs alone are gigantic, and not the bones they contain" – says that German biologist, and archæology has but to bow and submit to the decision.[226]

STILL MORE ASTOUNDING CONTRADICTIONS

That no gigantic skeletons have been hitherto found in the "tombs" is yet no reason to say there never were the remains of giants in them. *Cremation was universal* till a comparatively recent period – some 80, or 100,000 years ago. The real giants, moreover, were nearly all drowned with Atlantis. Nevertheless, the classics, as shown elsewhere, often speak of giant skeletons still excavated in their day. Besides this, human fossils may be counted on the fingers, as yet. No skeleton ever yet found is older than between 50, or 60,000 years,[227] and man's size

---

225 We take the following description from a scientific work. "The first of these animals (the alligator) designed with considerable skill, is no less than 250 ft. long. . . . . The interior is formed of a heap of stones, over which the form has been moulded in fine stiff clay. The great serpent is represented with open mouth, in the act of swallowing an egg of which the diameter is 100 ft. in the thickest part; the body of the animal is wound in graceful curves and the tail is rolled into a spiral. The entire length of the animal is 1,100 ft. This work is unique . . . . and there is nothing on the old continent which offers any analogy to it." Except its symbolism, however, of the serpent—the cycle of Time—swallowing Kosmos, the egg.

226 It might be better, perhaps, for FACT had we more *Specialists* in Science and fewer "authorities" on universal questions. One never heard that Humboldt gave authoritative and final decisions in the matter of *polypi*, or the nature of an excrescence.

227 57,000 years is the date assigned by Dr. Dowler to the remains of the human

was reduced from 15 to 10 or 12 feet, ever since the third sub-race of the Aryan stock, which sub-race – born and developed in Europe and Asia Minor under new climates and conditions – had become European. Since then, as said, it has steadily been decreasing. It is truer therefore to say, that the tombs alone are archaic, and not necessarily the bodies of men occasionally found in them; and that those tombs, since they are gigantic, must have contained giants,[228] or rather the ashes of generations of giants.

Nor were all such cyclopean structures intended for sepulchres. It is with the so-called Druidical remains, such as Carnac in Brittany and Stonehenge in Great Britain, that the traveling Initiates above alluded to had to do. And these gigantic monuments are all symbolic records of the World's history. They are *not* Druidical, but *universal*. Nor did the Druids build them, for they were only the heirs to the cyclopean lore left to them by generations of mighty builders and "magicians," both good and bad.

It will always be a subject of regret that history, rejecting *a priori* the actual existence of giants, has preserved us so little of the records of antiquity concerning them. Yet in nearly every mythology – which after all *is* ancient history – the giants play an important part. In the old Norse mythology, the giants, Skrymir and his brethren, against whom the sons of the gods fought, were potent factors in the histories of deities and men. The modern exegesis, that makes these giants to be the brethren of the dwarfs, and reduces the combats of the gods to the history of the development of the Aryan race, will only receive credence amongst the believers in the Aryan theory, as expounded by Max Müller. Granting that the Turanian races were typified by the dwarfs (Dwergar), and that a dark, round-headed, and dwarfish race was driven northward by the fair-faced Scandinavians, or Æsir,

skeleton found buried beneath four ancient forests at New Orleans on the banks of the Mississippi river

228 Murray says of the Mediterranean barbarians that they marveled at the prowess of the Atlanteans. "Their physical strength was extraordinary (witness indeed their cyclopean buildings), the earth shaking sometimes under their tread. Whatever they did, was done speedily. . . . . They were wise and communicated their wisdom to men" ("*Mythology*," p. 4).

the gods being like unto men, there still exists neither in history nor any other scientific work any anthropological proof whatever of the existence in time or space of a race of giants. Yet that such exist, relatively and *de facto* side by side with dwarfs, Schweinfurth can testify. The *Nyam-Nyam* of Africa are regular dwarfs, while their next neighbours (several tribes of comparatively fair-complexioned Africans) are giants when confronted with the Nyam-Nyams, and very tall even among Europeans, for their women are all above 6½ feet high. (*Vide* Schweinfurth's latest works.)

In Cornwall and in ancient Britain the traditions of these giants are, on the other hand, excessively common; they are said to live even down to the time of King Arthur. All this shows that giants lived to a later date amongst the Celtic than among the Teutonic peoples.

If we turn to the New World, we have traditions of a race of giants at Tarija on the eastern slopes of the Andes and in Ecuador, who combated gods and men. These old beliefs, which term certain localities "*Los campos de los gigantes*" – "the fields of giants," are always concomitant with the existence of Pliocene *mammalia* and the occurrence of Pliocene raised beaches. "All the giants are not under Mount Ossa," and it would be poor anthropology indeed that would restrict the traditions of giants to Greek and *Bible* mythologies. Slavonian countries, Russia especially, teem with legends about the *bogaterey* (mighty giants) of old, and their folklore, most of which has served for the foundation of national histories, their oldest songs, and their most archaic traditions, speak of the giants of old. Thus we may safely reject the modern theory that would make of the Titans mere symbols standing for cosmic forces. They were real living men, whether twenty or only twelve feet high. Even the Homeric heroes, who, of course, belonged to a far more recent period in the history of the races, appear to have wielded weapons of a size and weight beyond the strength of the strongest men of modern times.

> "Not twice ten men the mighty bulk could raise,
> Such men as live in these degenerate days."

If the fossil footprints from Carson, Indiana, U.S.A., are human, they indicate gigantic men. Of their genuineness there can remain no doubt. It is to be deplored that the modern and *scientific* evidence for gigantic men should rest on footprints alone. Over and over again, the skeletons of hypothetical giants have been identified with those of elephants and mastodons. But all such blunders before the days of geology, and even the traveler's tales of Sir John Mandeville, who says that *he saw giants 56 feet high* in India, only show that belief in the existence of giants has never, at any time, died out of the thoughts of men.

RACES OF GIANTS

That which is known and accepted is, that several races of gigantic men have existed and left distinct traces. In the journal of the Anthropological Institute (Vol. 1871, article by Dr. C. Carter Blake), such a race is shown as having existed at Palmyra and possibly in Midian, exhibiting cranial forms quite different from those of the Jews. It is not improbable that another such race existed in Samaria, and that the mysterious people who built the stone circles in Galilee, hewed Neolithic flints in the Jordan valley and preserved an ancient Semitic language quite distinct from the square Hebrew character – was of a very large stature. The English translations of the *Bible* can never be relied upon, even in their modern *revised* forms. They tell us of the *Nephilim*, translating the word by "giants," and further adding that they were "hairy" men, probably the large and powerful prototypes of the later satyrs so eloquently described by the patristic fancy, some of the Church Fathers assuring their admirers and followers that they had themselves seen these "Satyrs" – some alive, others pickled and preserved. The word "giants" being once adopted as a synonym of *Nephilim*, the commentators have since identified them with the sons of Anak. The filibusters who seized on the Promised Land found a pre-existing population far exceeding their own in stature, and called it a race of giants. But the races of really gigantic men had disappeared ages before the birth of Moses. This tall people existed in Canaan, and even in Bashan, and may have had representatives in the Nabatheans of Midian. They were of far greater stature than the undersized Jews.

Four thousand years ago their cranial conformation and large stature separated them from the children of Heber. Forty thousand years ago their ancestors may have been of still more gigantic size, and four hundred thousand years earlier *they must have been* in proportion to men in our days as the Brobdingnagians were to the Lilliputians. The Atlanteans of the middle period were called the Great Dragons, and the first symbol of their tribal deities, when the "gods" and the Divine Dynasties had forsaken them, was that of a giant Serpent.

The mystery veiling the origin and the religion of the Druids, is as great as that of their supposed fanes is to the modern Symbologist, but not to the initiated Occultists. Their priests were the descendants of the last Atlanteans, and what is known of them is sufficient to allow the inference that they were eastern priests akin to the Chaldeans and Indians, though little more. It may be inferred that they symbolized their deity as the Hindus do their Vishnu, as the Egyptians did their *Mystery God*, and as the builders of the Ohio Great-Serpent mound worshipped theirs – namely under the form of the "mighty Serpent," the emblem of the eternal deity TIME (the Hindu *Kâla*). Pliny called them the "*Magi* of the Gauls and Britons." But they were more than that. The author of "*Indian Antiquities*" finds much affinity between the Druids and the Brahmins of India. Dr. Borlase points to a close analogy between them and the *Magi* of Persia[229]; others will see an identity between them and the Orphic priesthood of Thrace, simply because they were connected, in their esoteric teachings, with the universal Wisdom Religion, and thus presented affinities with the exoteric worship of all.

WHERE PAGANISM AND CHRISTIANITY AGREE

Like the Hindus, the Greeks and Romans (we speak of the Initiates), the Chaldees and the Egyptians, the Druids believed in the doctrine of a succession of worlds, as also in that of seven "creations" (of new continents) and transformations of the face of the earth, and in a seven-

---

229 But the *Magi* of Persia were never Persians—not even Chaldeans. They came from a far-off land, the Orientalists being of opinion that the said land was Media. This may be so, but from what part of Media? To this we receive no answer.

fold night and day for each earth or globe (See "*Esoteric Buddhism*"). Wherever the Serpent with the egg is found, there this tenet was surely present. Their *Dracontia* are a proof of it. This belief was so universal that, if we seek for it in the esotericism of various religions, we shall discover it in all. We shall find it among the Aryan Hindus and Mazdeans, the Greeks, the Latins, and even among the old Jews and early Christians, whose modern stocks hardly comprehend now that which they read in their Scriptures. See what Seneca says in *Epistle* 9, and *Quæst. Nat.* III., c., ult.: "The world being melted and having re-entered the bosom of Jupiter, this god continues for some time to remain absorbed in himself and *concealed*, wholly immersed in contemplation. After which a new world springs from him. . . An innocent race of men and animals are produced anew. . . etc." Then again, when speaking of periodical mundane dissolution involving universal death, he (Seneca) says that "when the laws of nature shall be buried in ruin, and the last day of the world shall come, *the southern pole shall crush*, as it falls, all the regions of Africa, and the North pole shall overwhelm all the countries beneath its axis. *The affrighted sun shall be deprived of its light*; the palace of heaven falling to decay *shall produce at once both* life and death, and some kind of dissolution shall equally seize upon all deities, who thus shall return into their original chaos." (Quoted in "*Book of God*," p. 160.)

One might imagine oneself reading the Purânic account by Parasâra of the great *Pralaya*. It is nearly the same thing, idea for idea. Has Christianity nothing of the kind? It has, we say. Let the reader open any English *Bible* and read Chapter III of the *Second Epistle of Peter*, from verse iii. till the xivth, and he will find there the same ideas. . . "There shall come in the last days scoffers . . . saying, 'where is the promise of his coming? . . . . Since the fathers fell asleep all things continue as they were from the beginning of creation.' For, they are ignorant . . . . that by the word of God the heavens were of old, and *the earth standing out of the water and in the water: whereby the world that then was, being overflowed with water*, perished. But the heavens and the earth *that are now*, are reserved unto the fire. . . . wherein the heavens. . . . shall be dissolved, and elements shall melt with fervent heat. . . . we nevertheless look for *new heavens and new earth, etc., etc.*" If the interpreters chose to see in this a reference to creation, the deluge, and the promised coming of Christ, when they will live in a new Jerusalem in heaven, this is no fault of "Peter." What the writer of the *Epistles* meant was the destruction of this Fifth Race of ours by subterranean fires and inundations, and the appearance of new continents for the Sixth Root-Race. For the writers of these *Epistles* were all learned in symbology, if not in the sciences.

The Secret Doctrine, ii 747 – 757

GLOSSARY

A.

Absoluteness. When predicated of the UNIVERSAL PRINCIPLE, it denotes an abstract noun, which is more correct and logical than to apply the adjective "absolute " to that which has neither attributes nor limitations, nor can IT have any.

Adam (Heb.). In the *Kabalah* Adam is the "only-begotten", and means also "red earth". (See "Adam-Adami" in the *S.D.* II p. 452.) It is almost identical with *Athamas* or *Thomas*, and is rendered into Greek by *Didumos*, the "twin"– Adam, "the first", in chap. 1 of *Genesis*, being shown, "male-female."

Adam Kadmon *(Heb)*. Archetypal Man; Humanity. The "Heavenly Man" not fallen into sin; Kabalists refer it to the Ten *Sephiroth* on the plane of human perception. [w.w.w.]

In the *Kabalah* Adam Kadmon is the manifested *Logos* corresponding to our *Third Logos*; the Unmanifested being the first paradigmic ideal Man, and symbolizing the Universe in *abscondito*, or in its "privation" in the Aristotelean sense. The First *Logos* is the "Light of the World", the Second and the Third – its gradually deepening shadows.

Adept *(Lat.)*. *Adeptus*, "He who has obtained." In Occultism one who has reached the stage of Initiation, and become a Master in the science of Esoteric philosophy.

Âditi *(Sk.)*. The Vedic name for the *Mûlaprakriti* of the Vedantists; the abstract aspect of Parabrahman, though both unmanifested and unknowable. In the *Vedas* Âditi is the "Mother-Goddess", her terrestrial symbol being infinite and shoreless space.

Adwaita *(Sk.)*. A Vedânta sect. The non-dualistic (A-dwaita) school of Vedântic philosophy founded by Sankarâchârya, the greatest of the historical Brahmin sages. The two other schools are the Dwaita (dualistic) and the ViSishtadwaita; all the three call themselves Vedântic.

Adwaitin *(Sk.)*. A follower of the said school.

Æther *(Gr.)*. With the ancients the divine luminiferous substance which pervades the whole universe, the "garment" of the Supreme Deity, Zeus, or Jupiter. With the moderns, Ether, for the meaning of which in physics and chemistry see Webster's *Dictionary* or any other. In esotericism Æther is the third principle of the Kosmic Septenary; the Earth being the lowest, then the

Astral light, Ether and *Âkâsa* (phonetically *Âkâsha*) the highest.

Agathodæmon (*Gr.*). The beneficent, good Spirit as contrasted with the bad one, Kakodæmon. The "Brazen Serpent" of the *Bible* is the former; the flying serpents of fire are an aspect of Kakodæmon. The Ophites called Agathodæmon the *Logos* and Divine Wisdom, which in the Bacchanalian Mysteries was represented by a serpent erect on a pole.

Agni (*Sk.*). The God of Fire in the Veda; the oldest and the most revered of Gods in India. He is one of the three great deities: Agni, Vâyu and Sûrya, and also all the three, as he is the triple aspect of fire; in heaven as the Sun; in the atmosphere or air (Vâyu), as Lightning; on. earth, as ordinary Fire. Agni belonged to the earlier Vedic *Trimûrti* before Vishnu was given a place of honour and before Brahmâ and Siva were invented.

Agnishwattas (*Sk.*). A class of *Pitris*, the creators of the first ethereal race of men. Our solar ancestors as contrasted with the *Barhishads,* the "lunar" *Pitris* or ancestors, though otherwise explained in the *Purânas.*

Aham (*Sk.*). "I" – the basis of *Ahankâra*, Self-hood.

Ahankâra (*Sk.*). The conception of "I", Self-consciousness or Self- identity; the "I", the egotistical and *mâyâvic* principle in man, due to our ignorance which separates our "I" from the Universal ONE-SELF Personality, Egoism.

Ahura (*Zend.*). The same as *Asura*, the holy, the Breath-like. Ahura Mazda, the Ormuzd of the Zoroastrians or Parsis, is the Lord who bestows light and intelligence, whose symbol is the Sun (See "Ahura Mazda"), and of whom Ahriman, a European form of "Angra Mainyu" (q.v.), is the dark aspect.

Ahura Mazda (*Zend*). The personified deity, the Principle of Universal Divine Light of the Parsis. From Ahura or *Asura*, breath, "spiritual, divine" in the oldest *Rig Veda*, degraded by the orthodox Brahmans into *A -sura*, "no gods", just as the Mazdeans have degraded the Hindu *Devas* (Gods) into Dæva (Devils).

Ain Soph (*Heb.*). The "Boundless" or Limitless; Deity emanating and extending. [w.w.w.]

Ain Soph is also written *En Soph* and *Ain Suph*, no one, not even Rabbis, being sure of their vowels. In the religious metaphysics of the old Hebrew philosophers, the ONE Principle was an abstraction, like Parabrahmam, though modern Kabbalists have succeeded now, by dint of mere sophistry and paradoxes, in making a "Supreme God" of it and nothing higher. But with the early Chaldean Kabbalists Ain Soph is "without form or being", having "no likeness with anything else" (Franck, *Die Kabbala*, p. 126). That Ain Soph has never been considered as the "Creator" is proved by even such an orthodox Jew as Philo calling the "Creator" the *Logos*, who stands next the "Limitless One", and the "Second God". "The Second God is its (Ain Soph's) wisdom", says Philo (*Quaest. et Solut.*). Deity is NO-THING; it is nameless, and therefore called Ain Soph; the word *Ain* meaning NOTHING. (See Franck's *Kabbala*, p. 153 ff.)

Aitareya (*Sk.*). The name of an Aranyaka (Brâhmana) and a Upanishad of the *Rig Veda*. Some of its portions are purely Vedântic.

Akâsa (*Sk.*). The subtle, supersensuous spiritual essence which pervades all space; the primordial substance erroneously identified with Ether. But it is to Ether what Spirit is to Matter, or *Âtmâ* to *Kâma-rûpa*. It is, in fact, the Universal Space in which lies inherent the eternal Ideation of the Universe in its ever-changing aspects on the planes of matter and objectivity, and from which radiates the *First Logos*, or expressed thought. This is why it is stated in the *Purânas* that Âkâsa has but one attribute, namely sound, for sound is but the translated symbol of *Logos* – "Speech" in its mystic sense. In the same sacrifice (*the Jyotishtoma Agnishtoma*) it is called the "God Âkâsa". In these sacrificial mysteries Âkâsa is the all-directing 'and omnipotent Deva who plays the part of Sadasya, the superintendent over the magical effects of the religious performance, and it had its own appointed Hotri (priest) in days of old, who took its name. The Âkâsa is the indispensable agent of every *Krityâ* (magical performance) religious or profane. The expression "to stir up the Brahmâ", means to stir up the power which lies latent at the bottom of every magical operation, Vedic sacrifices being in fact nothing if not ceremonial magic. This power is the Âkâsa – in another aspect, *Kundalini* – occult electricity, the alkahest of the alchemists in one sense, or the universal solvent, the same *anima mundi* on the higher plane as the *astral light* is on the lower. "At the moment of the sacrifice the priest becomes imbued with the spirit of Brahmâ, is, for the time being, Brahmâ himself". (*Isis Unveiled*).

Alaya (*Sk.*). The Universal Soul (See *Secret Doctrine* Vol. I. pp. 47 *et seq.*). The name belongs to the Tibetan system of the contemplative *Mahâyâna* School. Identical with *Âkâsa* in its mystic sense, and with *Mulâprâkriti*, in its essence, as it is the basis or root of all things.

Amânasa (*Sk.*). The " Mindless", the early races of this planet; also certain Hindu gods.

Ambhâmsi (*Sk.*). A name of the chief of the *Kumâras* Sanat-Sujâta, signifying the "waters". This epithet will become more comprehensible when we remember that the later type of Sanat-Sujâta was Michael, the Archangel, who is called in the Talmud "the Prince of *Waters*", and in the Roman Catholic Church is regarded as the patron of gulfs and promontories. Sanat-Sujâta is the immaculate soñ of the immaculate mother (Ambâ or Aditi, chaos and space) or the "waters" of limitless space. (See *Secret Doctrine-*, Vol. I., p. 460.)

Amesha Spentas (*Zend*). Amshaspends. The six angels or divine Forces personified as gods who attend upon Ahura Mazda, of which he is the synthesis and the seventh. They are one of the prototypes of the Roman Catholic "Seven Spirits" or Angels with Michael as chief, or the "Celestial Host"; the " Seven Angels of the Presence". They are the Builders, Cosmocratores, of the Gnostics and identical with the Seven Prajâpatis, the *Sephiroth*, etc. (q.v.).

Ananta-Sesha (*Sk.*). The Serpent of Eternity – the couch of Vishnu during *Pralaya* (lit., endless remain).

Anaxagoras (*Gr.*) A famous Ionian philosopher who lived 500 B.C., studied philosophy under Anaximenes of Miletus, and settled in the days of Pericles at Athens. Socrates, Euripides, Archelaus and other distinguished men and philosophers were among his disciples and pupils. He was a most learned astronomer and was one of the first to explain openly that which was taught by Pythagoras secretly, namely, the movements of the planets, the eclipses of the sun and moon, etc. It was he who taught the theory of Chaos, on the principle that "nothing comes from nothing"; and of atoms, as the underlying essence and substance of all bodies, "of the same nature as the bodies which they formed".

These atoms, he taught, were primarily put in motion by Nous (Universal Intelligence, the Mahat of the Hindus), which Nous is an immaterial, eternal, spiritual entity; by this combination the world was formed, the material gross bodies sinking down, and the ethereal atoms (or fiery ether) rising and spreading in the upper celestial regions. Antedating modern science by over 2000 years, he taught that the stars were of the same material as our earth, and the sun a glowing mass; that the moon was a dark, uninhabitable body, receiving its light from the sun; the comets, wandering stars or bodies ; and over and above the said science, he confessed himself thoroughly convinced that the real existence of things, perceived by our senses, could not be demonstrably proved. He died in exile at Lampsacus at the age of seventy-two.

Androgyne Ray (*Esot.*). The first differentiated ray; the Second *Logos*; Adam Kadmon in the *Kabalah*; the "male and female created he them", of the first chapter of *Genesis*.

AnimaMundi (*Lat.*). The"Soul of the World", the same as the *Alaya* of the Northern *Buddhists*; the divine essence which permeates, animates and informs all, from the smallest atom of matter to man and god. It is in a sense the "seven-skinned mother" of the stanzas in the *Secret Doctrine*, the essence of seven planes of sentience, consciousness and differentiation, moral and physical. In its highest aspect it is *Nirvâna*, in its lowest Astral Light. It was feminine with the Gnostics, the early Christians and the Nazarenes; bisexual with other sects, who considered it only in its four lower planes. Of igneous, ethereal nature in the objective world of form (and then ether), and divine and spiritual in its three higher planes. When it is said that every human soul was born by detaching itself from the *Anima Mundi,* it means, esoterically, that our higher Egos are of an essence identical with **It,** which is a radiation of the ever unknown Universal ABSOLUTE.

Anthropomorphism *(Gr.).* From "anthropos" meaning man. The act of endowing god or gods with a human form and human attributes or qualities.

Anugîtâ *(Sk.).* One of the *Upanishads.* A very occult treatise. *(See The sacred Books of the East.)*

Anupâdaka *(Sk.).* Anupapâdaka, also Aupapâduka; means parentless", "self-existing", born without any parents or progenitors. A term applied to certain self-created gods, and the Dhyâni Buddhas.

Archæus *(Gr.).* "The Ancient." Used of the oldest manifested deity; a term employed in the *Kabalah* ; "archaic ", old, ancient.

Archangel *(Gr.).* Highest supreme angel. From the Greek *arch,* "chief" or "primordial", and *angelos,* "messenger ".

Archæus *(Gr.).* "The Ancient." Used of the oldest manifested deity; a term employed in the *Kabalah* ; "archaic ", old, ancient.

Archetypal Universe *(Kab.).* The ideal universe upon which the objective world was built. [w.w.w.]

Arûpa *(Sk.).* "Bodiless", formless, as opposed to *rûpa,* "body", or form.

Arvâksrotas *(Sk.).* The *seventh* creation, that of man, in the *Vishnu Purâna.*

Âryasangha *(Sk.)* The Founder of the *first* Yogâchârya School. This Arhat, a direct disciple of Gautama, the Buddha, is most unaccountably mixed up and confounded with a personage of the same name, who is said to have lived in Ayôdhya (Oude) about the fifth or sixth century of our era, and taught Tântrika worship in addition to the Yogâchârya system. Those who sought to make it popular, claimed that he was the same Âryasangha, that had been a follower of Sâkyamuni, and that he was 1,000 years old. Internal evidence alone is sufficient to show that the works written by him and translated about the year 600 of our era, works full of Tantra worship, ritualism, and tenets followed now considerably by the "red-cap" sects in Sikhim, Bhutan, and Little Tibet, cannot be the same as the lofty system of the early Yogâcharya school of pure Buddhism, which is neither northern nor southern, but absolutely esoteric. Though none of the genunine Yogâchârya books (the *Narjol chodpa*) have ever been made public or marketable, yet one finds in the *Yogâchârya Bhûmi Shâstra* of the *pseudo*-Âryasangha a great deal from the older system, into the tenets of which he may have been initiated. It is, however, so mixed up with Sivaism and Tantrika magic and superstitions, that the work defeats its own end, notwithstanding its remarkable dialectical subtilty. (See the *Theosophical Glossary*)

Astral Body, or Astral "Double". The ethereal counterpart or shadow of man or animal. The **Linga Sharira**, the "Doppelgäinger". The reader must not confuse it with the ASTRAL SOUL, another name for the lower *Manas*, or Kama-*Manas* so-called, the reflection of the HIGHER EGO.

Astral Light (*Occult*) The invisible region that surrounds our globe, as it does every other, and corresponding as the second Principle of Kosmos (the third being Life, of which it is the vehicle) to the *Linga Sharira* or the Astral Double in man. A subtle Essence visible only to a clairvoyant eye, and the lowest but one (*viz.*, the earth), of the Seven Akâsic or Kosmic Principles. Eliphas Levi calls it the great Serpent and the Dragon from which radiates on Humanity every evil influence. This is so; but why not add that the Astral Light gives out nothing but what it has received; that it is the great terrestrial crucible, in which the vile emanations of the earth (moral and physical) upon which the Astral Light is fed, are all converted into their subtlest essence, and radiated back intensified, thus becoming epidemics – moral, psychic and physical. Finally, the Astral Light is the same as the *Sidereal Light* of Paracelsus and other Hermetic philosophers. "Physically, it is the ether of modern science. Metaphysically, and in its spiritual, or occult sense, ether is a great deal more than is often imagined. In occult physics, and alchemy, it is well demonstrated to enclose within its shoreless waves not only Mr. Tyndall's *'promise* and potency of every quality of life'*, but also the *realization* of the potency of every quality of spirit. Alchemists and Hermetists believe that their *astral*, or sidereal ether, besides the above properties of sulphur, and white and red magnesia, or *magnes*, is the *anima mundi*, the workshop of Nature and of all the Kosmos, spiritually, as well as physically. The 'grand magisterium' asserts itself in the phenomenon of mesmerism, in the 'levitation' of human and inert objects; and may be called the ether from its spiritual aspect. The designation *astral* is ancient, and was used by some of the Neo-platonists, although it is claimed by some that the word was coined by the Martinists. Porphyry describes the celestial body which is always joined with the soul as 'immortal, luminous, and star-like'. The root of this word may be found, perhaps, in the Scythic *Aist-aer* – which means star, or the Assyrian *Istar*, which, according to Burnouf has the same sense." (*Isis Unveiled*.)

Asuras (*Sk.*). Exoterically, elementals and evil, gods – considered maleficent; demons, and *no* gods. But esoterically – the reverse. For in the most ancient portions of the *Rig Veda*, the term is used for the Supreme Spirit, and therefore the *Asuras* are spiritual and divine It is only in the last book of the *Rig Veda*, its latest part, and in the *Atharva Veda*, and the *Brâhmanas,* that the epithet, which had been given to Agni, the greatest Vedic Deity, to Indra and Varuna, has come to signify the reverse of gods. *Asu* means breath, and it is with his breath that Prajâpati (Brahmâ) creates the *Asuras*. When ritualism and dogma got the better of the Wisdom religion, the initial letter **a** was adopted as a negative prefix, and the term ended by signifying "not a god", and Sura only a deity. But in the *Vedas* the Suras have ever been connected with *Surya*, the sun, and regarded as *inferior* deities, devas.

Aswattha *(Sk.)* The *Bo-tree*, the tree of knowledge, *ficus religiosa.*

Avalokiteswara *(Sk.)* "The on-looking Lord" In the exoteric interpretation, he is Padmapâni (the lotus bearer and the lotus-born) in Tibet, the first divine ancestor of the Tibetans, the complete incarnation or Avatar of Avalokiteswara; but in esoteric philosophy Avaloki, the "on-looker", is the Higher Self, while Padmapâni is the Higher Ego or *Manas.* The mystic formula "Om mani padme hum" is specially used to invoke their joint help. While popular fancy claims for Avalokiteswara many incarnations on earth, and sees in him, not very wrongly, the spiritual guide of every believer, the esoteric interpretation sees in him the *Logos*, both celestial and human. Therefore, when the Yogâchârya School has declared Avalokiteswara as Padmâpani "to be the Dhyâni Bodhisattva of Amitâbha Buddha", it is indeed, because the former is *the spiritual reflex in the world of forms* of the latter, both being one – one in heaven, the other on earth.

Avatâra *(Sk.)* Divine incarnation. The descent of a god or some exalted Being, who has progressed beyond the necessity of Rebirths, into the body of a simple mortal. Krishna was an avatar of Vishnu. The Dalai Lama is regarded as an avatar of Avalokiteswara, and the Teschu Lama as one of Tson-kha-pa, or Amitâbha. There are two kinds of avatars: those born from woman, and the parentless, the *anupapâdaka.*

B.

Barhishad *(Sk.).* A class of the "lunar" *Pitris* or "Ancestors", Fathers, who are believed in popular superstition to have kept up in their past incarnations the household sacred flame and made fire-offerings. Esoterically the *Pitris* who evolved their shadows or *chhayas* to make there-with the first man. (See *Secret Doctrine*, Vol. II.)

Bhûta-sarga *(Sk.).* Elemental or incipient Creation, i.e., when matter was several degrees less material than it is now.

Bhûts (Sk.). *Bhûta.*: Ghosts, phantoms. To call them "demons", as do the Orientalists, is incorrect. For, if on the one hand, a Bhûta is "a malignant spirit which haunts cemeteries, lurks in trees, animates dead bodies, and deludes and devours human beings", in popular fancy, in India in Tibet and China, by Bhûtas are also meant "heretics" who besmear their bodies with ashes, or Shaiva ascetics (Siva being held in India for the King of Bhûtas).

Binah *(Heb.).* Understanding. The third of the 10 *Sephiroth*, the third of the Supernal Triad; a female potency, corresponding to the letter *hé* of the Tetragrammaton IHVH. Binah is called AIMA, the Supernal Mother, and "the great Sea". [w.w.w.]

Book of the Dead. An ancient Egyptian ritualistic and occult work attributed to Thot-Hermes. Found in the coffins of ancient mummies.

Brahma (*Sk.*). The student must distinguish between Brahma the neuter, and Brahmâ, the male creator of the Indian Pantheon. The former, Brahma or Brahman, is the impersonal, supreme and uncognizable Principle of the Universe from the essence of which all emanates, and into which all returns, which is incorporeal, immaterial, unborn, eternal, beginningless and endless. It is all-pervading, animating the highest god as well as the smallest mineral atom. Brahmâ on the other hand, the male and the alleged Creator, exists periodically in his manifestation only, and then again goes into pralaya, i.e., disappears and is annihilated.

Brahmâ's Day. A period of 2,160,000,000 years during which Brahmâ having emerged out of his golden egg (*Hiranyagarbha*), creates and fashions the material world (being simply the fertilizing and creative force in Nature). After this period, the worlds being destroyed in turn, by fire and water, he vanishes with objective nature, and then comes Brahmâ's Night.

Brahmâ's Night. A period of equal duration, during which Brahmâ. is said to be asleep. Upon awakening he recommences the process, and this goes on for an AGE of Brahmâ composed of alternate "Days", and "Nights", and lasting 100 years (of 2,160,000,000 years each). It requires fifteen figures to express the duration of such an age; after the expiration of which the *Mahapralaya* or the Great Dissolution sets in, and lasts in its turn for the same space of fifteen figures.

Brahmâ Vâch (*Sk.*) Male and female Brahmâ. Vâch is also some-times called the female logos; for Vâch means Speech, literally. (See *Manu* Book I., and *Vishnu Purâna.*)

Brahma Vidyâ (*Sk.*) The knowledge, the esoteric science, about the two Brahmas and their true nature.

Brahmâ Virâj. (*Sk.*) The same: Brahmâ separating his body into two halves, male and female, creates in them Vâch and Virâj. In plainer terms and *esotericlly* Brahmâ the Universe, differentiating, produced thereby material nature, Virâj, and spiritual intelligent Nature, Vâch – which is the *Logos* of Deity or the manifested expression of the eternal divine Ideation.

Brâhman (*Sk.*) The highest of the four castes in India, one supposed or rather fancying himself, as high among men, as Brahman, the ABSOLUTE of the Vedantins, is high among, or above the gods.

Brahmâputrâs (*Sk.*) The Sons of Brahmâ.

Buddha (*Sk.*). Lit., "The Enlightened". The highest degree of knowledge.

To become a Buddha one has to break through the bondage of sense and personality; to acquire a complete perception of the REAL SELF and learn not to separate it from all otherselves; to learn by experience the utter unreality of all phenomena of the visible Kosmos foremost of all; to reach a complete detachment from all that is evanescent and finite, and live while yet on Earth in the immortal and the everlasting alone, in a supreme state of holiness.

Buddhi *(Sk.).* Universal Soul or Mind. *Mahâbuddhi* is a name of Mahat (see "Alaya"); also the spiritual Soul in man (the sixth principle), the vehicle of Atmâ exoterically the seventh.

Buddhism. Buddhism is now split into two distinct Churches : the Southern and the Northern Church. The former is said to be the purer form, as having preserved more religiously the original teachings of the Lord Buddha. It is the religion of Ceylon, Siam, Burmah and other places, while Northern Buddhism is confined to Tibet, China and Nepaul. Such a distinction, however, is incorrect. If the Southern Church is nearer, in that it has not departed, except perhaps in some trifling dogmas due to the many councils held after the death of the Master, from the public or *exoteric* teachings of Sâkyamuni – the Northern Church is the outcome of Siddhârta Buddha's esoteric teachings which he confined to his elect Bhikshus and Arhats. In fact, Buddhism in the present age, cannot he justly judged either by one or the other of its exoteric popular forms. Real Buddhism can be appreciated only by blending the philosophy of the Southern Church and the metaphysics of the Northern Schools. If one seems too iconoclastic and stero:, and the other too metaphysical and transcendental, even to being overgrown with the weeds of Indian exotericism – many of the gods of its Pantheon having been transplanted under new names to Tibetan soil – it is entirely due to the popular expression of Buddhism in both Churches. Correspondentially they stand in their relation to each other as Protestantism to Roman Catholicism. Both err by an excess of zeal and erroneous interpretations, though neither the Southern nor the Northern *Buddhi*st clergy have ever departed from truth consciously, still less have they acted under the dictates of *priestocracy,* ambition, or with an eye to personal gain and power, as the two Christian Churches have.

C

Cain or Kayn *(Heb.)* In Esoteric symbology he is said to be identical with Jehovah or the "Lord God" of the fourth chapter of *Genesis.* It is held, moreover, that Abel is not his brother, but his female aspect. (See *Sec.Doct., sub voce.*)

Capricornus *(Lat.)* The 10th sign of the Zodiac (*Makâra* in Sanskrit), considered, on account of its hidden meaning, the most important among the constellations of the mysterious Zodiac. it is fully described in the *Secret Doctrine,* and therefore needs but a few words more. Whether, agreeably with exoteric statements, Capricornus was related in any way to the wet-nurse Amalthæa who fed Jupiter with her milk, or whether it was the god Pan who changed himself into a goat and left his impress upon the sidereal records, matters little. Each of the fables has its significance. Everything in Nature is intimately correlated to the rest, and therefore the students of ancient lore will not be too much surprised when told that even the seven steps taken in the direction of every one of the four points of the compass, or – 28 steps – taken by the new-born infant Buddha, are closely related to the 28 stars of the constellation of Capricornus.

Causal Body. This "body", which is no body either objective or subjective, but *Buddhi,* the Spiritual Soul, is so called because it is the direct cause of the Sushupti condition, leading to the *Turya* state, the highest state of *Samadhi.* It is called *Karanopadhi,* "the basis of the Cause", by the Târaka Raja Yogis; and in the Vedânta system it corresponds to both the *Vignânamaya* and *Anandamaya Kosha,* the latter coming next to *Atma,* and therefore being the vehicle of the universal Spirit. *Buddhi* alone could not be called a "Causal Body ", but becomes so in conjunction with *Manas,* the incarnating Entity or EGO.

Chakra *(Sk.)* A wheel, a disk, or the circle of Vishnu generally. Used also of a cycle of time, and with other meanings.

Chaldeans, or *Kasdim.* At first a tribe, then a caste of learned Kabbalists. They were the *savants,* the magians of Babylonia, astrologers and diviners. The famous Hillel, the precursor of Jesus in philosophy and in ethics, was a Chaldean. Franck in his *Kabbala* points to the close resemblance of the "secret doctrine" found in the *Avesta* and the religious metaphysics of the Chaldees.

Chaos *(Gr.)* The Abyss, the "Great Deep". It was personified in Egypt by the Goddess Neïth, anterior to all gods. As Deveria says, "the only God, without form and sex, who gave birth to itself, and without fecundation, is adored under the form of a Virgin Mother". She is the vulture-headed Goddess found in the oldest period of Abydos, who belongs, accordingly to Mariette Bey, to the first Dynasty, which would make her, even on the confession of the time-dwarfing Orientalists, about 7,000 years old. As Mr. Bonwick tells us in his excellent work on Egyptian belief – "Neïth, Nut, Nepte, Nuk (her names as variously read !) is a philosophical conception worthy of the nineteenth century after the Christian era, rather than the thirty-ninth before it or earlier than that". And he adds: " Neith or Nout is neither more nor less than the *Great Mother,* a yet the *Immaculate Virgin,* or female God from whom all things proceeded". Neïth is the "Father-mother" of the *Stanzas* of the *Secret Doctrine,* the Swabhavat of the Northern *Buddhists,* the *immaculate* Mother indeed, the prototype of the latest "Virgin" of all; for, as Sharpe says, "the Feast of Candlemas – in honour of the goddess Neïth – is yet marked in our Almanacs as Candlemas day, or the Purification of the Virgin Mary"; and Beauregard tells us of "the Immaculate

Conception of the Virgin, who can henceforth, as well as the Egyptian Minerva, the mysterious Neïth, boast of having come from herself, and of having given birth to God". He who would deny the working of cycles and the recurrence of events, let him read what Neïth was years ago, in the conception of the Egyptian Initiates, trying to popularize a philosophy too abstract for the masses; and then remember the subjects of dispute at the Council of Ephesus in 431, when Mary was declared Mother of God; and her Immaculate Conception forced on the World as by command of God, by Pope and Council in 1858. Neïth is *Swabhdvat* and also the Vedic *Aditi* and the Purânic *Akâsa*, for "she is not only the celestial vault, or ether, but is made to appear in a tree, from which she gives the fruit of the Tree of Life (like another Eve) or pours upon her worshippers some of the divine water of life". Hence she gained the favourite appellation of "Lady of the Sycamore", an epithet applied to another Virgin (Bonwick). (See *The Theosophical Glossary.*)

Chelâ (*Sk.*) A disciple, the pupil of a *Guru* or Sage, the follower of some adept of a school of philosophy (*lit.*, child).

Cherubim (*Heb.*) According to the Kabbalists, a group of angels, which they specially associated with the *Sephira* Jesod. in Christian teaching, an order of angels who are "watchers". *Genesis* places Cherubim to guard the lost Eden, and the O.T. frequently refers to them as guardians of the divine glory. Two winged representations in gold were placed over the Ark of the Covenant; colossal figures of the same were also placed in the Sanctum Sanctorum of the Temple of Solomon. Ezekiel describes them in poetic language. Each Cherub appears to have been a compound figure with four faces – of a man, eagle, lion, and ox, and was certainly winged. (See *The Theosophical Glossary.*)

Chhâyâ (*Sk.*) "Shade" or " Shadow". The name of a creature produced by Sanjnâ, the wife of Surya, from herself (astral body). Unable to endure the ardour of her husband, Sanjnâ left Chhâyâ in her place as a wife, going herself away to perform austerities. Chhâyâ is the astral image of a person in esoteric philosophy.

Chhaya **loka** (*Sk.*) The world of Shades; like Hades, the world of the *Eidola* and *Umbræ*. We call it *Kâmaloka*.

Chohan (*Tib.*) "Lord" or "Master" ; a chief; thus **Dhyan-Chohan** would answer to "Chief of the *Dhyanis*", or celestial Lights – which in English would he translated Archangels.

Chokmah (Heb) Wisdom; the second of the ten *Sephiroth*, and the second of the supernal Triad. A masculine potency corresponding to the Yod (I) of the Tetragrammaton IHVH, and to **Ab**, the Father. [w.w.w.]

Chréstos (*Gr.*) The early Gnostic form of Christ. It was used in the fifth century B.C. by Æschylus, Herodotus, and others. The *Manteumata pythochresta*, or the "oracles delivered by a Pythian god" "through a pythoness, are mentioned by the former (*Choeph*.901). *Chréstian* is not only "the seat of an oracle", but an offering to, or for, the oracle.

Chréstés is one who explains oracles, "a prophet and soothsayer", and Chrésterios one who serves an oracle or a god. The earliest Christian writer, Justin Martyr, in his first *Apology* calls his co-religionists Chréstians. It is only through ignorance that men call themselves Christians instead of Chréstians," says Lactantius (lib. iv., cap. vii.). The terms Christ and Christians, spelt originally Chrést and Chréstians, were borrowed from the Temple vocabulary of the Pagans. Chréstos meant in that vocabulary a disciple on probation, a candidate for hierophantship. When he had attained to this through initiation, long trials, and suffering, and had been "*anointed*" (i.e., "rubbed with oil", as were Initiates and even idols of the gods, as the last touch of ritualistic observance), his name was changed into *Christos*, the "purified", in esoteric or mystery language. In mystic symbology, indeed, *Christés*, or *Christos*, meant that the "Way", the Path, was already trodden and the goal reached ; when the fruits of the arduous labour, uniting the personality of evanescent clay with the indestructible INDIVIDUALITY, transformed it thereby into the immortal EGO. "At the end of the Way stands the *Chréstes*", the *Purifier*, and the union once accomplished, the *Chrestos*, the "man of sorrow", became *Christos* himself. Paul, the Initiate, knew this, and meant this precisely, when he is made to say, in bad translation : "I travail in birth again until Christ be formed in you" (Gal. iv.19), the true rendering of which is . . . "until ye form the *Christos* within yourselves" But the profane who knew only that Chréstés was in some way connected with priest and prophet, and knew nothing about the hidden meaning of *Christos*, insisted, as did Lactantius and Justin Martyr, on being called *Chréstians* instead of Christians. Every good individual, therefore, may find Christ in his "inner man" as Paul expresses it (Ephes. iii. 16,17), whether he be Jew, Mussulman, Hindu, or Christian. Kenneth Mackenzie seemed to think that the word *Chréstos* was a synonym of Soter, "an appellation assigned to deities, great kings and heroes," indicating "Saviour," – and he was right. For, as he adds:"It has been applied redundantly to Jesus Christ, whose name Jesus or Joshua bears the same interpretation. The name Jesus, in fact, is rather a title of honour than a name – the true name of the Soter of Christianity being Emmanuel, or God with us (*Matt*.i, 23.).Great divinities among all nations, who are represented as expiatory or self-sacrificing, have been designated by the same title." (*R. M. Cyclop*.) The Asklepios (or Æsculapius) of the Greeks had the title of *Soter*.

Codex Nazaraeus (Lat.) The "Book of Adam" – the latter name meaning *anthropos*, Man or Humanity. The Nazarene faith is called sometimes the Bardesanian system, though Bardesanes (B.C. 155 to 228) does not seem to have had any connection with it. True, he was born at Edessa in Syria, and was a famous astrologer and Sabian before his alleged conversion. But he was a well-educated man of noble family, and would not have used the almost incomprehensible Chaldeo dialect mixed with the mystery language of the Gnostics, in which the Codex is written. The sect of the Nazarenes was pre-Christian. Pliny and Josephus speak of the Nazarites as settled on the banks of the Jordan 150 years B.C. (*Ant.Jud.* xiii. p. 9); and Munk says that the "Naziareate was an institution established before the laws of Musah" or Moses. (Munk p. 169.) Their modern name is in Arabic – *El Mogtasila*; in European languages – the Mendæans or "Christians of St. John". (See "Baptism".) But if the term Baptists may well be applied to them, it is not with the Christian meaning: for while they were, and still are Sabians, or pure astrolaters, the Mendæans of Syria, called the Galileans, are pure polytheists, as every traveller in Syria and on the Euphrates can ascertain, once he acquaints himself with their mysterious rites and ceremonies. (*See Isis Unv. ii. 290, et seq.*) So secretly did they preserve their beliefs from the very beginning, that Epiphanius who wrote against the Heresies in the14th century confesses himself unable to say what they believed in (i. 122); he simply states that they never mention the name of Jesus, nor do they call themselves Christians (*loc. cit.* 190. Yet it is undeniable that some of the alleged philosophical views and doctrines of Bardesanes are found in the codex of the Nazarenes. (See Norberg's *Codex Nazaræous* or the "Book of Adam", and also "Mendæans ".)

Cosmic Gods. Inferior gods, those connected with the formation of matter.

Cosmic ideation (*Occult.*) Eternal thought, impressed on substance or spirit-matter, in the eternity ; thought which becomes active at the beginning of every new life-cycle.

Cosmocratores (*Gr.*). "Builders of the Universe", the "world architects", or the Creative Forces personified.

Crocodile. "The great reptile of Typhon." The seat of its "worship" was Crocodilopolis and it was sacred to Set and Sebak – its alleged creators. The primitive *Rishis* in India, the *Manus*, and Sons of Brahmâ, are each the progenitors of some animal species, of which he is the alleged "father"; in Egypt, each god was credited with the formation or creation of certain animals which were sacred to him. Crocodiles must have been numerous in Egypt during the early dynasties, if one has to judge by the almost incalculable number of their mummies. Thousands upon thousands have been excavated from the grottoes of Moabdeh, and many a vast *necropolis* of that Typhonic animal is still left untouched. But the Crocodile was only worshipped where his god and "father" received honours. Typhon (*q.v.*) had once received such honours and, as Bunsen shows, had been considered a great god. His words are, " Down to the time of Ramses B.C. 1300, Typhon was one of the most venerated and powerful gods, a god who pours blessings and life on the rulers of Egypt." As explained elsewhere, Typhon is the material aspect of Osiris. When Typhon, the Quaternary, *kills* Osiris, the triad or divine Light, and cuts it metaphorically into 14 pieces, and separates himself from the "god", he incurs the execration of the masses; he becomes the evil god, the storm and hurricane god, the burning sand of the Desert, the constant enemy of the Nile, and the "slayer of the evening beneficent dew", because Osiris is the ideal Universe, Siva the great Regenerative Force, and Typhon the material portion of it, the evil side of the god, or the Destroying Siva. This is why the crocodile is also partly venerated and partly execrated. The appearance of the crocodile in the Desert, far from the water, prognosticated the happy event of the coming inundation – hence its adoration at Thebes and Ombos. But he destroyed thousands of human and animal beings yearly – hence also the hatred and persecution of the Crocodile at Elephantine and Tentyra.

Cycle. From the Greek *Kuklos*. The ancients divided time into end less cycles, wheels within wheels, all such periods being of various durations, and each marking the beginning or the end of some event either cosmic, mundane, physical or metaphysical. There were cycles of only a few years, and cycles of immense duration, the great Orphic cycle, referring to the ethnological change of races, lasting 120,000 years, and the cycle of Cassandrus of 136,000, which brought about a complete change in planetary influences and their correlations between men and gods – a fact entirely lost sight of by modern astrologers.

D

Dæmon (*Gr.*) In the original Hermetic works and ancient classics it has a meaning identical with that of "god", "angel" or "genius". The Dæmon of Socrates is the incorruptible part of the man, or rather the real inner man which we call Nous or the rational divine Ego. At all events the Dæmon (or Daimon of the great Sage was surely not the demon of the Christian Hell or of Christian orthodox theology. The name was given by ancient peoples, and especially the philosophers of the Alexandrian school, to all kinds of spirits, whether good or bad, human or otherwise. The appellation is often synonymous with that of gods or angels. But some philosophers tried, with good reason, to make a just distinction between the many classes.

Daitya Guru (*Sk.*) The instructor of the giants, called *Daityas* (*q.v.*) Allegorically, it is the title given to the planet Venus-Lucifer, or rather to its indwelling Ruler, *Sukra*, a male deity (See *Sec. Doct..* ii. p. 30).

Daityas (*Sk.*) Giants, Titans, and exoterically demons, but in truth identical with certain *Asuras*, the intellectual gods, the opponents of the useless gods of ritualism and the enemies of *puja* sacrifices.

Dâkinî (*Sk.*) Female demons, vampires and blood-drinkers (*asra-pas*). In the *Purânas* they attend upon the goddess Kâli and feed on human flesh. A species of evil "Elementals" (*q.v.*).

Daksha (*Sk.*) A form of Brahmâ and his son in the *Purânas* But the *Rig Veda* states that "Daksha sprang from Aditi, and Aditi from Daksha", which proves him to be a personified correlating Creative Force acting on *all the planes*. The Orientalists seem very much perplexed what to make of him; but Roth is nearer the truth than any, when saying that Daksha is the spiritual power, and at the same time the male energy that generates the gods in eternity, which is represented by Aditi. The *Purânas* as a matter of course, anthropomorphize the idea, and show Daksha instituting "sexual intercourse on this earth", after trying every other means of procreation. The generative Force, spiritual at the commencement, becomes of course at the most material end of its evolution a procreative Force on the physical plane ; and so far the Purânic allegory is correct, as the Secret Science teaches that our present mode of procreation began towards the end of the third Root-Race.

Dangma (*Sk.*) In Esotericism a purified Soul. A Seer and an Initiate; one who has attained full wisdom.

Day of Brahmâ. See "Brahmâ's Day" etc.

Demeter The Hellenic name for the Latin Ceres, the goddess of corn and tillage. The astronomical sign, Virgo. The Eleusinian Mysteries were celebrated in her honour.

Demiurgic Mind. The same as "Universal Mind". Mahat, the first "product" of Brahmâ, or himself.

Demiurgos (*Gr*) The Demiurge or Artificer; the Supernal Power which built the universe. Freemasons derive from this word their phrase of "Supreme Architect ". With the Occultists it is the third manifested *Logos*, or Plato's "second god", the second logos being represented by him as the "Father", the only Deity that he dared mention as an Initiate into the Mysteries.

Demons. According to the Kabbalah, the demons dwell in the world of Assiah, the world of matter and of the "shells'" of the dead. They are the Klippoth. There are Seven Hells, whose demon dwellers represent the vices personified. Their prince is Samael, his female companion is Isheth Zenunim – the woman of prostitution: united in aspect, they are named "The Beast", Chiva. [w.w.w.]

Demon est Deus inversus (*Lat*) A Kabbalistic axiom; lit., "the devil is god reversed"; which means that there is neither evil nor good, but that the forces which create the one create the other, according to the nature of the materials they find to work upon.

Deva (*Sk.*). A god, a "resplendent" deity. Deva-Deus, from the root *div* "to shine". A Deva is a celestial being – whether good, bad, or indifferent. *Devas* inhabit "the three worlds", which are the *three planes* above us. There are 33 groups or 330 millions of them.

Deva Sarga (*Sk.*). Creation: the origin of the principles, said to be Intelligence born of the qualities or the attributes of nature.

Devachan (*Sk.*). The "dwelling of the gods". A state intermediate between two earth-lives, into which the EGO (Atmâ-*Buddhi-Manas*, or the Trinity made One) enters, after its separation from Kâma Rupa, and the disintegration of the lower principles on earth.

Devajnânas (*Sk.*). or *Daivajna*. The higher classes of celestial beings, those who possess divine knowledge.

Devaki (*Sk.*). The mother of Krishna. She was shut up in a dungeon by her brother, King Kansa, for fear of the fulfilment of a prophecy which stated that a son of his sister should dethrone and kill him. Notwithstanding the strict watch kept, Devaki was overshadowed by Vishnu, the holy Spirit, and thus gave birth to that god's *avatara*, Krishna. (See "Kansa".)

Deva-lôkas (*Sk.*). The abodes of the Gods or *Devas* in superior spheres. The seven celestial worlds above Meru.

Devamâtri (*Sk.*). Lit., "the mother of the gods". A title of Aditi, Mystic Space.

Dhyan Chohans (*Sk*). Lit., "The Lords of Light". The highest gods, answering to the Roman Catholic Archangels. The divine Intelligences charged with the supervision of Kosmos.

Dhyâna (*Sk.*). In Buddhism one of the six Paramitas of perfection, a state of abstraction which carries the ascetic practising it far above this plane of sensuous perception and out of the world of matter. Lit., "contemplation". The six stages of Dhyan differ only in the degrees of abstraction of the personal Ego from sensuous life.

Dhyani **Bodhisattyas** (*Sk.*). In Buddhism, the five sons of the *Dhyani-Buddhas*. They have a mystic meaning in Esoteric Philosophy.

Dhyani **Buddhas** (*Sk.*). They "of the Merciful Heart"; worshipped especially in Nepaul. These have again a secret meaning.

Dianoia (*Gr.*). The same as the *Logos*. The eternal source of thought, "divine ideation", which is the root of all thought. (See "Ennoia.")

Drakôn (*Gr.*) or Dragon. Now considered a "mythical" monster, perpetuated in the West only on seals,. &c., as a heraldic griffin, and the Devil slain by St. George, &c. In fact an extinct antediluvian monster In Babylonian antiquities it is referred to as the "scaly one" and connected on many gems with Tiamat the sea. "The Dragon of the Sea" is repeatedly mentioned. In Egypt, it is the star of the Dragon (then the North Pole Star), the origin of the connection of almost all the gods with the Dragon. Bel and the Dragon, Apollo and Python, Osiris and Typhon, Sigur and Fafnir, and finally St. George and the Dragon, are the same. They were all solar gods, and wherever we find the Sun there also is the Dragon, the symbol of Wisdom – Thoth-Hermes. The Hierophants of Egypt and of Babylon styled themselves "Sons of the Serpent-God" and "Sons of the Dragon". "I am a Serpent, I am a Druid", said the Druid of the Celto-Britannic regions, for the Serpent and the Dragon were both types of Wisdom, Immortality and Rebirth. As the serpent casts its old skin only to reappear in a new one, so does the immortal Ego cast off one personality but to assume another.

Druids. A sacerdotal caste which flourished in Britain and Gaul. They were Initiates who admitted females into their sacred order, and initiated them into the mysteries of their religion. They never entrusted their sacred verses and scriptures to writing, but, like the Brahmans of old, committed them to memory; a feat which, according to the statement of Cæsar took twenty years to accomplish. Like the Parsis they had no images or statues of their gods. The Celtic religion considered it blasphemy to represent any god, even of a minor character, under a human figure. It would have been well if the Greek and Roman Christians had learnt this lesson from the "pagan" Druids. The three chief commandments of their religion were: – "Obedience to divine laws; concern for the welfare of mankind; suffering with fortitude all the evils of life".

Dwapara *Yuga* (*Sk.*). The third of the "Four Ages" in Hindu Philosophy ; or the second age counted from below.

Dynasties. In India there are two, the Lunar and the Solar, or the *Somavansa* and the *Suryavansa*. In Chaldea and Egypt there were also two distinct kinds of dynasties, the *divine* and the *human*. In both countries people were ruled in the beginning of time by Dynasties of Gods. In Chaldea they reigned one hundred and twenty Sari, or in all 432,000 years; which amounts to the same figures as a Hindu Mahayuga 4,320,000 years. The chronology prefacing the *Book of Genesis* (English translation) is given "Before Christ, 4004". But the figures are a rendering by solar years. In the original Hebrew, which preserved a lunar calculation, the figures are 4,320 years. This "coincidence" is well explained in Occultism.

Dzyn or Dzyan (*Tib.*). Written also *Dzen*. A corruption of the Sanskrit Dhyan and *jnâna* (or *gnyâna* phonetically) – Wisdom, divine knowledge. In Tibetan, learning is called *dzin*.

E

Eden (*Heb.*). "Delight", pleasure. In *Genesis* the "Garden of Delight" built by God ; in the Kabbala the "Garden of Delight", a place of Initiation into the mysteries. Orientalists identify it with a place which was situated in Babylonia in the district of Karduniyas, called also Gan-dunu, which is almost like the Gan-eden of the Jews. (See the works of Sir H. Rawlinson, and G. Smith.) That district has four rivers, Euphrates, Tigris, Surappi, Ukni. The two first have been adopted without any change by the Jews; the other two they have probably transformed into " Gihon and Pison", so as to have something original. The following are some of the reasons for the identification of Eden, given by Assyriologists. The cities of Babylon, Larancha and Sippara, were founded before the flood, according to the chronology of the Jews.

"Surippak was the city of the ark, the mountain east of the Tigris was the resting place of the ark, Babylon was the site of the tower, and Ur of the Chaldees the birthplace of Abraham." And, as Abraham, "the first leader of the Hebrew race, migrated from Ur to Harran in Syria and from thence to Palestine", the best Assyriologists think that it is "so much evidence in favour of the hypothesis that Chaldea was the original home of these stories (in the *Bible*) and that the Jews received them originally from the Babylonians".

Ego (*Lat.*). " Self" ; the consciousness in man "I am I" – or the feeling of "I-am-ship". Esoteric philosophy teaches the existence of two Egos in man, the mortal or personal, and the Higher, the Divine and the Impersonal, calling the former "personality" and the latter "Individuality Egoity. From the word "Ego". Egoity means "individuality", never "personality", and is the opposite of egoism or "selfishness", the characteristic par excellence of the latter.

Elementals. Spirits of the Elements. The creatures evolved in the four Kingdoms or Elements – earth, air, fire, and water. They are called by the Kabbalists, Gnomes (of the earth), Sylphs (of the air), Salamanders (of the fire), and Undines (of the water). Except a few of the higher kinds, and their rulers, they are rather forces of nature than ethereal men and women. These forces, as the servile agents of the Occultists, may produce various effects; but if employed by" Elementaries" (*q.v.*) – in which case they enslave the mediums – they will deceive the credulous. All the lower invisible beings generated on the 5th 6th, and 7th planes of our terrestrial atmosphere, are called Elementals, Peris, Devs, Djins, Sylvans, Satyrs, Fauns, Elves, Dwarfs, Trolls, Kobolds, Brownies, Nixies, Goblins, Pinkies, Banshees, Moss People, White Ladies, Spooks, Fairies, etc., etc., etc.

Elementaries. Properly, the disembodied souls of the depraved; these souls having at some time prior to death separated from themselves their divine spirits, and so lost their chance for immortality; but at the present stage of learning it has been thought best to apply the term to the spooks or phantoms of disembodied persons, in general, to those whose temporary habitation is the Kâma Loka. Eliphas Lévi and some other Kabbalists make little distinction between elementary spirits who have been men, and those beings which people the elements, and are the blind forces of nature. Once divorced from their higher triads and their bodies, these souls remain in their *Kâma-rupic* envelopes, and are irresistibly drawn to the earth amid elements congenial to their gross natures. Their stay in the Kâma Loka varies as to its duration; but ends invariably in disintegration, dissolving like a column of mist, atom by atom, in the surrounding elements.

Elohîm (*Heb.*). Also *Alhim*, the word being variously spelled. Godfrey Higgins, who has written much upon its meaning, always spells it *Aleim*. The Hebrew letters are *aleph, lamed, hé,yod, mem*, and are numerically 1, 30, 5, 10, 40 = 86. It seems to be the plural of the feminine noun *Eloah*, ALH, formed by adding the common plural form IM, a masculine ending; and hence the whole seems to imply the emitted active and passive essences. As a title it is referred to "Binah" the Supernal Mother, as is also the fuller title IHVH ALHIM, Jehovah *Elohim*. As Binah leads on to seven succeedent Emanations, so " *Elohim*" has been said to represent a sevenfold power of godhead. [w.w. w.]

Emanation *The Doctrine of.* In its metaphysical meaning, it is opposed to Evolution, yet one with it. Science teaches that evolution is physiologically a mode of generation in which the germ that develops the foetus pre-exists already in the parent, the development and final form and characteristics of that germ being accomplished in nature; and that in cosmology the process takes place blindly through the correlation of the elements, and their various compounds. Occultism answers that this is only the *apparent* mode, the real process being Emanation, guided by intelligent Forces under an immutable LAW. Therefore, while the Occultists and Theosophists believe thoroughly in the doctrine of Evolution as given out by Kapila and Manu, they are *Emanationists* rather than *Evolutionists*. The doctrine of Emanation was at one time universal. It was taught by the Alexandrian as well as by the Indian philosophers, by the Egyptian, the Chaldean and Hellenic Hierophants, and also by the Hebrews (in their Kabbala, and even in *Genesis*). For it is only owing to deliberate mistranslation that the Hebrew word asdt has been translated "angels" from the Septuagint, when it means *Emanations, Æons*, precisely as with the Gnostics. Indeed, in Deuteronomy (xxxiii., 2) the word *asdt* or *ashdt* is translated as" fiery law", whilst the correct rendering of the passage should be "from his right hand went [not a fiery law, but a fire according to law "; viz., that the fire of one flame is imparted to, and caught up by another like as in a trail of inflammable substance. This is precisely emanation. As shown in Isis Unveiled : "In Evolution, as it is now beginning to he understood, there is supposed to be in all matter an impulse to take on a higher form – a supposition clearly expressed by Manu and other Hindu philosophers of the highest antiquity. The philosopher's tree illustrates it in the case of the zinc solution. The controversy between the followers of this school and the Emanationists may he briefly stated thus The Evolutionist stops all inquiry at the borders of ' the Unknowable "; the Emanationist believes that nothing can be evolved – or, as the word means, unwombed or born – except it has first been involved, thus indicating that life is from a spiritual potency above the whole."

En (or **Ain**) **Soph** (*Heb.*). The endless, limitless and boundless. The absolute deific Principle, impersonal and unknowable. It means literally "no-thing" i.e., nothing that could be classed with anything else. The word and ideas are equivalent to the Vedantic conceptions of Parabrahmn. [w.w.w.]

Some Western Kabbalists, however, contrive to make of IT, a personal "He", a male deity instead of an impersonal deity.

Epimetheus (*Gr.*). Lit., "He who takes counsel *after*" the event. A brother of Prometheus in Greek Mythology.

Epinoia (*Gr.*). Thought, invention, design. A name adopted by the Gnostics for the first passive Æon.

Eros (*Gr.*). Hesiod makes of the god *Eros* the third personage of the Hellenic primordial Trinity composed of Ouranos, Gæa and *Eros*. It is the personified procreative Force in nature in its abstract sense, the propeller to "creation" and procreation. Exoterically, mythology makes of *Eros* the god of lustful, animal desire, whence the term *erotic* esoterically, it is different. (See " Kâma".)

Esoteric (*Gr.*). Hidden, secret. From the Greek *esotericos*, "inner" concealed.

Esoteric Bodhism. Secret wisdom or intelligence from the Greek *esotericos* "inner", and the Sanskrit *Bodhi*, "knowledge", intelligence – in contradistinction to *Buddhi*, "the *faculty* of knowledge or intelligence" and Buddhism, the philosophy or Law of Buddha (the Enlightened). Also written " Budhism", from *Budha* (Intelligence and Wisdom) the Son of Soma.

Ether. Students are but too apt to confuse this with Akâsa and with Astral Light. It is neither, in the sense in which ether is described by physical Science. Ether is a material agent, though hitherto undetected by any physical apparatus; whereas Akâsa is a distinctly spiritual agent, identical, in one sense, with the Anima Mundi, while the Astral Light is only the seventh and highest principle of the terrestrial atmosphere, as undetectable as Akâsa and real Ether, because it is something quite on another plane. The seventh principle of the earth's atmosphere, as said, the Astral Light, is only the second on the Cosmic scale. The scale of Cosmic Forces, Principles and Planes, of Emanations – on the metaphysical – and Evolutions – on the physical plane – is the Cosmic Serpent biting its own tail, the Serpent reflecting the Higher, and reflected in its turn by the lower Serpent. The Caduceus explains the mystery, and the four-fold Dodecahedron on the model of which the universe is said by Plato to have been built by the manifested *Logos* – synthesized by the unmanifested First-Born – yields geometrically the key to Cosmogony and its microcosmic reflection – our Earth.

Evolution. The development of higher orders of animals from lower. As said in *Isis Unveiled*: "Modern Science holds but to a one-sided physical evolution, prudently avoiding and ignoring the higher or spiritual evolution, which would force our contemporaries to confess the superiority of the ancient philosophers and psychologists over themselves. The ancient sages, ascending to the UNKNOWABLE, made their starting- point from the first manifestation of the unseen, the unavoidable, and, from a strictly logical reasoning, the absolutely necessary creative Being, the Demiurgos of the universe. Evolution began with them from pure spirit, which descending lower and lower down, assumed at last a visible and comprehensible form, and became matter. Arrived at this point, they speculated in the Darwinian method, but on a far more large and comprehensive basis." (See "Emanation".)

Exoteric. Outward, public; the opposite of esoteric or hidden.

F

First Point. Metaphysically the first point of manifestation, the germ of primeval differentiation, or the point in the infinite Circle "whose centre is everywhere, and circumference nowhere". The Point is the *Logos*.

Fire (*Living*). A figure of speech to denote deity, the "One" life. A theurgic term, used later by the Rosicrucians. The symbol of the *living fire* is the sun, *certain of whose rays develope the fire of life in a diseased body, impart the knowledge of the future* to the sluggish mind, and stimulate to active function a certain psychic and generally dormant faculty in man. The meaning is very occult.

Fohat (*Tib.*). A term used to represent the active (male) potency of the Sakti (female reproductive power) in nature. The essence of cosmic electricity. An occult Tibetan term for *Daiviprakriti* primordial light: and in the universe of manifestation the ever-present electrical energy and ceaseless destructive and formative power. Esoterically, it is the same, *Fohat* being the universal propelling Vital Force, at once the propeller and the resultant.

G

Gabriel. According to the Gnostics, the "Spirit" or *Christos*, the "messenger of life", and Gabriel are one. The former "is called some-times the Angel Gabriel Hebrew 'the mighty one of God'," and took with the Gnostics the place of the *Logos*, while the Holy Spirit was considered one with the Æon Life, (see *Irenæus* I., xii.). Therefore we find Theodoret saying (in *Hævet. Fab.*, II vii.) : " The heretics agree with us (Christians) respecting the beginning of all things. But they say there is not one Christ (God), *but one above* and *the other below*. And this last *formerly dwelt in many;* but the Jesus, they at one time say is *from* God, at another they call him a Spirit;" The key to this is given in the esoteric philosophy. The "spirit" with the Gnostics was a female potency exoterically, it was the ray proceeding from the Higher *Manas*, the Ego, and that which the Esotericists refer to as the *Kâma Manas* or the lower personal Ego, which is radiated in every human entity by the Higher Ego or *Christos*, the god within us. Therefore, they were right in saying: "there is not one Christ, but one above and the other below". Every student of Occultism will understand this, and also that Gabriel – or "the mighty one of God" – is one with the Higher Ego. (See *Isis Unveiled*.)

Gæa (*Gr.*). Primordial Matter, in the Cosmogony of Hesiod; Earth, as some think; the wife of Ouranos, the sky or heavens. The female personage of the primeval Trinity, composed of Ouranos, Gæa and *Eros*.

Genesis. The whole of the Book of *Genesis* down to the death of Joseph, is found to he a hardly altered version of the Cosmogony of the Chaldeans, as is now repeatedly proven from the Assyrian tiles. The first three chapters are transcribed from the allegorical narratives of the beginnings common to all nations. Chapters four and five are a new allegorical adaptation of the same narration in the secret *Book of Numbers*; chapter six is an astronomical narrative of the Solar year and the seven *cosmocratores* from the Egyptian original of the Pymander and the symbolical visions of a series of *Enoichioi* (Seers) – from whom came also the *Book of Enoch*. The beginning of Exodus, and the story of Moses is that of the Babylonian Sargon, who having flourished (as even that unwilling authority Dr. Sayce tells us) 3750 B.C. preceded the Jewish lawgiver by almost 2300 years. (See *Secret Doctrine*, vol. II., pp. 691 et seq.) Nevertheless, *Genesis* is an undeniably esoteric work. It has not borrowed, nor has it disfigured the universal symbols and teachings on the lines of which it was written, but simply adapted the eternal truths to its own national spirit and clothed them in cunning allegories comprehensible only to its Kabbalists and Initiates. The Gnostics have done the same, each sect in its own way, as thousands of years before, India, Egypt, Chaldea and Greece, had also dressed the same incommunicable truths each in its own national garb. The key and solution to all such narratives can be found *only in the esoteric teachings*.

Genii (*Lat.*) A name for Æons, or angels, with the Gnostics. The names of their hierarchies and classes are simply legion.

Gnâna (*Sk.*) Knowledge as applied to the esoteric sciences.

Gnân *Devas* (*Sk.*) Lit., "the gods of knowledge". The higher classes of gods or devas; the "mind-born" sons of Brahmâ, and others including the *Manasa-putras* (the Sons of Intellect). Esoterically, our reincarnating Egos.

Gnânasakti (Sk.) The power of true knowledge, one of the seven great forces in Nature (*six*, exoterically).

Gnôsis (*Gr.*) Lit., "knowledge". The technical term used by the schools of religious philosophy, both before and during the first centuries of so-called Christianity, to denote the object of their enquiry. This Spiritual and Sacred Knowledge, the *Gupta Vidya* of the Hindus, could only be obtained by Initiation into Spiritual Mysteries of which the ceremonial "Mysteries" were a type.

Gnostics (*Gr.*) The philosophers who formulated and taught the Gnôsis or Knowledge (*q.v.*). They flourished in the first three centuries of the Christian era: the following were eminent, Valentinus, Basilides, Marcion, Simon Magus, etc. [w.w. w.]

Golden Age. The ancients divided the life cycle into the Golden, Silver, Bronze and Iron Ages. The Golden was an age of primeval purity, simplicity and general happiness.

Great Age. There were several "great ages" mentioned by the ancients. In India it embraced the whole Maha-manvantara, the "age of Brahmâ", each "Day" of which represents the life cycle of a chain – i.e. it embraces a period of seven Rounds. (See *Esoteric Buddhism*, by A. P. Sinnett.) Thus while a "Day" and a "Night" represent, as *Manvantara* and *Pralaya*, 8,640,000,000 years, an "age" lasts through a period of 311,040,000,000,000 years; after which the *Pralaya*, or dissolution of the universe, becomes universal. With the Egyptians and Greeks the "great age" referred only to the tropical or sidereal year, the duration of which is 25,868 solar years. Of the complete age – that of the gods – they say nothing, as it was a matter to he discussed and divulged only in the Mysteries, during the initiating ceremonies. The "great age" of the Chaldees was the same in figures as that of the Hindus.

Grihastha (*Sk.*) Lit., "a householder", "one who lives in a house with his family". A Brahman " family priest" in popular rendering, and the sarcerdotal hierarchy of the Hindus.

Gupta Vidyâ (*Sk.*) The same as Guhya Vidyâ; Esoteric or Secret Science; knowledge.

Guru (*Sk.*) Spiritual Teacher; a master in metaphysical and ethical doctrines; used also for a teacher of any science.

H

Hades (*Gr.*), or *Aïdes*. The "invisible", i.e., the land of the shadows, one of whose regions was Tartarus, a place of complete darkness, like the region of profound dreamless sleep in the Egyptian Amenti. Judging by the allegorical description of the various punishments inflicted therein, the place was purely Karmic. Neither Hades nor Amenti were the hell still preached by some retrograde priests and clergymen; but whether represented by the Elysian Fields or by Tartarus, Hades was a place of retributive justice and no more. This could only be reached by crossing the river to the "other shore", i.e. by crossing the river Death, and being once more reborn, for weal or for woe. As well expressed in Egyptian Belief: "The story of Charon, the ferryman (of the, Styx) is to be found not only in Homer, but in the poetry of many lands. The River must be crossed before gaining the Isles of the Blest. The Ritual of Egypt described a Charon and his boat long ages before Homer. He is Khu-en-ua, the hawk-headed steersman." (See "Amenti", "Hel" and "Happy Fields".)

Hanuman (Sk.) The monkey god of the *Ramayana*; the *generalissimo* of Rama's army; the son of Vayu, the god of the wind, and of a virtuous she-demon. Hanuman was the faithful ally of Rama and by his unparalleled audacity and wit, helped the Avatar of Vishnu to finally conquer the demon-king of Lanka, Ravana, who had carried off the beautiful Sita, Rama's wife, an outrage which led to the celebrated war described in the Hindu epic poem.

Heavenly Adam. The synthesis of the *Sephirothal* Tree, or of all the Forces in Nature and their informing deific essence. In the diagrams, the Seventh of the lower *Sephiroth, Sephira Malkhooth* – the Kingdom of Harmony – represents the feet of the ideal Macrocosm, whose head reaches to the first manifested Head. This Heavenly Adam is the *natura naturans*, the abstract world, while the Adam of Earth (Humanity) is the *natura naturata* or the material universe. The former is the presence of Deity in its universal essence; the latter the manifestation of the intelligence of that essence. In the *real Zohar* not the fantastic and anthropomorphic caricature which we often find in the writings of Western Kabbalists – there is not a particle of the personal deity which we find so prominent in the dark cloaking of the Secret Wisdom known as the Mosaic Pentateuch.

Hell. A term with the Anglo-Saxons, evidently derived from the name of the goddess **Hela** (*q.v.*), and by the Sclavonians from the Greek Hades: hell being in Russian and other Sclavonian tongues – *ad*, the only difference between the Scandinavian cold hell and the hot hell of the Christians, being found in their respective temperatures. But even the idea of those overheated regions is not original with the Europeans, many peoples having entertained the conception of an underworld climate; as well may we if we localise our Hell in the centre of the earth. All exoteric religions – the creeds of the Brahmans, *Buddhists*, Zoroastrians, Mahommedans, Jews, and the rest, make their hells hot and dark, though many are more attractive than frightful. The idea of a hot hell is an afterthought, the distortion of an astronomical allegory. With the Egyptians, Hell became a place of punishment by fire not earlier than the seventeenth or eighteenth dynasty, when Typhon was transformed from a god into a devil. But at whatever time this dread superstition was implanted in the minds of the poor ignorant masses, the scheme of a burning hell and souls tormented therein is purely Egyptian. Ra (the Sun) became the Lord of the Furnace in Karr, the hell of the Pharaohs, and the sinner was threatened with misery "in the heat of infernal fires". "A lion was there" says Dr. Birch "and was called the roaring monster". Another describes the place as "the bottomless pit and lake of fire, into which the victims are thrown" (compare *Revelation*). The Hebrew word *gaï-hinnom* (Gehenna) never really had the significance given to it in Christian orthodoxy.

Hermaphrodite (*Gr.*). Dual-sexed; a male and female Being, whether man or animal.

Hermes Trismegistus (*Gr.*). The "thrice great Hermes", the Egyptian. The mythical personage after whom the Hermetic philosophy was named. In Egypt the God Thoth or Thot. A generic name of many ancient Greek writers on philosophy and Alchemy. Hermes Trismegistus is the name of Hermes or Thoth in his human aspect, as a god he is far more than this. As *Hermes-Thoth-Aah*, he is Thoth, the moon, i.e., his symbol is the bright side of the moon, supposed to contain the essence of creative Wisdom, "the elixir of Hermes ". As such he is associated with the Cynocephalus, the dog-headed monkey, for the same reason as was Anubis, one of the aspects of Thoth. (See " Hermanubis".) The same idea underlies the form of the Hindu God of Wisdom, the elephant-headed Ganesa, or Ganpat, the son of Parvati and Siva. (See "Ganesa".) When he has the head of an *ibis*, he is the sacred scribe of the gods; but even then he wears the crown *atef* and the lunar disk. He is the most mysterious of gods. As a serpent, Hermes Thoth is the divine creative 'Wisdom. The Church Fathers speak at length of Thoth-Hermes. (See "Hermetic".)

Hermetic. Any doctrine or writing connected with the esoteric teachings of Hermes, who, whether as the Egyptian Thoth or the Greek Hermes, was the God of Wisdom with the Ancients, and, according to Plato, "discovered numbers, geometry, astronomy and letters". Though mostly considered as spurious, nevertheless the Hermetic writings were highly prized by St. Augustine, Lactantius, Cyril and others. In the words of Mr. J. Bonwick, " They are more or less touched up by the Platonic philosophers among the early Christians (such as Origen and Clemens Alexandrinus) who sought to substantiate their Christian arguments by appeals to these heathen and revered writings, though they could not resist the temptation of making them say a little too much. Though represented by some clever and interested writers as teaching pure monotheism, the Hermetic or Trismegistic books are, nevertheless, purely pantheistic. The Deity referred to in them is defined by Paul as that in *which* "we live, and move and have our being" – notwithstanding the "in Him" of the translators.

Higher Self. The Supreme Divine Spirit overshadowing man. The crown of the upper spiritual Triad in man – Atmân.

Hochmah (*Heb.*). See "Chochmah".

Humanity. Occultly and Kabbalistically, the whole of mankind is symbolised, by Manu in India; by Vajrasattva or Dorjesempa, the head of the Seven *Dhyani*, in Northern Buddhism; and by Adam Kadmon in the Kabbala. All these represent the totality of mankind whose beginning is in this androgynic protoplast, and whose end is in the Absolute, beyond all these symbols and myths of human origin. Humanity is a great Brotherhood by virtue of the sameness of the material from which it is formed physically and morally. Unless, however, it becomes a Brotherhood also intellectually, it is no better than a superior genus of animals.

I

Incarnations (*Divine*) or *Avatars*. The Immaculate Conception is as pre-eminently Egyptian as it is Indian. As the author of *Egyptian Belief* has it: "It is not the vulgar, coarse and sensual story as in Greek mythology, but refined, moral and spiritual "; and again the incarnation idea was found revealed on the wall of a Theban temple by Samuel Sharpe, who thus analyzes it: "First the god Thoth . . . as the messenger of the gods, like the Mercury of the Greeks (or the Gabriel of the first Gospel), tells the *maiden* queen Mautmes, that she is to give birth to a son, who is to be king Amunotaph III. Secondly, the god Kneph, the Spirit . . . . and the goddess Hathor (Nature) both take hold of the queen by the hands and put into her mouth the character for life, a cross, which is to be the life of the coming child", etc., etc. Truly divine incarnation, or the *avatar* doctrine, constituted the grandest mystery of every old religious system!

Individuality. One of the names given in Theosophy and Occultism to the Human Higher EGO. We make a distinction between the immortal and divine Ego, and the mortal human Ego which perishes. The latter, or "personality" (personal Ego) survives the dead body only for a time in the Kama Loka; the Individuality prevails forever.

Initiate. From the Latin *Initiatus*. The designation of anyone who was received into and had revealed to him the mysteries and secrets of either Masonry or Occultism. In times of antiquity, those who had been initiated into the arcane knowledge taught by the Hierophants of the Mysteries; and in our modern days those who have been initiated by the adepts of mystic lore into the mysterious knowledge, which, notwithstanding the lapse of ages, has yet a few real votaries on earth.

Initiation. From the same root as the Latin *initia,* which means the basic or first principles of any Science. The practice of initiation or admission into the sacred Mysteries, taught by the Hierophants and learned priests of the Temples, is one of the most ancient customs. This was practised in every old national religion. In Europe it was abolished with the fall of the last pagan temple. There exists at present but one kind of initiation known to the public, namely that into the Masonic rites. Masonry, however, has no more secrets to give out or conceal. In the palmy days of old, the Mysteries, according to the greatest Greek and Roman philosophers, were the most sacred of all solemnities as well as the most beneficent, and greatly promoted virtue. The Mysteries represented the passage from mortal life into finite death, and the experiences of the disembodied Spirit and Soul in the world of subjectivity. In our own day, as the secret is lost, the candidate passes through sundry meaningless ceremonies and is initiated into the solar allegory of Hiram Abiff, the "Widow's Son".

Inner Man. An occult term, used to designate the true and immortal Entity in us, not the outward and mortal form of clay that we call our body. The term applies, strictly speaking, only to the Higher Ego, the "astral man" being the appellation of the Double and of Kâma Rupa (*q.v.*) or the surviving *eidolon.*

Isis. In Egyptian *Issa,* the goddess Virgin-Mother; personified nature. In Egyptian or Koptic *Uasari,* the female reflection of *Uasar* or Osiris. She is the "woman clothed with the sun" of the land of Chemi. Isis Latona is the Roman Isis.

Iswara (*Sk.*). The "Lord" or the personal god – *divine Spirit in man. Lit.,* sovereign (independent) existence. A title given to Siva and other gods in India. Siva is also called Iswaradeva, or sovereign deva.

J

Jadoo (*Hind.*). Sorcery, black magic, enchantment.

Jadoogar (*Hind.*). A Sorcerer, or Wizard.

Jehovah (*Heb.*). The Jewish "Deity name J'hovah, is a compound of two words, *viz* of *Jah* (y, i, or j, *Yôdh,* the tenth letter of the alphabet) and *hovah* (Hâvah, or Eve)," says a Kabalistic authority, Mr. J. Ralston Skinner of Cincinnati, U.S.A. And again, "The word Jehovah, or *Jah-Eve,* has the primary meaning of existence or being as male female". It means Kabalistically the latter, indeed, and nothing more; and as repeatedly shown is entirely phallic. Thus, verse 26 in the IVth chapter of *Genesis,* reads in its disfigured translation . . . . "then began men to call upon the name of the Lord", whereas it ought to read correctly . . . . "then began men to call themselves by the name of *Jah-hovah*" or males and females, which they had become after the separation of sexes. In fact the latter is described in the same chapter, when Cain (the male or *Jah*) "rose up against Abel, his (*sister,* not) brother and slew him"(*spilt his blood,* in the original). Chapter IV of *Genesis* contains in truth, the allegorical narrative of that period of anthropological and physiological evolution which is described in the *Secret Doctrine* when treating of the third Root race of mankind. It is followed by Chapter V *as a blind*; but ought to be succeeded by Chapter VI, where the Sons of God took as their wives the daughters of men or of the giants. For this is an allegory hinting at the mystery of the Divine Egos incarnating in mankind, after which the hitherto senseless races "became mighty men, . . . men of renown" (v. 4), having acquired minds (*manas*) which they had not before.

Jhâna (*Sk.*) or *Jnana*. Knowledge; Occult Wisdom.

Jiva (*Sk.*). Life, as the Absolute; the Monad also or *"Atma-Buddhi"*.

Jivanmukta (*Sk.*). An adept or yogi who has reached the ultimate state of holiness, and separated himself from matter; a Mahatma, or *Nirvânee*, a "dweller in bliss" and emancipation. Virtually one who has reached Nirvâna during life.

Jivatma (*Sk.*). The ONE universal life, generally; but also the divine Spirit in Man.

Jnânam (*Sk.*). The same as "Gnâna", etc., the same as "Jhâna" (*q.v.*).

Jnâna Sakti (*Sk.*). The power of intellect.

Jupiter (*Lat.*). From the same root as the Greek Zeus, the greatest god of the ancient Greeks and Romans, adopted also by other nations. His names are among others: (1) Jupiter-Aërios; (2) Jupiter-Ammon of Egypt ; (3) Jupiter Bel-Moloch, the Chaldean; (4) Jupiter-Mundus, Deus Mundus, "God of the World"; (5) Jupiter-Fulgur, "the Fulgurant", etc.,etc.

K

Kabalah (*Heb.*). The hidden wisdom of the Hebrew Rabbis of the middle ages derived from the older secret doctrines concerning divine things and cosmogony, which were combined into a theology after the time of the captivity of the Jews in Babylon. All the works that fall under the esoteric category are termed Kabalistic.

Kabalist. From Q B L H, KABALA, an unwritten or oral tradition. The kabalist is a student of "secret science", one who interprets the hidden meaning of the Scriptures with the help of the symbolical *Kabala*, and explains the real one by these means. The Tanaim were the first kabalists among the Jews; they appeared at Jerusalem about the beginning of the third century before the Christian era. The books of *Ezekiel, Daniel, Henoch,* and the *Revelation* of St. John, are purely kabalistical. This secret doctrine is identical with that of

Chaldeans, and includes at the same time much of the Persian wisdom, or "magic". History catches glimpses of famous kabalists ever since the eleventh century. The Mediæval ages, and even our own times, have had an enormous number of the most learned and intellectual men who were students of the *Kabala* (or Qabbalah, as some spell it). The most famous among the former were Paracelsus, Henry Khunrath, Jacob Böhmen, Robert Fludd, the two Van Helmonts, the Abbot John Trithemius, Cornelius Agrippa, Cardinal Nicolao Cusani, Jerome Carden, Pope Sixtus IV., and such Christian scholars as Raymond Lully, Giovanni Pico de la Mirandola, Guillaume Postel, the great John Reuchlin, Dr. Henry More, Eugenius Philalethes (Thomas Vaughan), the erudite Jesuit Athanasius Kircher, Christian Knorr (Baron) von Rosenroth; then Sir Isaac Newton., Leibniz, Lord Bacon, Spinosa, etc., etc., the list being almost inexhaustible. As remarked by Mr. Isaac Myer, in his Qabbalah, the ideas of the Kabalists have largely influenced European literature.

Kabiri (*Phœn.*) or the *Kabirim*. Deities and very mysterious gods with the ancient nations, including the Israelites, some of whom – as Terah, Abram's father – worshipped them under the name of *Teraphim*. With the Christians, however, they are now devils, although the modern Archangels are the direct transformation of these same *Kabiri*. In Hebrew the latter name means "the mighty ones", *Gibborim*. At one time all the deities connected with fire – whether they were divine, infernal or volcanic – were called Kabirian.

Kadmon (*Heb.*). Archetypal man. See."Adam Kadmon".

Kaliyuga (*Sk.*). The fourth, the black or iron age, our present period, the duration of which us 432,000 years. The last of the ages into which the evolutionary period of man is divided by a series of such ages. It began 3,102 years B.C. at the moment of Krishna's death, and the first cycle of 5,000 years will end between the years 1897 and 1898.

Kalpa (*Sk.*). The period of a mundane revolution, generally a cycle of time, but usually, it represents a "day" and "night" of Brahmâ, a period of 4,320,000,000 years.

Kama (*Sk.*) Evil desire, lust, volition; the cleaving to existence. Kama is generally identified with *Mara* the tempter.

Kamadeva (*Sk.*). In the popular notions the god of love, a Visva-deva, in the Hindu Pantheon. As the *Eros* of Hesiod, degraded into Cupid by exoteric law, and still more degraded by a later popular sense attributed to the term, so is Kama a most mysterious and metaphysical subject. The earlier Vedic description of Kama alone gives the key-note to what he emblematizes. Kama is the first conscious, *all embracing desire* for universal good, love, and for all that lives and feels, needs help and kindness, the first feeling of infinite tender compassion and mercy that arose in the consciousness of the creative ONE

Force, as soon as it came into life and being as a ray from the ABSOLUTE. Says the *Rig Veda*, "Desire first arose in IT, which was the primal germ of mind, and which Sages, searching with their intellect, have discovered in their heart to be the bond which connects Entity with non-Entity", or *Manas* with pure *Atma-Buddhi*. There is no idea of sexual love in the conception. Kama is pre-eminently the divine desire of creating happiness and love; and it is only ages later, as mankind began to materialize by anthropomorphization its grandest ideals into cut and dried dogmas, that Kama became the power that gratifies desire on the animal plane. This is shown by what every *Veda* and some *Brahmanas* say. In the *Atharva Veda,* Kama is represented as the Supreme Deity and Creator. In the Taitarîya Brahmana, he is the child of Dharma, the god of Law and Justice, of Sraddha and faith. In another account he springs from the heart of Brahmâ. Others show him born from water, i.e., from primordial chaos, or the "Deep". Hence one of his many names, *Irâ-ja*, "the water-born"; and *Aja*, "unborn" ; and *Atmabhu* or "Self-existent". Because of the sign of *Makara* (Capricornus) on his banner, he is also called " Makara Ketu". The allegory about Siva, the "Great Yogin ", reducing Kama to ashes by the fire from his *central* (or third) *Eye*, for inspiring the Mahadeva with thoughts of his wife, while he was at his devotions – is very suggestive, as it is said that he thereby reduced Kama to his primeval spiritual form.

Kamaloka (*Sk.*). The *semi*-material plane, to us subjective and invisible, where the disembodied "personalities", the astral forms, called *Kamarupa* remain, until they fade out from it by the complete exhaustion of the effects of the mental impulses that created these eidolons of human and animal passions and desires; (See "Kam*Arupa*".) It is the Hades of the ancient Greeks and the Amenti of the Egyptians, the land of Silent Shadows; a division of the first group of the *Trailôkya*. (See "Kamadhâtu".)

Kamarupa (*Sk.*). Metaphysically, and in our esoteric philosophy, it is the subjective form created through the mental and physical desires and thoughts in connection with things of matter, by all sentient beings, a form which survives the death of their bodies. After that death three of the seven "principles" – or let us say planes of senses and consciousness on which the human instincts and ideation act in turn – viz., the body, its astral prototype and physical vitality, – being of no further use, remain on earth; the three higher principles, grouped into one, merge into the state of Devachan (*q.v.*), in which state the Higher Ego will remain until the hour for a new reincarnation arrives; and the *eidolon* of the ex-Personality is left alone in its new abode. Here, the pale copy of the man that was, vegetates for a period of time, the duration of which is variable and according to the element of materiality which is left in it, and which is determined by the past life of the defunct. Bereft as it is of its higher mind, spirit and physical senses, if left alone to its own senseless devices, it will gradually fade out and disintegrate. But, if forcibly drawn back into the terrestrial sphere whether by the passionate desires and appeals of the surviving friends or by regular necromantic practices – one of the most pernicious of which is mediumship – the "spook" may prevail for a period greatly exceeding the span of the natural life of its body. Once the Kam*Arupa* has learnt the way back to living human bodies, it becomes a vampire, feeding on the vitality of those who are so anxious for its company. In India these *eidolons* are called *Pisâchas,* and are much dreaded, as already explained elsewhere.

Karabtanos *(Gr.).* The spirit of blind or animal desire; the symbol of Kamarupa. The Spirit "without sense or judgment" in the Codex of the Nazarenes. He is the symbol of matter and stands for the father of the seven spirits of concupiscence begotten by him on his mother, the "Spiritus" or the Astral Light.

Kârana *(Sk.).* Cause (metaphysically).

Kârana Sarîra *(Sk.).* The "Causal body". It is dual in its meaning. Exoterically, it is Avidya, ignorance, or that which is the cause of the evolution of a human ego and its reincarnation ; hence the lower *Manas* esoterically – the causal body or Kâranopadhi stands in the Taraka Raja yoga as corresponding to *Buddhi* and the Higher " *Manas,*" or Spiritual Soul.

Kâranopadhi *(Sk.).* The basis or *upadhi* of Karana, the "causal soul". In Taraka Rajayoga, it corresponds with both *Manas* and *Buddhi.* See Table in the *Secret Doctrine,* Vol. I, p. 157.

Karma *(Sk.).* Physically, action: metaphysically, the LAW OF RETRIBUTION, the Law of cause and effect or Ethical Causation. Nemesis, only in one sense, that of bad Karma. It is the eleventh *Nidana* in the concatenation of causes and effects in orthodox Buddhism ; yet it is the power that controls all things, the resultant of moral action, the meta physical *Samskâra,* or the moral effect of an act committed for the attainment of something which gratifies a personal desire. There is the Karma of merit and the Karma of demerit. Karma neither punishes nor rewards, it is simply *the one* Universal LAW which guides unerringly, and, so to say, blindly, all other laws productive of certain effects along the grooves of their respective causations. When Buddhism teaches that "Karma is that moral kernel (of any being) which alone survives death and continues in transmigration ' or reincarnation, it simply means that there remains nought after each Personality but the causes produced by it ; causes which are undying, i.e., which cannot be eliminated from the Universe until replaced by their legitimate effects, and wiped out by them, so to speak, and such causes – unless compensated during the life of the person who produced them with adequate effects, will follow the reincarnated Ego, and reach it in its subsequent reincarnation until a harmony between effects and causes is fully reestablished. No "personality" – a mere bundle of material atoms and of instinctual and mental characteristics – can of course continue, as such, in the world of pure Spirit. Only that which is immortal in its very nature and divine in its essence, namely, the Ego, can exist for ever. And as it is that Ego which chooses the personality it will inform, after each Devachan, and which receives through these personalities the effects of the Karmic causes produced, it is therefore the Ego, that *self* which is the "moral kernel" referred to and embodied karma, "which alone survives death."

Kartikeya (*Sk*), or *Kartika*. The Indian God of War, son of Siva, born of his seed fallen into the Ganges. He is also the personification of the power of the *Logos*. The planet Mars. Kartika is a very occult personage, a nursling of the Pleiades, and a *Kumâra*. (See *Secret Doctrine*.)

Kether (*Heb.*). The Crown, the highest of the ten *Sephiroth*; the first of the Supernal Triad. It corresponds to the Macroprosopus, vast countenance, or Arikh Anpin, which differentiates into Chokmah and Binah. [w.w.w.]

Khem (*Eg.*). The same as Horus. "The God Khem will avenge his father Osiris"; says a text in a papyrus.

Kosmos (*Gr.*). The Universe, as distinguished from the world, which may mean our globe or earth.

Krishna (*Sk.*).. The most celebrated avatar of Vishnu, the "Saviour" of the Hindus and their most popular god. He is the- eighth Avatar, the son of Devaki, and the nephew of Kansa, the Indian King Herod, who while seeking for him among the shepherds and cow-herds who concealed him, slew thousands of their newly-born babes. The story of Krishna's conception, birth, and childhood are the exact prototype of the *New Testament* story. The missionaries, of course, try to show that the Hindus stole the story of the Nativity from the early Christians who came to India.

Krita-*Yuga* (*Sk.*). The first of the four Yugas or Ages of the Brahmans; also called *Satya-Yuga*, a period lasting 1,728,000 years.

Kriyasakti (*Gk.*). The power of thought; one of the seven forces of Nature. Creative potency of the *Siddhis* (powers) of the full Yogis.

Kronos (*Gr.*). Saturn. The God of Boundless Time and of the Cycles.

Kshetrajna or *Kshetrajneswara* (*Sk.*). Embodied spirit, the Conscious Ego in its highest manifestations; the reincarnating Principle; the "Lord" in us.

Kumâra (*Sk.*). A virgin boy, or young celibate. The first *Kumâras* are the seven sons of Brahmâ born out of the limbs of the god, in the so-called ninth creation. It is stated that the name was given to them owing to their formal refusal to "procreate their species", and so they "remained Yogis", as the legend says.

L

Lanoo (*Sk.*). A disciple, the same as "chela".

Laya or *Layam* (*Sk.*). From the root *Li* "to dissolve, to disintegrate" a point of equilibrium (*zero-point*) in physics and chemistry. In occultism, that point where substance becomes homogeneous and is unable to act or differentiate.

Lemuria. A modern term first used by some naturalists, and now adopted by Theosophists, to indicate a continent that, according to the *Secret Doctrine* of the East, preceded Atlantis. Its Eastern name would not reveal much to European ears.

Lha (*Tib.*). Spirits of the highest spheres, whence the name of Lhassa, the residence of the Dalaï-Lama. The title of Lha is often given in Tibet to some *Narjols* (Saints and Yogi adepts) who have attained great occult powers.

Lhamayin (*Tib.*). Elemental sprites of the lower terrestrial plane. Popular fancy makes of them demons and devils.

Linga or *Lingam* (*Sk.*). A sign or a symbol of abstract creation. Force becomes the organ of procreation only on this earth. In India there are 12 great Lingams of Siva, some of which are on mountains and rocks, and also in temples. Such is the *Kedâresa* in the Himalaya, a huge and shapeless mass of rock. In its origin the Lingam had never the gross meaning connected with the phallus, an idea which is altogether of a later date. The symbol in India has the same meaning which it had in Egypt, which is simply that the creative or procreative Force is divine. It also denotes who was the dual Creator – male and female, Siva and his Sakti. The gross and immodest idea connected with the phallus is not Indian but Greek and pre-eminently Jewish. The Biblical *Bethels* were real priapic stones, the " Beth-el" (phallus) wherein God dwells. The same symbol was concealed within the ark of the Covenant, the "Holy of Holies". Therefore the "Lingam" even as a phallus is not "a symbol of Siva" only, but that of every "Creator" or creative god in every nation, including the Israelites and their "God of Abraham and Jacob".

Linga Purâna (*Sk.*). A scripture of the Saivas or worshippers of Siva. Therein *Maheswara*, "the great Lord", concealed in the Agni Linga explains the ethics of life – duty, virtue, self-sacrifice and finally liberation by and through ascetic life at the end of the *Agni Kalpa* (the Seventh Round). As Professor Wilson justly observed "the Spirit of the worship (phallic) is as little influenced by the character of the type as can well be imagined. *There is nothing like the phallic orgies of antiquity; it is all mystical and spiritual.*"

Linga Sharîra (*Sk.*). The "body", i.e., the aerial symbol of the body. This term designates the *döppelganger* or the "astral body" of man or animal. It is the *eidolon* of the Greeks, the vital and *prototypal* body; the reflection of the men of flesh. It is born *before* and dies or fades out, with the disappearance of the last atom of the body.

Lipikas (*Sk.*). The celestial recorders, the "Scribes", those who record every word and deed, said or done by man while on this earth. As Occultism teaches, they are the agents of KARMA – the retributive Law.

Logos (*Gr.*). The manifested deity with every nation and people; the outward expression, or the effect of the cause which is ever concealed. Thus, speech is the *Logos* of thought; hence it is aptly translated by the "Verbum" and "Word" in its metaphysical sense.

Loka (*Sk.*). A region or circumscribed place. In metaphysics, a world or sphere or plane. The *Purânas* in India speak incessantly of seven and fourteen Lokas, above, and below our earth; of heavens and hells,

Lotus (*Gr.*). A most occult plant, sacred in Egypt, India and else where; called "the child of the Universe bearing the likeness of its mother in its bosom". There was a time "when the world was a golden lotus" (*padma*) says the allegory. A great variety of these plants, from the majestic Indian lotus, down to the marsh-lotus (bird's foot trefoil) and the Grecian "Dioscoridis", is eaten at Crete and other islands. It is a species of nymphala, first introduced from India to Egypt to which it was-not indigenous. See the text of *Archaic Symbolism* in the Appendix Viii. "The Lotus, as a Universal Symbol".

Lucifer (*Lat.*). The planet Venus, as the bright "Morning Star". Before Milton, Lucifer had never been a name of the Devil. Quite the reverse, since the Christian Saviour is made to say of himself in *Revelations* (xvi. 22.) "I am . . . the bright morning star" or Lucifer. One of the early Popes of Rome bore that name; and there was even a Christian sect in the fourth century which was called the *Luciferians.*

Lunar Gods. Called in India the Fathers, "*Pitris*" or the lunar ancestors. They are subdivided, like the rest, into seven classes or Hierarchies, In Egypt although the moon received less worship than in Chaldea or India, still Isis stands as the representative of Luna-Lunus, "the celestial Hermaphrodite". Strange enough while the modern connect the moon only with lunacy and generation, the ancient nations, who knew better, have, individually and collectively, connected their "wisdom gods" with it. Thus in Egypt the lunar gods are Thoth-Hermes and Chons; in India it is Budha, the Son of *Soma*, the moon; in Chaldea Nebo is the lunar god of Secret Wisdom, etc., etc. The wife of Thoth, *Sifix*, the lunar goddess, holds a pole with five rays or the five-pointed star, symbol of man, the Microcosm, in distinction from the Septenary Macrocosm. As in all theogonies a goddess precedes a god, on the principle most likely that the chick can hardly precede its egg, in Chaldea the moon was held as older and more venerable than the Sun, because, as they said, darkness precedes light at every periodical rebirth (or "creation") of the universe. Osiris although connected with the Sun and a Solar god is, nevertheless, born on Mount *Sinai*, because *Sin* is the Chaldeo-Assyrian word for the moon; so was

Dio-Nysos, god of Nyssi or *Nisi*, which latter appelation was that of Sinai in Egypt, where it was called Mount Nissa. The *crescent* is not – as proven by many writers – an ensign of the Turks, but was adopted by Christians for their symbol before the Mahommedans. For ages the crescent was the emblem of the Chaldean Astarte, the Egyptian Isis, and the Greek Diana, all of them Queens of Heaven, and finally became the emblem of Mary the Virgin. "The Greek Christian Empire of Constantinople held it as their palladium. Upon the conquest by the Turks, the Sultan adopted it . . . and since that, the crescent has been made to oppose the idea of the *cross*".

M

Macrocosm (*Gr.*). The "Great Universe" literally, or Kosmos.

Macroprosopus (*Gr.*). A Kabalistic term, made of a compound Greek word: meaning the Vast or Great Countenance (See "Kabalistic Faces"); a title of Kether, the Crown, the highest *Sephira*. It is the name of the Universe, called *Arikh-Anpin*, the totality of that of which Microprosopus or *Zauir-Anpin* "the lesser countenance", is the part and antithesis. In its high or abstract metaphysical sense, Microprosopus is Adam Kadmon, the *vehicle of Ain-Suph*, and the crown of the *Sephirothal* Tree, though since *Sephira* and Adam Kadmon are in fact one under two aspects, it comes to the same thing. Interpretations are many, and they differ.

Mahâ Buddhi (*Sk.*). *Mahat.* The Intelligent Soul of the World. The seven *Prakritis* or seven "natures" or planes, are counted from Mahâbuddhi downwards.

Mahâ Manvantara (*Sk.*). Lit., the great interludes between the "Manus". The period of universal activity. *Manvantara* implying here simply a period of activity, as opposed to *Pralaya*, or rest – without reference to the length of the cycle.

Mahâ Mâyâ (*Sk.*). The great illusion of manifestation. This universe, and all in it in their mutual relation, is called the great Illusion or *Mahâmâyâ* It is also the usual title given to Gautama the Buddha's Immaculate Mother – Mayâdêvi, or the "Great Mystery", as she is called by the Mystics.

Mahâ Pralaya (*Sk.*). The opposite of Mahâmanvantara, literally "the great Dissolution", the "Night" following the "Day of Brahmâ". It is the great rest and sleep of all nature after a period of active manifestation; orthodox Christians would refer to it as the "Destruction of the World".

Mahâ *Yuga* (*Sk.*). The aggregate of four *Yugas* or ages, of 4,320,000 solar years; a "Day of Brahmâ", in the Brahmanical system ; lit., "the great age".

Mahat (*Sk.*). Lit., "The great one". The first principle of Universal Intelligence and Consciousness. In the Purânic philosophy the first product of root-nature or *Pradhâna* (the same as Mulaprakriti); the producer of *Manas* the thinking principle, and of *Ahankâra*, egotism or the feeling of "I am I" (in the lower *Manas*).

Mahâtma. Lit., "great soul". An adept of the highest order. Exalted beings who, having attained to the mastery over their lower principles are thus living unimpeded by the "man of flesh", and are in possession of knowledge and power commensurate with the stage they have reached in their spiritual evolution. Called in Pali Rahats and Arhats.

Maitreya Buddha (*Sk.*). The same as the *Kalki Avatar* of Vishnu (the "White Horse" Avatar), and of Sosiosh and other Messiahs. The only difference lies in the dates of their appearances. Thus, while Vishnu is expected to appear on his white horse at the end of the present *Kali Yuga* age "for the final destruction of the wicked, the renovation of creation and the restoration of purity", Maitreya is expected earlier. Exoteric or popular teaching making slight variations on the esoteric doctrine states that Sakyamuni (Gautama Buddha) visited him in Tushita (a celestial abode) and commissioned him to issue thence on earth as his successor at the expiration of five thousand years after his (Buddha's) death. This would be in less than 3,000 years hence. Esoteric philosophy teaches that the next Buddha will appear during the seventh (sub) race of this Round. The fact is that Maitreya was a follower of Buddha, a well-known Arhat, though not his direct disciple, and that he was the founder of an esoteric philosophical school. As shown by Eitel (*Sanskrit-Chinese Dict.*), "statues were erected in his honour as early as B.C. 350".

Makâra (*Sk.*). "The Crocodile." In Europe the same as Capricorn; the tenth sign of the Zodiac. Esoterically, a mystic class of devas. With the Hindus, the vehicle of Varuna, the water-god.

Manas (*Sk.*). Lit., "the mind", the mental faculty which makes of man an intelligent and moral being, and distinguishes him from the mere animal; a synonym of *Mahat*. *Esoterically*, however, it means, when unqualified, the Higher EGO, or the sentient reincarnating Principle in man. When qualified it is called by Theosophists *Buddhi-Manas* or the Spiritual Soul in contradistinction to its human reflection – *Kâma-Manas*.

Manas, Kâma (*Sk.*). Lit., "the mind of desire." With the *Buddhi*sts it is the *sixth* of the Chadâyatana (*q.v.*), or the six organs of knowledge, hence the highest of these, synthesized by the seventh called *Klichta*, the spiritual perception of that which defiles this (lower) *Manas*, or the "Human-animal Soul", as the Occultists term it. While the Higher *Manas* or the Ego is directly related to *Vijnâna* (the 10th of the 12 Nidânas) – which is the perfect knowledge of all forms of knowledge, whether relating to object or subject in the nidânic concatenation of causes and effects; the lower, the Kâma *Manas* is but one of the *Indriya* or organs (roots) of

Sense. Very little can be said of the dual *Manas* here, as the doctrine that treats of it, is correctly stated only in esoteric works. Its mention can thus be only very superficial.

Manas Taijasi (*Sk.*). Lit., the "radiant" *Manas*; a state of the Higher Ego, which only high metaphysicians are able to realize and comprehend.

Mânasa or *Manaswin* (*Sk.*). "The efflux of the *divine* mind," and explained as meaning that this efflux signifies the *manasa* or divine sons of Brahmâ-Virâj. Nilakantha who is the authority for this statement, further explains the term "manasa" by *manomâtrasarira*. These *Manasa* are the *Arupa* or incorporeal sons of the Prajâpati Virâj, in another version. But as Arjuna Misra identifies Virâj with Brahmâ, and as Brahmâ is Mahat, the universal mind, the exoteric blind becomes plain. The *Pitris* are identical with the *Kumâra*, the Vairaja, the *Manasa*-Putra (mind sons), and are finally identified with the human "Egos".

Mânasa Dhyânis (*Sk.*). The highest *Pitris* in the *Purânas*; the Agnishwatthas, or Solar Ancestors of Man, those who made of Man a rational being, by incarnating in the senseless forms of semi-ethereal flesh of the men of the third race. (See Vol. II. of *Secret Doctrine*.)

Mânasas (*Sk.*). Those who endowed humanity with *manas* or intelligence, the immortal EGOS in men. (See "*Manas*".)

Mânava Dharma Shâstra – is the ancient code of law of, or by Manu.

Manu (*Sk.*). The great Indian legislator. The name comes from the Sanskrit root *man* "to think" – mankind really, but stands for Swâyambhuva, the first of the Manus, who started from *Swâyambhu*, "the self-existent" hence the *Logos*, and the progenitor of mankind. Manu is the first Legislator, almost a Divine Being.

Manus (*Sk.*). The fourteen Manus are the patrons or guardians of the race cycles in a *Manvantara*, or Day of Brahmâ. The primeval Manus are seven, they become fourteen in the *Purânas*.

Manushi or *Manushi Buddhas* (*Sk.*). Human Buddhas, Bodhisattvas, or incarnated *Dhyan Chohans*.

Manvantara (*Sk.*). A period of manifestation, as opposed to *Pralaya* (dissolution, or rest), applied to various cycles, especially to a Day of Brahmâ, 4,320,000,000 Solar years – and to the reign of one Manu – 308,448,000. (See Vol. II. of the *Secret Doctrine*, p. 68 *et. seq.*) Lit., *Manuantara* – between Manus.

Mârttanda, (*Sk.*). The Vedic name of the Sun.

Mâyâ (*Sk.*). Illusion ; the cosmic power which renders phenomenal existence and the perceptions thereof possible. In Hindu philosophy that alone which is changeless and eternal is called *reality* ; all that which is subject to change through decay and differentiation and which has therefore a begining and an end is regarded as *mâyâ* – illusion.

Monad (*Gr.*). The Unity, the *one* ; but in Occultism it often means the unified triad, *Atma-Buddhi-Manas,* or the duad, *Atma-Buddhi,* that immortal part of man which reincarnates in the lower kingdoms, and gradually progresses through them to Man and then to the final goal – Nirvâna.

Monas (*Gr.*). The same as the term *Monad* ; "Alone", a unit. In the Pythagorean system the duad emanates from the higher and solitary Monas, which is thus the "First Cause".

Moon. The earth's satellite has figured very largely as an emblem in the religions of antiquity; and most commonly has been represented as Female, but this is not universal, for in the myths of the Teutons and Arabs, as well as in the conception of the Rajpoots of India (see Tod, *Hist.*), and in Tartary the moon was male. Latin authors speak of Luna. and also of Lunus, but with extreme rarity. The Greek name is Selene, the Hebrew Lebanah and also Yarcah. In Egypt the moon was associated with Isis, in Phenicia with Astarte and in Babylon with Ishtar. From certain points of view the ancients regarded the moon also as Androgyne. The astrologers allot an Influence to the moon over the several parts of a man, according to the several Zodiacal signs she traverses; as well as a special influence produced by the house she occupies in a figure.

The division of the Zodiac into the 28 mansions of the moon appears to be older than that into 12 signs: the Copts, Egyptians, Arabs, Persians and Hindoos used the division into 28 parts centuries ago, and the Chinese use it still.

The Hermetists said the moon gave man an astral form, while Theosophy teaches that the Lunar *Pitris* were the creators of our human bodies and lower principles. (See *Secret Doctrine* 1. 386.) [w.w.w.]

Mummy. The name for human bodies embalmed and preserved according to the ancient Egyptian method. The process of mummification is a rite of extreme antiquity in the land of the Pharaohs, and was considered as one of the most sacred ceremonies. It was, moreover, a process showing considerable learning in chemistry and surgery. Mummies 5,000 years old and more, reappear among us a preserved and fresh as when they first came from the hands of the *Parashistes.*

Munis (*Sk.*). Saints, or Sages.

Mysteries. Greek *teletai,* or finishings, celebrations of initiation or the Mysteries. They were observances, generally kept secret from the profane and uninitiated, in which were taught by dramatic representation and other methods, the origin of things, the nature of the human spirit, its relation to the body, and the method of its purification and restoration to higher life.

Physical science, medicine, the laws of music, divination, were all taught in the same manner. The Hippocratic oath was but a mystic obligation. Hippocrates was a priest of Asklepios, some of whose writings chanced to become public. But the Asklepiades were initiates of the Æsculapian serpent-worship, as the Bacchantes were of the Dionysia; and both rites were eventually incorporated with the Eleusinia. The Sacred Mysteries were enacted in the ancient Temples by the initiated Hierophants for the benefit and instruction of the candidates. The most solemn and occult Mysteries were certainly those which were performed in Egypt by "the band of secret-keepers", as Mr. Bonwick calls the Hierophants. Maurice describes their nature very graphically in a few lines. Speaking of the Mysteries performed in Philæ (the Nile-island), he says that "it was in these gloomy caverns that the grand and mystic arcana of the goddess (Isis) were unfolded to the adoring aspirant, while the solemn hymn of initiation resounded through the long extent of these stony recesses". The word "mysteries" is derived from the Greek *muô,* "to close the mouth", and every symbol connected with them had, a hidden meaning. As Plato and many other sages of antiquity affirm, the Mysteries were highly religious, moral and beneficent as a school of ethics. The Grecian mysteries, those of Ceres and Bacchus, were only imitations of the Egyptian; and the author of *Egyptian Belief and Modern Thought,* informs us that our own "word *chapel* or *capella* is said to be the *Caph-El* or college of *El,* the Solar divinity". The well-known *Kabiri* are associated with the Mysteries. In short, the Mysteries were in every country a series of dramatic performances, in which the mysteries of cosmogony and nature, in general, were personified by the priests and neophytes, who enacted the part of various gods and goddesses, repeating supposed scenes (allegories) from their respective lives. These were explained in their hidden meaning to the candidates for initiation, and incorporated into philosophical doctrines.

N

Nâga (*Sk.*). Literally "Serpent". The name in the Indian Pantheon of the Serpent or Dragon Spirits, and of the inhabitants of Pâtâla, hell. But as Pâtâla means the *antipodes,* and was the name given to America by the ancients, who knew and visited that continent before Europe had ever heard of it, the term is probably akin to the Mexican Nagals the (now) sorcerers and medicine men. The *Nagas* are the Burmese *Nats,* serpent-gods, or "dragon demons". In Esotericism, however, and as already stated, this is a nick-name for the "wise men" or adepts in China and Tibet, the "Dragons." are regarded as the titulary deities of the world, and of various spots on the earth, and the word is explained as meaning adepts, yogis, and narjols. The term has simply reference to their great knowledge and wisdom. This is also proven in the ancient Sûtras and Buddha's biographies. The Nâga is ever a wise man, endowed with extraordinary magic powers, in South and Central America as in India, in Chaldea as also in ancient Egypt.

In China the "worship" of the Nâgas was widespread, and it has become still more pronounced since Nâgarjuna (the "great Nâga", the "great adept" literally), the fourteenth *Buddhist* patriarch, visited China. The "Nâgas" are regarded by the Celestials as "the tutelary Spirits or gods of the five regions or the four points of the compass and the centre, as the guardians of the five lakes and four oceans" (**Eitel**). This, traced to its origin and translated esoterically, means that the five continents and their five root-races had always been under the guardianship of "terrestrial deities", i.e., Wise Adepts. The tradition that Nâgas washed Gautama Buddha at his birth, protected him and guarded the relics of his body when dead, points again to the Nâgas being only wise men, Arhats, and no monsters or Dragons. This is also corroborated by the innumerable stories of the conversion of Nâgas to Buddhism. The Nâga of a lake in a forest near Râjagriha and many other "Dragons" were thus converted by Buddha to the good Law.

Nârada (*Sk.*). One of the Seven great *Rishis*, a Son of Brahmâ This "Progenitor" is one of the most mysterious personages in the Brahmanical sacred symbology. Esoterically Nârada is the Ruler of events during various Karmic cycles, and the personification, in a certain sense, of the great human cycle; a *Dhyan Chohan*. He plays a great part in Brahmanism, which ascribes to him some of the most occult hymns in the *Rig Veda*, in which sacred work he is described as "of the Kanwa family". He is called Deva-Brahmâ, but as such has a distinct character from the one he assumes on earth – or Pâtâla. Daksha cursed him for his interference with his 5,000 and 10,000 sons, whom he persuaded to remain Yogins and *celibates*, to be reborn time after time on this earth (*Mahâbhârata*). But this is an allegory. He was the inventor of the Vina, a kind of lute, and a great "lawgiver". The story is too long to be given here.

Nârâyana (*Sk.*). The "mover on the Waters" of space: a title of Vishnu, in his aspect of the Holy Spirit, moving on the Waters of Creation. (See *Mânu*, Book II.) In esoteric symbology it stands for the primeval manifestation of the *life-principle*, spreading in infinite Space.

Nâstika (*Sk.*). Atheist, or rather he who does not worship or recognize the gods and idols.

Nephesh (*Heb.*). Breath of life. *Anima, Mens, Vita,* Appetites. This term is used very loosely in the *Bible*. It generally means *prana* "life"; in the Kabbalah it is the animal passions and the animal Soul. [w.w.w.]. Therefore, as maintained in theosophical teachings, *Nephesh* is the synonym of the Prâna-Kâmic Principle, or the vital animal Soul in man. [H. P. B.]

Nidâna (*Sk.*). The 12 causes of existence, or a chain of causation, "a concatenation of cause and effect in the whole range of existence through 12 links". This is the fundamental dogma of *Buddhist* thought, "the understanding of which solves the riddle of life, revealing the insanity of existence and preparing the mind for Nirvâna". (Eitel's *Sans. Chin. Dict.*) The 12 links stand thus in their enumeration. (1) Jail, or birth, according to one of the four modes of entering the stream of life and reincarnation – or *Chatur Yoni (q.v.)*, each mode placing the being born in one of the six *Gâti* (q.v.). (2) *Jarârnarana*, or decrepitude and death, following the maturity of the *Skandhas* (q.v.). (3) *Bhava*, the Karmic agent which leads every new sentient being to be born in this or another mode of existence in the *Trailokya* and Gâti. (4) *Upâdâna*, the creative cause of *Bhava* which thus becomes the cause of *Jati* which is the effect; and this creative cause is the *clinging to life*. (5) Trishnâ, love, whether pure or impure. (6) *Vêdâna*, or sensation; perception by the senses, it is the 5th Skandha. (7) Sparsa, the sense of touch. (8) *Chadâyatana*, the organs of sensation. (9) *Nâmarûpa*, personality, i.e., a form with a name to it, the symbol of the unreality of material phenomenal appearances. (10) *Vijnâna*, the perfect knowledge of every perceptible thing and of all objects in their concatenation and unity. (11) *Samskâra*, action on the plane of illusion. (12) *Avidyâ*, lack of true perception, or ignorance. The Nidânas belonging to the most subtle and abstruse doctrines of the Eastern metaphysical system, it is impossible to go into the subject at any greater length.

Nirguna (*Sk.*). Negative attribute; unbound, or without *Gunas* (attributes), i.e., that which is devoid of all qualities, the opposite of Saguna, that which has attributes (*Secret Doctrine*, II. 95), e.g., Parabrahmam is *Nirguna*; Brahmâ, Saguna. *Nirguna* is a term which shows the impersonality of the thing spoken of.

Nirmânakâya (*Sk.*). Something entirely different in esoteric philosophy from the popular meaning attached to it, and from the fancies of the Orientalists. Some call the *Nirmânakâya* body "Nirvana with remains" (Schlagintweit, etc.) on the supposition, probably, that it is a kind of Nirvânic condition during which consciousness and form are retained. Others say that it is one of the *Trikâya* (three bodies), with the "power of assuming any form of appearance in order to propagate Buddhism" (Eitel's idea); again, that "it is the incarnate avatâra of a deity" (*ibid.*), and so on. Occultism, on the other hand, says: that *Nirmânakâya*, although meaning literally a transformed "body", is a state. The form is that of the adept or yogi who enters, or chooses, that *post mortem* condition in preference to the Dharmakâya or *absolute* Nirvânic state. He does this because the latter *kâya* separates him for ever from the world of form, conferring upon him a state of *selfish* bliss, in which no other living being can participate, the adept being thus precluded from the possibility of helping humanity, or even *devas*. As a *Nirmânakâya*, however, the man leaves behind him only his physical body, and retains every other "principle" save the Kamic – for he has crushed this out for ever from his nature, during life, and it can never resurrect in his post mortem state. Thus, instead of going into selfish bliss, he chooses a life of self-sacrifice, an existence which ends only with the life-cycle, in order to be enabled to help mankind in an invisible yet most effective manner. (See *The*

Voice of the Silence, third treatise, "The Seven Portals".) Thus a *Nirmânakâya* is not, as popularly believed, the body "in which a Buddha or a Bodhisattva appears on earth", but verily one, who whether a *Chutuktu* or a *Khubilkhan*, an adept or a yogi during life, has since become a member of that invisible Host which ever protects and watches over Humanity within Karmic limits. Mistaken often for a "Spirit", a Deva, God himself, &c., a *Nirmânakâya* is ever a protecting, compassionate, verily a *guardian* angel, to him who becomes worthy of his help. Whatever objection may be brought forward against this doctrine; however much it is denied, because, forsooth, it has never been hitherto made public in Europe and therefore since it is unknown to Orientalists, it must needs be "a myth of modern invention" – no one will be bold enough to say that this idea of helping suffering mankind at the price of one's own almost interminable self-sacrifice, is not one of the grandest and noblest that was ever evolved from human brain.

Nirvâna *(Sk.).* According to the Orientalists, the entire "blowing out", like the flame of a candle, the utter extinction of existence. But in the esoteric explanations it is the state of absolute existence and absolute consciousness, into which the Ego of a man who has reached the highest degree of perfection and holiness during life goes, after the body dies, and occasionally, as in the case of Gautama Buddha and others, during life. (See "Nirvânî".)

Nirvânî (ee) (Sk.). One who has attained *Nirvana* – an emancipated soul. That Nirvâna means nothing of the kind asserted by Orientalists every scholar who has visited China, India and Japan is well aware. It is *"escape* from misery" but only from that of matter, freedom from *Klêsha*, or *Kâma*, and the complete extinction of animal desires. If we are told that *Abidharma* defines Nirvâna "as a state of absolute annihilation", we concur, adding to the last word the qualification "of everything connected with matter or the physical world", and this simply because the latter (as also all in it) is illusion, *mâyâ*. Sâkya-mûni Buddha said in the last moments of his life that "the spiritual body is immortal" (See *Sans. Chin. Dict.*). As Mr. Eitel, the scholarly Sinologist, explains it: "The popular exoteric systems agree in defining Nirvâna *negatively* as a state of absolute exemption from the circle of transmigration; as a state of entire freedom from all forms of existence; to begin with, freedom from all passion and exertion; a state of indifference to all sensibility" and he might have added "death of all compassion for the world of suffering". And this is why the Bodhisattvas who prefer the *Nirmânakâya* to the Dharmakâya vesture, stand higher in the popular estimation than the Nirvânîs. But the same scholar adds that: "Positively (and esoterically) they define Nirvâna as the highest state of spiritual bliss, as absolute immortality through absorption of the soul (spirit rather) into itself, but *preserving individuality* so that, e.g., Buddhas, after entering Nirvâna, may reappear on earth" – i.e., in the future *Manvantara*.

Norns (*Scand.*). The three sister goddesses in the *Edda,* who make known to men the decrees of *Orlog* or Fate. They are shown as coming out of the unknown distances *enveloped in a dark veil* to the Ash Yggdrasil (*q.v.*), and "sprinkle it daily with water from the Fountain of Urd, that it may not wither but remain green and fresh and strong" (*Asgard and the Gods*). Their names are "Urd", the Past; "Werdandi", the Present; and "Skuld", the Future, "which is either rich in hope or dark with tears". Thus they reveal the decrees of Fate "for out of the past and present the events and actions of the future are born" (*loc. cit.*).

Nous. (*Gr.*). A Platonic term for the Higher Mind or Soul. It means Spirit as distinct from animal Soul – *psyche*; divine consciousness or mind in man: *Nous* was the designation given to the Supreme deity (third *logos*) by Anaxagoras. Taken from Egypt where it was called *Nout,* it was adopted by the Gnostics for their first conscious Æon which, with the Occultists, is the third *logos,* cosmically, and the third "principle" (from above) or *manas,* in man. (See "Nout".)

Nout. (*Gr.*). In the Pantheon of the Egyptians it meant the "One- only-One", because they did not proceed in their popular or exoteric religion higher than the third manifestation which radiates from the *Unknown* and the *Unknowable,* the first unmanifested and the second *logoi* in the esoteric philosophy of every nation. The Nous of Anaxagoras was the *Mahat* of the Hindu Brahmâ, *the first manifested* Deity – "the Mind or Spirit self-potent"; this creative Principle being of course the *primum mobile* of everything in the Universe – its Soul and Ideation. (See "Seven Principles" in man.)

O

Occult Sciences. The science of the secrets of nature – physical and psychic, mental and spiritual; called Hermetic and Esoteric Sciences. In the West, the Kabbalah may be named; in the East, mysticism, magic, and Yoga philosophy, which latter is often referred to by the Chelas in India as the *seventh* "Darshana" (school of philosophy), there being only *six* Darshanas in India known to the world of the profane. These sciences are, and have been for ages, hidden from the vulgar for the very good reason that they would never be appreciated by the selfish educated classes, nor understood by the uneducated; whilst the former might misuse them for their own profit, and thus turn the divine science into *black magic.* It is often brought forward as an accusation against the Esoteric philosophy and the Kabbalah that their literature is full of "a barbarous and meaningless jargon" unintelligible to the ordinary mind. But do not exact Sciences – medicine, physiology, chemistry, and the rest – do the same? Do not official Scientists equally veil their facts and discoveries with a newly coined and most barbarous Græco-Latin terminology? As justly remarked by our late brother, Kenneth Mackenzie – "To juggle thus with words, when the facts are so simple, is the art of the Scientists of the present time, in striking contrast to those of the XVIIth century, who called spades spades, and not 'agricultural implements '." Moreover, whilst their facts would be as simple and as comprehensible if rendered in ordinary language, the facts of Occult Science are of so abstruse a nature, that in most cases no words exist in European languages to express them; in addition to which our "jargon" is a *double* necessity – (a) for the purpose of describing clearly these *facts* to him who is versed in the Occult terminology; and (b) to conceal them from the profane.

Occultist. One who studies the various branches of occult science. The term is used by the French Kabbalists (See Eliphas Lévi's works). Occultism embraces the whole range of psychological, physiological, cosmical, physical, and spiritual phenomena. From the word occultus hidden or secret. It therefore applies to the study of the **Kabbalah**, astrology, alchemy, and all arcane sciences.

Oeaohoo, or *Oeaihwu*. The manner of pronunciation depends on the accent. This is an esoteric term for the six in one or the mystic seven. The occult name for the "seven vowelled" ever-present manifestation of the Universal Principle.

Ophiomorphos (*Gr.*). The same, but in its material aspect, as the Ophis-*Christos*. With the Gnostics the Serpent represented "Wisdom in Eternity".

Orlog (*Scand.*). Fate, destiny, whose agents were the three Norns, the Norse *Parcæ*.

Osiris. (*Eg.*). The greatest God of Egypt, the Son of Seb (Saturn), celestial fire, and of Neith, primordial matter and infinite space. This shows him as the self-existent and self-created god, the first manifesting deity (our third *Logos*), identical with Ahura Mazda and other " First Causes". For as Ahura Mazda is one with, or the synthesis of, the Amshaspends, so Osiris, the collective unit, when differentiated and personified, becomes Typhon, his brother, Isis and Nephtys his sisters, Horus his son and his other aspects. He was born at Mount Sinai, the Nyssa of the 0. T. (See- *Exodus* xvii. 15), and buried at Abydos, after being killed by Typhon at the early age of twenty-eight, according to the allegory. According to Euripides he is the same as Zeus and Dionysos or *Dio-Nysos* "the god of Nysa", for Osiris is said by him to have been brought up in Nysa, in Arabia "the Happy". Query: how much did the latter tradition influence, or have anything in common with, the statement in the *Bible*, that "Moses built an altar and called the name Jehovah Nissi", or Kabbalistically – "Dio-Iao-Nyssi"? (See *Isis Unveiled* Vol. II. p. 165.) The four chief aspects of Osiris were – Osiris-Phtah (Light), the spiritual aspect; Osiris-Horus (Mind), the intellectual *manasic* aspect; Osiris-Lunus, the " Lunar" or psychic, astral aspect; Osiris-Typhon, Daïmonic, or physical, material, therefore passional turbulent aspect. In these four aspects he symbolizes the dual Ego – the divine and the human, the cosmico-spiritual and the terrestrial.

Of the many supreme gods, this Egyptian conception is the most suggestive and the grandest, as it embraces the whole range of physical and metaphysical thought. As a solar deity he had twelve minor gods under him – the twelve signs of the Zodiac. Though his name is the "Ineffable", his forty-two attributes bore each one of his names, and his seven dual aspects completed the forty-nine, or 7 X 7; the former symbolized by the fourteen members of his body, or twice seven. Thus the god is blended in man, and the man is deified into a god.

As to his human development, he is, as the author of the *Egyptian Belief* has it . . . "One of the Saviours or Deliverers of Humanity . . . . As such he is born in the world. He came as a benefactor, to relieve man of trouble . . . . In his efforts to do good he encounters evil . . . and he is temporarily overcome. He is killed . . . Osiris is buried. His tomb was the object of pilgrimage for thousands of years. But he did not rest in his grave. At the end of three days, or forty, he rose again and ascended to Heaven. This is the story of his Humanity" (*Egypt. Belief*).

Ouranos (*Gr.*). The whole expanse of Heaven called the "Waters of Space", the Celestial Ocean, etc. The name very likely comes from the Vedic Varuna, personified as the water god and regarded as the chief Aditya among the seven planetary deities. In Hesiod's Theogony, Ouranos (or Uranus) is the same as Cœlus (Heaven) the oldest of all the gods and the father of the divine Titans.

P

Padma Kalpa (*Sk.*). The name of the last Kalpa or the preceding *Manvantara*, which was a year of Brahmâ.

Pagan (*Lat.*). Meaning at first no worse than a dweller in the country or the woods; one far removed from the city-temples, and therefore unacquainted with the state religion and ceremonies. The word "heathen" has a similar significance, meaning one who lives on the heaths and in the country. Now, however, both come to mean *idolaters*.

Pagan Gods. The term is erroneously understood to mean idols. The philosophical idea attached to them was never that of something objective or anthropomorphic, but in each case an abstract potency, a virtue, or quality in nature. There are gods who are divine planetary spirits (*Dhyan Chohans*) or *Devas*, among which are also our Egos. With this exception, and especially whenever represented by an idol or in anthropomorphic form, the gods represent symbolically in the Hindu, Egyptian, or Chaldean Pantheons – formless spiritual Potencies of the "Unseen Kosmos".

Palæolithic A newly-coined term meaning in geology "ancient stone" age, as a contrast to the term *neolithic*, the "newer" or later stone age.

Pandora (*Gr.*). A beautiful woman created by the gods under the orders of Zeus to be sent to Epimetheus, brother of Prometheus; she had charge of a casket in which all the evils, passions and plagues which torment humanity were locked up. This casket Pandora, led by curiosity, opened, and thus set free all the ills which prey on mankind.

Para (*Sk*.). "Infinite" and "supreme" in philosophy – the final limit.

Parabrahm (*Sk*.). "Beyond Brahmâ", literally. The Supreme Infinite Brahma, "Absolute" – the attributeless, the secondless reality. The impersonal and nameless universal Principle.

Paracelsus. The symbolical name adopted by the greatest Occultist of the middle ages – Philip Bombastes Aureolus Theophrastus von Hohenheim – born in the canton of Zurich in 1493. He was the cleverest physician of his age, and the most renowned for curing almost any illness by the power of talismans prepared by himself. He never had a friend, but was surrounded by enemies, the most bitter of whom were the Churchmen and their party. That he was accused of being in league with the devil stands to reason, nor is it to be wondered at that finally he was murdered by some unknown foe, at the early age of forty-eight. He died at Salzburg, leaving a number of works behind him, which are to this day greatly valued by the Kabbalists and Occultists. Many of his utterances have proved prophetic. He was a clairvoyant of great powers, one of the most learned and erudite philosophers and mystics, and a distinguished Alchemist. Physics is indebted to him for the discovery of nitrogen gas, or **Azote.**

Paramartha (*Sk*) Absolute existence.

Paranirvâna (*Sk*.). Absolute *Non-Being*, which is equivalent to absolute *Being* or "Be-ness", the state reached by the human Monad at the end of the great cycle (See *Secret Doctrine* I, 135). The same as *Paraniskpanna.*

Pentagon (*Gr*.), from *pente* "five", and *gonia* "angle" ; in geometry a plane figure with five angles.

Personality. In Occultism – which divides man into seven principles, considering him under the three aspects of the *divine*, the *thinking* or the *rational*, and the *animal* man – the lower *quaternary* or the purely astrophysical being; while by *Individuality* is meant the Higher Triad, considered as a Unity. Thus the *Personality* embraces all the characteristics and memories of one physical life, while the *Individuality* is the imperishable *Ego* which re-incarnates and clothes itself in one personality after another.

Phenomenon (*Gr*.). In reality "an appearance", something previously unseen, and puzzling when the cause of it is unknown. Leaving aside various kinds of phenomena, such as cosmic, electrical, chemical, etc., and holding merely to the phenomena of spiritism, let it be remembered that theosophically and esoterically every "miracle" – from the biblical to the theumaturgic – is simply a phenomenon, but that no phenomenon is ever a miracle, *i.e.*, something supernatural or outside of the laws of nature, as all such are impossibilities in nature.

Pitris (*Sk.*). The ancestors, or creators of mankind. They are of seven classes, three of which are incorporeal, *arupa*, and four corporeal. In popular theology they are said to be created from Brahmâ's side. They are variously genealogized, but in esoteric philosophy they are as given in the *Secret Doctrine*. In *Isis Unveiled* it is said of them "It is generally believed that the Hindu term means the spirits of our ancestors, of disembodied people, hence the argument of some Spiritualists that fakirs (and yogis) and other Eastern wonder-workers, are *mediums*. This is in more than one sense erroneous. The *Pitris* are not the ancestors of the present living men, but those of the human kind, or Adamic races; the spirits of human races, which on the great scale of descending evolution *preceded our races* of men, and they *were physically, as well as spiritually, far superior* to our modern pigmies. In *Mânava Dharma Shâstra* they are called the *Lunar Ancestors*." The *Secret Doctrine* has now explained that which was cautiously put forward in the earlier Theosophical volumes.

Planetary Spirits. Primarily the rulers or governors of the planets. As our earth has its hierarchy of terrestrial planetary spirits, from the highest to the lowest plane, so has every other heavenly body. In Occultism, however, the term "Planetary Spirit" is generally applied only to the seven highest hierarchies corresponding to the Christian archangels. These have all passed through a stage of evolution corresponding to the humanity of earth on other worlds, in long past cycles. Our earth, being as yet only in its fourth round, is far too young to have produced high planetary spirits. The highest planetary spirit ruling over any globe is in reality the "Personal God" of that planet and far more truly its "over-ruling providence" than the self-contradictory Infinite Personal Deity of modern Churchianity.

Plato. An Initiate into the Mysteries and the greatest Greek philosopher, whose writings are known the world over. He was the pupil of Socrates and the teacher of Aristotle. He flourished over 400 years before our era.

Popol Vuh. The Sacred Books of the Guatemalians. Quiché MSS., discovered by Brasseur de Bourbourg.

Pragna (*Sk.*) or *Prajna*. A synonym of *Mahat* the Universal Mind. The capacity for perception. (*S. D.*, I. 139) Consciousness.

Prajâpatis (*Sk.*). Progenitors; the givers of life to all on this Earth. They are seven and then ten – corresponding to the seven and ten Kabbalistic *Sephiroth*; to the Mazdean Amesha-Spentas, &c. Brahmâ the creator, is called Prajâpati as the synthesis of the Lords of Being.

Prakriti (*Sk.*). Nature in general, nature as opposed to Purusha – spiritual nature and Spirit, which together are the "two primeval aspects of the One Unknown Deity". (*Secret Doctrine*, I. 51.)

Pralaya (*Sk.*). A period of obscuration or repose – planetary, cosmic or universal – the opposite of *Manvantara* (*S. D.*, I. 370.).

Pramantha (*Sk.*). An accessory to producing the sacred fire by friction. The sticks used by Brahmins to kindle fire by friction.

Prâna (*Sk.*). Life-Principle ; the breath of Life.

Pranidhâna (*Sk.*). The fifth observance of the Yogis; ceaseless devotion. (See *Yoga Shâstras*, ii. 32.)

Pratyasarga (*Sk.*). In *Sankhya* philosophy the "intellectual evolution of the Universe" ; in the *Purânas* the 8th creation.

Prometheus (*Gr.*). The Greek *logos*; he, who by bringing on earth divine fire (intelligence and consciousness) endowed men with reason and mind. Prometheus is the Hellenic type of our *Kumâras* or *Egos*, those who, by incarnating in men, made of them latent gods instead of animals. The gods (or *Elohim*) were averse to men becoming "as one of us (*Genesis* iii., 22), and knowing "good and evil". Hence we see these gods in every religious legend punishing man for his desire to know. As the Greek myth has it, for stealing the fire he brought to men from Heaven, Prometheus was chained by the order of Zeus to a crag of the Caucasian Mountains.

Protogonos (*Gr.*). The "first-born"; used of all the manifested gods and of the Sun in our system.

Psyche (*Gr.*). The animal, terrestrial Soul; the lower *Manas*.

Purânas (*Sk.*). Lit., "ancient". A collection of symbolical and allegorical writings – eighteen in number now – supposed to have been composed by Vyâsa, the author of *Mahâbhârata*.

Purusha (*Sk.*). "Man", *heavenly man*. Spirit, the same as Nârâyana in another aspect. "The Spiritual Self."

Pymander (Gr.). The "Thought divine". The Egyptian Prometheus and the personified Nous or divine light, which appears to and instructs Hermes Trismegistus, in a hermetic work called "Pymander".

Q

Qabbalah (*Heb.*). The ancient Chaldean Secret Doctrine, abbreviated into *Kabala*. An occult system handed clown by oral transmission; but which, though accepting tradition, is not in itself composed of merely traditional teachings, as it was once a fundamental science, now disfigured by the additions of centuries, and by interpolation by the Western Occultists, especially by *Christian* Mystics. It treats of hitherto esoteric interpretations of the Jewish Scriptures, and teaches several methods of interpreting Biblical allegories. Originally the doctrines were transmitted "from mouth to ear" only, says Dr. W. Wynn Westcott, "in an oral manner from teacher to pupil who received them; hence the name Kabbalah, Qabalah, or Cabbala from the Hebrew root QBL, to receive. Besides this Theoretic Kabbalah, there was created a Practical branch, which is concerned with the Hebrew letters, as types a like of Sounds, Numbers, and Ideas." (See "Gematria", "Notaricon", " Temura".) For the original book of the *Qabbalah* – the *Zohar* – see further on. But the *Zohar* we have now is not the *Zohar* left by Simeon Ben Jochai to his son and secretary as an heirloom. The author of the present *approximation* was one Moses de Leon, a Jew of the XIIIth century. (See "Kabalah" and "Zohar".)

Qadmon, Adam, or *Adam Kadmon (Heb.)*. The Heavenly or Celestial Man, the Microcosm *(q.v.)*, He is the manifested *Logos*; the *third Logos* according to Occultism, or the Paradigm of Humanity.

R

Ra *(Eg.)*. The divine Universal Soul in its manifested aspect – the ever-burning light; also the personified Sun.

Rajasâs *(Sk.)*. The elder *Agnishwattas* – the Fire-*Pitris*, "fire" standing as a symbol of enlightenment and intellect.

Râkshasas (Sk.). *Lit.*, "raw eaters", and in the popular superstition evil spirits, demons. Esoterically, however, they are the *Gibborim* (giants) of the *Bible*, the Fourth Race or the Atlanteans. (See *Secret Doctrine*, II., 165.)

Reincarnation. The doctrine of rebirth, believed in by Jesus and the Apostles, as by all men in those days, but denied now by the Christians. All the Egyptian converts to Christianity, Church Fathers and others, believed in this doctrine, as shown by the writings of several. In the still existing symbols, the human-headed bird flying towards a mummy, a body, or "the soul uniting itself with its *sahou* (glorified body of the Ego, and also the *kâmalokic shell*) proves this belief. "The song of the Resurrection" chanted by Isis to recall her dead husband to life, might be translated "Song of Rebirth", as Osiris is collective Humanity. "Oh! Osiris [here follows the name of the Osirified mummy, or the departed], rise again in holy earth (matter), august mummy in the coffin, under thy corporeal substances", was the funeral prayer of the priest over the deceased. "Resurrection" with the Egyptians never meant the resurrection of the mutilated mummy, but of the *Soul* that informed it, the Ego in a new body. The putting on of flesh periodically by the Soul or the Ego, was a universal belief; nor can anything be more consonant with justice and Karmic law.

Rudras (Sk.). The mighty ones; the lords of the three upper worlds. One of the classes of the "fallen" or incarnating spirits; they are all born of Brahmâ.

Rûpa *(Sk.).* Body; any form, applied even to the forms of the gods, which are subjective to us.

S

Sacred Science. The name given to the *inner* esoteric philosophy, the secrets taught in days of old to the initiated candidates, and divulged during the last and supreme Initiation by the Hierophants.

Samvritisatya *(Sk.).* Truth mixed with false conceptions (Samvriti); the reverse of absolute truth – or *Paramârthasatya,* self-consciousness in absolute truth or reality.

Sanat Kumâra *(Sk.).* The most prominent of the seven *Kumâras,* the Vaidhâtra the first of which are called Sanaka, Sananda, Sanâtana and Sanat *Kumâra;* which names are all significant qualifications of the degrees of human intellect.

Sânkhya *(Sk.).* The system of philosophy founded by Kapila *Rishi,* a system of analytical metaphysics, and one of the six *Darshanas* or schools of philosophy. It discourses on numerical categories and the meaning of the twenty-five *tatwas* (the forces of nature in various degrees). This "atomistic school", as some call it, explains nature by the interaction of twenty-four elements with *purusha* (spirit) modified by the three gunas (qualities), teaching the eternity of *pradhâna* (primordial, homogeneous matter), or the self-transformation of nature and the eternity of the human Egos.

Sanskrit *(Sk.).* The classical language of the Brahmans, never known *nor spoken in its true systematized form* (given later *approximately* by Pânini), except by the initiated Brahmans, as it was pre-eminently "a mystery language". It has now degenerated into the so-called Prâkrita.

Saptarshi *(Sk.).* The seven *Rishis.* As stars they are the constellation of 'the Great Bear, and called as such the *Riksha* and *Chitrasikhandinas,* bright-crested.

Satya *Yuga (Sk.).* The golden age, or the age of truth and purity; the first of the four Yugas, also called Krita *Yuga.*

Secret Doctrine. The general name given to the esoteric teachings of antiquity.

Sephira *(Heb.)* An emanation of Deity; the parent and synthesis of the ten *Sephiroth* when she stands at the head of the *Sephiroth*al Tree; in the Kabbalah, *Sephira,*or the " Sacred Aged ", is the divine Intelligence (the same as Sophia or Metis), the first emanation from the "Endless" or Ain-Suph.

Sephiroth (*Heb.*). The ten emanations of Deity; the highest is formed by the concentration of the Ain Soph Aur, or the Limitless Light, and each: *Sephira* produces by emanation another *Sephira*. The names of the Ten *Sephiroth* are – 1. Kether – The Crown; 2. Chokmah – Wisdom; 3. Binah – Understanding; 4. Chesed- – Mercy; Geburah – Power; 6. Tiphereth – Beauty; 7. Netzach – Victory; 8. Hod – Splendour; 9. Jesod_Foundation; and 10. Malkuth – The Kingdom.

The conception of Deity embodied in the Ten *Sephiroth* is a very sublime one, and each *Sephira* is a picture to the Kabbalist of a group of exalted ideas, titles and attributes, which the name but faintly represents. Each *Sephira* is called either active or passive, though this attribution may lead to error; passive does not mean a return to negative existence; and the two words only express the relation between individual *Sephiroth*, and not any absolute quality. [w.w.w.]

Sesha (*Sk.*) *Ananta*, the great Serpent of Eternity, the couch of Vishnu; the symbol of infinite Time in Space. In the exoteric beliefs Sesha is represented as a *thousand*-headed and *seven*-headed cobra; the former the king of the nether world, called Pâtâla, the latter the carrier or support of Vishnu on the Ocean of Space.

Sharîra (Sarîra) (*Sk.*). Envelope or body.

Shekinah (*Heb.*). A title applied to Malkuth, the tenth *Sephira*, by the Kabbalists; but by the Jews to the cloud of glory which rested on the Mercy-seat in the Holy of Holies. As taught, however, by all the Rabbins of Asia Minor, its nature is of a more exalted kind, Shekinah being the veil of Akâsa, the Endless and the Absolute; hence a kind of Kabbalistic Mûlaprakriti. [w.w.w.]

Siddhas (*Sk.*). Saints and sages who have become almost divine also a hierarchy of *Dhyan Chohans*.

Sishta (*Sk.*). The great elect or Sages, left after every minor *Pralaya* (that which is called "obscuration" in Mr. Sinnett's *Esoteric Buddhism*), when the globe goes into its night or rest, to become, on its re-awakening, the seed of the next humanity. Lit. "remnant."

Siva (*Sk.*). The third person of the Hindu Trinity (the Trimûrti). He is a god of the first order, and in his character of Destroyer higher than Vishnu, the Preserver, as he destroys only to regenerate on a higher plane. He is born as Rudra, the *Kumâra*, and is the patron of all the Yogis, being called, as such, Mahâdeva the great ascetic, His titles are significant *Trilochana*, "the three-eyed", *Mahâdeva*, "the great god ", *Sankara*, etc., etc., etc.

Smaragdine Tablet of Hermes. As expressed by Eliphas Lévi,"this Tablet of Emerald is the whole of magic in a single page"; but India has a single word which, when understood, contains "the whole of magic ". This is a tablet, however, alleged to have been found by Sarai, Abraham's wife (!) *on the dead* *body of Hermes*. So say the Masons and Christian Kabbalists. But in Theosophy we call it an allegory. May it not mean that *Sarai-swati*, the wife of Brahmâ, or the goddess of secret wisdom and learning, finding still much of the ancient wisdom latent in the dead body of Humanity, revivified that wisdom? This led to the rebirth of the Occult Sciences, so long forgotten and neglected, the world over. The tablet itself, however, although containing the "whole of magic ", is too long to be reproduced here.

Soma (*Sk.*). The moon, and also the juice of the plant of that name used in the temples for trance purposes; a sacred beverage. Soma, the moon, is the symbol of the Secret Wisdom. In the *Upanishads* the word is used to denote gross matter (with an association of moisture) capable of producing life under the action of heat. (See " Soma-drink ".)

Soul. The **yuch**, or *nephesh* of the *Bible*; the vital principle, or the breath of life, which every animal, down to the infusoria, shares with man. In the translated *Bible* it stands indifferently for *life*, blood and soul. " Let us not kill his *nephesh* ", says the original text: "let us not kill *him* ", translate the Christians (*Genesis* xxxvii. 21), and so on.

Spirit. The lack of any mutual agreement between writers in the use of this word has resulted in dire confusion. It is commonly made synonymous with *soul*; and the lexicographers countenance the usage. In Theosophical teachings. the term "Spirit" is applied solely to that which *belongs directly to Universal Consciousness*, and which is its homogeneous and unadulterated emanation. Thus, the higher Mind in Man or his Ego (*Manas*) is, when linked indissolubly with *Buddhi*, a spirit; while the term "Soul", human or even animal (the lower *Manas* acting in animals as instinct), is applied only to Kâma-*Manas*, and qualified as the living soul. This is *nephesh*, in Hebrew, the "breath of life". Spirit is formless and *immaterial*, being, when individualised, of the highest spiritual substance – *Suddasatwa*, the divine essence, of which the body of the manifesting *highest Dhyanis* are formed. Therefore, the Theosophists reject the appellation " Spirits" for those phantoms which appear in the phenomenal manifestations of the Spiritualists, and call them "shells", and various other names. (See "Sukshma Sarîra".) Spirit, in short, is no entity in the sense of having form ; for, as *Buddhist* philosophy has it, where there is a form, there is a cause for pain and suffering. But each *individual* spirit – this individuality lasting only throughout the manvantaric life-cycle – may be described as a *centre of consciousness*, a self-sentient and self-conscious centre; a state, not a conditioned individual. This is why there is such a wealth of words in Sanskrit to express the different States of Being, Beings and Entities, each appellation showing the philosophical difference, the plane to which such *unit* belongs, and the degree of its spirituality or materiality. Unfortunately these terms are almost untranslatable into our Western tongues.

Sushupti Avasthâ (*Sk.*). Deep sleep; one of the four aspects of Prânava.

Sûtrâtman (*Sk.*). Lit., "the thread of spirit"; the immortal Ego, the Individuality which incarnates in men one life after the other, and upon which are strung, like beads on a string, his countless Personalities. The universal life-supporting air, *Samashti prau*; universal energy.

Svabhâvat (*Sk.*). Explained by the Orientalists as "plastic substance", which is an inadequate definition. Svabhâvat is the world-substance and stuff, or rather that which is behind it – the spirit and essence of substance. The name comes from *Subhâva* and is composed of three words – **su**, good, perfect, fair, handsome; **sva,** self; and **bkâva**, being, or *state of being*. From it all nature proceeds and into it all returns at the end of the life-cycles. In Esotericism it is called "Father-Mother". It is the plastic essence of matter.

Svasamvedanâ (*Sk.*). Lit., "the reflection which analyses itself "; a synonym of Paramârtha.

Svastika (Sk.). In popular notions, it is the Jaina cross, or the "four-footed" cross (*croix cramponnée*). In Masonic teachings, "the most ancient Order of the Brotherhood of the Mystic Cross" is said to have been founded by Fohi, 1,027 B.C., and introduced into China fifty-two years later, consisting of the three degrees. In Esoteric Philosophy, the most mystic and ancient diagram. It is "the originator of the fire by friction, and of the ' Forty-nine Fires'." Its symbol was stamped on Buddha's heart, and therefore called the " Heart's Seal". It is laid on the breasts of departed Initiates after their death ; and it is mentioned with the greatest respect in the *Râmâyana*. Engraved on every rock, temple and prehistoric building of India, and wherever *Buddhi*sts have left their landmarks; it is also found in China, Tibet and Siam, and among the ancient Germanic nations as Thor's Hammer. As described by Eitel in his *Hand-Book of Chinese* Buddhism. . (1) it is "found among Bonpas and *Buddhi*sts"; (2) it is "one of the sixty-five figures of the Sripâda" ; (it is "the symbol of *Esoteric Buddhism*" ; (4) "the special mark of all deities worshipped by the Lotus School of China". Finally, and in Occultism, it is as sacred to us as the Pythagorean *Tetraktys*, of which it is indeed the double symbol.

T

Tanha (*Pali*). The thirst for life. Desire to live and clinging to life on this earth. This clinging is that which causes rebirth or reincarnation.

Tanmâtras (*Sk.*). The types or rudiments of the five Elements; the subtle essence of these, devoid of all qualities and identical with the properties of the five basic Elements – earth, water, fire, air and ether; i.e., the *tanmâtras* are, in one of their aspects, smell, taste, touch, sight, and hearing.

Tetragrammaton. The four-lettered name of God, its Greek title: the four letters are in Hebrew " yod, hé vau, hé " ,or in English capitals, IHVH. The true ancient pronunciation is now unknown; the sincere Hebrew considered this name too sacred for speech, and in reading the sacred writings he substituted the title " Adonai ", meaning Lord. In the *Kabbalah*, **I** is associated with Chokmah, **H** with Binah, **V** with Tiphereth, and **H** final with Malkuth. Christians in general call IHVH Jehovah, and many modern Biblical scholars write it Yahveh. In the *Secret Doctrine*, the name Jehovah is assigned to *Sephira* Binah alone, but this attribution is not recognised by the Rosicrucian school of Kabbalists, nor by Mathers in his translation of Knorr Von Rbsenroth's *Kabbalah Denudata*: certain Kabbalistic authorities have referred Binah alone to IHVH, but only in reference to the Jehovah of the exoteric Judaism. The IHVH of the *Kabbalah* has but a faint resemblance to the God of the Old Testament. [w.w.w.]

The *Kabbalah* of Knorr von Rosenroth is no authority to the Eastern Kabbalists; because it is well known that in writing his *Kabbalah Denudata* he followed the modern rather than the ancient (Chaldean) MSS.; and it is equally well known that those MSS. and writings of the *Zohar* that are classified as "ancient", mention, and some even use, the Hebrew vowel or Massoretic points. This alone would make these would-be Zoharic books spurious, as there are no direct traces of the Massorah scheme before the tenth century of our era, nor any remote trace of it before the seventh.

Theosophia (*Gr.*). Wisdom-religion, or "Divine Wisdom". The substratum and basis of all the world-religions and philosophies, taught and practised by a few elect ever since man became a thinking being. In its practical bearing, Theosophy is purely divine ethics; the definitions in dictionaries are pure nonsense, based on religious prejudice and ignorance of the true spirit of the early Rosicrucians and mediæval philosophers who called themselves Theosophists.

Theosophists. A name by which many mystics at various periods of history have called themselves. The Neo-Platonists of Alexandria were Theosophists; the Alchemists and Kabbalists during the mediæval ages were likewise so called, also the Martinists, the Quietists, and other kinds of mystics, whether acting independently or incorporated in a brotherhood or society. All real lovers of divine Wisdom and Truth had, and have, a right to the name, rather than those who, appropriating the qualification, live lives or perform actions opposed to the principles of Theosophy. As described by Brother Kenneth R. Mackenzie, the Theosophists of the past centuries – " entirely speculative, and founding no schools, have still exercised a silent influence upon philosophy; and, no doubt, when the time arrives, many ideas thus silently propounded may yet give new directions to human thought. One of the ways in which these doctrines have obtained not only authority, but power, has been among certain enthusiasts in the higher degrees of Masonry. This power has, however, to a great degree died with the founders, and modern Freemasonry contains few traces of theosophic influence. However accurate and beautiful some of the ideas of Swedenborg, Pernetty, Paschalis, Saint Martin, Marconis, Ragon, and Chastanier may have been, they have but little direct influence on society." This is true of the Theosophists of the last three centuries, but not of the later ones. For the Theosophists of the current century have already visibly impressed themselves on modern literature, and introduced the desire and craving for some philosophy in place of the blind dogmatic faith of yore, among the most intelligent portions of human-kind. Such is the difference between past and modern THEOSOPHY.

Titans (*Gr.*). Giants of divine origin in Greek mythology who made war against the gods. Prometheus was one of them.

To On (*Gr.*). The "Being", the "Ineffable All" of Plato. He" whom no person has seen except the Son".

Tretâ *Yuga* (*Sk.*). The second age of the world, a period of 1,296,000 years.

Triad, or *the Three*. The ten *Sephiroth* are contemplated as a group of three triads: Kether, Chochmah and Binah form the supernal triad; Chesed, Geburah and Tiphereth, the second; and Netzach, Hod and Yesod, the inferior triad. The tenth *Sephira*, Malkuth, is beyond the three triads. [w.w.w.]

The above is orthodox Western Kabalah. Eastern Occultists recognise but one triad – – the upper one (corresponding to Atmâ-*Buddhi* and the " Envelope" which reflects their light, the three in one) – and count seven lower *Sephiroth*, everyone of which stands for a " principle", beginning with the Higher *Manas* and ending with the Physical Body – of which Malkuth is the representative in the Microcosm and the Earth in the Macrocosm.

Typhon (*Eg.*). An aspect or shadow of Osiris. Typhon is not, as Plutarch asserts, the distinct " Evil Principle " or the Satan of the Jews; but rather the lower cosmic "principles " of the divine body of Osiris, the god in them – Osiris being the personified universe as an ideation, and Typhon as that same universe in its material realization. The two in one are Vishnu-Siva. The true meaning of the Egyptian myth is that Typhon is the terrestrial and material envelope of Osiris, who is the indwelling spirit thereof. In chapter 42 of the *Ritual* (" Book of the Dead"), Typhon is described as "Set, formerly called Thoth". Orientalists find themselves greatly perplexed by discovering Set-Typhon addressed in some papyri as "a great and good god ", and in others as the embodiment of evil. But is not Siva, one of the Hindu *Trimûrti*, described in some places as "the best and most bountiful of gods ", and at other times, "a dark, black, destroying, terrible " and " fierce god"? Did not Loki, the Scandinavian Typhon, after having been described in earlier times as a beneficent being, as the god of fire, the presiding genius of the peaceful domestic hearth, suddenly lose caste and become forthwith a power of evil, a cold-hell Satan and a demon of the worst kind? There is a good reason for such an invariable transformation. So long as these dual gods, symbols of good and necessary evil, of light and darkness, keep closely allied, i.e., stand for a combination of differentiated human qualities, or of the element they represent – they are simply an embodiment of the average *personal* god. No sooner, however, are they separated into two entities, each with its two characteristics, than they become respectively the two opposite poles of good and evil, of light and darkness ; they become in short, two independent and distinct entities or rather *personalities*. It is only by dint of sophistry that the Churches have succeeded to this day in preserving in the minds of the few the Jewish deity in his primeval integrity. Had they been logical they would have separated Christ from Jehovah, light and goodness from darkness and badness. And this was what happened to Osiris Typhon ;but no Orientalist has understood it, and thus their perplexity goes on increasing. (See the *Theosophical Glossary*)

U

Upâdhi (*Sk.*). Basis; the vehicle, carrier or bearer of something less material than itself: as the human body is the *upâdhi* of its spirit, ether the *upâdhi* of light, etc., etc.; a mould; a defining or limiting substance.

V

Vâch (Sk.). To call Vâch "speech" simply, is deficient in clearness. Vâch is the mystic personification of speech, and the female *Logos*, being one with Brahmâ, who created her out of one-half of his body, which he divided into two portions; she is also one with Virâj (called the "female" Virâj) who was created in her by Brahmâ. In one sense Vâch is "speech" by which knowledge was taught to man; in another she is the "mystic, secret speech" which descends upon and enters into the primeval *Rishis*, as the "tongues of fire" are said to have "sat upon" the apostles. For, she is called "the female creator ", the "mother of the *Vedas* ", etc., etc. Esoterically, she is the subjective Creative Force which, emanating from the Creative Deity (the subjective Universe, its "privation ", or *ideation*) becomes the manifested "world of speech ", i.e., the *concrete expression of ideation*, hence the "Word" or *Logos*. Vâch is "the male and female" Adam of the first chapter of *Genesis*, and thus called "Vâch-Virâj" by the sages. (See *Atharva Veda*.) She is also "the celestial Saraswatî produced from the heavens ", a "voice derived from *speechless* Brahmâ" (*Mahâbhârata*); the goddess of wisdom and eloquence. She is called *Sata-rûpa*, the goddess of *a hundred forms*.

Vâhan(a) (*Sk.*). A vehicle, the carrier of something immaterial and formless. All the gods and goddesses are, therefore, represented as using vâhanas to manifest themselves, which vehicles are ever symbolical. So, for instance, Vishnu has during *Pralayas, Ânanta* the infinite" (Space), symbolized by the serpent Sesha, and during the *Manvantaras* – *Garuda* the gigantic half-eagle, half-man, the symbol of the great cycle; Brahma appears as Brahmâ, descending into the planes of manifestations on *Kâlahamsa*, the "swan in time or finite eternity"; Siva (phonet, Shiva) appears as the bull *Nandi;* Osiris as the sacred bull *Apis;* Indra travels on an elephant; Kârttikeya, on a peacock; Kâmadeva on *Makâra,* at other times a parrot; Agni, the universal (and also solar) Fire-god, who is, as all of them are, "a consuming Fire", manifests itself as a ram and a lamb, *Ajâ,* "the unborn"; Varuna, as a fish; etc., etc., while the vehicle of MAN is his body.

Vaishnava (*Sk.*). A follower of any sect recognising and worshipping Vishnu as the one supreme God. The worshippers of Siva are called *Saivas.*

Vaivaswata (*Sk.*). The name of the Seventh Manu, the forefather of the post-diluvian race, or our own fifth humankind. A reputed son of Sûrya (the Sun), he became, after having been saved in an ark (built by the order of Vishnu) from the Deluge, the father of Ikshwâku, the founder of the solar race of kings. (See "*Sûryavansa*".)

Vâyu (*Sk.*). Air: the god and sovereign of the air; one of the five states of matter, namely the *gaseous;* one of the five elements, called, as wind, *Vâta.* The *Vishnu Purâna* makes Vâyu King of the Gandharvas. He is the father of Hanumân, in the *Râmâyana.* The trinity of the mystic gods in Kosmos closely related to each other, are " Agni (fire) whose place is on earth; Vâyu (air, or one of the forms of Indra), whose place is in the air ; and Sûrya (the sun) whose place is in the air (*Nirukta.*) In esoteric interpretation, these three cosmic principles, correspond with the three human principles, Kâma, Kâma-*Manas* and *Manas,* the sun of the intellect.

Vedânta (*Sk.*). A mystic system of philosophy which has developed from the efforts of generations of sages to interpret the secret meaning of the *Upanishads* (*q.v.*). It is called in the *Shad-Darshanas* (six schools or systems of demonstration), *Uttara Mîmânsâ,* attributed to *Vyâsa,* the compiler of the *Vedas,* who is thus referred to as the founder of the Vedânta. The orthodox Hindus call Vedânta_a term meaning literally the "end of all (Vedic) knowledge " – *Brahmâ-jnâna,* or pure and spiritual knowledge of Brahmâ. Even if we accept the late dates assigned to various Sanskrit schools and treatises by our Orientalists, the Vedânta must be 3,300 years old, as Vyâsa is said to have lived I,400 years B.C. If, as Elphinstone has it in his *History of India,* the *Brahmanas* are the *Talmud* of the Hindus, and the *Vedas* the Mosaic books, then the *Vedânta* may be correctly called the *Kabalah* of India. But how vastly more grand! Sankarâchârya, who was the popularizer of the Vedântic system, and the founder of the *Adwaita* philosophy, is sometimes called the founder of the modern schools of the Vedânta.

Vedas (*Sk.*). The "revelation". the scriptures of the Hindus, from the root *vid*, "to know ", or "divine knowledge". They are the most ancient as well as the most sacred of the Sanskrit works. The *Vedas* , on the date and antiquity of which no two Orientalists can agree, are claimed by the Hindus themselves, whose Brahmans and Pundits ought to know best about their own religious works, to have been first taught orally for thousands of years and then compiled on the shores of Lake Mânasa-Sarovara (phonetically, *Mansarovara*) beyond the Himalayas, in Tibet.

The Vedic writings are all classified in two great divisions, exoteric and esoteric, the former being called *Karma-Kânda*, "division of actions or works ", and the *Jnâna Kânda*, "division of (divine) knowledge", the Upanishads (q.v.) coming under this last classification. Both departments are regarded as *Sruti* or revelation. To each hymn of the *Rig -Veda*, the name of the Seer or *Rishi* to whom it was revealed is prefixed. It, thus, becomes evident on the authority of these very names (such as Va*Sishta*, Viswâmitra, Nârada, etc.), all of which belong to men born in various manvantaras and even ages, that centuries, and perhaps millenniums, must have elapsed between the dates of their composition.

Vendîdâd (*Pahlavi*). The first book (*Nosk*) in the collection of Zend fragments usually known as the *Zend-Avesta*. The *Vendidâd* is a corruption of the compound-word "Vidaêvo-dâtern", meaning "the anti- demoniac law ", and is full of teachings how to avoid sin and defilement by purification, moral and physical – each of which teachings is based on Occult laws. It is a pre-eminently occult treatise, full of symbolism and often of meaning quite the reverse of that which is expressed in its dead-letter text. The *Vendîdâd*, as claimed by tradition, is the only one of the twenty-one Nosks (works) that has escaped the *auto-da-fé* at the hands of the drunken Iskander the Rûmi, he whom posterity calls Alexander the Great – though the epithet is justifiable only when applied to the brutality, vices and cruelty of this conqueror. It is through the vandalism of this Greek that literature and knowledge have lost much priceless lore in the Nosks burnt by him. Even the Vendidâd has reached us in only a fragmentary state. The first chapters are very mystical, and therefore called "mythical" in the renderings of European Orientalists. The two "creators" of "spirit-matter" or the world of differentiation – Ahura- Mazda and Angra-Mainyu (Ahriman) – are introduced in them, and also Yima (the first man, or mankind personified). The work is divided into *Fargards* or chapters, and a portion of these is devoted to the formation of our globe, or terrestrial evolution. (See *Zend-Avesta*.)

Vishnu (*Sk.*). The second person of the Hindu Trimûrti (trinity), composed of Brahmâ, Vishnu and Siva. From the root **vish**, "to pervade". in the *Rig - Veda*, Vishnu is no high god, but simply a manifestation of the solar energy, described as "striding through the seven regions of the Universe in *three* steps and enveloping all things with the dust (of his beams ".) Whatever may be the six other occult significances of the statement, this is related to the same class of types as the seven and ten *Sephiroth*, as the *seven* and *three* orifices of the perfect Adam Kadmon, as the seven "principles" and the higher triad in man, etc., etc. Later on this mystic type becomes a great god, the preserver and the renovator, he "of a thousand names – Sahasranâma ".

W

Wisdom. The " very essence of wisdom is contained in the Non- Being ". say the Kabbalists; but they also apply the term to the WORD or *Logos*, the Demiurge, by which the universe was called into existence. "The one Wisdom is in the Sound ", say the Occultists; the *Logos* again being meant by Sound, which is the substratum of Âkâsa. Says the *Zohar*, the " Book of Splendour" "It is the Principle of all the Principles, the mysterious Wisdom, the crown of all that which there is of the most High". (*Zohar*, iii., fol. 288, Myers *Qabbalah*.) And it is explained, "Above Kether is the Ayin, or Ens, i.e., Ain, the NOTHING". "It is so named because we do not know, and it is impossible to know, *that which there is in that Principle*, because . . . it is above Wisdom itself." (iii., fol. 288.) This shows that the real Kabbalists agree with the Occultists that the essence, or that which is in the principle of Wisdom, is still above that highest Wisdom.

Wisdom Religion. The one religion which underlies all the now-existing creeds. That "faith" which, being primordial, and revealed directly to human kind by their *progenitors* and informing EGOS (though the Church regards them as the "fallen angels"), required no "grace", nor *blind* faith to believe, for it was *knowledge*. (See "Gupta Vidyâ", Hidden Knowledge.) It is on this Wisdom Religion that *Theosophy is based*.

Y

Years of Brahmâ. The whole period of "Brahma's Age" (100 Years). Equals 311,040,000,000,000 years. (See "*Yuga* ".)

Yggdrasil (*Scand.*). The "World Tree of the Norse Cosmogony; the ash Yggdrasil ; the tree of the Universe, of time and of life". It has three roots, which reach down to cold Hel, and spread thence to Jotun heim, the land of the Hrimthurses, or " Frost Giants ", and to Midgard, the earth and dwelling of the children of men. Its upper boughs stretch out into heaven, and its highest branch overshadows Waihalla, the Devachan of the fallen heroes. The Yggdrasil is ever fresh and green, as it is daily sprinkled by the Norns, the three fateful sisters, the Past, the Present, and the Future, with the waters of life from the fountain of Urd that flows on our earth. It will wither and disappear only on the day when the last battle between good and evil is fought ; when, the former prevailing, life, time and space pass out of life and space and time. Every ancient people had their world-tree. The Babylonians had their "tree of life", which was the world-tree, whose roots penetrated into the great lower deep or Hades, whose trunk was on the earth, and whose upper boughs reached *Zikum*, the highest heaven above. Instead of in Walhalla, they placed its upper foliage in the holy house of Davkina, the "great mother" of Tammuz, the Saviour of the world – the Sun-god put to death by the enemies of light.

Yoga (*Sk.*). (1) One of the six Darshanas or schools of India; a school of philosophy founded by Patanjali, though the real Yoga doctrine, the one that is said to have helped to prepare the world for the preaching of Buddha, is attributed with good reasons to the more ancient sage Yâjnawalkya, the writer of the *Shatapatha Brâhmana*, of *Yajur Veda*, the *Brihad Âranyaka*, and other famous works. (2) The practice of meditation as a means of leading to spiritual liberation. Psycho-spiritual powers are obtained thereby, and induced ecstatic states lead to the clear and correct perception of the eternal truths, in both the visible and invisible universe.

Yogâchârya (*Sk.*). (1) A mystic school. (2) Lit., a teacher (*âchârya*) of Yoga, one who has mastered the doctrines and practices of ecstatic meditation – the culmination of which are the *Mahâsiddhis*. It is incorrect to confuse this school with the Tantra, or Mahâtantra school founded by Samantabhadra, for there are two Yogâchârya Schools, one esoteric, the other popular. The doctrines of the latter were compiled and glossed by Asamgha in the sixth century of our era, and his mystic tantras and mantras, his formularies, litanies, spells and mudrâ would certainly, if attempted without a *Guru*, serve rather purposes of sorcery and black magic than real Yoga. Those who undertake to write upon the subject are generally learned missionaries and haters of Eastern philosophy in general. From these no unbiassed views can be expected. Thus when we read in the *Sanskrit -Chinese Dictionary* of Eitel, that the reciting of mantras (which he calls " spells"!) " should he accompanied by music and distortions of the fingers (mudrâ), that a state of mental fixity (*Samâdhi*) might he reached ' – one acquainted, however slightly,. with the real practice of Yoga can only shrug his shoulders. These distortions of the fingers or ,mudrâ are necessary, the author thinks, for the reaching of Samâdhi, "characterized by there being neither thought nor annihilation of thought, and consisting of six-fold bodily (*sic*) and mental happiness (*yogi*) *whence would result endowment with supernatural miracle-working power*". Theosophists cannot be too much warned against such fantastic and prejudiced explanations.

Yuga (*Sk.*). A 1,000th part of a Kalpa. An age of the World of which there are four, and the series of which proceed in succession during the manvantaric cycle. Each *Yuga* is preceded by a period called in the *Purânas* Sandhyâ, twilight, or transition period, and is followed by another period of like duration called Sandhyânsa, "portion of twilight". Each is equal to one-tenth of the *Yuga*. The group of four Yugas is first computed by the *divine* years, or " years of the gods" – each such year being equal to 360 years of mortal men. Thus we have, in "divine" years :

	AGE	YEARS
1	Krita or Satya *Yuga*	4,000
	Sandhyâ	400
	Sandhyansa	400
		4,800

2	Tretâ *Yuga*	3,000
	Sandhyâ	300
	Sandhyânsa	300
		3,600

3	Dwâpara *Yuga*	2,000
	Sandhya	200
	Sandhyânsa	200
		2,400

4	Kali *Yuga*	1,000
	Sandhyâ	100
	Sandhyânsa	100
		1,200
	Total =	**12,000**

This rendered in years of mortals equals:

4,800	X	360	=	1,728,000
3,600	X	360	=	1,296,000
2,400	X	360	=	864,000
1,200	X	360	=	432,000
		Total	=	4,320,000

The above is called a *Mahâyuga* or *Manvantara*. 2,000 such *Mahâyugas*, or a period of 8,640,000 years, make a Kalpa the latter being only a "day and a night", or twenty-four hours, of Brahmâ. Thus an "age of Brahmâ", or one hundred of his divine years, must equal 311,040,000,000,000 of our mortal years. The old Mazdeans or *Magi* (the modern Parsis) had the same calculation, though the Orientalists do not seem to perceive it, for even the Parsi Moheds themselves have forgotten it. But their "Sovereign time of the Long Period" (*Zervan Dareghâ Hvadâta*) lasts 12,000 years, and these are the 12,000 *divine* years of a *Mahâyuga* as shown above, whereas the *Zervan Akarana* (Limitless Time), mentioned by Zarathustra, is the *Kâla*, out of space and time, of Parabrahm.

Z

Zend-Avesta (*Pahl.*). The general name for the sacred books of the Parsis, fire or sun worshippers, as they are ignorantly called. So little is understood of the grand doctrines which are still found in the various fragments that compose all that is now left of that collection of religious works, that Zoroastrianism is called indifferently Fire-worship, Mazdaism, or Magism, Dualism, Sun-worship, and what not. The *Avesta* has two parts as now collected together, the first portion containing the *Vendîdâd*, the *Vispêrad* and the *Yasna*; and the second portion, called the *Khorda Avesta* (Small Avesta), being composed of short prayers called Gâh, Nyâyish, etc. *Zend* means "a commentary or explanation", and *Avesta* (from the old Persian *âbashtâ*, "the law". (See Darmsteter.) As the translator of the Vendîdâd remarks in a foot note (see int. xxx.): "what it is customary to call 'the Zend language', ought to be named 'the Avesta language', the Zend being no language at all and if the word be used as the designation of one, it can be rightly applied only to the Pahlavi". But then, the Pahlavi itself is only the language into which certain original portions of the *Avesta* are translated. What name should be given to the old *Avesta* language, and particularly to the "special dialect, older than the general language of the *Avesta*" (Darmst.), in which the five Ghthas in the *Yasna* are written? To this day the Orientalists are mute upon the subject. Why should not the Zend be of the same family, if not identical with the Zen-sar, meaning also the speech explaining the abstract symbol, or the "mystery language," used by Initiates?

Zeus (*Gr.*). The "Father of the gods". *Zeus-Zen* is Æther, there fore Jupiter was called Pater Æther by some Latin races.

Zodiac (*Gr.*). From the word *zodion*, a diminutive of *zoon*, animal. This word is used in a dual meaning; it may refer to the fixed and intellectual Zodiac, or to the movable and natural Zodiac. "In astronomy", says Science, "it is an imaginary belt in the heavens 16° or 18° broad, through the middle of which passes the sun's path (the ecliptic) ."It contains the twelve constellations which constitute the twelve signs of the Zodiac, and from which they are named. As the nature of the *zodiacal light* – that elongated, luminous, triangular figure which, lying almost in the ecliptic, with its base on the horizon and its apex at greater and smaller altitudes, is to be seen only during the morning and evening twilights – is entirely unknown to science, the origin and real significance and occult meaning of the Zodiac were, and are still, a mystery, to all save the Initiates. The latter preserved their secrets well. Between the Chaldean star-gazer and the modern astrologer there lies to this day a wide gulf indeed; and they wander, in the words of Albumazar, "'twixt the poles, and heavenly hinges, 'mongst eccentricals, centres, concentricks, circles and epicycles", with vain pretence to more than *profane* human skill. Yet, some of the astrologers, from Tycho Braire and Kepler of astrological memory, down to the modern Zadkiels and Raphaels, have contrived to make a wonderful science from such scanty occult materials as they have had in hand from Ptolemy downwards. (See "Astrology".) To return to the astrological Zodiac proper, however, it is an imaginary circle passing round the earth in the plane of the equator, its first point being called Aries 0°. It is divided into twelve equal parts called "Signs of the Zodiac", each containing 30° of space, and on it is measured the right ascension of celestial bodies. The movable or natural Zodiac is a succession of constellations forming a belt of in width, lying north and south of the plane of the ecliptic. The precession of the Equinoxes is caused by the "motion" of the sun through space, which makes the constellations appear to move forward against the order of the signs at the rate of 501/3 seconds per year. A simple calculation will show that at this rate the constellation Taurus (Heb. *Aleph*) was in the first sign of the Zodiac at the beginning of the Kali *Yuga*, and consequently the Equinoctial point fell therein. At this time, also, Leo was in the summer solstice, Scorpio in the autumnal Equinox, and Aquarius in the winter solstice ; and these facts form the astronomical key to half the religious mysteries of the world- – the Christian scheme included. The Zodiac was known in India and Egypt for incalculable ages, and the knowledge of the sages (magi) of these countries, with regard to the occult influence of the stars and heavenly bodies on our earth, was far greater than profane astronomy can ever hope to reach to. If, even now, when most of the secrets of the Asuramayas and the Zoroasters are lost, it is still amply shown that horoscopes and judiciary astrology are far from being based on fiction, and if such men as Kepler and even Sir Isaac Newton believed that stars and constellations influenced the destiny of our globe and its humanities, it requires no great stretch of faith to believe that men who were initiated into all the mysteries of nature, as well as into astronomy and astrology, knew precisely in what way nations and mankind, whole races as well as individuals, would be affected by the so-called "signs of the Zodiac".

Zohar, or *Sohar*. A compendium of Kabbalistic Theosophy, which shares with the *Sepher Yetzirah* the reputation of being the oldest extant treatise on the Hebrew esoteric religious doctrines. Tradition assigns its authorship to Rabbi Simeon ben Jochai, AD. 80, but modern criticism is inclined to believe that a very large portion of the volume is no older than 1280, when it was certainly edited and published by Rabbi Moses de Leon, of Guadalaxara in Spain. The reader should consult the references to these two names. In *Lucifer* (Vol. I., p. 141) will be found also notes on this subject : further discussion will be attainable in the works of Zunz, Graetz, Jost, Steinschneider, Frankel and Ginsburg. The work of Franck (in French) upon the *Kabalah* may be referred to with advantage. The truth seems to lie in a middle path, viz., that while Moses de Leon was the first to produce the volume as a whole, yet a large part of some of its constituent tracts consists of traditional dogmas and illustrations, which have come down from the time of Simeon ben Jochai and the Second Temple. There are portions of the doctrines of the Zohar which bear the impress of Chaldee thought and civilization, to which the Jewish race had been exposed in the Babylonish captivity. Yet on the other hand, to condemn the theory that it is ancient in its entirety, it is noticed that the Crusades are mentioned; that a quotation is made from a hymn by Ibn Gebirol, A,D. 1050; that the asserted author, Simeon ben Jochai, is spoken of as more eminent than Moses; that it mentions the vowel-points, which did not come into use until Rabbi Mocha (AD. 570) introduced them to fix the pronunciation of words as a help to his pupils, and lastly, that it mentions -a comet which can be proved by the evidence of the context to have appeared in 1264. There is no English translation of the *Zohar* as a whole, nor even a Latin one.

Zoroaster. Greek form of Zarathustra (q.v.).

Zoroastrian. One who follows the religion of the Parsis, sun, or fire-worshippers.

For additional explanations of theosophical terminology, readers should consult *THE THEOSOPHICAL GLOSSARY* at http://www.theosophytrust.org/HPB_index.php.

Index

A

"Arjuna's doubt is the one which naturally arises in one who for the first time is brought face to face with the great duality of nature – or of God. This duality may be expressed metaphysically by the words thought and action, for these mean in this the same as ideation and expression. Brahman, as the unmanifested God, conceives the idea of the Universe, and it at once expresses itself in what is called creation by the Christian and by the scientist evolution. This creation or evolution is the action of God. With him there is no difference in time between the arising of the idea and its expression in manifested objects. Coming down to consider the 'created' objects, or the planes on which the thought of God has its expression through its own laws, we find the duality expressed by action and reaction, attraction and repulsion, day and night, outbreathing and inbreathing, and so on. When face to face with these, one is first confused by the multiplicity of objects, and we strive to find one simple thing, some law or doctrine, practice, dogma, or philosophy, by which, being known, happiness can be secured."

William Q. Judge

Notes on the Bhagavad-Gita, Chp II.

10016312R0025

Made in the USA
Charleston, SC
31 October 2011